Lambert's

# Worldwide Directory of Defense Authorities

## with International Defense Organizations and Treaties

### 1984

# Lambert's
# Worldwide Directory of Defense Authorities

## with International Defense Organizations and Treaties

## 1984

*Managing Editor*
**James L. Huskey**

*Senior Editor*
**Joel Weeks**

*Associate Editors*
**Geoffrey Basik**
**James Bigus**
**Anthony Czuczka**
**Patricia Krackov**
**Randall Purcell**
**Howard Sugar**

**Lambert Publications, Inc.**
1030 Fifteenth Street, N.W.
Washington, D.C. 20005 U.S.A.

International Standard Book Number: 0-939304-03-1
Library of Congress Catalog Number:  Pending

Printed and bound in the United States of America

---

**Lambert Publications, Inc.**
1030 Fifteenth Street, NW
Washington, D.C. 20005 U.S.A.
Telephone: (202) 682-1111 • Telex: 248597

# A Word from the Publisher

Defense spending worldwide in the 1980's has consistently exceeded half a trillion dollars every year. Defense has always been a preoccupation of governments, and the industry that supplies the arms needs of nations is a principal economic activity of man. It therefore seemed logical to this publisher that a directory which would describe the defense structure of every government while identifying the personnel responsible for maintaining that structure would serve a most useful purpose.

Thus the *Worldwide Directory of Defense Authorities* was conceived in 1981. For the preceding two years Lambert Publications had been engaged in the ambitious task of trying to compile a governmental directory for every country in the world, to be named the *Worldwide Government Directory*. When the effort was completed in 1981 and the book released, it quickly became established as an authoritative reference work. I am almost embarrassed to relate to you the number of unsolicited letters we received from high government and corporate officials expressing praise and thanks for what we had done.

Thus encouraged, we launched the *Defense Directory* project in the same year.

We now take great pride in presenting to you the fruits of that undertaking, this being the first of annual editions. The editorial development of this unique resource was quite complicated, as the information presented on these pages was not easily obtained. It took over two years of diligent investigation and research by dozens of editors to compile this volume, and we earnestly hope that you, our reader, will find the result satisfactory.

We have gathered, for the first time anywhere, over 25,000 entries for top military and civilian authorities in the defense forces of every country in the world. The entries for each country are presented so that you can readily determine the basic structure of each defense force. Ranks and titles are included, together with the address of each office, and telephone, telex, and cable information. Defense manpower and budgets, related economic data, bilateral and mulitlateral relationships, conclude the listing for each country. An appendix allows comparison of military ranks among nations.

A separate section of the Directory, Part II, lists the defense personnel in international organizations and identifies bilateral and multilateral treaties. Part III provides a map of each country, identifying the major army, navy, and air force bases, as well as important foreign bases.

In preparing this volume, no effort was spared in seeking confirmation of the names, addresses, telephones, telex, cables, and statistical data contained in the listings. Although we have endeavored to insure that all the information here meets the highest standards of accuracy, we cannot accept liability for errors or omissions, nor for any damages arising therefrom.

We wish to express our deepest gratitude to the many governments, international organizations, defense institutions, embassies and foreign missions the world over. Without their generous cooperation, the compilation of this Directory would have been impossible. We assure our readers that no payment was either solicited or accepted for the inclusion of any entries. Within our own organization, I particularly wish to thank our defense editorial team, James L. Huskey, Joel Weeks, Geoffrey Basik, James Bigus, Anthony Czuczka, Patricia Krackov, Randall Purcell, Howard Sugar and the many other individuals in the administrative, production, and marketing departments at Lambert whose hard work and dedication made the success of this effort inevitable.

We would welcome, and be grateful for, your suggestions and comments.

*Cyrus A. Ansary*
PUBLISHER

## Abbreviations & Titles Commonly Used in the Worldwide Directory of Defense Authorities
### (See Appendix A for Military Rank Abbreviations)

| | |
|---|---|
| Arq. | Arquitecto (Sp.) *Architect* |
| dott. | DoHore (Ital.) *Doctor* |
| Dr./dr. | Doctor, PhD |
| Dra. | Doctora/Doutora (Sp. and Port.) Female Doctor |
| Eng. | Engineer |
| H.E. | His Excellency |
| H.H. | His Highness |
| H.M. | His/Her Majesty |
| Hon. | Honourable |
| Ing. | Ingeniero/Ingénieur (Sp. and Fr.) *Engineer* |
| ir. | (Dutch) *Engineer* |
| jkh. | (Dutch) *Member of Nobility* |
| Judr. | (Czechoslovakia) *Doctor of Law* |
| Lic. | Licenciado (Sp.) *Law Degree recipient* |
| mr. | (Dutch) *Master of Laws* |
| Ret. | Retired |

# How to use the *Worldwide Directory of Defense Authorities*

Customary reference name of country, together with formal and national language names

Explanation of the chain of command and basic defense structure of the country

Armed forces manpower with breakdown by service

Identifies the titular leader of the country

Supreme military commander and immediate advisors

Formal name of office or other entity

Mailing address

Telephone, telex and cable information

Formal name of division or department within above office

Title of person within body

Additional portfolio

## SWEDEN
### Kingdom of Sweden
*Konungariket Sverige*

### Defense Establishment Command Structure and Force Organization

The King is nominal Commander-in-Chief of the Swedish armed forces. Civilian control is exercised in peacetime by the Defense Minister; in case of war, it is exercised by the Prime Minister. Operational control is vested with the Supreme Commander, who is under the direction of the Minister of Defense. The Supreme Commander is assisted in matters of central military planning by the integrated Defense Staff.

Overall military planning is carried out by the National Defense Council, which may include any member of Parliament summoned by the Prime Minister. The Defense Head Committee, comprised of the heads of all government agencies relevant to defense and, on the military side, by the Supreme Commander, implements the Council's recommendations.

Sweden is divided into six Military Command Areas, each of which is headed by a commanding general, supported by an integrated staff.

The armed forces are not fully integrated. The individual service commanders are responsible for the organization (including procurement) and training of their respective units. The country's defense is based on the principle of national service for all men and rapid mobilization of all trained conscripts.

**Total armed forces:** 64,500 (Army: 45,000;    Navy: 10,000;    Air Force: 9,500). **Para-military forces:** 550 (Coast Guard). **Total armed forces after mobilization:** 850,000 (in 72 hours).

### HEAD OF STATE

H. M. King Carl XVI Gustaf

**OFFICE OF H. M. THE KING**
*Kungl. Slottet*
*Slottsbacken*
*S-111 30 Stockholm*
*Telephone:   (8) 10 09 63*

King of Sweden and Commander-in-Chief ......H. M. Carl XVI Gustaf
Marshal of the Realm ............................Sten Rudholm
First Marshal of the Royal Court ....................Lennart Ahrén
Public Affairs Officer ..................Elisabeth Tarras-Wahlberg

**OFFICE OF THE PRIME MINISTER**
*S-103 33 Stockholm*
*Telephone:   (8) 763 1000*
*Telex:   17820 premier s*

Prime Minister ......................................Olof Palme
Under Secretary ....................................Odd Engström
Undersecretary of State ............................Ulf Larsson
Undersecretary of State ............................Kjell Larsson

**National Defense Council**

Chairman ..........................................Olof Palme
(Prime Minister)
Member.................................Gen. Lennart Ljung
(Supreme Commander, Armed Forces)
Member ..................................Vam. Bror Stefenson
(Chief, Defense Staff)
Member ...............................Holger Romander
(Chief, National Police Board)

# Table of Contents

## PART I
## Countries

# PART II

## International Defense Organizations, Treaties and Agreements

### A. Multilateral Defense Organizations, Treaties and Agreements

## B. Bilateral Defense Treaties and Agreements

# PART III

# Maps And Major Military Bases

# Appendices

# PART I
# COUNTRIES

# AFGHANISTAN

## Democratic Republic of Afghanistan
### *De Afghanistan Democrateek Jamhuriat* (Pushtu)
### *Jamhuriat Democrateek ye Afghanistan* (Dari)

### Defense Establishment Command Structure and Force Organization

The President of the Revolutionary Council is Commander-in-Chief of the armed forces of Afghanistan. Administrative matters relating to the military are the responsibility of the Ministry of Defense. Police security forces are under the jurisdiction of the Ministry of Interior.

**Total armed forces:** 46,000 (Army: 40,000;   Air Force: 6,000). **Para-military forces:** 30,000 (Gendarmerie).

## HEAD OF STATE

H. E. Babrak Karmal

**OFFICE OF THE PRESIDENT OF THE REVOLUTIONARY COUNCIL**
*Kabul*
Telephone:   25889

President of the Revolutionary Council, General Secretary of the Central Committee of the People's Democratic Party of Afghanistan (PDPA), and Commander-in-Chief ............................... Babrak Karmal
Vice President of the Revolutionary Council ........... Noor Ahmad Noor
Vice President of the Revolutionary Council ......... Abdul Rashid Aryan
Vice President of the Presidium of the Revolutionary Council .................................... Gul Aqa

**OFFICE OF THE PRIME MINISTER**
*Kabul*

Prime Minister, Chairman of the Council of Ministers and President of the State Planning Committee .................... Sultan Ali Keshtmand
Deputy Prime Minister ..................... Lt. Gen. Mohammed Rafi'
Deputy Prime Minister ....................................... Gol Dad
Deputy Prime Minister .................... Abdol Majid Sarbuland
Deputy Prime Minister ......................... Khalil Ahmad Abawi
Deputy Prime Minister ......................... Abdul Rashid Aryan

**MINISTRY OF NATIONAL DEFENSE**
*Zia Watt*
*Kabul*
Telephone:   25714

Minister ................................... Maj. Gen. Abdul Qader

**MINISTRY OF INTERIOR**
*Ahmad Shah Mena*
*Kabul*
Telephone:   32743

Minister .................... Brig. Gen. Sayyed Mohammed Gulabzoi

**STATE INFORMATION SERVICES**
*Kabul*

Director ................................... Maj. Gen. Najibollah

# DEFENSE FORCES

**ARMY**
*Ansari Watt*
*Kabul*

*Telephone: 25715*

| | |
|---|---|
| Chief of General Staff | Maj. Gen. Baba Jan |
| Head, Army Political Administration | Brig. Gen. Yasin Sadeqi |
| Commander, Armor | Brig. Gen. Ziaoddin |
| Commander, Armor | Brig. Gen. Abdorrahman |
| Commander, Infantry | Brig. Gen. Mohammed Aziz |
| Commander, Infantry | Brig. Gen. Mohammed Kazem |
| Commander, Infantry | Brig. Gen. Mohammed Asef |
| Commander, Infantry | Brig. Gen. Abdul Qodus Rashid |
| Commander, Artillery | Brig. Gen. Enzar Gol |
| Commander, Artillery | Brig. Gen. Mohammed Faruq |

**AIR AND DEFENSE FORCES**
*Snari Watt*
*Kabul*

*Telephone: 20740*

| | |
|---|---|
| Commander-in-Chief | Maj. Gen. Nazar Mohammad |
| Commander | Brig. Gen. Jura Beg |

**NATIONAL POLICE FORCE**
*Kabul*

Chief .........................................................

\* \* \* \* \*

# GENERAL DEFENSE DATA

**Manpower**

| | |
|---|---|
| Total Armed Forces | 46,000 |
| (See Page 19) | |
| Population | 15,328,000 |

**Spending**

| | |
|---|---|
| Military Expenditures | $97 million |
| Gross National Product | $3.23 billion |
| Military Expenditure as a Percentage of Gross National Product | 3% |
| Military Expenditure as a Percentage of Central Government Expenditure | 14.4% |

**Defense Treaties** *(See Part II for Additional Detail)*

Bilateral:    Czechoslovakia
Soviet Union

Multilateral:    Biological Weapons Convention
Limited Test Ban Treaty
Treaty on the Control of Arms on the Seabed
Treaty on the Non-Proliferation of Nuclear Weapons

# ALBANIA
## People's Socialist Republic of Albania
### *Republika Popullore Socialiste e Shqiperise*

### Defense Establishment Command Structure and Force Organization

The Minister of People's Defense is Commander-in-Chief of the Albanian People's Army. The Chief of the Army General Staff is the highest-ranking military official. The para-military forces and the People's Police are controlled by the Ministry of Internal Affairs.

The Navy and the Air Force are integral parts of the People's Army.

**Total armed forces**: 43,100 (Army: 30,000; Navy: 3,100; Air Force: 10,000). **Para-military forces**: 13,000 (State Security Force: 5,000; Frontier Guard: 8,000).

## HEAD OF STATE

H. E. Ramiz Alia

**PRESIDIUM OF THE PEOPLE'S ASSEMBLY**
*Tirana*

Chairman .............................................. Ramiz Alia

**OFFICE OF THE CHAIRMAN, COUNCIL OF MINISTERS**
*Tirana*

Chairman .............................................. Adil Carcani
Deputy Chairman .................................. Besnik Bekteshi
Deputy Chairman................................... Manush Myftiu

**MINISTRY OF PEOPLE'S DEFENSE**
*Tirana*

Minister and Commander-in-Chief,
    Albanian People's Army ........................... Prokop Murra
Deputy Minister ................................... Nazar Berberi
Deputy Minister .................................. Llambi Gegprifti
Deputy Minister ................................... Veli Llakaj
Deputy Minister ................................... Maliq Sadushi
Chief, Secretariat ................................ Ndreko Cabali
Secretary, Albanian Worker's Party Committee ............ Ali Vukatana
Chief, Culture and Propaganda Directorate ............... Bajran Balla
Deputy Chief, Culture and Propaganda Directorate .......... Mitat Duka
Deputy Chief, Culture and Propaganda Directorate ........... Foni Papa
Director, Political Directorate........................... Dilaver Poci
Deputy Director, Political Directorate ..................... Ziqiri Mero
Deputy Director, Political Directorate ....................... Ilo Prifti
Deputy Director, Political Directorate ................. Halim Ramohito
Deputy Director, Political Directorate ................. Xhemel Shehu
Director, Directorate of Productive Work .............. Taxhedin Baholli
Director-General, Directorate of Studies and Publications .... Bedri Dedja

**MINISTRY OF INTERNAL AFFAIRS**
*Tirana*

Minister ........................................... Hekuran Isai
Commander, People's Police........................... Kasem Kaci
Chief, Tirana People's Police ....................... Qemal Balluku

# DEFENSE FORCES

**ARMY**
**Albanian People's Army**
*c/o Ministry of People's Defense*
*Tirana*

| | |
|---|---|
| Chief, General Staff | Veli Llakaj |
| Deputy Chief, General Staff | Mendu Backa |
| Commander, Tirana Garrison | Bejto Isufi |
| Director, Enver Hoxha Military Academy (Tirana) | Enver Begeja |

**NAVY**
**Naval Command**

| | |
|---|---|
| Commander | Qamil Poda |
| Chief of Staff | Plani Mark |

**AIR FORCE**
**Air Command**

| | |
|---|---|
| Commander | Arif Hasko |
| Commander, Air Defense | Bejto Isufi |

\* \* \* \* \*

# GENERAL DEFENSE DATA

**Manpower**

| | |
|---|---|
| Total Armed Forces | 43,100 |
| (See Page 21) | |
| Population | 2,730,000 |

**Spending**

| | |
|---|---|
| Military Expenditures | $188 million |
| Gross National Product | $1.85 billion |
| Military Expenditure as a Percentage of Gross National Product | 10.1% |
| Military Expenditure as a Percentage of Central Government Expenditure | 11.5% |

**Defense Treaties** *(See Part II for Additional Detail)*

Bilateral:    None

Multilateral:    None

# ALGERIA
## Democratic and Popular Republic of Algeria
### al-Jumhuriyah al-Jaza'iriyah al-Dimuqratiyah al-Sha'biyah

## Defense Establishment Command Structure and Force Organization

The President unites the offices of Commander-in-Chief of the Armed Forces and Minister of Defense. He is advised on national security issues by the Supreme Security Council. While operational control of the armed forces is the responsibility of the Secretary General of the Ministry of Defense, the President often deals directly with the Commanders of the seven Regional Commands, as well as with the armed forces commanders.

**Total armed forces:** 168,000 (Army: 150,000;  Navy: 6,000;  Air Force: 12,000). **Paramilitary forces:** 24,000 (Gendarmerie).

## HEAD OF STATE

H. E. Chadli Bendjedid

**OFFICE OF THE PRESIDENT**
*El-Mouradia, Algiers*
*Telephone:  60 63 60*
*Telex:  52045-47*

President of the Democratic and Popular Republic, Secretary-General of the Party, and Supreme Commander of the Armed Forces ..................Chadli Bendjedid
Secretary-General of the Presidency..................Col. Larbi Belkhier
Secretary-General of the Government ................Mohamed Tayebi

**Supreme Security Council**
*(Haute Conseil de Sécurité)*

Chairman .........................................Chadli Bendjedid
(President of the Republic and Minister of Defense)
Member *(ex officio)* .............................Mohamed Hadj Yala
(Minister of Interior)
Member *(ex officio)* .......................Dr. Ahmed Taleb Ibrahimi
(Minister of Foreign Affairs)
Member *(ex officio)* .....................................Bitat Rabah
(Chairman of the Committee of National Defense, National Assembly)
Member *(ex officio)* ..........................(Presidential Appointee)
Member *(ex officio)* ..........................(Presidential Appointee)
Permanent Secretary .......................Col. Benabbes Ghezaiel

**MINISTRY OF NATIONAL DEFENSE**
*(Ministère de la Defense Nationale)*
*Avenue Ali Khoudja*
*Les Tagarins, Algiers*
*Telephone:  61 15 15, 63 14 76, 63 17 65*
*Telex:  52547 dz midef,*
*53975 dz midef*

President and Minister of National Defense .............Chadli Bendjedid
Vice-Minister, General Inspector General, NPA.....................Col. Abdallah Belhouchet
Secretary-General ...........................Col. Mustapha Benloucif
Director, Military Security ............Lt. Col. Medjedoub Lakehal Ayat
Director, External Relations.......................Cmdt. Bachir Kamel
Director, Instruction .............................Lt. Col. Yahia Rahal

# DEFENSE FORCES

## ARMED FORCES
**People's National Army—NPA**
*c/o Ministry of National Defense*
*Avenue Ali Khodja*
*Les Tagarins, Algiers*

*Telephone: 61 15 15, 63 14 76, 63 17 65*
*Telex: 52547 dz medef,*
*53975 dz midef*

President, Supreme Commander of the Armed Forces, and Minister of National Defense . . . . . . . . . . . . . . . . . . . . . . . . . . . . . . . . . .Chadli Benjedid
Inspector General, NPA . . . . . . . . . . . . . . . . . . . . .Col. Abdallah Belhouchet

### Political Commissariat
*(Commisaire Politique)*

Director . . . . . . . . . . . . . . . . . . . . . . . . . . . . . . . . . . . . . . .Col. Mohamed Alleg

### Cherchell Interarms Military Academy
*(Academie Militaire Interarmes—EMIA)*

Commander . . . . . . . . . . . . . . . . . . . . . . . . . . . . . . . .Col. El Hachemi Hadjres

## ARMY
*(Armée de Terre)*
*c/o Ministry of National Defense*
*Avenue Ali Khodja*
*Les Tagarins, Algiers*

*Telephone: 61 15 15, 63 14 76, 63 17 65*
*Telex: 52547 dz midef,*
*53975 dz midef*

Commander . . . . . . . . . . . . . . . . . . . . . . . . . . . . . . . . . . . .Chadli Bendjedid
Director, Combat Arms . . . . . . . . . . . . . . . . . .Lt. Col. Abdallah Boumedriss
Commander, First Military Region (Blida) . . . . . . . . . . . . . . . . . . .Col. Mohamed Attailia
Commander, Second Military Region (Oran) . . . . . . . . . . . . . . . . . . . . .Col. Kamel Abderahim
Commander, Third Military Region (Colomb-Bechar) . . . . . . . . . . .Lt. Col. Hachichi Zine El Abidine
Commander, Fourth Military Region (Ouargla) . . . . . . . . . . . . . . . . . . . .Col. Hocine Ben Maalem
Commander, Fifth Military Region (Constantine) . . . . . . . . . . . . . . . . . . . .Col. Khaled Nezzar
Commander, Sixth Military Region (Taman Rasset) . . . . . . . . . . . . . . . . . . . .Lt. Col. Lamine Zeroual
Commander, Seventh Military Region (Algiers) . . . . . . . . . . . . . . . . . . . . . . .Lt. Col. Ali Bouhadja

### Military College
*Blida*

Commandant . . . . . . . . . . . . . . . . . . . . . . . . . . . . . . . . . . . . . . . . .(Vacant)

### Army Information Service
*(Centre de Documentation de l'Armée)*
*B.P. 516*
*Alger Gare*

Director . . . . . . . . . . . . . . . . . . . . . . . . . . . . . . . . . . . . . . . . . . . .(Vacant)

## NAVY
*(Marine Nationale)*
*c/o Ministry of National Defense*
*Avenue Ali Khodja*
*Les Targarins, Algiers*

*Telephone: 61 15 15, 63 14 76, 63 17 65*
*Telex: 52547 dz midef,*
*53975 dz midef*

Commander . . . . . . . . . . . . . . . . . . . . . . . . . . . . . . . .Col. Rachid Ben Yelles
Deputy Director, Logistics . . . . . . . . . . . . . . . . . .Maj. Chabane Ghodbane
Deputy Director, Personnel . . . . . . . . . . . . . . . . . . . . . . . . . . . . . .Maj. Heddi
Commanding Officer of Fleet . . . . . . . . . . . . . . . . . . . . . . . . . .Maj. Zenasni

## AIR FORCE
*c/o Ministry of National Defense*
*Avenue Ali Khodja*
*Les Tagarins, Algiers*

Commander . . . . . . . . . . . . . . . . . . . . . . . . . . . .Lt. Col. Abdelhamid Abdelli
Deputy Director, Operations. . . . . . . . . . . . . . . . . .Maj. Farouk Ben Toubal
Director, Air Defense . . . . . . . . . . . . . . . .Lt. Col. Nourredine Ben Khoucha
Deputy Director, Technology . . . . . . . . . . . . . . . . . . . . . .Maj. Cheki Kamel

Telephone: *61 51 15, 63 14 76, 63 17 65*
Telex: *52547 dz midef,*
   *53975 dz midef*

Squadron Commander, C-130
   Transport . . . . . . . . . . . . . . . . . . . . . . . . . . . . . . . . Maj. Chouaib Oultache

**Military Aviation Directorate**
*(Direction de l'Air:*
   *Aviation Militaire)*

Director . . . . . . . . . . . . . . . . . . . . . . . . . . . . . . . Cdt. Belkacem Moassouni

**NATIONAL CONSTABULARY**
**Central Directorate of the**
   **National Constabulary**
*(Direction Centrale de la*
   *Gendarmerie Nationale)*
*c/o Ministry of National Defense*
*Avenue Ali Khodja*
*Les Tagarins, Algiers*

Telephone: *61 15 15, 63 14 76, 63 17 65*
Telex: *52547 dz midef,*
   *52975 dz midef*

Commander-in-Chief . . . . . . . . . . . . . . . . . . . . . . . Col. Mustapha Cheloufi
Chief of Staff . . . . . . . . . . . . . . . . . . . . . . . . . . . . . Lt. Col. Mohamed Touati

\* \* \* \* \*

## GENERAL DEFENSE DATA

**Manpower**
   Total Armed Forces . . . . . . . . . . . . . . . . . . . . . . . . . . . . . . . . . . . . . . . . . 168,000
      (See Page 23)
   Population . . . . . . . . . . . . . . . . . . . . . . . . . . . . . . . . . . . . . . . . . . . . 20,030,000

**Spending**
   Military Expenditures . . . . . . . . . . . . . . . . . . . . . . . . . . . . . . . . . . . . . . $796 million
   Gross National Product . . . . . . . . . . . . . . . . . . . . . . . . . . . . . . . . . . . . . $35.5 billion
   Military Expenditure as a Percentage of
      Gross National Product . . . . . . . . . . . . . . . . . . . . . . . . . . . . . . . . . . . . . 2.2%
   Military Expenditure as a Percentage of
      Central Government Expenditure . . . . . . . . . . . . . . . . . . . . . . . . . . . . . 7.6%

**Defense Treaties** *(See Part II for Additional Detail)*

   Bilateral:     Libya

   Multilateral:  League of Arab States
                  Organization of African Unity

# ANGOLA
## People's Republic of Angola

### Defense Establishment Command Structure
### and Force Organization

The President is Commander-in-Chief of the armed forces. Administration of the military is the responsibility of the Minister of Defense. The Commanders of the Army, Navy and Air Force hold the title of Vice Minister of Defense, and are responsible directly to the Minister.

**Total armed forces:** 37,500 (Army: 35,000;    Navy: 1,000;    Air Force: 1,500). **Para-military forces:** 510,000 (Militia Infantry: 10,000;    Organization of Popular Defense: 500,000).

### HEAD OF STATE

H. E. José Eduardo dos Santos

**OFFICE OF THE PRESIDENT**
*Luanda*

President of the People's Republic
and Commander-in-Chief . . . . . . . . . . . . . . . . . .José Eduardo dos Santos

**MINISTRY OF DEFENSE**
*(Ministério da Defesa)*
*Rua Silva Carvalho*
  *ex Quartel General*
*Luanda*
*Telex:   3138 def an*

Minister . . . . . . . . . . . . . . . . . . . . . . . . . . . . . . . . . . .Cel. Pedro María Tonha
First Vice Minister . . . . . . . . . . . . . . . . . . . . . . . . .Cel. João Luis Neto Xietu
Second Vice Minister and Commander,
  Air Force and Aerial Defense . . . . . . . . . . . . . . . . . . . . . . . . . . . .Ten. Cel.
  Antonio dos Santos Franca N'dalu
Vice Minister . . . . . . . . . . . . . . . . . . . . . . . . . . . .Cel. Julião Mateus Paulo
Vice Minister . . . . . . . . . . . . . . . . . . . . . . . . . . . . . . . . . . . . . . . . .(Vacant)
Vice Minister and Commander, Navy . . . . . . . . . . . . . . . . . . . . . . .Ten. Cel.
  Manuel Augusto Alfredo Orlog
Vice Minister and Commander,
  Army and Peoples Defense Organization . . . . . . . . . . . . . . . . . . .Ten. Cel.
  Paiva Domingos da Silva
Vice Minister and Political Commissar . . . . . . . . . . . . . . . . . . . . . .Ten. Cel.
  Francisco Magalhaes Paiva N'Vundu
State Secretary for Veterans Affairs . . . . . . . . . . . . . . . . . . . . . . . . . . .Cap.
  José Domingos Francisco Tuta

**MINISTRY OF STATE SECURITY**
*Luanda*

Minister . . . . . . . . . . . . . . . . . . . . . . . . . . . . . . .Cel. Julião Mateus Paulo
Vice Minister . . . . . . . . . . . . . . . . . . . . . . . . . . . . . .Cdt. Delfim de Castro

### DEFENSE FORCES

**ARMED FORCES**
*(Forcas Armadas Populares de*
  *Libertacao de Angola—FAPLA)*

Chief of Staff . . . . . . . . . . . . . . . . . . . . . . . . . . . . . . . . .João Neto Chieto
Political Commissar . . . . . . . . . . . . . . . . . . . . . . . . . . . . . . . . . . .Ten. Cel.
  Francisco Magalhaes Paiva N'Vundu

**Military Governors**
Cuando Cubango . . . . . . . . . . . . . . . . . . . . . .Major Manuel Francisco Tuta
Huambo . . . . . . . . . . . . . . . . . . . . . . . . . .Ten. Cel. João Ernesto dos Santos
Lula Sul . . . . . . . . . . . . . . . . . . . . . . . . . . . . . . . . .Major Celestino Bernardo
Malange . . . . . . . . . . . . . . . . . . . . . . . . . . . .Cel. Rodriguez Kissassunda
Mocamedes. . . . . . . . . . . . . . . . . . . . . . . . . . . . . . .Major Rafael Sapilinha
Mexico. . . . . . . . . . . . . . . . . . . . . . . . . . . . . . . . .Major Marques Monakapui

**ARMY**
*Luanda*

Commander......................Ten. Cel. Paiva Domingos da Silva

**NAVY**
*Luanda*

Commander..................Ten. Cel. Manual Augusto Alfreda Orlog

**AIR FORCE**
**Popular Angolan Air Forces**
  **and Anti-Aircraft Defense—**
  **FAPA-DA**
*Luanda*

Commander ...............Ten. Cel. Antonio dos Santos Franca N'dalu

**PARA-MILITARY FORCES**
**Organization of Popular Defense**
*Luanda*

Commander.......................Ten. Cel. Paiva Domingos da Silva

\* \* \* \* \*

# GENERAL DEFENSE DATA

**Manpower**
  Total Armed Forces...............................................37,500
    (See Page 27)
  Population ...................................................7,000,000

**Spending**
  Military Expenditures .........................................$115 million
  Gross National Product .........................................$3.2 billion
  Military Expenditure as a Percentage of
    Gross National Product ............................................3.5%
  Military Expenditure as a Percentage of
    Central Government Expenditure ................................24.7%

**Defense Treaties** *(See Part II for Additional Detail)*

  Bilateral:      Cuba
                  Soviet Union
                  Zambia

  Multilateral:   *Angola—Mozambique—Tanzania—Zambia:* Agreement con-
                    cerning joint defense strategy against external attack (1976)
                  *Angola—Zaire—Zambia:* Non-aggression pact (1979)
                  Organization of African Unity

**Military Rank Comparisons**
  See Appendix A.

# ANTIGUA AND BARBUDA

## Defence Establishment Command Structure and Force Organization

The Prime Minister is Commander-in-Chief of the armed forces. Administrative and operational control of the military is exercised by the Commander of the Antigua and Barbuda Defence Force.

## HEAD OF STATE

H. M. Queen Elizabeth II

**OFFICE OF THE GOVERNOR-GENERAL**
*St. John's*
*Telephone: 462-0003*

Governor-General ...................... Sir Wilfred Ebenezer Jacobs, K.C.V.O., O.B.E., Q.C.

**OFFICE OF THE PRIME MINISTER**
*Factory Road*
*St. John's*
*Telephone: 462-0773/79*
*Telex: 2127 ofprem ak*

Prime Minister and Commander-in-Chief .............. Vere C. Bird, Sr.

## DEFENCE FORCES

**ARMY**
**Antigua and Barbuda Defence Force**
*St. John's*
*Telephone: 462-3363, 462-1458*

Commander ..................................... Maj. Clyde Walker
Deputy Commander ............................. Lt. Trevor Thomas

**POLICE**
**Royal Antigua Police Force**
*St. John's*
*Telephone: 462-0125/28*

Commissioner......................................... Wright George
Deputy Commissioner ................................. Eric Potter

\* \* \* \* \*

## GENERAL DEFENCE DATA

**Manpower**
Total Armed Forces ....................................................
Population ....................................................76,500

**Spending**

Military Expenditures . . . . . . . . . . . . . . . . . . . . . . . . . . . . . . . . . . . . . . . . . . . . .

Gross National Product . . . . . . . . . . . . . . . . . . . . . . . . . . . . . . . . . . . . . .$22.8 billion

Military Expenditure as a Percentage of
  Gross National Product . . . . . . . . . . . . . . . . . . . . . . . . . . . . . . . . . . . . . . . . . . . .

Military Expenditure as a Percentage of
  Central Government Expenditure . . . . . . . . . . . . . . . . . . . . . . . . . . . . . . . . . . . . .

**Defense Treaties** *(See Part II for Additional Detail)*

Bilateral:     United States

Multilateral:  Regional Security System
               Treaty on the Control of Arms on the Seabed

# ARGENTINA
## Argentine Republic
### *República Argentina*

### Defense Establishment Command Structure and Force Organization

The Military Junta is the highest organ of the State and is comprised of the Chiefs of Staff of the three armed services. The President of Argentina is Head of the Executive Branch. A Military Committee, consisting of the President and the three service Chiefs of Staff, coordinate national security policy. A federal armed police, the Gendarmeria Nacional, perform frontier and domestic duties and are subordinate to the Army.

**Total armed forces:** 180,500 (Army: 125,000; Navy: 36,000; Air Force: 19,500). **Paramilitary forces:** 43,000 (Gendarmeria Nacional).

**MILITARY JUNTA**
*(Junta Militar)*
*Azopardo 250*
*1328 Buenos Aires*

Member, Ruling Junta . . . . . . . . . . . . . . . . . .Tte. Gral. Cristino Nicolaides
(Commander-in-Chief, Army)
Member, Ruling Junta . . . . . . . . . . . . . . . . . . . . . . . . .Alm. Ruben Franco
(Commander-in-Chief, Navy)
Member, Ruling Junta. . . . . . . . . . . . . . . .Gral. Brig. Augusto Jorge Hughes
(Commander-in-Chief, Air Force)

**Office of the President**
*(Oficina de la Presidencia)*
*Casa de Gobierno*
*Balcarece 50*
*1064 Buenos Aires*

*Telephone: (1) 46-9841, 33-7051*
*Telex: 21464 copre ar*

President of the
Republic . . . . . . . . . . .Gral. Div. (Ret.) Reynaldo Benito António Bignone
Head, Government Household . . . . . . . . . . . . . . .Cdte. Roberto Benito Moya
Under Secretary, Legal . . . . . . . . . . . . . . . . . . . .Cnel. Adolfo Ernesto Álvarez
Under Secretary, Technical . . . . . . . . . . . . . . . . . . . . .Cnel. Mário Zamboni

**MILITARY COMMITTEE**
*(Comité Militar)*

Member . . . . . . . . . . . . . . . . . . . . . . . . . . . . . .Tte. Gral. Cristino Nicolaides
(Commander-in-Chief, Army)
Member . . . . . . . . . . . . . . . . . . . . . . . . . . . . . .Vice Alm. Carlos Carpintero
(Commander-in-Chief, Navy)
Member . . . . . . . . . . . . . . . . . . . . . . . .May. Gral. Augusto Jorge Hughes
(Commander-in-Chief, Air Force)
Member . . . . . . . . . . . . . . . . . . . .Gral. Reynaldo Benito António Bignone

**SECRETARIAT OF PUBLIC INFORMATION**
*(Secretaría de Información Pública)*
*Casa de Gobierno*
*Balcarce 50*
*1063 Buenos Aires*

*Telephone: (1) 46-9841, 46-9849*
*Telex: (390) 122214, 121334*

Secretary, Public Information . . . . . . . . . . . . . . . .Cnel. Cladoveo Bappesti
Under Secretary, Operations . . . . . . . . . . . . . . . . . . . . .Cap. Héctor de Piro
Under Secretary, Planning. . . . . . . . . . . . . . . . . . . . .Cdte. Julio César Cotier

**SECRETARIAT OF PLANNING**
*(Secretaría de Planeamiento)*
*25 de mayo 459*

Secretary, Planning . . . . . . . . . . . . . . . . . . . . . . . . . . . .Brig. José Miret
Under Secretary, Information . . . . . . . . . . . . . . . . . . . . .Vice Cdte. (Ret.)
Juan Manuel Beverina

*1002 Buenos Aires*
*Telephone:   (1) 32-1474*

**SECRETARIAT OF STATE**
**INFORMATION**
*(Secretaría de Información*
*del Estado)*
*25 de mayo 11*
*1002 Buenos Aires*
*Telephone:   (1) 30-5531*

**MINISTRY OF DEFENSE**
*(Ministério de Defensa)*
*Paseo de Colon 255*
*1063 Buenos Aires*
*Telephone:   (1) 30-1294, 30-1561/69*
*Telex:   22200*

**ARMED FORCES**
*(Las Fuerzas Armadas)*
*Ave. Paseo Colon 255*
*1063-Buenos Aires*

**ARMY**
*(Ejército Argentino)*
*Azopardo 250*
*1328 Buenos Aires*
*Telephone:   (1) 34-0538, 34-2121, 33-0312*
*Telex:   22200*

    **Army General Staff**
    *(Estado Mayor General del Ejército)*
    *Azopardo 250-5 piso*
    *1328-Buenos Aires*
    *Telephone:   (1) 33-7907*

    **First Corps**
    *(1 Cuerpo del Ejército)*
    *Ave. Sante Fe 4857*
    *1425-Buenos Aires*
    *Telephone:   (1) 773-8667*

    **Second Corps, "Tte. Gral.**
    **Juan Carlos Sanchez"**
    *(II Cuerpo del Ejército)*
    *Sarmiento 1350*
    *2000-Roasrio-Pcia de Sante Fe*

Under Secretary, Coordination and
  Planning . . . . . . . . . . . . . . . . . . . . . . . . Vice Cdte. (Ret.) Jorge Bonnesere

Secretary, State Information  . . . . . . . . . . . . . . . May. Gral. Carlos Martínez

Minister . . . . . . . . . . . . . . . . . . . . . . . . . . . . . . . . . . . . . . Dr. Julio Martínez Vivot
Under Secretary . . . . . . . . . . . . . . . . . . . . . . . . . . . . . . Jorge António Monzo
President, Sports Federation
  of the Argentine Military . . . . . . . . . . . . . . Gral. Brig. Carlos Delia la Roca
President, Institute of Scientific
  & Technical Research  . . . . . . . . . . . . . Gral. Brig. Eduardo Osvaldo Garay
Director-General, General Office of
  Research & Development  . . . . . . . . . . . . . . Cdte. Horacio Juvenal Martín
National Director, National Office
  of the Antarctica  . . . . . . . . . . . . . . . . . Gral. Brig. Andres Aníbal Ferrero
Chief, Argentine Antarctic
  Institute . . . . . . . . . . . . . . . . . . . . . . Cap. Roberto Manuel Martínez Abal
Chief, Office of Civil Defense . . . . . . . . . . . . . . . . . . . . . . Brig. Bravo Deheza
Chief, Intelligence Headquarters . . . . . . . . . . . . . . . . . . . . . . . . . . . . . . . . . .

## DEFENSE FORCES

Chairman, Joint Chiefs of Staff . . . . . . . . . . . . . . . . . . . . . . . . . . . Alm. Busser
Chief, Armed Forces Council of War  . . . . . . . . Gral. Brig. Luis María Sages
Chief, Joint Chiefs of Staff
  Personnel . . . . . . . . . . . . . . . . . Gral. Brig. Héctor Raúl Rodríguez Espada
Chief of Operations, Joint Chiefs of Staff  . . . . . . . . Gral. Brig. Vicente Meli

Commander-in-Chief . . . . . . . . . . . . . . . . . . . . Tte. Gral. Cristino Nicolaides
Secretary General . . . . . . . . . . . . . . . . . . . . . Gral. Brig. Mário Alfredo Piotti
Under-Secretary General . . . . . . . . Gral. Brig. Jorge Ezequiel Suárez Nelson

Chief of Staff . . . . . . . . . . . . . . . . . . . . . . . . Gral. Div. Edgardo Nestor Calvi
Commander, Military
  Institutes . . . . . . . . . . . . . . . . . . . . . . . Gral. Div. Luis Santiago Martella

Commander . . . . . . . . . . . . . . . . . Gral. Div. Juan Carlos Ricardo Trimarco
Second-in-Command and
  Chief of Staff . . . . . . . . . . . . . . . . . . . . Gral. Brig. Julio Alfredo Fernández

Commander . . . . . . . . . . . . . . . . . . . . . Gral. Div. Eduardo Alfredo Esposito
Second-in-Command and
  Chief of Staff . . . . . . . . . . . . . . . . . . . . Gral. Brig. Alberto Carlos Lucena

**Third Corps**
*(III Cuerpo del Ejército)*
*Camino a la Calera-Km. 10, 5000-5101-*
*Cordoba-Pcia de Cordoba*

Commander ................... Gral. Div. Eugenio Guanabens Perello
Second-in-Command and
  Chief of Staff ..................... Gral. Brig. Nestor Ruben Castelli

**Fourth Corps, "Army of The Andes"**
*(IV Cuerpo del Ejército "Ejército*
*de los Andes)*
*Raul Díaz 1075, 6300-Santa Rosa-*
*Pcia de la Pampa*

Commander ........................ Gral. Div. Miguel Ángel Podesta
Second-in-Command and
  Chief of Staff ................ Gral. Brig. Américo Gerónimo Herrera

**Fifth Corps, "Julio Argentino Roca"**
*(V Cuerpo, "Julio Argentino Roca")*
*Calle Florida-Villa Floresta*
*8000-Bahía Blanca-Pcia de*
*Buenos Aires*

Commander .................. Gral. Div. Rodolfo Enrique Luis Wehner
Second-in-Command and
  Chief of State ................. Gral. Brig. Miguel Alfredo Mallea Gil

**Superior War College "Tte. Gral.**
**Luis Maria Campos"**
*(Escuela Superior de Guerra*
*"Tte. Gral. Luis María Campos")*
*Ave. Luis M. Campos 480*
*1426-Buenos Aires*

Director ........................... Gral. Brig. Carlos Antónío Binotti

**Superior Technical College "Gral.**
**de Div. Manuel Nicolas Savio"**
*(Escuela Superior Técnia "Gral. de*
*División Manuel Nicólas Savis")*
*Ave. Cabildo 15*
*1426-Buenos Aires*

Director ......................... Gral. Brig. Eduardo Osvaldo Garay

**National Military College**
*(Colegio Militar de la Nación)*
*1684-El Palomar-Pcia de Buenos Aires*

Director............................. Gral. Brig. Mário Jaime Sánchez

**NAVY**
*(Armada Argentina)*
*Edificio Libertad, Comodoro PY 2055*
*Buenos Aires, 1104*
*Telephone: (1) 32-5001 through 32-5009,*
*3127561*

Commander-in-Chief....................... Alm. Ruben Oscar Franco
Chief of Staff ........................ Vice Alm. Carlos Carpintero
Secretary-General, Navy ................ Contra Alm. Joaquin Gómez
Under Secretary-General, Navy..................... Cap. Héctor Monzo
Director-General, Naval Material ......... Contra Alm. Roque Manrique
Director-General, Naval Personnel ........... Contra Alm. Carlos Bonino
Chief, Naval Staff Logistics ............... Contra Alm. Eugenio Bezzola
Chief, Naval Staff Operations
  and Coordinator ...................... Vice Alm. Rodolfo Remotti
General Contractor, Navy ................ Contra Alm. Horacio Nadales
Director, Electricity and
  Machinery, Navy ..................... Contra Alm. Roque Manrique
Chief, Naval Aviation....................... Contra Alm. Rivero Kelly
Director, Personal Armaments............ Contra Alm. Norman Azcoieia
Chief, Marine Infantry of the General Staff ................ Cap. Daladriz
Commander, Naval Air Force .......................... Cap. Águila
Deputy Chief, Operations .................... Contra Alm. Mário Palet
Chief, Intelligence ............................ Contra Alm. Juan Iglesia

**Naval Offices**
*(Oficinas Navales)*
*Eduardo Madero 235*
*Buenos Aires*
*Telephone: (1) 33-7001/33-7009*

Prefect................................ Contra Alm. Salvio Menéndez
Director-General, Naval Instruction........... Contra Alm. Carlos Bonino
Director, Naval Air Material ...................... Contra Alm. Vignale
Chief, Usuaia Naval Base.............. Tte. Cdte. Julio Hugo Pérez Roca
Commander, 30th Naval Air Unit........... Cap. Alberto Eduardo Alonso

**Port Belgrano Naval Base**
*(Base Naval del Puerto Belgrano)*
*Provinde of Buenos Aires*
*Telephone:   8111*

| | |
|---|---|
| Naval Commander | Alm. Rodolfo Remotti |
| Chief of Staff, Naval Operations Command | Cap. Ángel M. Rodríguez |
| Commander, Marine Infantry | Contra Alm. Carlos Sosa |
| Commander, Naval Aviation | Contra Alm. Rivero Kelly |
| Commander, Naval Operations | Vice Alm. Rodolfo Remotti |
| Director, Naval War College | Contra Alm. Ángel Rodríguez |

**AIR FORCE**
*(La Fuerza Aérea Argentina)*
*Pedro Zanni 250'*
*Buenos Aires 1004*
*Telephone:   (1) 392-1333, 392-1346, 392-1446*

| | |
|---|---|
| Commander-in-Chief | May. Gral. Augosto Jorge Hughes |
| Chief of Staff | May. Brig. José María Insua |
| Commander, Air Operations | May. Brig. Teodoro Guillermo Waldner |
| Commander, Air Regions | May. Brig. Héctor René Roy |
| Commander, Material | Brig. Serafin Julio Iribarra |
| Commander, Instruction | May. Brig. Alfredo Ramón Berastegui |
| Commander, Air Defense | May. Brig. David Eduardo Giosa |
| Commander, 2nd Air Brigade | Cnel. Edel Oscar Martínez Via de Monte |
| Commander, 4th Air Brigade | Gral. Brig. Carlos Alberto de Blasis |

\* \* \* \* \*

# GENERAL DEFENSE DATA

**Manpower**

| | |
|---|---|
| Total Armed Forces | 180,500 |
| (See Page 31) | |
| Population | 28,593,000 |

**Spending**

| | |
|---|---|
| Military Expenditures | $2.8 billion |
| Gross National Product | $118 billion |
| Military Expenditure as a Percentage of Gross National Product | 2.4% |
| Military Expenditure as a Percentage of Central Government Expenditure | 12.8% |

**Defense Treaties** *(See Part II for Additional Detail)*

Bilateral:    United States

Multilateral:    Act of Chapultepec
Biological Weapons Convention
Inter-American Defense Board
Inter-American Treaty of Reciprocal Assistance
Treaty for the Prohibition of Nuclear Weapons in Latin
America (not ratified)

**Military Rank Comparisons**
See Appendix A.

# AUSTRALIA
## Commonwealth of Australia

### Defence Establishment Command Structure and Force Organization

The Governor-General, as representative of the Queen, has nominal control of the armed forces. Executive authority for the Australian defence forces is vested in the Prime Minister, who exercises this responsibility through the Minister for Defence. The Defence Secretary is the principal civilian adviser to the Minister for Defence on general policy and on the management and utilization of defence resources. The Minister's senior military advisor is the Chief of the Defence Force Staff, who commands through the three service Chiefs of Staff. The Chief of the Defence Force Staff and the Defence Secretary have equal status. The Minister for Defence is also advised by a Defence Council, which coordinates defence matters, and a Defence Committee, which advises on overall defence policy.

**Total armed forces:** 72,965 (Army: 32,843;    Navy: 17,450;    Air Force: 22,672).

### HEAD OF STATE

H. M. Queen Elizabeth II

### GOVERNOR-GENERAL

H. E. Sir Ninian Martin Stephen, A.K.,
G.C.M.G., K.B.E., K.St.J., G.C.V.O.

**OFFICE OF THE GOVERNOR-GENERAL**
*Governor House*
*Canberra, A.C.T. 2600*
*Telephone: (62) 81 1211*

Governor-General ....................... Sir Ninian Martin Stephen, A.K., G.C.M.G., K.B.E., K.St.J., G.C.V.O.

**OFFICE OF THE PRIME MINISTER**
*Core 6, Edmund Barton Building*
*Corner Broughton and Macquarie Sts.*
*Barton, A.C.T. 2600*
*Telephone: (62) 723955*
*Telex: 61616*

Prime Minister ............................ Robert Lee James Hawke
Deputy Prime Minister ............................... Lionel Bowen

**DEPARTMENT OF DEFENCE**
*Russell Offices*
*Canberra, A.C.T. 2600*
*Telephone: (62) 65 9111*
*(62) 65 3000*
*(after hrs.)*
*Telex: 62625*
*Cable: DEFENCE CANBERRA*

Minister for Defence ........................... Gordon Scholes, M.P.
Minister for Defence Support
and Minister Assisting the
Minister for Defence ................................... Brian Howe
Secretary, Department of Defence ...................... W. B. Pritchett
Deputy Secretary A ................................. N. J. Attwood
Deputy Secretary B ................................. A. K. Wrigley
Deputy Secretary C ................................. F. N. Bennett
Assistant Secretary, Quality Assurance and
Engineering Resources Policy Division .................. L. A. McGee

35

First Assistant Secretary,
  Force Development and Analysis Division . . . . . . . . . . . . . . .J. M. Moten
First Assistant Secretary,
  Programmes and Budgets Division . . . . . . . . . . . . . . . . . .D. M. McAlister
First Assistant Secretary, Industrial Division . . . . . . . . . . . . . .T. K. Hickman
First Assistant Secretary, Defence Facilities . . . . . . . . . . . . . . .N. R. Miller
First Assistant Secretary,
  Computing Services Division . . . . . . . . . . . . . . . . . . . . . .Dr. R. J. Turton
Director, Australian Counter Disaster
  College (Natural Disasters
  Organization) . . . . . . . . . . . . . . . . .Brig. I. G. C. Gilmore, O.B.E. (Ret.)
Director, Defence Signals Directorate . . . . . . . . . . . . . . . . . .T. W. S. James
First Assistant Secretary, Financial Services
  and Internal Audit Division . . . . . . . . . . . . . . . . . . . . . . .T. E. Sullivan
Assistant Secretary, Manpower Policy Division . . . . . . . . . . . . .P. E. Bazley

**Council of Defence**

Chairman . . . . . . . . . . . . . . . . . . . . . . . . . . . . . . . . . . . . .Gordon Scholes
(Minister of Defence)
Deputy Chairman . . . . . . . . . . .Air Chief Marshal Sir Neville P. McNamara
(Chief of Defence Force Staff)
Deputy Chairman . . . . . . . . . . . . . . . . . . . . . . . . . . . . . . .W. B. Pritchett
(Secretary for Defence)
Member (ex officio) . . . . . . . . . . . . . . . . . . . . . . . . . . . . . . . .Brian Howe
(Minister Assisting the Minister for Defence)
Member (ex officio) . . . . . . . . . . . . . . . . . . . . . . . . . .Vice Adm. D. W. Leach
(Chief of Naval Staff)
Member (ex officio) . . . . . . . . . . . . . . . . . . . . . . .Lt. Gen. Sir. P. H. Bennett
(Chief of General Staff)
Member (ex officio) . . . . . . . . . . . . . . . . . . . . .Air Marshal Selwyn D. Evans
(Chief of Air Staff)

**Defence Committee**

Chairman . . . . . . . . . . . . . . . . . . . . . . . . . . . . . . . . . . . . .W. B. Pritchett
(Secretary for Defence)
Member (ex officio) . . . . . . . . . . . . . . . . . . . . . .Sir Geoffrey Yeend, C.B.E.
(Secretary, Department of
Prime Minister and Cabinet)
Member (ex officio) . . . . . . . . . . . . . . . . . . . . . . . . . . . . . . . .J. O. Stone
(Secretary to Treasury)
Member (ex officio) . . . . . . . . . . . . . . . . . . . . . . . . . .P. G. F. Henderson
(Secretary, Department of
Foreign Affairs)
Member (ex officio) . . . . . . . . . .Air Chief Marshal Sir Neville P. McNamara
(Chief of Defence Staff)
Member (ex officio) . . . . . . . . . . . . . . . . . . . . . . .Vice Adm. D. W. Leach
(Chief of Naval Staff)
Member (ex officio) . . . . . . . . . . . . . . . . . . . . . .Lt. Gen. Sir P. H. Bennett
(Chief of General Staff)
Member (ex officio) . . . . . . . . . . . . . . . . . . . . .Air Marshal Selwyn D. Evans
(Chief of Air Staff)

**Policy Coordination Division**
*Telephone:   (62) 653048*

First Assistant Secretary, Policy Co-ordination . . . . . . . . . . . .N. D. McInnes
Director, Public Information . . . . . . . . . . . . . . . . . . .Air Comdr. T. C. Owen

**Strategic and International
  Policy Division**
*Telephone:   (62) 652849*

First Assistant Secretary, Strategic and
  International Policy . . . . . . . . . . . . . . . . . . . . . . . . . . . . .R. W. Cottrill
Assistant Secretary, Strategic Policy . . . . . . . . . . . . . . . . .A. G. Thompson
Senior Assistant Secretary, International Policy . . . . . . . . . . . .G. R. Marshall
Assistant Secretary, International Policy
  Anzus and UN . . . . . . . . . . . . . . . . . . . . . . . . . . . . . . . .R. K. Thomas

**Supply Division**
*Telephone:   (62) 664102*

Chief of Supply . . . . . . . . . . . . . . . . . . . . . . . . . .Maj. Gen. A. D. Powell
Director-General, Supply Army . . . . . . . . . . . . . . . . . . . .Brig. J. G. Cosson
Director-General, Supply Air Force . . . . . . . . . . .Air Comdr. R. R. Y. Candy
Director-General, Supply Navy . . . . . . . . . . . . . . . . . . . . .Cdr. I. Crawford

**Personnel Administration and Policy Division**

*Telephone: (62) 654899*

First Assistant Secretary, Personnel
Administration and Policy .............................P. J. Fogarty
Assistant Secretary, Civil Personnel ........................T. J. Parker
Assistant Secretary, Personnel, Navy ......................T. J. Keely
Assistant Secretary, Personnel, Army .....................R. H. Mills
Assistant Secretary, Personnel, Air Force .................L. Ludovicci

**Establishments Division**

*Telephone: (62) 663960*

Assistant Secretary, Organization
and Establishments ....................................B. E. Duke
Assistant Secretary, Management
Advisory Services .....................................J. H. Smith

**Joint Intelligence Organization**

*Telephone: (62) 654587*

Director, Joint Intelligence Organization ............Brig. J. Furner (Ret.)
Deputy Director, Civilian Joint
Intelligence Organization...............................N. L. Webb
Assistant Director, Economic Intelligence ................A. L. Campain
Assistant Director, Scientific and
Technical Intelligence ............................Dr. M. J. Barton
Assistant Director, Intelligence
Estimates .........................................D. J. Mannett

**Defence Industry and Materiel Policy Division**

*Telephone: (62) 653849*

First Assistant Secretary, Defence Industry
and Materiel Policy ...................................D. D. Wood
Special Adviser (Tactical Fighter Project) ...................A. F. Kent
Assistant Secretary, Industry Policy
and Planning.....................................Dr. M. K. McIntosh
Assistant Secretary, Project Planning
and Evaluation .......................................M. J. Welch
Assistant Secretary, Materiel Policy.......................P. V. Gerrans
Assistant Secretary, Industry Development.................G. M. Taylor

**Defence Communications System Division**

*Telephone: (62) 653780*

General-Manager, Defence
Communications Systems .............................I. H. Maggs
Assistant General-Manager,
Planning and Programming.............................M. F. Sage

**Defence Science and Technology Organization**

*Telephone: (62) 663399*

Chief, Defence Scientist .......................Prof. P. T. Fink, C.B.E.
Deputy Chief, Defence Scientist .........................G. E. Barlow
Superintendent, Science and
Technology Programmes........................Dr. M. E. G. Biffin
Assistant Secretary, Administration..........................(Vacant)
Assistant Secretary, Defence
Information Services ...................................F. B. Power

**Projects and Analytical Studies Division**

*Telephone: (62) 664302*

Controller, Projects and Analytical Studies .................W. Howard
Superintending Scientist, Major Projects .................J. H. L. Cohen
Superintending Scientist, External Relations ...............W. S. Howitt
Superintending Scientist, Analytical Studies ...............A. R. Taylor

**Research Laboratories**

Chief Superintendent, Aeronautical Research
Laboratories....................................Dr. G. L. Brown
Chief Superintendent, Advanced Engineering
Laboratory ........................................J. E. Lamprey
Chief Superintendent, Electronics Research
Laboratory....................................H. A. D'Assumpcao
Chief Superintendent, Weapons Systems
Research Laboratory ...............................J. W. Crompton
Chief Superintendent, Material Research
Laboratory...................................Dr. L. E. Samuels

**Defence Central Positions**
*(headed by service officers)*

Director-General, Service Conditions,
(Industrial Division) ....................... Comdr. A. R. Cumming
Controller, Establishments Division .......................... (Vacant)
Director-General, Natural
Disasters Organization .............. Maj. Gen. K. W. Latchford, A.O.
Director-General, Computer Operations .............. Brig. J. S. Kendell
Assistant General-Manager, Operations
and Engineering Defence Communications
System) .................................... Air Comdr. A. J. Benson
President, Australian Ordnance
Council ............................... Brig. M. H. MacKenzie-Orr

**Supply Division**
*Telephone:    (62) 664392*

Chief, Supply ................................ Maj. Gen. A. D. Powell
Director-General, Supply—Army ................... Brig. J. G. Cosson
Director-General, Supply—Air Force ......... Air Comdr. R. R. Y. Candy
Director-General, Movements
and Transport ........................ Air Comdr. K. W. Skillicorn
Director-General, Electrical and
Mechanical Engineering—Army .................... Brig. J. E. Faulks
Director-General, Army Quality Assurance ........... Brig. I. J. Meibusch

## DEFENCE FORCES

**ARMED FORCES**
**Defence Central Staff**
*Defence Force Headquarters*
*Russell Offices*
*Canberra, A.C.T. 2600*
*Telephone:    (62) 65 2858*
*Telex:    62625*

Chief, Defence Force Staff ........................ Air Chief Marshal
Sir Neville Patrick McNamara
K.B.E., A.E., G.C.V.O., G.C.M.G.
Assistant Chief, Defence Force Staff ..... Maj. Gen. P. C. Gration, O.B.E.

**Joint Military Operations
and Plans Division**
*Telephone:    (62) 654649*

Chief, Joint Operations and Plans .............. Rear Adm. I. H. Richards
Director-General, Joint Plans
and Operations ................................. Brig. G. J. Murphy
Director-General, Joint
Communications Electronics ................. Comdr. H. J. P. Adams
Commandant, Joint Services
Staff College ........................... Comdr. P. G. N. Kennedy
Deputy Director, Exercise
Kangaroo ............................... Air Comdr. G. W. Talbot

**ARMY**
**Australian Army**
*Russell Offices*
*Canberra, A.C.T. 2600*
*Telephone:    (62) 9111*
*Telex:    62053/62054*

Chief, General Staff ....................... Lt. Gen. Sir P. H. Bennett,
A.O., D.S.O., K.B.E.
Deputy Chief, General Staff ............... Maj. Gen. D. F. W. Engel,
A.O., O.B.E.
Chief, Operations ........................ Maj. Gen. L. G. O'Donnell
Deputy Chief, Operations ............... Brig. N. R. Smethurst, M.B.E.
Director-General, Operations and Plans .................. Brig. B. Wade
Chief, Personnel ......................... Maj. Gen. B. H. Hockney
Deputy Chief, Personnel ..................... Brig. A. B. Garland, A.M.
Chief, Logistics ................. Maj. Gen. D. C. J. Deighton, M.B.E.
Deputy Chief, Logistics ......................... Brig. R. D. Milliken
Director-General, Logistics
Development and Plans ..................... Brig. J. N. Stein, A.M.
Chief, Army Materiel (in
charge of procurement) ..................... Maj. Gen. K. J. Taylor
Chief, Army Reserve ...................... Maj. Gen. K. R. Murray,
A.O., O.B.E., E.D., Q.C.
Deputy Chief, Army Reserve ...................... Brig. K. R. Phillips

Director-General, Army
  Health Services............................Maj. Gen. W. B. James,
                                                       M.B.E., M.C., Q.H.P.
Director-General, Co-ordination
  and Organization .....................Brig. P. R. Badman, M.V.O.
Director-General, Army
  Development...............................Brig. F. K. Cole, A.M.
Director-General, Army
  Training ...................................Brig. T. F. H. Walker
Director-General, Personnel.............Brig. K. L. MacPherson, A.M.
Director-General, Army
  Legal Services...............................Brig. M. J. Ewing
Director, Army Medical
  Services................................Brig. W. O. Rogers, O.B.E.

## COMMANDS

**Field Force Command**

General Officer, Commanding ............Maj. Gen. J. D. Kelly, D.S.O.

**Logistic Command**
*P.O. Box 1932R*
  *G.P.O.*
*Melbourne VIC 3001*
*Telephone:  (3) 6976700*

General Officer, Commanding .................Maj. Gen. J. C. Hughes,
                                                       A.O., D.S.O., M.C.

**Training Command**
*P.O. Box 39*
*Darlinghurst,*
*NSW 2010*
*Telephone:  (2) 2372676*

General Officer, Commanding ..........Maj. Gen. D. M. Butler, D.S.O.

**First Division**
*Headquarters 1st Division*
*MILPO*
*Enoggera, QLD 4052*
*Telephone:  (7) 3545111*

Commander .......................Maj. Gen. D. A. Drabsch, M.B.E.

**Second Division**
*Headquarters 2nd Division*
*Moore Park Bks,*
*Moore Park Road*
*Paddington NSW 2021*
*Telephone:  (2) 330905*

Commander ...........................Maj. Gen. R. J. Sharp, E.D.

**Royal Military College**
*Duntroon, ACT 2601*
*Australia*
*Telephone:  (62) 663430*

Commander .........................Maj. Gen. H. J. Coates, M.B.E.

**NAVY**
**Royal Australian Navy—RAN**
*Russell Offices*
*Canberra, A.C.T. 2600*
*Telephone:  (62) 65 9111, 65 5142*
         *(after hours)*
*Telex:  62112*

Chief, Naval Staff..................Vice Adm. David Willoughby Leach,
                                                       A.O., C.B.E., M.V.O.
Deputy Chief, Naval Staff ................Rear Adm. G. J. H. Woolrych
Chief, Naval Materiel
  (In charge of procurement)............Rear Adm. W. J. Rourke, A.O.
Deputy Chief, Naval Material ......................Comdr. B. L. West
Chief, Naval Technical
  Services .........................Rear Adm. D. F. Lynam, C.B.E.
Chief, Naval Personnel.......................Rear Adm. D. J. Martin
Chief, Naval Operational
  Requirements and Plans ....................Rear Adm. I. W. Knox

Director-General, Naval
   Health Services . . . . . . . . . . . . . . . . . . . Surgeon Rear Adm. B. T. Treloar
Director-General, Fleet
   Maintenance . . . . . . . . . . . . . . . . . . . . . . . . . Comdr. D. G. Holthouse
Director-General, Naval
   Production . . . . . . . . . . . . . . . . . . . . . . . . . . Comdr. R. R. Calder, A.M.
Director-General, Naval
   Operational Requirements . . . . . . . . . . . . . Comdr. J. A. O'Farrell, A.M.
Director-General, Naval
   Plans and Policy . . . . . . . . . . . . . . . . . . . . . . Comdr. A. R. Horton, A.M.
Director-General, Naval
   Manpower . . . . . . . . . . . . . . . . . . . . . . . . . . . Comdr. B. G. Gibbs, A.M.
Director-General, Naval
   Personnel Services . . . . . . . . . . . . . . . . . . . . . . . . Comdr. J. L. Jobson
Director-General, Naval
   Training and Education . . . . . . . . . . . . . . . . . . . . . Comdr. R. M. Baird

**Naval Support Command**
*Remington Centre*
*175/183 Liverpool Street*
*Sydney NSW 2010*
*Telephone:   (2) 2662911*

Flag Officer, Naval
   Support Command . . . . . . . . . . . . . . . . . . . . . Rear Adm. K. Vonthethoff

**Australian Fleet Garden Island**
*New South Wales 2000*
*Telephone:   (2) 359 9111*

Flag Officer Commanding
   Her Majesty's Australian Fleet . . . . . . . . . . . . . Rear Adm. M. W. Hudson
Naval Officer Commanding
   Victoria Area (Melbourne) . . . . . . . . . . . . . . . . Comdr. R. W. Burnett
Naval Officer Commanding
   West Australia (Rockingham) . . . . . . . . . . . . . . . . . Comdr. D. J. Orr
Naval Officer Commanding
   Queensland (Brisbane) . . . . . . . . . . . . . . . . . . . . . Capt. E. T. Keane
Naval Officer Commanding
   North Australia (Darwin) . . . . . . . . . . . . . . . . . . Capt. C. M. G. Hole
Naval Officer Commanding
   South Australia
   (Port Adelaide) . . . . . . . . . . . . . . . . . . . . . . . . . Cdmr. D. E. Clinch
Naval Officer Commanding
   Tasmania (Hobart) . . . . . . . . . . . . . . . . . . . . . Cdmr. M. T. E. Shotter

**Royal Australian Naval College**
*HMAS Creswell*
*Jervis Bay, A.C.T. 2540*
*Telephone:   421007*

Commanding Officer . . . . . . . . . . . . . . . . . . . . . . . . . . . Capt. P. A. Ross

**AIR FORCE**
**Royal Australian Air Force—RAAF**
*Russell Offices*
*Canberra, A.C.T. 2600*
*Telephone:   (62) 65 9111*
*Telex:   62767*

Chief of the Air Staff . . . . . . . . . . . . . . . . . Air Marshal Selwyn David Evans,
                                                                            A.O., D.S.O., A.F.C.
Deputy Chief, Air Staff . . . . . . . . . . . . . . . . . . . . . . . . . Air Vice-Marshal
                                                                     H. A. Hughes, A.O., D.F.C.
Chief, Air Force Personnel . . . . . . . . . . . . . . . . Air Vice-Marshal R. E. Frost
Chief, Air Force Development . . . . . . . . . . . . . . Air Vice-Marshal P. J. Scully
Chief, Air Force Materiel
   (in charge of procurement) . . . . . . . . . . . . Air Vice-Marshal A. E. Heggen
Chief, Air Force Technical Services . . . . . . . . . . . . . . . . . Air Vice-Marshal
                                                                           J. A. Dietz, B.E.
Director-General, Supply—
   Air Force . . . . . . . . . . . . . . . . . . . . . . . Air Comdr. R. R. Y. Candy, A.M.
Director-General, Operations—
   Air Force . . . . . . . . . . . . . . . . . . . . . Air Comdr. W. G. McM. Richardson
Director-General, Material
   Definition . . . . . . . . . . . . . . . . . . . . . . . Air Comdr. J. H. Cox, D.F.C.
Director-General, Material
   Projects . . . . . . . . . . . . . . . . . . . . . . . . . . . . Air Comdr. W. E. Sansum

Director-General, Tactical
Fighter Project . . . . . . . . . . . . . . . . . . . . . . . . . . . . . . Air Comdr. H. J. Roser
Director-General, Technical
Plans . . . . . . . . . . . . . . . . . . . . . . . . . . . . . . . . . . . . . . . Air Comdr. R. A. Kee
Director-General,
Engineering . . . . . . . . . . . . . . . . . . . . . . . . . . . . . . . Air Comdr. B. J. Graf
Director-General, Policy
and Plans . . . . . . . . . . . . . . . . . . . . . . . . . . . . . Air Comdr. D. G. Cameron
Director-General, Operational
Requirements . . . . . . . . . . . . . . . . . . . . . . . Air Comdr. R. W. Bradford
Director-General, Manpower . . . . . . . . . . . . . . . . . . . . . . . . . . . Air Comdr.
E. A. Radford, A.M.
Director-General, Air Force
Health Services . . . . . . . . . . . . . . . . Air Vice-Marshal E. H. Stephenson,
O.B.E., M.S.C., L.R.C.P., M.R.C.S.,
D.I.H., A.F.O.M., Q.H.P.
Deputy Director, Air Force
Health Services . . . . . . . . . . . . . . . . . . . . . . . . . Air Comdr. G. W. Reed
Director-General, Personnel
Services . . . . . . . . . . . . . . . . . . . . . . . . . . . . . . . . . . . . . . . . . Air Comdr.
J. M. Chesterfield, A.M.
Judge Advocate General, RAAF . . . . . . . . . . . . . . . . . . . . . Air Vice-Marshal
The Hon. Mr. Justice M. M. Helsham,
D.F.C., B.A., L.L.B.(A)

## AIR FORCE COMMANDS

**Operational Command**
*Glenbrook*
*New South Wales*
*Telephone:   (2) 397111*

Commander . . . . . . . . . . . . . . . . . . . . . . . . . . . . Air Vice-Marshal R. N. Law

**Support Command**
*Melbourne, Victoria*
*Telephone:   (3) 6971111*

Commander . . . . . . . . . . . . . . . . . . Air Vice-Marshal B. H. Collings, A.F.C.

\* \* \* \* \*

# GENERAL DEFENCE DATA

**Manpower**
Total Armed Forces . . . . . . . . . . . . . . . . . . . . . . . . . . . . . . . . . . . . . . . . . . 72,965
(See Page 35)
Population . . . . . . . . . . . . . . . . . . . . . . . . . . . . . . . . . . . . . . . . . . . 15,011,000

**Spending**
Military Expenditures . . . . . . . . . . . . . . . . . . . . . . . . . . . . . . . . . . . . $3.2 billion
Gross National Product . . . . . . . . . . . . . . . . . . . . . . . . . . . . . . . . . . $142 billion
Military Expenditure as a Percentage of
Gross National Product . . . . . . . . . . . . . . . . . . . . . . . . . . . . . . . . . 2.3%
Military Expenditure as a Percentage of
Central Government Expenditure . . . . . . . . . . . . . . . . . . . . . . . . . . 9.1%

**Defence Treaties** *(See Part II for Additional Detail)*

Bilateral:       India
                 New Zealand
                 United States

Multilateral:    ANZUS
                 Biological Weapons Convention
                 Five-Power Defence Arrangements
                 Limited Test Ban Treaty
                 Multinational Force and Observers in Sinai
                 South-East Asia Collective Defence Treaty
                 Treaty on the Control of Arms on the Seabed
                 Treaty on the Non-Proliferation of Nuclear Weapons

# AUSTRIA
## Republic of Austria
### *Republik Österreich*

### Defense Establishment Command Structure
### and Force Organization

The Federal President is the Supreme Commander of the Austrian armed forces. In practice the head of the government, the Federal Chancellor, is responsible for defense matters. He in turn delegates operational control of the armed forces to the Minister of Defense.

The Inspector General is the highest-ranking military officer and the top adviser to the Minister of Defense. He is responsible for matters of military strategy and coordination. The Commander of the Army is charged mainly with ensuring operational readiness of the armed forces. The Air Force is an integral part of the Army.

The Defense Council is chaired by the Federal Chancellor. Its other members include the Inspector General as well as Members of Parliament and nonpartisan experts summoned by the Chancellor. The Council has a general advisory role.

**Total armed forces:** 49,350 (Army: 44,950;  Air Force: 4,400).

## HEAD OF STATE

Dr. Rudolf Kirchschläger

**OFFICE OF THE FEDERAL
  PRESIDENT**
*Hofburg, Leopoldinischer Trakt
1014 Vienna*

*Telephone: (222) 57 36 26, 57 36 28
Telex: 133484*

Federal President and Supreme
  Commander ............................Dr. Rudolf Kirchschläger

**OFFICE OF THE FEDERAL
  CHANCELLOR**
*Ballhausplatz 2
1014 Vienna*

*Telephone: (222) 66 15 0
Telex: 137090*

Federal Minister ...............................Dr. Fred Sinowatz

**Defense Council**
*(Verteidigungstrat)*

Chairman .......................................Dr. Fred Sinowatz
(Federal Chancellor)
Member .............................Dr. Friedhelm Frischenschlager
(Minister of Defense)
Member ......................................Gen. Heinrich Scharff
(Inspector General)

**FEDERAL MINISTRY FOR NATIONAL
  DEFENSE**
*(Bundesministerium für
  Landesverteidigung)*

Federal Minister ......................Dr. Friedhelm Frischenschlager
Chief of Cabinet ...........................Obst. Dr. Peter Corrieri
Director, Press and Information
  Service ...............................Dr. Klaus Sartorius-Thalborn

*Dampfschiffstr. 2*
*1030 Vienna*

*Telephone:   (222) 52 95 25*
*Telex:   112145 bmflv a*

| | |
|---|---|
| Director, Defense Policy Bureau | Obstlt. Karl Semlitsch |
| Director, Control Bureau | Bgdr. Friedrich Rötzer |

### Section I: Presidial and Legal Section
*(Präsidial- und Rechtssektion)*

| | |
|---|---|
| Chief | Dr. Adolf Kolb |
| Director, Division 1 (Legislative) | Gerhard Rauter |
| Director, Group A (Presidium) | Divr. Dr. Erich Fraydl |
| Director, Division 2 (Presidial) | Alois Rosenberger |
| Director, Division 3 (Presidial) | Obst. Dr. Friedrich Hötz |
| Director, Division 4 (Presidial) | Walter Kraus |
| Director, Division 5 (Legal) | Obst. Dr. Josef Seyfried |
| Director, Division 6 (Legal) | Dr. Heinrich Geusau |
| Director, Division 7 (Legal) | Dr. Friedrich Griessler |
| Director, Accounting | Heinrich Gruner |

### Section II: Personnel and Recruitment
*(Sektion für Personal- und*
*Ergänzungswesen)*
*Engerthstr. 226*
*1020 Vienna*

*Telephone:   (222) 24 36 61*

| | |
|---|---|
| Chief | Dr. Franz Sailler |
| Director, Group A (Personnel) | Dr. Peter Weihs |
| Directior, Group B (Recruitment) | Johann Ellinger |

### Section III: Army Command
*(See "Defense Forces")*

### Section IV: Armaments Procurement and Supply
*(Sektion für Rüstung, Beschaffung und*
*Versorgung)*
*Franz-Josefs-Kai 7-9*
*1011 Vienna*

*Telephone:   (222) 52 95 25*

| | |
|---|---|
| Chief | Gen. Dr. Raimund Truxa |

**Group A (Logistics)**

| | |
|---|---|
| Director | Divr. Franz Fikeis |
| Director, Planning and Operations Division | Obst. Richard Bondi |
| Director, Administrative Division | Obst. Gerhard Janzek-Hawlat |
| Director, Defense Industry Affairs Division | Dr. Walter Zeininger |

**Group B (Ordnance)**

| | |
|---|---|
| Director | Divr. Josef Fenz |
| Director, Ordnance and Munitions | Obst. Hans Kossik |
| Director, Military Vehicles and Fuels/Lubricants Division | Obstlt. Franz Bremm |
| Director, Aircraft, Electronics and Communications Division | Bgdr. Josef Schmalzer |

**Group C (Quartermaster Affairs)**

| | |
|---|---|
| Director | Divr. Eduard Uhl |
| Director, Military Economics Division | Obstlt. Raimund Truxa |
| Director, Quartermaster and Clothing Division | Bgdr. Dr. Gottfried Zauner |
| Director, Monetary and Accounts Division | Bgdr. Gustav Mayerhofer |
| Director, Medical Division | Divr. Dr. Johann Schmid |
| Director, Procurement and Sales Division | Bgdr. Helmut Fischer |
| Director, Defense Technology Division | Dr. Paul Vock |

### General Troop Inspectorate
*(Generaltruppeninspektorat)*
*Franz-Josefs-Kai 7-9*
*1011 Vienna*

*Telephone:   (222) 52 95 25*

| | |
|---|---|
| Inspector General | Gen. Heinrich Scharff |
| Director, General Staff Division | Obst. Karl Budik |
| Director, Attaché Division | Bgdr. Ignaz Attems |

**General Staff Group A**

| | |
|---|---|
| Director | Divr. Othmar Tauschitz |
| Director, Long-Term Planning Division | Obst. Ernest König |
| Director, Armament Planning Division | Obst. Karl Plienegger |
| Director, Organizational Division | Bgdr. Rudolf Striedinger |
| Director, Information Systems, Telecommunications and Electronics Division | Bgdr. Otto Horak |

**General Staff Group B**

Director ........................................Divr. Karl Liko
Director, Military Operations Division ...............Bgdr. Erich Eder
Director, Training and Manuals Division ....................(Vacant)
Director, Air Division .........................Obst. Josef Bernecker

**Inspection Group**

Director........................................Divr. Robert Lang
Director, Inspection Division ....................Bgdr. Hans Haufler

**Military Technology Agency**
*Albrecht-Kaserne*
*Engerthstr. 226*
*1024 Vienna*
*Telephone: (222) 24 36 61*

Commanding Officer ..........................Divr. Richard Rubik

**Army Materiel Agency**
*Heckenast-Burian Kaserne*
*Schwenkg. 47*
*1121 Vienna*
*Telephone: (222) 83 16 31*

Commanding Officer ........................Divr. Dr. Franz Schöner

**Army Construction and Survey Agency**
*Strausseng. 11*
*1050 Vienna*
*Telephone: (222) 57 15 31*

Commanding Officer......................Divr. Dr. Wolfgang Seibert

**Army Intelligence Agency**
*Kommandogebäude General Körner*
*Hütteldorferstr. 126*
*1142 Vienna*
*Telephone: (222) 92 66 51*

Commanding Officer ...........................Divr. Johann Ulrich

## DEFENSE FORCES

**ARMY**
**Army Command (Section III)**
*(Armeekommando)*
*Hütteldorfer Strasse 126*
*1142 Vienna*
*Telephone: (222) 92 66 51, 92 44 70*

Commander, Army ..........................Gen. Ernest Bernadiner
Chief of Staff ................................Divr. Viktor Fortunat
Director, Personnel Division ......................Obst. Günter Holly
Director, Publicity Division ........................Obst. Walter Gsell
Director, Special Training Division ...............Bgdr. Marius Dadak
Commanding Officer, National Defense
    Academy (Vienna) .............KorpsKdt. Lothar Brosch-Fohraheim
Military Vicar (Catholic) (Vienna) ......................Dr. Franz Zak
Evangelical Superintendent (Vienna).................Dr. Julius Hanak

**Operations Staff**

Director .........................................Divr. Fritz Wieser
Director, Intelligence and Security
    Division......................................Obst. Walter Schmit
Director, Operations and Preparation
    Division ..............................Bgdr. Johann Mittendorfer
Director, Air Operations Division .............Obst. Gerhard Keltscher
Director, Training Division ....................Obst. Alfred Schenner
Director, Communications Division................Bgdr. Ernest Stoiser
Director, Motorized Transport Division ..........Obst. Adalbert Bednar

**Supply Staff**

Director ......................................Divr. Josef Pollhammer
Director, Supply Division .........................Obst. Karl Marek
Director, Supply Management Division ............Obst. Wilfried Wöss

Director, Technical Division ....................Obst. Dr. Karl Becker
Director, Medical Division ..............Bgdr. Dr. Otto Zinn-Zinneburg
Director, Veterinary Division ..................Bgdr. Dr. Fritz Hampel

**Vienna Military Command**
*Radetzky-Kaserne*
*Panikeng. 2*
*1163 Vienna*
*Telephone:   (222) 92 66 61*

Commanding Officer .............................Divr. Karl Majcen

**First Corps Command**
*Glacisstr. 39-41*
*8011 Graz*
*Telephone:   (316) 33 5 61*

Commanding Officer ...........................Gen. Alexius Battyan
Commander, Burgenland ......................Divr. Siegbert Kreuter
Commander, Lower Austria .....................Divr. Ernst Maerker
Commander, Styria ..........................Divr. Hubert Albrecht

**Second Corps Command**
*Schwarzenberg-Kaserne*
*Block 1301*
*5071 Salzburg*
*Telephone:   (6222) 44 5 81*

Commanding Officer ...............KorpsKdt. Dr. Johann Tretter
Commander, Upper Austria ......................Divr. Karl Schöller
Commander, Tyrol ...........................Divr. Mathis Winfried
Commander, Carinthia ..................Divr. Maximilian Liebminger
Commander, Salzburg ......................................(Vacant)
Commander, Vorarlberg .....................Divr. Friedrich Materna

**Higher Commands**

Commander, First Mechanized Division
    (Baden)..............................Divr. August Ségur-Cabanac
Commander, Third Mechanized Brigade
    (Mautern) ................................Obst. Kurt Pirker
Commander, Fourth Mechanized Brigade
    (Linz) ..................................Obst. Günter Wild
Commander, Ninth Mechanized Brigade
    (Götzendorf) ............................Obst. Heinz Danzmayr

**AIR FORCE**
**Air Command**
*(Kommando Fliegerdivision)*
*Fliegerhorst Brumowski*
*3425 Langenlebarn*
*Telephone:   (2272) 23 08*

Commander....................................Divr. Gustav Golja

\* \* \* \* \*

## GENERAL DEFENSE DATA

**Manpower**
    Total Armed Forces ..............................................49,350
        (See Page 43)
    Population ..................................................7,510,000

**Spending**
    Military Expenditures...........................................$913 million
    Gross National Product .........................................$77 billion
    Military Expenditure as a Percentage of
        Gross National Product .........................................1.2%
    Military Expenditure as a Percentage of
        Central Government Expenditure ................................6.0%

**Defense Treaties** *(See Part II for Additional Detail)*

    Bilateral:     United States

    Multilateral:     Biological Weapons Convention
                      Limited Test Ban Treaty
                      Treaty on the Control of Arms on the Seabed
                      Treaty on the Non-Proliferation of Nuclear Weapons
                      United Nations Disengagement Observer Force
                      United Nations Force in Cyprus
                      United Nations Truce Supervision Organization

**Military Rank Comparisons**
    See Appendix A.

# BAHAMAS
## Commonwealth of the Bahamas

### Defence Establishment Command Structure and Force Organization

The Governor-General is Commander-in-Chief of the Defence Forces of the Bahamas. Operational and administrative control of the military is exercised by the Minister of Defence.

**Para-military forces:** 1,365. **Reserves:** 272.

### HEAD OF STATE

H. M. Queen Elizabeth II

### Governor-General

H. E. Sir Gerald Christopher Cash, G.C.M.G., K.C.V.O., O.B.E., J.P.

**OFFICE OF THE GOVERNOR-GENERAL**
*Government House*
*Government Hill*
*P.O. Box N-8301*
*Nassau, N.P.*
*Telephone: 332-1875, 332-1021*

Governor-General and
  Commander-in-Chief . . . . . . . . . . . . . . . . . . Sir Gerald Christopher Cash,
    G.C.M.G., K.C.V.O., O.B.E., J.P.
Aide-de-Camp and Inspector General . . . . . . . . . . . . . . . . . . . . . Ulric Smith

**CABINET OFFICE**
*Rawson Square*
*P.O. Box N-7147*
*Nassau, N.P.*
*Telephone: 322-2805*

Prime Minister and Minister
  of Defence . . . . . . . . . . . . . . . . Sir Lynden O. Pindling, K.C.M.G., M.P.
Secretary to the Cabinet . . . . . . . . . . . . (Mrs.) Margaret McDonald, C.B.E.
Under Secretary . . . . . . . . . . . . . . . . . . . . . . . . . . . . . . . . . . . Wendell Major
Deputy Permanent Secretary . . . . . . . . . . . . . . . . . . (Miss) Vernita Johnson

**MINISTRY OF DEFENCE**
*Rawson Square*
*P.O. Box N-3733*
*Nassau, N.P.*
*Telephone: 322-3220, 3221*

Prime Minister and Minister of
  Defence . . . . . . . . . . . . . . . . . . Sir Lynden O. Pindling, K.C.M.G., M.P.
Secretary to the Cabinet and
  Permanent Secretary, Ministry of
  Defence . . . . . . . . . . . . . . . . . . . (Mrs.) Margaret McDonald, C.B.E.
Deputy Permanent Secretary . . . . . . . . . . . . . . . . . . . . . . . . Samule Dean
First Assistant Secretary . . . . . . . . . . . . . . . . . . . . . . . . . . . . . . . (Vacant)

### DEFENCE FORCES

**ARMED FORCES**
**Defence Forces**
*Ministry of Defence*
*Rawson Square*
*P.O. Box N-3393*
*Nassau, N.P.*
*Telephone: 322-1994*

Commander, Defence Forces . . . . . . . . . . . . . . . Comdr. Christopher Belton
Squadron Commanding Officer . . . . . . . . . . . . . . . . . . Cdr. David B. King

**NAVY**
**HMBS** *Coral Harbour*
*Telephone:  7-7141, 7-7608*

Commander . . . . . . . . . . . . . . . . . . . . . . . . . . . . . . . . . . . . . . . . Capt. L. L. Smith

**AIR FORCE**
**Air Wing**
*Nassau*

Commander . . . . . . . . . . . . . . . . . . . . . . . . . . . . . . . . . . . . . . . David Henderson

**POLICE**
**Royal Bahamas Police Force**
*P.O. Box N-3020*
*Nassau, N.P.*
*Telephone:  322-4444*
*Cable:  COMPOL (Bah)*

Commissioner . . . . . . . . . . . . . . . . . . . . . . . . . . . . . . . . . Gerald A. Bartlett,
C.B.E., O.B.E., Q.P.M., C.P.M.
Deputy Commissioner . . . . . . . . . . . . . . . . . . . . Dudley T. Hanna, Q.P.M.
Assistant Commissioner . . . . . . . . . . . . . . . . . . . . . . . . . . . . Alonzo M. Butler
Assistant Commissioner . . . . . . . . . . . . . . . . . . . . . Keith V. Mason, Q.P.M.
Assistant Commissioner  . . . . . . . . . . Howard T. G. Smith, Q.P.M., C.P.M.

**New Providence District**
*Telephone:  2-4568*

Chief Superintendent . . . . . . . . . . . . . . . . . . . . . . . . . . . . . . G. O. Ifill, Sr.

**Police Air Wing**
*Telephone:  2-1647*

Chief . . . . . . . . . . . . . . . . . . . . . . . . . . . . . . . . . . . . . . . . . . G. O. Ifill, Sr.

**Security and Intelligence Branch**
*Telephone:  2-4088*

Assistant Commissioner . . . . . . . . . . . . . . . . . . . . . . . . . DSP B. K. Bonimy

**Internal Security Division**
*Telephone:  3-5361*

Assistant Commissioner  . . . . . . . . . Howard T. G. Smith, Q.P.M., C.P.M.

**Central Division**
*Telephone:  2-3114*

Commander . . . . . . . . . . . . . . . . . . . . . . . . . . . DSP Errol Farquarson, C.P.M.

**Southern Division**
*Telephone:  2-2197*

Commander . . . . . . . . . . . . . . . . . . . . . . . . . . . . . . . . . . ASP Oscar Sawyer

**Western Division**
*Telephone:  7-8551*

Commander . . . . . . . . . . . . . . . . . . . . . . . . . . . . . . . . . . . . . . . ASP Rahming

**Police College**
*Nassau, N.P.*
*Telephone:  5-8551*

Commander . . . . . . . . . . . . . . . . . . . . . . . Chief Superintendent Darville
Deputy Superintendent
(In charge of procurement) . . . . . . . . . . . . . . . . . . . . ASP Edmund Stubbs

* * * * *

# GENERAL DEFENCE DATA

**Manpower**
   Total Armed Forces . . . . . . . . . . . . . . . . . . . . . . . . . . . . . . . . . . . 1,365
      (See Page 49)
   Population . . . . . . . . . . . . . . . . . . . . . . . . . . . . . . . . . . . . . . . . . . 237,000

**Spending**

Military Expenditures . . . . . . . . . . . . . . . . . . . . . . . . . . . . . . . . . . . . . . . . . . . . . . . . . .

Gross National Product . . . . . . . . . . . . . . . . . . . . . . . . . . . . . . . . . . . . . . . . . .$1 billion

Military Expenditure as a Percentage of
  Gross National Product . . . . . . . . . . . . . . . . . . . . . . . . . . . . . . . . . . . . . . . . . . . . . .

Military Expenditure as a Percentage of
  Central Government Expenditure . . . . . . . . . . . . . . . . . . . . . . . . . . . . . . . . . . . . . .

**Defence Treaties** *(See Part II for Additional Detail)*

Bilateral:    United States

Multilateral:    Limited Test Ban Treaty
              Inter-American Defence Board
              Treaty for the Prohibition of Nuclear Weapons in
                Latin America
              Treaty on the Non-Proliferation of Nuclear Weapons

# BAHRAIN
## State of Bahrain
### *Dawlat Bahrain*

## Defence Establishment Command Structure and Force Organization

The Amir is Commander-in-Chief of the Bahrain Defence Force. His authority is exercised through the Minister of Defence and the Chief of Staff. The Navy and Air Wing form components of the Army.

**Total armed forces:** 2,550 (Army: 2,300;  Navy: 150;  Air Force: 100). **Para-military forces:** 2,680 (Coastguard: 180;  Police: 2,500).

## HEAD OF STATE

H. H. Sheikh Isa Bin Salman Al-Khalifa, K.C.M.G.

**OFFICE OF H. H. THE AMIR**
*P.O. Box 555*
*Manama*

*Telephone:   661451*
*Telex:   8666 qasar gj*

Amir of Bahrain and
　Commander-in-Chief . . . . . . . . . H. H. Sheikh Isa Bin Salman Al-Khalifa
Advisor to the Amir . . . . . . . . . . . . . . . . . . . . . . . . . . . . . . Ahmad Al-Umran
Chief of Amiri Court . . . . . . . . . . . . . . . . . . . . . . Yousuf Rahman Al-Dousiri
Administration Director . . . . . . . . . . . . . . . . . . . . . Khaled Yousuf Mattar

**OFFICE OF THE PRIME MINISTER**
*P.O. Box 1000*
*Manama*

*Telephone:   253361*
*Telex:   8228 karjia bn*

Prime Minister . . . . . . . . . . . . . . . . . . Sheikh Khalifa Bin Salman Al-Khalifa
Director of the Office of
　the Prime Minister . . . . . . . . . . . . . . . . Mohamed Ebrahim Al-Mutawa'a
Secretary to the Prime Minister . . . . . . . . . . . . . Abdulrahman Al-Mahmood

**MINISTRY OF DEFENCE**
*P.O. Box 245*
*West Rifa'a*
*Bahrain*

*Telephone:   665599*
*Telex:   8429 deffaa gj*

Heir Apparent and Minister
　of Defence . . . . . . . . . . . . . . . . . . . . . . Sheikh Hamad Bin Isa Al-Khalifa
Advisor . . . . . . . . . . . . . . . . . . . . . . . . . . . . . . . . . . . . . . . Maj. T. B. Johnson
Public Relations Officer . . . . . . . . . . . . . . . . . . . . . . . . . . . . . Ahmad Al-Absi

## DEFENCE FORCES

**ARMY**
**Bahrain Defence Force**
*Headquarters*
*Manama*

*Telephone:   665599*

Chief of Staff . . . . . . . . . . . . . . . . Brig. Gen. Khalifa bin Ahmed Al-Khalifa
Assistant Chief of Staff,
　Operations . . . . . . . . . . . . . . . . . . . . Col. Abdullah bin Sulam Al-Khalifa
Assistant Chief of Staff,
　for Personnel . . . . . . . . . . . . . . . . . . . . . . . . . . . Col. Hussain Ali A. Qader
Director of Training . . . . . . . . . Lt. Col. Hamed Bin Mohammed Al-Khalifa
Commanding Officer, Infantry
　Battalion Camp . . . . . . . . . . . . . . . . . . . . . . . . . . Col. Mohamed Mashel
Commanding Officer, Amiri
　Guard . . . . . . . . . . . . . . . . . . . . . . . . . . . . . . . . . . . . Col. Ibrahim Musla
Commanding Officer, Military
　Hospital . . . . . . . . . . . . . . . . . . . . . . . . . . . . . Col. Mohamed Al-Khalifa
Director, Military Medical
　Services . . . . . . . . . . . . . . . . . . . . . . Dr. Mohd Bin Abdulla Al-Khalifa

**Navy**
*c/o Bahrain Defence Force*
*Headquarters*
*Manama*
*Telephone:   665599*

Commander . . . . . . . . . . . . . . . . . . . . . . . . . . . . . . . . . . . Col. Khalil Rahman

**Air Wing**
*c/o Bahrain Defence Force*
*Headquarters*
*Manama*
*Telephone:   665599*

Commander . . . . . . . . . . . . . . . . . . . . . . . . . . . . . . . . . . . Maj. Nabil Kamal

\* \* \* \* \*

## GENERAL DEFENCE DATA

**Manpower**
    Total Armed Forces . . . . . . . . . . . . . . . . . . . . . . . . . . . . . . . . . . . . . . . . . . . 2,550
       (See Page 53)
    Population . . . . . . . . . . . . . . . . . . . . . . . . . . . . . . . . . . . . . . . . . . . . . . . . . 380,000

**Spending**
    Military Expenditures . . . . . . . . . . . . . . . . . . . . . . . . . . . . . . . . . . . . . $55 million
    Gross National Product . . . . . . . . . . . . . . . . . . . . . . . . . . . . . . . . . . $2.899 billion
    Military Expenditure as a Percentage of
      Gross National Product . . . . . . . . . . . . . . . . . . . . . . . . . . . . . . . . . . . . 1.9%
    Military Expenditure as a Percentage of
      Central Government Expenditure . . . . . . . . . . . . . . . . . . . . . . . . . . . . . . 6.6%

**Defence Treaties** *(See Part II for Additional Detail)*

      Bilateral:      Saudi Arabia
                   United Kingdom

      Multilateral:  Cooperation Council for the Arab States of the Gulf
                   League of Arab States

# BANGLADESH
## People's Republic of Bangladesh

### Defence Establishment Command Structure
### and Force Organization

The Chief Martial Law Administrator is Commander-in-Chief and Minister of Defence of the armed forces of Bangladesh.

**Total armed forces:** 83,000 (Army: 70,000; Navy: 6,000; Air Force: 7,000). **Para-military forces:** 66,000.

### HEAD OF STATE

Justice A. F. M. Ahsanuddin Chowdhury

### CHIEF EXECUTIVE AND HEAD OF THE GOVERNMENT

Lt. Gen. Hussain Muhammad Ershad

**OFFICE OF THE PRESIDENT**
*Bangabhaban*
*Dacca-2*
*Telephone: 404166, 404202, 404024*
*(President's Secretariat)*

President of the People's Republic in
    Charge of the President's Secretariat . . . . . . . . . . . . . . . . . Justice A. F. M. Ahsanddin Chowdhury
Secretary of the President's Secretariat . . . . . . . . . . . . . A. H. F. K. Sadeque

### CHIEF MARTIAL LAW ADMINISTRATOR
### AND COUNCIL OF ADVISORS

**OFFICE OF CHIEF MARTIAL LAW ADMINISTRATOR**
*Old Sangshad Bhaban*
*Airport Road*
*Dacca-15*

Chief Martial Law Administrator,
    and Head of Ministries of the
    C.M.L.A.'s Secretariat, Defence,
    Tourism, Cabinet Division
    and Establishment Division . . . . . . Lt. Gen. Hussain Muhammad Ershad ndc, psc
Principal Staff Officer to the Chief
    Martial Law Administrator . . . . . . . . . . . . Maj. Gen. Muzammel Hussain
General Staff to the Chief
    Martial Law Administrator . . . . . . . . . . . . . Maj. Gen. Nazirul Aziz Chisti
Deputy Chief Martial Law
    Administrator and Minister
    of Communications . . . . . . . . . . . . . . . . . . Rear Adm. Mahbub Ali Khan
Deputy Chief Martial Law
    Administrator and Minister of
    Energy and Mineral Resources . . . . . . . Air Vice-Marshal Sultan Mahmud

**C.M.L.A. SECRETARIAT**
*Double Protected Area*
*Bangladesh Secretariat*
*Dacca-2*

**Cabinet Division**
*Telephone: 404840*

Secretary . . . . . . . . . . . . . . . . . . . . . . . . . . . . Mohammad Mahbubuzzanan

**MINISTRY OF DEFENCE**
*Old High Court Building*
*Segunbagicha*
*Dacca-2*

*Telephone:   242638*

| | |
|---|---|
| Minister of Defence and Chief Martial Law Administrator | Lt. Gen. Hussain Muhammad Ershad ndc, psc |
| Secretary | Mr. M. Salahuddin Ahmed |
| Joint Secretary, Training | Brig. Amin Ahmed Chowdhury |
| Deputy Secretary | Aftabuddin Ahmed |
| Deputy Secretary | M. A. Khan |
| Deputy Secretary | A. K. M. Nurul Islam |
| Deputy Secretary | Ataul Huq |
| Deputy Secretary | A. T. M. Azizur Rahman |
| Deputy Secretary | Md. Shariful Huq |

**Defence Division**
*Telephone:   251644*

Secretary ........................................ Salauddin Ahmed

# DEFENCE FORCES

**ARMED FORCES**
**Office of the Commander-in-Chief of the Armed Forces**
*Dacca Cantonment*
*Dacca*

Chief Martial Law Administrator and Commander-in-Chief of the Armed Forces .............. Lt. Gen. Hussain Muhammad Ershad
Principal Staff Officer to the Commander-in-Chief ............. Maj. Gen. M. Atiqur Rahman

**ARMY**
*Army Headquarters*
*Dacca Cantonment*
*Dacca*

*Telephone:   310341-46*
*Telex:   642200 bj*
*(Ministry of Foreign Affairs)*

Chief of the General Staff ............... Maj. Gen. M. Noor Uddin Khan
Quartermaster General .............. Maj. Gen. Abdul Mannan Siddiqui
Adjutant General ......................................... (Vacant)
Commander, 9th Infantry Division Headquarters ................... Maj. Gen. Abdul Wahed
Commander, 11th Infantry Division Headquarters ..................... Maj. Gen. Abdus Salam
Commander, 26th Infantry Division Headquarters ................... Maj. Gen. Abdul Mannaf
Commander, 33rd Infantry Division Headquarters .................... Maj. Gen. Abdus Samad
Commander, 55th Infantry Division Headquarters ........ Maj. Gen. Sadiqur Rahman Chowdhury
Commander, Bogra Tank Depot ..................... Col. Ruhul Alam

**NAVY**
**Bangladesh Navy**
*Naval Headquarters*
*Dacca-13*

*Telephone:   600251-6*
*Telex:   602209 navy bj*
*Cable:   BANGLADESHNAVY*

Chief of Staff ........................ Rear Adm. Muhbub Ali Khan
Secretary to Chief of the Naval Staff .............. Lt. Cdr. Abdul Karim
Director of Naval Operations .................... Lt. Cdr. S. I. Mujtaba
Assistant Chief of Staff, Operations .............. Comdr. Sultan Ahmad
Assistant Chief of Staff, Material ............... Comdr. Khan Mohammad Julaluddin Akbar
Assistant Chief of Staff, Personnel ............... Comdr. Khan Mohammad Julaluddin Akbar
Assistant Chief of Staff, Logistics ........... Comdr. Fakhruddin Ahmad
Commodore Commanding, Chittagong ................. Comdr. Mohammad Mohaiminul Islam
Naval Officer-in-Charge, Khulna ................ Capt. Abu Zaher Nizam
Senior Naval Officer (Afloat) ........ Capt. Mohammad Mafizur Rahman

**Naval Store Depot**
*Naval Base*
*New Mooring*
*Chittagong*

Commanding Officer (Acting) .............. A. K. M. Abdul Karim Khan

## NAVAL TRAINING INSTITUTIONS

**BNS Issa Khan**
*New Mooring*
*Chittagong*

Commanding Officer ................Cdr. Mohammad Shamsul Huda

**BNS Titumir**
*Town Khalishpur*
*Khulna*

Commanding Officer .........................Capt. Abu Zaher Nizam

**BNS Shaheed Moazzam**
*Kaptai*
*Chittagong Hill Tract*

Commanding Officer ................Cdr. Mohammad Abul Quasem

## AIR FORCE
**Bangladesh Air Force—BAF**
*Air Headquarters*
*Dacca Cantonment*
*Dacca-6*

*Telephone:   310194-96*

Chief of Staff .....................Air Vice-Marshal Sultan Mahmud
Assistant Chief of Air Staff,
    Operation and Training............Air Comdr. Mumtazuddin Ahmed
Assistant Chief of Air Staff,
    Maintenance ...............Air Comdr. Chowdhury Abdul Mannan
Assistant Chief of Air Staff,
    Administration ..................Air Vice-Marshal Sultan Mahmud
Director, Air Intelligence .................Wing Cdr. Jawad-ur Rahim
Director, Training .......................Group Capt. Shamsul Alam
Assistant Director, Training ....................Flt. Lt. Nazrul Karim

**Directorate General of Defence**
    **Purchase—DGDP**
*New Airport Road*
*Tejgaon*
*Dacca*

Director-General ..........................Brig. Shamsuddin Ahmed

**Bangladesh Air Force Academy**
*B.A.F. Base*
*Matiur Rahman*

Commandant .........................Wing Cdr. Farhat S. A. Roomy

**Recruit Training School**
*B.A.F. Base*
*Zahurul Haque*

Commanding Officer ...................Wing Cdr. Khalihur Rahman

## BANGLADESH RIFLES
*Dacca*

Commander .......................Maj. Gen. Ram Gulam Muktadir
Deputy Commander .........................Brig. Matiur Rahman

\* \* \* \* \*

# GENERAL DEFENCE DATA

**Manpower**
    Total Armed Forces...............................................83,000
        (See Page 55)
    Population ................................................93,040,000

**Spending**
Military Expenditures . . . . . . . . . . . . . . . . . . . . . . . . . . . . . . . . . . . . . . . .$153 million
Gross National Product . . . . . . . . . . . . . . . . . . . . . . . . . . . . . . . . . . . . . . .$10.9 billion
Military Expenditure as a Percentage of
    Gross National Product . . . . . . . . . . . . . . . . . . . . . . . . . . . . . . . . . . . . . .1.4%
Military Expenditure as a Percentage of
    Central Government Expenditure . . . . . . . . . . . . . . . . . . . . . . . . . . . . . .6.4%

**Defence Treaties** *(See Part II for Additional Detail)*

Bilateral:    None

Multilateral:    Environmental Modification Convention
                Treaty on the Non-Proliferation of Nuclear Weapons

# BARBADOS

## Defence Establishment Command Structure and Force Organization

The Prime Minister is Minister of Defence and Chairman of the Defence Board, which is responsible for the Barbados Defence Force.

**Total armed forces:** 300.

## HEAD OF STATE

H. M. Queen Elizabeth II

## GOVERNOR-GENERAL

H. E. Sir Deighton Ward, G.C.M.G., G.C.V.O.

**OFFICE OF THE GOVERNOR-GENERAL**
*Government House*
*St. Michael*
*Telephone:  42 93497*

Governor-General . . . . . . . . . . . Sir Deighton Ward, G.C.M.G., G.C.V.O.

**OFFICE OF THE PRIME MINISTER**
*Government Headquarters*
*Bay Street*
*Bridgetown*
*Telephone:  60970*

Prime Minister and Minister
 of Defence *(pro tempore)* . . . . . . . . . . . . . J. M. G. M. Adams, Q.C., M.P.

**MINISTRY OF DEFENCE**
*Bridgetown*
*Telephone:  60970*

Minister and Prime Minister . . . . . . . . . . . . J. M. G. M. Adams, Q.C., M.P.

**Defence Board**

Chairman . . . . . . . . . . . . . . . . . . . . . . . . . J. M. G. M. Adams, Q.C., M.P.
(Prime Minister and Minister of Defence)
Vice Chairman . . . . . . . . . . . . . . . . . . . . . . . . . . . . . . . Rudyard E. C. Lewis
(Chief of Staff of the
Barbados Defence Force)

## DEFENCE FORCES

**BARBADOS DEFENCE FORCE**
**Headquarters**
*St. Ann's Fort*
*The Garrison*
*St. Michael*
*Telephone:  65949*

Chief of Staff . . . . . . . . . . . . . . . . . . . . . . . . . . . . Col. Rudyard E. C. Lewis

**POLICE**
**Royal Barbados Police Force**
*Central Police Station*
*Coleridge Street*
*Bridgetown*
*Telephone:   63840*

Commissioner . . . . . . . . . . . . . . . . . . . . . . . . . . . . . . . . . . . . . . . . . . . .Orville Durant
Deputy Commissioner . . . . . . . . . . . . . . . . . . . . . . . . . . . . . . . . . . . . .Cloris Boyce

\* \* \* \* \*

## GENERAL DEFENCE DATA

**Manpower**
   Total Armed Forces . . . . . . . . . . . . . . . . . . . . . . . . . . . . . . . . . . . . . . . . . . .300
      (See Page 59)
   Population . . . . . . . . . . . . . . . . . . . . . . . . . . . . . . . . . . . . . . . . . . . .252,000

**Spending**
   Military Expenditures . . . . . . . . . . . . . . . . . . . . . . . . . . . . . . . . . . . . . . .$2 million
   Gross National Product . . . . . . . . . . . . . . . . . . . . . . . . . . . . . . . . . . . . .$748 million
   Military Expenditure as a Percentage of
      Gross National Product . . . . . . . . . . . . . . . . . . . . . . . . . . . . . . . . . . .0.3%
   Military Expenditure as a Percentage of
      Central Government Expenditure . . . . . . . . . . . . . . . . . . . . . . . . . . . . . .1%

**Defence Treaties** *(See Part II for Additional Detail)*

   Bilateral:      None

   Multilateral:   Biological Weapons Convention
                   Regional Security System
                   Treaty for Prohibition of Nuclear Weapons in Latin
                      America
                   Treaty on the Non-Proliferation of Nuclear Weapons

# BELGIUM
## Kingdom of Belgium
*Royaume de Belgique* (French)
*Koninkrijk België* (Dutch)

### Defense Establishment Command Structure
### and Force Organization

The King is Commander-in-Chief of the Belgian armed forces. Executive authority over the military is exercised by the Prime Minister. Administrative and operational control of the armed forces is the responsibility of the Minister of Defense operating through a small Ministry of Defense which incorporates a General or Joint Staff and a Central Administrative Staff. A Ministerial Committee on Defense provides advice on security policy.

**Total armed forces:** 93,500 (Army: 68,700;   Navy: 4,300;   Air Force: 20,500). **Paramilitary forces:** 16,200.

### HEAD OF STATE

H. M. King Baudouin I

**OFFICE OF H. M. THE KING**
*Palais Royal/Koninklijk Paleis*
*Rue de Brederode*
*1000 Brussels*

*Telephone:  (2) 513 07 70*
*Telex:  21 376, 23 979 (Foreign Affairs)*

King of the Belgians and Commander-in-Chief .........H. M. Baudouin I
Grand Marshal of the Court........................Herman Dehennin
Chief of Cabinet ......................Jacques van Ypersele de Strihou
Press Attaché .......................................Marc van Craen

**OFFICE OF THE PRIME MINISTER**
*Rue de la Loi 16*
*1000 Brussels*

*Telephone:  (2) 513 80 20*
*Telex:  62400 prinim b*

Prime Minister.................................Dr. Wilfried Martens
Chief of Cabinet (General Policy) ..........................O. Coenen
Press Attaché .......................................Lou Del Clerck

**MINISTRY OF NATIONAL DEFENSE**
*(Ministère de la Defense Nationale)*
*Rue Lambermont 8*
*1000 Brussels*

*Telephone:  (2) 512 16 10*
*Telex:  61104 cabmod b*

Minister..........................................Freddy Vreven
Chief of Cabinet ....................................Joel De Smet
Assistant Chief of Cabinet ..........................Walter De Meyer
Assistant Chief of Cabinet and Councillor ..........Col. Marcel Terrasson
Councillor ......................................Herman Schoofs
Attache ...........................................Flor Cleemput
Attache, SAT .................................Lt. Col. Andre Jadin
Attache ............................Maj. Jean-Baptiste Heremans
Secretary of Cabinet ..........................Capt. Rene Lambinet
Military Press Attache ....................Lt. Col. Willy Demeuleneer
Civilian Press Attache ..............................Herman Meers
Head, Budget Affairs ..............................Franki Vanstapel

**Central Military Administration
of the Armed Forces—AMD**
*Quartier Reine Elisabeth*
*Rue d'Evere*
*1140 Brussels*

*Telephone:  (2) 243 32 11*

Chief ...........................................Lt. Gen. Geudvert
Director-General, Office of Personnel ..............Maj. Gen. J. De Mild
Director-General, Office of Finances ..............Maj. Gen. van Aubel

**General Civilian Administration—AGC**
*Quartier Reine Elisabeth*
*Rue d'Evere*
*1140 Brussels*
*Telephone:    (2) 243 31 11*

Director-General . . . . . . . . . . . . . . . . . . . . . . . . . . . . . . . . . . . . . . . . . . . .A. Maes
Secretary, Bureau of Methods . . . . . . . . . . . . . . . . . . . . . . . . . . . .A. De Mol
Director, Administration of Legal Affairs . . . . . . . . . . . . . . . . . . .Verschoore
Director, Administrative Affairs . . . . . . . . . . . . . . . .K. Vanden Wyngaerd

**Information Service of the Ministry**
    **of National Defense—SID**
*Quartier Reine Elisabeth*
*Rue d'Evere*
*1140 Brussels*
*Telephone:    (2) 243 39 55*

Director . . . . . . . . . . . . . . . . . . . . . . . . . . . . . . . . . . . . . . .Col. S. Vanderberghe

# DEFENSE FORCES

**ARMED FORCES**
**General Staff (Joint Staff)**
*Headquarters*
*Quartier Reine Elisabeth*
*Rue d'Evere*
*1140 Brussels*
*Telephone:    (2) 243 31 11*

Chief of Staff . . . . . . . . . . . . . . . . . . . . . . . . . . . . . . .Lt. Gen. M. Gysemberg
First Deputy Chief of Staff . . . . . . . . . . . . . . . . . . . . . .Lt. Gen. LeFebvre
Second Deputy Chief of Staff . . . . . . . . . . . . . . . . . . . . .Maj. Gen. Deliege
Chief, Medical Service . . . . . . . . . . . . . . . . . . . . . . . . . . . . .Maj. Gen. Leroy
Chief, Public Relations Section
    of the General Staff . . . . . . . . . . . . . . . . . . . . . . . . . . . . .Col. Y. Meugens

**SERVICES OF THE**
    **GENERAL STAFF**

**Intelligence—SGR**

Chief . . . . . . . . . . . . . . . . . . . . . . . . . . . . . . . . . . . . . . . . . . . .Maj. Gen. Tichon

**General Officers Service—SGP**
*Telephone:    (2) 243 31 11*

Chief . . . . . . . . . . . . . . . . . . . . . . . . . . . . . . . . . . . . . . . . . . . .Maj. Gen. Kermer

**Historical Service—SGR/CDH**
*Avenue de Cortenberg 79-81, bte 3*
*Kortenberglaan 79-81, bus 3*
*1040 Brussels*
*Telephone:    (2) 733 77 53*

Chief . . . . . . . . . . . . . . . . . . . . . . . . . . . . . . . . . . . . . . . . . . .Col. De Permentier

**Protocol Section—SGP**
*Telephone:    (2) 243 32 58*

Chief . . . . . . . . . . . . . . . . . . . . . . . . . . . . . . . . . . . . . . . . . . . . . . . .Maj. Brabant

**General Procurement Office—SGA**
*Telephone:    (2) 243 31 07*

Chief . . . . . . . . . . . . . . . . . . . . . . . . . . . . . . . . . . . . . . . . .Maj. Gen. M. Barrez

**General Construction Service—KGC**
*Telephone:    (2) 243 45 76*

Director-General . . . . . . . . . . . . . . . . . . . . . . . .Maj. Gen. R. De Brabander

**Interforces Service of Physical**
    **Education and Sports—BLS**
*Telephone:    (2) 243 40 27*

Chief . . . . . . . . . . . . . . . . . . . . . . . . . . . . . . . . . . . . . . . . . . . . . .Col. Kesteloot

## INSTITUTIONS OF MILITARY EDUCATION

**Royal Military School—ERM**
*Avenue de la Renaissance 30*
*Renaissancelaan 30*
*1040 Brussels*
*Telephone: (2) 733 97 94*

Commandant . . . . . . . . . . . . . . . . . . . . . . . . . . . . . . . . . .Maj. Gen. Boudin

**Royal Higher Institute of Defense— IRSD**
*Avenue de Cortenberg 115*
*Cortenberglaan 115*
*1040 Brussels*
*Telephone: (2) 733 97 94*

Commandant . . . . . . . . . . . . . . . . . . . . . . . . . . . . . . . . .Maj. Gen. P. Cremer

**School of Military Administration— ERDMMIL**
*Avenue de la Renaissance 31*
*Renaissancelaan 31*
*1040 Brussels*
*Telephone: (2) 733 97 94*

Commandant . . . . . . . . . . . . . . . . . . . . . . . . . . . . . . .Maj. Gen. De Craemer

**Royal School of the Medical Service— ERSM**
*Kazerne Leopold*
*G. de Crayerstraat 2*
*9000 Gent*
*Telephone: (91) 25 61 70*

Commandant . . . . . . . . . . . . . . . . . . . . . . . . . . . . . . . . . . . .Col. Van Acker

**Royal Cadet School—ERCAD**
*Dreve*
*1020 Brussels*
*Telephone: (2) 478 03 37*

Commandant . . . . . . . . . . . . . . . . . . . . . . . . . . . .Col. Janssens De Bisthoven

**Royal Military Institute of Physical Education—IRMEP**
*Caserne Slt. Antoine*
*4700 Eupen*
*Telephone: (87) 55 23 43*

Commandant . . . . . . . . . . . . . . . . . . . . . . . . . . . . . . . . . . . . . .Maj. Bodard

**Center of Recruitment and Selection— CRS**
*Caserne de Petit Chateau*
*Kazerne Klein Kasteeltje*
*1000 Brussels*
*Telephone: (2) 217 41 10*

Commandant . . . . . . . . . . . . . . . . . . . . . . . . . .Capt. (Force de) C. Verheyden

**ARMY**
*(Force Terrestre)*
*Army Headquarters*
*Quartier Reine Elisabeth*
*Rue d'Evere*
*1140 Brussels*
*Telephone: (2) 243 3111, 243 3380*

Chief of Staff . . . . . . . . . . . . . . . . . . . . . . . . . . . . .Lt. Gen. E. De Wilder
Deputy Chief of Staff . . . . . . . . . . . . . . . . . . . . . . .Maj. Gen. B. Derenne
Deputy Chief of Staff, Inspection . . . . . . . . . . . . . . . . . . . .Maj. Gen. R. Bats
Secretariat . . . . . . . . . . . . . . . . . . . . . . . . . . . . . . . . . . . . . .Capt. Dedeyne
Chief, Planning Division . . . . . . . . . . . . . . . . . . . . . . . . . . .Col. Van Calster
Chief, Studies . . . . . . . . . . . . . . . . . . . . . . . . . . . . . . . . . .Col. Castermans
Chief, International Relations . . . . . . . . . . . . . . . . . . . . . . .Col. Briquemont
Chief, Programming Division . . . . . . . . . . . . . . . . . . . . . . . .Col. Lheureaux
Chief, Synthesis . . . . . . . . . . . . . . . . . . . . . . . . . . . . . . . . . . . . .(Vacant)
Chief, Operations-Training . . . . . . . . . . . . . . . . . . . . . . .Lt. Col. Malherbe
Chief, Equipment-Logistics . . . . . . . . . . . . . . . . . . . . . . . .Lt. Col. Delhotte

| | |
|---|---|
| Chief, Organization-Personnel | Maj. Schellemans |
| Chief, Geshan Division | Col. Segers |
| Deputy Chief, Geshan Division | Col. Boving |
| Chief, Personnel | Lt. Col. De Clerck |
| Chief, Operations-Intelligence | Lt. Col. Couwenberg |
| Chief, Training | Col. Derwael |
| Chief, Infrastructure | Lt. Col. Van Daele |
| Chief, Public Relations | Lt. Col. Cambier |
| Chief, Budget | Lt. Col. Letouche |
| Chief, Special Staff and Control Division | Col. Saive |
| Chief, Finance Division | Lt. Col. Pirotte |
| Director, Medical Services | Col. M. D. Viaene |
| Chief, Technical Services | Col. Massart |

**Home Forces**
*Caserne Panguin*
*Warande 3*
*1980 Tervuren*

| | |
|---|---|
| Commander | Lt. Gen. Liebens |
| Chief of Staff | Col. Van Zwijnsvoorde |
| Deputy Commander, Training | Maj. Gen. Demesmaeker |
| Deputy Commander, Mobilization | Maj. Gen. Raes |
| Deputy Commander, Logistics | Maj. Gen. Juliam |

**Belgian Forces in West Germany—**
**Köln Weiden**

*(Forces Belges en Allemagne)*

| | |
|---|---|
| Commander, 1st Belgian Army Corps | Lt. Gen. De Boodt |
| Deputy Commander | Maj. Gen. Vanderhaegen |
| Deputy Commander, Fire Support | Maj. Gen. Gauchie |
| Commander, 1st Division | Maj. Gen. Depoorter |
| Commander, 16th Division | Maj. Gen. Maquet |

**NAVY**
*(Force Navale)*
*Naval General Staff*
*Quartier Reine Elisabeth*
*Rue d'Evere*
*1140 Brussels*

*Telephone:   (2) 243 31 19*

| | |
|---|---|
| Chief of Staff | Vice Adm. A. Schlim |
| Deputy Chief of Staff | Capt. F. Devillers |
| Deputy Chief of Staff, Logistics | Capt. H. Roufosse |
| Chief, Plans and Programs Section | Capt. J. Dewilde |
| Chief, Personnel and Instruction Section | Capt. F. De Swert |
| Chief, Operations, Training, Intelligence and Security Section | Cdr. C. Jacobs |
| Chief, Supply Section | Cdr. M. Bodet |
| Chief, Projects Bureau | Capt. Ch. Collard |
| Chief, Technical Section | Capt. Buys |
| Chief, Weapons Section | Cdr. van Begin |
| Chief, Assignment Section | Cdr. De Grande |
| Chief, Naval Training and Operations Command | Capt. P. van Damme |
| Chief, Logistical Command | Capt. H. Roufosse |

**Naval Procurement Service**
*(Under General Procurement Service,*
*  Ministry of National Defense)*
*Quartier Reine Elisabeth*
*Rue d'Evere*
*1140 Brussels*

| | |
|---|---|
| Chief | Cdr. Massart |

**Navy Instruction Command**
*Kazerne LTZ Billet V. Leopold*
*Debruynestraat 125*
*8310 Brugge*

| | |
|---|---|
| Commander | Capt. Th. Nevens |

**AIR FORCE**
*(Force Aérrienne)*
*Air Force General Staff*
*Quartier Reine Elisabeth*
*Rue d'Evere*
*1140 Brussels*

*Telephone:   (2) 243 31 11*

| | |
|---|---|
| Chief of Staff | Lt. Gen. Y. Dedeurwaeder |
| Vice Chief of Staff, Plans, Operations, and Personnel | Maj. Gen. A. Moriau |
| Vice Chief of Staff, Logistics | Maj. Gen. H. Robyns De Schneidauer |
| Commander, Air Force Tactics | Lt. Gen. V. Wils |
| Commander, Air Force Logistics | Maj. Gen. G. Sokay |
| Chief, Public Relations | Lt. Col. W. Bogaerts |

**Air Force Instruction and Training**  Commander ................................Maj. Gen. P. De Groof
*Quartier Roi Albert I*
*Rue de la Fusee 70*
*1130 Brussels*

\* \* \* \* \*

## GENERAL DEFENSE DATA

**Manpower**
    Total Armed Forces...............................................93,500
      (See Page 61)
    Population ...............................................9,881,000

**Spending**
    Military Expenditures .........................................$4 billion
    Gross National Product ......................................$122 billion
    Military Expenditure as a Percentage of
      Gross National Product .........................................3.4%
    Military Expenditure as a Percentage of
      Central Government Expenditure ...............................10.5%

**Defense Treaties** *(See Part II for Additional Detail)*

        Bilateral:      United Kingdom
                        United States
                        Zaire

        Multilateral:    Biological Weapons Convention
                        Environmental Modification Convention
                        Limited Test Ban Treaty
                        North Atlantic Treaty Organization
                        Treaty on the Control of Arms on the Seabed
                        Treaty on the Non-Proliferation of Nuclear Weapons
                        Western European Union

# BELIZE

## Defence Establishment Command Structure and Force Organization

The Governor-General is Commander-in-Chief of the Defence Forces of Belize. His authority is exercised through the Ministry of Defence. The United Kingdom maintains a permanent garrison at Camp Ladyville.

**Total armed forces:** 600 (Army).

## HEAD OF STATE

H. E. Dr. Minita E. Gordon

**OFFICE OF THE GOVERNOR GENERAL**
*Belmopan*
*Telephone: (8) 2521 (Private Secretary)*
*Telex: 211 bh*

Governor-General and Commander-in-Chief .......Dr. Minita E. Gordon
Private Secretary ............................(Mrs.) Margarita Castillo

**OFFICE OF THE PREMIER**
*Belmopan*
*Telephone: (8) 2346, 2344 (Finance)*
*Telex: 211 bh*

Prime Minister, Minister of Finance and Economic
    Development, and Minister of Foreign Affairs .......George Cadle Price
Secretary to the Cabinet & Chief of Protocol ................Orton Clarke

**MINISTRY OF DEFENCE AND HOME AFFAIRS**
*Belmopan*
*Telephone: (8) 7680, 2695*
*Telex: 211 bh*

Minister ...........................................Carl L. B. Rogers
Permanent Secretary ...............................Michael J. Hulse
Advisor ...............................................Maj. R. Fox

## DEFENCE FORCES

**ARMY**
**Belize Defence Force**
*P.O. Box 141*
*Price Barracks*
*Belize City*
*Telephone: (25) 2171-74*

Commandant........................Lt. Col. Christopher C. Galloway
Deputy Commander .....................Maj. Thomas H. Greenwood

**BRITISH FORCES, BELIZE**
*Camp Ladyville*
*Telephone: (25) 2192*
*Telex: 215 britfor bz*

Commander ................................Brig. Anthony J. Pollard

**POLICE DEPARTMENT**                    Commissioner . . . . . . . . . . . . . . . . . . . . . . . . . . . . . . . . . E. Maxwell Samuels
*Belmopan*
*Telephone:   (8) 2224*
*Telex:   211 bh*

＊ ＊ ＊ ＊ ＊

## GENERAL DEFENCE DATA

**Manpower**
　　Total Armed Forces . . . . . . . . . . . . . . . . . . . . . . . . . . . . . . . . . . . . . . . . . . . .600
　　　(See Page 67)
　　Population . . . . . . . . . . . . . . . . . . . . . . . . . . . . . . . . . . . . . . . . . . . . .150,000

**Spending**
　　Military Expenditures . . . . . . . . . . . . . . . . . . . . . . . . . . . . . . . . . . . . . . . . . . .
　　Gross National Product . . . . . . . . . . . . . . . . . . . . . . . . . . . . . . . . . . . . . . .$140 million
　　Military Expenditure as a Percentage of
　　　Gross National Product . . . . . . . . . . . . . . . . . . . . . . . . . . . . . . . . . . . . . . . . .
　　Military Expenditure as a Percentage of
　　　Central Government Expenditure . . . . . . . . . . . . . . . . . . . . . . . . . . . . . . . . . . .

**Defence Treaties** *(See Part II for Additional Detail)*

　　　Bilateral:　　United Kingdom
　　　　　　　　　United States

　　　Multilateral:　None

# BENIN
## People's Republic of Benin
### *République Populaire du Bénin*

## Defense Establishment Command Structure and Force Organization

The President is Minister of National Defense and Commander-in-Chief. The armed forces of Benin are composed of three units, the National Defense Forces, the Public Security Forces and the People's Militia. The National Defense Forces are deployed in two zones, South (Cotonou, Camp Guezo) and North (Parakou).

**Total armed forces:** 3,160 (Army: 3,000; Navy: 60; Air Force: 100). **Para-military forces:** 1,100 (Police).

## HEAD OF STATE

H. E. General Mathieu Kerekou

**OFFICE OF THE PRESIDENT AND CHIEF OF GOVERNMENT CHARGED WITH NATIONAL DEFENSE**
*B.P. 2028*
*Cotonou*

*Telephone:   30 00 90, 30 04 12*
*Telex:   5222 presirep ctnou*

**National Executive Council, Permanent Committee**

President of the People's Republic,
  Minister of National Defense,
  President of the National
  Executive Council and
  Commander-in-Chief ..................... Gen. Mathieu Kerekou

Head .............................. Gen. Mathieu Kerekou
    (President and Minister of National Defense)
Member ................................. Michel Alladaye
    (Minister of Interior and Public Security)
Member ................................ Tiamiori Adjibade
    (Minister of Foreign Affairs and Cooperation)
Member ........................... Lt. Col. Isidore Amoussou
    (Minister of Finance)
Member ......................... Col. Barthelemy Chouens
    (Minister of Industry, Mines and Energy)
Member .............................. Alidou Ba Boukary
    (Minister of State for Farms,
    Livestock and Fishing)
Member ................................. Zul-Kifl Salami
    (Minister of Plans, Statistics
    and Economic Analysis)
Member .............................. Manasse Ayayi
    (Minister of Commerce)
Member ............................... Girigissou Gado
    (Minister of Public Works,
    Construction and Housing)
Member ............................... Armand Montiero
    (Minister of Higher Education
    and Scientific Research)

Member . . . . . . . . . . . . . . . . . . . . . . . . . . . Tonakpou Gratiez Capo-Chichi
(Minister of Popular Culture and Literary)
Member . . . . . . . . . . . . . . . . . . . . . . . . . . . . . . Amidou Baba Moussa
(Minister of Information and Propaganda)
Member . . . . . . . . . . . . . . . . . . . . . . . . . . . Lt. Col. Francois Dossou
(Minister of Justice)

**MINISTRY OF INTERIOR AND
   PUBLIC SECURITY**
*Cotonou*
*Telephone: 30 11 06, 30 11 54*

Minister . . . . . . . . . . . . . . . . . . . . . . . . . . . . . . . Col. Michel Alladaye
Director General . . . . . . . . . . . . . . . . . . . . . . . . Raymond Fadonougbo
Director of State Police . . . . . . . . . . . . . . . . . . . . . Marc Guinikoukou

**MINISTRY OF NATIONAL DEFENSE**
*Cotonou*
*Telephone: 30 10 73*

Minister . . . . . . . . . . . . . . . . . . . . . . . . . . . . Gen. Mathieu Kerekou
Director General . . . . . . . . . . . . . . . . . . . . . . . Lt. Col. Pierre Koffi
Director, Studies and Planning . . . . . . . . . . . . . . . . . Maj. Aristide Boni
Director, Military Cooperation . . . . . . . . . . . . . . . . Maj. Seraphin Noukpo

# DEFENSE FORCES

**ARMED FORCES**
**People's Armed Forces of Benin—FAP**
*(Forces Armées Populaires de Benin)*
*Headquarters*
*Cotonou*

Chief of the General Staff, FAP . . . . . . . . . . . . . . Gen. Barthelemy Ohouens
Deputy Chief of the General Staff . . . . . . . . . . . . . . . . . Col. Michel Alladaye

**FORCES OF NATIONAL DEFENSE**
*(Forces de Defense Nationale)*

**Army**
*(Les Forces Terrestres)*
*Parakou*

Chief of Staff . . . . . . . . . . . . . . . . . . . . . . . . . . . Col. A. Mama Djoujou
Deputy Chief of Staff . . . . . . . . . . . . . . . . . . . . . . . . . . . . . . . . . . . . . . .
Commander, Infantry . . . . . . . . . . . . . . . . . . . . . . . . . . . . . . . . . . . . . . .
Commander, Para-Commando . . . . . . . . . . . . . . . . . . . . . . . . . . . . . . . . .
Commander, Reconnaissance . . . . . . . . . . . . . . . . . . . . . . . . . . . . . . . . .
Commander, Artillery . . . . . . . . . . . . . . . . . . . . . . . . . . . . . . . . . . . . . . .
Commander, Engineering . . . . . . . . . . . . . . . . . . . . . . M. Andre Atchade

**Navy**
*(Les Forces Maritimes)*

Commander . . . . . . . . . . . . . . . . . . . . . . . . . . . Lt. Bere Prosper Kiando

**Air Force**
*(Les Forces Aeriennes)*
*Cotonou*

Commander . . . . . . . . . . . . . . . . . . . . . . . . . . Capt. Christopher Fandohan

**FORCES OF PUBLIC SECURITY**
*(Forces de Securité Publique)*

Chief of Staff . . . . . . . . . . . . . . . . . . . . . . . . . . . Col. Raimi Issa Lawani
Deputy Chief of Staff . . . . . . . . . . . . . . . . . . . . . . Maj. Martin Azonhiho

**PEOPLE'S MILITIA**
*(Milice Populaire)*

Commander . . . . . . . . . . . . . . . . . . . . . . . . . . . Gen. Mathieu Kerekou

\* \* \* \* \*

## GENERAL DEFENSE DATA

**Manpower**

Total Armed Forces...............................................3,160
(See Page 69)
Population ...............................................3,636,000

**Spending**

Military Expenditures........................................$24 million
Gross National Product........................................$1 million
Military Expenditure as a Percentage of
Gross National Product .........................................2.2%
Military Expenditure as a Percentage of
Central Government Expenditure ...............................15.3%

**Defense Treaties** *(See Part II for Additional Detail)*

Bilateral:      France
United States

Multilateral:   Biological Weapons Convention
Economic Community of West African States
Limited Test Ban Treaty
Organization of African Unity
Treaty on the Non-Proliferation of Nuclear Weapons

# BERMUDA
## Colony of Bermuda

### Defence Establishment Command Structure
### and Force Organization

The Bermuda Constitution Order provides for internal self-government with the Governor as Commander-in-Chief. External security is the responsibility of the United Kingdom.

**Total armed forces:** 1,090 (Army: 675). **Police Force:** 415.

### HEAD OF STATE

H. M. Queen Elizabeth II

### GOVERNOR

(Vacant)

**OFFICE OF THE GOVERNOR**
*Government House*
*Pembroke 5-17*
Telephone:  292-2587
Telex:  3202 depgv ba

Governor and Commander-in-Chief .........................(Vacant)
Deputy Governor ...................................J. M. A. Herdman
Aide-de-Camp ....................................Maj. Randy Butler

**OFFICE OF THE PREMIER**
*The Cabinet Building*
*Front Street*
*Hamilton 5-24*
Telephone:  292-5501

Premier ....................................John W. Swan, J.P., M.P.
Minister without Portfolio ......................Sen. Charles T. Collis
Secretary to the Cabinet ..........................W. James Williams,
C.V.O., O.B.E., J.P.

**DEPARTMENT OF PUBLIC**
  **RELATIONS**
*The Cabinet Building*
*Front Street*
*Hamilton 5-24*
Telephone:  292-5501

Director .........................................(Mrs.) Valerie Smith
Assistant to the Director ................................(Vacant)
Information Officer ....................................(Vacant)

**DEFENCE DEPARTMENT**
*P.O. Box 146*
*Warwick*
Telephone:  298-2162

Administrator, Defence .........................Lt. Bernard Gibbons
Secretary, Defence Board .....................Lt. Col. Michael Darling
Chairman, Defense Medical Board ................Dr. Joseph H. Woolf

# DEFENCE FORCES

**ARMY**
**The Bermuda Regiment**
*P.O. Box 1006*
*Hamilton 5*

*or: Warwick Camp*
*South Shore Road*
*Warwick 7-01*

*Telephone:  298-1044*


**POLICE DEPARTMENT**
*Headquarters*
*Prospect*
*Devonshire 4-05*

*or: P.O. Box 530*
*Hamilton 5*

*Telephone:  5-0011*
*Telex:  3442*

Commanding Officer . . . . . . . . . . . . . . . . . . . . . . .Lt. Col. C. Eugene Raynor,
O.B.E., E.D.
Second-In-Commmand . . . . . . . . . . . . . . . . . . . . . .Maj. A. Gavin Shorto
Training Officer. . . . . . . . . . . . . . . . . . . . . . . . . . . . .Maj. John Drinkwater
Adjutant . . . . . . . . . . . . . . . . . . . . . . . . . . . . . . . . . .Capt. Nigel Richardson
Quartermaster . . . . . . . . . . . . . . . . . . . . . . . . . . .Capt. Henry W. Burnard
Regimental Sergeant Major . . . . . . . . . . . . . . . . . .W. O. 1 A. Eugene DeSilva
Commander, A Company . . . . . . . . . . . . . . . . . . . . .Capt. Alvin Daniels
Commander, B Company . . . . . . . . . . . . . . . . . . . . .Capt. Wendell Hollis

Commissioner. . . . . . . . . . . . . . . . . . . . . .Frederick Bean, O.P.M., C.P.M.
Deputy Commissioner . . . . . . . . . . . . . . . . . . . . . . .Clive Donald, C.P.M.
Assistant Commissioner, Crime . . . . . . . . . . . .James C. P. Hanlon, C.P.M.
Assistant Commissioner,
Uniform Branch . . . . . . . . . . . . . . . . . . . . . .Harold F. Moniz, C.P.M.

\* \* \* \* \*

# GENERAL DEFENCE DATA

**Manpower**
Total Armed Forces. . . . . . . . . . . . . . . . . . . . . . . . . . . . . . . . . . . . . . . . .1,090
    (See Page 73)
Population . . . . . . . . . . . . . . . . . . . . . . . . . . . . . . . . . . . . . . . . . . . . . . .72,000

**Spending**
Military Expenditures . . . . . . . . . . . . . . . . . . . . . . . . . . . . . . . . . . . . . . . .
Gross National Product . . . . . . . . . . . . . . . . . . . . . . . . . . . . . . . .$500 million
Military Expenditure as a Percentage of
    Gross National Product . . . . . . . . . . . . . . . . . . . . . . . . . . . . . . . . . . . . .
Military Expenditure as a Percentage of
    Central Government Expenditure . . . . . . . . . . . . . . . . . . . . . . . . . . . . . .

**Defence Treaties** *(See Part II for Additional Detail)*

Bilateral:    United States

Multilateral:  None

# BHUTAN
## Kingdom of Bhutan
*Druk Yul*

### Defence Establishment Command Structure and Force Organization

The King is Commander-in-Chief of the armed forces of Bhutan. India assists with the training of the Bhutanese Army.

**Total armed forces:** Approximately 4,000. **Militia Reserve:** 15,000.

### HEAD OF STATE

H. M. Jigme Singye Wangchuck

**OFFICE OF H. M. THE KING**
*Tashicho Dzong*
Telephone: 2590

King of Bhutan ........................ H. M. Jigme Singye Wangchuck

**ROYAL ADVISORY COUNCIL**
*Tashicho Dzong*
Telephone: 2339

| | |
|---|---|
| Chairman | Dasho J. Dorji |
| Councelor | Dasho Thukchhoe |
| Councelor | Dasho Rinzin Dorji |
| Councelor | Dasho Dawa Dem |
| Councelor | Dasho Kezang |
| Councelor | Dasho P. M. Ghaley |
| Councelor | Dasho Prahlad Gurung |
| Councelor | Lopon Rinchen |
| Councelor | Lopon Yonten Gyeltshen |

### DEFENCE FORCES

**ARMY**
**Royal Bhutan Army**
*Tashicho Dzong*
*Thimphu*
Telephone: 2308

| | |
|---|---|
| Chief of Army Staff | Maj. Gen. Lam Dorji |
| Staff Officer to Chief of Army Staff | Lt. Dorji Khandu |
| Personal Assistant to Chief of Army Staff | Sub. Maj. A. K. Gurung |
| Personnel Officer | Lt. Col. Rinchhen Tshering |
| Chief Administrative Officer | Lt. Col. Ratna Bahadur Gurung |
| Operations and Training Officer | Capt. Chhunjur Dorji |
| Intelligence Officer | Capt. Batoo Tshering |
| Chief Signal Officer | Maj. Passang Tshering Sherpa |
| Signal Officer | Lt. M. K. Chhetri |
| Pay and Accounts Officer | Lt. Kesang Dorji |
| Record Officer | Capt. Rinzin Gyeltshen |
| Defence Accounts Officer | Capt. Laphu Tshering |
| Officer Commanding, Constructions | Maj. Chachu Tshering |
| Chief Medical Officer | Dr. Tandin Dorji |
| Chief Maintenance Officer | Capt. Phugey |
| Mechanical Transport Officer | Capt. Rinzin Dorji |
| Officer Commanding, Arms and Ammunition Depot | Capt. Sonam Tshering |

Commander, Army Headquarters Wing . . . . . . . . . . . . . . Capt. Penjor Dorji
Camp Commandant . . . . . . . . . . . . . . . . . . . . . . . . . Capt. Rinchhen Khandu
Adjutant . . . . . . . . . . . . . . . . . . . . . . . . . . . . . . . . . . . . Capt. Andoo Tshering
Engineer Works and Buildings . . . . . . . . . . . . . . . . . . . . . Lt. Dago Chencho
Sports Officer . . . . . . . . . . . . . . . . . . . . . . . . . . . . . . . . . Capt. Kesang Jigmi

**Wangdiphodrang Exchange**
*Telephone: 203*

Commandant, RBA Training Centre . . . . . . . . Lt. Col. Tshewang Rinchhen
Adjutant, RBA Training Centre . . . . . . . . . . . . . . . . . . . . Capt. Singey Dorji
Quartermaster, RBA Training Centre . . . . . . . . . . . . . Capt. Dophu Tshering
Training Officer, RBA Training Centre . . . . . . . . . . . . . . . Capt. Sacha Dorji
Medical Officer, Military Hospital . . . . . . . . . . . . . . . . . . Dr. A. K. Mohanty

**Phuntsholing Exchange**
*Telephone: 236*

Zeopon, RBA Base Headquarters . . . . . . . . . . . . . . . . . Maj. Kinley Tshering

**Samdrup Jongkhar Exchange**
*Telephone: 45*

Officer Commanding, Det RBA . . . . . . . . . . . . Capt. Indrabahadur Chhetri

**ROYAL BHUTAN POLICE—RBP**
*Headquarters*
*Zilnen Nemyelling*
*Thimphu*
*Telephone: 2347, 2348, 2619*

Chief, Headquarters . . . . . . . . . . . . . . . . . . . . . Dungda Kesang Namgyel
Accounts Officer . . . . . . . . . . . . . . . . . . . . . . . . . Dechhab Sonam Penjore
Record Officer . . . . . . . . . . . . . . . . . . . . . . . . . . . . . Dezin N. Wangchuk
Special Branch . . . . . . . . . . . . . . . . . . . . . . . . . . Dechhab Karma Tenzin
Traffic Control . . . . . . . . . . . . . . . . . . . . . . . . . . . . . . . . . . . Dezin Tashi
Commander, Town Outpost . . . . . . . . . . . . . . . . . . Dezin Ugyen Sonam
Commanding Officer, RBP Wangdiphodrang
   Exchange . . . . . . . . . . . . . . . . . . . . . . . . . . . . . . . . . . . Dechhab Dorji
Police Range Officer, RBP Samdrup
   Jongkhar Exchange . . . . . . . . . . . . . . . . . . . . . Yongzin Zimba Dukpa

**ROYAL BODY GUARDS**
*Thimphu*
*Telephone: 2206, 2274*

Commandant . . . . . . . . . . . . . . . . . . . . . . . . . . . . . . . Maj. Hodo Tshering
Motor Transport Officer . . . . . . . . . . . . . . . . . . . . . . . . . Capt. D. Tshering
Commanding Officer, Third Company . . . . . . . . . . . . . . . Capt. V. Namgyel
Senior Officer . . . . . . . . . . . . . . . . . . . . . . . . . . . . . . Capt. Norbu Tshering
Senior Officer . . . . . . . . . . . . . . . . . . . . . . . . . . . . . . . Lt. Kado Tshering
Senior Officer . . . . . . . . . . . . . . . . . . . . . . . . . . . . . . . . Lt. Kipchu Dorji

\* \* \* \* \*

## GENERAL DEFENCE DATA

**Manpower**
Total Armed Forces . . . . . . . . . . . . . . . . . . . . . . . . . . . . . . . . . . . . . . . . . 4,000
   (See Page 75)
Population . . . . . . . . . . . . . . . . . . . . . . . . . . . . . . . . . . . . . . . . . . . 1,364,000

**Spending**
Military Expenditures . . . . . . . . . . . . . . . . . . . . . . . . . . . . . . . . . . . . . . . . .
Gross National Product . . . . . . . . . . . . . . . . . . . . . . . . . . . . . . . . . . . $116 million
Military Expenditure as a Percentage of
   Gross National Product . . . . . . . . . . . . . . . . . . . . . . . . . . . . . . . . . . . . . .
Military Expenditure as a Percentage of
   Central Government Expenditure . . . . . . . . . . . . . . . . . . . . . . . . . . . . . . .

**Defence Treaties** *(See Part II for Additional Detail)*

   Bilateral:     India

   Multilateral:  Biological Weapons Convention
                  Limited Test Ban Treaty

# BOLIVIA
## Republic of Bolivia
### *República de Bolivia*

### Defense Establishment Command Structure and Force Organization

The President is Commander-in-Chief of the armed forces. His authority is exercised through the Minister of Defense. The National Security Council provides guidance on defense policy matters.

**Total armed forces:** 26,600 (Army: 20,000; Navy: 2,600; Air Force: 4,000). **Para-military forces:** 5,000.

### HEAD OF STATE

H. E. Hernán Siles Zuazo

**OFFICE OF THE PRESIDENT**
*(Oficina de la Presidencia)*
*Palacio de Gobierno*
*Plaza Murillo*
*La Paz*

*Telephone: (2) 374-030, 374-033*
*Telex: 2461 presrep by, 5242 west coast, 2320 entel*

President of the Republic
and Commander-in-Chief ..............Cap. Gral. Hernán Siles Zuazo
Minister Secretary of the Presidency .............Horacio Poppe Martínez
Press and Information Secretary ..................Jorge González Roda

**Military Household**
*(Casa Militar)*

Chief .......................................Cnel. Edgar Claure Eaz

**Supreme Council of National Security**
*(Consejo Nacional de Seguridad)*

*Telephone: (2) 372-154*

President ..........................Contra. Alm. Renee Torres (Navy)
Chief of Cabinet...........................Cesar Ruiz Valarde (Army)
Member ...............................Cnel. Carlos Estrada (Army)

**MINISTRY OF NATIONAL DEFENSE**
*(Ministério de la Defensa Nacional)*
*Plaza Abaroa, Esq. 20 de Octubre*
*La Paz*

*Telephone: (2) 377-135, 344-135*
*Telex: 2448 mindef br, 5245 west coast*

Minister ....................................Lic. José Ortiz Mercado
Director, Logistics .......................Cnel. Mario Oxa Bustas
Director-General, Administration and
Budget .........................Cap. Corbata Jorge Lopez Arispe
Director, Planning ..............................Cnel. Hugo Buehzo

**CORPORATION OF THE ARMED FORCES FOR NATIONAL DEVELOPMENT**
*(Corporacion de las Fuerzas Armadas Para el Desarrollo Nacional)*
*Ave. 6 de Agosto No. 2649*
*La Paz*

*Telephone: (2) 37-7305*

General Manager .............................Elías Gutiérrez Ardaya
Director, Enterprises.................Cnel. Francísco Vasquez Alemam

# DEFENSE FORCES

**ARMED FORCES**
*(Fuerzas Armadas)*
*Gran Cuartel General de Miraflores*
*La Paz*

*Telephone:    (2) 37-8030, 37-0120*
*Telex:    5384 comanfab*

| | |
|---|---|
| Commander-in-Chief of the Armed Forces | Gral. Div. Alfredo Villaroel Barja |
| Inspector-General | Gral. Brig. Octavio Villavicencio |
| Chief, Department 1 | Gral. Brig. Hugo Jironda Flores |
| Chief, Department 2 | Cnel. Osvaldo Arroyo |
| Chief, Department 3 | Cnel. Gonzálo Saavedra Espinoza |
| Chief, Department 4 | Gral. Mario Escobar |
| Chief, Department 5 | Cnel. Carlos Calderon de la Riva |
| Chief, Department of Public Relations | May. Franklin William González |
| Chief, National School for Advanced Studies | Gral. Brig. Raul Ramallo Belarde |

**ARMY**
*(Ejército Boliviano)*
*Gran Cuartel General de Miraflores*
*La Paz*

*Telephone:    (2) 37-8180/81*
*Telex:    356682, 2538 comanejito bv*

| | |
|---|---|
| Commanding General of the Division | Simon Sejas Tordoya |
| Deputy Chief of Staff | Gral. Bgda. Walter Antezana Palacios |
| Commander, Tarapaca Region | Cnel. Sergio Osinaga |
| Commander, Ingavi Region | Cnel. Rolando Saravia |
| Commander, 8th Division (Santa Cruz) | Cnel. Gary Prado Salman |
| Commander, Special Forces Training Center—CITE | Cnel. Emilio Larza |

**NAVY**
*(Fuerza Naval Boliviana)*
*Gran Cuartel General de Miraflores*
*La Paz*

*Telex:    2519 naval br*
*(Estado Mayor General)*

| | |
|---|---|
| Commander | Vice Alm. Wilfredo de la Barra Saavedro |
| Chief of Naval Staff | José Antonio Oña Costas |
| Chief, Dept. 1, Personnel | Cap. Luis Arces Fredericksen |
| Chief, Dept. 2 | Cap. Fernándo Torres Alarcon |
| Chief, Dept. 3, Operations | Cap. Francísco Mariaca Salas |
| Chief, Dept. 4 | Cap. Felix Mendiola Galarza |
| Naval Inspector | Cap. Edmundo Pereida |

**Navy Military School**
*(Escuela Militar Naval)*

| | |
|---|---|
| Director | Cap. Anibal Gutiérrez |
| Director of Studies | Cap. Corbeta Julio Jiménez Valdivia |

**Navy Hydrological Service**
*(Dirección de Hidrografía)*

| | |
|---|---|
| Director | Cap. Alberto Saenz Klinsky |

**AIR FORCE**
*(Fuerza Aerea Boliviana)*
*Avenida Montes 734*
*La Paz*

*Telephone:    (2) 37-9050*
*Telex:    356682 comanem, 3350 comfab bv*

| | |
|---|---|
| Commander | Gral. Juan Muñoz Revollo |
| Chief, Air Force General Staff | Gral. Oscar Hinojosa |
| Chief, Department 1 EMFA | Cnel. Grover Rojas Senzano |
| Chief, Department 2 EMFA | Cnel. Edwin Greminger |
| Chief, Department 4 EMFA | Gral. Adalid Cuellar Peña |
| Chief, Department 6 EMFA | Cnel. Ernesto Mendoza |
| Chief, Department 7 EMFA | Cnel. Mario Guzman Moreno |

**POLICE FORCE**
*(Fuerza de Policia)*
*La Paz*

| | |
|---|---|
| Commander | Gral. Edi Cordero Márquez |
| Deputy Commander | Cnel. Nelsen Pereda Rosas |

\* \* \* \* \*

# GENERAL DEFENSE DATA

**Manpower**
Total Armed Forces............................................26,600
(See Page 77)
Population .................................................5,633,000

**Spending**

Military Expenditures . . . . . . . . . . . . . . . . . . . . . . . . . . . . . . . . . . . . . . . . .$178 million

Gross National Product . . . . . . . . . . . . . . . . . . . . . . . . . . . . . . . . . . . . . . . .$7.4 billion

Military Expenditure as a Percentage of
    Gross National Product . . . . . . . . . . . . . . . . . . . . . . . . . . . . . . . . . . . . . . .2.4%

Military Expenditure as a Percentage of
    Central Government Expenditure . . . . . . . . . . . . . . . . . . . . . . . . . . . . . .22.7%

**Defense Treaties** *(See Part II for Additional Detail)*

Bilateral:      United States

Multilateral:   Act of Chapultepec
                Biological Weapons Convention
                Inter-American Defense Board
                Inter-American Treaty of Reciprocal Assistance
                Treaty for the Prohibition of Nuclear Weapons in
                    Latin America
                Treaty on the Non-Proliferation of Nuclear Weapons

# BOTSWANA
## Republic of Botswana

### Defense Establishment Command Structure and Force Organization

The President is Commander-in-Chief of the armed forces. The Minister of Public Service, Broadcasting, and Information is the senior civilian adviser to the President on military matters and *de facto* Minister of Defense. All services form part of the Army (Botswana Defense Force).

**Total armed forces:** 3,000 (Army: 2,850; Air Wing: 150). **Para-military forces:** 1,260 (Police).

## HEAD OF STATE

H. E. Dr. Quett K. J. Masire

**OFFICE OF THE PRESIDENT**
*Private Bag 001*
*Gaborone*

*Telephone: 55434, 55431*
*Telex: 2414 bd*

President of the Republic ........................Dr. Quett K. J. Masire
Permanent Secretary to the President
   and Secretary of the Cabinet .......................Festus G. Mogae
Senior Private Secretary ...............................Louis Selepeng
Private Secretary (Social) .............................Bogatsu Pheto
Administrative Secretary ....................Lebang M. Mpotokwane

**MINISTRY OF PUBLIC SERVICE, BROADCASTING AND INFORMATION**
*Private Bag 001*
*Gaborone*

*Telephone: 55434, 55431*
*Telex: 2414 bd*
*Cable: PULA*

Minister ......................................Daniel K. Kwelagobe
Director, National Civil Service .................Honorius K. Kedikilwe

## DEFENSE FORCES

**ARMY**
**Botswana Defense Force—BDF**
*Private Bag X061*
*Gaborone*
*Sir Seretse Khama Barracks*
*Mogoditshane*

*Telephone: 45413, 51121*
*Telex: 2400 bd*

Commander .........................Maj. Gen. Mompati S. Merafhe,
                             B.P.M., F.O.M., D.S.O.
Deputy Commander ................Brig. Seretse Khama Ian Khama,
                                    F.O.M.
Chief, Logistics (in charge of
   procurement) ................................Col. Z. S. Ratshipa
Deputy Chief ...............................................Lt. Pheto

**BDF Air Wing**
*c/o BDF Headquarters*
*Gaborone*

*Telephone: 56213 (Gaborone)*

Commander...................................Capt. A. T. Scheffers

**BOTSWANA POLICE**
*Private Bag 0012*
*Gaborone*
*Telephone:    55232*

| | |
|---|---|
| Commissioner of Police | S. A. Hirschfeld |
| Deputy Commissioner of Police | N. S. Moleboge |
| Senior Assistant Commander of Police, Operations | N. S. Molefe |
| Assistant Commissioner of Police, Administration | N. L. Mangoye |
| Commanding Officer, Special Branch South Central (Gaborone) | A. K. Nyame |
| Commanding Officer, Special Branch Lobatse | S. Mothusi |
| Commanding Officer, Special Branch Francistown | S. D. Manyeneng |
| Commanding Officer, Special Branch North Central (Mahalapye) | F. Mangadi |
| Commander, Special Support Group | D. Radikolana |
| Divisional Commander, Divisional— Headquarters, Northern Division (Francistown) | M. D. Moloi |
| Commanding Officer, No. 1 District (Francistown) | J. G. Mazwiduma |
| Commanding Officer, No. 2 District (Serowe) | A. Matlapeng |
| Commanding Officer, No. 3 District (Gaborone) | B. Mabutho |
| Commanding Officer, No. 4 District (Lobatse) | S. M. Matsietsa |
| Commanding Officer, No. 5 District (Maun) | D. Sabuta |
| Commanding Officer, No. 6 District (Gantsi) | P. E. Mothokho |
| Commanding Officer, No. 7 District (Kasane) | K. L. Gabaake |
| Commanding Officer, No. 8 District (Mahalapye) | J. Mlotshwa |
| Commanding Officer, No. 10 District (Selibe Phikwe) | P. Marathe |

\* \* \* \* \*

## GENERAL DEFENSE DATA

**Manpower**

| | |
|---|---|
| Total Armed Forces | 3,000 |
| (See Page 81) | |
| Population | 975,000 |

**Spending**

| | |
|---|---|
| Military Expenditures | $24 million |
| Gross National Product | $711 million |
| Military Expenditure as a Percentage of Gross National Product | 3.5% |
| Military Expenditure as a Percentage of Central Government Expenditure | 6.4% |

**Defense Treaties** *(See Part II for Additional Detail)*

Bilateral:    United States

Multilateral:    Limited Test Ban Treaty
Organization of African Unity
Treaty on the Control of Arms on the Seabed
Treaty on the Non-Proliferation of Nuclear Weapons

# BRAZIL

## Federative Republic of Brazil
### *República Federativa do Brasil*

## Defense Establishment Command Structure and Force Organization

The President is the Commander-in-Chief of the Armed Forces of Brazil. He is advised on the formulation and execution of defense policy by the National Security Council, and on the development of war plans and organization by the Armed Forces General Staff. The Army, Navy and Air Force are independent services with their own Cabinet level ministries. There is no ministry for defense. A Military Cabinet is responsible for liaison with the armed forces ministries.

**Total armed forces:** 272,850 (Army: 182,750;   Navy: 47,300;   Air Force: 42,800). **Paramilitary forces:** 185,000.

## HEAD OF STATE

H. E. Gen. João Baptista de Oliveira Figueiredo

**OFFICE OF THE PRESIDENT**
*Palacio do Planalto*
*Praça 3 Poderes*
*Brasília-D.F.*
*Telephone:  (61) 211-1221, 211-2107*
*Telex:  1451, 1148, 1496*

President of the Republic and
Commander-in-Chief of the
Armed Forces . . . . . . . . . Gen. Ex.(RR) João Baptista Oliveira Figueiredo

**Military Cabinet of the Presidency**
*(Casa Militar da Presidencia)*
*Palacio do Planalto, 4 andar*
*70150 Brasília-D.F.*
*Telephone:  (61) 211-1411, 221-1305,*
*223-4534*
*Telex:  1451*

Minister-Chief . . . . . . . . . . . . . . . . . . . . . Gen. Bda. Rúbem Carlos Ludwig
Deputy Secretary . . . . . . . . . . . . . . . . . Cel. Luiz Henrique Abreu de Moraes

**Civilian Cabinet of the Presidency**
*(Casa Civil de Presidência)*
*Palacio do Planalto, 4 andar*
*70150 Brasília-D.F.*
*Telephone:  (61) 211-1210/12,*
*223-6564*

Minister-Chief. . . . . . . . . . . . . . . . . . . . . . . . . . . . . . . . . . . . . . . João Leitão
Deputy Secretary . . . . . . . . . . . . . . . . . . . . . . João Carlos Pessoa Fragoso

**National Intelligence Service**
*(Serviço Nacional de Informacões)*
*Palacio do Planalto, 4 andar, 70150*
*Brasília-D.F.*
*Telephone:  (61) 211-1221, 211-1660*
*Telex:  1451*

Minister-Chief . . . . . . . . . . . . . . . . . . . Gen. Div. Octavio Aguiar de Medeiros
Deputy Secretary . . . . . . . . . . . . . . . . . Cel. Ewerton Da Paixão Curado Fleury
Chief, Central Agency of
National Intelligence
Service . . . . . . . . . . . . . . . . . . Gen. Div. Newton Araujo de Oliveira e Cruz

**National Security Council**
*(Conselho de Segurança Nacional—*
*CSN)*

Special Minister for Land-Related
Issues and Chief of National
Security Council . . . . . . . . . . . . . . . . . . . . . . . Gen. Bda. Danilo Venturini

*Telephone:    211-1302, 211-1303*
*Telex:    611160*

| | |
|---|---|
| Executive Director | Cel. Francisco Fernandes |
| Member | Gen. João Baptista de Oliveira Figueiredo |
| | (President of the Republic) |
| Member | Aureliano Chaves de Mendonça |
| | (Vice President of the Republic) |
| Member | Gen. Div. Delio Jardim de Mattos |
| | (Minister of State) |
| Member | Gen. Ex. Walter Pires de Carvalho e Albuquerque |
| | (Minister of State, Army) |
| Member | Alte.-de-Esq. Maximiano Eduardo de Silva Fonseca |
| | (Minister of State, Navy) |
| Member | Gen. Bda. Waldir de Vasconcelos |
| | (Chief, Armed Forces General Staff) |
| Member | Gen. Tulio Chagas Noguera |
| | (Chief of Staff, Army) |
| Member | Alte.-de-Esq. José Calvante Aranda |
| | (Chief of Staff, Navy) |
| Member | Ten. Brig. Bertholino Joaquim |
| | (Chief of Staff, Air Force) |

## OFFICE OF THE VICE PRESIDENT
*Gabinete da Presidencia*
*SBS-Edf. Sede III, Banco do Brasil*
*70083 Brasília-D.F.*

*Telephone:    (61) 224-7369, 244-5769*
*Telex:    1040*

| | |
|---|---|
| Vice President | Dr. Antônio Aureliano Chaves de Mendonça |
| Chief of State | Cel. Venicio Alves da Cunha |

# DEFENSE FORCES

## ARMED FORCES
**Armed Forces General Staff**
*(Estado Maior das Forças Armadas)*
*Esplanada dos Ministerios*
*Bloco Q*
*70049 Brasília-D.F.*

*Telephone:    (61) 225-4605*
*                      223-5356*

| | |
|---|---|
| Chief of Staff | Gen. Bda. Waldir de Vasconcelos |
| Deputy Chief of Staff | Gen. Div. Mário Brum Negreiros |
| Chief, Public Relations Division | Moacyr Monteiro Baptista |

## ARMY
**Brazilian Army**
*(Exército Brasiléira)*
*Quartel-General do Exército*
*Setor Militar Urbano*
*Bloco A, 4 andar*
*70630 Brasília-D.F.*

*Telephone:    (61) 223-1932*
*Telex:    61113 mnex br*
*                611092 mnex br*

| | |
|---|---|
| Minister of State | Gen. Ex. Walter Pires de Carvalho e Albuquerque |
| Chief of Staff | Gen. Ex. Túlio Chagas Nogueira |
| Vice Chief of Staff | Gen. Div. Leonidas Pires Goncalves |
| Chief, Engineering and Communications Department | Gen. Ex. Jorge Sá Freire de Pinho |
| Chief, Ordnance Materiel Department | Gen. Ex. José Magalhães da Silveira |
| Chief, General Personnel Department | Gen. Ex. Mário de Mello Mattos |
| Chief, General Services Department | Gen. Ex. Enio Gouvêa dos Santos |
| Chief, Education and Research Department | Gen. Ex. Heraldo Tavares Alves |

**First Army**
*(1ʳ Exército)*
*Placio Duque de Caxias*
*   25-9 andar, Praca Duque de Caxias-*
*   Centro, 20455*
*Rio de Janeiro*

*Telephone:    (21) 283-2580*

| | |
|---|---|
| Commander | Gen. Ex. Heitor Luiz Gomes de Almeida |

**Second Army**
*Av. Sgt. Mário Kosel Filho*
*222-Ibirapuera*
*04090 São Paulo*
*Telephone:    (11) 282 8541*

Commander . . . . . . . . . . . . . . . . . . . . . . . . . . . .Gen. Ex. Sérgio de Ary Pires

**Third Army**
*Rua dos Andradas*
*562-4 andar-Centro*
*90.000 Porto Alegre*
*Telephone:    (512) 24 8749*

Commander . . . . . . . . . . . . . . . . . . . . . . . .Gen. Ex. Túlio Chagas Nogueira

**Fourth Army**
*BR 232-KM 12*
*Bairro Curado*
*50.000 Recife*
*Telephone:    (81) 251 2556*

Commander . . . . . . . . . . . . . . . . . . . . . . . .Gen. Ex. Enio Gouvêa dos Santos

**Amazonian Military Command**
*Estrada da Ponta Negra*
*69.000 Manaus*
*Telephone:    (92) 232 5721*

Commander . . . . . . . . . . . . .Gen. Ex. Euclydes de Oliveira Figueiredo Filho

**War College**
*(Escola Superior de Guerra)*
*Fortaleza de São João-Urca*
*22291 Rio de Janeiro*
*Telephone:    (21) 295 3595*

Commander . . . . . . . . . . . . . . . . . . . . . .Gen. Ex. Alzuir Benjamim Chaloub

**NAVY**
**Brazilian Navy**
*(Marinha Brasiléira)*
*c/o Ministry of Navy*
*Esplanada dos Ministérios*
*Bloco N, 2 andar*
*70055 Brasília-D.F.*
*Telephone:    223-6058, 224-1939*
*Telex:    2153102 mmar br*
*Cable:    MARINHA BRASILIA*

Minister . . . . . . . . . . . .Alte.-de-Esq. Maximiano Eduardo da Silva Fonseca
Chief of Staff, Navy . . . . . . . . . . . . . . . . . .Alte.-de-Esq. José Calvante Aranda
Deputy Chief . . . . . . . . . . . . . . . .C. Alte. Manoel José dos Passos Fernandes
Secretary-General, Navy
  (In charge of Supply,
  Administration, etc) . . . . . . . . . . . . .Alte.-de-Esq. Arthur Ricart da Costa
Chief, Naval Materiel . . . . . . . . . .Alte.-de-Esq. Raphael de Azevedo Branco
Chief of Naval Personnel. . . . . . . . . . . . . . . . . .Alte.-de-Esq. Alfredo Karam
Chief of Naval Operations and
  Director of Navigation . . . . . .Alte.-de-Esq. Paulo de Bonoso Duarte Pinto
Commander of the
  Marine Corps . . . . . . . . . . . . . . .Alte.-de-Esq. Domingos de Mattos Cortez

**Marine Corps**
*(Corpo de Fuzeleiros Navais)*
*Ilha das Cobras*
*Rio de Janeiro, 20091*
*Telephone:    253-4334, 253-2234*

Commandant . . . . . . . . . . . . . . . .Alte.-de-Esq. Domingos de Mattos Cortez

**AIR FORCE**
*(Força Aérea)*
*c/o Minisitry of Air Force*
*Esplanada dos Ministérios*
*Bloco M, 6 andar*
*70045 Brasília-D.F.*
*Telephone:    (61) 225-6405, 223-6409*
*Telex:    1152*
*Cable:    EMAER SBBR BRASILIA*

Minister of State . . . . . . . . . . . . . . . . . . . .Ten. Brig. Delio Jardim de Mattos
Chief of Staff . . . . . . . . . . . . . . . . . . . . . . . . . . . . . .Ten. Bertolino Joaquim
Vice Chief of Staff . . . . . . . . . . . . . . . .Brig. Tarso Magnus da Cunha Frota
Commander, Air General
  Command . . . . . . . . . . . . . . . .Ten. Brig. Alfredo H. Berenguer Cesar
Commander, Support
  General Command . . . . . . . . . . . . .Ten. Brig. Octavio Julio Moreira Lima
Commander, Civil Aviation
  Department . . . . . . . . . . . . . .Ten. Brig. Luiz Felippe C. de Lacerda Neto
Commander, Personnel
  General Command. . . . . . . . . . . . . . . . . . . .Ten. Saulo de Mattos Macedo

* * * * *

# GENERAL DEFENSE DATA

**Manpower**
Total Armed Forces..............................................272,850
(See Page 83)
Population ..............................................127,734,000

**Spending**
Military Expenditures.........................................$2.3 billion
Gross National Product.......................................$248.4 billion
Military Expenditure as a Percentage of
Gross National Product ...........................................0.9%
Military Expenditure as a Percentage of
Central Government Expenditure .................................9.3%

**Defense Treaties** *(See Part II for Additional Detail)*

Bilateral:    United States

Multilateral:    Act of Chapultepec
Biological Weapons Convention
Inter-American Defense Board
Inter-American Treaty of Reciprocal Assistance
Limited Test Ban Treaty
Treaty for the Prohibition of Nuclear Weapons in Latin
America

**Military Rank Comparisons**
See Appendix A.

# BRUNEI
## State of Brunei
*Negeri Brunei*

### Defence Establishment Command Structure and Force Organization

The Sultan is Supreme Commander of Brunei's armed forces, all of which are part of the Army. Under the terms of the Constitution, Brunei and the United Kingdom share responsibility for the State's defence and security. The British maintain a Gurkha Battalion in the country.

**Total armed forces:** 3,300 (Army: 2,850; Navy: 350; Air Force: 100). **Para-military forces:** 1,750 (Royal Brunei Police).

### THE SOVEREIGN

H. H. Sir Muda Hassanal Bolkiah Mu'issaddin Waddaulah

**OFFICE OF H. H. THE SULTAN**
*Bandar Seri Begawan*
*Telephone: 02-22301*
*Telex: bu 2234 istana*

Sultan of Brunei and Supreme
Commander . . . . . . . . . . . . . . . . . . . . . . H. H. Sir Muda Hassanal Bolkiah
Mu'issaddin Waddaulah

**OFFICE OF THE GENERAL ADVISER TO H. H. THE SULTAN**
*Bandar Seri Begawan*
*Telephone: 02-22301*
*Telex: bu 2234 istana*

General Adviser to
H. H. The Sultan . . . . . . . . . . . . . . . . . . . . . . . Pehin Dato Haji Isa Bin
Pehin Data Haji Ibrahim

**OFFICE OF THE CHIEF MINISTER**
*(Menteri Besar)*
*Bandar Seri Begawan*
*Telephone: 02-23225 (Private Branch Exchange), 02-22713*
*Telex: bu 2209 brugov*

Chief Minister
(Acting) . . . . . . . . . . Pehin Orang Kaya Laila Wiyaya Dato SeriSetia Awg
Haji Abd Aziz Bin Umar

### DEFENCE FORCES

**ARMY**
**Royal Brunei Malay Regiment—RBMR**
*(Askar Melayu Di-Raja Brunei)*
*Telephone: 02-31111 (Private Branch Exchange)*
*Telex: 2220 rbmr bu*

Commander . . . . . . . . . . . Brig. Yang Mulia Dato Seri Pahlawan N. Roberts
Deputy Commander . . . . . . . . . . . . . . . . . Col. Pehin Dato Haji Mohammed
Chief of Staff . . . . . . . . . . . . . . . . . . . . . Seri Begawan Sultan, Sir Omar Ali

**NAVY**
**Royal Brunei Navy—RBN**
*(Angkatan Laut Pertama Askar*
  *Melayu Di-Raja Brunei)*
*Muara Base Flotilla Brunei*
*Bandar Seri Begawan*
*Telephone:   02-72442, 72232*

Commander . . . . . . . . . . . . . . . . . . . . . . . . . . . . . . . . . . . .Lt. Col. A. H. Lorimer

**AIR FORCE**
**Royal Brunei Air Wing—RBAW**
*Berakas Camp, Brunei Town*
*Telephone:   31 111, Ext. 170*

Commander . . . . . . . . . . . . . . . . . . . . . . . . . . . . . . . . . . . . . . . . . . . . .

**ROYAL BRUNEI POLICE**
*Gadong*
*Bandar Seri Begawan*
*Telephone:   02-23901 (Private Branch*
              *Exchange)*
*Telex:   bu 2226 compol*

Commissioner . . . . . . . . . . . . . . .Pengiran Setia Raja Pengiran Haji Jaya Bin
Pengiran Haji Rajid

**BRITISH ARMY BRUNEI GARRISON**
*(Askar British Garrison Brunei)*
*Seria Camp*
*Telephone:   03-24101 (Private Branch*
              *Exchange) 22-541*
*Telex:   bu 3333 tpsbrun*

Garrison Commander . . . . . . . . . . . . . . . . . . . . . . .Lt. Col. V. J. Beauchamp

\* \* \* \* \*

## GENERAL DEFENCE DATA

**Manpower**
    Total Armed Forces. . . . . . . . . . . . . . . . . . . . . . . . . . . . . . . . . . . . . .3,300
      (See Page 87)
    Population . . . . . . . . . . . . . . . . . . . . . . . . . . . . . . . . . . . . . . . . . . . .252,000

**Spending**
    Military Expenditures . . . . . . . . . . . . . . . . . . . . . . . . . . . . . . . . . . .$195 million
    Gross National Product . . . . . . . . . . . . . . . . . . . . . . . . . . . . . . . . . . .$1.8 billion
    Military Expenditure as a Percentage of
      Gross National Product . . . . . . . . . . . . . . . . . . . . . . . . . . . . . . . . .10.8%
    Military Expenditure as a Percentage of
      Central Government Expenditure . . . . . . . . . . . . . . . . . . . . . . . . . . . .26.8%

**Defence Treaties** *(See Part II for Additional Detail)*

    Bilateral:     None

    Multilateral:   None

# BULGARIA
## People's Republic of Bulgaria
### *Narodna Republika Bulgariya*

## Defense Establishment Command Structure
## and Force Organization

The State Council, Bulgaria's supreme executive body, formally controls the country's armed forces and appoints their command staff. In practice, however, command of the military is vested in the Minister of National Defense. The State Council appoints the members of the Defense Council, an advisory entity that convenes mostly in times of emergency.

**Total armed forces:** 148,000 (Army: 105,000; Navy: 9,000; Air Force: 34,000). **Paramilitary forces:** 22,500 (Border Guard: 15,000; Security Police: 7,500). **People's Militia:** 150,000.

## HEAD OF STATE

Todor Zhivkov

**STATE COUNCIL**
*2 Dondoukov Boulevard*
*Sofia*

*Telephone:  8501*
*Telex:   22272 dsnr bg,*
*    22803 dsnrb bg*

| | |
|---|---|
| Chairman | Todor Zhivkov |
| First Deputy Chairman | Petur Tanchev |
| Deputy Chairman | Georgi Dzhagarov |
| Deputy Chairman | Mitko Grigorov |
| Deputy Chairman | Peko Takov |
| Deputy Chairman | Yaroslav Radev |
| Deputy Chairman | Georgi Atanasov |

**Defense Council**

| | |
|---|---|
| Chairman | Todor Zhivkov (Chairman, State Council) |
| Member *(ex officio)* | Gen. Dobri Dzhurov (Minister of National Defense) |
| Member *(ex officio)* | Col. Gen. Atanas Semerdzhiev (Chief, General Staff) |

**MINISTRY OF NATIONAL DEFENSE**
*3 Levski Street*
*Sofia*

*Telephone:   8621*

| | |
|---|---|
| Minister | Gen. Dobri Dzhurov |
| First Deputy Minister | Col. Gen. Khristo Dobrev |
| First Deputy Minister | Col. Gen. Atanas Semerdzhiev |
| Deputy Minister | Col. Gen. Mircho Asenov |
| Deputy Minister | Lt. Gen. Boris Karamfilov |
| Deputy Minister | Adm. Branimir Ormanov |
| Deputy Minister | Col. Gen. Tencho Papazov |
| Deputy Minister | Col. Gen. Boris Todorov |

**Main Political Administration**

| | |
|---|---|
| Chief | Col. Gen. Kiril Kosev |
| First Deputy | Lt. Gen. Mitko Mitkov |
| Deputy Chief | Maj. Gen. Petko Milushev |
| Deputy Chief | Maj. Gen. Ivan Shtilyanov |

**Civil Defense Administration**

| | |
|---|---|
| Chief | Col. Gen. Tencho Papazov |
| Deputy Chief | Maj. Gen. Georgi Kostov |
| Deputy Chief, Political Affairs | Lt. Gen. Nikola Atanasov |

| Construction Troops Administration | Chief ........................................Lt. Gen. Vasil Vasilev |
| | Chief of Staff...........................................Ivan Petrov |
| | Deputy Chief.................................Col. Mincho Minev |
| | Deputy Chief........................Maj. Gen. Yordon Todorov |
| | Deputy Chief...........................Maj. Gen. Anton Vulev |
| | Deputy Chief.............................Maj. Gen. Georgi Zlatev |

| Support Services Administration | Chief...................................Lt. Gen. German Germanov |

| Transportation Administration | Chief, Transport Troops ......................Maj. Gen. Mityu Kisov |
| | Chief, Political Department................Maj. Gen. Stoyan Semyenov |

# DEFENSE FORCES

**ARMED FORCES**
**General Staff**
*c/o Ministry of National Defense*
*3 Levski Street*
*Sofia*
*Telephone:   8621*

| Chief, General Staff ....................Col. Gen. Atanas Semerdzhiev |
| First Deputy...................................Lt. Gen. Stancho Mitev |
| Deputy Chief ................................Lt. Gen. Petko Dudov |
| Deputy Chief ................................Gen. Nikola Nedyalkov |

**ARMY**
**Bulgarian People's Army**
*c/o Ministry of National Defense*
*3 Levski Street*
*Sofia*
*Telephone:   8621*

| Commander, First Army ....................Lt. Gen. Lyubcho Toshkov |
| Commander, Second Army ....................Lt. Gen. Tsotso Tsotsov |
| Commander, Third Army ......................Lt. Gen. Stoyan Subev |

**NAVY**
**Bulgarian Navy**
*c/o Ministry of National Defense*
*3 Levski Street*
*Sofia*
*Telephone:   8621*

| Commander-in-Chief ............................Adm. Ivan Dobrev |
| Chief of Staff ..............................Vice Adm. Vasil Yanakiev |

**AIR FORCE**
**Air and Air Defense Forces**
*c/o Ministry of National Defense*
*3 Levski Street*
*Sofia*
*Telephone:   8621*

| Commander-in-Chief and Chief of Staff, Air and Air Defense Forces................................Col. Gen. Lyubcho Blagoev |

**PARA-MILITARY FORCES**
**Border Guard**
*(Under Ministry of Interior)*

| Chief, Border Guard ........................Maj. Gen. Stefan Tsanov |

\* \* \* \* \*

# GENERAL DEFENSE DATA

**Manpower**
Total Armed Forces..............................................148,000
(See Page 89)
Population ..................................................8,940,000

**Spending**
Military Expenditures .......................................... $3.7 billion
Gross National Product ........................................ $30.2 billion
Military Expenditure as a Percentage of
Gross National Product ....................................... 12.4%
Military Expenditure as a Percentage of
Central Government Expenditure ............................... 33.3%

**Defense Treaties** *(See Part II for Additional Detail)*

Bilateral:      Angola           Poland
                      Cambodia       Romania
                      Czechoslovakia   Soviet Union
                      German Demo-     Vietnam
                        cratic Republic   People's Demo-
                      Hungary         cratic Republic
                      Laos             of Yemen
                      Mongolia

Multilateral:    Biological Weapons Convention
                      Environmental Modification Convention
                      Limited Test Ban Treaty
                      Treaty on the Control of Arms on the Seabed
                      Treaty on the Non-Proliferation of Nuclear Weapons
                      Warsaw Treaty Organization

# BURMA
## Socialist Republic of the Union of Burma
*Pyidaungsu Myanma Nainggan-Daw*

### Defense Establishment Command Structure and Force Organization

The President is Commander-in-Chief and is advised on military matters by a Council Executive Committee composed of senior military officers. The Council of Ministers, as supreme executive body, is charged with the management of national defense and the maintenance of law and order.

The Minister of Defense is also Chief of Staff and as such exercises both administrative and operational control over the Burmese Armed Forces. The Defense Ministry is a tri-service organization that operates as a joint integrated headquarters.

The Burmese Armed Forces are divided for jurisdictional purposes into five area army commands and three regions for the navy.

**Total armed forces:** 179,000 (Army: 163,000; Navy: 7,000; Air Force: 9,000). **Paramilitary forces:** 73,000 (People's Police Force: 38,000; People's Militia: 35,000).

### HEAD OF STATE

H. E. U San Yu

**OFFICE OF THE PRESIDENT AND CHAIRMAN OF THE COUNCIL OF STATE**
*16, Windermere Park*
*Rangoon*
*Telephone: 32404*

President of the Socialist Republic and
Chairman of the Council of State ..........................U San Yu
Director-General, President's Office ...........Lt. Col. Aung Myint Baw

**OFFICE OF THE SECRETARY OF THE COUNCIL OF STATE**
*15/16 Windermere Park*
*Rangoon*
*Telephone: 32318, 32466 (Director General)*

Secretary, Council of State................................U Aye Ko
Director-General .....................................Col. Jin Hlaing

**OFFICE OF THE PRIME MINISTER**
*Ministers' Office*
*Rangoon*
*Telephone: 18742, 83742*

Prime Minister ...............................U Maung Maung Kha
Deputy Prime Minister .............................Thura U Tun Tin
Deputy Prime Minister .........................Gen. Thura Kyaw Htin

**MINISTRY OF DEFENSE**
*Shwedagon Pagoda Road*
*Rangoon*
*Telephone: 71611, 72185*
*Telex: 21316 milpro bm*
*(Procurement)*

Minister .......................................Gen. Thura Kyaw Htin
Officer General Staff .....................................Col. Hla Maw
Director, Military Appointments .................Brig. Gen. Soe Myint
Adjutant General .............................Maj. Gen. Saw Maung
Quartermaster General.........................Maj. Gen. Aung Khin
Inspector General ...................................Col. Ba Thein
Judge Advocate General ...............................Col. Sein Win

Director, Military Training and Plans ......................Col. Sein Ya
Director, Supply and Transport.....................Col. Soe Myint Win
Director, Ordnance .................................Col. Than Lwin
Director, Artillery and Armour ........................Col. Thet Waj
Director, Medical ..................................Col. Kan Nyunt
Director, Procurement..................................Col. Tin Gyi
Director, Military Accounts............................U Thein Han
Director, Defense Industries .........................Col. Htay Tint
Director, Signals ....................................Col. Tin Tun
Director, People's Militia
   and Public Relations ..............................Col. Sein Aung
Director, Military Engineers ........................Col. Aung Khin
Director, Electrical and Mechanical
   Engineers ........................................Col. Nyun Tin
Director, Resettlement ...............................Col. Myo Swe
Director, Historical Research ...................Cdr. Hla Shein (Navy)
Provost Marshal ...............................Lt. Col. Myint Lwin
Principal, National Defense College ..................Brig. Gen. Tin Oo

## DEFENSE FORCES

**ARMED FORCES**
*Signal Pagoda Road*
*Rangoon*

*Telephone:   81611*

Chief of Staff ...............................Gen. Thura Kyaw Htin

**ARMY**
**Burmese Army**
*Signal Pagoda Road*
*Rangoon*

*Telephone:   81611*

Vice Chief of Staff ..................................Lt. Gen. Tun Yi

**NAVY**
*Signal Pagoda Road*
*Rangoon*

*Telephone:   81611*

Vice Chief of Staff .....................Rear Adm. Maung Maung Win

**AIR FORCE**
*Signal Pagoda Road*
*Rangoon*

*Telephone:   81611*

Vice Chief of Staff ...............................Maj. Gen. Ko Gyi

\* \* \* \* \*

## GENERAL DEFENSE DATA

**Manpower**
   Total Armed Forces...............................179,000
      (See Page 93)
   Population ...............................36,166,000

**Spending**
   Military Expenditures ...........................$228 million
   Gross National Product ..........................$6 billion
   Military Expenditure as a Percentage of
      Gross National Product .......................3.8%
   Military Expenditure as a Percentage of
      Central Government Expenditure ...............22.1%

**Defense Treaties** *(See Part II for Additional Detail)*

   Bilateral:     United States

   Multilateral:   Limited Test Ban Treaty

# BURUNDI
## Republic of Burundi
*République du Burundi*

### Defense Establishment Command Structure and Force Organization

The President, as Minister of Defense and Commander-in-Chief, has direct control of the armed forces.

**Total armed forces:** 8,000 (Army: 7,800;    Navy: 50;    Air Force: 150). **Para-military force:** 1,500 (Police).

### HEAD OF STATE

H. E. Col. Jean-Baptiste Bagaza

**OFFICE OF THE PRESIDENT**
*Bujumbura*
*Telephone: 6063*
*Telex: 38 presibu bdi*

President of the Republic, Minister of
Defense and Commander-in-Chief ......... Col. Jean-Baptiste Bagaza

**MINISTRY OF NATIONAL DEFENSE**
*(Ministére de la Defense Nationale)*
*Bujumbura*

Minister of National Defense and
Commander-in-Chief ................... Col. Jean-Baptiste Bagaza
Secretary General ............................. Lt. Col. Paul Povota
Chief, Personnel, G1 ...................... Capt. Joseph Ndvwingoma
Chief, G2 (Security) ..................... Lt. Col. Laurent Ndabanezi
Chief, G3 ................................... Maj. Edmond Ndabazi
Director, School Unit *(Unite Ecole)* .......... Cdt. Etienne Sindahebura

**MINISTRY OF THE INTERIOR**
*(Ministére de l'Interieur)*
*Bujumbura*

Minister .................................. Lt. Col. Charles Kazatsa

### DEFENSE FORCES

**ARMED FORCES**
*(Forces Armeed Burundi)*
*Bujumbura*
*Telephone: 6700*

Chief of Staff, Armed Forces ............ Lt. Col. Hermenigilde Karenzo

**Naval Squadron**
*(Escadrille)*
*Telephone: 42 68*

Commander .....................................................

**Air Wing**
*(Armee de l'Air)*
*Telephone: 42 68, 37 41*

Commander .............................. Lt. Col. Libere Mahimana

**POLICE FORCE**
*(Gendarmerie)*

Commander . . . . . . . . . . . . . . . . . . . . . . . . . . . . . . . .Lt. Col. Stanislas Mandi
Deputy Commander . . . . . . . . . . . . . . . . . . . . . . .Lt. Col. Augustine Bakana

\* \* \* \* \*

# GENERAL DEFENSE DATA

**Manpower**
   Total Armed Forces . . . . . . . . . . . . . . . . . . . . . . . . . . . . . . . . . . . . . . . . . . . . .8,000
     (See Page 95)
   Population . . . . . . . . . . . . . . . . . . . . . . . . . . . . . . . . . . . . . . . . . . . .4,438,000

**Spending**
   Military Expenditures . . . . . . . . . . . . . . . . . . . . . . . . . . . . . . . . . . . . . . .$22 million
   Gross National Product . . . . . . . . . . . . . . . . . . . . . . . . . . . . . . . . . . . . .$881 million
   Military Expenditure as a Percentage of
     Gross National Product . . . . . . . . . . . . . . . . . . . . . . . . . . . . . . . . . . . . .2.6%
   Military Expenditure as a Percentage of
     Central Government Expenditure . . . . . . . . . . . . . . . . . . . . . . . . . . . . . .22.2%

**Defense Treaties** *(See Part II for Additional Detail)*

    Bilateral:    None

    Multilateral:   *Burundi—Rwanda—Zaire:* Mutual Security Pact (1966,
             1974)
           Organization of African Unity
           Treaty on the Non-Proliferation of Nuclear Weapons

# CAMEROON
## United Republic of Cameroon
### *République Unie du Cameroon*

## Defence Establishment Command Structure and Force Organization

The President is Commander-in-Chief. Administrative control of the military is exercised by the Minister of State in Charge of the Armed Forces. The Inspector General is vested with operational command and coordination responsibility for the defense forces.

**Total armed forces:** 7,250 (Army: 6,600;    Navy: 300;    Air Force: 350). **Para-military forces:** 5,000.

## HEAD OF STATE

H. E. Paul Biya

**OFFICE OF THE PRESIDENT**
*Yaoundé*
*Telephone: 22 01 12, 22 00 23*
*Telex: 8207 kn*

President of the United Republic and
Commander-in-Chief ....................................Paul Biya
Director of Civil Staff (with rank of Minister) ........Philémon Beb à Don

**Presidential Military Staff**
Chief, Military Staff .........................Col. Ousmanou Daouda
Head, Military Affairs Office ......................Lt. Col. Meillon M.
Head, Air Liaison Office ........................Capt. Jean Ze Eya'an
Aide de Camp ...............................Capt. Issa Ousmanou
Aide de Camp .........................Capt. Abdoulaye Tombouctou

**PERMANENT SECRETARIAT OF NATIONAL DEFENSE**
*(Secretariat Permanent à la Défense Nationale)*
*Telephone: 22 35 41*

Permanent Secretary ...................................Samule Kame
Director of Administration Regulations ............Abraham Mvendongo

**OFFICE OF THE PRIME MINISTER**
*Yaoundé*
*Telephone: 22 07 02, 22 07 69*
*Telex: 8221*

Prime Minister .................................Maigari Bello Bouba

**MINISTRY OF ARMED FORCES**
*(Ministère des Forces Armées)*
*Yaoundé*
*Telephone: 22 10 50, 22 11 22, 22 11 51*
*Telex: 8261 minfa kn*

Minister of State in Charge of
Armed Forces ..........................Dr. Abdoulaye Maikano
Secretary General ................................Meva'a M'eboutou
Technical Adviser to the Minister....................Lt. Col. Mgamaleu
Technical Adviser to the Minister ............Capt. de Corvette Leberre
Chief, Military Secretariat .....................Lt. Col. Narcisse Eyango
Chief, Division of Budget and
Administration Management ..................Lt. Col. Fidèle Nkam
Chief, Military Security Service ............C. E. Mohamadou Abdoulaye
Chief, Military Justice ................................Ndebi Mpondy
Director, Office of Personnel ..................Lt. Col. Nyemeg Bissek
Director, Armed Forces Medical Corps ..........Col. Kamdoum Charles

Director, Office of Education and
Regulations . . . . . . . . . . . . . . . . . . . . . . . . . . . . . . . . .Col. Jean Nganso Sunji
Deputy Director, Office of Education and
Regulations . . . . . . . . . . . . . . . . . . . . . . . . . . . . .Lt. Col. Moukouri Mbappe

**Offices of Procurement**

Director, Office of Materials
*(Direction des Services Materiel)* . . . . . . . . . . . . . . . . . .Col. Malongue Titus
Officer in Charge of Procurement . . . . . . . .Cdt. Philemon Nguele Amougou
Director, Office of Supply Services
*(Direction des Services Intendants)* . . . . . . . . . . . . . . . . . . . . .Col. Abakaka

# DEFENSE FORCES

**ARMED FORCES**
*Yaoundé*
*Telephone:    22 36 00, 22 35 00, 22 22 00*

Inspector-General, In Charge of Coordination
of Armed Forces . . . . . . . . . . . . . . . . . . . . .Gen. de Div. Pierre Semengue

**Center for Interforce Coordination**
*(Centre Interarmées de Coordination)*

Inspector-General . . . . . . . . . . . . . . . . . . . . . .Gen. de. Div. Pierre Semengue
Deputy Inspector-General, Coordination . . . . . . . . .Lt. Col. Pierre Samabo
Deputy Inspector-General, Inspection . . . . . . . . . . . . . . . . . . . . . . . . . . . . .
Chargé d'études . . . . . . . . . . . . . . . . . . . . . . . . . . . . . . . .C. B. Robert Mbuh
Commander, Headquarters Command
(Commandement du Quartier Général) . . . . . . . . . . .Col. Ngoura Belladji
Commander, Force Intervention
Command . . . . . . . . . . . . . . . . . . . . . .Col. Abdoulaye Oumarou Garoua
Commander, Corps of Engineers Command . . . . . . . . . .Col. René Youmba
Commander, Schools and Instruction Centers
Command . . . . . . . . . . . . . . . . . . . . . . . . . . . . . . . . . .Col. Mpay Philippe
Commander, Signals Command . . . . . . . . . . . . . . . . . .Lt. Col. Joseph Sing
Commander, National Armed Forces Instruction
Center (CIFAN) . . . . . . . . . . . . . . . . . . . . . . .C. B. Hector Marie Tchemo
Commander, Armed Forces National Training
Center . . . . . . . . . . . . . . . . . . . . . . . . . . . . . . . . .C. B. James  Chi Ngafor

**External Services**

Commander, 1st Military Sector (Central-South
East, HQ Ebolowa) . . . . . . . . . . . . . . . . . . . .Lt. Col. Guillaume Mbomback
Commander, Sub Sector Bertoua,
151st Company . . . . . . . . . . . . . . . . . . . . . . . . . . .Lt. Col. Tanka Songola
Commander, 2nd Military Sector
(Seaboard, HQ Douala) . . . . . . . . . . . . . . . . . . . .Lt. Col. John Abel Kweti
Commander, 3rd Military Sector
(North West, HQ Bafoussam) . . . . . . . . . . . . . . . . . . . . . . .Lt. Col. Mpay
Commander, 4th Military Sector
(North, HQ Garoua) . . . . . . . . . . . . . . . . . . . . . . .Lt. Col. Etoga Mbarga
Commander, Sub Sector Maroua . . . . . . . . . . . . . . . . . . . . . . . . . . . . . . . . .

**ARMY**
*(Forces Terrestres)*
*Yaoundé*
*Telephone:    23 11 22, 23 22 00, 23 22 02*

Commander . . . . . . . . . . . . . . . . . . . . . . . . . . . . .Col. James Tataw Tabe
Chief of Staff . . . . . . . . . . . . . . . . . . . . . . . . . . . . .C. B. Martin Sinkam
Commander, 21st Infantry Battalion . . . . . . . . . . . . . .C. B. Michael Ngen
Commander, 23rd Infantry Battalion . . . . . . . . . . . . . . .C. B. Robert Mbu
Commander, 24th Infantry Battalion . . . . . . . . . . . .C. B. Albert Ambassa
Commander, 32nd Infantry Battalion . . . . . . . . . . .Lt. Col. Sylvester Mang

**NAVY**
*(Forces Navales)*
*Douala*

Commander . . . . . . . . . . . . . . .Capt. de Corvette Guillaume Ngouah Ngally

**AIR FORCE**
*(Forces Aériennes)*
*Douala*

*Telephone: 42 43 20, 42 20 55, 42 39 75*
*Telex: 5519*

Commander ..............................Cdt. Paul Yakana Guemba

**NATIONAL CONSTABULARY**
*(Gendarmerie Nationale)*
*Yaoundé*

Delegate General...............................Mr. Ibrahim Wadjiri
Chief of Staff ....................................Col. Joseph Kalla
Chief, Correspondent Bureau....................Adjt. Samuel Abessolo
Chief, Defense Mobilization Bureau ..............Capt. Paul Messanga

**Gendarmerie Administrative and Technical Center**

Commander .......................................Col. Isidore Obama
Chief, Materiel Bureau............................Lt. Grégoire Bineli
Commander, Gendarmerie School ........Lt. Col. Louis-Jean Lambidjeck

**Legions**

Commander, Republican Guard.....................................
Legion de la Garde Republicaine ..................Lt. Col. Ibrahim Sale
Commander, Central South Legion ...Lt. Col. Laurent-Claude Angouan'd
Commander, Coastal Legion ...................Col. Abdoulaye Oumaro
Commander, Western Legion................Lt. Col. Douala Massango
Commander, Eastern Legion ...............C. E. Gaus Fombo Fomuso
Commander, Northern Legion ......................Col. Saly Oumarou
Commander, South-Western Legion ....Lt. Col. Marc Guillaume Nguidjol
Commander, North-Western Legion ............C. E. Ze Akono Clément

\* \* \* \* \*

# GENERAL DEFENSE DATA

**Manpower**
Total Armed Forces ...............................................7,250
(See Page 97)
Population ...................................................9,049,000

**Spending**
Military Expenditures.........................................$86 million
Gross National Product .......................................$5.8 billion
Military Expenditure as a Percentage of
Gross National Product ...............................................1.5%
Military Expenditure as a Percentage of
Central Government Expenditure ..................................9.1%

**Defense Treaties** *(See Part II for Additional Detail)*

Bilateral:     France
               Libya
               United States

Multilateral:  Organization of African Unity
               Treaty on the Non-Proliferation of Nuclear Weapons

**Military Rank Comparisons**
See Appendix A.

# CANADA

## Defence Establishment Command Structure and Force Organization

The Governor-General of Canada, in his capacity as the representative of H. M. Queen Elizabeth II, is titular Commander-in-Chief of the Canadian Armed Forces. The Minister of Defence, specifically, and the Cabinet, generally, are accountable to Parliament for all matters relating to national defence including the setting and implementation of defence policy. The Chief of the Defence Staff, senior military advisor to the Minister of Defence, is charged with control and administration of the armed forces.

As the armed forces are a unified structure, there are no distinct services. Forces are arranged by function into six commands: Maritime Command, Mobile Command, Air Command, Communications Command, Canadian Forces Europe and Canadian Forces Training System. Each command reports to the Chief of the Defence Staff. Mobile Command controls army combat forces, and Maritime Command naval forces. Air Command controls all air forces, but Maritime Command has operational control of maritime aircraft of Air Command on the Atlantic and Pacific Coasts. The armed forces are also organized into six geographical regions to provide liaison with provincial and territorial authorities (Atlantic, Eastern, Central, Prairie, Pacific and Northern).

**Total armed forces:** 82,905 (Mobile Command: 19,098;　Maritime Command: 11,150; Air Command: 23,991;　Communication Command: 3,147;　Canadian Forces Europe: 5,537; Canadian Forces Training System: 8,864;　National Defence Headquarters Staff: 11,118). **Para-military forces:** 20,861 (Royal Canadian Mounted Police, Coast Guard and Canadian Rangers).

## HEAD OF STATE

H. M. Queen Elizabeth II

## GOVERNOR-GENERAL

H. E. The Rt. Hon. Edward R. Schreyer

**OFFICE OF THE GOVERNOR-GENERAL**
*Government House*
*1 Sussex Drive*
*Ottawa, Ontario K1A OA1*
*Telephone: 749-5933*
*Telex: 053-3280*

Governor-General and Commander-in-Chief . . . . . . . . Edward R. Schreyer
Secretary to the Governor-General . . . . . . . . . . . . . . . . . . . . . . . . E. U. Butler

**OFFICE OF THE PRIME MINISTER**
*Langevin Block*
*Ottawa, Ontario K1A OA2*
*Telephone: 992-4211*
*Telex: 053-3208*

Prime Minister . . . . . . . . . . . . . . . . . . . . . . . . . . . . . Pierre Elliott Trudeau
Secretary to the Cabinet . . . . . . . . . . . . . . . . . . . . . . . . . G. F. Osbaldeston

**DEPARTMENT OF NATIONAL DEFENCE**
*101 Colonel By Drive*
*Ottawa, Ontario K1A OK2*
*Telephone: 996-4450*
*Telex: 053-4218*

Minister ........................................J. Gilles Lamontagne
Deputy Minister.........................................D. B. Dewar

**Assistant Deputy Minister, Policy**
*Telephone: 922-3458, 922-2869*

Assistant Deputy Minister, Policy........................J. F. Anderson
Associate Assistant Deputy Minister,
    Policy .....................................Maj. Gen. C. M. Kinney
Chief, Policy Planning ..........................A. de W. Mathewson
Director, Strategic Policy Planning .......................D. C. Thillaye
Director, Socio-economic Strategic Planning..............P. C. Skippon
Director, Scientific and Technological
    Strategic Planning ....................................E. Ellington
Director-General, Policy Planning.................Brig. Gen. L. Skaalen
Director, Continental Policy .....................Col. R. W. Buskard
Director, International Policy.......................Col. R. G. Gentles
Director, Arms Control Policy .......................W. M. Beckett
Chief, Strategic Program .........................J. G. R. Hutcheson
Director-General, Defence Program............................Vacant
Director, Program Analysis...................Capt. (N) W. J. Broughton
Director, Program Control...............................R. G. A. Clare
Director, Defence Services Program
    Information System .........................Lt. Col. G. G. Hynes
Director-General, Organization and
    Manpower....................................Brig. Gen. S. A. Millar
Director, Manpower Control and Organization ...........A. L. Altwasser
Director, Establishment Requirements ...............Col. I. D. Isbester
Director, On-Site Manpower Evaluation
    Program .........................................L. D. Richards
Chief, Evaluation ...........................Maj. Gen. C. M. Kinney
Director-General, Evaluation Services ..................J. E. Dumbrille
Chief, Operational Research Analysis
    Establishment (CORAE)..........................Dr. G. R. Lindsey
Deputy Chief, ORAE ......................Brig. Gen. P. H. G. Carew
Director-General, General Analysis .....................S. H. Woodend
Director, Strategic Analysis ...............................K. J. Calder
Director, Social and Economic Analysis ...................Dr. J. J. Conn
Director, Mathematics and Statistics ..............Dr. M. A. Weinberger
Director, Manpower Analysis ...........................J. R. Hudson
Director, Logistics Analysis ...........................K. R. Kavanagh
Director-General, Operational Research....................D. A. Grant
Director, Maritime Operational Research .................C. L. R. Unwin
Director, Land Operational Research ......................W. P. Doyle
Director, Air Operational Research .................Dr. R. C. Brereton

**Assistant Deputy Minister, Personnel**
*Telephone: 922-7582*

Assistant Deputy Minister ...........................Lt. Gen. J. Vance
Executive Assistant/ADM ......................Lt. Col. U. Neugebauer
Associate Assistant Deputy Minister, Personnel ............W. R. Green
Executive Assistant/AADM (Per) ...............Lt. Col. M. C. Sweeney
Personnel Management Policy
    Study Group............................Comdr. W. B. Hotsenpillen
Director Personnel Legal Services ....................Col. R. L. Martin
Director Women Personnel .......................Col. A. M. Bélanger
Director-General, Official Languages ....................G. A. Sullivan
Assistant Director-General Official Languages .............D. J. Slimman
Director-General, Personnel Relations ....................J. R. Dalzell
Director-General, Personnel Services ...........Brig. Gen. P. F. Maxwell
Director-General, Compensation and Benefits .............D. W. Digby
Director-General, Personnel Co-ordination .................G. A. White
Chief, Personnel Development....................Maj. Gen. J. A. Fox

Director-General, Personnel Research
and Development . . . . . . . . . . . . . . . . . . . . . . . . . . . . . . . . . .W. M. Ritchie
Director-General, Recruiting Educational
and Training . . . . . . . . . . . . . . . . . . . . . . . . . . . . .Brig. Gen. D. J. McLaws
Chief, Personnel Careers and Senior
Appointments . . . . . . . . . . . . . . . . . . . . . . . . . . .Maj. Gen. B. R. Campbell
Director-General, Personnel Careers
Officers . . . . . . . . . . . . . . . . . . . . . . . . . . . . . . . . . . .Brig. Gen. R. L. Bell
Director-General, Personnel Careers
Other Ranks . . . . . . . . . . . . . . . . . . . . . . . . . . . . .Comdr. F. W. Crickard
Chaplain-General, Protestant . . . . . . . . . . . . . . . .Brig. Gen. O. A. Hopkins
Chaplain-General, Roman Catholic . . . . . . . . . . . . .Brig. Gen. G. E. Travers
Director-General, Manpower Utilization . . . . . . . .Brig. Gen. J. A. Williams
Director-General Classification . . . . . . . . . . . . . . . . . . . . . . . . . . . .C. Poiré
Director-General, Civilian Personnel . . . . . . . . . . . . . . . . . . . . . .R. P. Moir
Surgeon-General . . . . . . . . . . . . . . . . . . . . . . . .Maj. Gen. J. A. G. R. Dupuis
Deputy Surgeon-General . . . . . . . . . . . . . . . . . . . .Brig. Gen. R. W. Fassold
Director-General, Dental Services . . . . . . . . . . . . . .Brig. Gen. J. N. Wright

**Assistant Deputy Minister, Materiel**

*Telephone:   922-8473*

Assistant Deputy Minister . . . . . . . . . . . . . . . . . . . . . . . . . . . . .J. R. Killick
Associate Assistant Deputy Minister,
Materiel . . . . . . . . . . . . . . . . . . . . . . . . . . . . . . . . .Maj. Gen. R. N. Senior
Director-General, Material Administration
and Programs . . . . . . . . . . . . . . . . . . . . . . . . . . . .Brig. Gen. R. B. Screaton
Director, Logistic Operations . . . . . . . . . . . . . . . . . . . . . . .Col. D. G. Lewis
Director, Materiel Management Systems . . . . . . . . . . . . .Lt. Col. J. M. Flynn
Director, Materiel Administration and Services . . . . . . . . . . . . .C. A. Leech
Director, Documentation and Drawing Services . . . . . . . . . . . . .C. B. Keane
Director, Patent Administration . . . . . . . . . . . . . . . . . . . . . . . . .K. P. Aspila
Director-General, International Programs . . . . . . . . . . . . . . . . .D. M. Kettle
National Liaison Officer . . . . . . . . . . . . . . . . . . . . . . . . . . . . .R. J. Emerson
Director, Defence Sales Support . . . . . . . . . . . . . . . . . . . . . . . . .D. A. Bell
Director, Armaments Co-operation . . . . . . . . . . . . . . . . . . . .M. J. Montague
Project Management Office CF-18 . . . . . . . . . . .Brig. Gen. R. G. Slaunwhite
Project Management Office Canadian
Patrol Frigate . . . . . . . . . . . . . . . . . . . . . . . . . . . . . . .Cmdre. E. J. Healey
Project Management Office, NATO Airborne,
Early Warning and Control System . . . . . . . . . . . . . .Lt. Col. G. L. Hegge
Chief, Engineering and Maintenance . . . . . . . . . .Maj. Gen. G. MacFarlane
Director, Engineering and Maintenance
Planning and Standardization . . . . . . . . . . . . . . . . . . . . . .Col. J. A. Torck
Engineering and Maintenance Policy Section . . . . . . . . . . . . . .H. P. Neilson
Engineering and Maintenance Support . . . . . . . . . . . . .Lt. Col. J. M. Savage
Standardization Section . . . . . . . . . . . . . . . . . . . . . . . . . . . . . . . . . . . . . .
Director-General, Maritime Engineering
and Maintenance . . . . . . . . . . . . . . . . . . . . . . . . . . . . . .Comdr. E C. Ball
Director-General, Aerospace Engineering
and Maintenance . . . . . . . . . . . . . . . . . . . . . . . . . .Brig. Gen. W. Gelling
Director, Aerospace Project Management . . . . . . . . . . . .Col. R. I. McDowell
Director, Aircraft Engineering
and Maintenance . . . . . . . . . . . . . . . . . . . . . . . . . . . . . .Col. J. D. Young
Director, Aerospace Combat Systems . . . . . . . . . . . . .Col. G. A. Kerr-Wilson
Director, Avionics and Simulator
Engineering . . . . . . . . . . . . . . . . . . . . . . . . . . . . . . . . . .Col. G. G. Kemp
Director, Aerospace Support
Engineering . . . . . . . . . . . . . . . . . . . . . . . . . .Lt. Col. F. P. Harvey-Smith
Director-General, Land
Engineering and Maintenance . . . . . . . . . . . . . .Brig. Gen. J. G. R. Doucet
Director-General, Communications and
Electronics Engineering and Maintenance . . . . . .Brig. Gen. P. E. Woods
Chief, Supply . . . . . . . . . . . . . . . . . . . . . . . . . . . . . . . . . . . .M. E. Metusiak
Director, Supply Policy Control and
Administration . . . . . . . . . . . . . . . . . . . . . . . . . . . . . . . . . .M. H. Powell

Contract Settlement ...........................Lt. Col. W. R. Roueche
Senior, Energy and Environment
    Management Committee .............................E. R. Forster
Director of Law/Material Services....................Lt. Col. C. F. Blair
Director-General, Supply Systems ...............Brig. Gen. J. P. Leclerc
Director, Supply Management .......................Col. J. G. Goguen
Director, Supply Resources and Operations .............Col. B. D. Hanly
Director, Cataloguing and Identification ....................K. M. Roy
Director, Materiel Authorization...............Lt. Col. R. T. Macfarlane
Director, Food Services ...........................Lt. Col. R. Grenier
Director-General, Procurement
    and Supply (996-4900) ....................................Vacant
Director, Procurement and
    Supply Services (996-6214) .....................Col. W. P. Whelan
Director, Programs and Personnel...............Lt. Col. G. C. Tousignant
Director, Initial Provisioning Section ..............Lt. Col. H. E. Hartung
Director, Repair and Overhaul Section .................Cdr. P. C. Martin
Director, Procurement and Supply Finances ...........Col. H. A. Cooper
Director, Policy and Procedures .........................L. Villeneuve
Director, Audit .......................................J. D. Marshall
Director, Financial Operations ....................Lt. Col. W. J. Cormier
Director, Procurement and Supply
    Maritime (995-0934)...................................G. D. Hines
Director, Capital Development .........................D. S. McNicol
Director, Operations and Maintenance ............Lt. Col. C. H. Lionais
Director, Procurement and Supply Aerospace
    (993-2737) .........................................W. Grayson
Director, Capital and Development ....................A. J. Macdonald
Director, Operations and Maintenance
    Programs .....................................Lt. Col. J. E. Brabant
Director, Procurement and Supply Land
    (992-9725)........................................Col. W. E. R. Little
Director, Vehicle Acquisition and MRs
    (995-3072) .........................................A. Loschiuk
Director, Ammunition and Armament ...............Lt. Col. R. T. Sing
Director, Procurement and Supply Communications
    and Electronics (996-7124)............................G. L. Martin
Director, Capital Procurement (996-7094) ................R. N. Sturgeon
Director, Inventory Control Operational
    and Maintenance Procurement of
    Communication and Electronic Materiel
    (996-5800) ........................................J. C. Plummer
Director, Research and Development ..........Lt. Col. R. K. Waterhouse
Director, Procurement and Supply Common User ........Col. R. A. Allan
Director, Clothing, Fuel, Foods, Publications ............O. B. Sheldrick
Director, Furniture, Tools .......................Lt. Col. M. R. Beyreis
Director-General, Transportation ................Brig. Gen. S. B. Roach
Director-General, Ammunition ......................Col. J. A. F. Huot
Director, Ammunition Operations ...................Lt. Col. J. M. Flynn
Director, Ammunition Maintenance
    Engineering ...................................Cdr. N. T. Malcolm
Director, Ammunition Resources and Plans.................A. Churchill
Director-General Quality Assurance .....................W. H. Casley
Chief, Construction and Properties................Maj. Gen. J. A. Stuart
Project Manager, St. Jean Project Office .....................B. Gravel
Director-General, Quartering....................Brig. Gen. D. M. Gray
Director-General, Construction .......................R. H. Walsworth
Director-General, Works...............................Col. C. Allan
Director-General, Properties and Utilities ...................C. J. Crowe
Chief, Research and Development .......................E. J. Bobyn
Deputy Chief, Research and Development
    Laboratories....................................Dr. D. Schofield
Director, Science and Technology,
    Ordonnance and Vehicles ............................F. Jackson

Director, Science and Technology,
    Sensors and Electromagnetics .........................R. S. Thomas
Director, Science and Technology,
    Human Performance .............................Dr. L. A. Kuehn
Deputy Chief, Research and Development,
    Development ..................................Dr. G. T. Pullan
Director, Technology Application Co-ord ...................D. G. Gage
Director, Technology Application Maritime ............Dr. J. C. Moldon
Director, Technology Application Land ...........Lt. Col. R. T. Preston
Director, Technology Application, Air ....................N. E. Jeffrey
Director, Technology Application, Comm/Elec ..............K. Peebles
Deputy Chief, Research and Development, Plans....................
Director, Scientific Planning ...............................P. Brooks
Director, Extramural Scientific Activities ......................J. Koop
Director-General, Research and
    Development Services ..........................Dr. H. Waterman
Director, Research and Development Program
    Co-ordination ..................................B. G. McRoberts
Director, Technology Transfer
    and Exploitation ......................................H. K. Clark
Director, Administration, Research
    and Development ..............................J. P. Lafreniére
Director, Scientific Information Services...............N. M. Wildgoose
Customer Services Centre .............................B. J. Campbell

**Assistant Deputy Minister Finance**
*Telephone:    992-0359*

Assistant Deputy Minister ...............................L. E. Davies
Associate Assistant Deputy Minister,
    Finance ..........................................Maj. Gen. R. Ringma
Director-General, Audit .............................P. G. Northover
Director-General, Management
    Services.................................Brig. Gen. D. P. Harrison
Director-General Financial Policy and Procedures ...........W. F. Power
Director-General, Financial
    Administration...........................Brig. Gen. R. M. Bergin

**Defence Research
    Establishment Ottawa**
*Shirley Bay K1A OZ4*
*Telephone:    596-9356*

Chief, CDREO .........................................C. R. Iverson

**Communications Security
    Establishment—CCSE**
*Confederation Heights*
*Telephone:    998-4229*

Chief, CCSE ...........................................P. R. Hunt

**National Defence Medical
    Centre**
*Telephone:    733-6600*

Commandant and Chief, Medicine .................Brig. Gen. F. Knight
Commandant, NDMC Detachment
    DHQ/MIR...............................Lt. Col. B. M. O'Hearn
Deputy Commandant ..............................Maj. E. Seeger
Commander, 1 Dental Unit HQ .................Lt. Col. V. J. Lanctis

## DEFENCE FORCES

**ARMED FORCES**
**Defence Staff**
*101 Colonel By Drive*
*Ottawa, Ontario K1A OK2*
*Telephone:    992-5054*
*Telex:    053-4218*

Chief of the Defence Staff .......................Gen. G. C. E. Thériau
Vice Chief of the Defence Staff ...............Vice Adm. D. N. Mainguy
Deputy Chief of the Defence Staff ...............Lt. Gen. F. R. Richard

**Office of the Chief of the Defence Staff**

*Telephone:　992-5054*

Chief . . . . . . . . . . . . . . . . . . . . . . . . . . . . . . . . . . . . . . . . . .Gen. G. C. E. Thériaut
Judge Advocate General . . . . . . . . . . . . . . . . . . . . . . .Brig. Gen. F. Karwandy
Deputy Judge Advocate General . . . . . . . . . . . . . . . . . . .Col. G. L. Waterfield
Deputy Judge Advocate General, Advisory . . . . . . . . . . . . .Col. P. R. Partner
Chief Judge Advocate . . . . . . . . . . . . . . . . . . . . . . . . . . . . . .Col. J. P. Letellier
Director-General, Departmental
　　Administrative Services . . . . . . . . . . . . . . . . . . . . . . . . . . . . . . . .C. Gauther
Director, National Defence Inquiries . . . . . . . . . . . . . . . . . . . .F. H. Sashaw
Director-General, Information . . . . . . . . . . . . .Brig. Gen. J. M. L. Bourgeois
Head, Media Inquiries . . . . . . . . . . . . . . . . . . . . . . . . . . . . . . . . . . . . . . . . . . .
Head, Policy, Evaluation and Plans . . . . . . . . . . . . . . . . . . . . . .W. B. Myers
Director, Information Services . . . . . . . . . . . . . . . . . . . . . . .Col. J. G. Boulet
Director, Exhibitions and Displays . . . . . . . . . . . . . . . . . . . .Maj. G. R. Nagy
Director, Parliamentary Affairs . . . . . . . . . . . . . . . . . . . . . . . . . . . .G. L. Alarie

**Office of the Vice Chief of the Defence Staff**

*Telephone:　992-3433*

Vice Chief . . . . . . . . . . . . . . . . . . . . . . . . . . . . .Vice Adm. D. N. Mainguay
Chief, Intelligence and Security . . . . . . . . . . . . . . . . .Maj. Gen. A. Pickering
Director, Security . . . . . . . . . . . . . . . . . . . . . . . . . . . . . . . . . . .Col. R. T. Hall
Director, Police Operations . . . . . . . . . . . . . . . . . . .Lt. Col. R. E. Gladstone
Director, Personnel Security . . . . . . . . . . . . . . . . . . . .Lt. Col. E. W. Roberts
Director, Protective Security . . . . . . . . . . . . . . . . . . . . . . .Lt. Col. F. A. Leigh
Dirrector, Defence Intelligence . . . . . . . . . . . . . . . . . . . .Col. C. R. Simonds
Director, Foreign Liaison . . . . . . . . . . . . . . . . . . . . . . . . . . . . .Col. H. Gold
Chief, CIS Multilingual Section,
　　Translation Bureau Section of State . . . . . . . . . . . . . . . . . . . .T. Showalter
Director, Scientific and Technical
　　Intelligence . . . . . . . . . . . . . . . . . . . . . . . . . . . . . . . . . . .Dr. N. J. Hopkins
Commander Defence Liaison Staff Washington . . . . .Maj. Gen. R. Sturgess
Commander Defence Liaison Staff London . . . . . . . .Brig. Gen. C. B. Snider

**Office of the Deputy Chief of the Defence Staff**

*Telephone:　992-3355*

Deputy Chief . . . . . . . . . . . . . . . . . . . . . . . . . . . . . . . . .Lt. Gen. F. R. Richard
Director, Operational Programs Co-ordination . . . . . . . . . . . .Col. J. R. Lines
Director-General Military Plans and
　　Operations . . . . . . . . . . . . . . . . . . . . . . . . . . . . . . . . . . .Brig. Gen. A. C. Brown
Director, Military Operations Co-ordination . . . . . . . . . . .Col. R. W. Found
Director, Military Plans Co-ordination . . . . . . . . . . . . .Col. W. D. Wellsman
Director, Operational Guidance Co-ordination . . . . . . . . .Col. M. D. Calnan
Director, Nuclear, Biological and
　　Chemical Co-ordination . . . . . . . . . . . . . . . . . . .Lt. Col. E. D. Champagne
Director, Standardization Co-ordination . . . . . . . . .Lt. Col. J. C. Berezowski
Director, Mobilization Planning . . . . . . . . . . . . . . . . . . . . .Col. A. L. Geddry
Director, U.S. Army Research,
　　Development and Standardization
　　Group—Canada Representative . . . . . . . . . . . . . . . . . . .Col. C. G. Ramsey
Director, Australian Army Senior
　　Standardization Representative . . . . . . . . . . . . . . . . . . . .Maj. J. R. James
Director, British Army Standardization
　　Representative . . . . . . . . . . . . . . . . . . . . . . .Lt. Col. D. H. G. Corsellis
Director-General, Reserves and Cadets . . . . . . . . . . . . .Brig. Gen. P. Senecal
Director, Cadets . . . . . . . . . . . . . . . . . . . . . . . . . . . . . . .Col. H. L. Broughton
Director, Reserves . . . . . . . . . . . . . . . . . . . . . . . . . .Lt. Col. A. J. R. H. Neadow
Director, Associations . . . . . . . . . . . . . . . . . . . . . . . . . .Lt. Col. B. C. Glover
Secretary, Conference of Defence Associations . . . . . . . . . .Lt. Col. T. Hayes
Director-General, Military Engineering
　　Operations . . . . . . . . . . . . . . . . . . . . . . . . . . . . . . . . . .Col. J. K. Matheson
Director, Military Engineering Operations . . . . . . . . . . .Col. A. J. Tattersall
Director, Military Engineering Requirements . . . . . .Lt. Col. J. D. W. Peters
Director, Military Engineering Plans . . . . . . . . . . . . .Lt. Col. R. M. Gienow
Director, Cartography . . . . . . . . . . . . . . . . . . . . . . . . . . .Col. R. A. Grainger
Director-General, Communications and
　　Electronics Operations . . . . . . . . . . . . . . . . . . . . . . . . . . .Col. B. J. Bennett
Director, Communications and Electronics
　　Operations . . . . . . . . . . . . . . . . . . . . . . . . . . . . . . . .Lt. Col. E. M. MacLeod

Director, Communications Security . . . . . . . . . . . . . . . . . . . . . . . W. D. Moyes
Director, Frequency Spectrum Management . . . . . . . . Lt. Col. A. J. Beemer
Director, Electronic Warfare . . . . . . . . . . . . . . . . . . . . . . . Lt. Col. D. J. Ross
Director, Communications and Electronics
    Plans and Requirements . . . . . . . . . . . . . . . . . . . . . . . . Lt. Col. D. H. Brown
Director, International Communications
    and Electronics Co-ordination . . . . . . . . . . . . . . . . . . Lt. Col. G. L. Mowry
Chief of Reserves . . . . . . . . . . . . . . . . . . . . . . . . . . . . . . . Maj. Gen. J. J. Dunn
Director-General, Land
    Doctrine and Operations . . . . . . . . . . . Brig. Gen. A. J. G. D. deChastelain
Director, Land Operations and Infantry . . . . . . . . . . . . . . . . Col. E. C. Quinn
Director, Land Requirements and Artillery . . . . . . . . . . Col. H. R. Wheatley
Director, Project Management Office TCCCS . . . . . . . . . . Lt. Col. D. Banks
Director, Land Combat Development
    and Armour . . . . . . . . . . . . . . . . . . . . . . . . . . . . . . . . . . . . . . . Col. C. Milner
Chief, Maritime Doctrine and Operations . . . . . . . . . . Rear Adm. J. C. Wood
Director, Maritime Operations
    Plans and Reserves . . . . . . . . . . . . . . . . . . . . . . . Capt. (Navy) J. B. O'Reilly
Director, Maritime Requirements Sea . . . . . . . Capt. (Navy) M. H. D. Taylor
Director, Maritime Force Development . . . . . . . . . . . . . . . . . Cdr. D. Cogdon
Director, Auxiliary Vessels . . . . . . . . . . . . . . . . . . . . . . . . . . . F. C. Allwood
Director-General Air Doctrine
    and Operations . . . . . . . . . . . . . . . . . . . . . . . . . . . Brig. Gen. R. G. Hayman
Director, Air Operations, Training
    and Nuclear Weapons . . . . . . . . . . . . . . . . . . . . . . . . . . . . Col. P. G. Harle
Director, Air Regulations and
    Traffic Services . . . . . . . . . . . . . . . . . . . . . . . . . . . . Lt. Col. R. W. Hawkins
Director, Meteorology and Oceanography . . . . . . . . . . . . Dr. J. M. R. Asselin
Director, Air Requirements . . . . . . . . . . . . . . . . . . . . . . . . . Col. H. A. Sievert
Director, Air Plans . . . . . . . . . . . . . . . . . . . . . . . . . . . . . . Col. G. E. McArthur
Director, Maritime Aviation . . . . . . . . . . . . . . . . . . . . . . . . . Col. W. J. Read
Director, Land Aviation . . . . . . . . . . . . . . . . . . . . . . . Lt. Col. H. F. E. Swain
Deputy Commander, North American
    Aerospace (NORAD) Command . . . . . . . . . . . Lt. Gen. D. C. Mackenzie

## CANADIAN FORCES COMMANDS

**Mobile Command**
*Mobile Command Headquarters*
*St. Hubert, P.Q.*
*J3Y 5T5*

Commander . . . . . . . . . . . . . . . . . . . . . . . . . . . . . . . . . Lt. Gen. C. H. Belzile

**Air Command**
*Air Command Headquarters*
*Westwin, Manitoba*
*R2R OTO*

Commander . . . . . . . . . . . . . . . . . . . . . . . . . . . . . . . . . . . Lt. Gen. P. Manson

**Maritime Command**
*Maritime Command Headquarters*
*FMO Halifax, Nova Scotia*
*B3K 2XO*

Commander . . . . . . . . . . . . . . . . . . . . . . . . . . . . . . . . . . . Vice Adm. J. Woods

**Maritime Forces Pacific**
*Maritime Forces Pacific Headquarters*
*FMO Victoria, British Columbia*
*VOS 1BO*

Commander . . . . . . . . . . . . . . . . . . . . . . . . . . . . . . Rear Adm. G. L. Edwards

**Canadian Forces Europe**
*Canadian Forces Europe Headquarters*
*CFPO 5000*
*Belleville, Ontario*
*KOK 3RO*

Commander . . . . . . . . . . . . . . . . . . . . . . . . . . . . . . . Maj. Gen. D. Whiteman

**Northern Region**
*Northern Region Headquarters*
*Evans Block*
*P.O. Box 6666*
*Yellowknife, N.W.T.*
*X1A 2R3*

Commander.....................................Brig. Gen. B. Baile

**Communication Command**
*Communication Command Headquarters*
*Ottawa, Ontario*
*K1A OK2*

Commander .................................Brig. Gen. G. Simpson

\* \* \* \* \*

# GENERAL DEFENCE DATA

**Manpower**
Total Armed Forces...............................................82,905
  (See Page 101)
Population ................................................24,469,000

**Spending**
Military Expenditures.........................................$4.5 billion
Gross National Product ......................................$243 billion
Military Expenditure as a Percentage of
  Gross National Product ........................................1.9%
Military Expenditure as a Percentage of
  Central Government Expenditure ................................7.8%

**Defence Treaties** *(See Part II for Additional Detail)*

Bilateral:    Federal Republic        Sweden
                of Germany            Switzerland
              France                  United States
              Norway

Multilateral: Biological Weapons Convention
              Environmental Modifications Convention
              Limited Test Ban Treaty
              North Atlantic Treaty Organization
              Treaty on the Control of Arms on the Seabed
              Treaty on the Non-Proliferation of Nuclear Weapons

# CAPE VERDE
## Republic of Cape Verde

### Defense Establishment Command Structure
### and Force Organization

The President is Commander-in-Chief of the People's Revolutionary Armed Forces. Administrative matters are the responsibility of the Minister of Defense.

**Total armed forces:** 1,000 (Army: 900; Navy: 50; Air Force: 50).

### HEAD OF STATE

H. E. Aristides María Pereira

**OFFICE OF THE PRESIDENT**
*Rua Guerra Mendes 14*
*Praia*

*Telephone: 260*
*Telex: 51 prep cv*
*Cable: PRESCV PRAIA*

President of the Republic and Commander-in-Chief
of the People's Revolutionary Armed Forces . . . . . Aristides María Pereira

**OFFICE OF THE PRIME MINISTER**
*Praca 12 de Septembro*
*Praia*

*Telephone: 248*
*Telex: 52 govern cv*
*Cable: PREMCV PRAIA*

Prime Minister . . . . . . . . . . . . . . . . . . . . . . . . . . . . . . . Pedro Verona Pires

**MINISTRY OF DEFENSE**
*Rua Unidade Guine*
*Praia*

*Telephone: 448*
*Cable: DEFSEC PRAIA*

Minister . . . . . . . . . . . . . . . . . . . . . . . . . . . Col. Honorio Chantre Fortes
Director, Ideological Affairs . . . . . . . . . . . . . . . . . . . . . . . . . Al Varotavares

### DEFENSE FORCES

**ARMED FORCES**
**Peoples Revolutionary**
   **Armed Forces—FARP**
*Rua Unidade Guine*
*Praia*

*Telephone: 448*
*Cable: DEFSEC PRAIA*

Commander-in-Chief and President of the
   Republic . . . . . . . . . . . . . . . . . . . . . . . . . . . . . Aristides María Pereira
Chief of Staff . . . . . . . . . . . . . . . . . . . . . . . . . . . . . . . Angelo Dantas
Commander, Mindelo Military Region . . . . . . . . . . . . . . . . . . . . . . . . . . .
Commander, Sal Military Region . . . . . . . . . . . . . . . . . . . . . . . . . . . . . .
Commander, Praia Military Region . . . . . . . . . . . . . . . . . . . . . . . . . . . . .

**ARMY**
*Rua Unidade Guine*
*Praia*

Commander . . . . . . . . . . . . . . . . . . . . . . . . . . . . . . Col. Silvino M. da Luz

* * * * *

## GENERAL DEFENSE DATA

**Manpower**

Total Armed Forces ...............................................1,000
(See Page 109)
Population ...................................................293,000

**Spending**

Military Expenditures..........................................$3 million
Gross National Product.........................................$97 million
Military Expenditure as a Percentage of
Gross National Product ........................................3.4%
Military Expenditure as a Percentage of
Central Government Expenditure ...............................3.7%

**Defense Treaties** *(See Part II for Additional Detail)*

Bilateral:       None

Multilateral:    Biological Weapons Convention
Environmental Modification Convention
Limited Test Ban Treaty
Organization of African Unity
Treaty on the Control of Arms on the Seabed
Treaty on the Non-Proliferation of Nuclear Weapons

# CENTRAL AFRICAN REPUBLIC
## *République Centrafricaine*

### Defense Establishment Command Structure and Force Organization

The President, as Minister of National Defense and Chief of Staff of the Armed Forces, commands the military.

**Total armed forces:** 2,300 (Army: 2,000; Air Force: 300). **Para-military forces:** 1,500.

### HEAD OF STATE

H. E. Gén. d'Armée André Kolingba

**OFFICE OF THE PRESIDENT**
*(Palais de la Renaissance)*
*Bangui*
*Telephone: 61 03 23*
*Telex: 5253 presirep rc*
*5300 presicab rc (Cabinet)*

President of the Military Committee
  for National Recovery, Minister
  of National Defense, and Chief of
  Staff of the Armed Forces . . . . . . . . . . . . . Gén. d'Armée André Kolingba
Chief, Military Cabinet of
  the Presidency . . . . . . . . . . . . . . . . . . . . . . . . . Lt. Col. Joseph Songomali

**MINISTRY OF NATIONAL DEFENSE AND VETERANS AFFAIRS**
*Bangui*
*Telephone: 61 46 11, 61 30 11*
*Telex: 5298 mindica rc*

Minister . . . . . . . . . . . . . . . . . . . . . . . . . . . . . Gén. d'Armée André Kolingba
State Secretary . . . . . . . . . . . . . . . . . . . . . . . . . . . . . Lt. Col. François Diallo

### DEFENSE FORCES

**ARMY**
*(Forces Armées Centrafricaine—FACA)*
*c/o Ministry of National Defense*
*Bangui*
*Telephone: 61 26 11, 61 36 11*
*Telex: 5298 rc*

Chief of Staff of the Armed Forces
  and President of the Republic . . . . . . . . . . . Gén. d'Armée André Kolingba
Commander, Communications Company . . . . . . . . . . Sous Lt. Noel Gamago
Bureau of Social Services, FACA . . . . . . . . . . . Madame Celestine N'Guengo
Director, Military Engineering . . . . . . . . . . . . . . . . . . . . . . Cdt. Aimé Kassa

**Materiel Service**
*(Service du Materiel)*
*Telephone: 61 42 66*
*Telex: 5298 rc*

Director . . . . . . . . . . . . . . . . . . . . . . . . . . . . . . . . . . Capt. François Mobebou

**Military Engineering**
*Telephone: 61 25 66*
*Telex: 5298 rc*

Chief . . . . . . . . . . . . . . . . . . . . . . . . . . . . . . . . . . . . . . . . . . Cdt. Aimé Kassa

**Quartermaster General**
*(Quartier Générale)*
*Camp de Roux*
*Telephone: 61 04 00, 61 40 11*

Quartermaster General . . . . . . . . . . . . . . . . . . . . . . . . . . . . . . . . . . . . . . .

**Intervention Regiment**
*Camp Kassai*
*Telephone: 61 39 80, 61 39 85*

Commander ........................................... Cdt. Mi'ango

**NAVY**
*(Marine Nationale)*
*c/o Ministry of National Defense*
*Bangui*
*Telephone: 61 26 11, 61 40 44*
*Telex: 5298 rc*

Chief of Staff and President
of the Republic ...................... Gén. d'Armée André Kolingba

**AIR FORCE**
*(Armée de l'Air)*
*c/o Ministry of National Defense*
*Bangui*
*Telephone: 61 07 55*
*Telex: 5298 rc*

Chief of Staff ............................ Cdt. Ngoudou Touritiango

**NATIONAL CONSTABULARY**
*(Gendarmerie Centrafricaine)*
*Bangui*
*Telephone: 61 22 00, 61 49 78*

Commander ...................... Chief d'Éscadron Goze-Guy Gabriel
Commander, Territorial Brigade.................... Adjt. Koumbe Fidel
Commander, Mobile Legion .............. Capt. Mogoniaka Dieudonne
Commander, PK9 Brigade
  (M'Baiki Route)........................... Maréchal des Logis Chef
                                              A. Komatchleze Victor
Commander, PK12 Brigade
  (D'Amara Route).............................. Adjt. Bende Patrice
Director, Gendarmerie School .............. Capt. Zounemathi Leonard

**POLICE**
*(Police Centrafricaine)*
*Bangui*
*Telephone: 61 19 44, 61 28 55*

Director General ............................... Jean Willybird Sacko

\* \* \* \* \*

## GENERAL DEFENSE DATA

**Manpower**
Total Armed Forces................................................ 2,300
  (See Page 111)
Population .................................................... 2,471,000

**Spending**
Military Expenditures ........................................ $12 million
Gross National Product ...................................... $690 million
Military Expenditure as a Percentage of
  Gross National Product ............................................ 1.8%
Military Expenditure as a Percentage of
  Central Government Expenditure .................................. 8.9%

**Defense Treaties** *(See Part II for Additional Detail)*

Bilateral:     France

Multilateral:  Organization of African Unity
               Limited Test Ban Treaty
               Treaty on the Control of Arms on the Seabed
               Treaty on the Non-Proliferation of Nuclear Weapons

**Military Rank Comparisons**
See Appendix A.

# CHAD
## Republic of Chad
### *République du Tchad*

### Defense Establishment Command Structure and Force Organization

The President is Commander-in-Chief of the armed forces of Chad. He exercises his authority through the Minister of Defense, and is advised on defense policy by a High Military Council.

**Total armed forces:** 3,200 (Army: 3,000; Air Force: 200). **Para-military forces:** 6,000.

## HEAD OF STATE

Hissein Habré

**OFFICE OF THE PRESIDENT**
*N'Djamena*
*Telephone:   32-15, 32-80*
*Telex:   5201 presirep*

Head of State and Supreme
Chief of Armed Forces .............................. Hissein Habré
Chief of Military Cabinet ........................... Cdt. Galjam Negal

**MINISTRY OF STATE FOR DEFENSE, VETERANS AND DISABLED VETERANS**
*N'Djamena*
*Telephone:   32-15, 31-58*

Minister ........................................... Routouan Yoma
State Secretary ..................................... Daoud Dinefour

**MINISTRY OF INTERIOR AND SECURITY**
*N'Djamena*

Minister ........................................... Taher Guinassou
State Secretary .................................... Mbailao Beral Moise

## DEFENSE FORCES

**ARMED FORCES**
*N'Djamena*
*Telephone:   23-11*

Commander-in-Chief ................................. Idriss Dèby
Adjoint ........................ Cdt. de Battalion Gane Bang Zamtato

**ARMY**
*N'Djamena*

Commander ................................... Capt. Gopina Hussan
Adjoint ............................................ Hakouma Ali

**AIR FORCE**
*N'Djamena*

Commander ............................... Lt. Mornadji Mbaisambé
Adjoint ............................................ Assi Bousso

\* \* \* \* \*

# GENERAL DEFENSE DATA

**Manpower**

Total Armed Forces. . . . . . . . . . . . . . . . . . . . . . . . . . . . . . . . . . . . . . . . . . . . . .3,200
    (See Page 113)
Population . . . . . . . . . . . . . . . . . . . . . . . . . . . . . . . . . . . . . . . . . . . . . .4,852,000

**Spending**

Military Expenditures . . . . . . . . . . . . . . . . . . . . . . . . . . . . . . . . . . . . . . . .$22.2 million
Gross National Product . . . . . . . . . . . . . . . . . . . . . . . . . . . . . . . . . . . . . . .$590 million
Military Expenditure as a Percentage of
    Gross National Product . . . . . . . . . . . . . . . . . . . . . . . . . . . . . . . . . . . . . . . . .3.7%
Military Expenditure as a Percentage of
    Central Government Expenditure . . . . . . . . . . . . . . . . . . . . . . . . . . . . . . . . . .33%

**Defense Treaties** *(See Part II for Additional Detail)*

Bilateral:      France
                Nigeria

Multilateral:   Limited Test Ban Treaty
                Organization of African Unity
                Treaty on the Non-Proliferation of Nuclear Weapons

**Military Rank Comparisons**
See Appendix A.

# CHILE
## Republic of Chile
### *República de Chile*

### Defense Establishment Command Structure
### and Force Organization

The President is the Commander-in-Chief of the armed forces of Chile. The Government Junta, comprised of the Navy and Air Force Commanders-in-Chief, an Army Representative and the Director of the Police, maintains operational control of the military. The Ministry of Defense handles administrative matters.

**Total armed forces:** 97,000 (Army: 53,000;   Navy: 29,000;   Air Force: 15,000). **Paramilitary forces:** 27,000 (Carabineros).

## HEAD OF STATE

H. E. Cap. Augusto Pinochet Ugarte

**OFFICE OF THE PRESIDENT**
*(Oficina de la Presidencia)*
*Palacio de la Moneda*
*Santiago*

*Telephone: (2) 22 12 02*
*Telex: 240518 cmpjg cl*

President of the Republic and
  Commander-in-Chief . . . . . . . . . . . . . . . . . .Cap. Gral. del Ejército (Ret.)
                                     Augusto Pinochet Ugarte
Secretary General . . . . . . . . . . . . . . .Brig. Gral. Santiago Sinclair Ageneder

**GOVERNMENT JUNTA**
*(Junta del Gobierno)*
*Edificio Diego Portales*
*Santiago*
*Telephone: (2) 22 12 02*

Chairman . . . . . . . . . . . . . . . . . . . . . . . . .Alm. José Toríbio Merino Castro
                                   (Commander-in-Chief, Navy)
Member . . . . . . . . . . . . . . . . . . . . . .Tte. Gral. César Raúl Benavides Escobar
                                    (Army Representative)
Member . . . . . . . . . . . . . . . . . . . . . . . . .Air Gral. Fernando Matthei Aubel
                            (Commander-in-Chief, Air Force)
Member . . . . . . . . . . . . . . . . . . . . . . . . . . . . .Gral. César Mendoza Duran
                              (General Director, Police Force)

**MINISTRY OF NATIONAL DEFENSE**
*(Ministério de Defensa Nacional)*
*Plaza Bulnes*
*Santiago*

*Telephone: (2) 71-05-51*
*Telex: 240573 minde cl*

Minister . . . . . . . . . . . . . . . . . . . . . . . . . . .Vice Alm. Patricio Carvajal Prado
Commander, Guard Company of the
  Ministry of National Defense . . . . . . . . . . . . . . . . . . . . .Cap. Leonel Díaz
Director, Sports Federation of the Armed
  Forces and the National Police . . . . . . . . . . . . . . . . .Cnel. Emilio Moraga
Secretary, Education Council of the
  Armed Forces . . . . . . . . . . . . . . . . . . . . . . . . . . . . . .Cdte. Francisco Vargas
Secretary, Supreme Council of
  National Defense . . . . . . . . . . . . . . . . . . . . . . . . . . . . . .Cnel. Fdo. Silva V.
Director General, Civil Defense of Chile . . . . . . . . . . . .Cnel. Diego Grez G.
Director General, Recruitment and
  Mobilization for the Armed Forces . . . . . . . . .Gral. Brig. César Manríquez

**National Defense Staff**
*(Estado Mayoe de Defensa Nacional)*
*Plaza Bulnes*
*Santiago*
*Telephone: (2) 71 5685*

Chief (FACH) . . . . . . . . . . . . . . . . . . . .May. Gral. Pablo Saldias Maripangue
Deputy Chief (Army) . . . . . . . . . . . . . . . . . . . . . . .Gral. Brig. Gabriel Pizarro
Auditor (Navy) . . . . . . . . . . . . . . . . . . . . . . . . . . . . . .Cdte. Enrique Guzman
Chief, Planning . . . . . . . . . . . . . . . . . . . . . . . . . . . . . . .Cdte. Gustavo Leal
Adjutant, E.M.D.N. (Army) . . . . . . . . . . . . . . . . . . . . .Cdte. Gustavo Leal

Chief, Department of Economic
Analysis (Navy) . . . . . . . . . . . . . . . . . . . . . .Cnel. Emilio De La Mahotiere
Chief, Department I, Organization . . . . . . . . . . . . .Cnel. Alfonso Straub G.
Chief, Department III, Operations, (Navy) . . . . . . . .Cdte. Ruben Scheihing
Chief, Department IV . . . . . . . . . . . . . . . . . . . . . . . .Cnel. Rolando Lagos
Chief, Department VI, Telecommunications . . . . . . . . .Cap. Arnoldo Luna
Secretary, J.E.M.D. . . . . . . . . . . . . . . . . . . . . . . . . .Brig. Hugo Sepulveda

**Office of the Undersecretary
of the Army**
*(Oficina del Sub-Secretario del Ejército)*
*Plaza Bulnes*
*Santiago*
*Telephone:  (2) 72 2868*

Undersecretary . . . . . . . . . . . . . . . . . . . . . . . . . .Cnel. Renato Fuenzalida
Chief, Department I, Administration . . . . . . . . . . . . . . . .May. Javier Urbina
Chief, Department III, Audit . . . . . . . . . . . . . . . . . . .May. Ricardo Carrasco
Chief, Department IV, Finances . . . . . . . . . . . . . . .May. René Valenzuela
Chief, Information Section . . . . . . . . . . . . . . . . . . . . . . . . . . .Ana Villarroel

**Office of the Undersecretary
of the Navy**
*(Oficina del Sub-Secretario de la
Armada)*
*Galvez 45 P 3*
*Santiago*
*Telephone:  (2) 81 449*

Undersecretary . . . . . . . . . . . . . . . . . . . . . .Cap. Alfredo Gallejos Villalobos
Chief, Administration Department . . . . . . . . . . . . . . . .Manuel Concha G.
Auditor. . . . . . . . . . . . . . . . . . .Cap. Frageta (JT) Folo Toyos C. Renato Silva
Chief, Pension Department . . . . . . . . . . . . . . . . . . . . . . . . . . . . . . . . . . . . .
Chief, Budget Department . . . . .Cap. Corbeta (AB) Guillermo Cespedes G.

**Office of the Undersecretary
of Aviation**
*(Oficina del Sub-Secretario de Aviación)*
*Santiago*

Undersecretary . . . . . . . . . . . . . . . . . . . . . . . . . . . .Cnel. Jaime Parra Santos
Chief, Department I, Analysis and
Administration . . . . . . . . . . . . . . . . . . . . . . . . . . . . . . . . . . . . . .Pedro Ramírez
Chief, Department II, Technical Budget
and Finances . . . . . . . . . . . . . . . . . . . . . . . . . . . . . . . . . .Cdte. Raul Aranda
Chief, Department III, Social . . . . . . . . . . . . . . . . . . . .Guillermo Galleguillos
Chief, Department IV, Aviation Archives . . . . . . . . . . .Jaime De La Fuente
Chief, Department of Personnel
and Administration . . . . . . . . . . . . . . . . . . . . . . . . . . . . . . .Federico Lagos

**Office of the Undersecretary
of National Police**
*(Oficina del Sub-Secretario
de la Policía)*
*Teatinos 20*
*Santiago*
*Telephone:  (2) 60 480*

Undersecretary . . . . . . . . . . . . . . . . . . . . . . . . . .Cnel. Rigoberto Gonzalez
Chief, Department I, Decrees . . . . . . . . . . . . . . . . . . . . . . .Raul Pirattini R.
Chief, Department II, Administration . . .Tte. Cnel. (I) Marcos Ibacache R.

**Office of the Undersecretary
of Investigations**
*(Oficina del Sub-Secretario de
Investigaciones)*

Undersecretary . . . . . . . . . . . . . . . . . . . . . . . . . . .Cap. Nav. Carlos Pinto C.

## DEFENSE FORCES

**ARMY**
*(Ejército de Chile)*
*Plaza Bulnes*
*Santiago*
*Telephone:  (2) 83 721*

Commander-in-Chief . . . . . . . . .Cap. Gral. Augusto Pinochet Ugarte (Ret.)
Vice Commander-in-Chief . . . . . . . . . . . . . . . . . .Gral. Julio Canessa Robert
Chief of Staff . . . . . . . . . . . . . . . . . . . . . . . . . . . .Gral. Rafael Ortiz Navarro
Commander, Antarctic Command . . . . . . . . . . . . . . .Tte. Cnel. Juan Morales
Commander, Telecommunication
Supply and Maintenance . . . . . . . . . . . . . . . . . . .Gral. Brig. Carlos Ojeda
Chief, Engineer Command . . . . . . . . . . . . . . . .Brig. Christian Ackerknecht
Chief, Telecommunications Command. . . . . . . . . .Gral. Brig. Carlos Ojeda
Chief, War Academy. . . . . . . . . . . . . . . . . . . . . . . . . . . . .Cnel. Jaime Nuñez
Chief, Military Polytechnical Academy . . . . . . . . . . .Cnel. Raúl Dinator M.
Chief, Military Institute Command . . . . . . . . . . . . . . . .Cnel. Oscar Vargas
Chief, Transportation Headquarters . . . . . . . . . . .Brig. Gral. Pedro Howard

Chief, Institute of Investigation and
     Control . . . . . . . . . . . . . . . . . . . . . . . . . . . . . . . . . . . .Cnel. Rolando Rojas L.
Chief, Institute of Military Hospital . . . . . . . . . . . . . . . .Cnel. Hans Zipelline
Director, Army Armaments Factory . . . . . . . . . . . .Brig. Luis Alberto Reyes
Director, Military School . . . . . . . . . . . . . . . . . . . . . . . .Cnel. Oscar Vargas
Director, Military Health . . . . . . . . . . . . . . . . . .Gral. Brig. Jorge Verdugo A.

**Administrative Support Command**
*(Comando Administrativo de Apoyo)*

Telephone:    (2) 22 2635

Chief . . . . . . . . . . . . . . . . . . . . . . . . . . . . . . . . . . . . . . . . . . . . . . . . . . . .(Vacant)
Chief, Javiera Carrera Technical Academy . . . . . . . . . . .Cnel. Mário Álvarez
Chief, Judicial Section . . . . . . . . . . . . . . . . . . . . . .Gral. Brig. Fernando Lyon
Chief, Religious Services . . . . . . . . . . . . . . . . . .Gral. Brig. Francisco Gillmore
Chief, Acquisitions and Bookkeeping . . . . . . . . .Gral. Brig. Julio Fernandez

**NAVY**
*(Armada de Chile)*
*Galvez 45, 7*
*Santiago*

Telephone:    (2) 72 52 72
Telex:   230443 ctcv cl
     *(Centro de Telecommunicaciones
       Navales Valparaiso)*

Commander-in-Chief . . . . . . . . . . . . . . . . .Alm. José Toribio Merino Castro
Chief, Navy General Staff . . . . . . . . . . . . . . . .Vice Alm. Maurice Poisson E.
Auditor General of the Navy . . . . . . . . .Contra Alm. J. T. Aldo Montagna B.
Director, Shipyards and Armory of the Navy . . . . . . . . . .Alm. Oscar Paredes

**Marine Corps**
*(Infantería de Marina)*

Telephone:    (31) 55971

Commander . . . . . . . . . . . . . . . . . . . . . . . .Contra Alm. Pablo Wunderlich P.
Chief of Staff . . . . . . . . . . . . . . . . . . . . . . .Cap. Navio Guillermo Toledo Leal

**Office of General Services**
*(Oficina de Servicios Generales)*
*(In Charge of Procurement)*
*Prat 620*
*Valparaiso*

Telephone:    (2) (31)-52379

Director General . . . . . . . . . . . . . . . . . . . . . . . .Vice Alm. German Guesalaga
Director, Naval Armaments . . . . . . . . . . .Contra Alm. Guillermo Le Maitre
Director, Naval Ingenierigs . . . . . . . . . . . . . .Contra Alm. Luis Lara Marshall
Director, Supply . . . . . . . . . . . . . . . . . . . . .Contra Alm. Pedro Larrond-Jara
Comptroller of the Navy . . . . . . . . . . . . . . . . . .Contra Alm. Navajas Irigoyen

**Office of Personnel**
*(Oficina del Personal)*

Telephone:    (31)-50992

Director General, Personnel . . . . . .Contra Alm. Ramon Undurraga Carvajal
Director, Naval Education . . . . . . . . . . . .Contra Alm. Jorge Sepúlveda Ortíz
Director, Naval Health . . . . . . . . . . . . . .Contra Alm. René Miguieles Orellana

**Office of Maritime Territories**
*(Oficina de Territorios Maritimos)*

Telephone:    (31)-55912

Director General, Maritime
     Territories . . . . . . . . . . . . . . . . . . . .Contra Alm. Victor Larenas Quisada

**Naval Aviation Command**
*(Comando de Aviación Naval)*
*Base Naval El Belloto*
*Correo Naval Valparaiso*
*Belloto 266*

Commander-in-Chief, Naval Aviation . . . . . . . . . . . . . . .Contra Alm. Huber

**I Naval Zone**
*(I Zona Naval)*
*Correo Naval*
*Valparaiso*

Telephone:    (31)-55438

Commander-in-Chief . . . . . . . . . . . .Vice Alm. Luis De Los Rios Echeverría

**II Naval Zone**
*(II Zona Naval)*
*Correo Naval*
*Talcahuano*

Telephone:    (42)-42515

Commander-in-Chief . . . . .Contra Alm. Osvaldo Schwarzenberg Steemeier

**III Naval Zone**
*(III Zona Naval)*
*Correo Naval*
*Dunta Arenas*
*PTA Arenas 22021*

Commander-in-Chief . . . . . . . . . . . . . . . . . . . . . . . . Vice Alm. Jorge Baeze

**Naval Fleet**
*(Flota Naval)*
*Correo Naval*
*Valparaiso*

Commander-in-Chief . . . . . . . . . . . . . . . . . . Contra Alm. Rolando García

**AIR FORCE**
*(Fuerza Aérea)*
*Plaza Bulnes*
*Santiago*

*Telephone:   (2) 8 6543*

Commander . . . . . . . . . . . . . . . . . . Gral. de Aviación Fernando Matthei A.
Chief of Staff . . . . . . . . . . . . . . . . . . . . . Gral. de Aviación Carlos Desgroux C.
Commander, National Garrison (Chief of Second Air
   Brigade—Santiago) . . . . . . . . . . . . . . . . . . Gral. de Brig. Av. Ramon Vega
Chief, Aerial Photography . . . . . . . . . . . . . . Cdte. de Gruppo Oscar Boronig
Chief, Personnel . . . . . . . . . . . . . . . . . . . . . Gral. de Brig. Vicente Rodriguez
Inspector General and Director
   of Operations . . . . . . . . . . . . . . . . . . . . . . . . Gral. de Aviación Mario Lopez
Deputy Director, Operations . . . . . . . . . . . . . . . . . . . . Cnel. Carlos Carrasco
Director of Meteorology . . . . . . . . . . . . . . . . . . Cdte. de Gruppo Federico Roll
Director, Aeronautic Technical School . . . . . . . . . . . . . Cnel. Victor Ramirez
Chief, Computer Data and Processing Dept. . . . . . . . . . . . . . . . Jorge Canon
Comptroller General . . . . . . . . . . . . . . . . . . . . Gral. de Brig. Enrique Montero
Director, Civil Aeronautics . . . . . . . . . . . . . . Gral. de Brig. Nelson Sepulveda
Commander, General Depot and Deputy
   Director of Electronic Development
   Engineering and Maintenance . . . . . . . . . . . . . . Gral. de Brig. Fritz Dreyer
Chief, Air Force Public Relations . . . . . . . . . . . . . . . Cnel. Daniel Moraga L.

\* \* \* \* \*

# GENERAL DEFENSE DATA

**Manpower**
   Total Armed Forces . . . . . . . . . . . . . . . . . . . . . . . . . . . . . . . . . . . . . . . . . . . . . 97,000
      (See Page 115)
   Population . . . . . . . . . . . . . . . . . . . . . . . . . . . . . . . . . . . . . . . . . . . . . . 11,323,000

**Spending**
   Military Expenditures . . . . . . . . . . . . . . . . . . . . . . . . . . . . . . . . . . . . $567 million
   Gross National Product . . . . . . . . . . . . . . . . . . . . . . . . . . . . . . . . . . . . $23 billion
   Military Expenditure as a Percentage of
      Gross National Product . . . . . . . . . . . . . . . . . . . . . . . . . . . . . . . . . . . . . 2.4%
   Military Expenditure as a Percentage of
      Central Government Expenditure . . . . . . . . . . . . . . . . . . . . . . . . . . . . . 9.8%

**Defense Treaties** *(See Part II for Additional Detail)*

   Bilateral:       United States

   Multilateral:   Act of Chapultepec
                     Inter-American Defense Board
                     Inter-American Treaty of Reciprocol Assistance
                     Limited Test Ban Treaty
                     Treaty on the Prohibition of Nuclear Weapons in Latin
                        America

**Military Rank Comparisons**
   See Appendix A.

# CHINA

## People's Republic of China
### *Zhonghua Renmin Gongheguo*

## Defense Establishment Command Structure
## and Force Organization

The Chairman of the Military Commission of the Chinese Communist Party's Central Committee is the Commander-in-Chief of the armed forces. The military services are unified into the People's Liberation Army (PLA) and are under the direct command of the Ministry of National Defense. The PLA is structured regionally. The Commander of each of the eleven Military Regions is in direct control of all PLA forces in that region, including naval, air, and militia forces.

Military ranks, abolished in 1965 in the early days of the cultural revolution, have not yet been reestablished, though there are indications that they soon will be.

**Total armed forces:** 4,000,000 (Army: 3,150,000;  Navy: 360,000;  Air Force: 490,000).

## HEAD OF STATE

Li Xiannian

**NATIONAL PEOPLE'S CONGRESS**
*Beijing*

Chairman, Standing Committee . . . . . . . . . . . . . . . . . . . . . . . . . . . Ye Jianying

**STATE COUNCIL**
*c/o State Council Secretariat*
*Beijing*
*Telephone:  666453*

Premier . . . . . . . . . . . . . . . . . . . . . . . . . . . . . . . . . . . . . . . . . . . Zhao Ziyang
Vice Premier . . . . . . . . . . . . . . . . . . . . . . . . . . . . . . . . . . . . . . . . Wan Li
Vice Premier. . . . . . . . . . . . . . . . . . . . . . . . . . . . . . . . . . . . . . . . Yao Yilin
State Councillor . . . . . . . . . . . . . . . . . . . . . . . . . . . . . . . . . . . . . Fang Yi
State Councillor. . . . . . . . . . . . . . . . . . . . . . . . . . . . . . . . . . . . . . Gu Mu
State Councillor. . . . . . . . . . . . . . . . . . . . . . . . . . . . . . . . . . . . . . Yu Qiuli
State Councillor . . . . . . . . . . . . . . . . . . . . . . . . . . . . . . . . . . . . . Kang Shi'en
State Councillor . . . . . . . . . . . . . . . . . . . . . . . . . . . . . . . . . . . . . Chen Muhua
State Councillor . . . . . . . . . . . . . . . . . . . . . . . . . . . . . . . . . . . . . Bo Yibo
State Councillor . . . . . . . . . . . . . . . . . . . . . . . . . . . . . . . . . . . . . Ji Pengfei
State Councillor. . . . . . . . . . . . . . . . . . . . . . . . . . . . . . . . . . . . . . Zhang Jingfu
State Councillor . . . . . . . . . . . . . . . . . . . . . . . . . . . . . . . . . . . . . Huang Hua
State Councillor . . . . . . . . . . . . . . . . . . . . . . . . . . . . . . . . . . . . . Zhang Aiping

**MILITARY COMMISSION OF THE**
**CHINESE COMMUNIST PARTY**
**TWELFTH CENTRAL COMMITTEE**
*Beijing*

Chairman and Commander-in-Chief . . . . . . . . . . . . . . . . . . . Deng Xiaoping
Vice Chairman . . . . . . . . . . . . . . . . . . . . . . . . . . . . . . . . . . . . . Ye Jianying
Vice Chairman . . . . . . . . . . . . . . . . . . . . . . . . . . . . . . . . . . . . . Xu Xiangqian
Vice Chairman . . . . . . . . . . . . . . . . . . . . . . . . . . . . . . . . . . . . . Nie Rongzhen
Secretary General . . . . . . . . . . . . . . . . . . . . . . . . . . . . . . . . . . Yang Shangkun
Member . . . . . . . . . . . . . . . . . . . . . . . . . . . . . . . . . . . . . . . . . . Xiao Hua
Member, Standing Committee . . . . . . . . . . . . . . . . . . . . . . . . . Chen Xillian
Member, Standing Committee . . . . . . . . . . . . . . . . . . . . . . . . . Zhang Aiping
Member, Standing Committee . . . . . . . . . . . . . . . . . . . . . . . . . Han Xianchu
Member, Standing Committee . . . . . . . . . . . . . . . . . . . . . . . . . Su Yu
Member, Standing Committee . . . . . . . . . . . . . . . . . . . . . . . . . Wang Ping
Member, Standing Committee . . . . . . . . . . . . . . . . . . . . . . . . . Wang Zhen
Member, Standing Committee . . . . . . . . . . . . . . . . . . . . . . . . . Wei Guoqing

119

| | |
|---|---|
| Member, Standing Committee | Xu Shiyou |
| Member, Standing Committee | Yang Dezhi |
| Member, Standing Committee | Yang Shangkun |
| Member, Standing Committee | Yang Yong |
| Member, Standing Committee | Zhang Tingfa |

**MINISTRY OF NATIONAL DEFENSE**
*Huangsi Dajie*
*Andingmenwai*
*Beijing*
*Telephone:    440518, 667343*

| | |
|---|---|
| Minister | Zhang Aiping |
| Vice Minister | Xu Shiyou |
| Vice Minister | Xiao Jingguang |
| Vice Minister | Yang Dezhi |

**Foreign Affairs Bureau**

| | |
|---|---|
| Director | Chai Chengwen |
| Deputy Director | Gan Mai |
| Deputy Director | Liu Zhenlen |
| Deputy Director | Xi Yi |
| Deputy Director | Shen Shoaoxing |
| Deputy Director | Yin Zuozhen |
| Deputy Director | Zhang Bingyu |
| Deputy Director | Zhao Chenzheng |
| Deputy Director | Zhu Kaiyin |
| Director, Protocol Department | Liu Guangming |
| Director, Third Division | |
| Deputy Director, Third Division | Dong Ligong |

**MINISTRY OF STATE SECURITY**
*Beijing*

| | |
|---|---|
| Minister | Ling Yun |

# DEFENSE FORCES

**ARMY**
**Chinese People's Liberation Army—PLA**
*Beijing*

**General Staff Headquarters**

| | |
|---|---|
| Chief of Staff | Yang Dezhi |
| Assistant to the Chief of Staff | Han Huaizhi |
| Assistant to the Chief of Staff | Liu Kai |
| Assistant to the Chief of Staff | Xu Xin |
| Deputy Chief of Staff | Chi Haotian |
| Deputy Chief of Staff | He Zhengwen |
| Deputy Chief of Staff | Li Da |
| Deputy Chief of Staff | Liu Huaquing |
| Deputy Chief of Staff | Wang Shangrong |
| Deputy Chief of Staff | We Xiuquan |
| Deputy Chief of Staff | Yang Chengwu |
| Deputy Chief of Staff | Yang Yong |
| Deputy Chief of Staff | Zhang Aiping |
| Deputy Chief of Staff | Zhang Zhen |

**Chinese Communist Party Committee**

| | |
|---|---|
| First Secretary | Yang Dezhi |
| Second Secretary | Yang Yong |

**Antichemical Warfare Troops Department**

| | |
|---|---|
| Director | |
| Deputy Director | Wu Gezhi |

**Armament Department**

| | |
|---|---|
| Director | |
| Deputy Director | Wang Luotian |

**Intelligence Department**

| | |
|---|---|
| Director | |
| Deputy Director | Huang Zhengji |

**Military Training Department**
Director.............................................................
Deputy Director ........................................Han Fudong
Deputy Director ....................................Zhang Donghuan
Member ..................................................Dai Jiong

**Radar Department**
Director.............................................Qu Peiyong

**Signal Department**
Director...........................................Jiang Wen

**PLA Logistics Academy**
Commandant ........................................................
First Political Commissar .........................................

**PLA Military Academy**
Commandant ...........................................Xiao Ke
First Political Commissar .........................................

**PLA Political Academy**
Commandant ...........................................Lin Hao
First Political Commissar .........................................

**General Logistics Department**
Director ..............................................Hong Xuezhi
Deputy Director .........................................Fan Ziyu
Deputy Director .....................................Feng Yongshun
Deputy Director ..........................................He Biao
Deputy Director ..........................................Li Yuan
Deputy Director ......................................Rao Zhengxi
Deputy Director .....................................Sun Hongzhen
Deputy Director ......................................Xu Guangyi
Deputy Director ....................................Zhang Ruguang
Deputy Director....................................Zhang Xianyue
Political Commissar ....................................Wang Ping
Deputy Political Commissar ......................Bai Xiangguo
Deputy Political Commissar .........................Cao Siming
Deputy Political Commissar..........................Chen Ying
Deputy Political Commissar ............................Li Yao
Chief of Staff .......................................Wang Zixiu
Deputy Chief of Staff....................................Chen Lei
Deputy Chief of Staff ...............................Lui Lumin

**Foreign Affairs Department**
Director...........................................Wang Xiushen

**Ordnance Department**
Director.............................................................
Deputy Director ...................................Zhang Huanxin

**Public Health Department**
Director ............................................Zhang Xiang
Deputy Director ..................................Yang Dingchen

**General Political Department of the People's Liberation Army**
Director..............................................Wei Guoqing
Deputy Director .........................................Fu Zhong
Deputy Director.......................................Gan Weihan
Deputy Director ..........................................Hua Nan
Deputy Director.......................................Huang Yukun
Deputy Director.........................................Liang Biye
Deputy Director.........................................Shi Jinqian
Deputy Director .....................................Yan Jinsheng
Deputy Director .....................................Zhu Yunqian
Deputy Secretary General ...............................Li Wei
Deputy Secretary General ............................Yao Kang

**Liberation Army Daily** *(Jiefangjun Bao)*
Director . . . . . . . . . . . . . . . . . . . . . . . . . . . . . . . . . . . . . . . . . . . . . . . . . . . Liu Zongzhuo
Deputy Director . . . . . . . . . . . . . . . . . . . . . . . . . . . . . . . . . . . . . . . . . . . . Lu Liang

**Culture Department**
Director . . . . . . . . . . . . . . . . . . . . . . . . . . . . . . . . . . . . . . . . . . . . . . . . . . Liu Baiyu
Deputy Director . . . . . . . . . . . . . . . . . . . . . . . . . . . . . . . . . . . . . . . . . . . . Zhou Zhitong

**Mass Work Department**
Director . . . . . . . . . . . . . . . . . . . . . . . . . . . . . . . . . . . . . . . . . . . . . . . . . . Lu Cunfu

**Organization Department**
Director . . . . . . . . . . . . . . . . . . . . . . . . . . . . . . . . . . . . . . . . . . . . . . . . . . .
Deputy Director . . . . . . . . . . . . . . . . . . . . . . . . . . . . . . . . . . . . . . . . . . . . Fang Zhengbo

**National Defense Scientific and Technological Commission**
Chairman . . . . . . . . . . . . . . . . . . . . . . . . . . . . . . . . . . . . . . . . . . . . . . . . . Zhang Aiping
Vice Chairman . . . . . . . . . . . . . . . . . . . . . . . . . . . . . . . . . . . . . . . . . . . . . Chen Bin
Vice Chairman . . . . . . . . . . . . . . . . . . . . . . . . . . . . . . . . . . . . . . . . . . . . Ding Henggao
Vice Chairman . . . . . . . . . . . . . . . . . . . . . . . . . . . . . . . . . . . . . . . . . . . . Qian Xuesen
Vice Chairman . . . . . . . . . . . . . . . . . . . . . . . . . . . . . . . . . . . . . . . . . . . . Zhang Zhenhuan
Vice Chairman . . . . . . . . . . . . . . . . . . . . . . . . . . . . . . . . . . . . . . . . . . . . Zhu Guangya
Political Commissar . . . . . . . . . . . . . . . . . . . . . . . . . . . . . . . . . . . . . . . . Li Youguang

**National Defense Industry Office**
Director . . . . . . . . . . . . . . . . . . . . . . . . . . . . . . . . . . . . . . . . . . . . . . . . . . Hong Xuezhi
Deputy Director . . . . . . . . . . . . . . . . . . . . . . . . . . . . . . . . . . . . . . . . . . . . Su Jing (f)
Deputy Director . . . . . . . . . . . . . . . . . . . . . . . . . . . . . . . . . . . . . . . . . . . . Wang Hui
Deputy Director . . . . . . . . . . . . . . . . . . . . . . . . . . . . . . . . . . . . . . . . . . . . Xie Guang
Deputy Director . . . . . . . . . . . . . . . . . . . . . . . . . . . . . . . . . . . . . . . . . . . . Ye Zhengda
Deputy Director . . . . . . . . . . . . . . . . . . . . . . . . . . . . . . . . . . . . . . . . . . . . Zheng Hantao
Deputy Director . . . . . . . . . . . . . . . . . . . . . . . . . . . . . . . . . . . . . . . . . . . . Zou Jiahua

**People's Liberation Army Military Court**
President . . . . . . . . . . . . . . . . . . . . . . . . . . . . . . . . . . . . . . . . . . . . . . . . . Tian Jia

**Physical Culture and Sports Commission of the People's Liberation Army**
Chairman . . . . . . . . . . . . . . . . . . . . . . . . . . . . . . . . . . . . . . . . . . . . . . . . . Han Fudong
Vice Chairman . . . . . . . . . . . . . . . . . . . . . . . . . . . . . . . . . . . . . . . . . . . . Zhou Zhitong

**Armoured Forces**
Commander . . . . . . . . . . . . . . . . . . . . . . . . . . . . . . . . . . . . . . . . . . . . . . Huang Xinting
Deputy Commander . . . . . . . . . . . . . . . . . . . . . . . . . . . . . . . . . . . . . . . . Cheng Shicai
Deputy Commander . . . . . . . . . . . . . . . . . . . . . . . . . . . . . . . . . . . . . . . . Deng Jiatai
Deputy Commander . . . . . . . . . . . . . . . . . . . . . . . . . . . . . . . . . . . . . . . . He Jinnian
Deputy Commander . . . . . . . . . . . . . . . . . . . . . . . . . . . . . . . . . . . . . . . . Lin Bin
Deputy Commander . . . . . . . . . . . . . . . . . . . . . . . . . . . . . . . . . . . . . . . . Zhang Wenzhou
Political Commissar . . . . . . . . . . . . . . . . . . . . . . . . . . . . . . . . . . . . . . . . Mo Wenhua
Deputy Political Commissar . . . . . . . . . . . . . . . . . . . . . . . . . . . . . . . . . Niu Mingzhi
Chief of Staff . . . . . . . . . . . . . . . . . . . . . . . . . . . . . . . . . . . . . . . . . . . . . Yan Zhenheng

**Engineering Corps**
Commander . . . . . . . . . . . . . . . . . . . . . . . . . . . . . . . . . . . . . . . . . . . . . . Tan Shanhe
Deputy Commander . . . . . . . . . . . . . . . . . . . . . . . . . . . . . . . . . . . . . . . . Xu Guoxian

**Railway Corps**
Commander . . . . . . . . . . . . . . . . . . . . . . . . . . . . . . . . . . . . . . . . . . . . . . Chen Zaidao
Deputy Commander . . . . . . . . . . . . . . . . . . . . . . . . . . . . . . . . . . . . . . . . Qi Qianzhai
First Political Commissar . . . . . . . . . . . . . . . . . . . . . . . . . . . . . . . . . . . Lu Zhengcao
Second Political Commissar . . . . . . . . . . . . . . . . . . . . . . . . . . . . . . . . . Kuang Fuzhao

**Political Department**
Director . . . . . . . . . . . . . . . . . . . . . . . . . . . . . . . . . . . . . . . . . . . . . . . . . .
Adviser . . . . . . . . . . . . . . . . . . . . . . . . . . . . . . . . . . . . . . . . . . . . . . . . . . Zhang Chongwen

**Capital Construction Engineering Corps**
Director of General Office and Secretary,
    Chinese Communist Party Committees . . . . . . . . . . . . . . . . . . . . . Li Renlin
Director . . . . . . . . . . . . . . . . . . . . . . . . . . . . . . . . . . . . . . . . . . . . . . . . . . Zhang Kongxiu

|  |  |  |
|---|---|---|
|  | Deputy Director | Wang Sen |
|  | Deputy Director | Zhu Guang |
|  | Political Commissar | Gu Mu |
|  | Deputy Political Commissar | Yang Jie |
| **Artillery** | Commander | Song Chengzhi |
|  | Political Commissar | Jin Rubai |
|  | Deputy Commander | Gao Cunxin |
|  | Deputy Commander | Kong Congzhou |
|  | Deputy Commander | Li Maozhi |
|  | Deputy Commander | Su Jin |
|  | Political Commissar | Jin Rubai |
|  | Deputy Political Commissar | Ouyang Yi |
|  | Deputy Political Commissar | Yang Yisheng |
| **Second Artillery**<br>*(Chinese Strategic Rocket Units)* | Commander | Li Shuiqing |
|  | Deputy Commander | Liao Chengmel |
|  | Deputy Commander | Sheng Zhihua |
|  | Political Commissar | Chen Heqiao |
|  | Deputy Political Commissar | Liu Lifeng |
|  | Deputy Political Commissar | Wang Zonghuai |

## MILITARY REGIONS AND DISTRICTS

| **Beijing Military Region** | First Secretary, Chinese Communist Party Committee | |
|---|---|---|
|  | Commander | Qin Jiwei |
|  | Political Commissar | Yuan Shengping |
|  | **Hebei Military District** | |
|  | Commander | Ma Hui |
|  | First Political Commissar | Jin Ming |
|  | **Nei Mongol Military District** | |
|  | Commander | Huang Hou |
|  | First Political Commissar | Zhou Hui |
|  | **Shanxi Military District** | |
|  | Commander | Geng Shuming |
|  | First Political Commissar | Huo Shillian |
| **Chengdu Military Region** | First Secretary, Chinese Communist Party Committee | |
|  | Commander | You Taizhong |
|  | Political Commissar | Xu Liqing |
|  | Political Commissar | Zhong Hanhua |
|  | **Sichuan Military District** | |
|  | Commander | Zhao Wenjin |
|  | First Political Commissar | Tan Qilong |
|  | **Xizang Military District** | |
|  | Commander | Xi Jinwu |
|  | First Political Commissar | Yin Fatang |
| **Fuzhou Military Region** | First Secretary, Chinese Communist Party Committee | Yang Chengwu |
|  | Commander | Yang Chengwu |
|  | Political Commissar | Fu Kuiqing |
|  | Political Commissar | Jiang Weiqing |
|  | Political Commissar | Li Zhimin |
|  | Political Commissar | Liao Zhigao |
|  | Political Commissar | Ni Nanshan |
|  | **Fujina Military District** | |
|  | Commander | Cong Dezi |
|  | First Political Commissar | Liao Zhigao |

**Jiangxi Military District**
Commander . . . . . . . . . . . . . . . . . . . . . . . . . . . . . . . . . . . . . . . . . Xin Jinjie
First Political Commissar . . . . . . . . . . . . . . . . . . . . . . . . . . . . Jiang Weiqing

**Guangzhou Military Region**

First Secretary, Chinese Communist Party Committee . . . . . . . . . . . . . . . . . .
Commander . . . . . . . . . . . . . . . . . . . . . . . . . . . . . . . . . . . . . . . . Wu Kehua
Political Commissar . . . . . . . . . . . . . . . . . . . . . . . . . . . . . . . . . . Wang Meng
Political Commissar . . . . . . . . . . . . . . . . . . . . . . . . . . . . . . . . . Zhu Yunqian

**Guangdong Military District**
Commander . . . . . . . . . . . . . . . . . . . . . . . . . . . . . . . . . . . Hao Shengwang
First Political Commissar . . . . . . . . . . . . . . . . . . . . . . . . . . . . Ren Zhongyi

**Guangxi Military District**
Commander . . . . . . . . . . . . . . . . . . . . . . . . . . . . . . . . . . . . Zhang Xudeng
First Political Commissar . . . . . . . . . . . . . . . . . . . . . . . . . . . Qiao Xiaoguang

**Hainan Military District**
Commander . . . . . . . . . . . . . . . . . . . . . . . . . . . . . . . . . . . . . . Jinag Hai
First Political Commissar . . . . . . . . . . . . . . . . . . . . . . . . . . . . . . . Luo Tian

**Hunan Military District**
Commander . . . . . . . . . . . . . . . . . . . . . . . . . . . . . . . . . . . . Liu Zhanrong
First Political Commissar . . . . . . . . . . . . . . . . . . . . . . . . . . . . Mao Zhiyong

**Jinan Military Region**

First Secretary, Chinese Communist Party Committee . . . . . Xiao Wangdong
Commander . . . . . . . . . . . . . . . . . . . . . . . . . . . . . . . . . . . . . Rao Shoukun
First Political Commissar . . . . . . . . . . . . . . . . . . . . . . . . . . . Xia Wangdong

**Shandong Military District**
Commander . . . . . . . . . . . . . . . . . . . . . . . . . . . . . . . . . . . . . . Zhao Feng
First Political Commissar . . . . . . . . . . . . . . . . . . . . . . . . . . . . . . . Su Yiran

**Kunming Military Region**

First Secretary, Chinese Communist Party Committee . . . . . . . . Liu Zhijian
Commander . . . . . . . . . . . . . . . . . . . . . . . . . . . . . . . . . . . . . Zhang Xhixiu
First Political Commissar . . . . . . . . . . . . . . . . . . . . . . . . . . . . Liu Zhijian

**Guizhou Military District**
Commander . . . . . . . . . . . . . . . . . . . . . . . . . . . . . . . . . . . . . . . Ren Ying
First Political Commissar . . . . . . . . . . . . . . . . . . . . . . . . . . . . . Chi Biqing

**Yunnan Military District**
Commander . . . . . . . . . . . . . . . . . . . . . . . . . . . . . . . . . . . Zhang Haitang
First Political Commissar . . . . . . . . . . . . . . . . . . . . . . . . . . . An Pingsheng

**Lanzhou Military Region**

First Secretary, Chinese Communist Party Committee . . . . . . . . . . . . . . . . . .
Commander . . . . . . . . . . . . . . . . . . . . . . . . . . . . . . . . . . . . . . . Du Yide
First Political Commissar . . . . . . . . . . . . . . . . . . . . . . . . . . . . . . Xiao Hua

**Gansu Military District**
Commander . . . . . . . . . . . . . . . . . . . . . . . . . . . . . . . . . . . . . . . . Li Bin
First Political Commissar . . . . . . . . . . . . . . . . . . . . . . . . . . . . . . Feng Jixin

**Ningxia Military District**
Commander . . . . . . . . . . . . . . . . . . . . . . . . . . . . . . . . . . . . . Chen Jiedi
First Political Commissar . . . . . . . . . . . . . . . . . . . . . . . . . . . . . . Li Xuezhi

**Oinghai Military District**
Commander . . . . . . . . . . . . . . . . . . . . . . . . . . . . . . . . . . . Wu Shengrong
First Political Commissar . . . . . . . . . . . . . . . . . . . . . . . . . . . . Liang Buting

**Shaanxi Military District**
Commander . . . . . . . . . . . . . . . . . . . . . . . . . . . . . . . . . . . Sun Hongdao
First Political Commissar . . . . . . . . . . . . . . . . . . . . . . . . . . . . Ma Wenrui

**Nanjing Military Region**

First Secretary, Chinese Communist Party Committee . . . . . . . Guo Linxiang
Commander . . . . . . . . . . . . . . . . . . . . . . . . . . . . . . . . . . . . . . Nie Fengzhi
First Political Commissar . . . . . . . . . . . . . . . . . . . . . . . . . . . . Guo Linxiang

**Anhui Military District**
Commander . . . . . . . . . . . . . . . . . . . . . . . . . . . . . . . . . . . . . . . . .Yu Guangmao
First Political Commissar . . . . . . . . . . . . . . . . . . . . . . . . . . . . .Zhang Jingfu

**Jinagsu Military District**
Commander . . . . . . . . . . . . . . . . . . . . . . . . . . . . . . . . . . . . . . . . .Lin Yousheng
First Political Commissar . . . . . . . . . . . . . . . . . . . . . . . . . . . . . . . . .Xu Jiatun

**Zhejiang Military District**
Commander . . . . . . . . . . . . . . . . . . . . . . . . . . . . . . . . . . . . . . . . .Guan Junting
First Political Commissar . . . . . . . . . . . . . . . . . . . . . . . . . . . . . . . . .Tie Ying

**Shenyang Military Region**

First Secretary, Chinese Communist Party Committee . . . . . . . . .Li Desheng
Commander . . . . . . . . . . . . . . . . . . . . . . . . . . . . . . . . . . . . . . . . .Li Desheng
First Political Commissar . . . . . . . . . . . . . . . . . . . . . . . . . . .Liao Hansheng

**Heilongjiang Military District**
Commander . . . . . . . . . . . . . . . . . . . . . . . . . . . . . . . . . . . .Zhao Xianshun
First Political Commissar . . . . . . . . . . . . . . . . . . . . . . . . . . . .Yang Yichen

**Jilin Military District**
Commander . . . . . . . . . . . . . . . . . . . . . . . . . . . . . . . . . . . . . . . . .He Youfa
First Political Commissar . . . . . . . . . . . . . . . . . . . . . . . . . . . . .Wang Enmao

**Liaoning Military District**
Commander . . . . . . . . . . . . . . . . . . . . . . . . . . . . . . . . . . . . . . . . .Yang Dayi
First Political Commissar . . . . . . . . . . . . . . . . . . . . . . . . . . . . . . . .Guo Feng

**Urumqi Military Region**

First Secretary, Chinese Communist Party Committee . . . . . . . . .Wang Feng
Commander . . . . . . . . . . . . . . . . . . . . . . . . . . . . . . . . . . . . . . . . .Xiao Quanfu
First Political Commissar . . . . . . . . . . . . . . . . . . . . . . . . . . . . .Wang Feng

**East Xinjiang Military District**
Commander . . . . . . . . . . . . . . . . . . . . . . . . . . . . . . . . . . . . . . . . .Kong Xinye
Political Commissar . . . . . . . . . . . . . . . . . . . . . . . . . . . . . . . . . . . .Lu Kejie

**North Xinjiang Military District**
Commander . . . . . . . . . . . . . . . . . . . . . . . . . . . . . . . . . . . . . . . . .
First Political Commissar . . . . . . . . . . . . . . . . . . . . . . . . . . . . . . . . .

**South Xinjiang Military District**
Commander . . . . . . . . . . . . . . . . . . . . . . . . . . . . . . . . . . . . . . . . .
Political Commissar . . . . . . . . . . . . . . . . . . . . . . . . . . . . . .Huang Youxia

**Wuhan Military Region**

First Secretary, Chinese Communist Party Committee . . . . . . .Li Chengfang
Commander . . . . . . . . . . . . . . . . . . . . . . . . . . . . . . . . . . . . . .Zhang Caiqian
First Political Commissar . . . . . . . . . . . . . . . . . . . . . . . . . . .Li Chengfang

**Henan Military District**
Commander . . . . . . . . . . . . . . . . . . . . . . . . . . . . . . . . . . . . . . . . .Shang Kan
First Political Commissar . . . . . . . . . . . . . . . . . . . . . . . . . . . . . . . .Liu Jie

**Hubei Military District**
Commander . . . . . . . . . . . . . . . . . . . . . . . . . . . . . . . . . . . . . .Chu Chuanyu
First Political Commissar . . . . . . . . . . . . . . . . . . . . . . . . . . . .Chen Pixian

**NAVY**
*Beijing*

Commander . . . . . . . . . . . . . . . . . . . . . . . . . . . . . . . . . . . . . . . . . .Ye Fei
First Deputy Commander . . . . . . . . . . . . . . . . . . . . . . . . . . . .Liu Daosheng
Deputy Commander . . . . . . . . . . . . . . . . . . . . . . . . . . . . . .Deng Zhaoxiang
Deputy Commander . . . . . . . . . . . . . . . . . . . . . . . . . . . . . . . .Fang Qiang
Deputy Commander . . . . . . . . . . . . . . . . . . . . . . . . . . . . . . . . . . .Fu Jize
Deputy Commander . . . . . . . . . . . . . . . . . . . . . . . . . . . . . . .Gao Zhenjia
Deputy Commander . . . . . . . . . . . . . . . . . . . . . . . . . . . . . .Kong Zhaonian
Deputy Commander . . . . . . . . . . . . . . . . . . . . . . . . . . . . . .Ma Zhongquan
Deputy Commander . . . . . . . . . . . . . . . . . . . . . . . . . . . . . . .Mei Jiasheng
Deputy Commander . . . . . . . . . . . . . . . . . . . . . . . . . . . . . . .Wang Wanlin
Deputy Commander . . . . . . . . . . . . . . . . . . . . . . . . . . . . . . .Yang Guoyu
Deputy Commander . . . . . . . . . . . . . . . . . . . . . . . . . . . . . . . .Zhou Renjie

|  |  |
|---|---|
| Deputy Commander | Zhou Xihan |
| Political Commissar | Li Yaowen |
| Deputy Political Commissar | Fang Zhengping |
| Deputy Political Commissar | Kang Zhiqiang |
| Deputy Political Commissar | Lu Rencan |
| Deputy Political Commissar | Wang Xin |
| Deputy Chief of Staff | Fan Chaofu |
| Deputy Chief of Staff | Fan Yukang |
| Deputy Chief of Staff | Hu Pengfei |
| Deputy Chief of Staff | Lin Zhen |
| Deputy Chief of Staff | Xu Mingde |

**Chinese Communist Party Committee**

| First Secretary | Ye Fei |
|---|---|
| Secretary | Yu Shanfu |

**Armament and Technical Department**

| Director | |
|---|---|
| Deputy Director | Wang Anzhi |

**Logistics Department**

| Director | |
|---|---|
| Deputy Director | Hou Xiangzhi |

**Commands**

**East Sea Fleet** *(Shanghai)*

| Commander | Xie Zhenghao |
|---|---|
| Deputy Commander | Gao Xiceng |
| Deputy Commander | Wang Xueqing |
| Deputy Commander | Xie Zhenghao |
| Deputy Commander | Zhang Chaozhong |
| Political Commissar | Huang Zhongxue |
| Deputy Political Commissar | Li Gongyan |
| Deputy Political Commissar | Song Xianzhang |
| Chief of Staff | Tian Zuocheng |
| Deputy Chief of Staff | Huang Shengtian |

Chinese Communist Party Committee

| First Secretary | Fang Zhengping |
|---|---|
| Political Department Director | |
| Deputy Director | Wang Yong |

**North Sea Fleet** *(Qingdao, Shandong)*

| Commander | Yang Li |
|---|---|
| Political Commissar | Kang Zhiqiang |
| Political Commissar | Yu Xifeng |
| Deputy Political Commissar | Fu Xichu |

**South Sea Fleet** *(Zhanjiang, Guangdong)*

| Commander | |
|---|---|
| Political Commissar | Duan Dezhang |
| Deputy Political Commissar | Zang Banyou |

**AIR FORCE**
*Beijing*

| Commander | Zhang Tingfa |
|---|---|
| Deputy Commander | Cao Lihuai |
| Deputy Commander | Cheng Jun |
| Deputy Commander | He Tingyi |
| Deputy Commander | Wu Fushan |
| Deputy Commander | Zhang Jihui |
| Political Commissar | Gao Houliang |
| Deputy Political Commissar | Huang Liqing |
| Deputy Political Commissar | Liu Shichang |
| Chief of Staff | Ma Zhanmin |
| Chief of Staff | Yang Fuzhen |
| Chief of Staff | Yao Jun |
| Chief of Staff | Zhang Zhong |
| Adviser | Li Shian |
| Adviser | Xue Shaoqing |

| **Chinese Communist Party Committee** | First Secretary.........................................Zhang Tingfa |
| | Second Secretary.......................................Gao Houliang |
| | Third Secretary.........................................Cao Lihuai |
| **Logistics Department** | Director...............................................Huang Yonggui |
| | Deputy Director.......................................Duan Shikai |
| **Political Department** | Director.............................................................. |
| | Deputy Director.......................................Gao Dexiang |

\* \* \* \* \*

## GENERAL DEFENSE DATA

**Manpower**
Total Armed Forces.............................................4,000,000
   (See Page 119)
Population.................................................1,055,304,000

**Spending**
Military Expenditures.........................................$47 billion
Gross National Product.......................................$552 billion
Military Expenditure as a Percentage of
  Gross National Product.........................................8.5%
Military Expenditure as a Percentage of
  Central Government Expenditure.............................57.3%

**Defense Treaties** *(See Part II for Additional Detail)*

Bilateral:    Egypt              Mali
                Equatorial Guinea   Sudan
                Guinea           Tanzania
                Japan           Yemen Arab
                Democratic People's   Republic
                  Republic of Korea

Multilateral:   Protocol II of Treaty for the Prohibition of Nuclear Weapons
                in Latin America

# COLOMBIA
## Republic of Colombia
### *República de Colombia*

## Defense Establishment Command Structure and Force Organization

The President is the Commander-in-Chief of the armed forces of Colombia. He is advised on security policy by the Supreme Council of National Defense. The Minister of National Defense has administrative authority over the armed forces. The President exercises operational control of the military through the Commander-General of the armed forces.

**Total armed forces:** 67,800 (Army: 57,000;    Navy: 7,000;    Air Force: 3,800). **Paramilitary forces:** 50,000 (Police).

## HEAD OF STATE

H. E. Belisario Betancur Caurtas

**OFFICE OF THE PRESIDENT**
*(Oficina de la Presidencia)*
*Palacio de Maringo*
*Carrera 8 No. 7-26*
*Bogotá*
*Telephone:   284-3300*
*Telex:   44281 magr co*

President of the Republic
and Commander-in-Chief . . . . . . . . . . . . . . Dr. Belisario Betancur Cuartas
General Secretary . . . . . . . . . . . . . . . . . . . . . . . . . . . . . . Dr. Alfonso Espina
Private Secretary . . . . . . . . . . . . . . . . . . . . . . . . . . . Diana Turbay de Hoyos
Designate for Presidency . . . . . . . . . . . . . . . . . . . . . . . . . . Dr. Álvaro Gómez

**Supreme Council of National Defense**
*(Consejo Supremo de Defensa Nacional)*

Member *(ex officio)* . . . . . . . . . . . . . . . . . . . . . . . . Gral. Fernando Landazabal
(Minister of National Defense)
Member *(ex officio)* . . . . . . . . . . . . . . . . . . . . . . . . . . . . Dr. Rodrigo Escobar
(Minister of Government)
Member *(ex officio)* . . . . . . . . . . . . . . . . . . . . . . . . . . . Dr. Rodrigo Lloreda
(Minister of Foreign Affairs)
Member *(ex officio)* . . . . . . . . . . . . . . . . . . . . . . . . . . Dr. Edgar Gutiérrez
(Minister of Finance & Public Affairs)
Member *(ex officio)* . . . . . . . . . . . . . . . . . . . . . . . Dr. Bernardo Ramírez
(Minister of Communications)
Member *(ex officio)* . . . . . . . . . . . . . . . . . . . . . . . . . . . . . . Dr. Jaime Pinzón
(Minister of Labor & Social Security)
Member *(ex officio)* . . . . . . . . . . . . . . . . . . . . . . . . . . . . Dr. José F. Isaza
(Minister of Public Works & Transportation)
Member *(ex officio)* . . . . . . . . . . . . . . . . . . . . . . Gral. Gustavo Matamoros
(Commander of the Military Forces)

**MINISTRY OF NATIONAL DEFENSE**
*(Ministério de Defensa Nacional)*
*Avenida El Dorado,*
*CAN- Ofic. 250*
*Bogotá*
*Telephone:   266-9300*
*Telex:   46261 brtrij co*

Minister . . . . . . . . . . . . . . . . . . . . . . . . . Gral. Fernándo Landazabal Reyes
Secretary-General . . . . . . . . . . . . . May. Gral. Miguel Francísco Vega Uribe
Deputy Secretary-General . . . . . . . Gral. Brig. Jorge Hernando Vega Torres
Deputy, National Police . . . . . . . . . . . . Gral. Brig. Desiderio Vera Jaimes
Chief, Systems Division . . . . . . . . . . . . . . . . . . . . Alm. Alberto Cubillos Peña
Chief, Liaison Office . . . . . . . . . . . . . . . . Cnel. José Ignacio Mendoza Cuello
Chief, General Services Division . . . . . . . . . . . . Cnel. Hernán Zapata Velez
Chief, Office of News and
Information . . . . . . . . . . . . . . . . . . . . Cnel. José Gregorio Torres Ramirez

Military Vicar (Chaplaincy) . . . . . . . . . . . . Cnel. Ariel Gutiérrez Marulanda
Chief, Planning Office . . . . . . . . . . . . . . . . . . Cap. Domingo López Archila
Chief, Legal Office . . . . . . . . . . . . . . . . . Tte. Cnel. Jesús M. Castro Suarez
Chief, Financial Division . . . . . . . . . . . . . . . . . . . . . . Tte. Raúl Castro Ante

## DEFENSE FORCES

**ARMED FORCES**
*(El Comando General de las Fuerzas*
*Militares)*
*Avenida El Dorado*
*Bogotá*
*Telephone: 244-422*
*Telex:*

Commander-General . . . . . . . . . . . . . . . Gral. Gustavo Matamoros D'Costa
Chief of Joint Chiefs of Staff . . . . . . . May. Gral. Guillermo Jaramillo Berrio
Inspector-General . . . . . . . . . . . . . . . . . May. Gral. Hernan Hurtado Vallejo
District Attorney . . . . . . . . . . . . . . . . . . May. Gral. Rafael Samudio Molina
Director, Superior War College . . . . . . . May. Gral. Manuel Jaime Guerrero
Deputy Director, Superior
    War College . . . . . . . . . . . . . . Gral. Brig. Manuel Jaime Forero Quinones
Chief, Department 1 . . . . . . . . . . . . . . Gral. Brig. Horacio Garcia Rodríguez
Chief, Department 2 . . . . . . . . . . . . . . Gral. Brig. Hernando Zuluaga García
Chief, Department 3 . . . . . . . . . . . . . . Gral. Brig. Jimmy Needy Rocha Rubio
Chief, Department 4 . . . . . . . . . . Gral. Brig. Luis Enrique Díaz Sanmiguel
Commander, Southern
    Command . . . . . . . . . . . . . . . Gral. Brig. Jaime de Jesús Gomez Martínez
Director, Central Military
    Hospital . . . . . . . . . . . . . . . . . . . . Gral. Brig. José Ignacio Posada Duarte

**ARMY**
*(Ejército Nacional)*
*Ministério de Defensa Nacional,*
*Avenida El Dorado-CAN-*
*Ofic. 250*
*Bogotá*

Commander . . . . . . . . . . . . . . . . . . . . . . May. Gral. Bernardo Lema Henao
Chief of Staff . . . . . . . . . . . . . . . May. Gral. José María Arbalaez Caballero
Inspector-General . . . . . . . . . . . . . . May. Gral. Luis Alberto Andrade Anaya
Director, Intendance
    (Quartermaster) . . . . . . . . . . . . . . . Tte. Cnel. Luis A. Guerrero Martínez
Director, Engineers . . . . . . . Gral. Brig. Joaquín Gustavo Gomez Villamizar
Director, Recruitment . . . . . . . Gral. Brig. Daniel Enrique Garcia Echeverry
Director, Instruction . . . . . . . . . . . . . Gral. Brig. José Nelson Mejia Henao
Chief, Department of Administration
    and Budget . . . . . . . . . . . . . . . . . . . Cnel. Gustavo Adolfo Monroy Salas
Commander, Logistical Support
    Brigade . . . . . . . . . . . . . . . . . . . . Cnel. José Orlando Hincapie Ocampo
Director, Communications . . . . . . . . . . . . . . Cnel. Carlos A. Pinto Achury
Director of Administration . . . . . . . Tte. Cnel. Felix Hernando Silva Torres
Commander, Maintenance
    Battalion . . . . . . . . . . . . . . . . . . . . Tte. Cnel. Bernardo Lombo Vanegas
Commander, 1st Division . . . . . . . . . . . . . . . . . May. Gral. José Leal Barrera
Commander, 2nd Division . . . . . . May. Gral. Diego Alfonso González Ossa
Commander, 1st Brigade (Covaca) . . . . . . . . . . . . . . . . . . . . . . . Brig. Gral.
                                                                Jesús Armado Arias Cabrales
Commander, 2nd Brigade
    (Atlantico) . . . . . . . . . . . . . . . . . . . . Gral. Brig. Enrique Varon Valencia
Commander, 3rd Brigade
    (Valle) . . . . . . . . . . . . . . . . . . . . Gral. Brig. Jesús Jammasait Yussef Arias
Commander, 4th Brigade
    (Antioquia) . . . . . . . . . . . . . . . . Gral. Brig. António José Gonzalez Prado
Commander, 5th Brigade
    (Tolima) . . . . . . . . . . . . . . . . . . . . . Gral. Brig. Ernesto Lopez Ramírez
Commander 6th Brigade
    (Tolima) . . . . . . . . . . . . . . . Gral. Brig. José Alirio Alvarado Hernández
Commander, 7th Brigade
    (Meta) . . . . . . . . . . . . . . . . . . . . . . Gral. Brig. Fernando Gomez Barros
Commander, 8th Brigade
    (Quindio) . . . . . . . . . . . . . . . . . . . . Gral. Brig. Ernesto Caviedes Hoyos
Commander, 9th Brigade
    (Huila) . . . . . . . . . . . . . . . . . Gral. Brig. Manuel Alberto Murillo Herrera
Commander, 10th Brigade
    (Tolima) . . . . . . . . . . . . . . . . . . . . Gral. Brig. Alberto González Herrera

**NAVY**
*(La Amrada Colomibana)*
*Ministério de Defensa Nacional,*
*Avenida El Dorado-CAN-*
*Ofic. 235*
*Bogotá*
*Telephone:  244-4291*

Commander . . . . . . . . . . . . . . . . . . . . . . . . . . . Alm. Héctor Calderon Salazar
Deputy Commander . . . . . . . . . . . . . . Contra Alm. Rafael H. Grau Araujo
Commander, Navy Infantry . . . . . . Gral. Brig. Numa Pompillo Rojas Currea
Chief, Pacific Naval Base Projects . . . Contra Alm. Jorge Edgar Garay Rubio
Director, Maritime and Ports . . . . Contra Alm. Juan Pablo Rairan Hernández
Chief, Dept. EMN-2 . . . . . . . . . . . Contra Alm. Luis Felipe Mantilla Duarte
Inspector-General . . . . . . . . . . . . . . . . . . . . . . Cnel. Arnold Arnedo Cardona
Director, Revolving Fund . . . . . . . . . . . . . . . . . Cap. Gustavo Piñeda Gallo
Director, Economy and Finance . . . . . . . . . . . Cap. Ramiro Rodríguez Zarta
Secretary, XI Inter-American
    Naval Conference . . . . . . . . . . . . . . . . . . . Cap. Roberto Montoya Robledo
Chief, Department M-1 . . . . . . . . . . . . . . . . Cap. Saturnino Rodríguez Melo
Director, Sanitation . . . . . . . . . . . . . . . . . Cap. Luis Raphael Cotes Marquez
Director, Materials . . . . . . . . . . . . . . . . . . . . Cap. Miguel G. Ruan Trujillo
Chief of Staff, Naval Infantry . . . . . . . . . . . Cnel. Gabriel Mario Morales H.
Chief, Department M-6 . . . . . . . . . . . . . . . . . . . . Cap. Jorge Cadena Mutis
Director, Personnel . . . . . . . . . . . . . . . . . . . . Benjamin Gamarra Murillo
Chief, Department M-3 . . . . . . . . . . . . . . Cap. Luis Guillermo Riano Fajardo
Chief, Department M-5 . . . . . . . . . . . . . . . . . . . . . Cap. Carlos Prieto Avila
Chief, Department M-4 . . . . . . . . . . . . . . . . Cap. Carlos A. Olmus Restrepo

**AIR FORCE**
*(La Fuerza Aerea Colombiana)*
*Ministério de Defensa Nacional,*
*Avenide El Dorado -CAN-*
*Ofic. 207*
*Bogotá*
*Telephone:  263-2170*

Commander . . . . . . . . . . . . . . . . . . . . . . . Gral. Angel María Gomez Jauregui
Deputy Commander . . . . . . . . . . . . . . Gral. May. Augusto Moreno Guerrero
Chief, Logistical Support . . . . . . . Gral. May. Mário Enrique Plazas Galindo
Inspector-General . . . . . . . . . . . . . . . . . Gral. Brig. Gilberto Franco Vasquez
Director, Military Aviation
    School . . . . . . . . . . . . . . . . . . . . . . . . Gral. Brig. Alberto Guzman Molina
Commander, Air Combat
    Command No. I (Cund) . . . . . . . . Gral. Brig. Alfonso Amaya Maldonado
Commander, Air Combat
    Command No. III (Atlantico) . . Gral. Brig. Luis Enrique Murillo Alvarez
Commander, Air Tactical Support
    Command . . . . . . . . . . . . . . . . . . . . . Gral. Brig. Ciro Alberto Leal Barrera
Chief, Department EMA-3 . . . . . . . . . . . . . . Cnel. Horacio Galeano Zuluaga
Director, Revolving Fund . . . . . . . . . . . . . . . Cnel. Florentino Ayala Carreno
Chief, Instruction and Training . . . . . . . . . Cnel. Alvaro Sarmiento Landinez
Director, Air Operations . . . . . . . . . . . . . . Cnel. José Domingo Viloria Mier
Chief, Aviation Infantry . . . . . . . . . . . . . . . . . Cnel. Jonas Franco Pereiro
Chief, Department EMA-4 . . . . . . . . . . Cnel. Hernando Monsalve Figueroa
Chief, Department EMA-1 . . . . . . . . . . . . . . . Cnel. Luis Cipagauta Arenas
Commander, Air Maintainence
    Command (Cund) . . . . . . . . . . . . . . . . . . . . . . . Cnel. Mario Piñeda Gallo
Commander, Military Air
    Transport Command . . . . . . . . . Cnel. Antónío Aimer Satizabal Victoria
Director, Non-Commissioned
    Officers School . . . . . . . . . . . . . . . . Tte. Cnel. José Nehil Heredia Sabogal

\* \* \* \* \*

# GENERAL DEFENSE DATA

**Manpower**
    Total Armed Forces . . . . . . . . . . . . . . . . . . . . . . . . . . . . . . . . . . . . . . . . . . . 67,800
        (See Page 129)
    Population . . . . . . . . . . . . . . . . . . . . . . . . . . . . . . . . . . . . . . . . . . . . . . . 26,631,000

**Spending**
    Military Expenditures . . . . . . . . . . . . . . . . . . . . . . . . . . . . . . . . . . . . . . $350 million
    Gross National Product . . . . . . . . . . . . . . . . . . . . . . . . . . . . . . . . . . . . . . . $32 billion
    Military Expenditure as a Percentage of
        Gross National Product . . . . . . . . . . . . . . . . . . . . . . . . . . . . . . . . . . . . . . . 1.1%

Military Expenditure as a Percentage of
Central Government Expenditure .................................10.3%

**Defense Treaties** *(See Part II for Additional Detail)*

Bilateral:      United States

Multilateral:   Act of Chapultapec
Central American Democratic Community (Observer)
Inter-American Defense Board
Inter-American Treaty of Reciprocal Assistance
Multinational Force and Observers in Sinai
Treaty for the Prohibition of Nuclear Weapons in
Latin America

**Military Rank Comparisons**
See Appendix A.

# COMOROS

## The Federal Islamic Republic of the Comoros
### *République Féderale et Islamique des Comores*

### Defense Establishment Command Structure and Force Organization

The President is the Commander-in-Chief of the armed forces. Administrative and operational control of the military is the responsibility of the Minister of Defense.

**Total armed forces:** 800.

## HEAD OF STATE

H. E. Ahmed Abdallah Abderemane

**OFFICE OF THE PRESIDENT**
*B.P. 521*
*Moroni*

*Telephone: 22 32, 22 17*
*Telex: 233 presirep*

President of the Federal
  Islamic Republic......................Ahmed Abdallah Abderemane
Staff Director ...............................Nadjib Dakoine
Secretary-General.............................Said Ahmed Cheick
Legal Adviser................................Ibrahim Abdallah
Special Adviser.................................Salim Ben Ali

**OFFICE OF THE PRIME MINISTER**
*B.P. 421*
*Moroni*

*Telephone: 24 13*
*Telex: 233 presirep*

Prime Minister ........................................Ali Mroudjae

**MINISTRY OF DEFENSE**
*B.P. 246*
*Moroni*

*Telephone: 26 46*
*Telex: 219 presirep*

Minister............................................Ahmed Abdou

## DEFENSE FORCES

**ARMED FORCES**
*P.O. Box 246*
*Moroni*

*Telephone: 26 46*
*Telex: 233 presirep*

Chief of Staff .....................Chef de Bataillon Ahmed Mohamed

**FEDERAL MILITARY POLICE AND
  NATIONAL DEFENSE CONSTABULARY**
*Moroni*

*Telephone: 26 46*

Commander....................................Capt. Abdourazakou
Director, Information Center for
  Armed Forces and the Constabulary ..........Chef de Bataillon Boyer

\* \* \* \* \*

# GENERAL DEFENSE DATA

**Manpower**
Total Armed Forces . . . . . . . . . . . . . . . . . . . . . . . . . . . . . . . . . . . . . . . . . . . . . .800
  (See Page 133)
Population . . . . . . . . . . . . . . . . . . . . . . . . . . . . . . . . . . . . . . . . . . . . . . . .442,000

**Spending**
Military Expenditures . . . . . . . . . . . . . . . . . . . . . . . . . . . . . . . . . . . . . .$2.9 million
Gross National Product . . . . . . . . . . . . . . . . . . . . . . . . . . . . . . . . . . . . .$78.8 million
Military Expenditure as a Percentage of
  Gross National Product . . . . . . . . . . . . . . . . . . . . . . . . . . . . . . . . . . .2.7%
Military Expenditure as a Percentage of
  Central Government Expenditure . . . . . . . . . . . . . . . . . . . . . . . . . . . . .16.0%

**Defense Treaties** (*See Part II for Additional Detail*)

Bilateral:      None

Multilateral:   Organization of African Unity

**Military Rank Comparisons**
See Appendix A.

# CONGO
## People's Republic of the Congo
### *République Populaire du Congo*

### Defense Establishment Command Structure and Force Organization

The President is Commander-in-Chief and Minister of Defense. The Chief of the General Staff is responsible for administrative matters relating to the military as well as direct command of the armed forces.

**Total armed forces:** 9,550 (Army: 9,000; Navy: 200; Air Force: 350).

### HEAD OF STATE

H. E. Col. Denis Sassou-Nguesso

**OFFICE OF THE PRESIDENT**
*Palais du Peuple*
*Brazzaville*

*Telex:* 5210 precongo kg
5325 presirep kg

President of the People's Republic,
Minister of National Defense, and
Commander-in-Chief ....................Col. Denis Sassou-Nguesso

**OFFICE OF THE PRIME MINISTER**
*Palais du Peuple*
*Brazzaville*

*Telex:* 5210 precongo kg

Prime Minister.............................Col. Louis-Sylvain Goma

**MINISTRY OF NATIONAL DEFENSE**
*(Ministère de la Defense Nationale)*
*Brazzaville*

*Telex:* 5210 precongo kg

Minister of National Defense
and Commander-in-Chief ................Col. Denis Sassou-Nguesso
Delegate Minister at the
Presidency of the Republic
Charged with Defense ................Col. Raymond Damase N'Gollo
Chief of Cabinet ..........................Capt. Alexis Bruno Kouku

### DEFENSE FORCES

**ARMED FORCES**
**People's National Army**
*(Armée Populaire Nationale—APN)*
*B.P. 138*
*Brazzaville*

*Telephone:* 94 07 46
*Telex:* 5210 precongo kg

Chief, General Staff .........................Col. Emmanuel Elenga
Director, Directorate of
International Relations .................Lt. Col. Innocent Mboungou
Director, Directorate of
Instruction and Combat Preparation ....................Capt. Gatse
Director, Directorate of Logistics ....................Lt. Col. Kouamba
Director, Directorate of
Military Material, Automobiles,
Missiles and Armored Vehicles ................Capt. Richard Tsonga
Director, Directorate of Fuels
and Lubricants................................Cdt. Benjamin Ntasa
Director, Directorate of Engineering ................Cdt. Eugene-Marie
Director, Directorate of Health ..................Lt. Col. Durang-Abel

135

Director, Directorate of Signals
and Communications .......................Capt. Onesieme Engoya
Director, Directorate of Artillery .................Commandant Bakotila
Director, Directorate of
Anti-Aircraft Defense....................Capt. Albert Silvan Ngouma
Director, Political Directorate....................Capt. Eduard Okombi
Director, Directorate of
Administration ...............................Capt. Bernard Ngoyi
Director, Directorate of
Counter Espionage .........................Lt. Daniel Mbon-Okona
Director, Directorate of Operations ..............Capt. Etienne Malonga

**ARMY**
**Land Forces**
*(Forces Armées Terrestres)*
*B.P. 138*
*Brazzaville*

*Telephone:   81 21 04*
*Telex:   5210 precongo kg*

Chief, Army Staff ...........................Capt. Henri Eboundita

**Regional Commands**
Commander, First Military
Region (Point Noire) .......................Capt. Michel Gangouo
Commander, Second Military
Region (Loubomo) ...............................Cdt. Essouba
Commander, Third Military
Region (Brazzaville).......................Lt. Col. Paul Kouma
Commander, Fourth Military
Region (Djambalo) .....................................
Commander, Fifth Military
Region (Onando) .................................Capt. Balou
Commander, Sixth Military
Region (Onesso).....................................
Commander, Seventh Military
Region (Impfondo) .................................Capt. Mpika

**NAVY**
*(Marine Nationale)*
*Brazzaville*

*Telex:   5210 precongo kg*

Chief, Navy Staff...........................Capt. de Corvette Lt. Jean

**AIR FORCE**
*Brazzaville*

*Telex:   5210 precongo kg*

Chief, Air Force Staff (Acting) ........................Capt. Makosso

**PEOPLE'S MILITIA**
*Brazzaville*

*Telex:   5210 precongo kg*

Commander .......................................Michel Ngakola

\* \* \* \* \*

# GENERAL DEFENSE DATA

**Manpower**
Total Armed Forces................................................9,550
(See Page 135)
Population ..................................................1,641,000

**Spending**
Military Expenditures .........................................$48 million
Gross National Product......................................$1.189 billion
Military Expenditure as a Percentage of
Gross National Product ..........................................4.1%
Military Expenditure as a Percentage of
Central Government Expenditure ................................14.4%

**Defense Treaties** *(See Part II for Additional Detail)*

    Bilateral:      France

    Multilateral:   Biological Weapons Convention
                      Defense Council of Equatorial Africa
                      Organization of African Unity
                      Treaty on the Control of Arms on the Seabed
                      Treaty on the Non-Proliferation of Nuclear Weapons

**Military Rank Comparisons**
See Appendix A.

# COSTA RICA
## Republic of Costa Rica
### *República de Costa Rica*

## Defense Establishment Command Structure
## and Force Organization

The President of the Republic is the Commander-in-Chief of all public forces. Costa Rica has no established military force, but a Civil Guard, Rural Guard, and National Police are responsible for internal security. The Civil Guard is under the direction of the Ministry of Public Security, while the Rural Guard falls under the jurisdiction of the Ministry of Government. The National Police are administered by the Ministry of Justice.

**Para-military forces:** 7,000 (Civil Guard: 5,000;    Rural Guard: 2,500).

## HEAD OF STATE

H. E. Luis Alberto Monge Alvarez

**OFFICE OF THE PRESIDENT**
*(Oficina de la Presidencia)*
*Casa Presidencial*
*Apartado 10089*
*San José 1000*

*Telephone:   25-3211*
*Telex:   2106 preside*

President of the Republic and
   Commander-in-Chief ...............Lic. Luis Alberto Monge Alvarez
First Vice President .........................Lic. Alberto Fait Lozano
Second Vice President ...................Lic. Armando Arauz Águilar

**MINISTRY OF PUBLIC SECURITY**
*(Ministério de Seguridad Pública)*
*Apartado 1006*
*San José 1000*

*Telephone:   23-2395, 21-4606*

Minister .......................Lic. Angel Edmundo Solano Calderón
Vice Minister ...............................................Johnny Campos
Director, Department of Plans and Operations.........May. Carlos Porras
Director, National Security.....................Cnel. Francísco Tacsan
Director-General, Civil Guard.......................Cnel. Oscar Vidal
First Commissioner ............................Tte. Issac Amador
Second Commissioner .......................May. Ernesto Chincilla
Third Commissioner...........................Tte. Cnel. Mario Rojas
Fourth Commissioner ........................................(Vacant)
Fifth Commissioner .........................Tte. Cnel. Daniel Morera
Chief, Military Police .......................May. José Aniseto Vargas
Chief, Alajuela Command ...........................May. Jorge Rojas
Chief, Cartago Command ..........................May. Jorge Solano
Chief, Heredia Command .........................May. Geraldo Ruiz
Chief, Liberia Command ...............Tte. Cnel. José Ramón Montero
Chief, Limon Command ......................May. Carlos Luis Flores
Chief, Puntarenas Command ....................May. Alfredo Azofeta
Chief, North Command .....................Tte. Cnel. Rodrigo Rivera
Chief, Atlantic Command ..........................May. Jorge Cedeño
Chief, South Command .................May. Marco Daniel Calderón

**MINISTRY OF GOVERNMENT**
*(Ministério de Gobernación)*
*Apartado 544*
*San José 1000*

*Telephone:   23-2395*

Minister ...................................Lic. Alfonso Carro-Zuniga
Chief, Rural Guard ...........................Cnel. Benito Zeledon

**MINISTRY OF JUSTICE**
*(Ministério de Justicia)*
*Apartado 1006*
*San José 1000*
*Telephone:   23-7344*

Minister . . . . . . . . . . . . . . . . . . . . . . . . . . . . . . . . . . . .Lic. Carlos José Gutiérrez
Vice Minister . . . . . . . . . . . . . . . . . . . . . . . . . . . . . . . . .Enrique Rojas Franco
Director, National Police . . . . . . . . . . . . . . . . . . . . . . . . .Cnel. Marco Múñoz
Chief, National Police School . . . . . . . . . . . . . . . .Tte. Cnel. Eliseo Uba Dura

\* \* \* \* \*

## GENERAL DEFENSE DATA

**Manpower**
    Total Armed Forces . . . . . . . . . . . . . . . . . . . . . . . . . . . . . . . . . . . . . . . .7,000
      (See Page 139)
    Population . . . . . . . . . . . . . . . . . . . . . . . . . . . . . . . . . . . . . . . .2,396,000

**Spending**
    Military Expenditures . . . . . . . . . . . . . . . . . . . . . . . . . . . . . . . . . . .$13.9 million
    Gross National Product . . . . . . . . . . . . . . . . . . . . . . . . . . . . . . . . . . . .$4.2 billion
    Military Expenditure as a Percentage of
      Gross National Product . . . . . . . . . . . . . . . . . . . . . . . . . . . . . . . . . .0.3%
    Military Expenditure as a Percentage of
      Central Government Expenditure . . . . . . . . . . . . . . . . . . . . . . . . . .2.6%

**Defense Treaties** *(See Part II for Additional Detail)*

      Bilateral:    United States

      Multilateral:  Act of Chapultepec
                Central-American Democratic Community
                Council for Central-American Defense
                Inter-American Defense Board
                Inter-American Treaty of Reciprocal Assistance
                Limited Test Ban Treaty
                Treaty on the Non-Proliferation of Nuclear Weapons

**Military Rank Comparisons**
    See Appendix A.

# CUBA
## Republic of Cuba
*República de Cuba*

### Defence Establishment Command Structure and Force Organization

The President is the Commander-in-Chief of the Revolutionary Armed Forces of Cuba. He deals directly with the commanders of the operational formations. Administration of the military is the primary responsibility of the Minister of the Revolutionary armed forces. The Council of Ministers is empowered to fix the size of the security forces and decide on their organization.

**Total armed forces:** 127,000 (Army: 100,000;  Navy: 11,500;  Air Force: 16,000). **Paramilitary forces:** 168,500  (State Security: 15,000;  Frontier Guards: 3,500;  Youth Labor Army: 100,000;  Territorial Militia: 50,000).

### HEAD OF STATE

Cdte. Fidel Castro Ruz

**OFFICE OF THE PRESIDENT**
*(Oficina de la Presidencia)*
*Ciudad de la Habana*

President and Commander-in-Chief . . . . . . . . . . . . . Cdte. Fidel Castro Ruz

**OFFICE OF THE FIRST VICE PRESIDENT**
*(Oficina de la Vice Presidencia)*
*Ciudad de la Habana*

First Vice President and Minister of the Revolutionary Armed Forces . . . . . . . . . . . . . . . . Gral. Raúl Castro Ruz

**MINISTRY OF THE REVOLUTIONARY ARMED FORCES**
*(Ministério de las Fuerzas Armadas Revolucionaries—MINFAR)*
*Revolucionarias Nivel Central Minfar*
*Plaza de la Revolución*
*Ciudad de la Habana*
*Telex: 511151 Minfar hab*

President and Commander-in-Chief . . . . . . . . . . . . . Cdte. Fidel Castro Ruz
First Vice President and Minister of the
  Revolutionary Armed Forces . . . . . . . . . . . . . . . . Gral. Raúl Castro Ruz
First Vice Minister and Chief of
  the General Staff . . . . . . . . . . . . . . . . Gral. de Div. Senen Casas Regueiro
First Vice Minister . . . . . . . . . . . . . . Gral. de Div. Abelardo Colomé Ibarra
Vice Minister and Chief, Central
  Political Directorate . . . . . . . . . . . . . . Gral. de Div. Sixto Batista Santana
Vice Minister and Chief, Antiaircraft
  Denfense and Revolutionary
  Air Force . . . . . . . . . . . . . . . . . . . . . . . . . Gral. de Div. Julio Casas Regueiro
Vice Minister, Armament
  and Technology . . . . . . . . . . . . . . . . . . Gral. Brig. Francísco Cruz Bourzac
Vice Minister, Civil Defense . . . . . . . . . . Gral. Brig. Juan Escalona Reguera
Vice Minister and Chief of the
  Youth Labor Army—EJT . . . . . . . . . . Gral. Rigoberto García Fernández
Vice Minister . . . . . . . . . . . . . . . . . . . . . . . . Gral. Arnaldo T. Ochoa Sánchez
Vice Minister and Chief, Rear Services . . . . . . Gral. Brig. Carlos Rodés Moro
Vice Minister and Chief,
  Cuban Revolutionary Navy . . . . . . . Vice Alm. Aldo Santamaría Cuadrado

**Directorate of Foreign Relations**
*(Dirección de Relaciones Exteriores)*

Chief . . . . . . . . . . . . . . . . . . . . . . . . . . . . . . . Cnel. Diego E. González Pérez
Deputy Chief . . . . . . . . . . . . . . . . . . . . . . . . . . . . Cnel. José C. Quevedo Pérez
Chief, Unidentified Section . . . . . . Tte. Cnel. Salvador Kindelan Rodríguez

Chief, Unidentified Section . . . . . . . . . .Tte. Cnel. Juan E. Oliveros Galbán
Official . . . . . . . . . . . . . . . . . . . . . . . . . . . . . . . .Tte. Cnel. Eddy Ávila Trujillo
Official . . . . . . . . . . . . . . . . . . . . . . . . . . . . . .May. Arnoldo Delgado Cueto
Official . . . . . . . . . . . . . . . . . . . . . . . . . . .May. Eduardo Delado Rodríguez
Official . . . . . . . . . . . . . . . . . . . . . . . . .Tte. Cnel. Ernesto A. Llanes Fleitas
Official . . . . . . . . . . . . . . . . . . . . . . . . . . .May. Manuel Nieves Rodríguez
Official . . . . . . . . . . . . . . . . . . . . . . . . . . . . . . .Tte. Cnel. Roberto Nuñez

**Economic-Administrative Directorate**
*(Dirección Administrativa-Económica)*

Chief . . . . . . . . . . . . . . . . . . . . . . . . . . . . . . . . . . . .Eleuterio Ávila Góngora

**Directorate of Human Resources**
*(Dirección de Recursos Humanos)*

Chief . . . . . . . . . . . . . . . . . . . . . . . . . . . . . . . . .Tte. Cnel. Juan Díaz Oliva

**Directorate of Military Tribunals**
*(Dirección de Tribunales Militares)*

Chief, Legal Services . . . . . . . . . . . . . . . . . .Cnel. Roberto Paralada Nápoles
Principal Military Prosecutor,
   Legal Services . . . . . . . . . . . . . . . . . . . . . . .Cnel. Mário Albarellos García
Deputy Military Prosecutor,
   Legal Services . . . . . . . . . . . . . . . .Tte. Cnel. Pedro Enrique Salazar Miró

**Patriotic Military Education Commission**
*(Comisión Militar de Educación Patriótica)*

Chairman . . . . . . . . . . . . . . . . . . . . . . . . . . . . . . .Gral. Raúl Castro Ruz
Executive Vice President . . . . . . . . . . . . . . . . . . . .Cnel. Gregorio Junco Díaz
Vice President . . . . . . . . . . . . . . . . . . . .Gral. Brig. William Galvez Rodríguez
Secretary . . . . . . . . . . . . . . . . . . . . . . . . . . . . . .Tte. Cnel. Julio Rego López
Chief, Organization and
   Patriotic-Military Education . . . . . . . . . .Tte. Cnel. César Rodríguez Díaz
President, National
   Executive Committee . . . . . . . . . . . .Gral. Brig. William Gálvez Rodríguez
Chief, Foreign Relations Section . . . . . . . . . .Tte. Cnel. José Álvarez Alemán
Chief, Communications Section . . . . . . . . . . . .Cap. Cipriano Sánchez Peña
President, National Council
   of Military Studies . . . . . . . . . . . . . . . . . . .Tte. Cnel. Haroldo Castro Mesa

**Civil Defense National Staff**
*(Estado Mayor de la Defensa Civil)*

Vice Minister . . . . . . . . . . . . . . . . . . . . . .Gral. Brig. Juan Escalona Reguera
Chief . . . . . . . . . . . . . . . . . . . . . . . . . . . . . . . . .Cnel. Pedro Altez Monistiról
Chief, General Staff Political Section . . . . . .Tte. Cnel. Luis Valladares León
Chief, Operations . . . . . . . . . . . . . . . . . . . . . . . . . . .May. Eugenio Bárcena
First Officer, Combat Training Section . . . . . . . .Cap. Heriberto Díaz Pérez

**Territorial Militia Troops**
*(Milicias de Tropas Territoriales—MTT)*
*Havana City Province*

Commander . . . . . . . . . . . . . . . . . . . . . .Gral. Brig. Rolando Kinderlán Bles
Official . . . . . . . . . . . . . . . . . . . . . . . . . . . . . . . . . . . . . .May. Pedro Garbalo
Official . . . . . . . . . . . . . . . . . . . . . . . . . . .Gral. Brig. Samuel Rodiles Planas
Chief, Central Havana Municipality . . . . . . . . . . . . . . . . . . . .Nelson Negrin
Official . . . . . . . . . . . . . . . . . . . . . . . . . . . . . . . . . . . . . .Fnu Díaz Armas
Chief, First Battalion . . . . . . . . . . . . . . . . . . . . . . . . . . . . . .Jorge Miranda
Official, 10th of October Municipality . . . . . . . . .Tte. Francísco Rodríguez
Assistant to the President,
   Sanctus Spiritus Province . . . . . . . . . . . . . . . . . .Cnel. Marcelo Martínez
President Official, Camaguey Province . . . . . . . . . . . . .Cnel. Gerardo Cabral
Commander, General Maximo Gómez Division . . . . .Ulises Rosales del Tora
President Military Adviser,
   Santiago de Cuba Province . . . . . . . . . . . . . .Cnel. Raúl Barrera González
Official . . . . . . . . . . . . . . . . . . . . . . . . . . . . .May. Romarico Navarro López
Official . . . . . . . . . . . . . . . . . . . . . . . . . . . . . . . . . .Cnel. Fnu Peña Vega
President Military Adviser, Granma Province . . . . . . . . . . . . . . . . . . . . . . .
Chief, Bayamo Municipality . . . . . . . . . .Tte. Cnel. Roberto Pérez Toranzo
President Military Adviser,
   Isle of Youth Municipality . . . . . . . . . . . . . . . . . .May. Delio Rodríguez

# DEFENSE FORCES

**ARMED FORCES**
**Armed Forces General Staff**
*(Estado Mayor General)*

Chief of the General Staff . . . . . . . . . . . . Gral. de Div. Senén Casas Regueiro
Director of the General Staff . . . . . . . . . . . . . . . . . . . . . Cnel. Pedro González
First Deputy Chief . . . . . . . . . . . . . . . . . . . Gral. Brig. Jorge Suárez Lorenzo
Deputy Chief and Chief,
    Communications Directorate . . . . . . . . . . . . . . . Cnel. Mário Cruz Samada
Chief, Political Section . . . . . . . . . . . . . . . . . . . Cap. Alfredo Salas Labrada
Chief, Political Section . . . . . . . . . . . . . . . . . . . . Cnel. José M. García Trujillo
Chief, Directorate of Operations . . . . . . . . . . . . . . Cnel. Fnu Díaz González
Chief, Directorate of Artillery . . . . Gral. Brig. José Arnaldo Morfa González
Chief, Directorate of Armor,
    Directorate for Chemical Defense . . . . . . . . . . May. Evaristo Pérez Medina
Chief, Directorate for Engineering . . . . . . Tte. Cnel. Ramón Andollo Valdeś
Chief, Directorate of Organization
    and Mobilization . . . . . . . . . . . . . . . . . . . . Cnel. Arnaldo Trutié Mantilla
Chief, Directorate for Planning
    and Organization . . . . . . . . . . . . . . . . . . . . . . . . Tte. Cnel. José R. Legro
Chief, Directorate for Cadres . . . . . . . . . . . Gral. Brig. Venancio Rivas Pérez
Chief, Military Counter-intelligence Directorate . . . . . . . . . . . . . . . . . . . . . . .
Chief, Planning and Economy Directorate . . . . . . . . . . . . . . . . . . . . . . . . . . .
Chief, Finance Directorate . . . . . . Gral. Brig. Juan António Rodríguez Pérez
Chief, Security Battalion . . . . . . . . . . . . . . . . . . Cnel. Eloy Rodríguez Téllez
Chief, Central Directorate for
    Construction and Housing . . . . . . . . . . . . . . . . Cnel. Carlos Lahite Lahera

**Central Political Directorate**
*(Dirección Política Central)*

Chief and Vice Minister . . . . . . . . . . . . . . Gral. de Div. Sixto Batista Santana
First Deputy Chief . . . . . . . . . . . . . . . . . . . . Cnel. Armando Saucedo Yero
Second Deputy Chief . . . . . . . . . . . . . . . . . Ship Cap. Eladio Calvo González
Official . . . . . . . . . . . . . . . . . . . . . . . . . . Tte. Cnel. Vicente Campos Barrios
Official . . . . . . . . . . . . . . . . . . . . . . . . . . . . Tte. Cnel. Alfredo Darna Rivero
Official . . . . . . . . . . . . . . . . . . . . . . . . Tte. Cnel. German Gómez Caicedo
Official . . . . . . . . . . . . . . . . . . . . . . . . . . . . . . . . . Cnel. José A. González
Official . . . . . . . . . . . . . . . . . . . . . . . . . . . . . . . . Cap. Gaspar Hernández
Official . . . . . . . . . . . . . . . . . . . . . . . . . . . . . . Humberto Hernández García
Official . . . . . . . . . . . . . . . . . . . . . Tte. Cnel. Eustaquio Izquierdo Miranda
Official . . . . . . . . . . . . . . . . . . . . . . . . . . . Tte. Cnel. Gustavo Milián Rivero
Official . . . . . . . . . . . . . . . . . . . . . . . . . . Tte. Cnel. Orlando de la O. Navarro
Official . . . . . . . . . . . . . . . . . . . . . . . . . . . . . . Tte. Cnel. Julio César Rosie
Chief, Directorate for
    Organizational Worl . . . . . . . . . . Tte. Cnel. Santiago Hernández Caceres
Secretary, Party Committee Adjunct to
    the Central Political Directorate . . . . . . . . Cnel. Diego E. González Pérez
President, Electrical Committee . . . . . . . . . . . Cnel. Armando Saucedo Yero
Chief, Organization Section . . . . . . . . . . . . . . . . . . . . . . . . . . . . . . . . . . . . . .
Chief, Directorate for
    Propaganda Agitation . . . . . . . . . . . . . . . Cap. Nav. Eladio Calvo González
CDF-FAR National Secretariat . . . . . . . . Tte. Cnel. Lázaro Martín Gutiérrez
Chief, Union of Young
    Communists (UJC) Section . . . . . . . . . . . . . . . . Cap. Juan Chávez Arteaga
Chief, History Section . . . . . . . . . . . . . . . . . . Cnel. Thelma Bornot Pubillones
Chief, FAR's Central House . . . . . . . . . . . . . . . . . . . . . Tte. Col. Oscar Azua
Chief, Propaganda Section . . . . . . . . . . . . . May. Carlos Eloy García Trápaga
Director, FAR Film Studies
    (ECIFAR) . . . . . . . . . . . . . . . . . . . . . . . Tte. Cnel. Francísco Soto Acosta
Chief, Press, Radio and Television Section . . . . . Tte. Cnel. Angel Rodríguez
Director, Senior Party School of FAR . . . . . . . . . . . Cap. Nieves Milán Goyos
Chief, Social Sciences Section . . . . . . . . . . . . . . . . Tte. Cnel. José M. Delgado
Director, Verde Olivo Magazine . . . . . . . . Tte. Cnel. Eduardo Yassells Ferrer
Director, Trabajo Politico Magazine . . . . . . . . . . . . . . . . . . . . . . . . . . . . . . . .

**Directorate for Combat Training and Military Training Centers**
*(Preparación Combativa y Centros de Enseñanza Militar)*

| | |
|---|---|
| Chief | Miguel A. Lorente León |
| Deputy Chief | |
| Chief, Physical Training Section | Tte. Cnel. Roberto Díaz Fabregat |
| President, MINFAR Sports Committee | Gral. de Div. Arnaldo T. Ochoa Sánchez |
| Director, Directorate of Military Training Centers and Noncombat Training | Cnel. Jorge Díaz García |
| Chief, Noncombat Training Section | Tte. Cnel. Emilio Robaina Figueredo |
| Director, General Máximo Gómez Revolutionary Armed Forces Academy (Senior Service School) | Gral. Brig. Manuel Fernádez Falcón |
| Director, General António Maceo Interservice School | Cnel. José Palacios Suaŕez |
| Director, Comandante Camilo Cienfuegos Artillery School, La Cabana, Havana | Tte. Cnel. Adán Hernández Gutiérrez |
| Director, Military Technical Institute, Marianao, Havana | Tte. Cnel. Evidio Fumero Valdés |
| Director, Comilo Cinfuegos Military Vocational Schools | Tte. Cnel. Miguel Ángel Díaz Ibáñez |
| Director, Major José Sierra Ramos Special Studies Center | May. Juan Domínguez Sánchez |
| Director, School of Economic Management | Cap. Juan Miranda Lezcano |

**Rear Services**
*(Logistics)*
*(Servicios Logísticos)*

| | |
|---|---|
| Chief | Gral. Brig. Carlos Rodés Moros |
| Deputy Chief | Col. Miguel Bisbé Suaŕez |
| Chief of Staff | Tte. Cnel. Enrique Batille Callejas |
| Chief, Directorate of Fuels and Lubricants | Eng. Tte. Cnel. José Bisbé Suárez |
| Chief, Directorate of Provisions (Dirección de Viveres) | |
| Chief, Directorate of Military Commerce (Dirección de Comercio Militar) | Cnel. Primitivo Henríquez Hernández |
| Chief, Military Unit Number 2778 (Central Supply Depot) | |
| Chief, Directorate of Medical Services | Guillermo Rodríguez del Pozo |
| Director, Higher Institute of Military Medicine (ISMM) | Jorge Martínez Ribalta |
| Director, Directorate of Transportation and Roads | |

**Directorate of Armaments and Technology**
*(Directorio de Armamentos y Technología)*

| | |
|---|---|
| Chief | Gral. Brig. Francísco Cruz Bourzac |
| Chief, Directorate of Industrial, Enterprises, Political Section | Cnel. Victor António Bernál Leon |
| President, Central Committee for Inter-Enterprise Emulation | Cnel. Augusto Martínez Sánchez |
| Chief, Directorate of Tanks and Transports | May. Victor Hugo Padrón |

**Youth Labor Army**
*(Ejército de Mano de Obra Juvenil)*

| | |
|---|---|
| Chief and Vice Minister | May. Brig. Rigoberto García Fernádez |
| Deputy Chief | Cnel. Emilio Morales |
| Deputy Chief | May. Rafael Morales |
| Deputy Chief | EJT Tte. Cnel. Roberto Santos Sanduy |
| Deputy Chief | Cnel. Luis Alfonso Zayas Ochoa |
| Chief of Staff | Cnel. René Nuñez Alvarado |
| Chief, Political Section | Maximo Chapelín Sabater |
| Chief, Directorate of Operations | |
| Chief, Technical Directorate | EJT Tte. Cnel. Humberto Vásquez |
| Chief, Directorate of Instruction | EJT Cap. Amalia Catala Álverez |
| Chief, Cadre Directorate | EJT May. Domingo González Mendoza |

Chief, Combat Training
  Directorate . . . . . . . . . . . . . . . . . . . . . .EJT Cnel. Alberto Vásquez García
Chief, Organization and Mobilization . . . . . . . .EJT Tte. Cnel. Jesús Padilla
Chief, Rear Services. . . . . . . . . . . . . . . . . . . . . . . . . . . . . . . . . . . . . . . . . . . .
Chief, Production . . . . . . . . . . . . . . . . . . . . . . . . . . . .May. Rafael Morales

# ARMY
## Armies and Army Corps
*(Los Ejército y Cuerpos del Ejército)*

**Isle of Youth Military Region**

Chief . . . . . . . . . . . . . . . . . . . . . . . . . .Gral. Brig. Marcelo Verdcia Perdomo
Chief of Staff . . . . . . . . . . . . . . . . . . . . . . . . . . . . . . . .Tte. Cnel. Pablo Bercelo
Chief, Political Section . . . . . . . . . . . . . . . . . . . .Tte. Cnel. Sergio Fernández

**Western Army**

Chief . . . . . . . . . . . . . . . . . . . . . . . . . . . .Gral. Brig. Joaquín Quinta Solás
First Deputy Chief . . . . . . . . . . . . . . . . . . .Gral. Brig. Samuel Rodiles Planas
Chief of Staff . . . . . . . . . . . . . . . . . . . . . . . . . . . .Cnel. Carlos Lezcano Pérez
Chief, Political Section . . . . . . . . . . . . .Tte. Cnel. Juan Luis Charón Duarte
Chief, Combat Training . . . . . . . . . . . . . . . . . . .Cnel. Lorenzo García Frias
Chief, Rear Services . . . . . . . . . . . . . . . . . .Gral. Brig. Julio Fernández Pérez
Chief, Operations . . . . . . . . . . . . . . . . . . . . . . . . .Cnel. Amel Escalante Colas
Chief, Equipment . . . . . . . . . . . . . . . . . . . . . .Cnel. Fernándo Navo Álvarez
Chief, Education . . . . . . . . . . . . . . . . . . . . . . . . . . . . . . . . . . .Tte. Nilo García
Chief, Medical Services . . . . . . . . . . . . . .Tte. Cnel. Pedro Rodríguez Fonseca

### Troop Units
Chief, Military Unit Number 1011
  (Armored Division) . . . . . . . . . . . . . . . . .Gral. Brig. Ramón Pardo Guerra
Chief, Military Unit Number 1700 . . . . . . . . . . . . . . . . . . . . . . . . . . . . . . . . .
Chief, Military Unit Number 1787 . . . . . . . . . . . . . . . . . . . . . . . . . . . . . . . . .
Official, Military Unit Number 2721 . . . . . . . . . .Cnel. Emilio Herrera Guada
Chief, Military Unit Number 2862 . . . . . . . . . . . . . . . . . . . . . . . . . . . . . . . . .
Chief, Military Unit Number 3234
  (Infantry Division) . . . . . . . . . . . . . . . .Gral. Brig. Leopoldo Cintras Frias
Chief, Military Unit Number 4279 . . . . . . . . . . . . . . . . . . . . . . . . . . . . . . . . .
Chief, Artillery Division,
  Cabana Fortress . . . . . . . . . . . . . . . . . . .Tte. Cnel. Hugo Pérez González
Official . . . . . . . . . . . . . . . . . . . . . . . . . . . . . . .Cap. Miguel Barbán Vásquez
Official . . . . . . . . . . . . . . . . . . . . . . . . . .Primer Tte. António Cruz Escalona
Chief, Great Havana Garrison . . . . . . .Gral. Brig. Roberto T. Viera Estrada
Chief, Rinar del Rio Army Corps . . . . . . . . .Cnel. Jesús Almeida Hernández

**Central Army**

Chief . . . . . . . . . . . . . . . . . . . . .Gral. de Div. Raúl Menéndez Tomassevich
Official . . . . . . . . . . . . . . . . . . . . . . .Tte. Cnel. José Pablo Lleonart Machado
Official . . . . . . . . . . . . . . . . . . . . . . . . . . .Gral. Brig. Jorge Suárez Lorenzo
Official . . . . . . . . . . . . . . . . . . . . . . . . .Tte. Cnel. Faustino Tamayo Quesada
Chief of Staff . . . . . . . . . . . . . . . . . . . . . . . . .Tte. Cnel. René García Herrera
Chief, Political Section . . . . . . . . . . . . .Tte. Cnel. Ibrahim Alfonso Victorero
Chief, Combat Training. . . . . . . . . . . . . . . . . . . . .May. José Roig Palenzuela
Chief, Medical Services . . . . . . . . . . . . . .Tte. Cnel. José González Arévalo
Chief, Communications Unit . . . . . . . . . .Premier Tte. Ramón Gálvez Pérez

### Troop Units
Chief, Training Regiment
  Political Section . . . . . . . . . . . . . . . . . . . .Tte. Cnel. Benito Marabal Acosta
Chief, Military Unit Number 1116 . . . . . . . . . . . . . .Cnel. Edgardo Vasquez
Chief, Military Unit Number 1410 . . . . . .Cnel. Carlos Carballos Betancourt
Chief, Military Unit Number 1890 . . . . . . . . . . . . . . . . . . . .Cnel. Raúl Pérez
Chief, Military Unit Number 2447 . . . . . .May. Enrique Rodríguez González
Chief, Military Unit Number 3224 . . . . . . . . . . .Tte. Cnel. Pablo Ávila Morell
Chief, Las Villas Army Corps . . . . . . . . .Brig. Gral. Orlando Lorenzo Castro

**Eastern Army**

Chief ........................May. Gral. Rogelio Acevedo González
Deputy Chief ......................Gral. Brig. Samuel Rodiles Planas
Official ...............................Gral. Brig. René Ávila Ochoa
Official ...............................Gral. Brig. Victor Chueg Colas
Official ...............................Tte. Cnel. Orlando González
Official .......................Tte. Cnel. Fernándo Muguercía Cata
Official ...............................Cnel. Orgelino Pérez Peña
Official, Civil Defense ..................Tte. Cnel. José R. Ricardo
Chief of Staff ...........................................................
Chief, Political Section ....................Cnel. Oscar Puig Céspedes
Chief, Combat Training .........................Emilio Samper
Chief, Rear Services ...................Cnel. José Nivaldo Causse Pérez
Chief, Medical Services ...........Tte. Cnel. Severino Cabrera González
Chief, Military Tribunal ...................May. Juan Montejo Benítez

**Troop Units**

Chief, Guantánamo Frontier Brigade ..........May. José Castillo Carballo
Chief of Staff ........................Cap. Adalberto Segura Meneses
Chief, Military Unit Number 1090 ....................................
Chief, Military Unit Number 1321 ....................................
Chief, Military Unit Number 1632 ....................................
Chief, Military Unit Number 1654 ....................................
Chief, Military Unit Number 1668 .........May. Eudy Figueredo Vásquez
Chief, Military Unit Number 1690 ....................................
Chief, Military Number 1973 ......Tte. Cnel. Miguel Bustamante del Toro
Chief, Military Unit Number 2012 ....................................
Chief, Military Unit Number 2034 ....................................
Chief, Military Unit Number 2431 ....................................
Chief, Military Unit Number 2463 ....................Cap. Argelio Fabre
Chief, Military Unit Number 2520 ....................................
Chief, Military Unit Number 2545 ..........Cnel. Wilfredo Rosales Aleaga
Chief, Military Unit Number 2632 ....................................
Chief, Military Unit Number 2810 ....................................
Chief, Military Unit Number 2840 ....................................
Chief, Military Unit Number 2847 .............May. Virgilio Hernández
Chief, Military Unit Number 2969 ....................................
Chief, Military Unit Number 3065 ....................................
Chief, Military Unit Number 3128 ....................................
Chief, Military Unit Number 3338 ....................................
Chief, Military Unit Number 3586 ....................................
Chief, Military Unit Number 3906 .................Tte. Amalia Cribeiro
Chief, Military Unit Number 5254 ....................................
Chief, Sapper Engineering Regiment .....Tte. Cnel. Gabriel Bada Arnedo
Official ...........................Tte. Sinencio Céspedes Rosales
Official ...........................Cap. Dioscórides Ferrer Arminán
Chief, Company Army Corps ........Gral. Brig. Roberto T. Viera Estrada
Chief, Holguin Army Corps ...............Gral. Brig. Victor Schueg Colas
Chief, Angolan Expeditionary Forces ..................................
Chief, Ethiopian Expeditionary Forces ................................

**NAVY**
**Cuban Revolutionary Navy**
*(Marina de Guerra*
*Revolucionária-MCR)*

Chief and Vice Minister ............Vice Alm. Aldo Santamaría Cuadrado
First Deputy Chief, Chief of Staff ................Cap. Pedro Perera Ruiz
Deputy Chief ....................Cap. Julio Hernandez Fernández
Chief, Political Section .............Cap. Gonzálo González de la Rosa
Deputy Chief, Political Section ...............Cap. Miguel Valle Miranda
Chief, Union of Young
    Communists (UJC) Subsection .........Tte. Arnaldo Rodríguez Fuentes
Chief, Rear Services.................................................
Chief, Combat Training ...................Cap. Amado González Ávila

**Base Commands**

Chief, Havana Naval Base ............................................
Chief, Nariel Naval Base ............................................
Chief, Cienfuegos Naval Base ..........Cap. Generoso Escudero González

| | |
|---|---|
| **Operational Commands** | Chief, Western Naval District . . . . . . . . Contra Alm. Pedro Pérez Betancourt |
| | Chief, Western Naval Flotilla |
| |    (*Flotilla de la Guatdia* |
| |    *Desembatco del Granma*) . . . . . . . . . . . . . Cap. Leonardo Díaz Rodríguez |
| | Chief, Torpedo Boat Flotilla . . . . . . . . . . . . . . . . . . . . . . . . . . . . . . . . . . . |
| | Chief, Submarine Chaser Fleet . . . . . . . . . . . . . . Cap. Emilio Saborit Arzuaga |
| | Chief, Central Naval District . . . . . . . . . Cap. Sabino Hernández Goinochea |

| | |
|---|---|
| **Shore Commands** | Director, Naval Academy |
| |    (Punta Santa Ana) . . . . . . . . . . . . . Contra Alm. José L. Cuza Téllez-Girón |
| | Director, Training Center for |
| |    Junior Specialists . . . . . . . . . . . . . . . . . Gral. Brig. Juan Rodríguez Acosta |
| | Chief, General Repairs Depot . . . . . . . . . . . . Cap. Armando Ojeda Bartumeu |
| | President, Cuban Institute |
| |    of Hydrography . . . . . . . . . . . . . . . . . . . . . . Cap. Joel Chaveco Hernández |

| | |
|---|---|
| **AIR FORCE** | Chief . . . . . . . . . . . . . . . . . . . . . . . . . . . . . Gral. de Div. Julio Casas Regueiro |
| **Anti-Aircraft Defense and** | First Deputy Chief . . . . . . . . . . . . . . . . . . . . . . . . . . . . . . . Cnel. Ricardo Díaz |
| **Revolutionary Air Force—DAAFAR** | Deputy Chief . . . . . . . . . . . . . . . . . . . . . . . . . . . . . Ladislao Branda Columbie |
| *(Fuerza Aérea Revolucionária* | Chief of Staff . . . . . . . . . . . . . . . . . . . . . . . . . . . Cnel. Tomás Benítez Martínez |
| *y de Defensa)* | Chief, Political Section . . . . . . . . . . . . . . . . . . . . . . . . . Marcelion Rodríguez |
| | Chief, Training Center for |
| |    Junior Specialists . . . . . . . . . . . . . . . . . . . . . . . . . . . . . . . . . . . . . . |
| | Chief, Aviation Repair Base . . . . . . . . . . . . . . Tte. Cnel. Ángel R. Lugo Torre |
| | Director, Yuri Gagarin Military |
| |    Industrial Enterprise . . . . . . . . . . . . . . . . Tte. Cnel. Gerado Chávez López |
| | Director, Great October Socialist |
| |    Revolution Military Enterprise |
| |    (Repair Depot) . . . . . . . . . . . . . . . . . . . . . . . . . . . . May. Samuel Savariego |

| | |
|---|---|
| **Components** | Official, Air Force |
| |    (Cosmonaut Trainee) . . . . . . . . . . . . . . May. José Armando López Falcón |
| | Official, Air Force (Cosmonaut) . . . . . . . . . Cnel. Arnaldo Tamayo Méndez |
| | Chief, Western Air Brigade (Bay of |
| |    Pigs Guard Aerial Brigade) . . . . . . . . . . . . Cnel. Ruben Martínez Puentes |
| | Chief, Missile Troops . . . . . . . . . . . . . . Gral. Brig. Armando Choy Rodríguez |
| | Chief, Central Anti-Aircraft Missile Brigade |
| |    (Santa Clara Battle Guard Brigade) . . . . . . Tte. Cnel. Nivio Sánchez Arce |
| | Chief, Western Anti-Aircraft |
| |    Missile Brigade . . . . . . . . . . . . . . . . . . . . . . . Cnel. Carlos Lamas Rodríguez |
| | Chief, Anti-Aircraft Missile Group for |
| |    the Defense of the Capital . . . . . . . . . . . . . . . . . . . Cap. Fernándo Cabrera |
| | Chief, Radio Technical Troops . . . . . . . . . . . . . Cnel. Enrique Dorta Marrero |
| | Chief, Anti-Air Defense of |
| |    the Ground Troops . . . . . . . . . . . . . . . . Cnel. Ricardo Hernández Merino |
| | Chief, Military Unit Number 3063 |
| |    (Holguin Air Base) . . . . . . . . . . . . . . . . . . . . . . Victor Rodríguez López |

\* \* \* \* \*

# GENERAL DEFENSE DATA

**Manpower**
   Total Armed Forces . . . . . . . . . . . . . . . . . . . . . . . . . . . . . . . . . . . . . . . . . . . 127,000
      (See Page 141)
   Population . . . . . . . . . . . . . . . . . . . . . . . . . . . . . . . . . . . . . . . . . . . . . . . . 9,771,000

**Spending**
Military Expenditures . . . . . . . . . . . . . . . . . . . . . . . . . . . . . . . . . . . . . . . . . . . . .$1.1 billion
Gross National Product . . . . . . . . . . . . . . . . . . . . . . . . . . . . . . . . . . . . . . . . . . .$18.4 billion
Military Expenditure as a Percentage of
    Gross National Product . . . . . . . . . . . . . . . . . . . . . . . . . . . . . . . . . . . . . . . . .6.2%
Military Expenditure as a Percentage of
    Central Government Expenditure . . . . . . . . . . . . . . . . . . . . . . . . . . . . . . . .8.2%

**Defense Treaties** *(See Part II for Additional Detail)*

Bilateral:    Angola
              United States

Multilateral:  Biological Weapons Convention
               Environmental Modification Convention

**Military Rank Comparisons**
See Appendix A.

# CYPRUS

## Republic of Cyprus
*Demokratia Kyprou* (Greek)
*Kzbrzs* (Turkish)

### Defence Establishment Command Structure
### and Force Organization

The Cypriot National Guard is responsible to the President of the Republic of Cyprus. Administrative control of the Guard is exercised by the Minister of the Interior and Defence. Operational command of the military is vested in the Commander-in-Chief of the Guard.

**Total armed forces:** 10,000 (National Guard): **Para-military forces:** 3,000 (Police).

## HEAD OF STATE

H. E. Spyros Kyprianou

**OFFICE OF THE PRESIDENT**
*Nicosia*
*Telephone:  (21) 47767*

President of the Republic of Cyprus . . . . . . . . . . . . . . . . . . Spyros Kyprianou
Minister to the President . . . . . . . . . . . . . . . . . . . . . . . . . Dinos Michaelides
Under Secretary to the President . . . . . . . . . . . . . . . . . . . . Patroclos Stravrou
Director-General, Ministry to the President . . . . . . . . . . . . . Linos Shacallis

**Press and Information Office**

Director (Acting) . . . . . . . . . . . . . . . . . . . . . . . . . . . . . . . . . . . K. Psyllides

**MINISTERY OF THE INTERIOR
   AND DEFENCE**
*25 Demophon Street*
*Nicosia*
*Telephone:  (21) 402105, 402509*

Minister . . . . . . . . . . . . . . . . . . . . . . . . . . . . . . . . . . Christodoulos Veniamin
Deputy Minister of the Interior . . . . . . . . . . . . . . . . . . . . . . . . . Elias Eliades
Director-General (Interior) . . . . . . . . . . . . . . . . . . . . . . . . Kyriacos Christofi
Director-General (Defence) . . . . . . . . . . . . . . . . . . . . . . . . Nicos Phylactou
Commissioner, Civil Defence . . . . . . . . . . . . . . . . . . . . Modestos Pentaliotis
President, Military Court . . . . . . . . . . . . . . . . . . . . . . . Col. Soterios Efetzis
Deputy President, Military Court . . . . . . . . . . . . Lt. Christophoraos Tseligas
Military Attorney . . . . . . . . . . . . . . . . . . . . . . . . . . . . Maj. Stylianos Tamasios

**District Administrations**

District Officer, Nicosia (Acting) . . . . . . . . . . . . . . . . . . Andreas Papagavriel
District Officer, Limassol (Acting) . . . . . . . . . . . . . . . . Antonios Frangoudes
District Officer, Famagusta (Acting) . . . . . . . . . . . . . . . . . . Kokos Marcou
District Officer, Larnaca . . . . . . . . . . . . . . . . . . . . . . . . . . . . Kokos Marcou
District Officer, Paphos (Acting) . . . . . . . . . . . . . . . . . . Andreas Yiannacou

## DEFENCE FORCES

**CYPRUS NATIONAL GUARD**
*Nicosia*
*Telephone:  (21) 402513, 403187*

Commander-in-Chief . . . . . . . . . . . . . . . . . . Lt. Gen. Nicolaos Papanayiotou
Deputy Commander . . . . . . . . . . . . . . . . . . . . . . Maj. Gen. George Azinas
Chief of Staff . . . . . . . . . . . . . . . . . . . . . Brig. Gen. Euripedes Tsadamouras
Commander, Greek Contingent
   in Cyrpus . . . . . . . . . . . . . . . . . . . . . Brig. Gen. Athanasios Constantinedes

**POLICE**
*Nicosia*

Chief of Police . . . . . . . . . . . . . . . . . . . . . . . . . . . . . . . . . . . . . . Savvas Antoniou
Deputy Chief of Police . . . . . . . . . . . . . . . . . . . . . . . . . Theophanis Demetriou
Assistant Chief of Police . . . . . . . . . . . . . . . . . . . . . . . . . . Odysseas Lambrou
Assistant Chief of Police . . . . . . . . . . . . . . . . . . . . . . . . Kypros Mourouzides

\* \* \* \* \*

# GENERAL DEFENCE DATA

**Manpower**
  Total Armed Forces . . . . . . . . . . . . . . . . . . . . . . . . . . . . . . . . . . . . . . 10,000
    (See Page 149)
  Population . . . . . . . . . . . . . . . . . . . . . . . . . . . . . . . . . . . . . . . . . . . . 642,000

**Spending**
  Military Expenditures . . . . . . . . . . . . . . . . . . . . . . . . . . . . . . . . . . $32 million
  Gross National Product . . . . . . . . . . . . . . . . . . . . . . . . . . . . . . . . . . $2 billion
  Military Expenditure as a Percentage of
    Gross National Product . . . . . . . . . . . . . . . . . . . . . . . . . . . . . . . . . 1.6%
  Military Expenditure as a Percentage of
    Central Government Expenditure . . . . . . . . . . . . . . . . . . . . . . . . . 7.8%

**Defence Treaties** *(See Part II for Additional Detail)*

  Bilateral:     None

  Multilateral:  Biological Weapons Convention
                 Environmental Modification Convention
                 Limited Test Ban Treaty
                 Treaty on the Control of Arms on the Seabed
                 Treaty of Establishment
                 Treaty on the Non-Proliferation of Nuclear Weapons

# CZECHOSLOVAKIA
## Czechoslovak Socialist Republic
### *Ceskoslovenska Socialisticka Republika*

### Defense Establishment Command Structure and Force Organization

The President is Commander-in-Chief of the armed forces. He heads the Defense Council, a policy-making body that has formal responsibility for the country's defense. Operational control of both the Army and the Air and Air Defense Forces is exercised by the Minister of National Defense.

**Total armed forces:** 196,500 (Army: 142,500; Air Force: 54,000). **Para-military forces:** 135,500 (People's Militia: 126,000; Border Troops: 11,000; Civil Defense: 2,500).

## HEAD OF STATE

Judr. Gustav Husak. CSc.

**CHANCELLERY OF THE PRESIDENT**
*119 08 Prague 1 Hrad*
*Telephone: 2101, 534541*

President of the Republic and
    Commander-in-Chief......................Judr. Gustav Husak, CSc.
Head of the President's Chancellery ................Ing. Frantisek Salda
Chief, Military Office ........................Lt. Gen. Miroslav Rybak

**Defense Council**

Chairman...................................Judr. Gustav Husak, CSc.
Deputy Chairman ........................Lubomir Strougal (Premier)
Member..............................................Peter Colotka
Member.........................................Gen. Martin Dzur
Member...........................................Vaclav Hula
Member ............................................Josef Kempný
Member ............................................Jozef Lenárt
Member ........................................Col. Gen. Karel Rusov

**OFFICE OF THE FEDERAL GOVERNMENT PRESIDUM**
*nabr. Kpt. Jarose 4*
*125 09 Prague 1*

Premier.......................................Judr. Lubomir Štougal
Deputy Premier and Premier,
    Czech Government ...................................Jozef Korčak
Deputy Premier and Premier,
    Slovak Government.................Prof. Judr. Peterf Colotka, C.Sc.
Director ...........................................Augustin Hubka
Chief, Division for Defense
    and Security ..................................Lt. Gen. Alois Gros
Press Secretary.....................................Frantisek Kouřil
Director, Secretariat for Foreign
    Affairs and Protocol .........................Ota Kchwarzenberger

**FEDERAL MINISTRY OF NATIONAL DEFENSE**
*nam. Svobody 471*
*160 01 Prague 6*
*Telephone: 330822*
*Telex: 121616 mno c, 121741 mno c*

Minister.........................................Gen. Martin Dzur
First Deputy Minister .........................Col. Gen. Karel Rusov
First Deputy Minister ......................Col. Gen. Miloslav Blahnik
Deputy Minister ...............................Lt. Gen. Jan Lux
Deputy Minister ...........................Lt. Gen. Josef Martinec
Deputy Minister ......................Lt. Gen. Josef Marusak, CSc.
Deputy Minister ..............................Lt. Gen. Jozef Remek

Deputy Minister . . . . . . . . . . . . . . . . . . . . . . . . . . . .Lt. Gen. Miloslav Zika
Deputy Minister . . . . . . . . . . . . . . . . . . . . . . . . . .Lt. Gen. Ferdinand Hanzel
Press Secretary . . . . . . . . . . . . . . . . . . . . . . . . . . . . . . . .Lt. Col. Juraj Rubau
Director, Inspectorate of the Minister . . . . . . . . . . .Maj. Gen. Zoltan Jakus
Director, Office of the Minister . . . . . . . . . . . . . . . . .Col. Frantisek Palenik
Chief, Political Section . . . . . . . . . . . . . . . . . . . . . .Maj. Gen. Josef Svoboca
Chief, Main Political Directorate . . . . . . . . . . . . . .Col. Gen. Antonin Brabec
Deputy Chief, Political Directorate . . . . . . . . . . . .Maj. Gen. Jaroslav Klicha
Deputy Chief, Political Directorate . . . . . . . . . . . . . . . .Lt. Gen. Jiři Nečas
Deputy Chief, Political Directorate . . . . . . . . . . . . .Maj. Gen. Cyril Rabusic

# DEFENSE FORCES

**ARMY**
**Czechoslovak People's Army**
*c/o Federal Ministry of National Defense*
*nam. Svobody 471*
*160 01 Prague 6*
*Telephone:   330822*
*Telex:   121616 mno c 121741 mno c*

Chief, General Staff . . . . . . . . . . . . . . . . . . . . . . .Col. Gen. Miloslav Blahník
Deputy Chief, General Staff . . . . . . . . . . . . . . . . . . . . .Lt. Col. Josef Turošík
Director, Foreign Liaison Office
    (General Staff) . . . . . . . . . . . . . . . . . . . . . . . . . . . .Maj. Gen. Michal Choma

**Eastern Military District—VVO**
*Headquarters*
*Trencin*
*(Slovakia)*

Commander . . . . . . . . . . . . . . . . . . . . . . . . . . . . . . .Lt. Gen. Jozef Hrebik
Chief, Political Directorate . . . . . . . . . . . . . . . . . . . .Lt. Gen. Jozef Kovacik
Deputy . . . . . . . . . . . . . . . . . . . . . . . . . . . . . . . . . .Maj. Gen. Ivan Dzamko
Deputy . . . . . . . . . . . . . . . . . . . . . . . . . . . . . . . . . .Maj. Gen. Jaroslav Kryl
Deputy . . . . . . . . . . . . . . . . . . . . . . . . . . . . . . . .Maj. Gen. Zdislav Sedlaček
Deputy . . . . . . . . . . . . . . . . . . . . . . . . . . . . . . . . .Maj. Gen. Karel Zatopek
Bratislava Garrison Commander . . . . . . . . . . . . . . . . . . . . .Col. Jozef Figura

**Western Military District—ZVO**
*Headquarters*
*Tabor*
*(Bohemia and Moravia)Tabor*

Commander . . . . . . . . . . . . . . . . . . . . . . . . . . . .Col. Gen. Frantisek Veselý
Chief, Political Directorate . . . . . . . . . . . . . . . . . . .Maj. Gen. Julius Hasana
Deputy . . . . . . . . . . . . . . . . . . . . . . . . . . . . . . .Maj. Gen. Frantisek Janošek
Deputy . . . . . . . . . . . . . . . . . . . . . . . . . . . . . . .Maj. Gen. Vojtech Kantner
Deputy . . . . . . . . . . . . . . . . . . . . . . . . . . . . . . . . .Maj. Gen. Jozef Mikulec
Deputy . . . . . . . . . . . . . . . . . . . . . . . . . . . . . . . . .Lt. Gen. Milan Václavík
Prague Garrison Commander . . . . . . . . . . . . . . . . .Maj. Gen. Stepan Bunzak

**Directorates and Administrations**

Commander, Combat Preparedness . . . . . . . . . . . . . .Lt. Gen. Miloslav Zika
Commander, Rear Services . . . . . . . . . . . . . . . . . . . . . . . . . .Lt. Gen. Jan Lux
Commander, Central Home Army
    (Prague) . . . . . . . . . . . . . . . . . . . . . . . . . . . . . . . . .Col. Vnislav Duchek
Director, Central Military Hospital . . . . . . . . . . . . . . .Maj. Gen. Josef Sabo
Commander, Chemical Troops . . . . . . . . . . . . . . . . . . . . . . . . .Jan Franko
Commander, Engineer Troops . . . . . . . . . . . . . . . . . . .Maj. Gen. Jiri Lelek
Director, Financial Directorate . . . . . . . . . . . . . . .Maj. Gen. Josef Hamaria
Director, Medical Services . . . . . . . . . . . . . . . . . .Maj. Gen. Bohumil Indra
Director, Military Courts . . . . . . . . . . . . . . . . . . . . . . . . .Col. Jan Borgula
Director, Military Education . . . . . . . . . . . . . . . .Maj. Gen. Josef Mikulec
Director, Personnel . . . . . . . . . . . . . . . . . . . . . . . . . .Lt. Gen. Pavel Papac
Commander, Railroad Troops . . . . . . . . . . . . . . .Maj. Gen. Vladimir Čihak
Commander, Signals Troops . . . . . . . . . . . . . . . .Maj. Gen. Ladislav Stack
Commander, Tank Services . . . . . . . . . . . . . . . . . .Maj. Gen. Zdenek Jasek
Chief, Troop Services Section . . . . . . . . . . . . . . . . . . . . . . . .Alena Spanova

**Academic Institutions**

Commandant, Antonin Zapotocky
    Military Academy (Brno) . . . . . . . . . . . . . . . . . . . . .Lt. Gen. Josef Čepický
Commandant, Ludvik Svoboda Ground Forces
    Military College (Vyskov) . . . . . . . . . . . . . . . . . . . . . . . . . . . . .V. Roucka

**AIR FORCE**
**Air and Air Defense Forces**
*c/o Federal Ministry of National Defense*
*nam. Svobody 471*
*160 01 Prague 6*

*Telephone:    330822*
*Telex:    121616 mno c 121741 mno c*

Commander ...................................Lt. Gen. Josef Remek
Deputy Commander .......................Maj. Gen. Jarolsav Stecha
Commander, 7th Air Defense Army...............Lt. Gen. Michal Prelac
Commander, 10th Air Army.......................................
Commandant, Military
    Aeronautical Institute (Kosice) ..............Maj. Gen. Leonard Sabol
Commander, Artillery and
    Rocket Troops..........................Lt. Gen. Miroslav Pelousek
Chief, Political Directorate .................Maj. Gen. Bohumil Jarabek

**CIVIL DEFENSE**
*c/o Federal Ministry of National Defense*
*nam. Svobody 471*
*160 01 Prague 6*

*Telephone:    330822*
*Telex:    121616 mno c, 121741 mno c*

Commander .................................Lt. Gen. Josef Marušek
Chief of Staff ................................Col. Mewtodej Pospišil

**PEOPLE'S MILITIA**

Commander...................................Josef Lenart
Chief of Staff ........................................Mikulas Uher

\* \* \* \* \*

# GENERAL DEFENSE DATA

**Manpower**
    Total Armed Forces..............................196,500
        (See Page 151)
    Population ................................15,369,000

**Spending**
    Military Expenditures.........................$6.1 billion
    Gross National Product.......................$125.5 billion
    Military Expenditure as a Percentage of
        Gross National Product .........................4.9%
    Military Expenditure as a Percentage of
        Central Government Expenditure ...............15.5%

**Defense Treaties** *(See Part II for Additional Detail)*

|             |                        |                      |
|-------------|------------------------|----------------------|
| Bilateral:  | Afghanistan            | Poland               |
|             | Bulgaria               | Romania              |
|             | Ethiopia               | Soviet Union         |
|             | German Demo-           | Vietnam              |
|             |   cratic Republic      | People's Democratic  |
|             | Hungary                |   Republic of Yemen  |
|             | Laos                   |                      |

Multilateral:    Biological Weapons Convention
                 Environmental Modification Convention
                 Limited Test Ban Treaty
                 Treaty on the Non-Proliferation of Nuclear Weapons
                 Warsaw Treaty Organization

# DENMARK
## Kingdom of Denmark
### *Kongeriget Danmark*

## Defense Establishment Command Structure and Force Organization

The Queen is nominal Commander-in-Chief of the armed forces. Actual authority lies with the Minister of Defense, who is responsible to the Federal Diet and the Prime Minister. The Minister of Defense is advised by the Defense Council. Operational control is exercised by the Chief of Defense; the three services are integrated under his command.

In a crisis, field command would be transferred to the Commander, Operational Forces Denmark. Within NATO, this officer is Commander, Allied Forces Baltic Approaches (COMBALTAP). In the Danish chain of command, the Commander, Operational Forces Denmark is subordinate to the Chief of Defense.

The voluntary Home Guard forms an integral part of the Danish national defense structure. It has its own command which is under direct control of the Minister of Defense.

**Total armed forces:** 31,200 (Army: 18,000; Navy: 5,800; Air Force: 7,400). **Home Guard:** 78,000.

## HEAD OF STATE

H. M. Queen Margrethe II

**OFFICE OF H. M. THE QUEEN**
*Amalienborg*
*1257 Copenhagen*

*Telephone: (1) 14 36 28, 14 41 33*

Queen of Denmark and Commander-in-Chief, Danish Armed Forces . . . . . . . . . . . . H. M. Queen Margrethe II

**OFFICE OF THE PRIME MINISTER**
*Christiansborg Palace*
*1218 Copenhagen K*

*Telephone: (1) 11 30 38*
*Telex: 27027 statsm dk*

Prime Minister . . . . . . . . . . . . . . . . . . . . . . . . . . . . . . . . . . . Poul Schlüter
Principal Personal Assistant . . . . . . . . . . . . . . . . . . . . . Lars Teit Hansen

**MINISTRY OF DEFENSE**
*Slotsholmgade 10*
*1216 Copenhagen K*

*Telephone: (1) 11 62 60*
*Telex: 27190*

Minister . . . . . . . . . . . . . . . . . . . . . . . . . . . . . . . . . . . . . . . . . . Hans Engell
Private Secretary . . . . . . . . . . . . . . . . . . . . Troels Schaldemose-Nielsen
Permanent Under Secretary . . . . . . . . . . . . . . . . . . . . P. Verner Christiansen
Deputy Permanent Under Secretary . . . . . . . . . . . . . . . . . . Erik H. Sørensen
Deputy Permanent Under Secretary . . . . . . . . . . . . . . Mogens Frederiksen
Head, Organization, Training and
　　Readiness Division . . . . . . . . . . . . . . . . . . . . Maj. Kristian Andersen
Head, Personnel Division . . . . . . . . . . . . . . . . . . . . . . . . Else K. Sørensen
Head, Payroll Division . . . . . . . . . . . . . . . . . . . . . . . . . . Maj. Bent Frank
Head, NATO Affairs and International
　　Law Division . . . . . . . . . . . . . . . . . . . . . . . . . . . . . . . . . Jørgen Wahl
Head, Budget and Efficiency Division . . . . . . . . . . . . . . . . . . . Birgit Reeh
Head, Building Planning and
　　Maintenance Division . . . . . . . . . . . . . . . . . . . . . . . . . . Jørgen Haarh

Head, Juridical Affairs Division . . . . . . . . . . . . . . . . . . . . . . . . . .Verner Gyde
Head, Accounting Division . . . . . . . . . . . . . . . . . . . .Erik Henriksen
Head, Auditing Division . . . . . . . . . . . . . . . . . . . . . . . . . .Sven Scheving
Director, Geodetic Institute . . . . . . . . . . . . . . . . . . . . . . . . .F. Wiinblad
Director, Defense Intelligence Service . . . . . . . . . . . . . .Capt. M. M. Telling
Head, Contracting Division . . . . . . . . . . . . . . . . . . . . . . . . .Troels Lauritzen

## DEFENSE FORCES

**ARMED FORCES**
**Defense Command**
*(Forsvarskommandoen)*
*P.O. Box 202*
*2950 Vedbaek*

*Telephone:   (2) 89 22 55*
*Telex:   40171 sigvb dk*

Chief of Defense . . . . . . . . . . . . . . . . . . . . . . . . . . . . . .Gen. Knud Jørgensen
Chief of Defense Staff . . . . . . . . . . . . . . . . . . . . . . .Vice Adm. S. E. Thiede
Inspector-General, Royal Danish Army . . . . . . .Maj. Gen. H. M. H. Boysen
Inspector-General, Royal Danish Navy . . . . . . . . . . .Rear Adm. N. F. Lange
Inspector-General, Royal Danish Air Force . . . . . . . . .Maj. Gen. P. Thorsen
Deputy Chief of Staff, Personnel . . . . . . . . . . . . . .Maj. Gen. P. B. Krogen
Deputy Chief of Staff, Operations . . . . . . . . . . . . . . .Maj. Gen. B. E. Amled
Deputy Chief of Staff, Materiel . . . . . . . . . . . . .Rear Adm. J. P. Rasmussen
Deputy Chief of Staff, Finances . . . . . . . . . . . .Maj. Gen. A. H. Christensen
Chief, Public Information Service . . . . . . . . . . . . . .Maj. K. Brøns-Hansen

**Defense Council**

Member *(ex officio)* . . . . . . . . . . . . . . . . . . . . . . . . . .Gen. Knud Jørgensen
(Chief of Defense)
Member *(ex officio)* . . . . . . . . . . . . . . . . . . . . . . . . .Vice Adm. S. E. Thiede
(Chief, Defense Staff)
Member *(ex officio)* . . . . . . . . . . . . . . . . . . . . . . . . . . . . .Lt. Gen. O. K. Lind
(Commander, Operational Forces Denmark)
Member *(ex officio)* . . . . . . . . . . . . . . . . . . . . . . .Maj. Gen. H. M. H. Boysen
(Inspector-General, Royal Danish Army)
Member *(ex officio)* . . . . . . . . . . . . . . . . . . . . . . . . .Rear Adm. N. F. Lange
(Inspector-General, Royal Danish Navy)
Member *(ex officio)* . . . . . . . . . . . . . . . . . . . . . . . . .Maj. Gen. P. Thorsen
(Inspector-General, Royal Danish Force)

**Defense College**
*(Forsvarsakademiet)*
*Østerbrogades Kaserne*
*2100 Copenhagen 0*

Commanding Officer . . . . . . . . . . . . . . . . . . . . . . . . . . . . . . .Col. J. Gerstoft

**ARMY**
**Royal Danish Army**
*(Haeren)*
*P.O. Box 202*
*2950 Vedbaek*

*Telephone:   (2) 89 22 55*
*Telex:   40171*

Inspector-General, Royal Danish Army . . . . . . .Maj. Gen. H. M. H. Boysen
Commander, Eastern Land
    Command (Ringsted) . . . . . . . . . . . . . . .Maj. Gen. N.-A. Rye Andersen
Commander, Western Land
    Command (Århus) . . . . . . . . . . . . . . . . . . . . . .Maj. Gen. H. T. Havning
Commander, Jutland Division
    (Fredericia) . . . . . . . . . . . . . . . . . . . . . . . . .Maj. Gen. H. Dencker
Commander, Military Region VI
    (Copenhagen) . . . . . . . . . . . . . . . . . . . . . . . . . . . . . . .Col. P. C. Jessen

**Army Materiel Command**
*Arsenalvej 55*
*9800 Hjørring*

*Telephone:   (8) 92 61 11*

Chief . . . . . . . . . . . . . . . . . . . . . . . . . . . . . . . . . . .Maj. Gen. K. H. Nielsen

**Army Academy**
*(Haerens Officersskole)*
*Frederiksberg Slot*
*Roskildevej 28*
*2000 Copenhagen*

Commanding Officer . . . . . . . . . . . . . . . . . . . . . . . . . .Col. N. E. A. Møller

**NAVY**
**Royal Danish Navy**
*(Søvaernet)*
*P.O. Box 202*
*2950 Vedbaek*

Inspector-General, Royal Danish Navy . . . . . . . . . . Rear Adm. N. F. Lange
Flag Officer . . . . . . . . . . . . . . . . . . . . . . . . . . . . . . Rear Adm. J. O. Fischer
Commander, Copenhagen Naval
   Base . . . . . . . . . . . . . . . . . . . . . . . . . . . . . . . . . . . . Capt. P. Wessel-Tolvig

    **Naval Materiel Command**
    *Holmen*
    *1433 Copenhagen K.*
    *Telephone:   (1) 54 13 13*

Chief . . . . . . . . . . . . . . . . . . . . . . . . . . . . . . . . . . Rear Adm. M. E. Michelsen

    **Naval Academy**
    *(Søvaernets Officersskole)*
    *Holmen*
    *1433 Copenhagen K.*

Commanding Officer . . . . . . . . . . . . . . . . . . . . . . . . . . . . . Capt. J. Thorsen

**AIR FORCE**
**Royal Danish Air Force**
*(Flyvevåbnet)*
*P.O. Box 202*
*2950 Vedbaek*
*Telephone:   (2) 89 22 55*

Inspector-General, Royal Danish Air Force . . . . . . . . Maj. Gen. P. Thorsen
Commander, Tactical Air
   Command (Kølvrå) . . . . . . . . . . . . . . . . . . . . . . . Maj. Gen. C. S. Børgesen

    **Air Materiel Command**
    *P.O. Box 130*
    *3500 Vaerløse*
    *Telephone:   (2) 97 95 00*

Chief . . . . . . . . . . . . . . . . . . . . . . . . . . . . . . . . . . . . . . Maj. Gen. J. Skjøth

    **Air Force Academy**
    *(Flyvevabnets Officersskole)*
    *Jonstrup*
    *2750 Ballerup*

Commanding Officer . . . . . . . . . . . . . . . . . . . . . . . . . . . . . Col. F. Tingleff

**HOME GUARD**
*Home Guard Command*
*(Hjemmevaernskommandoen)*
*Kastellet 82*
*2100 Copenhagen 0*

Chief, Home Guard . . . . . . . . . . . . . . . . . . . . . . . Maj. Gen. J. Andreassen
Civilian Commissioner . . . . . . . . . . . . . . . . . . . . . . . . . . . . . . P. Søgaard

\* \* \* \* \*

## GENERAL DEFENSE DATA

**Manpower**
    Total Armed Forces . . . . . . . . . . . . . . . . . . . . . . . . . . . . . . . . . . . . 31,200
       (See Page 155)
    Population . . . . . . . . . . . . . . . . . . . . . . . . . . . . . . . . . . . . . . . . 5,125,000

**Spending**
    Military Expenditures . . . . . . . . . . . . . . . . . . . . . . . . . . . . . . . $1.7 billion
    Gross National Product . . . . . . . . . . . . . . . . . . . . . . . . . . . . . $69.6 billion
    Military Expenditure as a Percentage of
       Gross National Product . . . . . . . . . . . . . . . . . . . . . . . . . . . . . . 2.5%
    Military Expenditure as a Percentage of
       Central Government Expenditure . . . . . . . . . . . . . . . . . . . . . . . . 6%

**Defense Treaties** *(See Part II for Additional Detail)*

Bilateral:     United Kingdom
               United States

Multilateral:  Biological Weapons Convention
               Environmental Modification Convention
               Limited Test Ban Treaty
               North Atlantic Treaty Organization
               Treaty on the Control of Arms on the Seabed
               Treaty on the Non-Proliferation of Nuclear Weapons

# DJIBOUTI
## Republic of Djibouti
*Jumhuriyat Djibouti*

### Defense Establishment Command Structure and Force Organization

The President is Commander-in-Chief of the Armed Forces and exercises his authority through the Minister of National Defense. Naval and air forces are under Army command. The Gendarmerie is responsible for internal security and is administered by the Ministry of the Interior.

**Total armed forces:** 2,700 (Army: 2,600; Navy: 20; Air Force: 80). **Para-military forces:** 2,100 (Gendarmerie).

## HEAD OF STATE

H. E. Gouled Aptidon Hassan

**OFFICE OF THE PRESIDENT**
*P.O. Box 6*
*Djibouti*
*Telephone: 35 02 01, 35 01 77*
*Telex: 5871 presiden dj*

President of the Republic and Commander-in-Chief of the Armed Forces ........................ H. E. Gouled Aptidon Hassan
Director of Cabinet .............................. Ismail Guedi Hared
Principal Private Secretary ....................... Ismail Omar Guelleh
Secretary-General ............................ Osman Bogoreh Bouh

**OFFICE OF THE PRIME MINISTER**
*P.O. Box 2086*
*Djibouti*
*Telephone: 35 14 94*
*Telex: 5871 presiden dj*

Prime Minister and Minister of Port Affairs .......................... Gourad Hamadou Barkat
Director of Cabinet and Principal Private Secretary (Acting) ............................ Ahmed Waiss

**MINISTRY OF NATIONAL DEFENSE**
*P.O. Box 42*
*Djibouti*
*Telephone: 35 20 34*
*Telex: 5871 presiden dj*

Minister ..................................... Mohamed Loita Habib
Secretary-General ............................. Omar Chirdon Abass

**MINISTRY OF THE INTERIOR**
*P.O. Box 33*
*Djibouti*
*Telephone: 35 07 91*
*Telex: 5871 presiden dj*

Minister ......................................... Ali Chidron Youssef
Commissioner, Central Police ..................... Ali Ibrahim Goudal

## DEFENSE FORCES

**ARMY**
*(Armée Nationale)*
*Djibouti*

Chief of General Staff ......................... Col. Ali Mehidal Waiss
Deputy Chief of General Staff ................. Maj. Omar Barreh Darar
Commander, First Infantry Regiment ..... Lt. Col. Fabhi Ahmed Houssein

*Telephone:   35 11 56*
*Telex:   5871 presiden dj*

Commander, Intervention
   Commando Regiment . . . . . . . . . . . .Capt. Haissama Mohamed Houmed
Commander, Frontier
   Commando Group  . . . . . . . . . . . . . . .Capt. Mohamed Abdillahi Chireh

**Navy**
*Djibouti*

Commanding Officer . . . . . . . . . . . . . . . . . . . . . . . . .Capt. Ahmed Yonis Saad

*Telephone:   35 05 05 Ext. 344*
*Telex:   5871 presiden dj*

**Air Force**
*Djibouti*

Commanding Officer . . . . . . . . . . . . . . . . . . . . .Lt. Houssein Djama Ibrahim

*Telephone:   35 05 05 Ext. 350*
*Telex:   5871 presiden dj*

**GENDARMERIE**
*(Gendarmerie National)*
*B.P. 14*
*Djibouti*

Commanding Officer . . . . . . . . . . . . . . . . . . . . . . .Capt. Hoche Robleh Idleh
Commander, National Security Force  . . . . . . . . . .Maj. Yacin Yabeh Galeb

*Telephone:   35 34 71*
*Telex:   5871 presiden dj*

**FRENCH FORCES, DJIBOUTI**
*(Forces Françaises)*
*Djibouti*

Commander . . . . . . . . . . . . . . . . . . . . . . . . . . . . . . . . . . . .Gen. Jean Failler
Chief of Staff . . . . . . . . . . . . . . . . . . . . . . . . . . . . . . . . . . . . .Maj. Bouchery
Assistant Commander, Air Force . . . . . . . . . . . . . . . . . . . . . . .Col. Cloarec
Commander, French Naval Forces . . . . . . . . . . . . . . . .Adm. Claude Corbier

*Telephone:   35 39 73*

\* \* \* \* \*

# GENERAL DEFENSE DATA

**Manpower**
   Total Armed Forces . . . . . . . . . . . . . . . . . . . . . . . . . . . . . . . . . . . . . . . . .2,700
      (See Page 159)
   Population . . . . . . . . . . . . . . . . . . . . . . . . . . . . . . . . . . . . . . . . . . . .306,000

**Spending**
   Military Expenditures . . . . . . . . . . . . . . . . . . . . . . . . . . . . . . .$3.1 million
   Gross National Product . . . . . . . . . . . . . . . . . . . . . . . . . . . . . .$350 million
   Military Expenditure as a Percentage of
      Gross National Product . . . . . . . . . . . . . . . . . . . . . . . . . . . . . . .0.8%
   Military Expenditure as a Percentage of
      Central Government Expenditure . . . . . . . . . . . . . . . . . . . . . . . . .4.5%

**Defense Treaties** *(See Part II for Additional Detail)*

   Bilateral:    France

   Multilateral:   League of Arab States
                Organization of African Unity

# DOMINICA
## Commonwealth of Dominica

### Defence Establishment Command Structure
### and Force Organization

The Police are responsible for internal security. External security is the responsibility of the United Kingdom.

**Police:** 500–1,000.

## HEAD OF STATE

H. M. Queen Elizabeth II

**OFFICE OF THE PRESIDENT**
*Roseau*
*Telephone:   445-2054, 455-2064*

President . . . . . . . . . . . . . . . . . . . . . . . . . . . . . . . . . . . . . . . H. E. Aurelius Marie

**OFFICE OF THE PRIME MINISTER**
*Roseau*
*Telephone:   (445) 2171*
*Telex:   613 ext do*
*Cable:   EXTERNAL DOMINICA*

Prime Minister and Minister of
    Finance and Foreign Affairs . . . . . . . . . . . . . Ms. Eugenia Charles, L.L.B.

## DEFENCE FORCES

**POLICE**
*Police Headquarters*
*Barth Road*
*Telephone:   (445) 2222, 2221*

Commissioner of Police . . . . . . . . . . . . . . . . . . . . . . . . . . . . . . . . O.N. Philips

\* \* \* \* \*

## GENERAL DEFENCE DATA

**Manpower**
    Total Armed Forces. . . . . . . . . . . . . . . . . . . . . . . . . . . . . . . . . . . . . . . . . . . 500–1,000
    Population . . . . . . . . . . . . . . . . . . . . . . . . . . . . . . . . . . . . . . . . . . . . . . . . 80,000

**Spending**
    Military Expenditures . . . . . . . . . . . . . . . . . . . . . . . . . . . . . . . . . . . . . . . . . .
    Gross National Product . . . . . . . . . . . . . . . . . . . . . . . . . . . . . . . . . . . . . . . . $35 million
    Military Expenditure as a Percentage of
        Gross National Product . . . . . . . . . . . . . . . . . . . . . . . . . . . . . . . . . . . . . . . .
    Military Expenditure as a Percentage of
        Central Government Expenditure . . . . . . . . . . . . . . . . . . . . . . . . . . . . . . .

**Defence Treaties** *(See Part II for Additional Detail)*

    Bilateral:      United States

    Multilateral:   Regional Security System
                    Treaty on the Control of Arms on the Seabed

# DOMINICAN REPUBLIC

*República Dominicana*

## Defense Establishment Command Structure and Force Organization

The President is Supreme Chief of the Armed Forces. He appoints the Secretary of State for the Armed Forces, who handles defense policy-making and supervision. Administration is the primary responsibility of the three service Chiefs of Staff. The National Police, a para-military force, is under the control of the Secretary of State for the Interior and Police, but the Director-General of this body is an army officer.

**Total armed forces:** 24,500 (Army: 14,000;  Navy: 4,500;  Air Force: 6,000). **Para-military forces:** 10,000 (National Police).

## HEAD OF STATE

H. E. Silvestre Antonio Guzman Fernández

**OFFICE OF THE PRESIDENT**
*(Oficina de la Presidencia)*
*Palacio Nacional*
*Calle Moises Garcia*
*Santo Domingo*

*Telephone:  689-1131, 687-7495,*
*Telex:  RCA (326) 4299 secpre dr,*
*         RCA (326) 4499, ACR/ITT*
*         OO11 secpres*

President of the Republic and Supreme Chief
of the Armed Forces ......................Dr. Salvador Jorge Blanco
Administrative Secretary of the Presidency......Lic. José María Hernández
Administrative Under Secretary
of the Presidency ......................Dr. Ramón Martínez Aponte

**OFFICE OF THE VICE PRESIDENT**
*(Oficían de la Vice Presidencia)*
*Palacio Nacional*
*Calle Moises García*
*Santo Domingo*

*Telephone:  689-1131, 687-7495*
*Telex:  RCA (326) 4299 secpre dr,*
*         RCA (326) 4499, ACR/ITT*
*         0011 secpres*

Vice President .............................................(Vacant)

**MINISTRY OF INTERIOR AND POLICE**
*(Ministério de Gobernación y Policía)*
*(in charge of National Police)*
*Centro de los Heroes*
*Santo Domingo*

*Telephone:  533-2186, 533-1716,*
*            533-7202*

Secretary of State ..............................Prof. Guillermo Rivera
Under Secretary of State ...........................Gral. Brig. Benito
Under Secretary of State ...............................Juan Jiménez
Under Secretary of State .........................Monción Leonardo

# DEFENSE FORCES

**ARMED FORCES**
*(Las Fuerzas Armadas Dominicana)*
*Plaza de la Independencia*
*Avenida 27 de Febrero*
*Santo Domingo*
*Telephone:   533-5131, 533-0055,*
*532-3046*

Secretary of State, Armed Forces, and
  Chief of General Staff . . . . . . . . . . . . . Tte. Gral. Ramíro Matos González

**ARMY**
*(Ejército Nacional)*
*Plaza de la Independencia*
*Avenida 27 de Febrero*
*Santo Domingo*
*Telephone:   533-5131, 533-0055, 532-3046*

Chief of Staff . . . . . . . . . . . . . . . . . . . . . . . Tte. Manuel A. Lachapelle Suero
Deputy Chief of Staff . . . . . . . . . . . . . . . . . . . . Gral. Brig. Ernesto Cruz Brea

**NAVY**
*(Marina de Guerra)*
*Base Naval 27 de Febrero*
*Villa Duarte*
*Santo Domingo*
*Telephone:   682-2946, 688-8395, 688-7333*
*Telex:   ACR/ITT (346) 0521*

Chief of Staff . . . . . . . . . . . . . . . . . . . . . . Vice Alm. Arturo Borda Betances
Deputy Chief of Staff . . . . . . . . . . . . . Contra. Alm. Manuel Montes Arache
Under Secretary of State . . . . . . . . Contra. Alm. Nestor Julio González Diaz

**AIR FORCE**
*(La Fuerza Aérea Dominicana)*
*Base Aéreo de San Isidro*
*San Isidro*
*Santo Domingo*
*Telephone:   594-0770/3481, 533-0055,*
*532-3046*

Chief of Staff . . . . . . . . . . . . . . . . . . May. Gral. Fernando E. Cruz Mendez
Deputy Chief of Staff . . . . . . . . . . . . Gral. Brig. Luis José Martínez Cabrera
Under Secretary of State . . . . . . . . . . . . . May. Gral. Pablo Garrldo Medicine

**NATIONAL POLICE**
*(Policía Nacional)*
*Telephone:   682-2151*
*(Under the Minister of Interior*
*and Police)*

Chief . . . . . . . . . . . . . . . . . . . . . . . . . . . . . . May. Gral. José Feliz Hermida
Chief, Secret Service . . . . . . . . . . . . . . Brig. Gral. Manuel Imbert Sánchez

\* \* \* \* \*

# GENERAL DEFENSE DATA

**Manpower**
  Total Armed Forces . . . . . . . . . . . . . . . . . . . . . . . . . . . . . . . . . . . . . . . . . 24,500
    (See Page 163)
  Population . . . . . . . . . . . . . . . . . . . . . . . . . . . . . . . . . . . . . . . . . . . . . . . 6,013,000

**Spending**
  Military Expenditures . . . . . . . . . . . . . . . . . . . . . . . . . . . . . . . . . . . . . . $95 million
  Gross National Product . . . . . . . . . . . . . . . . . . . . . . . . . . . . . . . . . . . . . $6.1 billion
  Military Expenditure as a Percentage of
    Gross National Product . . . . . . . . . . . . . . . . . . . . . . . . . . . . . . . . . . . . 1.5%
  Military Expenditure as a Percentage of
    Central Government Expenditure . . . . . . . . . . . . . . . . . . . . . . . . . . . . . . 9.1%

**Defense Treaties** *(See Part II for Additional Detail)*

Bilateral:  United States

Multilateral: Act of Chapultepec
      Biological Weapons Convention
      Inter-American Defense Board
      Inter-American Treaty of Reciprocal Assistance
      Limited Test Ban Treaty
      Treaty on the Control of Arms on the Seabed
      Treaty on the Non-Proliferation of Nuclear Weapons
      Treaty for the Prohibition of Nuclear Weapons in Latin
       America

# ECUADOR
## Republic of Ecuador
### *República del Ecuador*

### Defense Establishment Command Structure
### and Force Organization

The President of the Republic, as Commander-in-Chief, has responsibility for all defense matters. Both the National Security Council and the Joint Chiefs of Staff of the Armed Forces provide guidance and advice to the President on military issues. Internal security is the responsibility of the National Civil Police, which is under the direction of the Ministry of Government.

**Total armed forces:** 38,000 (Army: 30,000;   Navy: 4,000;   Air Force: 4,000). **Para-military forces:** 5,800.

## HEAD OF STATE

H. E. Dr. Osvaldo Hurtado Larrea

**OFFICE OF THE PRESIDENT**
*(Oficina del Presidencia)*
*Palacio Nacional*
*Garcia Moreno 1043*
*Quito*

*Telephone:   (2) 211300, 216300*
*Telex:   2 23751, 2 2351 prerep ed,*
*2 2354 mingeb ed*
*(Ministério de Gobierno)*

President of the Republic and
Commander-in-Chief . . . . . . . . . . . . . . . . . . . .Dr. Osvaldo Hurtado Larrea

**National Security Council**
*(Consejo de Seguridad Nacional)*

Chairman . . . . . . . . . . . . . . . . . . . . . . . . . . . . . . . . . . .Gral. Luis Pineiros

**MINISTRY OF NATIONAL DEFENSE**
*(Ministério de Defensa Nacional)*
*Exposición N 208*
*Quito*

*Telephone:   (2) 216150, 216160*
*Telex:   2 2703*

Minister . . . . . . . . . . . . . . . . . . . . .May. Gral. (Ret.) Jorge Maldonado Mino
Under-Secretary . . . . . . . . . . . . . . . .Gral. Div. Edmundo Vivero Burbano
Director, Department of Public Relations . . . . . .May. Gral. Eugenio Ortega

## DEFENSE FORCES

**ARMED FORCES**
*(Las Fuerzas Armadas Ecuatorianas)*
*c/o Ministry of National Defense*
*Exposición No. 208*
*Quito*

*Telephone:   (2) 21 80 49*
*Telex:   2 2381 cc ffaa ed*
*(Comando Conjunto de las Fuerzas*
*Armadas)*

Commander-in-Chief and President
of the Republic . . . . . . . . . . . . . . . . . . . . . . . .Dr. Osvaldo Hurtado Larrea

**Joint Chiefs of Staff of the Armed Services**
*(Estado Mayor Conjunto de los Servicios Armadas)*
Telephone: 21 80 49

| | |
|---|---|
| Chief of Staff | Tte. Gral. Jorge Arceniegas Salazar |
| Commander, Navy | Vice Alm. Mário Jaramillo de Castillo |
| Commander, Air Force | Tte. Gral. Héctor Vasconez López |
| Commander, Army | Tte. Gral. Jorge Arceniegas Salazar |
| Chief of Staff, Joint Command | Gral. Grivaldo Niño Tapia |

**ARMY**
*(Ejército)*
c/o Ministry of National Defense
Exposición N 208
Quito
Telephone: (2) 510902
Telex: 2 2703

| | |
|---|---|
| Chief of Staff | Tte. Gral. Jorge Arceniegas |
| Deputy Chief of Staff | Tte. Gral. René Vargas |

**Infantry Brigades**

| | |
|---|---|
| Commander, Chinche | Brig. Gral. Félix Mena |
| Commander, Guayas | Gral. Jorge Borbua Bohorquez |
| Commander, Porteche | Cdte. Ericson Garzón |

**NAVY**
*(Armada del Ecuador)*
c/o Ministry of National Defense
Exposición N 208
Quito
Telephone: (2) 518 222
Telex: 2 2351 cgmarn ed

| | |
|---|---|
| Commander | Vice Alm. Mário Jaramillo del Castillo |
| Chief, Naval Operations | Vice Alm. Victor Hugo Garces |
| Director, Communications | |
| Inspector General | Vice Alm. Santiago Coral |
| Chief, Public Relations | Cap. Yeziv Jaramillo |
| Chief, Financial Administration | Contra Alm. Marco Villalba |
| Director, Maritime Development | Contra Alm. Aníbal Carrillo |
| Director, Technical Personnel | Contra Alm. Ramón Apolo |
| Commander, Zone 1 | Vice Alm. Mário Jaramillo del Castillo |
| Commander, Zone 2 | Cap. Francisco Bita Kabbes |
| Commander, Zone 3 | Contra Alm. Aníbal Carrio Baez |

**General Staff of the Navy**
*(Estado Mayor General de la Marina Ecuatoriana)*
Exposición N 208
Quito
Telephone: 51888

| | |
|---|---|
| Chief of Staff | Vice Alm. Carlos Flores |

**Coast Guard**
*(Guardacostas)*
c/o Ministry of National Defense
Exposición N 208
Quito
Telephone: (2) 518888, 514563
(Inspector General)

| | |
|---|---|
| Chief of Staff | Contra Alm. Jorge Guerirolo |
| Inspector General | Contra Alm. Fausto Cevallos |

**AIR FORCE**
*(Fuerza Aérea Ecuatoriana)*
c/o Ministry of National Defense
Casilla 3143
Quito
Telephone: (2) 210080/213602
Telex: 2 2706

| | |
|---|---|
| Commander | Tte. Gral. Héctor Bolivar Vasconez Lopez |
| Deputy Commander | Tte. Gral. Bolivar Mora Ventamilla |
| Chief, Public Relations | Cnel. Mário Pérez |
| Director, Civil Aviation | Brig. Gral. Armando Duran |
| Director, Operations & Planning Department | Brig. Gral. Jorge Andrade |
| Chief, Materials Group | Brig. Gral. Raúl López |
| Commander, First Air Zone, Mariscal Sucre Air Base | Brig. Gral. Galo Paz Minio |
| Director General, Instruction, Mariscal Sucre Air Base | Brig. Gral. Fausto Sevilla |
| Director, Academy of Air Warfare | Cnel. Galo Bustos |
| Commander, Air Force Technical College | Cnel. Alfredo Chacón |

**NATIONAL CIVIL POLICE**
*(La Policía Nacional y Civil)*
*Mideros y Cuenca*
*Quito*

*Telephone:* *(2) 510212*
  *(Under Ministry of Government)*
*Telex:* *2 2311 dce ed*
     *(Dirección Nacional de Defensa*
       *Civil)*

Commander.......................................Gral. Jorge Castro

\* \* \* \* \*

## GENERAL DEFENSE DATA

**Manpower**
  Total Armed Forces.............................................38,000
    (See Page 167)
  Population ...............................................8,537,000

**Spending**
  Military Expenditures .......................................$185 million
  Gross National Product......................................$10.2 billion
  Military Expenditure as a Percentage of
    Gross National Product ........................................1.8%
  Military Expenditure as a Percentage of
    Central Government Expenditure ...............................10.2%

**Defense Treaties** *(See Part II for Additional Detail)*

     Bilateral:     Italy

     Multilateral:  Act of Chapultepec
                    Biological Weapons Convention
                    Inter-American Defense Board
                    Inter-American Treaty of Reciprocal Assistance
                    Limited Test Ban Treaty
                    Treaty of Tlatelolco
                    Treaty on the Non-Proliferation of Nuclear Weapons

# EGYPT

## Arab Republic of Egypt

*Jumhuriyat Misr al-Arabiyah*

### Defence Establishment Command Structure and Force Organization

The President is Supreme Commander of the Egyptian Armed Forces. He presides over the National Defence Council, the highest-level defence policy-making body. Overall readiness and administration of the military establishment is the responsibility of the Commander of the Armed Forces. The Chief of Staff of the Army is also Deputy Commander of the Armed Forces and plays a primary role in wartime operations. The separate Air Defense Command incorporates the Army and Air Force units connected with air defence. It is commanded by the Assistant Minister for Air Defence.

**Total armed forces:** 452,000 (Army: 320,000; Navy: 20,000; Air Force: 27,000; Air Defense Command: 85,000). **Para-military forces:** 278,000.

### HEAD OF STATE

H. E. Mohamed Husni Mubarak

**OFFICE OF THE PRESIDENT**
*Oruba Palace*
*Oruba St. Heliopolis*
*Cairo*
*Telephone: 830788*
*Telex: 331 psi un (Exterior Communications), 92148 psi un (Secretariat for Information)*

President of the Republic and
  Supreme Commander, Egyptian
  Armed Forces..........................Mohamed Husni Mubarak
Assistant.........................................Eng. Sayed Marei
Assistant .........................................Mamdouh Salem
Minister of State for the Presidency .................Hassan Al-Tohamy
Director of Office for Foreign Affairs......................Osama El Bas

**National Defence Council**

Chairman ..............................Mohamad Husni Mubarak
  (President and Supreme Commander)
Member *(ex officio)* ....................................Field Marshal
  Mohamad Abd al-Halim Abu-Ghazala
  (Minister of Defence)
Member *(ex officio)* .............Maj. Gen. Gamal al-Din al-Said Ibrahim
  (Minister of State for War Production)
Member *(ex officio)* ...........................Gen. Kamal Hasan Ali
  (Minister of Foreign Affairs)
Member *(ex officio)* .....................Hassan Sulayman Abu Basha
  (Minister of Interior)
Member *(ex officio)* ...........................Mustafa Kamal al-Said
  (Minister of Economy and Foreign Trade)
Member *(ex officio)* .........................Maj. Gen. Nabil Shoukry
  (Commander-in-Chief)
Member *(ex officio)* .......................Gen. Mahmoud Abdullah
  (Director, Intelligence)
Member *(ex officio)* .................Maj. Gen. Abd Rab al-Nabi Hafez
  (Army Chief of Staff)
Member *(ex officio)* ...................Vice Adm. Anwar Kinawi Higzi
  (Navy Chief of Staff)
Member *(ex officio)* .......................Maj. Gen. Ali al-Mutawwa
  (Air Force Chief of Staff)
Member *(ex officio)* .............................Gen. Sayed Hamdy
  (Assistant Minister, Air Defence)

**OFFICE OF THE VICE PRESIDENT**
*Al Gomhouria Square*
*Cairo*
*Telephone:   910288, 910914, 910438, 910042*

Vice President . . . . . . . . . . . . . . . . . . . . . . . . . . . . . . . . . . . . . . . . . .(Vacant)

**OFFICE OF THE PRIME MINISTER**
*Magles Al Shaab Street*
*Cairo*
*Telephone:   26457, 27370*
*Telex:   93794 wazra un*

Prime Minister . . . . . . . . . . . . . . . . . . . . . . . . .Dr. Ahmed Fuad Muhi al-Din
Deputy Prime Minister. . . . . . . . . . . . . . . . . . . . .Gen. Kamal Hasan Ali
Deputy Prime Minister . . . . . . . . . . . . . . . . . . . . . . . . . . . . .Field Marshal
                           Mohamad Abd al-Halim Abu-Ghazala
Deputy Prime Minister, Production . . . . . . . . . . . . .Ahmad Izz al-Din Hilal
Deputy Prime Minister, Public Services . . . . . . . . . . .Mustafa Kamal Hilmi

**MINISTRY OF DEFENCE AND**
   **MILITARY PRODUCTION**
*Kobry Al Kobba*
*23 July Street*
*Cairo*
*Telephone:   833377, 837133*

Minister and Deputy Premier . . . . . . . . . . . . . . . . . . . . . . . . . .Field Marshal
                           Mohamad Abd al-Halim Abu Ghazala
Minister of State
   for War Production . . . . . . . . .Maj. Gen. Gamal al-Din al-Sayyid Ibrahim
Assistant Minister, Air Defence . . . . . . . . . . . . . . . . . . . .Gen. Sayed Hamdy
Assistant Minister, Technology
   Affairs and Procurement . . . . . . . . . . . . . . . .Maj. Gen. Mustafa Sadek
Military Research Office . . . . . . . . . . . . . . . . . . . . .Gen. Samir Yosri Awad
Director of Military Housing
   and Construction . . . . . . . . . . . . . . . . . . . .Gen. Hosni Mohamed Wahba
Director of Military Education and
   Civil Defense . . . . . . . . . . . . . . . . . . . . . . . . . . . .Maj. Gen. Fahim Shadid
Director of Military Intelligence . . . . . . . . . . . . . . .Gen. Mahmoud Abdullah
Director of the Institute of
   Military Research . . . . . . . . . . . . . . . . . . . . . . . . .Gen. Samir Yosri Sedki
Director of Military Justice . . . . . . . . . . . . . . . . . . . . . . . .Gen. Samir Fadel
Director of Irrigation . . . . . . . . . . . . . . . . . . . . . . . . . .Gen. Fouad Mohamed

## DEFENCE FORCES

**ARMED FORCES**
*Kobry Al Kobba*
*23rd July Street*
*Cairo*
*Telephone:   836822, 879810*

Supreme Commander . . . . . . . . . . . . . . . . . . . . .Mohamad Hosni Mubarak
Commander, Egyptian
   Armed Forces  . . . . .Field Marshal Mohamad Abdal-Halim Abu-Ghazala
Deputy Commander and
   Army Chief of Staff . . . . . . . . . . . .Gen. Ibrahim Abdel Ghafour El Orabi

**ARMY**
**Egyptian Army**
*Kobry Al Kobba*
*23rd July Street*
*Cairo*
*Telephone:   836822, 879810*

Chief of Staff . . . . . . . . . . . . . . . . . . .Gen. Ibrahim Abdel Ghafour El Orabi
Chief of Operations. . . . . . . . .Gen. Ahmed Salah Ad-Din Abd al-Halim Saad
Deputy Chief of Operations . . . . . . . . . . .Brig. Gen. Mohamed Alaa Barakat
Chief of Staff, Infantry . . . . . . . . . . . . . . . . . . . .Gen. Adel Sulliman Daoud
Chief of Staff, Commandos . . . . . . . . . . . . . . . . . . . . .Cdr. Hassan Al Zayate
Commander, Western Military Region . . . . . . . .Gen. El Sayed Ahmad Nasr
Chief of General Staff, Western
   Military Region . . . . . . . . . . . . . . . . . . . .Gen. Mohamed Nogati Ibrahim
Commander, Northern
   Military Region . . . . . . . . . . . . . .Gen. Kamal Eddine Mahmoud Hanafi
Chief, Army Intelligence . . . . . . . . . . . . . . . . . . . . . . . . . . . . .Gen. Shorrab
Deputy Chief  . . . . . . . . . . . . . . . . . . . . . . . . . . .Maj. Gen. Nabih Youssef
Chief, Repairs and Engineering. . . . . . . . . . . . . . . .Brig. Gen. George Ezzat
Chief, Materials and Construction . . . . . . . . . . . . . .Gen. Ahmad Lutfi Zaha
Commander, Engineering Corps . . . . . . . .Gen. Moshen Abdul Fattah Sedki
Commander, Signal Corps . . . . . . . . . . . . . . . . . .Gen. Ibrahim Fayez Sabri
Commander, Republican Guard . . . . . . . . . . . . . . . . . . . . . . .Gen. El Masri
Commander, Artillery . . . . . . . . . . . . . . . . . . . . . . . .Gen. Mouniv Chach

**NAVY**
**Egyptian Navy**
*Kobry Al Kobba*
*23rd July Street*
*Cairo*
*Telephone: 836822, 879810*

Commander......................................Vice Adm. Ali Gad
Deputy Commander and
   Chief of Staff ......................Vice Adm. Anwar Kinawi Higazi

**AIR FORCE**
**Egyptian Air Force**
*Kobry Al Kobba*
*23rd July Street*
*Cairo*
*Telephone: 836822, 879810*

Commander ..............Air Marshall Mohamad Abd al-Hamid Hilmy
Deputy Commander and Chief of Staff........Maj. Gen. Ali al-Mutawwey
Chief, Administration ................................................
Chief, Operations .................................................
Chief, Training ........................................Gen. Ali Ziko
Commander, Advanced Studies .............Gen. Abdel Monen Al Tawil
Chief, Engineering ................................................
Chief, Supply ....................................................
Commander, Fayid Air Base ....................Brig. Gen. Abdel Nasr
Commander, Heliopolis Air Defence
   Brigade ................................Col. Abdul Monsour
Mirage Wing Commander..........................Col. Ahmad Shafik
Chief of Staff, 222nd Tactical Fighter Wing...........Lt. Col. Sakr Reda
Deputy Commander ...........................Lt. Col. Ahmed Atef

**AIR DEFENCE COMMAND**
*Cairo*

Commander ...................................Gen. Sayed Hamdy
Chief of Staff ............................Maj. Gen. Magdi Suleiman

\* \* \* \* \*

## GENERAL DEFENCE DATA

**Manpower**
   Total Armed Forces..............................................452,000
     (See Page 171)
   Population ...................................................44,740,000

**Spending**
   Military Expenditures...........................................$1.3 billion
   Gross National Product.........................................$22.6 billion
   Military Expenditure as a Percentage of
     Gross National Product .............................................6.0%
   Military Expenditure as a Percentage of
     Central Government Expenditure ...............................16.4%

**Defense Treaties** *(See Part II for Additional Detail)*

Bilateral:
| | |
|---|---|
| China | Sudan |
| France | United States |
| Israel | Zaire |
| Soviet Union | |

Multilateral:   Environmental Modification Convention
     League of Arab States (Suspended)
     Limited Test Ban Treaty
     Organization of African Unity
     Treaty on the Non-Proliferation of Nuclear Weapons

# EL SALVADOR
## Republic of El Salvador
### *República de El Salvador*

## Defense Establishment Command Structure
## and Force Organization

The President exercises his authority as Commander-in-Chief through the Minister of Defense, whom he appoints. The Chief of the General Staff has operational control over the three services as well as the National Guard, National Police, and Treasury Police.

El Salvador is divided into three military defense zones. The Minister of National Defense appoints the civilian departmental commanders, who serve in a military capacity.

**Total armed forces:** 23,000 (Army: 22,400;   Navy: 300;   Air Force: 300). **Para-military forces:** 8,500 (National Guard: 3,300;   National Police: 3,500;   Treasury Police: 1,700).

## HEAD OF STATE

Dr. Alvaro A. Magaña

**OFFICE OF THE PRESIDENCY**
*(Oficina de la Presidencia)*
*Casa Presidencial*
*San Salvador*

*Telephone:   241172 218280*
*Telex:   30344 re sal*

| | |
|---|---|
| President and Commander-in-Chief | Dr. Ávaro A. Magaña |
| First Vice President | Raúl Molina |
| Second Vice President | Dr. Mauricio Gutiérrez Castro |
| Third Vice President | Dr. Pablo Mauricio Alverque |

**MINISTRY OF THE PRESIDENCY**
*(Ministério de la Presidencia)*
*Casa Presidencial*
*San Salvador*

*Telephone:   241172, 218280*
*Telex:   30344 rs sal*

| | |
|---|---|
| Minister of the Presidency | Dr. Francisco José Guerrero |
| Personal Secretary of the Presidency | Dr. Roberto Suarez Suay |
| Secretary of Information of the Presidency | Luis Lagos |
| Chief of Presidential Staff | Cnel. Edmundo Palacios |

**MINISTRY OF DEFENSE AND
  PUBLIC SECURITY**
*(Ministério de Defensa
  y de Sequridad Pública)*
*Palacio Nacional*
*San Salvador*

*Telephone:   220233, 214944*
*Telex:   218228, 30345 depf sal*

| | |
|---|---|
| Minister | Gral. Carlos Eugenio Vides Casanova |
| Vice Minister | Cnel. Rafael Flores Lima |
| Chief, Finance Department | Cnel. Jorge Alberto Rivera |
| Chief, Public Relations Department | Cnel. Marco Aurelio González |
| Chief, Logistics Department | Cnel. Joaquím Molina Barrera |

## DEFENSE FORCES

**ARMED FORCES**
**General Staff of the Armed Forces**
*(Estado Mayor General de las Fuerzas
  Armadas)*
*Km. 5 Carretera a Santa Tecla*
*Telephone:   23794, 237382*

| | |
|---|---|
| Chief of the General Staff | Cnel. Alberto Reyes Meña |
| Personal Secretary | May. Aviles |
| Deputy Chief | (Vacant) |

**Center of Studies of the Armed Forces**
*(Centro de Estudios de las Fuerzas
    Armadas)*
*Doble Via a Santa Tecla*
*San Salvador*
*Telephone:   23794, 237382*

Director . . . . . . . . . . . . . . . . . . . . . . . .Cnel. Oscar Edgardo Casanova Vejar

**Armed Forces Supply Office**
*(Intendencia de las Fuerzas
    Armadas)*
*Pasaje Merazo*
*Telephone:   257249, 257252*

Chief . . . . . . . . . . . . . . . . . . . . . . . . . . . .Cnel. Daniel Bustamante Caballero

**ARMY**
*(Ejército Nacional)*
*Km. 5, Carret. a Santa Tecla*
*Departamento de la Libertad*
*San Salvador*
*Telephone:   237166*

Chief of Staff of Army and Security
    Forces . . . . . . . . . . . . . . . . . . . . . . . . . . . . . . . . .Cnel. Alberto Reyes Meña
Deputy Chief . . . . . . . . . . . . . . . . . . . . . . . . .Cnel. Rafael Flores Lima
Commander, 1st Brigade . . . . . . . . . . . . . . . . . . . . . .Cnel. Adolfo Blandon
Commander, 2nd Brigade . . . . . . . . . .Cnel. Oscar Edgardo Casanova Vejar
Commander, 3rd Brigade . . . . . . . . . . . . . . . . . . . . . . . . . . . . . . . . . . . . . .
Commander, 4th Brigade  . . . . . . . . . . . . .Cnel. Mário António Morales Ruiz
Commander, 5th Brigade  . . . . . . . . . . . . . . . . . .Cnel. Dionicio Hernández

**NAVY**
*(Marina Nacional)*
*c/o Ministry of Defense*
*San Salvador*
*Telephone:   223234, 222999, 225056*

Commander . . . . . . . . . . . . . . . . .Cnel. Roberto de Jesús Monterrosa Bonilla

**AIR FORCE**
*(Fuerza Aérea)*
*Ilopango, Casset, Panamericana*
*San Salvador*
*Telephone:   272015*
*Telex:   20347 fas*

Chief . . . . . . . . . . . . . . . . . . . . . . . . . . . . . . . . . . .Cnel. Juan Rafael Bustillo
Deputy Chief and Commander,
    Ilopango Air Base . . . . . . . . . . . . . . . . . . . . . . . . . . . . .Cnel.Saúl Zelaya

**NATIONAL POLICE**
*(Policia Nacional)*
*San Salvador*
*Telephone:   224422 (ext. 14)*

Chief . . . . . . . . . . . . . . . . . . . . . . . .Cnel. y Dr. Carlos Reynaldo Lopez Nuila

**TREASURY POLICE**
*(Policia de Hacienda)*
*San Salvador*

Chief . . . . . . . . . . . . . . . . . . . . . . . . . . . . . . . . . . . . .Cnel. Nicolas Carranza

**NATIONAL GUARD**
*(Guardia Nacional)*
*San Salvador*

Chief . . . . . . . . . . . . . . . . . . . . . . . . . . . . . . . . . . . . . . . . . . . . . .(Vacant)

\* \* \* \* \*

# GENERAL DEFENSE DATA

**Manpower**
    Total Armed Forces . . . . . . . . . . . . . . . . . . . . . . . . . . . . . . . . . . . . . . . . . . .23,000
        (See Page 175)
        Population  . . . . . . . . . . . . . . . . . . . . . . . . . . . . . . . . . . . . . . . . . . . .4,617,000

**Spending**
Military Expenditures . . . . . . . . . . . . . . . . . . . . . . . . . . . . . . . . . . . . . . . . $85 million
Gross National Product . . . . . . . . . . . . . . . . . . . . . . . . . . . . . . . . . . . . . . $3.3 billion
Military Expenditure as a Percentage of
   Gross National Product . . . . . . . . . . . . . . . . . . . . . . . . . . . . . . . . . . . .2.5%
Military Expenditure as a Percentage of
   Central Government Expenditure . . . . . . . . . . . . . . . . . . . . . . . . . . . . .13.7%

**Defense Treaties** *(See Part II for Additional Detail))*

Bilateral:       United States

Multilateral:    Central-American Democratic Community
                 Council for Central-American Defense
                 *El Salvador—Guatemala—Honduras*: Informal Agreement
                    (1981)
                 Inter-American Defense Board
                 Inter-American Treaty of Reciprocal Assistance
                 Limited Test Ban Treaty
                 Treaty on the Non-Proliferation of Nuclear Weapons
                 Treaty for the Prohibition of Nuclear Weapons in Latin
                    America

**Military Rank Comparisons**
See Appendix A.

# EQUATORIAL GUINEA
## Republic of Equatorial Guinea
*Repúblic de Guinea Ecuatorial*

### Defense Establishment Command Structure and Force Organization

The President of the Supreme Military Council is Minister of Defense and Commander-in-Chief of the armed forces of Equatorial Guinea.

**Total armed forces:** 1,550 (Army: 1,400; Navy: 100; Air Force: 50). **Para-military forces:** 2,000 (Police).

### HEAD OF STATE

H. E. Col. Teodoro Obaing Nguema Mbasogo

**OFFICE OF THE PRESIDENT**
*Malabo*

President of the Supreme
    Military Council . . . . . . . . . . . . . .Col. Teodoro Obaing Nguema Mbasogo
First Vice President and Member
    of the Supreme Military Council . . . . . . . . . . . . . . . . . . . . . . . . . .(Vacant)
Second Vice President and Member
    of the Supreme Military Council . . . . . . . . .Capt. Christino Seriche Bioko
Chief, Presidential Security . . . . . . . . . . . . . . . . . . . . . .A. Ondo Nguema
Technical Director, Military Cabinet . . . . . . . . . . .Lt. Antonio Mba Nguema

**MINISTRY OF NATIONAL DEFENSE**
*Malabo*

President of the Supreme Military Council
    and Minister of Defense . . . . . . . .Col. Teodoro Obiang Nguema Mbasogo

**MINISTRY OF THE INTERIOR**
*Malabo*

Minister . . . . . . . . . . . . . . . . . . . . . . . . . . . . . . . .Lt. Felipe Oyono Manyana

### DEFENSE FORCES

**ARMED FORCES**
**National Guard**
*(Guardia Nacional)*
*Malabo*

Commander . . . . . . . . . . . . . . . . . . . .Col. Teodoro Obiang Nguema Mbasogo
Inspector-General of the
    Armed Forces . . . . . . . . . . . . . . .Lt. Col. Fructuoso Mba Onana Nchama
Chief of General Staff . . . . . . . . . . . . . . . . . . .Capt. Melanio Ebendeng Nsomo
Technical Secretary . . . . . . . . . . . . . . . . . . . . . . .Capt. Melchor Ndong Mba
Deputy Technical Secretary . . . . . . . . . . . . . . . . .Capt. Francisco Ngua Edu
Director of Security . . . . . . . . . . . . . . . . .2nd Lt. Isidoro Eyi Mesuy Andeme
Military Commander (Rio Muni) . . . . . . . . . . . . . . . . .Capt. Jose Moro Mba

**Police**
*Malabo*

Senior Police Commissioner (Bioko) . . . . . . . . . .Insp. Reginaldo Chicampo
Senior Police Commissioner (Rio Muni) . . . . . .Insp. Anacleto Ejapa Bolekia

\* \* \* \* \*

## GENERAL DEFENSE DATA

**Manpower**
Total Armed Forces . . . . . . . . . . . . . . . . . . . . . . . . . . . . . . . . . . . . . . . . . . . . . . . 1,550
    (See Page 179)
Population . . . . . . . . . . . . . . . . . . . . . . . . . . . . . . . . . . . . . . . . . . . . . . . . . . . . 260,000

**Spending**
Military Expenditures . . . . . . . . . . . . . . . . . . . . . . . . . . . . . . . . . . . . . . . . . $2.5 million
Gross National Product . . . . . . . . . . . . . . . . . . . . . . . . . . . . . . . . . . . . . . . . . $100 million
Military Expenditure as a Percentage of
    Gross National Product . . . . . . . . . . . . . . . . . . . . . . . . . . . . . . . . . . . . . . . . 2.5%
Military Expenditure as a Percentage of
    Central Government Expenditure . . . . . . . . . . . . . . . . . . . . . . . . . . . . . . . . . . . . . . .

**Defense Treaties** *(See Part II for Additional Detail)*

Bilateral:      China

Multilateral:   Organization of African Unity

# ETHIOPIA

## Defense Establishment Command Structure
## and Force Organization

The Chairman of the Provisional Military Administrative Council (the Derg) is Commander-in-Chief of the armed forces. The Minister of Defense is responsible for administrative matters relating to the military.

**Total armed forces:** 250,500 (Army: 244,500;  Navy: 2,500;  Air Force: 3,500). **Paramilitary forces:** 169,000 (Police force: 9,000;  People's Militia: 150,000;  People's Protection Brigades: 10,000).

## HEAD OF STATE

Lt. Col. Mengista Haile Mariam

**OFFICE OF THE CHAIRMAN**
*P.O. Box 1013*
*Addis Ababa*
*Telephone: 12 34 00*

Chairman of the Provisional Military Administrative Council (PMAC), Chairman of the Commission for Organizing the Party of the Working People of Ethiopia (COPWE), and Commander-in-Chief of the Revolutionary Army . . . . . . . . . . . . . Lt. Col. Mengista Haile Mariam
Deputy Chairman . . . . . . . . . . . . . . . . . . . . . . . . . . . . . . Lt. Col. Fisseha Desta
Senior Minister . . . . . . . . . . . . . . . . . . . . . . . . . . . . . . . . Hailu Yemanu
Deputy Senior Minister . . . . . . . . . . . . . . . . . . . . . . . . Amanuel Amde Mikael
Chief Political Adviser . . . . . . . . . . . . . . . . . . . . . . . . . . . . . . Imru Mikael

**OFFICE OF THE SECRETARY-GENERAL AND ASSISTANT SECRETARY-GENERAL**
*P.O. Box 5707*
*Addis Ababa*
*Telephone:   11 30 00*

Secretary-General . . . . . . . . . . . . . . . . . . . . Capt. Wodgeress Fikre-Selassie

**MINISTRY OF NATIONAL SECURITY**
*P.O. Box 125*
*Addis Ababa*
*Telephone:   15 57 36*

Minister . . . . . . . . . . . . . . . . . . . . . . . . . . . . . . . Col. Tesfaye Wolde Selassie
Permanent Secretary . . . . . . . . . . . . . . . . . . . . . . . . . . Moges Habte-Mariam

**MINISTRY OF NATIONAL DEFENSE**
*P.O. Box 125*
*Churchill Road*
*Addis Ababa*

*Telephone:   44 55 55*
*Telex:   21261 mond addis*

Minister . . . . . . . . . . . . . . . . . . . . . . . . . . . . . Lt. Gen. Tesfaye Gabre-Kidan
Deputy Minister . . . . . . . . . . . . . . . . Brig. Gen. Haile Giorgis Habte-Mariam
Deputy Minister . . . . . . . . . . . . . . . . . . . . . Brig. Gen. Abebe Wolde-Mariam

181

# DEFENSE FORCES

**ARMED FORCES**
*c/o Ministry of National Defense*
*P.O. Box 125*
*Addis Ababa*

*Telephone:    44 55 55*

Commander-in-Chief and Chairman
  of the Provisional Military
   Administrative Council................Lt. Col. Mengista Haile Mariam
Chief of Staff (Acting)............Brig. Gen. Haile Giorgis Habte-Mariam
Chief, Political Department (Army)......Brig. Gen. Gebreyes Wolde Hana

**ARMY**
*c/o Ministry of National Defense*
*P.O. Box 125*
*Addis Ababa*

*Telephone:    44 55 55*

Commander, Ground Forces .................Brig. Gen. Kefelegn Yibza
Commander, Southern Regions ..............Brig. Gen. Zewde Gebreyes
Commander, Mekit Forces...................Brig. Gen. Abdullah Umer
Adjunct Commander, Eastern Regions .....Brig. Gen. Getachew Gedamu
Adjunct Commander, Wukaw Force ...........Brig. Gen. Husein Ahmed
Chief of Staff, Asmara .......................Gen. Mesfin Guebrekal

**NAVY**
*Naval Headquarters*
*P.O. Box 1637*
*Addis Ababa*

*Telephone:    11 33 55*
*Telex:    21261 mond*

Commander ....................................Cdr. Tesfaye Berhanu
Deputy Commander ...............................Capt. Belege Belete
Deputy Commander .......................Capt. Makonnen Abraham
Deputy Commander ...............................Capt. Sirak Alemu
Deputy Commander ............................Capt. Mersha Girma
Deputy Commander ...........................Capt. Getachew Sium
Chief, Procurement Office ......................Cdr. Gebru Demssie
Commander, Military Training College ................Lt. Abebe Tefera

**AIR FORCE**
*c/o Ministry of National Defense*
*P.O. Box 125*
*Addis Ababa*

*Telephone:    44 55 55*

Commander....................................Brig. Gen. Fanta Belai

**POLICE FORCE**
*Addis Ababa*

Chief.............................Brig. Gen. Negussie Wolde Micheal

\* \* \* \* \*

# GENERAL DEFENCE DATA

**Manpower**
  Total Armed Forces.............................................250,500
    (See Page 181)
  Population ................................................30,569,000

**Spending**
  Military Expenditures .........................................$427 million
  Gross National Product .......................................$4.4 billion
  Military Expenditure as a Percentage of
    Gross National Product ....................................9.7%
  Military Expenditure as a Percentage of
    Central Government Expenditure ...............................42.6%

**Defence Treaties** *(See Part II for Additional Detail)*

    Bilateral:     Kenya
                Soviet Union
                United States
                People's Democratic Republic of Yemen

    Multilateral:   Aden Tripartite Alliance
                Biological Weapons Convention
                Organization of African Unity
                Treaty on the Control of Arms on the Seabed
                Treaty on the Non-Proliferation of Nuclear Weapons

# FIJI

## Defence Establishment Command Structure and Force Organization

The Prime Minister has responsibility for the armed forces of Fiji. His authority is exercised through the Commander of the Royal Fiji Military Forces.

**Total armed forces:** 2,051 (Army: 1,924;    Navy: 127). **Para-military forces:** 1,500 (Police).

## HEAD OF STATE

H. M. Queen Elizabeth II

## GOVERNOR-GENERAL

H. E. Ratu Sir George Cakabau

**OFFICE OF THE GOVERNOR-GENERAL**
*P.O. Box 119*
*Suva*
*Telephone:   22700, 22847, 22485*
*Telex:   2167 fosec fj*

Governor-General . . . . . . . . . . . . . . . . . . . . .H. E. Ratu Sir George Cakabau

**OFFICE OF THE PRIME MINISTER**
*Government Buildings*
*Victoria Parade*
*Suva*
*Telephone:   211201*
*Telex:   2167 fosec fj*

Prime Minister . . . . . . . . . . . . . . . . . . . . . .Rt. Hon. Ratu Sir Kamisese Mara

**MINISTRY FOR HOME AFFAIRS**
*Government Buildings*
*Victoria Parade*
*Suva*
*Telephone:   211401, 211210*
*Telex:   2342 homesec fj*
*Cable:   HOMEC FJ*

Minister for Home Affairs . . . . . . . . . . . . . .Ratu William Brown Toganivalu
Permanent Secretary . . . . . . . . . . . . . . . . . . . . . .Col. Mosese V. Buadromo
Principal Assistant Secretary . . . . . . . . . . . . . . . . . . . . . . . . . . . . . .I. S. Tulele

## DEFENCE FORCES

**ARMY**
**Royal Fiji Military Forces—RFMF**
*Headquarters*
*Queen Elisabeth Barracks*
*Maddocks Road*
*Nabua*
*Telephone:   22801*
*Telex:   2157*
*Cable:   HQRFMF FJ*

Commander, Royal Fiji Military Forces . . . . . . . . Col. Ratu Epeli Nailatikau
Chief of Staff of the Army . . . . . . . . . . . . . . . . . . . .Lt. Col. Sitiveni L. Rabuka
Commander, UNIFIL Contingent . . . . . . . . . . . . . . . .Illaisa Kacisolomani
Commander, MFO Contingent . . . . . . . . . . . . . . . .Lt. Col. Inosi Tawakedrav

**NAVY**
**Royal Fiji Military Force Navy Squadron**
*H.M.F.S. Viti*
*P.O. Box 102*
*Suva*

*Telephone:   313506*
*Telex:   2157*
*Cable:   HQRFMF*

Commander, RFMF Naval
    Squadron . . . . . . . . . . . . . . . . . . . . . . . . . . . . .Cdr. Stanley B. Brown, O.B.E.
Commander, Patrol Squadron . . . . . . . . . . . . . . . . . . . . . .Lt. Cdr. David Lane

**POLICE**
**Royal Fiji Police Force**
*MacArthur Street*
*Ratu Sukuna House*

*Telephone:   312999*

Commissioner of Police . . . . . . . . . . . . . . . . . . . . . . . . . . . . . . . . . .P. U. Raman
Deputy Commissioner . . . . . . . . . . . . . . . . . . . . . . . . . . . . . .M. K. Tuisawau

\* \* \* \* \*

# GENERAL DEFENCE DATA

**Manpower**
    Total Armed Forces . . . . . . . . . . . . . . . . . . . . . . . . . . . . . . . . . . . . . . .2,051
        (See Page 183)
    Population . . . . . . . . . . . . . . . . . . . . . . . . . . . . . . . . . . . . . . . . . . .654,000

**Spending**
    Military Expenditures . . . . . . . . . . . . . . . . . . . . . . . . . . . . . . . . . . .\$9 million
    Gross National Product . . . . . . . . . . . . . . . . . . . . . . . . . . . . . . . . .\$1 billion
    Military Expenditure as a Percentage of
        Gross National Product . . . . . . . . . . . . . . . . . . . . . . . . . . . . . . . .0.9%
    Military Expenditure as a Percentage of
        Central Government Expenditure . . . . . . . . . . . . . . . . . . . . . . . . .3.3%

**Defence Treaties** *(See Part II for Additional Detail)*

    Bilateral:     None

    Multilateral:  Biological Weapons Convention
                   Limited Test Ban Treaty
                   Multinational Force and Observers in the Sinai
                   Treaty on the Non-Proliferation of Nuclear Weapons

# FINLAND
## Republic of Finland
*Suomen Tasavalta*

### Defense Establishment Command Structure
### and Force Organization

The President of the Republic is Supreme Commander of the Defense Forces. The Minister of Defense, who is responsible to the Parliament, deals with legislative, budgetary and administrative matters.

The Finnish armed forces have an integrated command which is headed by the Commander-in-Chief of the Defense Forces. The Chiefs of the Navy, the Air Force and the Military Areas are his subordinates. The Commander-in-Chief reports directly to the President of the Republic.

The Prime Minister presides over the National Defense Council, which performs an advisory function.

**Total armed forces:** 36,900 (Army: 31,400;   Navy: 2,500;   Air Force: 3,000). **Paramilitary forces:** 3,600 (Border Guard, under Minister of the Interior).

## HEAD OF STATE

H. E. Mauno Koivisto

**OFFICE OF THE PRESIDENT**
*Pohjoisesplanadi 1*
*00170 Helsinki 17*

*Telephone: (0) 661 133, 631 459*
*Telex: 124636 umin sf*

President of the Republic and
    Supreme Commander of the Defense Forces . . . . . . . . . . Mauno Koivisto
Secretary General . . . . . . . . . . . . . . . . . . . . . . . . . . . . . . . . Juhani Perttunen

**OFFICE OF THE PRIME MINISTER**
*Aleksanterinkatu 3D*
*00170 Helsinki 17*

*Telephone: (0) 1681*
*Telex: 124636 umin sf*

Prime Minister . . . . . . . . . . . . . . . . . . . . . . . . . . . . . . . . . . . . . . Kalevi Sorsa

**National Defense Council**

Chairman . . . . . . . . . . . . . . . . . . . . . . . . . . . . . . . . . . . . . . . . . Kalevi Sorsa
(Prime Minister)
Member . . . . . . . . . . . . . . . . . . . . . . . . . . . . . . . . . Veikko Pihlajamäki
(Minister of Defense)
Member . . . . . . . . . . . . . . . . . . . . . . . . . . . . . . . . . . . Gen. Lauri Sutela
(Commander-in-Chief, Defense Forces)
Member . . . . . . . . . . . . . . . . . . . . . . . . . . . . . Lt. Gen. Jaakko Valtanen
(Chief, General Headquarters)
Member . . . . . . . . . . . . . . . . . . . . . . . . . . . . . . . . . . Paavo Väyrynen
(Minister for Foreign Affairs)
Member . . . . . . . . . . . . . . . . . . . . . . . . . . . . . . . . . . . . . . Ahti Pekkala
(Minister of Finance)
Member . . . . . . . . . . . . . . . . . . . . . . . . . . . . . . . . . . . Seppo Lindblom
(Minister of Trade and Industry)
Member . . . . . . . . . . . . . . . . . . . . . . . . . . . . . . . . . . . . Matti Luttinen
(Minister of the Interior)

**MINISTRY OF DEFENSE**
*Eteläinen Makasiinikatu 8*
*PL 31*
*00130 Helsinki 13*

*Telephone:    (0) 625 801*
*Telex:    124667*

| | |
|---|---|
| Minister | Veikko Pihlajamäki |
| Permanent Undersecretary | Lt. Gen. Aimo Pajunen |
| Director, Defense Research Agency (Ylöjärvi) | Col. Pentti Karppanen |
| Director, Defense Topography Office | Col. Lauri Vilkko |
| Director, Weapons Testing Institute | Lt. Col. Timo Erola |
| Inspector, Anti-Aircraft Artillery | Col. Aimo Heinaro |
| Inspector, Engineering | Col. Eino Hurmerinta |
| Inspector, Signals | Col. Raimo Penttinen |
| Chief, Security | Col. Niilo Kohonen |
| Chief, Maintenance | Maj. Gen. Alpo Kantola |
| Chief Medical Officer | Maj. Gen. Kimmo Koskenvuo |
| Chief Veterinarian | Col. Mati Waris |
| Chief, War Economics | Lt. Gen. Pentti Väyrynen |
| Chief, War Equipment | Col. Uolevi Anthoni |

# DEFENSE FORCES

**ARMED FORCES**
**General Headquarters,**
   **Finnish Defense Forces**
*(Pääesikunta)*
*Eteläinen Makasiininkatu 8*
*PL 919*
*00101 Helsinki 10*

*Telephone:    (0) 625 801*
*Telex:    124667 hkipe sf*

| | |
|---|---|
| Commander-in-Chief | Gen. Lauri Sutela |
| Chief, General Headquarters | Lt. Gen. Jaakko Valtanen |
| Chief, General Staff | Lt. Gen. Rolf Stewen |
| Chief, Foreign Section | Col. Raimo Jokinen |
| Quartermaster General | Maj. Gen. Matti Vanonen |
| Chief, Command Section | Maj. Gen. Keijo Tuominen |
| Chief, Intelligence Service | Maj. Gen. Raimo Heiskanen |
| Chief, Training Section | Maj. Gen. Raimo Viita |
| Inspector, Military Education | (Vacant) |
| Inspector, Infantry | Maj. Gen. Raimo Katona |
| Inspector, Field Artillery | Col. Allan Aarnio |
| Inspector, Coast Artillery | Col. Pentti Aulaskari |

**General Staff**
*(Yleiesikunta)*

| | |
|---|---|
| Chief | Lt. Gen. Rolf Wilhelm Stewen |
| Chief, Planning Division | Lt. Col. Niska Juhani |
| Chief, Organization Division | Col. Martti Palmén |
| Chief, Operations Division | Col. Ilkka Halonen |
| Chief, Intelligence Division | Col. Aulis Tuominen |
| Head, Examination Bureau | Col. Raimo Hastio |
| Chief, Foreign Division | (Vacant) |
| Chief, Command Division | Col. Pentti Karvonen |
| Chief, Information Division | Lt. Col. Antero Karvinen |

**Training Staff**
*(Koulutusesikunta)*

| | |
|---|---|
| Chief | Maj. Gen. Raimo Viita |
| Chief, Training Division | Col. Petter Parikka |
| Chief, Infantry Bureau | Lt. Col. Heikki Koskelo |
| Chief, Field Artillery Bureau | Lt. Col. Tauno Heikkilä |
| Chief, Coastal Artillery Bureau | Lt. Col. Jarmo Simola |
| Chief, Anti-Aircraft Artillery Bureau | Lt. Col. Mikko Virrankoski |
| Chief, Defense Bureau | Col. Niilo Kohonen |
| Chief, Engineering Division | Col. Aarre Ahonen |
| Chief, Signals Division | Col. Erkki Itkonen |

**Maintenance Staff**
*(Huoltoesikunta)*

| | |
|---|---|
| Chief | Maj. Gen. Alpo Kantola |
| Chief, Maintenance Division | Col. Eero Lampikoski |
| Chief, Transport Division | Col. Solmu Mattila |
| Chief, Ordnance Division | Col. Raimo Sihvola |
| Chief, Quartermaster Division | Comdr. Teuvo Kuparinen |
| Chief, Medical Division | Lt. Col. Matti Ponteva |
| Chief, Veterinary and Food Hygiene Division | Col. Matti Waris |

| | |
|---|---|
| **Procurement Staff**<br>*(Hankintaosasto)* | Chief ........................................Lt. Gen. Pentti Väyrynen<br>Chief, War Economy Division ........................Col. Jussi Kivelä<br>Chief, Procurement Division ...........................Sulo Gillberg<br>Chief, Technical Division ....................Lt. Gen. Kauko Räsänen<br>Chief, Weapons Technology Division.................Col. Paavo Heimo<br>Chief, Electrical Division ....................Col. Pentti Kolehmainen |
| **Military Chaplaincy**<br>*(Kirkollistoimisto)* | Chief/Field Chaplain.................................Kari Vappula |

**ARMY**
*(Maavoimat)*
*Eteläinen Makasiininkatu 8*
*PL 919*
*00101 Helsinki 10*

*Telephone:   (0) 625 801*
*Telex:   124667 hkipe sf*

**South Finland Military Area**
*Hämeenlinna/Tavastehus*

Commander...............................Maj. Gen. Keijo Tuominen
Chief of Staff........................................Col. Leo Vehmas
Chief, Helsinki Military District........................Col. Olli Rekola
Chief, Länsi-Uudsimaa Military
   District (Helsinki) ...............................Col. Pertti Envall
Chief, Itä—Uudenmaa Military
   District (Tuusula) ...........................Col. Yrjö Yki-Järvinen
Chief, Hämeelinna Military
   District (Hämeelinna)...........................Lt. Col. Pentti Lyly
Chief, Lahti Military
   District (Lahti) .............................Lt. Col. Veikko Simola

**Troop Units**
Commander, Armored Brigade
   (Parolanummi) ..............................Col. Matti Aaltonen
Commander, Armored Vehicle
   Battalion (Parolanummi).....................Lt. Col. Tauno Ylänne
Commander, Häme Infantry
   Battalion (Parolanummi) ..................Lt. Col. Martti Keskitalo
Commander, Infantry Battalion
   (Hämeenlinna) ............................Lt. Col. Asko Sivula
Commander, Uudenmaa
   Brigade (Dragsvik) ........................Col. Hans Christensen
Commander, Häme Mounted
   Infantry Battalion (Lahti) .................Lt. Col. Harri Virtapohja
Commander, Kaarti Battalion
   (Helsinki) .................................Lt. Col. Heikki Ahlqvist
Commander, Uudenmaa Infantry
   Battalion (Santahamina) ....................Lt. Col. Olli Heiskanen
Commander, Coast Infantry
   Battalion (Upinniemi) ......................Lt. Col. Ilmo Kekkonen
Commander, Suomen Linna Coast
   Artillery Regiment (Santahamina) ...................Col. Torsti Lahti
Commander, Hanko Coast Artillery
   Battery (Hanko) ..............................Lt. Col. Timo Sario
Commander, Helsinki Air Defense
   Regiment (Hyrylä) ..........................Col. Rauli Helminen
Commander, Signals Regiment
   (Riihimäki) ............................Lt. Col. Matti Savonheimo

**North Finland Military Area**
*Oulu/Uleåborg*

Commander ............................Maj. Gen. Erkki Laatikainen
Chief of Staff ......................................Col. Pertti Ylätupa
Chief, Oulu Military District (Oulu) .............Lt. Col. Joe Lehtilä
Chief, Raahe Military District (Oulainen).........Lt. Col. Kaarlo Hietala

Chief, Kajaani Military
District (Kajaani) .......................Lt. Col. Jouko-Juhani Hälvä
Chief, Kemi Military District (Kemi) ..............Lt. Col. Matti Skyttä
Chief, Rovaniemi Military
District (Rovaniemi) ................................Col. Arvi Aro

**Troop Units**
Commander, Pohja Brigade (Oulu) ................Col. Pekka Mustonen
Commander, Kainuu Brigade (Kajaani) ............Col. Heikki Koskelo
Commander, Infantry Brigade
(Sodankylä).................................Col. Tuomo Tuominen
Commander, Oulu Air Defense
Artillery (Oulu) ............................Lt. Col. Seppo Takamaa
Commander, Rovaniemi Air Defense
Artillery (Rovaniemi) ..........................Lt. Col. Ahti Lappi
Commander, First Independent
Signals Company (Oulu) .......................Maj. Jaakko Hurme

**Southeast Finland Military Area**
*Kouvola*

Commander .................................Maj. Gen. Erkki Annala
Chief of Staff .................................Col. Aarne Palmen
Chief, Kouvola Military District (Kouvola) ............Col. Arvo Vilhunen
Chief, Lappeenranta Military
District (Lappeenranta).......................Lt. Col. Antti Lehtola
Chief, Mikkeli Military
District (Mikkeli)............................Lt. Col. Yrjö Larikka
Chief, Savonlinna Military
District (Savonlinna) ....................Lt. Col. Antti Hautaniemi

**Troop Units**
Commander, Karjala Brigade (Vekaranjärvi) ...........Col. Pertti Kilkki
Commander, Savo Brigade (Mikkeli)..............Col. Hannu Arovaara
Commander, Kymi Infantry
Battalion (Hamina) ........................Lt. Col. Matti Suokas
Commander, Uudenmaa Mounted
Battalion (Lappeenranta).....................Lt. Col. Matti Kopra
Commander, Karjala Artillery
Regiment (Vekaranjärvi) .........................Col. Pekka Aitero
Commander, Coast Artillery
Battery (Kyminlinna) ...................Lt. Col. Teuvo Rönkkönen
Commander, Salpausselkä Air
Defense Artillery (Kouvola) .................Lt. Col. Arvo Toivonen
Commander, Kymi Engineer
Battalion (Koria)..........................Lt. Col. Reijo Raasakka

**Southwest Finland Military Area**
*Turku/Åbo*

Commander ....................................Gen. Lauri Koho
Chief of Staff ..............................Col. Veikko Vesterinen
Chief, Turku Military
District (Turku) ...........................Col. Kauko Laamanen
Chief, Satakunta Military
District (Pori) ............................Col. Vilho Aspinjaakko

**Troop Units**
Commander, Pori Brigade
(Säkylä) ..................................Col. Markku Salonen
Commander, Satakunta Artillery
Regiment (Niinisalo) ..........................Col. Reijo Kuusisto
Commander, Turku Coast Artillery
Regiment (Turku) ............................Col. Jukka Karvinen
Commander, Turku Air Defense
Artillery (Turku)........................Lt. Col. Heikki Happonen
Commander, Second Independent
Signals Company (Turku)..........................Maj. Unto Peri

**Savo-Karjala Military Area**
*Kuopio*

Commander . . . . . . . . . . . . . . . . . . . . . . . . . . . . . . . Maj. Gen. Ilkka Halonen
Chief of Staff . . . . . . . . . . . . . . . . . . . . . . . . . . . . Lt. Col. Jaakko Aatolainen
Chief, Kuopio Military District (Kuopio) . . . . . . . . . . . . Col. Esko Hevenoja
Chief, Joensuu Military District (Joensuu) . . . . . . . . . . Col. Raimo Savolahti

**Troop Units**
Commander, Karjala Infantry
    Battalion (Kontioranta) . . . . . . . . . . . . . . . . . . . . . . Lt. Col. Risto Koppinen
Commander, Northern Karjala
    Artillery (Ylämylly) . . . . . . . . . . . . . . . . . . . . . . . Lt. Col. Raimo Kaukonen

**Inner Finland Military Area**
*Luonetjärvi*

Commander . . . . . . . . . . . . . . . . . . . . . . . . . . . . . Maj. Gen. Martti Alatalo
Chief of Staff . . . . . . . . . . . . . . . . . . . . . . . . . . . . . . Col. Kalevi Markkula
Chief, East Tampere Military
    District (Tampere) . . . . . . . . . . . . . . . . . . . . . . . . . . Col. Timo Marjola
Chief, West Tampere Military
    District (Tampere) . . . . . . . . . . . . . . . . . . . . . . . . Lt. Col. Erkki Kolkka
Chief, Jyväskylä Military
    District (Jyväskylä) . . . . . . . . . . . . . . . . . . . . . . Lt. Col. Pertti Seppänen
Chief, Suolahti Military
    District (Äänekoski) . . . . . . . . . . . . . . . . . . . . . . Lt. Col. Seppo Nieminen

**Troop Units**
Commander, Central Finland
    Engineer Battalion (Keuruu) . . . . . . . . . . . . . . . . . . Lt. Col. Matti Lukkari
Commander, Central Finland
    Signals Battalion (Keuruu) . . . . . . . . . . . . . . . . . Lt. Col. Heikki Näremaa

**Pohjanmaa Military Area**
*Vaasa/Vasa*

Commander . . . . . . . . . . . . . . . . . . . . . . . . . . . . . . Maj. Gen. Erkki Vanninen
Chief of Staff . . . . . . . . . . . . . . . . . . . . . . . . . . . . . Lt. Col. Esko Nieminen
Chief, Vaasa Military District (Vaasa) . . . . . . . . . . . . . Lt. Col. Veijo Rutanen
Chief, Seinäjoki Military
    District (Seinäjoki) . . . . . . . . . . . . . . . . . . . . . . . . Col. Yrjö Maunula
Chief, Kokkola Military
    District (Kokkola) . . . . . . . . . . . . . . . . . . . . . . . Lt. Col. Matti Lehtonen

**Troop Unit**
Commander, Vaasa Coast Artillery
    Battery (Vaasa) . . . . . . . . . . . . . . . . . . . . . . . . . Lt. Col. Pentti Väyrynen

**Army Academies**

Commanding Officer, War
    College (Helsinki) . . . . . . . . . . . . . . . . . . . . . . . . Maj. Gen. Risto Setälä
Commanding Officer, Military
    Academy (Santahamina) . . . . . . . . . . . . . . . . . . . . . . . Col. Sami Sihvo
Commanding Officer, Combat
    School (Kerava) . . . . . . . . . . . . . . . . . . . . . . . . . . Col. Hannu Särkiö
Commanding Officer, Reserve
    Officers' School (Hamina) . . . . . . . . . . . . . . . . . . . Col. Jorma Pullinen

**NAVY**
*(Merivoimat)*
*Merivoimien Esikunta*
*PL 167*
*SF-00161 Helsinki 16*

*Telephone: (0) 176681*
*Telex: 12466 hkime sf*

Commander of the Navy . . . . . . . . . . . . . . . . . . . . . . Rear Adm. Jan Klenberg
Chief of Staff . . . . . . . . . . . . . . . . . . . . . . . . . . . . . . Capt. Lassi Hirvonen
Chief Engineer . . . . . . . . . . . . . . . . . . . . . . . . Capt. Esko Huhta-Koivisto
Chief, Training Division . . . . . . . . . . . . . . . . . . . . . . Cdr. Kari Dahlbo
Chief, General Staff Division . . . . . . . . . . . . . . . . . . Cdr. Osmo Tuomi
Chief, Signals Division . . . . . . . . . . . . . . . . . . . . . . Lt. Cdr. Risto Rasku
Chief, Ordnance Division . . . . . . . . . . . . . . . . . . . . Cdr. Matti Jyrämä
Chief, Naval Division . . . . . . . . . . . . . . . . . . . . . . . Cdr. Pekka Heikkilä
Chief, Procurement . . . . . . . . . . . . . . . . . . . . . . . . . Cdr. Aarni Lehti

**Coast Fleet** *(Turku)*

Commander . . . . . . . . . . . . . . . . . . . . . . . . . . . . . . . . Capt. Juha Tikka
Chief of Staff . . . . . . . . . . . . . . . . . . . . . . . . . . . . . . Cdr. Jalo Reinivuo
Commander, Attack Fleet . . . . . . . . . . . . . . . . . . Cdr. Kauko Neittamo
Commander, Support Fleet . . . . . . . . . . . . . . . . . . . . Cdr. Juoko Visa

Commander, Minesweeping Fleet . . . . . . . . . . . . . . . . .Lt. Cdr. Visa Auvinen
Commander, Patrol Fleet . . . . . . . . . . . . . . . . . . . . .Lt. Cdr. Seppo Sarelius
Commander, Turku Naval Base . . . . . . . . . . . . .Capt. Erkkui Uosokeinen
Commander, Helsinki Naval Base . . . . . . . . . . . . . . . .Cdr. Unto Suhonen
Commanding Officer, Naval
    Academy (Suomenlinna) . . . . . . . . . . . . . . . . . . . . . . .Capt. Erik Wihtol

**AIR FORCE**
*(Ilmavoimat)*
*Ilmavoimien Esikunta*
*PL 30*
*SF-41161 Tikkakoski*
*Telephone:   (41) 751322*
*Telex:   28132 ilmae sf*

Commander of the Air Force . . . . . . . . . . . . . . . . . . . . .Gen. Rauno Meriö
Chief of Staff . . . . . . . . . . . . . . . . . . . . . . . . . . . . . . . . . .Col. Kari Korttila
Chief, General Staff Division . . . . . . . . . . . . . . . .Lt. Col. Heikki Nikunen
Chief, Training Division . . . . . . . . . . . . . . . . . . . .Lt. Col. Raimo Rasehorn
Chief, Signals Division . . . . . . . . . . . . . . . . . . . .Lt. Col. Matti Antikainen
Chief, Procurement . . . . . . . . . . . . . . . . . . . . . . . .Lt. Col. Matti Keskinen

**Air Force Units**

Commander, Lappi Air
    Wing (Rovaniemi) . . . . . . . . . . . . . . . . . . . . . . . . . . . .Col. Pertti Jokinen
Commander, Satakunta Air
    Wing (Tampere) . . . . . . . . . . . . . . . . . . . . . . . . . . . . . . . .Col. Eero Urpo
Commander, Karjala Air
    Wing (Rissala) . . . . . . . . . . . . . . . . . . . . . . . . . . . . . . . .Col. Pertti Tolla
Commander, Transport
    Squadron (Utti) . . . . . . . . . . . . . . . . . . . . . . .Lt. Col. Osmo Kopponen
Commander, Reconnaissance
    Squadron (Tikkakoski) . . . . . . . . . . . . . . . . . . . . . .Maj. Erkki Ikonen
Commanding Officer, Air Force
    Academy (Kauhava) . . . . . . . . . . . . . . . . . . . . . .Col. Pertti Tapanainen

**BORDER GUARD**
*(Rajavartiolaitos)*
*(under Interior Minister)*
*PL 3*
*SF-00131 Helsinki*
*Telephone:   (90) 625801*

Commander . . . . . . . . . . . . . . . . . . . . . . . . . . . . . .Gen. Erkki Kirjavainen
Deputy Commander . . . . . . . . . . . . . . . . . . . . .Maj. Gen. Stig-Erik Malmen
Chief, Training Division . . . . . . . . . . . . . . . . . . .Col. Paavali Turpeeniemi
Chief, Ground and Air Division . . . . . . . . . . . . . . . . . . . . .Col. Matti Autio
Chief, Naval Division . . . . . . . . . . . . . . . . . . . . . .Comdr. Jorma Kaisalo
Chief, Signals Division . . . . . . . . . . . . . . . . . . . . . . .Lt. Col. Matti Ropo
Chief, Procurement . . . . . . . . . . . . . . . . . . . . . .Lt. Col. Seppo Kaikkonen
Chief, Administration . . . . . . . . . . . . . . . . . . . . . . . . . . . .Juhani Uusitalo

**Field Commanders**

Commander, Kaakkois-Suomi
    Border Guard Province (Imatra) . . . . . . . . . . . . . . .Col. Tauno Miettinen
Commander, Pohjois-Karjala
    Border Guard Province (Onttola) . . . . . . . . . . . . . . .Col. Teuvo Paanila
Commander, Kainuu Border
    Guard Province (Kajaani) . . . . . . . . . . . . . . . . . . . .Lt. Col. Eino Rainula
Commander, Lappi Border
    Guard Province (Rovaniemi) . . . . . . . . . . . . . . . . . .Col. Jarmo Mattila
Commander, Suomenlahti Naval
    Guard Province (Helsinki) . . . . . . . . . . . . . . . . . . . .Cdr. Heimo Iivonen
Commander, Saaristomei Naval
    Guard Province (Turku) . . . . . . . . . . . . . . . . . . . . .Cdr. Seppo Kanerva
Commander, Pohjanlahti Naval
    Guard Province (Vaasa) . . . . . . . . . . . . . . . . . . . . .Cdr. Esa Salonsaari
Commanding Officer, Border
    Guard Training School (Imatra) . . . . . . . . . . . . . . .Lt. Col. Jorma Jokinen
Commanding Officer, Border
    Guard Naval Training School (Espoo) . . . . . . . . .Lt. Cdr. Juoko Isohanni

\* \* \* \* \*

# GENERAL DEFENSE DATA

**Manpower**

Total Armed Forces . . . . . . . . . . . . . . . . . . . . . . . . . . . . . . . . . . . . . . . . . . . . . . . .36,900
   (See Page 185)
Population . . . . . . . . . . . . . . . . . . . . . . . . . . . . . . . . . . . . . . . . . . . . . . . . . . .4,816,000

**Spending**

Military Expenditures . . . . . . . . . . . . . . . . . . . . . . . . . . . . . . . . . . . . . . . . . . .$781 million
Gross National Product . . . . . . . . . . . . . . . . . . . . . . . . . . . . . . . . . . . . . . . . . .$47.1 billion
Military Expenditure as a Percentage of
   Gross National Product . . . . . . . . . . . . . . . . . . . . . . . . . . . . . . . . . . . . . . . .1.7%
Military Expenditure as a Percentage of
   Central Government Expenditure . . . . . . . . . . . . . . . . . . . . . . . . . . . . . . . . .7.6%

**Defense Treaties** *(See Part II for Additional Detail)*

    Bilateral:     Soviet Union

    Multilateral:   Biological Weapons Convention
                *Finland—France—Soviet Union—United Kingdom*: Paris
                    Peace Treaty restricting the size and armament of Finnish
                    armed forces
                Limited Test Ban Treaty
                Treaty on the Control of Arms on the Seabed
                Treaty on the Non-Proliferation of Nuclear Weapons

# FRANCE
## French Republic
### *République Française*

## Defense Establishment Command Structure and Force Organization

The President of the Republic is Commander-in-Chief of the armed forces. He presides over the Supreme Defense Council and the Defense Committee. The Prime Minister plans and implements military operations through the Secretariat General of National Defense and the Minister of Defense. The Minister of Defense is responsible for the administration of the defense forces.

**Total armed forces:** 452,850 (Army: 314,200; Navy: 68,000; Air Force: 100,400). **Paramilitary forces:** 83,000 (Gendarmerie).

## HEAD OF STATE

H.E. François Mitterand

**OFFICE OF THE PRESIDENT**
*Palais de l'Elysée*
*55 et 57, rue du Faubourg-Saint-Honore*
*75008 Paris*

*Telephone: (1) 261-51-00*
*Telex: 650127 prvo paris*

| | |
|---|---|
| President of the Republic and Commander-in-Chief | François Mitterand |
| General Secretary of the Presidency | Jean-Louis Bianco |
| Assistant General Secretary | Jaque Fourniar |
| Director of the Cabinet | André Rousselet |
| Special Chief of Staff to the President | Gén. Jean Saulnier |
| Special Assistant to the President | Paul Legatte |
| Special Advisor to the President | Jacques Attali |

**Supreme Defense Council**

| | |
|---|---|
| Chairman | François Mitterand (President of the Republic) |
| Member | Pierre Mauroy (Prime Minister) |
| Member | Claude Cheysson (Minister of Foreign Affairs) |
| Member | Charles Hernu (Minister of Defense) |
| Member | Jacques Delors (Minister of Economy and Finance) |
| Member | Gaston Deffere (Minister of Interior and Decentralization) |
| Member | Gén. d'Armée de Barry (General Secretary for National Defense) |

**MINISTRY OF DEFENSE**
*(Ministere de la Défense)*
*14, rue Saint Dominique*
*75 Paris*
*75997 Paris Armées*

*Telephone: (1) 555-95-20*
*Telex: 270003 defnat paris*

| | |
|---|---|
| Minister | Charles Hernu |
| Director, Military and Civil Staff | François Bernard |
| Chargé de Mission | Jean Francois Dubos |
| Chief, Civilian Staff | Serge Daëll |
| Chief, Military Staff | Rear Adm. René Hugues |

193

**State Secretary**
(Secretaire d'État aupres du Ministère
    de la Défénse)

State Secretary . . . . . . . . . . . . . . . . . . . . . . . . . . . . . . . . . . . . . François Autain
Director State Secretary Staff . . . . . . . . . . . . . . . . . . . . . . . . . . . . . . . . .

**Group for Strategic Planning
    and Studies**
(Groupe de Planification et d'Etudes
    Stratégiques)
10 rue Saint
    Dominique 7em
Postal Address: 14,
    rue Saint Dominique
75997 Paris Armées

Director . . . . . . . . . . . . . . . . . Ingenieur en Chef de l'Armement Gén. Delaye

**Committee of the Chiefs of Staff**

Member (ex officio) . . . . . . . . . . . . . . . . . . . . . . . . . . . . . . . . Charles Hernu
(Minister of Defense)
Member (ex officio) . . . . . . . . . . . . . . . . . . . . . . . . . . . . . Gén. Jannou Lacaze
(Chief of Staff, Armed Forces)
Member (ex officio) . . . . . . . . . . . . . . . . . . . . . . . . . . Gén. Bernard Capillon
(Chief of Staff, Air Force)
Member (ex officio) . . . . . . . . . . . . . . . . . . . . . . . . . . . . . Gén. René Imbot
(Chief of Staff, Army)
Member (ex officio) . . . . . . . . . . . . . . . . . . . . . . . . . . . Gén. Yves Leenardt
(Chief of Staff, Navy)

**General Comptrol of the Armed Forces**
(Controle Général des Armées)
231 bd. St. Germain 7em
Postal Address: 14, rue
    Saint Dominique
75997 Paris Armées
Telephone:    (1) 544-39-59

Comptroller General . . . . . . . . . . . . . . . . . . . . . . . . . . . . . . . . Henri Blandin

**Directorate of the Gendarmery and
    Military Justice**
(Direction de la Gendarmerie et de la
    Justice Militaire)
35, rue Saint Didier
75775 Paris
Cedex 16
Telephone:    (1) 505-14-47

Director . . . . . . . . . . . . . . . . . . . . . . . . . . . . . . . . . . . . . . . Charles Barbeau
Chief of Staff . . . . . . . . . . . . . . . . . . . . . . . . . . Chef d'Escadron Denis Picard

**Directorate for Military Engineering
    Industrial Affairs and Programs**
(Direction des Programmes et des
    Affaires Industrielles de
    l'Armement)
231 bd. St. Germain 7em
Postal Address: 14, rue
    Saint Dominique
75997 Paris Armées

Director . . . . . . . . . . . . . . . . . Ingenieur Gén. de 2eme Classe de l'Armement
Jean-Pierre Benichou
Director Adjoint Charged With Technical
    Liaisons and General Studies . . . . . . . . . . . . . . . . . . . . . . Niels Aschehoug
Deputy Director, Planning and
    Programs Division . . . . . . . . . . . . . . . . . . . . . . . . . . . Pierre Maisonneuve
Director, Bureau of Aeronautic and
    Electronics Programs . . . . . . . . . . . . . . . . . . . . . . . . . . . . . . Guy Monnet
Director, Bureau of Naval Materials . . . . . . Ingenieur en Chef de l'Armement
Remon-Bauvais
Director, Bureau of Terrestrial Materials  . Ingenieur en Chef de l'Armement
Remon-Bauvais
Director, Bureau of Missiles Programs . . . . . . . . . . . . . . . . . . . . . P. Dumas
Deputy Director, Division
    of Industrial Affairs . . . . . . . . . . . Ingenieur en Chef de l'Armement Rame

**Directorate of International Affairs**
*(Direction des Affairs Internationales)*
*231 bd. St. Germain 7ᵉᵐ*
*Postal Address: 14, rue*
 *Saint Dominique*
*75997 Paris Armées*
*(Responsible for all Matters of*
 *International Cooperation and*
 *Exportation of Weaponry)*
*Telephone:    (1) 555-95-20*

Director ...... Ingenieur Gén. de 1ᵉʳᵉ Classe de l'Armement Marc Cauchie
Director Adjoint ..... Ingenieur Gén. de 2ᵉᵐᵉ Classe de l'Armement Audran

**Subdirectorate for Studies and**
 **Coordination**

Director, Bureau of Relations With
 Ministry of Foreign Affairs ...... Ingenieur en Chef de l'Armement Conze
Director, Bureau of Economic Studies
 Section for Foreign
 Weaponry Information ..... Ingenieur en Chef de l'Armement Labernede
Director, Bureau of Public Relations
 Section for Demonstrations in France
 *(Organisation des Salons en France)* ........ Lt.-Col. Bernard LeCornec

**Subdirectorate for Cooperation**

Director, Section for Training Programs,
 Authorisations for Visits and Scholarships ............. Capt. de Fregate
 Jean Loup Legal de Kerangal
Director, Section for Cooperation
 Programs Formulation ...... Ingenieur en Chef de l'Armement Normand

**Directorate of Nuclear Experimentation**
 **Centers**
*(Direction des Centres*
 *d'Experimentation Nucleaires)*
*Base Aérienne No. 102*
*78129 Villacoublay*
*Telephone:    (3) 630-23-49*

Director ................................ Vice Amr. d'Escadre Fages
Deputy Director ......................................... Gal Lewin
Deputy Director.................................. Jean de Laborderie

**Department of Public Relations and**
 **Information for the Armed Forces**
*231 bd. St. Germain 7ᵉᵐᵉ*
*Postal Address: 14,*
 *rue Saint Dominique*
*75997 Paris Armées*
*Telephone:    (1) 555-9420*

Chief, Department ....................... Col. d'Auber De Peyrelongue
Deputy Chief ................................... Col. Jacques Bouley

**General Delegation for Military**
 **Engineering**
*(Delegation Génerale pour l'Armement)*
*Postal Address: 14,*
 *rue Saint Dominique*
*75997 Paris Armées*

General Delegate ................................................
Assistant Delegate .......... Ingenieur Gén. de 1ᵉʳᵉ Classe de l'Armement
 Alain Guigue
Military Advisor, Army ........................ Col. Bernard LeMaire
Military Advisor, Navy ...................... Capt. de Vaisseau Spilliaert
Military Advisor, Air Force .......................... Col. André Merold

**Directorate for General Administration**
 **and Personnel of Military Engineering**
*(Direction des Personnels et des Affaires*
 *Génerales de l'Armement*
*231 bd. St. Germain 7ᵉᵐᵉ*
*Postal Address: 14,*
 *rue Saint Dominique*
*75997 Paris Armées*
*Telephone:    (1) 555-95-20*

Director ............................................. Raoul Roger

**Subdirectorate Tactical Technical
  Assistance**

Director, Sales Service and Market
  Studies for Armaments Abroad . . . . . . . Ingenieur en Chef de L'Armement
  Bernard Retat

**Technical Directorate for Land
  Weaponry**
*(Direction Technique des Armements
  Terrestres)*

Director . . . . . . . Ingenieur Gén. de 1ere Classe de l'Arment Claude Engerand
Assistant Director and Chief
  of Technical Services . . . . . . . Ingenieur Gén. de 1ere Classe Michel Marest
Chief of Staff . . . . . . . . Ingenieur Gén. de 2eme Classe de l'Armement Nicolas

**Technical Directorate for Naval
  Construction**
*(Direction Technique des Constructions
  Navales)*
*2 rue Royal 18e*
*75200 Naval*

Director . . . . . . . . . . . . Ingenieur Gén. de 1ere Classe de l'Armement Barbery
Assistant Director, Head of Industrial
  Department . . . . . . . Ingenieur Gén. de 1ere Classe de l'Armement Wiener

**Technical Directorate for Aeronautical
  Constructions**
*(Direction Techniques des Constructions
  Aéronautiques)*
*26 bd. Victor*
*75015 Paris*
*75996 Paris Armées*
*Telephone:  (1) 552-93-21*

Director . . . . Ingenieur Gén. de 1ere Classe de l'Armement Georges Bousquet
Assistant Director . . . . . . . . . . Ingenieur Gén. de 1ere Classe de l'Armement
  François de Butz

**Directorate of Weaponry Techniques
  and Research**
*(Direction des Récherches Etudes et
  Techniques d'Armement)*
*26 bd. Victor*
*75996 Paris Armées*
*Telephone (1) 552-43-21*

Director . . . . . . Ingenieur Gén. de 1ere Classe de l'Armement Jean Carpentier
Scientific Director . . . . . . . . . . . . . . . . Expert Scientifique Pierre L'allemand

**Technical Directorate for Missiles**
*(Direction Technique des Engins)*
*26 bd. Victor*
*75996 Paris Armées*
*Telephone:  (1) 552-43-21*

Director . . . . . . . . . . . . . . . . . . . Ingenieur Gén. de 1ere Classe d'Armement
  Antonin Collet-Billon
Assistant Director . . . . . . . . . . Ingenieur Gén. de 1ere Classe de l'Armement
  Jacques Bataille

**Central Department of Computers and
  Telecommunications**
*(Service Central des Télé-
  communications et de l'Informatique)*
*2 bis bd. Victor*
*75015 Paris*
*Postal Address: 14,
  rue Saint Dominique*
*75997 Paris Armées*

Chief of Department . . . . . . . . . Ingenieur Gén. de 1ere Classe de l'Armement
  Jacques Alberge
Assistant Chief . . . . . . . . . . . . . . . . . . Ingenieur de 2eme Classe Yves Garnier

**General Administrative Secretariat**
*(Secretariat Géneral pour
  l'Administration)*
*14 rue Saint Dominique*
*75997 Paris Armées*

General Secretary . . . . . . . Inspecteur Gén. des Finances Phillipe LaCarriere
Charge de Mission . . . . . . . . . . . . . . . . . . . . . Controleur des Armées Chabod

**Directorate of Financial Departments**
*(Direction des Services Financiers)*
*14 rue Saint Dominique 7eme*
*75997 Paris Armées*
*Telephone:  (1) 555-39-59, 555-95-20*

Director . . . . . . . . . . . . . . . Controleur Gén. de Armées Jacques Barthelemy
Assistant Director . . . . . . . . . . . . . . . . . . . . . . . . . . . . . Amr. Civ. LaLauze

**Underdirectorate of International
and General Affairs**
*(Sous Direction des Affaires Generales
et Internationales)*
*1 pl. Joffre*
*75700 Paris*
*Telephone:    (1) 555-92-30*

Deputy Directeur .....................................Alain Marchais

**Directorate of Judicial Matters**
*(Direction des Affaires Juridiques)*
*231 bd. St. Germain 7ᵉᵐᵉ*
*Postal Address: 14,*
*rue Saint Dominique*
*75997 Paris Armées*
*Telephone:    (1) 555-95-20*

Director .......................................JeanClaude Roqueplo
Department Head................................Jacques Daumard

**Directorate of Civil Personnel**
*(Direction des Personnels Civils)*
*10 rue Saint Dominique 7ᵉᵐᵉ*
*75997 Paris Armées*

Director .........................................Maurice Rampant

## DEFENSE FORCES

**ARMED FORCES**
**Armed Forces Chief of Staff**
*(Etat Major des Armées)*
*231 bd. St. Germain*
*Paris 7ᵉᵐ*
*Mailing Address: 14,*
*rue Saint Dominique*
*75997 Paris Armées*
*Telephone:    544-39-59, 555-95-20*

Chief of Staff ....................Gén. d'Armée Jeannou Lacaze
Director, Armed Forces Staff ......Gén. de Corps Aérien Jean-Paul Arbelet
Deputy Chief of Staff .....................Gen. de Brig. Noël du Payrat
Deputy Chief of Staff ......................Vice Amr. d'Escadre Fages

**Division of Logistical Organization**
*(Division "Organisation Logistique")*

Chief ...................................Gén. de Brig. Jean Barbotin

**Division of Plans, Programs, Budget**
*(Division "Plans, Programmes,
Budget")*

Chief .......................................Gén. de Brig. Jean Gossot
Director, Classical Programs and International-
Cooperation in Armaments ...........................Col. B. Roux
Director, Biological Chemical and
Nuclear Programs .....................Capt. de Vaisseau Jean Adam

**Division of Electronics, Signals and
Computers**
*(Division "Transmissions-
Electronique-Informatique")*

Chief ...........................................Contre-Amr. Morel
Director, Material Studies,
Electronic Warfare ...........................Col. Pierre Peleton
Director, Protection of Electronic Signals ............Lt.-Col. George Gay
Director, Computer Command System ...........Lt.-Col. Guy Thebault

**Division of Employment**
*(Division, "Emploi")*

Chief............................................Contre-Amr. Bonavita
Director, Operational Studies ....................Col. Bernard Housset
Director, European Theater Forces ....................Col. Pierre David
Director, Overseas Forces, Intervention Forces
and Naval Forces.........................................Col. Goze
Director, Bureau of Air, Land and
Sea Transport ..............................Col. Etienne Courjaret

**Division of Nuclear Forces**
*(Division, "Forces Nucleaires")*

Chief ........................Gén. de Brig. Aérienne Francois Mermet

**Division of External Relations**
*(Division, "Relations Exterieurs")*

Chief ........................... Gén. de Brig. Aérienne Andre Ortolo
Head, International Relations in
   Military Defense ............ Capt. de Vaisseau Phillipe de Gorosturzu
Head, Military Technical Assistance
   and Cooperation ................................ Col. Bernard Rieu
Head, Liaison for Foreign Military Personnel
   in France .................................... Lt.-Col. Michel Galtier
Head, French Military Attaches Abroad ............... Col. Jean Crespin

**Center for the Utilisation of Military**
  **Intelligence**
*(Centre d'Exploitation du*
  *Renseignement Militaire)*
*14, rue Saint Dominique*
*75997 Paris Armées*
*Telephone:    (1) 555-95-20*

Chief .............................................. Col. Paul Hanrion

**Central Directorate of Armed Forces**
  **Health Department**
*(Direction Central du Service de Sante*
  *des Armées)*
*Hotel des Invalides 7ᵉᵐ*
*Postal Address: 14,*
  *rue Saint Dominique*
*75997 Paris Armées*
*Telephone:    (1) 555-92-30*

Director ............ Médecin Gén. Inspecteur Charles Tournies Lasserue
Deputy Director .......... Médecin Gén. Inspecteur Raymond Mautalen

**Central Directorate of Fuels for**
  **Armed Forces**
*(Direction Centrale des Essences des*
  *Armées)*
*Fort de Vanve 27,*
  *bd. de Stalingrad*
*B. P. 163, 92241 Malakoft*
*Postal Address: 14,*
  *rue Saint Dominique*
*75997 Paris Armées*

Director ............ Ingenieur Gén. Militaire de 1ᵉʳᵉ Classe Gilbert Borde
Deputy Director ............... Ingenieur en Chef Militaire de 1ᵉʳᵉ Classe
                      Michel Bouchet

**ARMY**
*Armée de Terre*
*231 bd. St. Germain 7ᵉᵐ*
*Postal Address: 14,*
  *rue Saint Dominique*
*75997 Paris Armées*
*Telephone:    (1) 555-95-20*

**Supreme Council of the Army**
President ........................................ Charles Hernu
                     (Minister of Defense)
Member ................................ Gén. de l'Armée René Imbot
                  (Chief of Staff, Army)
Member ................................ Gén. d'Armée Jean Bire
         (Inspecteur Gén. de l'Armée de Terre)

**General Staff of the Army**
*(Etat-Major de 1'Armée de Terre)*

Chief of Staff, Army ....................... Gén. d'Armée René Imbot
Chief Executive Officer ......................... Gén. de Brig. Moreau
Director, Army Staff Division .................... Gén. Maurice Schmitt
Deputy Chief of Staff, Operations ...................................
Deputy Chief of Staff, Organisation
   Logistics .............................. Gén. de Brig. Albert Billard
Director, Financial and Planning Studies Division ......................
Director, Bureau of International Relations .......... Col. Serge Douceret
Director, Logistics Division ............................... Col. Paravy
Director, Methods of Engagement Division ...........................
Director, Army Technical Section ............... Gén. de Div. Bosshardt
Director, Light Air Craft
   Army Commands .................... Gén. de Brig. Herve Navereau

Director, Army Personnel
   Directorate.................................Gén. de Div. Louis Pitel
Deputy Director ...............................Col. Gayral
Director, Army Service Corps
   Directorate....Intendant Gén. de 1ᵉʳᵉ Classe Veran Cambon de Lavalette
Adjoint ....................Intendant Gén. de 1ᵉʳᵉ Classe Jean Turdiex
Director, Central Engineering
   Directorate .........................Gén. de Div. Michell Blesbois
Adjoint ......................................................
Director, Central Directorate
   of Army Signals ..........................Gén. de. Div. Robert Dey

**Army Schools**
*(Commandement des Ecoles de l'Armée*
   *de Terre)*
*Caserne de Lourcine*
*37 bd. de Port-Royal 13ᵉ*
*75998 Paris Armées*
*Telephone: (1) 555-95-20*

Commander .....................Gén. de Corps d'Armée Andre Sciard
Adjoint ............................Gén. de Brig. Raymond Varenne
Commandant (St. Cyr) .....................Gén. de Div. Forry Gilbert

**Central Directorate of Army Equipment**
*(Direction Centrale du Materiel*
   *de Terre)*
*Fort de Vanes 27 bd. Stalingrad*
*92240 Malakoff*
*Postal Address: 14,*
   *rue Saint Dominique*
*75997 Paris Armées*
*Telephone: (1) 657-11-37*

Director .................................Gén. de Brig. Pierre Vigier
Adjoint ..............................Gén. de Div. Jacques Loubile

**Military Region Commands**

**3rd Army Corps and 1st Military**
   **Region—Paris**
*(3ᵉᵐ Corps dArmée et 1ᵉʳ*
*Region—Paris)*
*Hotel des Invalides*
*Postal Address 14,*
   *rue Saint Dominique*
*75997 Paris Armées*
*Telephone: (1) 555-92-30*

Military Governor of Paris and Commander
   of the First Military Region .......Gén. de Corps d'Armée Alban Barthez
Regional Director of Staff .........Gén. de Corps d'Armée Georges Roidet

**Second Military Region—Lille**
*14 rue Desmaziéres*
*59938 Lille Armées*
*Telephone: (20) 06-92-00*

Commander .......................Gén. de Corps d'Armée Alain Bizard

**Third Military Region—Rennes**
*Quartier Marguerite, bd. J. Cartier*
*35998 Rennes Armées*
*Postal Address: Hotel du Quartier*
   *General*
*12 rue de Corbin*
*Telephone: (99) 50-55-71*

Commander .....................Gén. de Corps d'Armée Maitre Alfred

**Fourth Military Region—Bordeaux**
*29 rue Vital-Carles*
*33998 Bordeaux Armées*
*Telephone: (56) 90-91-20*

Commander ...................................Gén. de Corps d'Armée
              Vincent de Paul Gourlez de la Motte
Regional Director of Staff, General Headquarters......................

**Fifth Military Region—Lyon**
*38 Avenue Marechal—Foch 6em*
*69998 Lyon Armées*
*Telephone: (7) 869-81-02*

Military Governor of Lyon and Commander
of the Fifth Military Region . . . . . . . . . . . . . . . . . .Gén. de Corps d'Armée
Wilfrid Boone Arbod Borssat de Laperousse
Regional Director of Staff,
General Headquarters . . . . . . . . . . . .Gén. de Corps d'Armée Rene Xhaard

**Sixth Military Region—Metz**
*Palais de Gouverneur*
*9 rue de la Citadelle*
*57998 Metz Armées*
*Telephone: (8) 763-53-00*

Military Governor of Metz and Commander of the
Sixth Military Region . . . . . . . . . . . .Gén. de Corps d'Armée Pierre Multon
Regional Director of Staff . . . . . . . . . . . . . . . . . . . . . . . . . . . . . . . . . . . . .
Commander, First Army and
Military Governor of Strasbourg . . . . . . . .Gén. d'Armée Jacques de Barry

**NAVY**
*(Marine)*
*2 rue Royale 8em*
*Postal Address: 15,*
*rue Laborde*
*75200 Paris*

**Supreme Council of the Navy**
President . . . . . . . . . . . . . . . . . . . . . . . . . . . . . . . . . . . . . . . . . .Charles Hernu
Member *(ex officio)* . . . . . . . . . . . . . . . . . . . . . . . . . . . . . . . .Adm. Leenhardt
(Vice President and Chief of Staff)
Member *(ex officio)* . . . . . . . . . .Vice Amr. d'Escadre Gerard de Castelbajac
(Inspector General of the Navy)

**General Staff of the Navy**
*(Etat-Major de la Marine)*

Chief of Staff, Navy . . . . . . . . . . . . . . . . . . . . . . . . . . .Amr. Yves Leenhardt
Chief Executive Officer . . . . . . . . . . . .Capt. de Vaisseau Jean-Claude Sajous

**Naval Staff**
*(Etat-Major)*

Director . . . . . . . . . . . . . . . . . . . . . . . . . . . .Vice Amr. d'Escadre Beaussant
Deputy Chief of Staff, Operations . . . . . . . . . . . . . . .Contre-Amr. Le Meledo
Deputy Chief of Staff, Plans . . . . . . . . . . . . . . . . . . . . .Vice Amr. Gagliardi
Deputy Chief of Staff, Materials . . . . . . . . . . . . . . . . . . . .Contre-Amr. Denis
Deputy Chief of Staff, Logistics . . . . . . . . . . . . . . . . . .Contre-Amr. Moyon
Chief, Naval Aeronautics Division . . . . . . . . . . . . . .Vice Amr. Maurice Soulet
Director, Naval Technical Section of
Signals and Computers . . . . . . . .Ingenieur Gén. des Telecommunications
Guy Gerbier
Adjoint Director . . . . . . . . . . . . . . . . . . . . . . . . . . . . . . . . . . . .Icta. Labesse
Director, Directorate of Navy Military
Personnel . . . . . . . . . . . . . . . . . . . . . . . . . . .Vice Amr. d'Escadre Lejeune
Adjoint Director . . . . . . . . . . . . . . . . . . . . . . . .Contre-Amr. André Bougeois
Director, Central Directorate of
Naval Paymastership . . . . . . . . . . . . . . . . . . . . . .Commissaire Gén. Petit
Adjoint Director . . . . . . . . . . . . . . . . . . . . . . . .Commissaire Gén. Casanova
Director, Central Directorate of Naval and
Building Construction . . . . . . . . . . . . . . . . . . . . .Ingenieur Gén. Barbery
Central Secretariat . . . . . . . . . . . . . . . . . . . . . . . . . . . . . . . . .Ipeta. Massoni
Department Chief, Central Department of
Naval Aeronautics . . . . . . . . . . . . . . . . . . . . . . . . . .Vice Amr. Alain Fatou
Director, Department of Naval Hydrography and
Oceanography . . . . . . . . . . . . . . . . . . . .Ingenieur Gén. Comolet-Tirman

**The Naval Academy**
*(Académie de Marine)*
*3 Avenue Octave-Gereard 7em*
*Postal Address: 15 75340 Paris*
*Cedex 07*
*Telephone: (1) 260-33-30*
*Poste 27333*

President . . . . . . . . . . . . . . . . . . . . . . . . . . . . . . . . . . . . . . . . . . . . . . . . . . . .

**Naval Forces Command Atlantic Squadron**
*(Escadre de l'Atlantique)*
*29240 Brest Naval*

Commander . . . . . . . . . . . . . . . . . . . . . . . . . . .Contre-Amr. Alain Coatanea

**Mediterranean Fleet**
*(Escadre de la Mediterranée)*
*83800 Toulon Naval*

Commander ............................................Vice Amr. Louzeau
Commander, Aircraft and
   Aircraft Carrier ...................................Contre-Amr. Klotz

**Submarine Forces and Strategic**
   **Oceanic Forces**
*(Forces Sous-Marines et Forces*
   *Oceanique Stratégique)*
*Centre Commandant Mille*
*75998 Paris Armées*

Commander .......................Vice Amr. d'Escadre Bonnemaison
Commander, Attack Submarine ....................Contre-Amr. Bisson

**Naval Unit of Trials and Measures**
*(Groupe Naval d'Essais et de Mesures)*
*29240 Brest Naval*

Commander ...........................Capt. de Vaisseau René Pinget

**Maritime Air Patrol**
*(Aviation de Patrouille Maritime)*
*Escale d'Aéronautique Naval*
*93350 Le Bourget*

Commander ................................Contre-Amr. Ghesquière

**Indian Ocean Maritime Forces**
*(Zone Maritime de l'Ocean Indien)*
*15 rue de Laborde*
*75200 Paris Naval*

Commander .......................Contre-Amr. Dominique Lefebvre

## MARITIME REGIONS

**First Maritime Region**
*47 rue Emmanuel-Liais*
*50107 Cherbourg*
*Telephone: (33) 52-66-45*

Maritime Prefect .........................Contre-Amr. Phillipe Crouzat

**Second Maritime Region**
*Le Chateau*
*29240 Brest Naval*
*Telephone: (98) 80-12-00*

Maritime Prefect ..............Vice Amr. d'Escadre Brac De La Perriere

**Third Maritime Region**
*83800 Toulon Naval*
*Telephone: (94) 41 40 20*

Maritime Prefect and Commander-in-Chief
   for the Mediterranean ..........Vice Amr. d'Escadre Jean Paul Orosco

## AIR FORCE
*(Armée de l'Air)*
*26 bd. Victor*
*75015 Paris*
*75996 Paris Armées*
*Telephone: (1) 552-43-21*

**Supreme Council of the Air Force**
President .........................................Charles Hernu
                                        (Minister of Defense)
Member *(ex officio)* .........Gén. de l'Armée Aérienne Bernard Capillon
Member *(ex officio)* ......Gén. de l'Armée Aérienne Phillipe Archambeand
                      (Inspector General of the Air Force)

    **General Staff of the Air Force**
    *(Etat-Major de 1'Armée de l'Air)*

Chief of Staff, Air Force .......Gén. de l'Armée Aérienne Bernard Capillon
Chargé de Mission .................Gén. de Brig. Aérienne Yvon Le Coz
Chief Executive Officer ..........Gén. de Brig. Aérienne Jacques Bourillet
Director of Staff ....................Gén. de Div. Aérienne Paul Huguet
Deputy Chief of Staff, Plans .................................
Deputy Chief of Staff, Operations ................Gén. de Brig. Aérienne
                                       Roger Pessidous
Deputy Chief of Staff, Logistics ...............................
Director, Directorate for Military
    Air Traffic ....................Gén. de Brig. Aérienne Jean Vedrine
Chief, Air Force Center for Photographic
    Interpretation ..............................Lt. Col. Celestin Cocot

Director, Directorate of Air Force
Military Personnel . . . . . . . . . . . .Gén. de Corps Aérien Jean-Louis Bonnet
Adjoint Director . . . . . . . . . . . . . . .Gén. de Brig. Aérienne Claude Carreau
Director, Central Directorate of Air Force
Commisariat . . . . . . . . . . . . . . . . .Commissaire Gén. de Div. Aérienne
Jean-Louis Bajard
Adjoint Director . . . . . . . . . . . . . . .Commissaire Gén. de Brig. Aérienne
Bernard Auvergne
Director, Central Directorate of Air Force
Equipment . . . . . . . . . . . . . . . . . . .Gén. de Div. Aérienne Paul Simonet
Adjoint Director . . . . . . . . . . . . . . .Gén. de Brig. Aérienne Jean Sabatey
Director, Directorate of Ground
Organisation . . . . . . . . . . . . . . . . . . . . . . .Gén. de Div. Jean Anquetil
Adjoint Director . . .Ingenieur en Chef des Ponts et Chaussées Andre Schmit
Military Adjoint . . . . . . . . . . . . . . . . . . . . . . . . . . . . . .Col. Henri Chapus

## SPECIALISED HIGH COMMANDS OF THE AIR FORCE
*(Grands Commandements Specialisés de l'Armée de l'Air)*

**Aerial Defense Command and Air Command of Aerial Defense Forces**
*(Commandement de la Defense Aérienne et Commandement "Air" des Forces de Defense Aérienne)*
*95150 Taverny*

*Telephone:    (3) 964-98-70*

Commander . . . . . . . . . . . . . . . . .Gén. de Corps Aérien Theodore Mahlberg

**Strategic Air Forces Command**
*(Commandement des Forces Aériennes Stratégiques)*
*95150 Taverny*

*Telephone:    (3) 964-98-70*

Commander . . . . . . . . . . . . . . . . . . . . .Gén. de Corps Aérien Elie Humbert

**Military Air Transport Command**
*(Commandement du Transport Aérien Militaire)*
*Base Aérienne 107*
*78129 Villacoublay*

*Telephone:    (3) 630-23-88*

Commander . . . . . . . . . . . . . . . . . . . . .Gén. de Brig. Aérienne Paul Clariond

**Air Force Schools Command**
*(Commandement des Ecoles de l'Armée de l'Air)*
*Base Aérienne 107*
*78129 Villacoublay*

*Telephone:    (3) 630-23-88*

Commander . . . . . . . . . . . . . . . . . . . . .Gén. de Corps Aérien Henri Gimbert

**Air Force Signals Command**
*(Commandement des Transmissions de l'Armée de l'Air)*
*Base Aérienne 107*
*78129 Villacoublay*

*Telephone:*

Commander . . . . . . . . . . . . . . . . . . . . .Gén. de Brig. Aérienne Louis Iribarne

**Air Engineering Command**
*(Commandement du Genie de l'Air)*
*Base Aérienne 107*
*78129 Villacoublay*

*Telephone:    (3) 630-23-88*

Commander . . . . . . . . . . . . . . . . .Gén. de Brig. Aérienne Michel de Touchet

**Aerial Regions First Region and Tactical Air Force—Metz**
*(Force Aérienne Tactique et 1ᵉʳ Region—Metz*

Commander ...................... Gén. de Corps Aérien Michel Forget
Executive Officer,
(Commandant en Second) ........ Gén. de Brig. Aérienne Alain Suquet

**Second Region—Villacoublay**
*Base Aérienne 107*
*78129 Villacoublay*
*Telephone:    (3) 630-23-88*

Region Commander...............................................

**Third Region—Bordeaux**
*(Gironde)*
*1 Place Jean-Moulin*
*33998 Bordeaux Armées*
*Telephone:    56-52-62-15*

Region Commander ........................... Gén. de Div. Aérienne
Jean de Boretgel de Chassay

**Fourth Region**
*21 bd. du Roy-Rene*
*13898 Aix-en-Provence Armées*
*Telephone:    91-27-75-01*

Region Commander ........ Gén. de Div. Aérienne Pierre-Claude Lauzeral

**National Office Aerospacial Research**
*(Office National d'Etudes et de Récherches Aérospaciales O.N.E.R.A.)*
*29 Avenue de la Division-Leclerc*
*92320 Chatillon*
*Telephone:    (1) 657-11-60*
*Telex:    ONERA 260907 F*

President............................. Ingenieur Gén. Andre Jouffret
Vice President ................. Ingenieur Gén. Jean-Claude Carpentier

\* \* \* \* \*

## GENERAL DEFENSE DATA

**Manpower**
Total Armed Forces............................................ 492,850
   (See Page 193)
Population ................................................. 54,174,000

**Spending**
Military Expenditures ........................................ $25.5 billion
Gross National Product ...................................... $634 billion
Military Expenditure as a Percentage of
   Gross National Product .................................... 4.0%
Military Expenditure as a Percentage of
   Central Expenditure........................................ 19.4%

**Defense Treaties** *(See Part II for Additional Detail)*

Bilateral:

| | |
|---|---|
| Benin | Mauritania |
| Cameroon | Monoco |
| Central African | Morocco |
|   Republic | Niger |
| Chad | Portugal |
| Congo | Saudi Arabia |
| Djibouti | Senegal |
| Egypt | Soviet Union |
| Federal Republic | Spain |
|   of Germany | Togo |
| Gabon | Tunisia |
| Ivory Coast | United Kingdom |
| Lebonon | United States |
| Libya | Zaire |
| Madagascar | |

Multilateral:

*France—Finland—Soviet Union—United Kingdom:* Paris Peace Treaty restricting the size and armament of Finnish armed forces (1947)

Multinational Force and Observers in the Sinai

North Atlantic Treaty Organization

Protocol II of Treaty of Tlatelolco

Western European Union

United Nations Interim Force in Lebanon

United Nations Truce Supervision Organization

**Military Rank Comparisons**
See Appendix A.

# GABON

## Gabonese Republic
### *Republique Gabonaise*

### Defense Establishment Command Structure and Force Organization

The President is Supreme Chief of the Armed Forces, and exercises his authority through the Minister of National Defense.

**Total armed forces:** 2,170 (Army: 1,500;  Navy: 170;  Air Force: 500). **Para-military forces:** 2,800 (Coast Guard, National Constabulary and National Police Force).

## HEAD OF STATE

H. E. El Hadj Omar Bongo

**OFFICE OF THE PRESIDENT**
*B.P. 546*
*Libreville*

*Telephone: 72 26 90*
*Telex: 5211 presigab, 5301 presigab*

President of the Republic and Supreme Chief
of the Armed Forces . . . . . . . . . . . . . . . Gen. d'Armée Aérienne de Reserve
El Hadj Omar Bongo
Commander-in-Chief,
Presidential Guard . . . . . . . . . . . . . . Gén. de Corps d'Armée Martin Louis
Chief, B2 (Bureau of Military Investigation) . . . . . . . . . Col. Roland Mandec
Colonel of the Guard . . . . . . . . . . . . . . . . . . . . . . . . . . . Lt. Col. Bettencourt

**OFFICE OF THE PRIME MINISTER**
*B.P. 91*
*Libreville*

*Telephone: 72 21 62*
*Telex: 5409*

Prime Minister, Minister of Interministerial
Coordination and the Reform of State and
Mixed Economy Enterprises, and President
of the National Consultative Council . . . . . . . . . . . . . . . . . Léon Mebiame
Secretary of State to the Prime Minister . . . . . Joachim Mogouim-Di Mahotes

**MINISTRY OF NATIONAL DEFENSE AND VETERANS AFFAIRS, CHARGED WITH NATIONAL SECURITY**
*B.P. 546*
*Libreville*

*Telephone: 72 22 61*

Minister . . . . . . . . . . . . . . . . . . . . . . . . . . . . . . . . . . . Julien Mpouho Epigat
Secretary-General . . . . . . . . . . . . . . . . . . . . . . . . . . Gen. Jean Fernand Roux
Deputy Secretary-General . . . . . . . . . . . . . . . . . . . . . . . . . . . . . . Col. Matega
Director, Office of Veterans Affairs . . . . . . . . . . . . . . . . Col. Thardin Roux
Inspector, Security Forces . . . . . . . . . . . . . . . . . . . . . . Gen. Germain Teale

## DEFENSE FORCES

**ARMY**
**Land and Naval Forces**
*(Forces Terrestres et Navales—FTN)*
*B.P. 2126*
*Libreville*

*Telephone: 72 21 55, 72 19 40*

Commander-in-Chief, Land and Naval Forces . . . . . Gén. de Corps d'Armée
Danial Ba Oumar
Chief of Staff . . . . . . . . . . . . . . . . . . . . . . . . . . . . . Gen. de Brig. Idriss Ngari
Deputy Chief of Staff . . . . . . . . . . . . . . . . . . . . . Col. Maj. Ella Abessolo Paul
Inspector-General, Armed Forces
and Military Engineering . . . . . . . . . . Gén. de Brig. Ehya Obiang Thomas
Chief, Engineering and Construction . . . . . . . . . Lt. Maj. Mounanga Badini
Central Director, Commisariat . . . . . . . . . . . . . . Cdt. Rantonga Barthelemy
Army Materiel Officer . . . . . . . . . . . . . . . . . . . . . . . . . . . . . . . . . Lt. Lendibi
Commander, Armored
Reconaissance Squadron . . . . . . . . . . . . . . . . Lt. Maj. Dimu Andjona J.L.
Commander, Parachute Battalion . . . . . . . . . . . . . . . . . . . . . . . Lt. Col. Oyini
Director, Mouila Instruction Center . . . . . . . . . . . . . . . . . . . Capt. Schneider

**Regional Commands**

Commander, 1st Military Region (Estuaire) . . . . . . . . . . . . . . . . . . . . . . . . . . . .

Commander, 2nd Military Region
(Wolen-N'Ten) . . . . . . . . . . . . . . . . . . . .Capt. Maj. Edouard Nkilly Edjo

Commander, 3rd Military Region
(Ogooue-Ivindo) . . . . . . . . . . . . . . . . . . . . . . .Lt. Maj. Jerome Ngamoua

Commander, 4th Military Region (Ogooue-Lolo). .Lt. Col. T. Baptiste Tabu

Commander, 5th Military Region (Hante Ogoone) . . . . . . . . . . . . . . . . . . . . .

Commander, 6th Military Region (N'Gounie) . . . . .Capt. Edouard Nzamba

Commander, 7th Military Region
(Nyanga) . . . . . . . . . . . . . . . . . . . . . . . . .Chef de Batallion André Ngomal

Commander, 8th Military Region (Ogooue Maritime) . . . . . . . . . . . . . . . . .

Commander, 9th Military Region (Moyen Ogooue) . . . . . . . . . . . . . . . . . . .

**AIR FORCE**
*(Forces Aériennes)*
*B.P. 10070*
*Libreville*

*Telephone:    73 24 75, 73 27 08*
*Telex:    5348 aag*

Chief of Staff . . . . . . . . . . . . . . . . . . . . . . . . . . . . .Gén. d'Armée Jacques Mvé

**NATIONAL CONSTABULARY**
*(Gendarmerie)*
*Libreville*

*Telephone:    73 20 36*

Commander-in-Chief, National
Constabulary . . . . . . . . . . . . . . . . . . . .Gén. de Corps d'Armée Andre Nzong

Chief of General Staff . . . . . . . . . . . . . . . .Col. Maj. Germain Henri Pounah

Director of Staff . . . . . . . . . . . . . . . . . . . . . . . . . . . . . . . . . . .Col. Maj. Tsinga

Chief, Burrak Division . . . . . . . . . . . . . . . . . . . . . . . . . . . .Capt. Max Massala

Chief of Staff, Mobile Constabulary . . . . . . . . .Lt. Col. Joachim Toulekima

**NATIONAL POLICE FORCES**
*(Forces de Police Nationale—FPN)*
*Libreville*

*Telephone:    73 20 36*

Commander-in-Chief, Police Forces . . . . . . . . . . . . .Gén. de Corps d'Armée
Jean Bonniface Assele

Director, Police Staff . . . . . . . . . . . . . . . . . . . . .Lt. Col. Maj. Mathieu Akouré

Technical Counselor . . . . . . . . . . . . . . . . . .Gén. de Div. Theodore Nkomah

Chief of Staff . . . . . . . . . . . . . . . . . . . . . . . . . . . . . . . . . . . .Col. Andre Eyeghe

\* \* \* \* \*

# GENERAL DEFENSE DATA

**Manpower**

Total Armed Forces . . . . . . . . . . . . . . . . . . . . . . . . . . . . . . . . . . . . . . . . . . .2,170
(See Page 205)

Population . . . . . . . . . . . . . . . . . . . . . . . . . . . . . . . . . . . . . . . . . . . . . . .662,000

**Spending**

Military Expenditures . . . . . . . . . . . . . . . . . . . . . . . . . . . . . . . . . . . . .$11 million

Gross National Product . . . . . . . . . . . . . . . . . . . . . . . . . . . . . . . . . . .$2.8 billion

Military Expenditure as a Percentage of
Gross National Product . . . . . . . . . . . . . . . . . . . . . . . . . . . . . . . . . . . .0.4%

Military Expenditure as a Percentage of
Central Government Expenditure . . . . . . . . . . . . . . . . . . . . . . . . . . . . .1.1%

**Defense Treaties** *(See Part II for Additional Detail)*

Bilateral:    France

Multilateral:    Limited Test Ban Treaty
Organization of African Unity
Treaty on the Non-Proliferation of Nuclear Weapons

**Military Rank Comparisons**
See Appendix A.

# GAMBIA
## Republic of The Gambia

### Defense Establishment Command Structure and Force Organization

The President is Commander-in-Chief of all defense and police forces. The Gambia Field Force is the Gambian component of the defense forces of the Senegambia confederation and is controlled by the Ministry of the Interior. The defense protocol, signed January 12, 1983, envisages parallel military structures in the Gambia and Senegal, with national units being designated for the confederal force. Organizationally, the Gambia Field Force is administered as part of the Gambia Police Force.

**Total armed forces:** 355 (Gambia Field Force: 280;   Navy: 50;   Air Force: 25). **Paramilitary forces:** 400 (Police).

### HEAD OF STATE

H. E. Alhaji Sir Dawda Kairaba Jawara, G.M.R.G., G.C.M.G.

**OFFICE OF THE PRESIDENT**
*State House*
*Banjul*
*Telephone: 200, 662*
*Telex: 2204 presof gv*

President of the Republic and
  Minister of Defense . . . . . . . . . . . . . . . . Alhaji Sir Dawda Kiraba Jawara, G.M.R.G., G.C.M.G.
Secretary-General . . . . . . . . . . . . . . . . . . . . . . . . . . . . . Dr. J. Ayo-Langley
Confidential Secretary . . . . . . . . . . . . . . . . . . . . . . . . . (Mrs.) Judith Johnson

**OFFICE OF THE VICE PRESIDENT**
*State House*
*Banjul*
*Telephone: 243, 263*

Vice President . . . . . . . . . . . . . . . . . . . . . . . . . . . . . Bakary B. Darbo, M.P.
Permanent Secretary . . . . . . . . . . . . . . . . . . . . . . . . . . . Alfaseni Kuli N'Jie

**MINISTRY OF THE INTERIOR**
*Banjul*

Minister . . . . . . . . . . . . . . . . . . . . . . . . . . . . . . Alhaji Alieu E. W. F. Badjie
Parliamentary Secretary . . . . . . . . . . . . . . . . . . . . Alhaji Jallow Sanneh, M.P.
Permanent Secretary . . . . . . . . . . . . . . . . . . Alhaji Momadou Lamin Auber

### DEFENSE FORCES

**GAMBIA POLICE**
*Banjul*
*Telephone: 210*

Commissioner of Police . . . . . . . . . . . . . . . . . . . Alhaji Mass Momodou Jarra
Assistant Commissioner of Police . . . . . . . . . . . . . . . . . . . . . . . . M. B. Khan
Commander, Gambia Field Force . . . . . . . . . Alhaji Momodou N'Dow-N'Jie
Commander, Police Immigration . . . . . . . . . . . . . . . . . . I. J. K. Tambajang
Commander, Police Prosecutions . . . . . . . . . . . . . . . . . . . . . . . . S. W. Riley
Commander, Police C.I.D. . . . . . . . . . . . . . . . . . . . . . . . Alhaji O. W. Nicol
Officer Commanding, 'T' Division . . . . . . . . . . . . . . . . . . . . . B. E. Baldeh
Officer Commanding, 'A' Division . . . . . . . . . . . . . . . . . . . . . O. A. Touray
Chief, Harbor Police . . . . . . . . . . . . . . . . . . . . . . . . . . . . . . . . . . . . . . . . .
Officer Commanding, 'W' Division . . . . . . . . . . . . . . . . . . . . . E. A. Gomez
Officer Commanding, 'B' Division . . . . . . . . . . . . . . . . . . . . . . T. S. Bojang
Officer Commanding, 'C' Division . . . . . . . . . . . . . . . . . Bakary K. Bojang
Chief Fire Officer . . . . . . . . . . . . . . . . . . . . . . . . . . . . . . . . . . . . Z. B. King

\* \* \* \* \*

# GENERAL DEFENSE DATA

**Manpower**

Total Armed Forces ...................................................355
   (See Page 207)
Population ...................................................635,000

**Spending**

Military Expenditures ...........................................$2.97 million
Gross National Product ...........................................$149 million
Military Expenditure as a Percentage of
   Gross National Product ...............................................0.6%
Military Expenditure as a Percentage of
   Central Government Expenditure ...................................3.4%

**Defense Treaties** *(See Part II for Additional Detail)*

Bilateral:      Senegal

Multilateral:   Economic Community of West African States
                Organization of African Unity
                Limited Test Ban Treaty
                Treaty on the Non-Proliferation of Nuclear Weapons

*Note: The Confederation of Senegambia was formed on Feb. 1, 1982, to bring about the integration of Senegal and Gambia's security services, armed forces, and economic and monetary systems.*

*There is a government of the Confederation, composed of members of the two individual governments. The President of Senegal serves as the President of the Confederation, and the President of the Gambia is the Vice-President. A Council of Ministers has also been formed.*

# GERMAN DEMOCRATIC REPUBLIC
## (East Germany)
### *Deutsche Demokratische Republik*

### Defense Establishment Command Structure and Force Organization

The Council of State has responsibility for defense and security matters. The National Defense Council advises the Council of State and provides policy guidance for the Ministry of Defense. The Minister of Defense directly commands all three services of the armed forces.

**Total armed forces:** 166,000 (Army: 113,000;   Navy: 15,000;   Air Force: 38,000). **Paramilitary forces:** 71,000.

**COUNCIL OF STATE**
*(Staatsrat)*
*Marx-Engels-Platz*
*1020 Berlin*

*Telephone: 230 (Central Protocol)*
*Telex: 1152408 stra dd*

| | |
|---|---|
| Chairman | Erich Honecker |
| Deputy Chairman | Willi Stoph |
| Deputy Chairman | Dr. Manfred Gerlach |
| Deputy Chairman | Gerald Götting |
| Deputy Chairman | Prof. Dr. Heinrich Homann |
| Deputy Chairman | Horst Sindermann |
| Deputy Chairman | Paul Verner |
| Member | Kurt Anclam |
| Member | Werner Felfe |
| Member | Prof. Dr. Kurt Hager |
| Member | Brunhilde Hanke |
| Member | Friedrich Kind |
| Member | Prof. Dr. Lothar Kolditz |
| Member | Egon Krenz |
| Member | Dr. Günter Mittag |
| Member | Margarete Müller |
| Member | Alois Pisnik |
| Member | Bernhard Quandt |
| Member | Werner Seifert |
| Member | Dr. Klaus Sorgenicht |
| Member | Paul Strauss |
| Member | Ilse Thiele |
| Member | Harry Tisch |
| Member | Prof. Dr. Johanna Töpfer |
| Member | Rosel Walther |
| Secretary | Heinz Eichler |

**NATIONAL DEFENSE COUNCIL**
*(Nationaler Verteidigungsrat)*

| | |
|---|---|
| Chairman | Erich Honecker |
| Secretary | GenObst Fritz Streletz |

**MINISTRY OF NATIONAL DEFENSE**
*(Ministerium für Nationale Verteidigung)*
*126 Strausberg*
*Berlin*

*Telephone: 527 9861*

| | |
|---|---|
| Minister and General of the Army | ArmeeGen Heinz Hoffmann |
| Deputy Minister | GenLt Klaus-Dieter Baumgarten (Chief of the Border Troops) |
| Deputy Minister | Adm Wilhelm Elm (Chief of People's Navy) |
| Deputy Minister | GenObst Werner Fleissner (Chief of Technology and Weapons) |
| Deputy Minister | GenLt Joachim Goldbach (Chief of Rear Services) |

Deputy Minister .............................GenObst Heinz Kessler
(Chief of Political Main Administration)
Deputy Minister ........................GenObst Wolfgang Reinhold
(Chief of the Air Force and Air Defense Command)
Deputy Minister ........................GenObst Horst Stechbarth
(Chief of the Ground Forces)
Deputy Minister .............................GenObst Fritz Streletz
(Chief of the Main Staff)
Deputy Minister ................................GenLt Fritz Peter
(Chief of Civil Defense)

**Main Staff**
*(Hauptstab)*

Chief .........................................GenObst Fritz Streletz
Deputy Chief ...............................GenLt Hellmut Arnold
Deputy Chief................................GenMaj Kurt Gottwald
Deputy Chief .............................GenMaj Edwin Maseberg
Chief Inspector .............................GenLt Helmut Borufka

**Political Main Administration**
*(Politische Hauptverwaltung)*

Chief.........................................GenObst Heinz Kessler
Deputy Chief ...............................GenLt Horst Brünner
Deputy Chief................................GenLt Ernst Hampf

**Rear Services**
*(Rückwärtige Dienste)*

Chief .......................................GenLt Joachim Goldbach
Deputy Chief ...............................GenLt Georg Steiger

**Civil Defense**
*(Zivilverteidigung)*

Chief ..........................................GenLt Fritz Peter
Deputy Chief ...............................GenMaj Rolf Fischer
Deputy Chief ...................................Obst Klaus Rude
Deputy Chief................................GenMaj Rudi Schütz
Deputy Chief ................................Obst Werner Sedlick
Deputy Chief ...............................GenMaj Kurt Sommer

**Military Academies**

Commanding Officer, Air Force and
   Air Defense Academy (Kamenz) ..................GenMaj Hans Süss
Commanding Officer, Rosa
   Luxemburg Border Troops
   Academy (Plauen) .........................GenMaj Werner Ebertz
Commanding Officer, Ernst
   Thalmann Land Forces Academy (Löbau) .......GenLt Werner Winter
Commanding Officer, Friedrick Engels
   Military Academy (Dresden) ...........GenLt Hans-Joachim Wiesner
Commanding Officer, Karl Liebknecht
   Naval Academy (Stralsund)...................VAdm Wilhelm Nordin
Commanding Officer, Wilhem Pieck
   Political Military School (Berlin)..........GenMaj Werner Wunderlich

**Administration**

Chief, Artillery and Rocket Troops..............GenLt Günter Bormann
Chief, Cadres..................................GenLt Harold Ludwig
Chief, Catering ...............................Obst Horst Schmiedes
Chief, Chemical Services ........................GenMaj Otto Heinz
Chief, Communications ......................GenMaj Walter Paduch
Chief, Construction .........................GenLt Fritz Ludwig
Chief, Intelligence Administration ................GenLt Theo Gregori
Chief, Medical .............................GenLt Gerhard Rehwald
Chief, Military Intelligence ...................GenMaj Alexander Karin
Chief, Physical Culture and Sports ..................Obst Arno Mücke
Chief, Technology and Weapons .............GenObst Werner Fleissner
Chief, Transport .............................GenMaj Siegfried Gräfe
Chief, Vehicle Affairs .......................GenMaj Günter Kackow

**Departments**

Chief, Cartographical Services (Halle/Saale) ........Obst Herbert Scharlo
Chief, Finance ...............................GenLt Heinz Tappert

Chief, International Relations ................GenMaj Heinrich Winkler
Chief, Legal Department ..................GenObst Lothar Krumbiegel
Chief, Press Department ....................Obst Wolfgang Lehmann
Chief, Protocol Department .......................Obst Willi Wollny
Chief, Tank Services .....................GenMaj Gerhard Storbeck

## DEFENSE FORCES

Commander-in-Chief and
    Minister of Defense.....................ArmeeGen Heinz Hoffmann

**ARMED FORCES**
**National People's Army**
*(Nationale Volksarmee)*
*Schnellerstrasse 1/4*
*119 Berlin*

*Telephone: 635 2881*

**ARMY**
**Ground Forces**
*(Landstreitkräfte)*
*Schnellerstrasse 1/4*
*119 Berlin*

*Telephone: 635 2881*

Chief .......................................GenObst Horst Stechbarth
Deputy Chief ...............................GenMaj Heinz Gerloff
Deputy Chief...............................GenLt Heinz Handke
Deputy Chief ..............................GenMaj Harry Kleffel
Deputy Chief ...............................GenLt Werner Rothe
Deputy Chief................................GenLt Klaus Winter
Deputy Chief................................GenLt Horst Zander

**Border Troops**
*(Grenztruppen)*

Commander.........................GenLt Klaus-Dieter Baumgarten
Deputy Commander ......................GenLt Gerhard Lorenz
Deputy Commander ..................GenMaj Heinz-Ottomar Thieme
Deputy Commander ..........................GenMaj Karl Wilhelm
Commander, Central Command ...............GenMaj Bernhard Geier
Commander, Northern Command .................GenMaj Harold Bär
Commander, Southern Command ..............GenMaj Walter Tanner
Commandant, East Berlin City Command .......GenLt Karl-Heinz Drews
Deputy Commandant ......................GenMaj Wolfgang Conrad
Deputy Commandant.............................Obst Lothar Hartig
Deputy Commandant .................Obst Manfred Hummel (Political)
Deputy Commandant .........................Obst Manfred Thomas
Deputy Commandant ..............................Wilhelm Walter

**Army Districts and Divisions**

Commander, Southern Military District (Leipzig) ......GenLt Horst Skerra
Commander, 4th Motorized Infantry Division
    (Erfurt) .........................................Obst Egon Gleau
Commander, 11th Motorized Infantry Division
    (Halle/Saale) .............................GenMaj Manfred Zeh
Commander, 7th Tank Division (Dresden) ..........Obst Günter Möckel
Commander, Northern Military District
    (Neurbrandenburg) .....................GenLt Manfred Gehmert
Commander, 1st Motorized Infantry Division
    (Potsdam)..............................GenMaj Siegfried Zabelt
Commander, 8th Motorized Infantry Division
    (Schwerin) ..................................Obst Ulrich Betmann
Commander, 9th Tank Division (Eggesin) ...........GenMaj Horst Sylla

**District Commands**
*(Wehrbezirkskommandos)*

Chief, Berlin (East) ...........................GenMaj Heinz Exner
Chief, Cottbus ......................GenMaj Günter Bretschneider
Chief, Dresden .............................GenMaj Rudi Mädler
Chief, Erfurt ..............................Obst Oskar Poschmann
Chief, Frankfurt/Oder .....................GenMaj Rudi Lindner
Chief, Gera ...................................Obst Horst Klimpel
Chief, Halle/Saale.............................GenMaj Franz Rös
Chief, Karl-Marx-Stadt ..................GenMaj Manfred Raupach
Chief, Leipzig.................................Obst Günther Diedrich

Chief, Magdeburg . . . . . . . . . . . . . . . . . . . . . . . . . . . . . .GenMaj Heinz Schieck
Chief, Neubrandenburg . . . . . . . . . . . . . . . . . . . . .GenMaj Franz Schindhelm
Chief, Potsdam . . . . . . . . . . . . . . . . . . . . . . . . . . .GenMaj Horst Kalkbrenner
Chief, Rostock . . . . . . . . . . . . . . . . . . . . . . . . . . . . . . . . . .Obst Hans Ziems
Chief, Schwerin . . . . . . . . . . . . . . . . . . . . . . . . . . . . . . .Obst Alfred Walter
Chief, Suhl . . . . . . . . . . . . . . . . . . . . . . . . . . . . . . . .Obst Günter Brodowski

**NAVY**
**People's Navy**
*(Volksmarine)*
*Schnellerstrasse 1/4*
*119 Berlin*

*Telephone:   635 2881*

Chief . . . . . . . . . . . . . . . . . . . . . . . . . . . . . . . . . . . . .Adm Wilhelm Ehme
Deputy Chief . . . . . . . . . . . . . . . . . . . . . .KAdm Lothar Heineke (Training)
Deputy Chief . . . . . . . . . . . . . . . . . . . . .VAdm Gustav Hesse (Chief of Staff)
Deputy Chief . . . . . . . . . . . . . . . . . . . . .VAdm Hans Hofman (Rear Services)
Deputy Chief . . . . . . . . . . . . . . . . . . . . . . . .VAdm Günter Kutzschebauch
(Political Administration)

**AIR FORCE**
**Air and Air Defense Command**
*(Luftstreitkrafte und Luftverteidigung)*
*Schnellerstrasse 1/4*
*119 Berlin*

*Telephone:   635 2881*

Chief . . . . . . . . . . . . . . . . . . . . . . . . . . . . . . .Genobst Wolfgang Reinhold
Deputy Chief . . . . . . . . . . . . . . . . . . . . . . . . . . . . . . .GenMaj Klaus Baars
Deputy Chief . . . . . . . . . . . . . . . . . . . . . . . . . . . . . .GenLt Martin Pahnke
Deputy Chief . . . . . . . . . . . . . . . . . . . . . . . . . . . . . . .GenLt Alfred Vogel
(Chief of Political Administration)

\* \* \* \* \*

# GENERAL DEFENSE DATA

**Manpower**

Total Armed Forces . . . . . . . . . . . . . . . . . . . . . . . . . . . . . . . . . . . . . . . . . .166,000
(See Page 209)
Population . . . . . . . . . . . . . . . . . . . . . . . . . . . . . . . . . . . . . . . . . . .16,738,000

**Spending**

Military Expenditures . . . . . . . . . . . . . . . . . . . . . . . . . . . . . . . . . . . . .$8.3 billion
Gross National Product . . . . . . . . . . . . . . . . . . . . . . . . . . . . . . . . . . .$146 billion
Military Expenditure as a Percentage of
Gross National Product . . . . . . . . . . . . . . . . . . . . . . . . . . . . . . . . . . . . . . .5.7%
Military Expenditure as a Percentage of
Central Government Expenditure . . . . . . . . . . . . . . . . . . . . . . . . . . . . . .11.1%

**Defense Treaties** *(See Part II for Additional Detail)*

Bilateral:    Angola              People's Democratic
Bulgaria              Republic of Yemen
Czechoslovakia    Poland
Ethiopia            Soviet Union
Hungary            Tanzania
Mozambique        Vietnam

Multilateral:  Biological Weapons Convention
Environmental Modification Convention
Limited Test Ban Treaty
Treaty on the Control of Arms on the Seabed
Treaty on the Non-Proliferation of Nuclear Weapons
Warsaw Treaty Organization

**Military Rank Comparisons**
See Appendix A.

# FEDERAL REPUBLIC OF GERMANY
## (West Germany)
### *Bundesrepublik Deutschland*

## Defense Establishment Command Structure and Force Organization

In peacetime, the Federal Minister of Defense is Commander-in-Chief and has responsibility for both the administrative control and the operational readiness of the armed forces. In case of war, this authority would pass to the Federal Chancellor, although in practice the major components of the West German armed forces would be commanded by NATO officers.

The Defense Minister is Chairman of the Federal Security Council, a cabinet committee that coordinates security policy. The Inspector General is the principal military adviser to the Minister of Defense and the Federal Government. He chairs the Armed Forces Defense Council, which provides interservice policy guidance. In matters of administration and planning, the Inspectors of each service and the Surgeon General are subordinate to the Inspector General. In military matters, the service chiefs report directly to the Minister of Defense.

The Territorial Army remains under national control even in times of war. It provides training and support for the Field Army and functions as a home defense force.

**Total armed forces:** 495,000 (Army: 335,000 including 38,000 Territorial Army; Navy: 36,400; Air Force: 105,900). **Para-military forces:** 20,000 (Border Police).

## HEAD OF STATE

Prof. Dr. Karl Carstens

**OFFICE OF THE FEDERAL PRESIDENT**
*Kaiser-Friedrich-Str. 16-18*
*5300 Bonn 1*

*Telephone: (228) 2001*
*Telex: 886393*

| | |
|---|---|
| Federal President | Prof. Dr. Karl Carstens |
| Personal Assistant | Dr. Helmut Rückriegel |
| Chief of Staff and Secretary | Hans Neusel |

**OFFICE OF THE FEDERAL CHANCELLOR**
*Adenauerallee 99-103*
*5300 Bonn 1*

*Telephone: (228) 5601*
*Telex: 886591*

| | |
|---|---|
| Federal Chancellor | Dr. Helmut Kohl |
| State Minister | Dr. Philipp Jenninger |
| State Minister | Friedrich Vogel |
| Parliamentary State Secretary | Peter Lorenz |

**Federal Security Council**
*(Bundessicherheitsrat)*

| | |
|---|---|
| Chairman | Dr. Helmut Kohl (Federal Chancellor) |
| Member | Hans-Dietrich Genscher (Minister of Foreign Affairs) |
| Member | Dr. Friedrich Zimmermann (Minister of the Interior) |
| Member | Dr. Manfred Wörner (Minister of Defense) |

Member .................................. Dr. Gerhard Stoltenberg
(Minister of Finance)
Member .................................. Dr. Otto Lambsdorff
(Minister of Economy)

**FEDERAL MINISTRY OF DEFENSE**
*(Bundesministerium der Verteidigung)*
*Hardthöhe*
*5300 Bonn 1*

*Telephone: (228) 121*
*Telex: 886575 bwd, 886583 bwd,*
*886788*

Federal Minister and Commander-in-Chief ......... Dr. Manfred Wörner
Parliamentary State Secretary ..................... Peter K. Würzbach
State Secretary ................................. Dr. Joachim Hiehle
State Secretary ................................. Dr. Lothar Rühl
Chief, Information and Press Staff ............... Obst Jürgen Reichardt
Chief, Planning Staff ........................... Dr. Hans Rühle
Chief, Organizational Staff ....................... Christian Weigeldt

**Personnel Division**

*Telephone: (228) 12 83 53*

Director ................................... GenLt Hans Kubis
Deputy Director ............................ Dr. Kurt Servatius
Chief, Civilian Personnel Section ..................... Elmar Fischer
Chief, Central Military
    Personnel Section ..................... BrigGen Roland Lankers
Chief, Army Officers Section .................. BrigGen Horst Albrecht
Chief, Air Force Officers Section .............. BrigGen Johann Gärtner
Chief, Navy Officers/Medical/
    Special Personnel Section .............. KptzS Hansdieter Christmann

**Budget Division**

*Telephone: (228) 12 22 65-66*

Director ................................... Paul Firmenich
Chief, Financial Planning/General and
    Personnel Budgeting/Treasury Section ................. Adolf Fischer
Chief, Materiel Budgeting/Research and
    Development/International Section ..................... Hans Wenz

**Administrative and Legal Division**

*Telephone: (228) 12 25 41-45*

Director ............................... Hans Joachim Hildebrandtl
Chief, Administrative Law/Legal Administration/
    Military Chaplaincy ......................... Dr. Hans Mensching
Chief, General Legal Affairs Section ................. Dr. Hans Böttcher
Chief, Military Administration Section ........ Dr. Hans-Günter Schwenk

**Billeting, Real Estate and**
  **Construction Division**

*Telephone: (228) 12 33 44-45*

Director ................................... Dr. Heinz Schaefgen
Chief, Billeting ............................. Dr. Hans-Joachim Korte
Chief, Real Estate ................................. Dr. Hans Müller

**Social Affairs Division**

*Telephone: (228) 12 29 12-15*

Director ................................... Alfred Zumkeller
Chief, General Social Affairs .................. BrigGen Winfried Vogel
Chief, Troops and Civil Servants
    Welfare Section ............................... Hans-Peter Riegel
Chief, Job Training Section ..................... Ingeborg Buchberger

**Medical Inspectorate**

*Telephone: (228) 12 26 66, 12 26 38*

Surgeon General ............................ Dr. Hans-Joachim Linde
Deputy Director and Medical Chief of Staff ...... Dr. Wolfgang Scheunert
Chief, Medical Section ...................... Dr. Karl-Wilhelm Wedel
Chief, Medical Field Service Station ................. Dr. Hans Sautter

**Ordnance Division**

*Telephone: (228) 12 91 40-41*

Director ................................... Karl Helmut Schnell
Deputy Director, Defense Technology ..................... Peter Runge
Deputy Director, Economic Affairs................... Wolfgang Ruppelt
Chief, Planning and Program Section .................. Wilfried Heins
Chief, Defense Research Section ..................... Dr. Heinz Glaser
Chief, Central Affairs ........................... Dr. Klaus Bosse
Chief, Foreign Relations Section ..................... Joachim Heyden
Chief, Army Materiel Section ......................... Karl Heinz Otte
Chief, Air Force Materiel Section..................... Erhard Letzel

|  |  |
|---|---|
| Chief, Navy Materiel Section | Norbert Roy |
| Chief, Operations and Intelligence Materiel Section | Dr. Lothar Weber |

**Office of Procurement and Defense Technology**
*Konrad-Adenauer-Ufer 2-6*
*5400 Koblenz*
*Telephone: (261) 4001*

|  |  |
|---|---|
| Director | Dr. Otto Greve |

**Military Chaplains**

|  |  |
|---|---|
| Director, Catholic Chaplaincy (Bonn) | Dr. Ernst Niermann |
| Director, Evangelical Chaplaincy (Bonn) | Reinhard Gramm |

## DEFENSE FORCES

**ARMED FORCES**
**Armed Forces High Command**
*(Führungsstab der Bundeswehr)*
*P.O. Box 1328*
*5300 Bonn 1*
*Telephone: (228) 1 21*
*Telex: 886575*

|  |  |
|---|---|
| Inspector General | Gen Wolfgang Altenburg |
| Deputy Inspector General | GenLt Walter Windisch |
| Chief of Staff, Armed Forces High Command | KAdm Klaus Rehder |
| Chief, Education/Personnel/ Training Section | Dr. Dietrich Genschel |
| Chief, Military Intelligence Section | BrigGen Jörn Söder |
| Chief, Defense Policy and Operations Section | GenMaj Hans Peter Tandecki |
| Chief, Organization | Johann Grillmeier |
| Chief, Logistics | BrigGen Horst Hauke |
| Chief, Planning | BrigGen Johannes Nebe |
| Chief, Telecommunications/ Electronics | FltlAdm Willi Krauss |

**Federal Armed Forces Security Council**
*(Militärischer Führungsrat)*

|  |  |
|---|---|
| Chairman | Gen Wolfgang Altenburg (Inspector General) |
| Member | GenLt Walter Windisch (Deputy Inspector General) |
| Member | GenLt Meinhard Glanz (Chief of Staff, Army) |
| Member | VAdm Ansgar Bethge (Chief of Staff, Navy) |
| Member | GenLt Eberhard Eimler (Chief of Staff, Air Force) |
| Member | Dr. Hans-Joachim Linde (Surgeon General) |

**ARMY**
*(Heer)*
*P.O. Box 1328*
*5300 Bonn 1*
*Telephone: (228) 1 21*
*Telex: 886575*

|  |  |
|---|---|
| Inspector of the Army | GenLt Meinhard Glanz |
| Deputy Inspector | GenLt Heinz Kasch |
| Chief of Staff | GenMaj Gerhard Deckert |
| Chief, Education/Personnel/ Training Section | BrigGen Harald Schulz |
| Chief, Military Intelligence Section | Obst Joachim Geyer |
| Chief, Operations | BrigGen Adolf Lorenz |
| Chief, Organization | BrigGen Hubertus Senff |
| Chief, Logistics | BrigGen Erich Schwemmle |
| Chief, Planning | BrigGen Kurt Barthel |
| Chief, Ordnance | Obst Hartmut Schmidt-Petri |

**First Army Corps**
*Einsteinstr. 40-44*
*4400 Münster*
*Telephone: (251) 40646*

|  |  |
|---|---|
| Commander | GenLt Dr. Gerhard Wachter |
| Commander, 1st Armored Divison (Hannover) | GenMaj Henning von Ondarza |
| Commander, 3rd Armored Divison (Buxtehude) | GenMaj Wolfgang Tebbe |

Commander, 6th Mechanized
Division (Neumünster) ........................GenMaj Dieter Clausz
Commander, 7th Armored
Division (Unna) ...........................GenMaj Erich Dietrichs
Commander, 11th Mechanized
Division (Oldenburg) .......................GenMaj Johann Hoster

**Second Army Corps**
*Kienlesbergstrasse*
*7900 Ulm*

*Telephone:   (731) 61181*

Commander ...............................GenLt Leopold Chalupa
Commander, 4th Mechanized
Divison (Regensburg) ..................GenMaj Wolfgang Odendahl
Commander, 1st Airborne
Divison (Bruchsal) ..................GenMaj Christoph-Adolf Fürus
Commander, 1st Mountain Division
(Garmisch-Partenkirchen).....................GenMaj Horst Netzler
Commander, 10th Armored Division
(Sigmaringen) ...........................GenMaj Werner Lange

**Third Army Corps**
*Rizzastr. 1-3*
*5400 Koblenz*

*Telephone:   (261) 10021*

Commander ...........................GenLt Hans-Joachim Mack
Commander, 2nd Mechanized
Division (Kassel) .......................GenMaj Manfred Fanslau
Commander, 5th Armored
Division (Diez).....................GenMaj Dr. Franz Uhle-Wettler
Commander, 12th Armored
Division (Veitshöchheim) .......................GenMaj Lutz Moek

**Territorial Command, Schleswig-
Holstein and German
Representative to Allied Forces
Northern Europe**
*Niemannsweg 220*
*2300 Kiel 1*

*Telephone:   (431) 3 07 71*

Commander ................................KAdm Rudolf Deckert

**Territorial Command, North**
*Kaldenkirchnerstr. 121-155*
*4050 Mönchengladbach*

*Telephone:   (2161) 1 20 11-17*

Commander................................GenMaj Konrad Manthey

**Territorial Command, South**
*Römerstr. 104*
*6900 Heidelberg 1*

*Telephone:   (6221) 2 71 22*

Commander................................GenMaj Helmut Komossa

**District Command I**
(see Territorial Command, Schleswig-
Holstein)

**District Command II**
*(Lower Saxony, Bremen)*
*Hans-Böckler-Allee 18*
*3000 Hannover 1*

*Telephone:   (511) 5311*

Commander .........................GenMaj Horst-Dieter Kallerhoff

**District Command III**
*(North Rhine-Westphalia)*
*Lenaustr. 29*
*4000 Düsseldorf 30*

*Telephone:   (211) 63 30 01*

Commander ............................GenMaj Wolfhard Galinsky

**District Command IV**
*(Hesse, Rhineland-Palatinate, Saar)*
*Freiligrathstr. 6*
*6500 Mainz*
*Telephone: (6131) 5 70 31*

Commander ................................GenMaj Martin Holzfuss

**District Command V**
*(Baden-Württemberg)*
*Nürnbergerstr. 184*
*7000 Stuttgart 50*
*Telephone: (711) 61 98 61*

Commander ...........................GenMaj Ruprecht von Butler

**District Command VI**
*(Bavaria)*
*Dachauer Strasse 128*
*8000 Munich 19*
*Telephone: (89) 13 00 01*

Commander..................................GenMaj Rudolf Meyer

**Administrative Headquarters**

Chief, District I (Kiel) ...................................Ulrich Behnel
Chief, District II (Hannover) .......................Karl Heinz Backes
Chief, District III (Düsseldorf) ................Hartmut Meyer-Truelsen
Chief, District IV (Wiesbaden) .......................Günther Petersen
Chief, District V (Stuttgart) ........................Waldemar Gressl
Chief, District VI (Munich) ............................Albert Köhler

**NAVY**
*(Marine)*
*P.O. Box 1328*
*5300 Bonn 1*
*Telephone: (228) 1 21*
*Telex: 886575*

Inspector of the Navy ..........................VAdm Ansgar Bethge
Deputy Inspector and Chief of Staff ..........KAdm Hans Hermann Vohs
Chief, Education/Personnel/Training Section ......FltlAdm Heinz Hallier
Chief, Intelligence ............................KptzS Jochen Mehner
Chief, Operations ......................FltlAdm Hans Friedrich Meisner
Chief, Organization .....................KptzS Konrad Ehrensberger
Chief, Logistics ...............................KptzS Alfons Teipel
Chief, Planning ..............................KptzS Walter Günther
Chief, Ordnance .....................FltlAdm Klaus Jürgen Steindorff
Commander-in-Chief, Fleet .....................VAdm Günter Fromm

**AIR FORCE**
*(Luftwaffe)*
*P.O. Box 1328*
*5300 Bonn 1*
*Telephone: (228) 1 21*
*Telex: 886575*

Inspector of the Air Force ......................GenLt Eberhard Eimler
Deputy Inspector............................GenLt Paul Sommerhoff
Chief of Staff ...............................GenMaj Hartmut Gülzow
Chief, Education/Personnel/
   Training Section......................BrigGen Dr. Jürgen Schreiber
Chief, Intelligence ......................Obst Karl Heinz Wiesmath
Chief, Operations...................................Obst Uwe Vieth
Chief, Organization .......................BrigGen Manfred Philipp
Chief, Logistics ................................Obst Peter Klatte
Chief, Planning ...........................BrigGen Rolf Thiemann
Chief, Ordnance ............................BrigGen Fritz Schulz
Chief, MRCA Weapons System Section ....................Hans Ambos
Commander, General Air Force Office ..............GenLt Günter Raulf
Commander, Air Force Tactical Command .....GenLt Hans-Jörg Kuebart
Commander, Air Force Supply Command .....GenLt Claus Thierschmann

**PARA-MILITARY FORCES**
**Border Police**
*(Bundesgrenzschutz)*
*(under Ministry of Interior)*

Inspector (Commanding Officer) ......................Karlheinz Amft
Deputy ..........................................Alwin Strecker

* * * * *

## GENERAL DEFENSE DATA

**Manpower**
Total Armed Forces . . . . . . . . . . . . . . . . . . . . . . . . . . . . . . . . . . . . . . . . . . . .495,000
  (See Page 213)
Population . . . . . . . . . . . . . . . . . . . . . . . . . . . . . . . . . . . . . . . . . . . . . .61,697,000

**Spending**
Military Expenditures . . . . . . . . . . . . . . . . . . . . . . . . . . . . . . . . . . . . . . . .$27.7 billion
Gross National Product . . . . . . . . . . . . . . . . . . . . . . . . . . . . . . . . . . . . . . .$848 billion
Military Expenditure as a Percentage of
  Gross National Product . . . . . . . . . . . . . . . . . . . . . . . . . . . . . . . . . . . . . . .3.3%
Military Expenditure as a Percentage of
  Central Government Expenditure . . . . . . . . . . . . . . . . . . . . . . . . . . . . . . .22.5%

**Defense Treaties** *(See Part II for Additional Detail)*

     Bilateral:     Soviet Union
                    United States

     Multilateral:  Limited Test Ban Treaty
                    North Atlantic Treaty Organization
                    Treaty on the Control of Arms on the Seabed
                    Treaty on the Non-Proliferation of Nuclear Weapons

**Military Rank Comparisons**
See Appendix A.

# GHANA
## Republic of Ghana

### Defense Establishment Command Structure and Force Organization

The Chairman of the Provisional National Defense Council (PNDC) is Commander-in-Chief of the Armed Forces. The PNDC is the main national policy-making body. It is advised on defense issues by the People's Defense Committee.

**Total armed forces:** 14,700 (Army: 12,000; Navy: 1,200; Air Force: 1,500). **Para-military forces:** 5,000 (Border Guard).

### HEAD OF STATE

H. E. Flt. Lt. Jerry John Rawlings

**OFFICE OF THE CHAIRMAN, PROVISIONAL NATIONAL DEFENSE COUNCIL—PNDC**
*The Castle, Osu*
*P.O. Box 1627*
*Accra*
*Telephone: 65415*

Chairman and Commander-in-Chief of the Armed Forces ............................ Flt. Lt. Jerry John Rawlings
Chief, Defense Staff .......................... Brig. Samuel K. Baafi
Coordinator, Armed Forces Defense Committee........ Joseph Adjei Boadi
Member ............................................. Ama Ata Aideo
Member.............................................. Mrs. Anaa Enin
Secretary of Information ................................. Ato Austin

**MINISTRY OF DEFENSE**
*Burma Camp*
*Accra*
*Telephone: 75608*
*Telex: 2077 burma camp accra*

Secretary.................................... Na Polkuu Konkuu Chiiri
Chief of Procurement .......................... Lt. Col. Dattey-Acquia

### DEFENSE FORCES

**ARMED FORCES**
*c/o Ministry of Defense*
*Burma Camp*
*Accra*
*Telephone: 76111*
*Telex: 2077 burma camp accra*

Commander-in-Chief of the Armed Forces................................... Flt. Lt. Jerry John Rawlings
Chief of Staff (PNDC Secretariat) ................ Brig. Samuel K. Baafi

**ARMY**
*Army Headquarters*
*Flagstaff House*
*Accra*
*Telephone: 76603*
*Telex: 2077 burma camp accra*

Chief, Army Staff and Army Commander........... Brig. Arnold Quainoo
Director, Operations and Planning....................... Lt. Col. Odei
First Brigade Commander .......................... Col. David Klutsuy
Second Brigade Commander ..................... Col. Siedua Ayuma

**NAVY**
*Navy Headquarters*
*Burma Camp*
*Accra*

*Telephone: 77695*
*Telex: 2077 burma camp accra*

Chief, Naval Staff and Naval Commander . . . . . . . . . . Capt. Joseph Oppong
Commander, NOIC Eastern Naval
    Command . . . . . . . . . . . . . . . . . . . . . . . . . . . . . . . Cdr. E. K. Aryeetey
Commander, NOIC Western
    Naval Command . . . . . . . . . . . . . . . . . . . . Cdr. Benjamin Ohene-Kwapong

**AIR FORCE**
*Air Force Headquarters*
*Burma Camp*
*Accra*

*Telephone: 77656*
*Telex: 2077 burma camp*

Chief, Air Staff and Acting Commander,
    Air Force . . . . . . . . . . . . . . . . . . . . . . . . . . . . Group Capt. J. E. A. Kotei
Commander, Accra Air Station . . . . . . . . . . . . . . . Wing Cdr. John A. Bruce
Commander, Takordi Air Station . . . . . . . . . . . . . . . . . . . . . . . . . (Vacant)
Commander, Tamale Air Station . . . . . . . . . . . . . . . . . . . Group Capt. Doke

**POLICE**
*Police Headquarters*
*Accra*

*Telephone: 2244*

Inspector-General . . . . . . . . . . . . . . . . . . . . . . . . . . . . . . . . . . . . . . Kugblnu
Deputy Inspector-General, Administration . . . . . . . . . . . . . . . J. K. Owusu

\* \* \* \* \*

## GENERAL DEFENSE DATA

**Manpower**
    Total Armed Forces . . . . . . . . . . . . . . . . . . . . . . . . . . . . . . . . . . . . 14,700
      (See Page 219)
    Population . . . . . . . . . . . . . . . . . . . . . . . . . . . . . . . . . . . . . . 12,943,000

**Spending**
    Military Expenditures . . . . . . . . . . . . . . . . . . . . . . . . . . . . . . . $46 million
    Gross National Product . . . . . . . . . . . . . . . . . . . . . . . . . . . . . $11.2 billion
    Military Expenditure as a Percentage of
      Gross National Product . . . . . . . . . . . . . . . . . . . . . . . . . . . . . . . 0.4%
    Military Expenditure as a Percentage of
      Central Government Expenditure . . . . . . . . . . . . . . . . . . . . . . . . . 3.7%

**Defense Treaties** *(See Part II for Additional Detail)*

    Bilateral:     United States

    Multilateral:    Biological Weapons Convention
                Economic Community of West African States
                Environmental Modification Convention
                Limited Test Ban Treaty
                Organization of African Unity
                Treaty on the Control of Arms on the Seabed
                Treaty on the Non-Proliferation of Nuclear Weapons
                United Nations Interim Force in Lebanon

# GREECE
## Hellenic Republic
### *Elleniki Demokratia*

## Defense Establishment Command Structure and Force Organization

The Prime Minister, who is also the Minister of Defense, commands the armed forces. He is advised by the Supreme Council of Defense and Foreign Policy *(Kysea)*, a consultative body comprised of several ministers and deputies. The Prime Minister's authority is exercised through the Chief of the Hellenic National Defense General Staff, who handles administrative and operational matters concerning the military. The position of Chief of the General Staff is rotated among the three service chiefs.

**Total armed forces:** 158,500 (Army: 115,000; Navy: 19,500; Air Force: 24,000). **Paramilitary forces:** 25,000 (Gendarmerie).

## HEAD OF STATE

H. E. Constantine Karamanlis

**OFFICE OF THE PRESIDENT**
*17 Stisichorou Street*
*Athens, T. T. 138*
*Telephone: (1) 72 831*

President . . . . . . . . . . . . . . . . . . . . . . . . . . . . . . . . . Constantine Karamanlis

**OFFICE OF THE PRIME MINISTER**
*Maximos Building*
*Athens*
*Telephone: (1) 724 0654*
*Telex: 214333 gspm gr*

Prime Minister and Minister
   of Defense . . . . . . . . . . . . . . . . . . . . . . . . . . . . . Andreas Papandreou
Minister to the Prime Minister . . . . . . . . . . . . . . Agamemnon Koutsogiorgas

    **Supreme Council of Defense and**
      **Foreign Policy**
    *Kysea*

Chairman . . . . . . . . . . . . . . . . . . . . . . . . . . . . . . . Andreas Papandreaou
     (Prime Minister and Minister of Defense)
Member *(ex officio)* . . . . . . . . . . . . . . . . . . . . . . . . . . . . . Gerasimos Arsenis
     (Minister of Coordination/National Economy)
Member *(ex officio)* . . . . . . . . . . . . . . . . . . . . . . . . . Ioannis Skoularikis
     (Minister of Public Order)
Member *(ex officio)* . . . . . . . . . . . . . . . . . . . . . Ioannis Charalambopoulos
     (Minister of Foreign Affairs)
Member *(ex officio)* . . . . . . . . . . . . . . . . . . . . Adm. Theodoros Deyannis, HN
     (Chief of the General Staff)
Member *(ex officio)* . . . . . . . . . . . . . . . . . . . . . . Agamemnon Koutsogiorgas
     (Minister to the Prime Minister)

**MINISTRY OF NATIONAL DEFENSE**
*Holargos, Athens*
*Telephone: (1) 642 6947*
     *(Foreign Relations)*
     *464 4874, 646 5201*
*Telex: 216780 rkqa gr*

Minister and Prime Minister . . . . . . . . . . . . . . . . . . . . Andreas Papandreaou
Under Secretary . . . . . . . . . . . . . . . . . . . . . . . . . . . . Antonios Drosoyiannis
Under Secretary . . . . . . . . . . . . . . . . . . . . . . . . . . . . . Pafsanias Zakolikos
Adjutant . . . . . . . . . . . . . . . . . . . . . . . . . . . . . Maj. Constantinos Polyzoes
Chief, Minister's Military Office . . . . . . . . . . . . . . . . Brig. Ioannis Tzanakis

# DEFENSE FORCES

## ARMED FORCES
**Hellenic National Defense General Staff—HNDGS**
*Holargos, Athens*
*Telephone: (1) 646 5201, 5301*

Chief, HNDGS ........................ Adm. Theodoros Deyannis, HN
Deputy Chief A .......................... Lt. Gen. Nik Lazaridis, HA
Deputy Chief B ............... Lt. Gen. Ioannis Dimakoyannis, HAF
Director, First Joint
   Staff Group ................... Maj. Gen. Sotirios Kontoyannis, HAF
Director, Second Joint
   Staff Group .................... Maj. Gen. Mich. Moustopoulos, HA
Director, Third Joint
   Staff Group ...................... Maj. Gen. Andr. Karadimas, HA
Director, Fourth Joint
   Staff Group .................... Comdr. Periandros Lampiris, HN
Director, Seventh Joint
   Staff Group, (Public
   Relations) ........................ Comdr. Athanasios Kantas, HN
Chief, Office of Foreign
   Affairs/Protocol ................................. Vas. Chroneas

## ARMY
**Hellenic Army**
*Holargos, Athens*
*Telephone: (1) 646 5301, 5201*

Chief, Hellenic Army General Staff—
   HAGS ........................... Lt. Gen. Dimitrios Panagopoulos
Deputy Chief A, HAGS ............. Lt. Gen. Alexandros Kalenteridis
Deputy Chief B, HAGS .............. Lt. Gen. Athanasios Papanikolaou
Commander, First Army
   Headquarters ....................... Lt. Gen. Vassilios Kourkafas
Commander, Hellenic Military
   Command Interior & Islands ........... Lt. Gen. Panayotis Panourgias
Commanding General, Athens ................ Lt. Gen. Manuel Skoulas
Inspector General, HAGS .................... Lt. Gen. Kimon Vimblis
Director, Second Staff
   Office (Information) ................... Brig. Gen. Miltiadis Laskaris

### Procurement Directorate
*Y.P. Rouf*
*Athens, Greece*

Director .............................. Lt. Gen. Loukas Athanasenas

## NAVY
**Hellenic Navy**
*Holargos, Athens*
*Telephone: (1) 644 3331*
*(Foreign Relations)*
*652 0401, 654 2011*

Chief, Hellenic Navy General Staff—HNGS ... Vice Adm. Nikolaos Pappas
Deputy Chief, HNGS ...................... Rear Adm. Elias Perissakis
Inspector General, HNGS ............... Rear Adm. Sotirios Georgiadis
Chief, Hellenic Fleet ................... Vice Adm. Athanasios Giogezas
Commander, Hellenic
   Naval Training ................. Rear Adm. Konstantinos Metallinos
Commander, Hellenic
   Naval Logistics ...................... Rear Adm. Aristomenis Kelaidis
Director, Second Staff
   Office (Information) ...................... Capt. Athanasios Vennis

### Procurement Office
*Hellenic Navy Command*
*2 Paparijoparilou Street*
*Athens*

Director .............................. Comdr. Dimitrios Tomaras

## AIR FORCE
**Hellenic Air Force**
*Holargos*
*Athens*
*Telephone: (1) 642 8101, 642 8411*

Chief, Hellenic Air Force General Staff—
   HAFGS .................................. Lt. Gen. Nikolaos Kouris
Deputy Chief, HAFGS .................... Maj. Gen. Ioannis Marinakis
Inspector General .................... Maj. Gen. Harilaos Angelopoulos
Chief, Tactical Air Force ................... Lt. Gen. Ioannis Hatziris
Commander, Air Training
   Command ........................ Maj. Gen. Anastasios Karadimas
Director, Second Staff
   Office (Information) ................... Col. Panayotis Stratigopoulos

**Air Materiel Command**
*(In charge of Procurement)*
*Hellenic Air Force*
*15 Mesogeion Street*
*Athens*

Director . . . . . . . . . . . . . . . . . . . . . . . . . . . . .Lt. Gen. Dimitrios Apostolakis

\* \* \* \* \*

## GENERAL DEFENSE DATA

**Manpower**
Total Armed Forces. . . . . . . . . . . . . . . . . . . . . . . . . . . . . . . . . . . . . . . . . . . . . .158,500
    (See Page 221)
Population . . . . . . . . . . . . . . . . . . . . . . . . . . . . . . . . . . . . . . . . . . . . . . .9,743,000

**Spending**
Military Expenditures. . . . . . . . . . . . . . . . . . . . . . . . . . . . . . . . . . . . . . . . . .$2.4 billion
Gross National Product. . . . . . . . . . . . . . . . . . . . . . . . . . . . . . . . . . . . . . . .$44.6 billion
Military Expenditure as a Percentage of
    Gross National Product . . . . . . . . . . . . . . . . . . . . . . . . . . . . . . . . . . . . . . . .5.4%
Military Expenditure as a Percentage of
    Central Government Expenditure . . . . . . . . . . . . . . . . . . . . . . . . . . . . . .23.5%

**Defense Treaties** *(See Part II for Additional Detail)*

    Bilateral:     United States

    Multilateral:   Biological Weapons Convention
                 Limited Test Ban Treaty
                 North Atlantic Treaty Organization
                 Treaty of Establishment
                 Treaty on the Non-Proliferation of Nuclear Weapons

# GRENADA
## State of Grenada

### Defence Establishment Command Structure
### and Force Organization

The Governor-General is nominal Commander-in-Chief of the armed forces. Executive authority is vested in the Prime Minister who is also Minister of Defence. Administrative and operational control of the military is exercised by the Commander of the Armed Forces.

**Total armed forces:** 1,500 (Army).

### HEAD OF STATE

H. M. Queen Elizabeth II

### GOVERNOR-GENERAL

H. E. Sir Paul Scoon, G.C.M.G., O.B.E.

**OFFICE OF THE GOVERNOR-GENERAL**
*St. George's*

*Telephone: 2401*
*Telex: 3423 grenex ga*
*(Ministry of External Affairs)*

Governor-General and
Commander-in-Chief ............. Sir Paul Scoon, G.C.M.G., O.B.E.

**REVOLUTIONARY COUNCIL**
*St. George's*

*Telephone: 2225*

| | |
|---|---|
| Member | Maurice Bishop (Prime Minister) |
| Member | Sydbey Ambrose |
| Member | Bernard Coard |
| Member | Caldwell Taylor |
| Member | Unison Whitman |
| Member | Fitzroy Bain |
| Member | Selwyn Strachan |
| Member | Basil Gahagan |
| Member | George Louison |
| Member | Kendrick Radix |
| Member | Leon Cornwall |
| Member | Vincent Cornwall |
| Member | Vincent Noel |
| Member | Gellineau James |
| Member | Hudson Austin |
| Member | Simon Charles |
| Member | Dr. Bernard Gittens |
| Member | Claudette Pitt |
| Member | Jacquelin Creft |
| Member | Liam James |
| Member | Lynden Rhamdanny |
| Member | Norris Bain |

**OFFICE OF THE PRIME MINISTER AND MINISTRIES OF DEFENCE, INFORMATION, INTERIOR, AND CARRIACOU AFFAIRS**
*St. George's*
*Telephone: 2225*
*Telex: 3457 pmgren ga*

Prime Minister and Minister of Defence, Information, Interior, and Carriacou Affairs . . . . . . . . . . Maurice Bishop

**MINISTRY OF COMMUNICATION, WORKS AND LABOUR**
*St. George's*

Minister, Secretary of State for Defence and the Interior, and Commander of the Armed Forces . . . . . . . . . . . . . . . . . . . . . . . . . . . . . . Gen. Hudson Austin

**MINISTRY OF DEFENCE**
*St. George's*
*Telephone: 2225*

Minister of Defence and Prime Minister . . . . . . . . . . . . . . . . Maurice Bishop

## DEFENCE FORCES

**ARMED FORCES**
**People's Revolutionary Army**
*St. George's*
*Telephone: 2265*

Commander, Armed Forces . . . . . . . . . . . . . . . . . . . . . . . . . . Hudson Austin

**POLICE**
**Grenada Police Service**
*St. George's*
*Telephone: 2244*

Commissioner . . . . . . . . . . . . . . . . . . . . . . . . . . . . . . . . . . . . . Ian St. Bernard

\* \* \* \* \*

## GENERAL DEFENCE DATA

**Manpower**
Total Armed Forces . . . . . . . . . . . . . . . . . . . . . . . . . . . . . . . . . . . . . . 1,500
(See Page 225)
Population . . . . . . . . . . . . . . . . . . . . . . . . . . . . . . . . . . . . . . . . . . 109,000

**Spending**
Military Expenditures . . . . . . . . . . . . . . . . . . . . . . . . . . . . . . . . . . . . . . . .
Gross National Product . . . . . . . . . . . . . . . . . . . . . . . . . . . . . . . . . . . . . . $70 million
Military Expenditure as a Percentage of Gross National Product . . . . . . . . . . . . . . . . . . . . . . . . . . . . . . . . . . . . . . . .
Military Expenditure as a Percentage of Central Government Expenditure . . . . . . . . . . . . . . . . . . . . . . . . . . . . . . .

**Defence Treaties** (*See Part II for Additional Detail*)

Bilateral:        None

Multilateral:    Treaty on the Control of Arms on the Seabed
                 Treaty on the Non-Proliferation of Nuclear Weapons
                 Treaty for the Prohibition of Nuclear Weapons in Latin
                     America

# GUATEMALA
## Republic of Guatemala
### *República de Guatemala*

### Defense Establishment Command Structure and Force Organization

The Chief of State of Guatemala is Commander-in-Chief of the armed forces and exercises his control through the Minister of Defense. The Minster of Defense is responsible for making key military appointments, and shares operational control of the armed forces with the Army Chief of Staff. The Navy and Air Force are subordinate to the Army Chief of Staff in operational matters.

**Total armed forces:** 19,050 (Army: 17,500;   Navy: 950;   Air Force: 600). **Para-military forces:** 9,500 (National Police).

## CHIEF OF STATE

H. E. Oscar Huberto Mejía Victores

**OFFICE OF THE PRESIDENT**
*(Oficina de la Presidencia)*
*Palacio Nacional*
*Guatemala City*

*Telephone:   (2) 212112, 222666*
*Telex:   5325 relpub gu*
*(Public Relations)*

Chief of State and
   Commander-in-Chief . . . . . . . . . . . . . . . . . .Oscar Huberto Mejía Victores
Military Chief, National Palace . . . . . . . . . . . . . .Cnel. Pedro Vidal Cifuentes

**PRESIDENTIAL HOUSE**
*(Casa Presidencial)*
*6 Avenida y 5 Calle Zona 1*
*Guatemala City*

*Telephone:   (2) 23933*
*Telex:   5331 capres gu*

Military Chief, Presidential Staff . . . . .Cnel. Victor Manuel Argueta Villaira
Deputy Chief . . . . . . . . . . . . . . . . . . . . . . . . . . . . . . .Cnel. Mário Enríquez
Third in Command . . . . . . . . . . . . . . . . . . . . . . . .Cnel. Florencio Castellanos
Commander, Presidential Guard . . . . . . . . . . .Cnel. Jaime Rabanales-Reyes

**MINISTRY OF NATIONAL DEFENSE**
*(Ministério de la Defensa Nacional)*
*Palacio Nacional*
*Guatemala City*

*Telephone:   (2) 21212, 20001-2*
*Telex:   248368*

Minister . . . . . . . . . . . . . . . . . . . . . . . . .Gral. Oscar Humberto Mejía Victores
Vice Minister . . . . . . . . . . . . . . . . . . . . . . .Cnel. Carlos Enríque Vides Reinoso
Secretary General . . . . . . . . . . . . . . . . . . . . . . . . . . . . . .Cnel. Gustavo Pinto

## DEFENSE FORCES

**ARMY**
*(Ejército Guatemalteco)*
*Ministry of Defense*
*Palacio Nacional*
*Guatemala City*

*Telephone:   (2) 21212, 28162*
*(Chief of Staff)*

Chief of Staff . . . . . . . . . . . . . . . . . . . . . . .Gral. Héctor Mário López Fuentes
Vice Chief of Staff . . . . . . . . . . . . . .Cnel. Héctor Alejandro Gramjo-Morales

**General Staff of the Army**
*(Estado Mayor General del Ejército)*

Chief, Personnel Department . . . . . . . . . . . . . Cnel. José Luis Ángeles Juarez
Chief, Intelligence Department . . . . . . . . . . . . . . . Cnel. Mauricio Rodríguez
Chief, Operations Department . . . . . . . . . . . Cnel. Luis E. Mendoza García
Chief, Logistics Department . . . . . . . . . Cnel. Jorge Manuel Estrada Estévez
Chief, 5th Department . . . . . . . . . . . . . . . . . . . . . Cnel. Mario Enrique Paiz
Secretary . . . . . . . . . . . . . . . . . . . . . . . . Cnel. Manuel Javier López Blanco
Protocol Official . . . . . . . . . . . . . . . . . . . . . . . . . . . Cnel. Carlos Lazo A.
Chief, Army Supply Service . . . . . . . . . . . . . . . Cnel. Alfredo Rego Lemus
Chief, Military Health Services . . . . . . . . Cnel. Roberto Sagas Tume Aquino
Chief, Army Transmissions Service . . . . . . . . . . . . . Cnel. Edgar Hernández
Chief, Army Geographic Service . . . . . . Cnel. Lionel Anibal Rivera Morataya
Chief, Army Department
    of Finances . . . . . . . . . . . . . . . . . . . . . . . Cnel. Jorge Dorturo Rivero
Chief, Military Auditor . . . . . . . . . . . . . . Cnel. Marco Antónío Ortíz Andrino
Director, Military Hospital . . . . . . . . . . . . . . . Cnel. Dr. Arturo Pinzón A.
Chief, Army Publications . . . . . . . . . . . . . . . . . . . . . . . . . . . . . . . (Vacant)
Auditor of War, Military
    Zone "GJRB" . . . . . . . . . . . . . . . . . . . Cnel. Lic. Ricardo Vides Menendez
Manager, Army Social
    Security Institute . . . . . . . . . . . . . . . . . . . . Cnel. Carlos Arroyave Castillo
Chief, Army Commissary . . . . . . . . . . . . . Cnel. Juan Francisco Aguilar Oliva
Chief, Army Department
    of Justice . . . . . . . . . . . . . . . . . . . . . . . Cnel. Lic. Felix Roman Beteta Paz
Director, Polytechnical
    School (Military Academy) . . . . . . . . . . . . Cnel. Alvaro Barahona Escobar
Director, Military Studies Center . . . . . . . Cnel. Cesar Augusto Caceres Rojas

**Commands**

Commander, Mariscal Zavala Military Brigade
    (Guatemala City) . . . . . . . . . . . . . . . . . . . . . . . . . . . . Cnel. Guido Abdala
Commander, "Justo Rufino Barrios" Military
    Zone Headquarters (Guatemala City) . . . . . . . . . . Cnel. Eliu Rego Lemus
Commander, Presidential Honor Guard . . . . . . . . . . . . Cnel. Jaime Hernan

**NAVY**
*(Marina de Guerra)*
*Department of Izabal*
*Guatemala City*
*Telephone:  (2) 0480102*

Commander . . . . . . . . . . . . . . . . . . . . . . . . Cap. Francisco Torres Cheguen
Deputy Commander . . . . . . . . . . . . . . . . . . . . . . . . . . . . . . . . . . . . . . . .
Commander, Sipacate
    Naval Base (Pacific) . . . . . . . . . . . . . . . . Cap. Juan Mariano Girón Pelaez
Deputy Commander,
    Santo Tomas de Castillas
    Naval Base (Atlantic) . . . . . . . . . . . . . . . . . . . . . . . . . . . . . . . . . . . . .

**AIR FORCE**
*(Fuerza Aerea Guatemalteca)*
*Avenida Hincapié, Base Aerea La Aurora,*
    *Zona 13*
*Guatemala City*
*Telephone:  (2) 64081*

Commander . . . . . . . . . . . . . . . . . . Cnel. Fernando Alfonso Castillo-Ramírez
Deputy Commander . . . . . . . . . . . . . . . . . . . . . . . Cnel. Guillermo Ponciano
Commander and Captain,
    La Aurora International
    Air Terminal . . . . . . . . . . . . . . . . . . . . . . . . . . Cnel. Ruben Suchini Paiz

**NATIONAL POLICE**
*(Policía Nacional)*
*Guatemala City*

Director-General . . . . . . . . . . . . . . . . . . . . Cnel. Hernan Orestes Ponce Nitsch
Deputy Director-General . . . . . . . . . . . . . . . . . . . . . . . . Cnel. Ricardo Pinto

**TREASURY POLICE**
*(Policía de Hacienda)*
*Guatemala City*

Commander . . . . . . . . . . . . . . . . . . . . . . . . . . . . . . . . . . . . . . . Cnel. Hichos

\* \* \* \* \*

## GENERAL DEFENSE DATA

**Manpower**

Total Armed Forces..............................................19,050
(See Page 227)
Population ....................................................7,537,000

**Spending**

Military Expenditures .........................................$65 million
Gross National Product.........................................$7.8 billion
Military Expenditure as a Percentage of
Gross National Product ..........................................0.8%
Military Expenditure as a Percentage of
Central Government Expenditure ................................5.8%

**Defense Treaties** *(See Part II for Additional Detail)*

Bilateral:    United States

Multilateral:    Act of Chapultepec
Biological Weapons Convention
Council for Central-American Defense
Inter-American Defense Board
Inter-American Treaty of Reciprocal Assistance
Limited Test Ban Treaty
Treaty for the Prohibition of Nuclear Weapons in Latin
America
Treaty on the Non-Proliferation of Nuclear Weapons

**Military Rank Comparisons**

See Appendix A.

# GUINEA
## People's Revolutionary Republic of Guinea
### *République Populaire Revolutionnaire de Guinée*

### Defense Establishment Command Structure and Force Organization

The President is Commander-in-Chief of the armed forces. Administrative and operational control is the responsibility of the Minister of the People's Army.

**Total armed forces:** 9,900 (Army: 8,500;     Navy: 600;     Air Force: 800). **Para-military forces:** 9,200 (People's Militia).

## HEAD OF STATE

H. E. Ahmed Sékou Touré

**OFFICE OF THE PRESIDENT**
*Conakry*
*Telephone:   44 11 47, 44 11 22*
*(Secretary-General of the Government)*
*Telex:   623 p r g ckry*

President of the People's Revolutionary
Republic and Commander-in-Chief . . . . . . . . . . . . . Ahmed Sékou Touré
Secretary-General of the Presidency . . . . . . . . . . . . . . El Hadj Salifou Touré
Secretary-General of the Government . . . . . . . . . . . . . Sadan Moussa Touré

**OFFICE OF THE PRIME MINISTER**
*Conakry*
*Telephone:   44 17 41*
*Telex:   646 pernis ckry*

Prime Minister . . . . . . . . . . . . . . . . . . . . . . . . . . . . . . . . Dr. Lansana Béovogui

**MINISTRY OF THE PEOPLE'S ARMY**
*(Ministère de l'Armée Populaire)*
*B.P. 1000*
*Conakry*
*Telephone:   44 16 36*

Minister . . . . . . . . . . . . . . . . . . . . . . . . . . . . . Gén. El Hadk Lansana Diané
Chief of Staff . . . . . . . . . . . . . . . . . . . . . . . . . . . . . . . Gen. Toya Conde

## DEFENSE FORCES

**ARMY**
**Ground Forces**
*(Armée de Terre)*
*Conakry*
*Telephone:   44 16 54*

Chief of Staff . . . . . . . . . . . . . . . . . . . . . . . . . . . . Col. Kourouma Somah

**NAVY**
*Conakry*
*Telephone:   44 33 37*

Chief of Staff . . . . . . . . . . . . . . . . . . . . . . . . . Capt. Mohamed Lamine Sako

**AIR FORCE**
*(Armée de l'Air)*
Conakry
Telephone: 46 15 51

Chief of Staff . . . . . . . . . . . . . . . . . . . . . . . . . . . . Capt. Abdourahmane Kaba

**NATIONAL MILITIA**
*(Milice Nationale)*
Conakry
Telephone: 46 24 81

Chief of Staff . . . . . . . . . . . . . . . . . . . . . . . . . . Capt. Sékou Ahamadou Touré

**CAMP ALPHA YA YA**
*Conakry*

Commander of the Camp . . . . . . . . . . . . . . . . . . . . . . . . Capt. Sidiki Condé

* * * * *

## GENERAL DEFENSE DATA

**Manpower**
Total Armed Forces . . . . . . . . . . . . . . . . . . . . . . . . . . . . . . . . . . . . . . . . . . . .9,900
  (See Page 231)
Population . . . . . . . . . . . . . . . . . . . . . . . . . . . . . . . . . . . . . . . . . . . .5,278,000

**Spending**
Military Expenditures . . . . . . . . . . . . . . . . . . . . . . . . . . . . . . . . . . . . . . . . . . . .
Gross National Product . . . . . . . . . . . . . . . . . . . . . . . . . . . . . . . . . . . . . . . . $1.6 billion
Military Expenditure as a Percentage of
  Gross National Product . . . . . . . . . . . . . . . . . . . . . . . . . . . . . . . . . . . . . . . . . . . .
Military Expenditure as a Percentage of
  Central Government Expenditure . . . . . . . . . . . . . . . . . . . . . . . . . . . . . . . . . . .

**Defense Treaties** *(See Part II for Additional Detail)*

Bilateral:     China             Soviet Union
                  Liberia          United States
                  Sierra Leone

Multilateral:   Economic Community of West African States
                  Organization of African Unity

# GUINEA-BISSAU
## Republic of Guinea-Bissau
*República do Guiné-Bissau*

### Defense Establishment Command Structure
### and Force Organization

The President is Commander-in-Chief, Minister of the People's Revolutionary Armed Forces, and Minister of National Security. Administrative duties are exercised by the Vice Minister of the People's Revolutionary Armed Forces, and the Vice Minister of National Security.

**Total armed forces**: 6,300 (Army: 6,000;  Navy: 250;  Air Force: 50). **Para-military forces**: 5,000.

## HEAD OF STATE

H. E. Brig. Gen. Joao Bernardo Vieira

**REVOLUTIONARY COUNCIL**
*Bissau*

President and Commander-in-Chief . . . . . . Brig. Gen. João Bernardo Vieira
Vice President . . . . . . . . . . . . . . . . . . . . . . . . . . . . . . . Victor Saude María
Member . . . . . . . . . . . . . . . . . . . . . . . . . . . . . . . . . . . . . . . . Paulo Correia
Member . . . . . . . . . . . . . . . . . . . . . Gen. Manuel Saturniono da Costa
Member . . . . . . . . . . . . . . . . . . . . . . . . . . . . Gen. Buota Nambatcha
Member . . . . . . . . . . . . . . . . . . . . . . . . . . . . . . Samba Lamine Mane
Member . . . . . . . . . . . . . . . . . . . . . . . . . . . . . . . Gen. Iafai Camara
Member . . . . . . . . . . . . . . . . . . . . . . . . . . . . Capt. Benghate Na Beate
Member . . . . . . . . . . . . . . . . . . . . . . . . . . . Dr. Victor Freire Monteiro
Advisor . . . . . . . . . . . . . . . . . . . . . . . . . . . . . . . . . Eng. Mário Cabral
Advisor . . . . . . . . . . . . . . . . . . . . . . . . . . . . . . Dr. João Cruz Pinto
Advisor . . . . . . . . . . . . . . . . . . . . . . . . . . . . . . . . . . . . Joseph Turpín

**MINISTRY OF THE PEOPLES REVOLUTIONARY ARMED FORCES**
*Bissau*
*Telephone: 213240, 213175*
*Telex: 249*

Minister . . . . . . . . . . . . . . . . . . . . . . . . Brig. Gen. João Bernardo Vieira
Vice Minister . . . . . . . . . . . . . . . . . . . . . . . . . . . . . . . . . . Iafai Camara
Secretary of State, Veterans Affairs . . . . . . . . . . . . . . Col. Braima Bangura
Delegate of the Peoples' Armed Revolutionary
    Forces . . . . . . . . . . . . . . . . . . . . . . . . . . . . . . . . . Cdr. Pedro Ramos

**MINISTRY OF NATIONAL SECURITY**

Minister . . . . . . . . . . . . . . . . . . . . . . . Brig. Gen. João Bernardo Vieira
Vice Minister . . . . . . . . . . . . . . . . . . . . . . . . Jose Alfaia Pinto Pereira

## DEFENSE FORCES

**ARMED FORCES**
**Peoples Revolutionary Armed Forces—FARP**
*Bissau*

Commander-in-Chief . . . . . . . . . . . . . . . . Brig. Gen. João Bernardo Vieira
Chief of Staff . . . . . . . . . . . . . . . . . . . . . . . . . . . . José Lopez da Silva
Deputy Chief of Staff . . . . . . . . . . . . . . . . . . . . . . . . Col. Lucio Soares

**ARMY**
*Bissau*

Chief of Staff . . . . . . . . . . . . . . . . . . . . . . . . . . . . . . . . . . Col. Silva
Deputy Chief of Staff . . . . . . . . . . . . . . . . . . . . . . . . . Col. Nancassa
Chief, Armoured Units . . . . . . . . . . . . . . . . . . . . . . Jose Marcos Vieira

**NAVY**
*(Marinha de Guerra)*
*Bissau*
*Telephone:   212556, 213536*

Chief of Staff ....................................Col. Buato Na'Batcha
Commander, Naval Forces (Bissau)......................Lt. Col. Lima

**AIR FORCE**
**People's Aviation**
*Bissau*
*Telephone:   213934*

Commander ...........................................Col. Bera
Assistant Commander ...........................Maj. Carlos Gomés

\* \* \* \* \*

## GENERAL DEFENSE DATA

**Manpower**
Total Armed Forces ...............................................6,300
    (See Page 233)
Population .....................................................23,000

**Spending**
Military Expenditures...........................................$8 million
Gross National Product.........................................$134 million
Military Expenditure as a Percentage of
  Gross National Product ...............................................6.4%
Military Expenditure as a Percentage of
  Central Government Expenditure ................................6.6%

**Defense Treaties** *(See Part II for Additional Detail)*

Bilateral:  Portugal
Soviet Union

Multilateral:  Biological Weapons Convention
Organization of African Unity
Treaty on the Control of Arms on the Seabed
Treaty on the Non-Proliferation of Nuclear Weapons

# GUYANA
## Cooperative Republic of Guyana

### Defence Establishment Command Structure and Force Organization

The President is Minister of Defence and National Security and Commander-in-Chief of the Armed Forces of Guyana. All services are combined under the Guyana Defence Force. The Police are administered by the Ministry of Home Affairs.

**Total armed forces:** 7,000 (Army: 6,850; Navy: 150). **Para-military forces:** 5,000.

## HEAD OF STATE

H. E. Linden Forbes Sampson Burnham

**OFFICE OF THE EXECUTIVE PRESIDENT**
*Vlissengen Road*
*Georgetown*
Telephone: *(2) 626-668*

President of the Cooperative Republic, Minister of Defence and Commander-in-Chief of the Armed Forces . . . . . . . . . Linden Forbes Sampson Burnham, O.E., S.C.
Vice President, Parliamentary Affairs, State and Party Relations . . . . . . . . . . . . Bishwaishwer Ramsaroop, M.P.
Head of the Presidential Secretariat . . . . . . . . . . . . . . . C. E. Douglas, M. P.

**OFFICE OF THE PRIME MINISTER**
*Parliament Buildings*
*Brickdam*
*Georgetown*
Telephone: *(2) 692-515*

Prime Minister and First Vice President, Mobilization, Public Service and Information . . . . . . . . Ptolemy Alexander Reid, O. E.
Minister . . . . . . . . . . . . . . . . . . . . . . . . . . . Yvone Harewood Benn, M. P.

**MINISTRY OF HOME AFFAIRS**
*6 Brickdam*
*Georgetown*
Telephone: *(2) 63310*

Senior Minister . . . . . . . . . . . . . . . . . . . . . . . . . . . Jeffrey Thomas, M. P.

## DEFENCE FORCES

**ARMED FORCES**
**Guyana Defence Force—GDF**
*Defence Force Headquarters*
*Camp Ayanganna*
*Thomas Lands*
*Georgetown*
Telephone: *(2) 68451-5, 68426, 69246*

Commander, GDF . . . . . . . . . . . . . . . . . . . . . . . Col. David Arthur Granger
Chief of Staff . . . . . . . . . . . . . . . . . . . . . . . . . . . Brig. N. G. McLean
Commandant, People's Militia . . . . . . . . . . . . . . . . . . Col. C. B. L. Morgan
Deputy Commandant, People's Militia . . . . . . . . . . Lt. Col. Watson Joseph
Commander, 1st Infantry Brigade . . . . . . . . . . . . . . . . Lt. Col. M. Munroe
General Staff Officer 1 . . . . . . . . . . . . . . . . . . . . . . Lt. Col. R. B. Mitchell
Commanding Officer, Maritime Corps . . . . . . . . . . . . . . . Lt. Col. H. Hinds
Aide to Chief of Staff (Public Relations) . . . . . . . . . . . Capt. W. E. Sargeant

**POLICE**
*c/o Ministry of Home Affairs*
*6 Brickdam*
*Georgetown*
Telephone: *(2) 71551*

Commissioner . . . . . . . . . . . . . . . . . . . . . . . . . . . Lloyd A. Barker, D.S.S.
Deputy Commissioner, Administration . . . . . . . . Balram Raghubir, D.S.M.
Deputy Commissioner, Crime . . . . . . . . . . . . Cecil "Skip" Roberts, D.S.M.

**GUYANA NATIONAL SERVICE**
*45 Regent Road*
*Bourda*
*Telephone:  (2) 57966*

Director-General.....................................Col. Joseph Singh
Deputy Director-General, Administration .....Lt. Col. Charwin Burnham
Deputy Director-General, Production .............Lt. Col. John Piggott

\* \* \* \* \*

## GENERAL DEFENCE DATA

**Manpower**
    Total Armed Forces ..............................................7,000
        (See Page 235)
    Population ...................................................870,000

**Spending**
    Military Expenditures.......................................$21 million
    Gross National Product.....................................$544 million
    Military Expenditure as a Percentage of
      Gross National Product ..........................................3.9%
    Military Expenditure as a Percentage of
      Central Government Expenditure .................................5.9%

**Defense Treaties** *(See Part II for Additional Detail)*

    Bilateral:    United States

    Multilateral:  None

# HAITI
## Republic of Haiti
*République d'Haiti*

### Defense Establishment Command Structure
### and Force Organization

The President of Haiti is Supreme and Effective Chief of the Armed Forces and exercises his command through the Secretary of State for the Interior and National Defense. Operational control of the military is vested in the Chief of General Staff.

**Total armed forces:** 7,500 (Army: 7,000; Navy: 300; Air Force: 200). **Para-military forces:** 14,900 (National Security Volunteers).

## HEAD OF STATE

H. E. Jean-Claude Duvalier

**DEPARTMENT OF THE PRESIDENCY**
*(Bureau de la Présidence)*
*Palais Nacionale*
*Port-au-Prince*

*Telephone: (1) 2-4020*
*Telex: 0068 palais*
*0431 depres*
*(Ministère A La Présidence)*

President-for-life of the Republic
and Supreme and Effective
Chief of the Armed Forces................H. E. Jean-Claude Duvalier
Private Secretary ...........................Claude Auguste Douyon
Secretary of State, Presidency ...................Jean-Marie Chanoine

**DEPARTMENT OF THE INTERIOR
AND NATIONAL DEFENSE**
*(Departement de l'Interieur et de la
Defense Nationale)*
*Palais des Ministères*
*Port-au-Prince*

*Telephone: (1) 2-2885*

Secretary of State .............................Dr. Roger La Fontant
Under Secretary.......................................Mr. Pierre Louis

## DEFENSE FORCES

**ARMY**
*(L' Armée de Terre)*
*Grand Quartier General*
*Place des Heros de l'Independance*
*Port-au-Prince*

*Telephone: (1) 2-3935*
*Telex: 0391*

Chief of the General Staff ......................Lt. Gen. Roger St. Albin
Deputy Chief of Staff ......................Brig. Gen. Henri Namphy

**Military Departments**
Commander, Presidential Guard ........Gen. of Brig. Gracia C. Jacques
Commander, Dessalines Barracks ...............Col. Carl Michel Nicolas
Commander, Port-au-Prince Police ...................Col. Albert Pierre
Commander, "Leopards" .....................Lt. Col. Raymond Cabrol

**Medical Corps**
*Service de Sanité*
*Hospital Militaire de Port-au-Prince*
*Telephone: (1) 20504*

Commander .............................Col. Dr. Ange-Marie Gousse
Deputy-Commander ...................Lt. Col. Dr. Roland Guillaume

237

**Engineers Corps**
*Corps du Génie*
*St. Martin*
*Telephone: (1) 21223*

Commander . . . . . . . . . . . . . . . . . . . . . . . . . . . . . . . . . . . . . . . . . . Col. Raymond Oriol

**Signal Corps**
*Service des Transmissions*
*Fort National*
*Port-au-Prince*

Commander . . . . . . . . . . . . . . . . . . . . . . . . . . . . . . . . . . . . . . Maj. Gabriel Painson

**NAVY**
*(Marine Haitien)*
*Base Navale Hammerton*
*Killick*
*Bizoton*
*Telephone:   (1) 4-053*

Chief of Staff . . . . . . . . . . . . . . . . . . . Cap. de Vaisseau Claude Dorsainville

**AIR FORCE**
*(Corps d'Aviation)*
*Avenue Somoza, Bowen*
*Field*
*Delmas*
*Port-au-Prince*
*Telephone:   (1) 2-2031*

Commander . . . . . . . . . . . . . . . . . . . . . . . . . . . . . . . . . . . . . . . Col. Roger Cazeau
Deputy Commander . . . . . . . . . . . . . . . . . . . . . . . . . . . . Lt. Col. Gesner Bruno

\* \* \* \* \*

# GENERAL DEFENSE DATA

**Manpower**
    Total Armed Forces . . . . . . . . . . . . . . . . . . . . . . . . . . . . . . . . . . . . . . . . . . . . . . . . 7,500
       (See Page 237)
    Population . . . . . . . . . . . . . . . . . . . . . . . . . . . . . . . . . . . . . . . . . . . . . . 6,054,000

**Spending**
    Military Expenditures . . . . . . . . . . . . . . . . . . . . . . . . . . . . . . . . . . . . . . . . . . . $18 million
    Gross National Product . . . . . . . . . . . . . . . . . . . . . . . . . . . . . . . . . . . . . . . . . . $1.3 billion
    Military Expenditure as a Percentage of
       Gross National Product . . . . . . . . . . . . . . . . . . . . . . . . . . . . . . . . . . . . . 1.4%
    Military Expenditure as a Percentage of
       Central Government Expenditure . . . . . . . . . . . . . . . . . . . . . . . . . . . . . 7.7%

**Defense Treaties** *(See Part II for Additional Detail)*

    Bilateral:    United States

    Multilateral:    Act of Chapultepec
                Inter-American Defense Board
                Inter-American Treaty of Reciprocal Assistance
                Treaty on the Non-Proliferation of Nuclear Weapons
                Treaty for the Prohibition of Nuclear Weapons in Latin
                   America

# HONDURAS
## Republic of Honduras
### *República de Honduras*

## Defense Establishment Command Structure and Force Organization

The President is Commander-in-Chief, exercising his authority through the Chief of the Armed Forces, who is selected for a five year term by Congress. Administration of the military is the responsibility of the Ministry of Defense.

**Total armed forces:** 13,000 (Army: 11,500; Navy: 300; Air Force: 1,200). **Public Security Force:** 3,000.

## HEAD OF STATE

H. E. Dr. Roberto Suazo Cordova

**OFFICE OF THE PRESIDENT**
*(Oficina de la Presidencia)*
*6 Avenida, 1 Calle*
*Tegucigalpa*
*Telephone: 22-8287, 22-5867, 22-6428*
        *(Press Secretary)*

President of the Republic
  and Commander-in-Chief
  of the Armed Forces . . . . . . . . . . . . . . . . . . . . .Dr. Roberto Suazo Córdova
Minister of the Presidency . . . . . . . . . . . . . . . .Carlos Roberto Flores Facussi

**MINISTRY OF NATIONAL DEFENSE**
*(Ministério de la Defensa Nacional)*
*Palacio de los Ministérios*
*Tegucigalpa*
*Telephone: 22-9551*
*Telex: 1129 mmrree ho*
        *(Ministério de Relaciones Exteriores)*

Minister of Defense . . . . . . . . . . . . . . . . . . . . . .Cnel. Amilcar Suazo Castillo
Vice Minister of Defense . . . . . . . . . . . . . . . . . . . .Tte. Cnel. René Paz Alfaro
Minister for Interior and Justice . . . . . . . . . . . . . . . . . . . . . . . . . . .Oscar Mejia

## DEFENSE FORCES

**DEPARTMENT OF THE ARMED FORCES**
*(Departamento de las Fuerzas Armadas)*
*Cuartel General Fuerzas Armadas*
*Tegucigalpa*
*Telephone: 22-3257, 22-8565 (Chief of Staff)*

Commander-in-Chief and
  President of the Republic . . . . . . . . . . . . . . . .Dr. Roberto Suazo Córdova
Chief of the Armed Forces . . . . . . . . . .Gral. Brig. Gustavo Álvarez Martínez
Adjutant General, Armed Forces . . . . . . . . . . . . . . . .Tte. Cnel. José Álvarez
Auditor General, Armed Forces . . . . . . . . . . .Cnel. Efraín González Muñoz
Paymaster General, Armed Forces . . . . . .Tte. Cnel. Carlos Aguirre Corrales
Inspector, General, Army . . . . . . . . . . .Cnel. Marco António Rosales Abella

**General Staff of the Armed Forces**
*(Estado Mayor General de las Fuerzas Ármadas)*

Joint Chief of Staff . . . . . . . . . . . . . . . . . . . . . . . . . . . .Cnel. José Bueso Rosa
Chief, Personnel Department . . . . . . .Tte. Cnel. Leone A. Gutiérrez Minera
Chief, Intelligence Department . . . . . . . . . . . .Tte. Cnel. Juan Lopez Grijalva
Chief, Operations Department . . . . . . . . . . . . . . . . . .Cnel. Wilfredo Sánchez
Chief, Logistics Department . . . . . . . . . . . . . . . . . . . .Tte. Cnel. Julio Pérez
Director, Command & General
  Staff School . . . . . . . . . . . . . . . . . . . . . . . . . .Cnel. Rodolfo Bonilla Blanco

Director, Advanced Officers School . . . . . Tte. Cnel. Carlos Reyes Barahona
Director, Gral. Francisco Morazon
    School . . . . . . . . . . . . . . . . . . . . . . . . . . . . . . Tte. Cnel. Lufti Azzad Matute
Director, National Police School
    (Esnapo) . . . . . . . . . . . . . . . . . . . . . . . . . . May. Cristobal Simón Romero

## NAVAL FORCES
*(Fuerzas Navales)*
*Cuartel General*
*Tegucigalpa*
*Telephone:   22-5545*

Commander . . . . . . . . . . . . . . . . . . . . . . . . . . . . . . Cnel. Ruben Montoya
Deputy Commander and
    Chief of the Naval Staff . . . . . . . Cap. de Fragata Edmundo Torres Chavez
Chief, Personnel Department . . . . . . Cap. de Corbeta Claudio Lainez Coello
Chief, Operations Department . . . . . . . . . . . . . . . . . . . . . . . . Cap. Cano
Chief, Logistics Department . . . . . . . . Cap. de Corbeta Arnulfo Cantarero L.

## AIR FORCE
*(La Fuerza Áerea Hondureña)*
*Base Aerea HAM*
*Toncontín*
*Tegucigalpa*
*Telephone:   33-6393*

Commander . . . . . . . . . . . . . . . . . . . . . . . Cnel. de Av. Walter Lopez Reyes
Chief of Staff . . . . . . . . . . . . . . . . . . . . . Cnel. de Av. Ernesto Zepeda Andino
Commander, Cnel. Hernan Acosta
    Air Base . . . . . . . . . . . . . . . . . . . . . . . . May. de Av. Oscar A. Servellón
Commander, Cnel. Armando
    Escalon Air Base . . . . . . . . . . . . . . . . . . May. de Av. Luis Isidro Aguilar
Commander, Cnel. Héctor
    Caracciolo Air Base . . . . . . . . . . . . . . . May. de Av. Alberto Urcina Reyes
Director, Military Aviation School . . . . . . . May. de Av. Héctor Castro Cabus
Chief, EMA-1 . . . . . . . . . . . . . . . . . . Tte. Cnel. de Av. Roberto Mendoza E.
Chief, EMA-2 and EMA-3 . . . . . . . . . Cnel. de Av. Edgardo Mejía Ramírez
Chief, EMA-4 . . . . . . . . . . . . . . . . . . . Tte. Cnel. de Av. Marco Tulio Rivera

## PUBLIC SECURITY FORCE
*(Fuerza de Seguridad Publica)*
*Palacio de los Ministérios*
*Tegucigalpa*
*Telephone:   22-9551*

Commander-General . . . . . . . . . . . . . . . . . . . . . . . Cnel. Daniel Bali Castillo
Chief of the General Staff . . . . . . . . . . . . . . . . Cnel. Héctor Ventura Piñeda

\* \* \* \* \*

# GENERAL DEFENSE DATA

**Manpower**
    Total Armed Forces . . . . . . . . . . . . . . . . . . . . . . . . . . . . . . . . . . . . . . . . . . 13,000
        (See Page 239)
    Population . . . . . . . . . . . . . . . . . . . . . . . . . . . . . . . . . . . . . . . . . . . . 4,103,000

**Spending**
    Military Expenditures . . . . . . . . . . . . . . . . . . . . . . . . . . . . . . . . . . . $43 million
    Gross National Product . . . . . . . . . . . . . . . . . . . . . . . . . . . . . . . . . . . $2.3 billion
    Military Expenditure as a Percentage of
        Gross National Product . . . . . . . . . . . . . . . . . . . . . . . . . . . . . . . . . . . 1.9%
    Military Expenditure as a Percentage of
        Central Government Expenditure . . . . . . . . . . . . . . . . . . . . . . . . . . . 7.9%

**Defense Treaties** *(See Part II for Additional Detail)*

    Bilateral:     United States

    Multilateral:    Act of Chapultepec
                    Biological Weapons Convention
                    Central-American Democratic Community
                    *Honduras—Guatemala—El Salvador*: Informal Agreement
                        (1981)
                    Inter-American Defense Board
                    Inter-American Treaty of Reciprocal Assistance
                    Limited Test Ban Treaty
                    Treaty for the Prohibition of Nuclear Weapons in Latin
                      America
                    Treaty on the Non-Proliferation of Nuclear Weapons

**Military Rank Comparisons**
See Appendix A.

# HONG KONG
## Crown Colony of Hong Kong

### Defence Establishment Command Structure and Force Organization

The United Kingdom has responsibility for the security of Hong Kong. The Commander of the British Forces Hong Kong Garrison has control over all military forces of the Crown Colony. The local Auxiliary Defence units, consisting of the Royal Hong Kong Regiment and the Royal Hong Kong Auxiliary Air Force, are administered by the Hong Kong government, but would come under British command if called to active duty in time of war.

**Total armed forces: 8,500. Auxiliary Defence units: 815.**

### HEAD OF STATE

H. M. Queen Elizabeth II

### GOVERNOR

H. E. Sir Edward Youde, G.C.M.G., M.B.E.

**OFFICE OF THE GOVERNOR**
*Government House*
*Hong Kong*
*Telephone: 5-232031*

Governor . . . . . . . . . . . . . . . . . . . . . . . . . . . . . . . . . H. E. Sir Edward Youde, G.C.M.G., M.B.E.

**GOVERNMENT SECRETARIAT**
*Executive Council*
*Lower Albert Road*
*Hong Kong*
*Telephone: 5-95527, 95406 (Chief Secretary)*

Governor and Chief of the
Executive Council . . . . . . . . . . . . . . . . . . . . . . . H. E. Sir Edward Youde, G.C.M.G., M.B.E.

Chief Secretary and Member
of the Executive Council . . . . . . . . . . . Sir. Philip Haddon-Cave, K.B.E., C.M.G., J.P.

Commander-in-Chief of the
British Forces and Member
of the Executive Council . . . . . . . . . . . . . Maj. Gen. J. L. Chapple, C.B.E.

**Security Branch**
*Government Secretariat*
*Lower Albert Road*
*Hong Kong*
*Telephone: 7-3380 govhr*

Secretary . . . . . . . . . . . . . . . . . . . . . . . L. M. Davies, C.M.G., O.B.E., J.P.
Deputy Secretary . . . . . . . . . . . . . . . . . . J. R. Heywood, O.B.E., E.D., J.P.

**Office of Government Information Services**
*Beaconsfield House, 6th floor*
*Queen's Road, Central,*
*Victoria, Hong Kong*
*Telephone: 5-233191*
*Cable: INFORMS, HONG KONG*

Director . . . . . . . . . . . . . . . . . . . . . . . . . . . . . . . . . . . . . . . . . . . . . . . . . . .
Assistant to the Director . . . . . . . . . . . . . . . . . . . . . . . . . . . . . Y. L. V. Sharma

# DEFENCE FORCES

**ARMED FORCES**
**British Forces Hong Kong**
*Victoria Barracks*
*Hong Kong*
*Telephone:   5-238111, 5-222259*
*Telex:   85966 remv hx*

Commander . . . . . . . . . . . . . . . . . . . . . . . . . . .Maj. Gen. J. L. Chapple, C.B.E.
Deputy Commander . . . . . . . . . . . . . . . . . . . . . . .Brig. R. J. Hodges, O.B.E.

**Joint Service Public Relations Staff**
*H.M.S. Tamar*
*British Forces Post Office 1*
*Hong Kong*
*Telephone:   5-284724, 5-284739*

Director . . . . . . . . . . . . . . . . . . . . . . . . . . . . . . . .Maj. Christopher Warren

**Gurkha Field Force**
*British Forces Post Office 1*
*Hong Kong*
*Telephone:   0-9837101*

Commander . . . . . . . . . . . . . . . . . . . . . . . . . . .Brig. R. M. Llewellyn, O.B.E.

**NAVY**
**Royal Navy**
*H.M.S. Tamar*
*Hong Kong*
*Telephone:   5-238111, 5-28933700,*
*5-239230*

Commander . . . . . . . . . . . . . . . . . . . . . . . . . . . . .Capt. A. A. Waugh

**AIR FORCE**
**Royal Air Force**
*British Forces Post Office 1*
*Hong Kong*
*Telephone:   0-9837400, 5-238111*

Commander . . . . . . . . . . . . . . . . . . . . . . . . . . . . .Group Capt. D. B. Hives

**ROYAL HONG KONG REGIMENT**
**(THE VOLUNTEERS)**
*Regimental Headquarters*
*Sports Road, Happy Valley,*
*Hong Kong*
*Telephone:   5-761371, 5-762663*

Commanding Officer . . . . . . . . . . . . . . . . . . . . . . . . .Lt. Col. M. P. Barneby
Operations Officer . . . . . . . . . . . . . . . . . . . . . . . . . .Maj. D. G. P. Scholfield
Departmental Secretary . . . . . . . . . . . . . . . . . . . . . . .Francis K. F. Chan
Quartermaster . . . . . . . . . . . . . . . . . . . . . . . . .Maj. A. A. Cornish, B. E. M.
Regimental Officer . . . . . . . . . . . . . . . . . . . . . . . . .W. O. I. D. P. H. Rose
Regimental Officer . . . . . . . . . . . . . . . . . . . . . . . . . . . . . .Poon Pak-wah
Regimental Officer . . . . . . . . . . . . . . . . . . . . . . . . . .(Mrs.) Susan Chim
Senior Clerk, Finance Administration . . . . . . . . . . . . . . . . .Yue Tung-hing
Chief, Accounts Office
    Regimental Armourer . . . . . . . . . . . . . . . . . . . . . . . .Tang Pui-Ching
Chief, Quartermaster Stores . . . . . . . . . . . . . . . . . . . .Cheng Pak-cheung
Chief, A Squadron Office . . . . . . . . . . . . . . . . . . . . . .W. O. H. J. Cooney
Chief, B Squadron Office . . . . . . . . . . . . . . . . . . . .W. O. H. A. H. Patterson
Chief, C Squadron Office . . . . . . . . . . . . . . . . . . . .W. O. H. A. A. Nicholas
Chief, D Squadron Office . . . . . . . . . . . . . . . . . . . . .W. O. H. J. L. Budd
Chief, Support Squadron Office . . . . . . . . . . . . . . . . . .W. O. H. J. A. Frost

**ROYAL HONG KONG AUXILIARY**
**AIR FORCE**
*Hong Kong International Airport*
*Airport Tunnel East Exit*
*Kowloon*
*Telephone:   3-8298418, 3-3297625*
*Telex:   64166 auxaf hx*

Hon. Air Commander . . . . . . . . . . . . . . . . . . . . . . . . .Air Cdr. G. J. Bell,
                                                                                      O.B.E., A.E., J.P.
Commanding Officer  . . . . . . . . . . . . . . . . . . . .Wing Cdr. R. G. Penlington,
                                                                                      O.B.E., A.E.
Staff Officer . . . . . . . . . . . . . . . . . . . . . . . .Sqn. Ldr. J. G. Shawcross, A.E.
Departmental Secretary . . . . . . . . . . . . . . . . . . . . . . . . . . . . .K. L. Wong
General Officer  . . . . . . . . . . . . . . . . . . . . . . . . . . . . . . . . .K. S. Mark

**Flight Operations**
*Telephone:   3-8298414*

Officer Commanding,
   Operations . . . . . . . . . . . . . . . . . . . . . . . .Sqn. Ldr. J. G. Shawcross, A.E.
Officer Commanding, Flying
   (Auxiliary) . . . . . . . . . . . . . . . . . . . . . . . . . . .Sqn. Ldr. A. P. Asprey, A.E.
Training Officer (Helicopter
   QHI RAF) . . . . . . . . . . . . . . . . . . . . . . . . . . . . . . . .Flt. Lt. M. R. D. Butt
Pilot (Fixed Wing) and
   Training Officer (Basic) . . . . . . . . . . . . . .Flt. Lt. M. A. Wightman, A.E.
Pilot (Fixed Wing Standard) . . . . . . . . . . . . . . . . . . . . . .Flt. Lt. T. J. Frame
Pilot (Fixed Wing) . . . . . . . . . . . . . . . . . . . . . . . . . . . .Flt. Lt. P. C. Alley
Pilot (Helicopter) . . . . . . . . . . . . . . . . . . . . . . . . .Flt. Lt. P. J. S. Curtis, A.E.
Pilot (Helicopter) . . . . . . . . . . . . . . . . . . . . . . . . . . .Flt. Lt. M. W. Catlow
Crewman Officer . . . . . . . . . . . . . . . . . . . . . . . . . . . . .Flt. Lt. R. W. Brown

**Engineering**
*Telephone:   3-8298411*

Senior Technical Officer . . . . . . . . . . . . . . . . . . . .Sqn. Ldr. G. M. McIntosh
Supplies Supervisor . . . . . . . . . . . . . . . . . . . . . . . . . . . . . . . . . . . .K. Y. Pau

**ROYAL HONG KONG POLICE FORCE**
*Headquarters*
*Arsenal Street*
*Telephone:   5-2842284*

Commissioner . . . . . . . . . . . . . . . . . . . . . . . . . . . . . . . . . . . . .R. T. M. Henry,
                        M.V.O., O.B.E., Q.P.M., C.P.M.
Deputy Commissioner,
   Operations . . . . . . . . . . . . . . . . . . . . . . . . . . . . . . . . . . . . . . . . .P. T. Moor,
             O.B.E., Q.P.M., C.P.M., F.B.I.M., J.P.
Deputy Commisioner, Management . . . . . .C. W. B. Purdon, C.B.E., M.C.
Police Administration Officer . . . . . . . . . . . . . . . . . . . . . . .J. F. Yaxlev, J.P.
Director, Public Relations . . . . . . . . . . . . . . . . . . . . . .E. F. Taylor, C.P.M.

\* \* \* \* \*

# GENERAL DEFENCE DATA

**Manpower**
   Total Armed Forces. . . . . . . . . . . . . . . . . . . . . . . . . . . . . . . . . . . . . . . . . . .8,500
     (See Page 243)
   Population . . . . . . . . . . . . . . . . . . . . . . . . . . . . . . . . . . . . . . . . .5,272,000

**Spending**
   Military Expenditures . . . . . . . . . . . . . . . . . . . . . . . . . . . . . . . . . . . . . . . . . . .
   Gross National Product . . . . . . . . . . . . . . . . . . . . . . . . . . . . . . . . . . . . .24.2 billion
   Military Expenditure as a Percentage of
     Gross National Product . . . . . . . . . . . . . . . . . . . . . . . . . . . . . . . . . . . . . . . . .
   Military Expenditure as a Percentage of
     Central Government Expenditure . . . . . . . . . . . . . . . . . . . . . . . . . . . . . . . .

**Defence Treaties** *(See Part II for Additional Detail)*

    Bilateral:    None

    Multilateral:   None

# HUNGARY
## Hungarian People's Republic
### *Magyar Nepköztarsasag*

### Defense Establishment Command Structure and Force Organization

The President of the Presidential Council is the nominal Commander-in-Chief. Administrative and operational control of the armed forces is exercised by the Minister of Defense. The National Defense Committee advises the Minister of Defense. It would direct military activities in time of war. All services form part of the Army.

**Total armed forces:** 106,700 (Army: 85,700;  Air Force: 21,000). **Para-military forces:** 75,000 (Border Guard: 15,000;  Workers' Militia: 60,000).

## HEAD OF STATE

Pal Losonczi

**OFFICE OF THE PRESIDENT**
*Kossuth L. ter*
*Budapest V*

*Telephone:  12 26 00*
*Telex:  225 547 mtbp h*

President and Commander-in-Chief ...................... Pál Losonczi
Deputy President ..................................... Sándor Gáspár
Deputy President ............................ Dr. Rezsö Trautmann

**MINISTRY OF DEFENSE**
*Pelffy Gy.u. 7-11*
*Budapest V*

*Telephone:  32 25 00*
*Telex:  225 424 rex h*

Minister ............................. Gen. of the Army Lajos Czinege
Under Secretary of State ...................... Col. Gen. Karoly Csemi
Deputy Minister ............................ Lt. Gen. Ferenc Karpati
Deputy Minister ............................... Lt. Gen. Pal Kovacs
Deputy Minister ............................. Lt. Gen. Jozsef Pacsek
Director, Foreign Affairs Department ................. Col. Tibor Tordai
Deputy Director, Foreign Affairs Department ............. Laszlo Berecki
Director, Intelligence Directorate .............. Maj. Gen. Ferenc Szücs
Director, Investment and Maintenance
  Directorate ........................... Maj. Gen. Dezsö Horvath
Director, Maintenance and Placement
  Department ............................... Lt. Col. Jozsef Fabian
Director, Military Supply Service ....................... Zoltan Szoradi
Director, Personnel Directorate .................. Lt. Gen. Sándor Rácz

## DEFENSE FORCES

**ARMY**
**Hungarian People's Army**
*Ministry of Defense*
*Pelffy Gy.u. 7-11*
*Budapest V*

*Telephone:  32 25 00*
*Telex:  225 424 rex h*

Chief, General Staff ........................... Col. Gen. István Oláh
First Deputy Chief, General Staff ............ Maj. Gen. Gyula Reményi
Deputy Chief, Ground Forces ................. Maj. Gen. Mihály Török
Deputy Chief ...................... Maj. Gen. László Damó
Deputy Chief ...................... Maj. Gen. Sándor Kiss
Deputy Chief ...................... Maj. Gen. Ferenc Szücs
Deputy Chief ...................... Maj. Gen. Tibor Toth
Inspector General ......................... Maj. Gen. Andras Lénárt

|  |  |
|---|---|
| | Secretary, Hungarian Socialist Workers' Party Committee ...........................Maj. Gen. Dezsö Papp |
| | Director, Main Training Directorate ..............Lt. Gen. Jozsef Pacsek |
| | Commander, Territorial Rear Defense Command ................................Lt. Gen. Miklos Darányi |
| **Main Political Directorate** | Director .....................................Lt. Gen. Ferenc Kárpáti |
| | First Deputy Director ...............................Istvan Horváth |
| | Deputy Director ..........................................Béla Ádám |
| | Deputy Director.......................................Col. Károly Bán |
| **Budapest Garrison** | Commander ................................Maj. Gen. Mihály Farkas |
| | Deputy Commander .............................Lt. Col. Károly Biro |
| | Deputy Commander ............................Lt. Col. Károly Sipos |
| **National Air Defense Command** | Commanding Officer..........................Maj. Gen. János Stock |
| **National Civil Defense Command** | Commanding Officer ............................................... |
| | Deputy Commanding Officer .......................Col. Imre Perger |
| **Military Academies** | Commanding Officer, Lajos Kossuth Military Academy ..........................Maj. Gen. Barna Kazai |
| | Commanding Officer, Karikas Frigyes Military College ................................Col. János Halász |
| | Commanding Officer, Zalka Mate Technical Military Academy ...........................György Paal |
| | Commanding Officer, György Killian Technical Air Force Academy ..............Maj. Gen. Tivadar Brassoi |

\* \* \* \* \*

## GENERAL DEFENSE DATA

**Manpower**
Total Armed Forces ..............................................106,700
(See Page 247)
Population ...................................................10,714,000

**Spending**
Military Expenditures...........................................$2.5 billion
Gross National Product .........................................$58 billion
Military Expenditure as a Percentage of
Gross National Product ...........................................4.4%
Military Expenditure as a Percentage of
Central Government Expenditure ..................................8.7%

**Defense Treaties** *(See Part II for Additional Detail)*

Bilateral:

| Bulgaria | Romania |
|---|---|
| Czechoslovakia | Soviet Union |
| German Democratic Republic | People's Democratic Republic of Yemen |
| Poland | |

Multilateral:
Biological Weapons Convention
Environmental Modification Convention
Limited Test Ban Treaty
Treaty on the Control of Arms on the Seabed
Treaty on the Non-Proliferation of Nuclear Weapons
Warsaw Treaty Organization

# ICELAND
## Republic of Iceland
### *Lydveldid Island*

## Defense Establishment Command Structure
## and Force Organization

Iceland does not have military forces of its own. The Ministry of Foreign Affairs handles the country's defense concerns, and the Ministry of Justice is responsible for the Police and Coast Guard. The Defense Council acts as the primary link between the government and NATO forces on the island.

**Police:** 400.    **Coast Guard:** 135.

## HEAD OF STATE

H. E. Vigdís Finnbogadóttir

**OFFICE OF THE PRESIDENT**
*Stjornrrádid*
*v/Laekjargötu*
*101 Reykjavík*
*Telephone:  15525, 25000*

President of the Republic ........................Vigdís Finnbogadóttir
Secretary to the President ..........................Halldor Reynisson

**OFFICE OF THE PRIME MINISTER**
*Stjornarrádid*
*v/Laekjargötu*
*101 Reykjavík*
*Telephone:  25000*

Prime Minister..............................Dr. Gunnar Thoroddsen
Secretary-General ..........................Gudmundur Benediktsson
Deputy Secretary-General ............................Gisli Arnason
Assistant to the Minister ......................Jon Ormur Halldörsson

**MINISTRY FOR FOREIGN AFFAIRS**
*Hverfisgätu 115*
*105 Reykjavík*
*Telephone:  25000*
*Telex:  2050, 2025 extern*

Minister .........................................Olafur Jóhannesson
Permanent Under Secretary .........................Ingrui Ingvasson
Deputy Permanent Under Secretary ..................Hannes Hafstein

**Icelandic Defense Council**

Chairman ...........................................Helgi Agustsson
Member ..........................................Hallgrimur Dalberg
Member .........................................Hoeskuldur Olafsson
Member .............................................Valtyr Gudjonsson
Member................................................Hannes Gudmundsson
Member............................................Capt. Erick D. McVadoon
Member................................................Col. Jerry E. Smith
Member......................................Cdr. Geoffrey R. Greiveldinger
Observer .........................................M. Allen Saunders

**MINISTRY OF JUSTICE AND
ECCLESIASTICAL AFFAIRS**
*Arnarhváli*
*v/Lindargötu*
*101 Reykjavík*
*Telephone:  25000*
*Telex:  2224 isdoms*

Minister............................................Fridjón Thórdarson
Secretary-General ......................................Baldur Moller
Deputy Secretary-General ......................Olafur W. Stefansson

# DEFENSE FORCES

**POLICE**
*Reykjavík*

Chief of Police ...................................................
Deputy Chief ....................................................
Deputy .......................................Arnar Gudmundsson
Deputy ...........................................Erla Jónsdottir
Police Captain ...............................Njördur Snaehólm

**COAST GUARD**
*Seljavegi 32*
*101 Reykjavík*
*Telephone: 102330*

Director ...................................Gunnar Bergsveinsson

\* \* \* \* \*

# GENERAL DEFENSE DATA

**Manpower**
Total Armed Forces ...................................................535
(See Page 249)
Population ...................................................233,000

**Spending**
Military Expenditures ...................................................
Gross National Product ...................................$2.7 billion
Military Expenditure as a Percentage of
Gross National Product ...................................................
Military Expenditure as a Percentage of
Central Government Expenditure ...................................................

**Defense Treaties** *(See Part II for Additional Detail)*

Bilateral: United States

Multilateral: Biological Weapons Convention
Limited Test Ban Treaty
North Atlantic Treaty Organization
Treaty on the Control of Arms on the Seabed
Treaty on the Non-Proliferation of Nuclear Weapons

# INDIA
## Republic of India
### *Bharat*

## Defence Establishment Command Structure and Force Organization

The President is Supreme Commander of the Indian Armed Forces and exercises his authority through the Prime Minister. Defense policy, however, is the responsibility of the Political Affairs Committee of the Cabinet. The Defence Minister exercises administrative and operational control over the military. He is counseled by the Defence Minster's Committee and the Defence Ministery's Productive and Supply Committee. A Chiefs of Staff Committee advises the Government on all important matters of defence strategy and inter-service policy.

The Ministry of Defence is comprised of four Departments: Defence, Defence Production, Defence Supplies, and Defence Research and Development. Although the three services are under the general control of the Ministry, they normally function directly under their respective Chief of Staff. A special branch of Ministry of Finance controls military expenditure and advises the Minister of Defence on the financial aspects of defence policy. Several organizations under the Ministry of Defence handle inter-service logistical and support functions.

**Total armed forces:** 1,104,000 (Army: 944,000; Navy: 47,000; Air Force: 113,000).
**Para-military forces:** 260,000 (Border Security Force: 85,000; Other: 175,000).

## HEAD OF STATE

H. E. Neelam Sanjiva Reddy

**OFFICE OF THE PRESIDENT**
*Rashtrapati Sachivalaya*
*New Delhi 110 011*
*Telephone: 374 930, 375 321/211*

President and Supreme Commander,
   Indian Armed Forces.............................Giani Zail Singh
Secretary to the President ..................................V. K. Dar
Military Secretary to the President ..............Maj. Gen. S. S. Jamwall
Press Secretary to the President .....................K. Suryanarayana

**OFFICE OF THE VICE PRESIDENT**
*Up-Rashtrapati Sachivalaya*

Vice President ............................Mohammad Hidayatullah
Secretary to the Vice President..........................A. N. Oberai

**OFFICE OF THE PRIME MINISTER**
*South Block, Gate No. 6*
*New Delhi 110 011*
*Telephone: 272 312, 382 160, 374 185*

Prime Minister, Chairman of the Planning
   Commission, Minister of Atomic Energy,
   Space, Science and Technology ..................Mrs. Indira Gandhi
Secretary to the Prime Minister ..........C. R. Krishanaswamy Rao Sahib
Cabinet Secretary.......................................S. S. Grewal

**MINISTRY OF DEFENCE**
*South Block-11*
*New Delhi 110 011*
*Telephone: 372 380, 373 033*
*Telex: c/o Ministry of External Affairs*
*313192*

Minister ...........................Ramaswamy Iyer Venkataraman
Defence Secretary.......................................P. K. Kaul
Deputy Minister ...............................Shrik. P. Singh Deo
Director General, National Cadet Corps ........Maj. Gen. Narinder Singh
Director, Armed Forces Medical Services ....Lt. Gen. V. V. S. Pratapa Rao
Commandant, National Defence College ...........Vice Adm. R. V. Arte

**251**

# DEFENCE FORCES

## ARMY
**Indian Army**
*Army House*
*4 King George's Avenue*
*New Delhi 100 011*

*Telephone: 371 632, 371 512*
*Telex: 313622*

### Army Commands

Chief of the Army Staff .......................Gen. K. V. Krishna Rao
Vice Chief of the Army Staff ......................Lt. Gen. S. K. Sinha
Deputy Chief of the Army Staff .....................Lt. Gen. H. Kaul
Adjutant General ...........................Lt. Gen. N. S. Cheema
Quartermaster General .......................Lt. Gen. M. M. L. Ghai
Master General of the Ordnance .................Lt. Gen. T. B. Nanda
Engineer-in-Chief...............................Lt. Gen. P. R. Puri
Director of Military Operations .................Lt. Gen. C.N. Somanna

General Officer in Charge, Southern Command .....Lt. Gen. T. S. Oberoi
General Officer in Charge, Eastern Command.......Lt. Gen. A. S. Vaidya
General Officer in Charge, Western Command.......Lt. Gen. K. Sundarji
General Officer in Charge, Central Command .......Lt. Gen. H. C. Dutta
General Officer in Charge, Northern Command...Lt. Gen. M. L. Chhibber

## NAVY
**Indian Navy**
*Naval Headquarters*
*12 King George's Avenue*
*New Delhi 110011*

### Navy Commands

Chief, Naval Staff ..........Adm. Oscar Stanley Dawson, PVSM, AVSM
Vice Chief, Naval Staff.........Vice Adm. Sardari Lal Sethi, AVSM, NM
Deputy Chief, Naval Staff ........Vice Adm. Subimal Mookerjee, AVSM
Assistant Chief, Policy & Planning...................Adm. K. K. Nayyer
Chief, Personnel ......................Vice Adm. J. G. Nadkamic
Chief, Material ...............................Vice Adm. A. K. Bhatia
Director, Naval Operations ...................Rear Adm. L N. Ramdas

Flag Officer Commanding-in-Chief,
   Western Naval Command
   (Bombay) ......................Vice Adm. Manohar Prehlad Awati,
                                                   Vr C, PVSM
Flag Officer Commanding-in-Chief,
   Eastern Naval Command
   (Vishakhapatnam) ..............Vice Adm. Mehir Kymar Roy, AVSM
Flag Officer Commanding-in-Chief,
   Southern Naval Command
   (Cochin).........Vice Adm. Radha Krishin Hariram Tahiliani, AVSM
Flag Officer Commanding
   Western Fleet ...........................Vice Adm. K. K. Nayyar
Flag Officer Commanding
   Eastern Fleet............................Rear Adm. I. J. S. Khurana

## AIR FORCE
**Indian Air Force**
*Air House*
*23 Akbar Road, Vayu Bawan*
*New Delhi 110011*

*Telephone: 372 517, 370 231, 372 521*
*Telex: 32257 iaf kp*

### Air Force Commands

Chief of the Air Staff .................Air Chief Marshal Dilbagh Singh
Vice Chief of the Air Staff ......................Air Marshal T. S. Brar
Deputy Chief of the Air Staff ...................Air Marshal C. V. Gole
Air Officer In Charge, Maintenance .............Air Marshal C. S. Naik
Air Officer In Charge, Personnel ..................Air Marshal S. Jena

Air Officer Commanding-in-Chief,
   Western Air Command .....................Air Marshal L. M. Katre
Air Officer Commanding-in-Chief,
   South Western Air Command ................Air Marshal J. R. Bhasin
Air Officer Commanding-in-Chief,
   Eastern Air Command ....................Air Marshal MSD Wollen
Air Officer Commanding-in-Chief,
   Central Air Command ..................Air Marshal B. W. Chauhan
Air Officer Commanding-in-Chief,
   Maintenance Command.................Air Marshal K. I. S. Chhabra
Air Officer Commanding-in-Chief,
   Training Command ..........................Air Marshal EPR Nair

\* \* \* \* \*

## GENERAL DEFENSE DATA

**Manpower**

Total Armed Forces . . . . . . . . . . . . . . . . . . . . . . . . . . . . . . . . . . . . . . . . . . . . . 1,104,000
   (See Page 251)
Population . . . . . . . . . . . . . . . . . . . . . . . . . . . . . . . . . . . . . . . . . . . . . . . 723,762,000

**Spending**

Military Expenditures . . . . . . . . . . . . . . . . . . . . . . . . . . . . . . . . . . . . . . . . $4.5 billion
Gross National Product . . . . . . . . . . . . . . . . . . . . . . . . . . . . . . . . . . . . . . . $159 billion
Military Expenditure as a Percentage of
   Gross National Product . . . . . . . . . . . . . . . . . . . . . . . . . . . . . . . . . . . . . . . . 2.8%
Military Expenditure as a Percentage of
   Central Government Expenditure . . . . . . . . . . . . . . . . . . . . . . . . . . . . . . . . 16%

**Defense Treaties** *(See Part II for Additional Detail)*

   Bilateral:     Soviet Union
                  United States

   Multilateral:   Biological Weapons Convention
                  Environmental Modification Convention
                  Limited Test Ban Treaty
                  Treaty on the Control of Arms on the Seabed

# INDONESIA
## Republic of Indonesia
*Republik Indonesia*

### Defense Establishment Command Structure and Force Organization

The President is the Supreme Commander of the Armed Forces. Directly responsible to him are the Minister of Defense and Security (the principal adviser to the President in matters pertaining to defense and security), and the Commander-in-Chief of the Armed Forces, who exercises operational control over the military.

**Total armed forces:** 248,000 (Army: 180,000; Navy: 40,000; Air Force: 28,000). **Paramilitary forces:** 140,000. (Police: 28,000. Police Mobile Brigade: 12,000. Militia: 100,000).

## HEAD OF STATE

H. E. Soeharto

**OFFICE OF THE PRESIDENT**
*Bina Graha*
*Jl. Veteran No. 17*
*Jakarta*
*Telephone: 21) 341079, 884656*

President and Supreme Commander of the Armed
    Forces . . . . . . . . . . . . . . . . . . . . . . . . . . . . . . . . . . . . . . . . H. E. Soeharto
Minister of State and State Secretary . . . . . . . . . . . . . . . Soedharmona, S. H.

**OFFICE OF THE VICE PRESIDENT**
*Jl. Merdeka Selatan 6*
*Jakarta*
*Telephone: 21) 357080*

Vice President . . . . . . . . . . . . . . . . . . . . . . . . H. E. Umar Wirahadikusumah

**OFFICE OF COORDINATING MINISTER FOR POLITICAL AFFAIRS AND SECURITY**
*(Menko Polkam)*
*Jl. Merdeka Barat 15*
*Jakarta*
*Telephone: 21) 371619, 358770*

Coordinating Minister . . . . . . . . . . . . . . . . . . . . . . . . . . . . . . H. E. Soerono

**DEPARTMENT OF DEFENSE AND SECURITY**
*(Dephankam)*
*Jl. Merdeka Barat 13*
*Jakarta*

Minister of Defense (*Menhankam*) . . . . . . . . . . . . . . . . . . . . Gen. S. Poniman
Inspector General . . . . . . . . . . . . . . . . . . . . . . . . . . . . . . . . . . . . . . . (Vacant)
Secretary General . . . . . . . . . . . . . . . . . . . . . . . . . . . . . . . . . . . . . . . (Vacant)
Director General . . . . . . . . . . . . . . . . . . . . . . . . . . . . . . . . . . . . . . . . (Vacant)

## DEFENSE FORCES

**ARMED FORCES**
**Indonesian National Military Forces**
*(Tentara National Indonesia-Ankatan)*

**Armed Forces General Staff**
Commander-in-Chief of the Armed Forces . . . . . . . . . . Gen. L. B. Moerdani
Assistant, Intelligence, and Chief, Strategic
    Intelligence Center . . . . . . . . . . . . . . . . . . . . . . . . . . . . . . . . . . . . (Vacant)

255

Assistant, Operations ...........................Maj. Gen. M. Sanif
Assistant, Personnel and Manpower
   Development.........................Lt. Gen. Soekemi Soemantri
Assistant, Logistics .....................Maj. Gen. Dading Kalbaudi
Assistant, Territorial ...................Maj. Gen. A. Rivai Harahap
Assistant, Communications and Electronics ...........Vice Air Marshal
                    Tedjo Suwarno
Assistant, General Planning..................Rear Adm. F. M. Parapat
Assistant, Socio-Political Affairs ...............Brig. Gen. Geonarso S.F.
Assistant, Civil Service .....................Maj. Gen. Satibi Darwis
Assistant, Finance............................Lt. Gen. Sarwono
Assistant, Public Security and Order ............Maj. Gen. Drs. Poerwata
Assistant, International Cooperation ....Maj. Gen. Sukotjo Tjokroatmodjo
Inspector, Operations.....................Brig. Gen. Mardjan Saragih
Main Inspector, General Affairs .................................
Chief, ABRI Military Police .......................Brig. Gen. Kartojo
Chief, Research and Development Center
   (PUSLITBANG) ......................Brig. Gen. Theo Sumantri
Chief, Survey and Mapping.....................Comdr. D. U. Martojo
Chief, Health Center ...............Brig. Gen. Dr. Kurnia Natadisastra
Chief, General Supplies Agency ............Maj. Gen. Dading Kalbuadi
Chief, Civil Service Development Agency ......Maj. Gen. Widodo Mulatto
Chief, Mental Development Center ...........Comdr. Dr. Tarmizi Taher
Chief, National Reserve Center (PUSCADWAS) ....Maj. Gen. R. A. Saleh
Chief, Historical Center............................Col. Gatot Surjadi
Chief, Legal Board (BABINKUM) .................Col. M. Jailani, S.H.
Chief, Liaison Office ..........................Col. R. Hasanoeddin
Deputy Assistant, Intelligence ....................Brig. Gen. Subiyakto
Commandant, HQ Corps.....................Brig. Gen. Slamet Sawidji

**Command for the Restoration of**
**  Security and Public Order**
*(Komando Pemulihan Keamanan Dan*
*  Ketertiban-Kopkamtib)*
*Jl. Merdeka Barat 13/14*
*Jakarta*
*Telephone:  21) 365261*

Commander ...................................Gen. L. B. Moerdani

**National Security and Defense Council**
*(Wanhankamnas)*

Secretary-General .................Lt. Gen. Achmad Wiranatakusumah
Deputy Secretary General ...............Vice Adm. Machmud Subarkah

**Defense Area Commands**
*(Komando Wilayah Pertahanan-*
*  Kowilhan)*

Commander, Kowilhan I (Sumatra-West,
  Kalimantan) ..........................Lt. Gen. Soesilo Sudarman
Chief of Staff .........................Brig. Gen. Istianto Soewargono
Commander, Kowilhan II
(Java, Madura, Lesser Sunda Islands) ...........Lt. Gen. Yogi S. Memet
Chief of Staff ................................Brig. Gen. Sumanto
Commander, Kowilhan III
  (Sulawesi, rest of Kalimantan) ...................Lt. Gen. Soepardjo
Commander, Kolwilhan IV
  (Moluccas, West Irian) .........Lt. Gen. (Marine) Kahpi Suriadiredja
Chief of Staff ...................................Col. Ketut Wirasata

## FUNCTIONAL COMMANDS

**National Air Defense Command**
*(Kohanudnas)*
*Halim Perdana Kusumah*
*Jakarta*
*Telephone:  21) 801852*

Commander ............................Air Vice Marshal Iskandar
Chief of Staff ...............................Air Cmdr. Sumankno I.

**National Strategic Command**
*(Kostranas)*
*Jl. Merdeka Selatan 10*
*Jakarta*
*Telephone: 21) 351921*

Commander ............................... Air Vice Marshal Rusman
Chief of Staff ............................... Brig. Gen. Rabain Jafar

**Indonesian Armed Forces Academy**
*(Akabri)*
*Jl. Gondangdia Lama 1-8*
*Jakarta*
*Telephone: 21) 325721*

Commander ............................... Lt. Gen. Julius Henuhili
Governor, Army Section ................... Maj. Gen. Sudiman Saleh
Governor, Navy Section ...................... Rear Adm. Sugiatmo
Governor, Air Section ...................... Air Vice Marshal Soejitno
Governor, Police Section...................... Brig. Gen. R. Noerjono

**Armed Forces Command and Staff Colleges**
*(Sesko Abri)*
*Jl. Wirayudha 1*
*Bandung*
*Telephone: 838852*

Commander ............................... Vice Adm. Prasodjo Mahdi
Deputy Commander ............................... Maj. Gen. Achir
Commandant ...................... Maj. Gen. Joni Abd. Rachman
Commandant Bagian Laut........................ Rear Adm. Suwarso
Commandant Bagian Darat ................... Maj. Gen. B. Soemitro
Commandant Bagian Udara ........... Air Vice Marshal Luli Wardiman
Commandant Bagian Kepolisian...... Maj. Gen. Drs. Utaryo Soerjawinata

**National Defense College**
*(Lemhanas)*
*Jl. Kebon Sirih 24-30*
*Jakarta*

Governor ............................... Lt. Gen. Sutopo Yuwono
Vice Governor ............................... Mr. Ilen Surianegara
Staff ............................... Brig. Gen. Drs. Soemargono

**ARMY**
**Indonesian National Military Forces—Army**
*(Tentara National Indonesia-Ankatan Darat-TNI-AD)*
*Markas Besar Angkatan Darat,*
*Jl. Merdeka Utara No. 2*
*Jakarta*
*Telephone: 21) 551403, 351403*

Chief of Staff............................... Lt. Gen. Rudini
Deputy Chief of Staff....................................... (Vacant)
Inspector General ...................... Maj. Gen. Untung Sridadi
Assistant, Security ...................... Maj. Gen. Soelarso
Assistant, Operations ...................... Maj. Gen. Soeweno
Assistant, Personnel ...................... Maj. Gen. Soeharto
Assistant, Planning and Budget ................... Brig. Gen. Darsojo
Assistant, Logistics ...................... Maj. Gen. Harum Suwardi
Assistant, Territory...................... Maj. Gen. A. Rivai Harahap
Inspector, Finance ...................... Brig. Gen. S. M. Simorangkir
Chief, General Secretariat............................... Col. Darodji
Chief, Cooperatives Center ............. Brig. Gen. Saptadji Hadiprawira
Chief, Information Center ................... Brig. Gen. Jhonet Hutomo
Chief, Topographical Service ............... Col. Rahardjo Dirdjosaputro
Chief, Health Service...................... Brig. Gen. Dr. Ngesti Utomo
Chief, Personnel Administration Service ................... Col. Selardi
Chief, Communications and Electronics............... Brig. Gen. Pitoyo
Chief, Financial Service ...................... Brig. Gen. Hary Kiswarto
Chief, Liaison Office ...................... Lt. Col. Mokhtar Yamin
Chief, Military Ground Transportation
    Department ............................... Brig. Gen. Hartedjo
Chief, Engineers Department ................... Brig. Gen. Heru Gunadi
Chief, Ordnance Department ................... Brig. Gen. M. Soejono
Chief, General Supplies Service ................... Brig. Gen. Ishak Odang
Chief, R & D Service ............................... Col. Darwanto
Commander, Development, Research and
    Education Command ................... Lt. Gen. Bambang Triantoro
Commander, Industry ...................... Brig. Gen. A. H. Pane
Commandant, Infantry Center ................... Brig. Gen. Simanjuntak
Commandant, Cavalry Center ................... Brig. Gen. Makadada
Commandant, Artillery Center ................... Brig. Gen. Rosadi
Commandant, Air Defense Artillery Center ........... Brig. Gen. Dirham
Commander, Sandi Yudha Troops Command
    Kopassandha) ............................... Brig. Gen. Wirmojo
Commandant, Intelligence Center .............. Brig. Gen. Adam Saleh

Commander, Strategic Reserve Command (*KOSTRAD*) .........(Vacant)
Commander, Aviation ...............Brig. Gen. Widodo Sastroamidjojo
Chief of Staff, KOSTRAD ........................Brig. Gen. Suripto
Chief of Staff, Capital Garrison .............Brig. Gen. Eddy Nalapraya

**Army Regional Commands**
*(Komando Daerah Militer-Kodam)*

Commander, Kodam I (Iskandarmuda) .............Col. N. Narundana
Commander, Kodam II (Bukit Barisan) .........Brig. Gen. Harsudijono
Commander, Kodam III (17 Agustus) ...............Maj. Gen. Sarwono
Commander, Kodam IV (Sriwijaya)............Brig. Gen. Ari Bandyoko
Commander, Kodam V (Jaya) ................Maj. Gen. Try Soetrisno
Commander, Kodam VI (Siliwangi) ..........Maj. Gen. Eddy Sudradjat
Commander, Kodam VII (Diponegoro).............Maj. Gen. Soegiarto
Commander, Kodam VIII (Brawijaya) .............Maj. Gen. Moergito
Commander, Kodam IX (Mulawarman) ........Brig. Gen. Henry Santoso
Commander, Kodam X (Lambung Mangkurat) ......Brig. Gen. Samsudin
Commander, Kodam XII (Tanjung Pura) ........Brig. Gen. I. B. Sudjana
Commander, Kodam XIII (Merdeka)................................
Commander, Kodam XIV (Hasanudin) .............Brig. Gen. Soetedjo
Commander, Kodam XV (Pattimura) .............Brig. Gen. Soekoso
Commander, Kodam XVI (Udayana) .............Brig. Gen. D. Soetarto
Commander, Kodam XVII
    (Cendrawasih).......................Brig. Gen. Sembiring Meliala

**NAVY**
**Indonesian National Military Forces—Navy**
*(Tentara Nasional Indonesia-Angkatan*
    *Laut-TNI-AL)*
*Markas Besar Angkatan Laut*
*Jl. Gunung Sahari No. 66*
*Jakarta*

*Telephone:    21) 363051, 349641*

Chief of Staff .....................Vice Adm. M. Romly
Deputy Chief of Staff ................Vice Adm. T. Asikin Natanegara
Inspector General.......................Read Adm. Imam Muharam
Inspector, General Affairs .................Rear Adm. Hartono D.
Assistant, Security .......................Rear Adm. Subardo
Assistant, Personnel .....................Rear Adm. J. H. Salu
Assistant, Logistics ......................Rear Adm. Hartono M.
Assistant, Planning and Budget .........Rear Adm. Kusnandar, M.S.C.
Assistant, Operations .........................Rear Adm. Handogo
Chief, Communications and Electronic
    Service ..................................Comdr. Satmoko Soenjoto
Chief Personnel Administration Service .................Comdr. Moearif
Chief, Information Service ..................Comdr. E. H. Mangeweang
Chief, Material Service...........................Comdr. Yatidjo
Chief, Hydrographic Service ....................Comdr. P. L. Katoppo
Chief, Financial Service ......................Comdr. Drs. M. Ashaf
Chief, Legal Service .........................Comdr. Sofyan Huri
Chief, Manpower Distribution Service ...........Comdr. Ilham Sumarno
Chief, Health Service.............Comdr. Dr. Soesanto Mangunsadjito
Main Inspector, Treasury ......................Comdr. Teguh Santoso
Chief, Historical Service .............Brig. Gen. (Manne) Bedjo Sumitro
Chief, Research and Development Service .....Comdr. Ir. Wiyoto Sukarso
Chief, Data Collecting and Processing Center .....Comdr. Suyoso Sukarno
Chief, General Secretariat.......................Comdr. W. Rahadi
Chief, Mental Development
    Service .....................Brig. Gen. (Marine) H. Djoko Supriadi
Chief, Naval Provost .............Brig. Gen (Marine) Herman Moedjiroen
Chief, Liaison Office .........................Maj. Bambang Sugeng
Commander, Marine Corps ...............................(Vacant)
Chief of Staff, Marine Corps .............Brig. Gen. (Marine) Muntaram

**Naval Regional Commands**
*(Komando Daerah Angkatan Laut-*
    *Kodaeral)*

Commander, KODAERAL I .....................Comdr. Anwar Affandi
Commander, KODAERAL II ..........................Comdr. Aboe
Commander, KODAERAL III ..................Rear Adm. Rusdi Rusli
Commander, KODAERAL IV ................Rear Adm. Gatot Suwardi
Commander, KODAERAL VI........................Comdr. Bintoro
Commander, KODAERAL VII ....................Comdr. Sri Waskito
Commander, KODAERAL IX....................Comdr. R. Soepangat
Commander, KODAERAL X .........................Comdr. Basuki

Commander, Military Seaborne Command
(*KOLINLAMIL*) ......................... Rear Adm. Adang Safaat
Commander, Indonesian Fleet .............. Rear Adm. Rudolf Kasenda
Commander, Nusantara Squadron
(*ESKATARA*) ............................. Comdr. Inman Taufiq
Commanding General, Education
Command ...................... Maj. Gen. Suharmo Hariantho
Commandant, HQ Corps ......................... Col. (MAR) Subais
Chief, Aviation Service ............................. Col. Purnomo
Chief of Staff, KOLINLAMIL .................. Col. Ena Djaja Suparta
Commandant, Tanjung Priok Naval Base ......... Lt. Col. Haris Permadi
Deputy Assistant Security ........................ Col. Basuki Suyoto

## AIR FORCE
**Indonesian National Military Forces—
Air Force**
*(Tentara Nasional Indonesia-Angkatan
Udara-TNI-AU)*
*Markas Besar Angkatan Udara*
*Jl. Gatot Subroto No. 72*
*Jakarta*

*Telephone: 21) 774055, 772395*

Chief of Staff ................................. Air Marshal Soekardi
Deputy Chief of Staff ......................... Air Vice Marshal Utomo
Inspector General .................. Air Vice Marshal D. R. Kamarudin
Main Inspector, General Affairs ................. Air Comdr. Sumarno
Assistant, Planning and Budget .......... Air Vice Marshal Ibnu Subroto
Assistant, Security ........................... Air Vice Marshal Soekotjo
Assistant, Operations ...................... Air Vice Marshal Hartono
Assistant, Personnel ....................... Air Vice Marshal Sumitro
Assistant, Logistics .......................... Air Vice Marshal Soebagio
Chief, Financial Service ....................... Air Comdr. Suwarto
Chief, Communications and Electronic Service ....... Air Comdr. Sabardjo
Chief, Aerial Navigation Service .................... Air Comdr. Susetyo
Chief, Aerial Topographic Service ............... Air Comdr. Suhardjo
Chief, Research and Development Service ..... Air Comdr. Drs. Subagjo H.
Deputy Assistant, Security ..................... Air Comdr. Soetardjo
Assistant Officer, Security ............................. Col. Isnain
Assistant Officer, Security Development .................. Col. Partono
Assistant Officer, Aerial Intelligence ............... Col. Willy Kairupan
Commanding General, Unified Air Combat
Command (*KOPATDARA*) ................ Air Marshal Aried Rijadi
Commanding General, Education
Command ....................... Air Vice Marshal Sobirin Misbah
Chief, Information Service ............ Air Comdr. Soetardjo Moewalladi
Commanding General Quick Reaction Force
Command (*KOPASGAT*) ................... Air Comdr. Sugiantoro
Chief, Liaison Office ...................... Maj. Arijanto Saleh
Commander, Halim Perdanakusuma Air Base ...... Air Comdr. Suparman
Administrator, Halim Perdanakusuma International
Airport ........................................ Col. Suhardono
Commanding General Air Force Material
Command (*KOMATAU*) ................ Air Vice Marshal B. Parwoto
Commandant, Command and Staff
College ........................... Air Vice Marshal Luli Wardiman

### Air Force Regional Commands
*(Komando Daerah Angkatan Udara-
Kodau)*

Commander, Kodau I .................... Air Comdr. Wardojo Kusumo
Commander, Kodau III ......................... Air Comdr. Siboen
Commander, Kodau IV ................... Air Vice Marshal I. Suwongso
Commander, Kodau V ................. Air Vice Marshal Suti Harsono
Commander, Kodau VII ...................... Air Comdr. Sudarma

## POLICE
**Police of the Republic of Indonesia**
*(Kepolisian Republic Indonesia)*
*J. Trunojoyo 3*
*Jakarta*
*Telephone: 21) 348537*

Chief of the Police ..................... Lt. Gen. Drs. Anton Sudjarwo
Deputy Chief ............................. Maj. Gen. Pamudji
Director, Criminal ...............................................

### Police Regional Commands
*(Komando Daerah Kepolisian—Kodak)*

Chief, Kodak I ................................. Brig. Gen. Hardjono
Chief, Kodak II ......................... Brig. Gen. J. F. R. Montolalu

Chief, Kodak III................................Brig. Gen. Soetopo P.
Chief, Kodak IV ...........................Brig. Gen. Drs. Hudioro
Chief, Kodak V .........................Brig. Gen. Soejono Soentahir
Chief, Kodak VI .....................................................
Chief, Kodak VII ....................................................
Chief, Kodak VIII .........................Maj. Gen. Drs. Moerjono
Chief, Kodak IX............................Maj. Gen. Drs. Kafandi
Chief, Kodak X ............................Maj. Gen. Hartawan
Chief, Kodak XI...........................Brig. Gen. Drs. Pamoedji
Chief, Kodak XII ....................Brig. Gen. Darmawan Soedarsono
Chief, Kodak XIII ..........................Brig. Gen. R. Istambul
Chief, Kodak XIV.................Brig. Gen. Herman Soedjanadiwirya
Chief, Kodak XVI............................Brig. Gen. R. Sudjoko
Chief, Kodak XVII..........................Brig. Gen. Soedarmadji

\* \* \* \* \*

## GENERAL DEFENSE DATA

**Manpower**

Total Armed Forces...........................................248,000
  (See Page 255)
Population ................................................157,595,000

**Spending**

Military Expenditures......................................$1.6 billion
Gross National Product....................................$56.7 billion
Military Expenditure as a Percentage of
  Gross National Product ........................................2.8%
Military Expenditure as a Percentage of
  Central Government Expenditure ..............................10.2%

**Defense Treaties** *(See Part II for Additional Detail)*

Bilateral:    United States

Multilateral:  Limited Test Ban Treaty
        Treaty on the Non-Proliferation of Nuclear Weapons

# IRAN
## Islamic Republic of Iran
### *Jomhori-e-Islami-e-Iran*

## Defense Establishment Command Structure and Force Organization

The Leader of the Revolution, Ayatollah Ruhollah Khomeini, is the Commander-in-Chief of the armed forces. The National Defense Council advises him on appointments and defense policy.

It is not clear whether the order of battle that existed under the former regime (before 1979) is still valid. Some of the same divisions appear to be in existence under their old designations, but there are significant changes that are not yet on public record. There has been some attempt to integrate regular army units with the Revolutionary Guard. The Guard has units in each district of the larger cities and towns and in many villages. Each of these units has a commander as well as a representative of the Imam, usually a local clergyman, who oversees the Islamic content of the Guard's activities.

**Total armed forces:** 235,000 (Army: 150,000;   Revolutionary Guard: 40,000;   Navy: 10,000;   Air Force: 35,000). **Para-military forces:** 35,000.

## LEADER OF THE REVOLUTION AND FOUNDER OF THE ISLAMIC REPUBLIC

Ayatollah Ruhollah Khomeini

## HEAD OF STATE

Hojjat-ol-Islam Sayyed-Ali Khamenei

**OFFICE OF THE PRESIDENT**
*Teheran*
*Telephone:  6161*

President ........................Hojjat-ol-Islam Sayyed-Ali Khamenei

**National Defense Council**

Chairman .......................Hojjat-ol-Islam Sayyed-Ali Khamenei
(President)
Imam's Deputy ...........................Hojjat-ol-Islam Ali Akbar
Hashemi-Rafsanjani
Member ......................Mir-Hosein Mousavi-Khamenei
(Prime Minister)
Member ...............................Brig. Gen. Zahir-Nezhad
(Chief of the Joint Staff of the Armed Forces)
Member ...............................Col. Mohammad Salimi
(Minister of Defense)
Member ...............................Mohsen Reza'i
(Commander of the Revolutionary Guards)
Member ...............................Col. Mo'inpur
(Commander of the Air Force)
Member ...............................Azizi
(Deputy Foreign Minister)
Member ...............................Kamal Kharazi
(Chief, War Propaganda Office and
Director, Islamic News Agency)

**261**

**OFFICE OF THE PRIME MINISTER**
*Pastor Avenue*
*Teheran*
*Telephone: 6161*
*Telex: prim ir 213113*

Prime Minister . . . . . . . . . . . . . . . . . . . . . Mir-Hosein Mousavi-Khamenei

    **Defense Commission of the Parliament**

President . . . . . . . . . . . . . . . . . . . . . . . . . . . . . . Hojjat-ol-Islam Ruhani

    **Ministry of Defense**
    *Teheran*

Minister . . . . . . . . . . . . . . . . . . . . . . . . . . . . . . Col. Mohammad Salimi

# DEFENSE FORCES

**ARMED FORCES**
**Joint Staff of the Armed Forces**

Chief . . . . . . . . . . . . . . . . . . . . . . . Brig. Gen. Qasem Ali Zahir-Nazhad

**ARMY**
**Islamic Ground Forces**
*c/o Ministry of Defense*
*Teheran*

Commander . . . . . . . . . . . . . . . . . . . . . . . . . . Col. Ali Seyyad-Shirazi
Director of Mobilization . . . . . . . . . . . . . . . . . . . . . . . . . . . . . . . Salek
**Commands**
Commander, 77th Division (Meshed) . . . . . . . . . . . . . . . . . . . . . . . . . .
Commander, 64th Division (Urumiyeh) . . . . . . . . . . . . . . . . . . . . . . . . .
Commander, 28th Division (Kurdistan) . . . . . . . . . . . . . . . . . . . . . . . . .
Commander, 55th Airborne Brigade (Khuzistan) . . . . . . . . . . . . . . . . . .
Commander, 128th Division (Sanada) . . . . . . . . . . . . . . . . . . . . . . . . . .
Commander, Division (Qazvin) . . . . . . . . . . . . . . . . . . . . . . . . . . . . . .
Commander, Division (Tabriz) . . . . . . . . . . . . . . . . . . . . . . . . . . . . . .
Commander, Division (Bushehr) . . . . . . . . . . . . . . . . . . . . . . . . . . . . .

**NAVY**
*c/o Ministry of Defense*
*Teheran*

Commander . . . . . . . . . . . . . . . . . . . . Capt. Bahram Afzali Khochik-Bidjari
Deputy Commander . . . . . . . . . . . . . . . . . . . . . . . . . . . . . . Col. Amir Jalali
Director of Political/Ideological Office . . . . . . . . . . . . . . . . . . . . . . . Elahi

**AIR FORCE**
*c/o Ministry of Defense*
*Teheran*

Commander . . . . . . . . . . . . . . . . . . . . . . Col. Mohammad Hasan Mo'inpur

**ISLAMIC REVOLUTIONARY GUARD CORPS**
*Teheran*

Minister of Revolutionary Guards . . . . . . . . . . . . . . . . . . . . Mohsen Rafiqdust
Commander-in-Chief . . . . . . . . . . . . . . . . . . . . . . . . . . . . . Mohsen Reza'i
Deputy Commander . . . . . . . . . . . . . . . . . . . . . . . . . . . . . . . Sham'khani
Imam's Deputy . . . . . . . . . . . . . . . . . . . . . . . . . Hojjat-ol-Islam Maha Elati

**GENDARMARIE**
*Teheran*

Commander . . . . . . . . . . . . . . . . . . . . . . . . . . . . . . . . . Col. Kuchek-Zadeh

**NATIONAL POLICE**
*Teheran*

Commander . . . . . . . . . . . . . . . . . . . . . . . . . . . . . . . . . . Col. Khalil Samimi

\* \* \* \* \*

# GENERAL DEFENSE DATA

**Manpower**
    Total Armed Forces . . . . . . . . . . . . . . . . . . . . . . . . . . . . . . . . . . . 235,000
      (See Page 261)
    Population . . . . . . . . . . . . . . . . . . . . . . . . . . . . . . . . . . . . . 41,203,000

**Spending**

| | |
|---|---|
| Military Expenditures | $4.4 billion |
| Gross National Product | $112.1 billion |
| Military Expenditure as a Percentage of Gross National Product | 3.9% |
| Military Expenditure as a Percentage of Central Government Expenditure | 11.5% |

**Defense Treaties** *(See Part II for Additional Detail)*

Bilateral:     United States

Multilateral:  Biological Weapons Convention
Limited Test Ban Treaty
Treaty on the Control of Arms on the Seabed
Treaty on the Non-Proliferation of Nuclear Weapons

# IRAQ
## Republic of Iraq
### *Jumhuriyat al-Iraq*

## Defense Establishment Command Structure and Force Organization

The President, who is Chairman of the Revolutionary Command Council, holds the rank of Field Marshal and is Commander-in-Chief of the armed forces of Iraq. The Minister of Defense has responsibility for administrative matters. Operational control over the entire armed forces is vested with the Chief of the General Staff (who is also Chief of Staff of the Army). The Navy operates as part of the Army. The People's Army augments the regular forces, and serves as a palace guard.

**Total armed forces:** 342,250 (Army: 300,000; Navy: 4,250; Air Force: 38,000). **Paramilitary forces:** 250,000 (People's Army).

## HEAD OF STATE

H. E. Saddam Hussein

**OFFICE OF THE PRESIDENT OF THE REPUBLIC AND PRIME MINISTER**
*Presidential Palace Kara'adat Marim*
*Baghdad*
*Telex: 2299 alqasr ik*

President of the Republic, Prime Minister, and Commander-in-Chief . . . . . . . . . . . . . Field Marshal Saddam Hussein
Vice President . . . . . . . . . . . . . . . . . . . . . . . . . . . . . . Taha Moheddin Maruf
Minister of State . . . . . . . . . . . . . . . . . . . . . . . . . . . . . . . . . . Hashim Hasan
Minister of State . . . . . . . . . . . . . . . . . . . . . . . . . . . Abdallah Isma'il Ahmad
Minister of State . . . . . . . . . . . . . . . . . Arshad Muhammad Ahmad Al-Zibari
Minister of State . . . . . . . . . . . . . . . Obaidallah Mustapha Al-Barazani
Minister of State for Foreign Affairs . . . . . . . . . . . . . . . . . . . . Hamid Alwan

**Revolutionary Command Council**
*Baghdad*

Chairman . . . . . . . . . . . . . . . . . . . . . . . . . . . . . . . . . . . . . . . Saddam Hussein
Vice Chairman . . . . . . . . . . . . . . . . . . . . . . . . . . . . . . . . . . . . Izzat Ibrahim

**MINISTRY OF DEFENSE**
*Bab Al-Muadam*
*Baghdad*
*Telephone: (1) 8889071*
*Telex: 21 2201 mi def ik*

Deputy Prime Minister and Minister of Defense . . . . . . . . . . . . . . . . . . . . . . . . . . . . Adnan Khairallah

## DEFENSE FORCES

**ARMED FORCES**
*c/o Ministry of Defense*
*Bab Al-Muadam*
*Baghdad*
*Telephone: (1) 8889071*

Chief of the General Staff and Ground Forces . . . . . . . . . Lt. Gen. Abdul al-Jabbar Khalil Shanshal
Deputy Chief of General Staff . . . . . . . . . . . . . . . . . . . . . . Mohammad Tayyib Daud Kashmulah
Chief, Political Staff . . . . . . . . . . . . . . . . . . . . . . . . Maj. Salam Abdul Wahid
Commander, I Corps (Northern sector) . . . . . . . . . . . . . . . . . . . . . . . . . . . . . . . . . . . . . . . . . . .
Commander, II Corps (Central sector) . . . . . . . . . . . . . . . . . . . . . . . . . . . . . . . . . . . . . . . . . . .

Commander, III Corps
  (East of Basra)............................Gen. Mohammed Qasim
Commander, IV Corps
  (East of Amarah) ................Maj. Gen. Hisham Sabah al-Fakhri

**NAVY**
*c/o Ministry of Defense*
*Bab Al-Muadam*
*Baghdad*
*Telephone:  (1) 8889071*

Commander........................Col. Kaske Rashid Jamil Al-Basri

**AIR FORCE**
*c/o Ministry of Defense*
*Bab Al-Muadam*
*Baghdad*
*Telephone:  (1) 8889071*

Chief of Staff ..............................Maj. Mohammad Hanash
Chief, Air Defense .....................Brig. Gen. Mohammad Rashid

**THE PEOPLE'S ARMY**
*Baghdad*

Commander and First
  Deputy Prime Minister .....................Taha Yassin Ramadan

\* \* \* \* \*

# GENERAL DEFENSE DATA

**Manpower**
  Total Armed Forces...............................................342,250
    (See Page 265)
  Population ...............................................14,034,000

**Spending**
  Military Expenditures.........................................$2.98 billion
  Gross National Product........................................$38.9 billion
  Military Expenditure as a Percentage of
    Gross National Product .........................................7.6%
  Military Expenditure as a Percentage of
    Central Government Expenditure ...............................14.9%

**Defense Treaties** *(See Part II for Additional Detail)*

  Bilateral:    France
                Jordan
                Soviet Union

  Multilateral:  League of Arab States
                 Limited Test Ban Treaty
                 Treaty on the Control of Arms on the Seabed
                 Treaty on the Non-Proliferation of Nuclear Weapons

# IRELAND
## Irish Republic
### *Eire*

## Defence Establishment Command Structure and Force Organization

The President is Supreme Commander of the armed forces. Administrative control is exercised through the Minister of Defence, who is advised by a Council of Defence. The Chief of Staff acts as executive commander, and the commanders of the Air Corps and Naval Service are operationally subordinate to him.

Ireland is divided into three military commands (Eastern, Southern, and Western).

**Total armed forces:** 16,390 (Army: 14,554; Navy: 1,200; Air Force: 636). **Para-military forces:** 24,000 (Reserve Defence Force).

## HEAD OF STATE

H. E. Dr. Patrick J. Hillery

**OFFICE OF THE PRESIDENT**
*Phoenix Park*
*Dublin 8*
*Telephone: (1) 772815*

President and Supreme Commander . . . . . . . . . . . . . . . . Dr. Patrick J. Hillery

**DEPARTMENT OF DEFENCE**
*(An Roinn Cosanta)*
*Parkgate Street*
*Dublin 8*
*Telephone: (1) 771881*
*Telex: 5250 ARM EI*

Minister of Defence . . . . . . . . . . . . . . . . . . . . . . . . . . . . . . . . . Patrick Cooney
Minister of State . . . . . . . . . . . . . . . . . . . . . . . . . . . . . . . . . . Sean Barrett
Secretary . . . . . . . . . . . . . . . . . . . . . . . . . . . . . . . . . . . . . . . R. O'Sullivan
Assistant Secretary . . . . . . . . . . . . . . . . . . . . . . . . . . . . . . . . . . M. Crowe
Assistant Secretary . . . . . . . . . . . . . . . . . . . . . . . . . . . . . . . . . . G. Scully
Assistant Secretary . . . . . . . . . . . . . . . . . . . . . . . . . . . . . . . . . S. Brosnan
Finance Officer . . . . . . . . . . . . . . . . . . . . . . . . . . . . . . . . . . . M. Burgess

**Council of Defence**

Chairman . . . . . . . . . . . . . . . . . . . . . . . . . . . . . . . . . . . . . . . Patrick Cooney
(Minister of Defence)
Member . . . . . . . . . . . . . . . . . . . . . . . . . . . . . . . . . . . . . . . . Sean Barrett
(Minister of State)
Member . . . . . . . . . . . . . . . . . . . . . . . . . . . . . . . . . . . . . . . . R. O'Sullivan
(Secretary of Defence)
Member . . . . . . . . . . . . . . . . . . . . . . . . . . . . . . . . . . . Lt. Gen. Louis Hogan
(Chief of Staff)
Member . . . . . . . . . . . . . . . . . . . . . . . . . . . Maj. Gen. William Prendergast
(Adjutant-General)
Member . . . . . . . . . . . . . . . . . . . . . . . . . . . . Maj. Gen. John Gallagher
(Quartermaster-General)

267

# DEFENCE FORCES

**ARMY**
*c/o Department of Defence*
*Parkgate Street*
*Dublin 8*
*Telephone: (1) 771881*
*Telex: 5250 ARM EI*

Chief of Staff . . . . . . . . . . . . . . . . . . . . . . . . . . . . . . . . . . . .Lt. Gen. Louis Hogan

### Office of the Chief of Staff

Assistant Chief of Staff . . . . . . . . . . . . . . . . . . . . . . .Brig. Gen. Sean F. Casey
Director, Operations . . . . . . . . . . . . . . . . . . . . . . . . . . . . .Col. Vincent Savino
Director, Training Section . . . . . . . . . . . . . . . . . . . . . .Col. Brendan Cassidy
Director, Planning and Research Section . . . . . . . . . . .Col. Edward Sheehy
Director, Intelligence Section . . . . . . . . . . . . . . . . . . . . . . . . . .Col. John Egan
Director, Reserve Force Section . . . . . . . . . . . . . . . . . . . .Col. James Parker
Commanding Officer, Observer Corps . . . . . . . . . . . . . . .Col. John Connole

### Office of the Adjutant-General

Adjutant-General . . . . . . . . . . . . . . . . . . . . . .Maj. Gen. William Prendergast
Deputy Adjutant-General . . . . . . . . . . . . . . . . . . . . . . . . . . .Col. James Croke
Deputy Judge Advocate-General . . . . . . . . . . . . . . . . . . . . . . .Col. P. Jordan
Director of Military Police
    and Provost Marshal . . . . . . . . . . . . . . . . . . . . . . . . . . . . . .Col. Frank Kelly
Head Chaplain to the Forces . . . . . . . . . . . . . . . . . . . .Rev. Fr. Edward Dunne

### Office of the Quartermaster-General

Quartermaster-General . . . . . . . . . . . . . . . . . . . . . .Maj. Gen. John Gallagher
Deputy Quartermaster-General . . . . . . . . . . . . . . . . . . . .Col. Thomas Waters

### Technical and Supply Staff

Director, Artillery Corps . . . . . . . . . . . . . . . . . . . . . . . . . . . .Col. C. McGuinn
Director, Cavalary Corps . . . . . . . . . . . . . . . . . . . . . . .Col. Francis Lawless
Director, Engineer Corps . . . . . . . . . . . . . . . . . . . . . . . . .Col. James Seward
Director, Signals Corps . . . . . . . . . . . . . . . . . . . . . . . . . . .Col. Edward Doyle
Director, Ordnance Corps . . . . . . . . . . . . . . . . . . . . . . .Col. James Dowdall
Director, Supply and
    Transport Corps . . . . . . . . . . . . . . . . . . . . . . . . . . . . . . .Col. P. Connolly
Director, Medical Corps . . . . . . . . . . . . . . . . . . . . . . . . . . . .Col. A. O'Connor

### Regional Commands

Commanding Officer, Eastern Command . . . . . . . .Brig. Gen. G. O'Sullivan
Commanding Officer, Southern Command . . . . . . . . . .Brig. Gen. D. Byrne
Commanding Officer, Western Command . . . . . . .Brig. Gen. T. J. Hartigan
Commanding Officer, Curragh Command . . .Brig. Gen. T. M. McDumphy

**NAVY**
**Irish Naval Service**
*Naval Headquarters*
*c/o Department of Defence*
*Parkgate Street*
*Dublin 8*
*Telephone: (1) 771881*
*Telex: 5250 ARM EI*

Flag Officer, Naval Service . . . . . . . . . . . . . . . . . . .Comdr. Liam S. Moloney
Commanding Officer, Naval
    Base & Dockyard . . . . . . . . . . . . . . . . . . . . . . . . . . . . . .Capt. W. J. Brett
Marine Engineering Superintendent . . . . . . . . . . . . . . . . .Capt. J. R. Guthrie
Commanding Officer, Naval Depot . . . . . . . . . . . . . . . .Comdr. J. A. Deasy
School Commandant, Naval School . . . . . . . . . . . . . . .Lt. Cdr. E. McNamara

### Procurement and Logistics Office

*Naval Headquarters*
*c/o Department of Defence*
*Parkgate Street*
*Dublin 8*
*Telephone: (1) 771881, Ext. 149*
*Telex: 5250 ARM EI*

Commander . . . . . . . . . . . . . . . . . . . . . . . . . . . . . . . . . . . . . .P. A. O'Mahony

**AIR FORCE**
**Irish Air Corps**
*Air Corps Headquarters*
*c/o Department of Defence*
*Parkgate Street*
*Dublin 8*

*Telephone:   (1) 771881*
*Telex:   5250 ARM EI*

Commander, Air Corps, and Director
 of Military Aviation . . . . . . . . . . . . . . . . . . . . . . . Brig. Gen. J. M. Connolly
Commander, Air Corps Group . . . . . . . . . . . . . . . . . . . . . Col. B. McMahon
Operations Officer, Air Corps Group . . . . . . . . . . . . . . . . Lt. Col. J. P. Kelly
Executive Officer, Air Corps . . . . . . . . . . . . . . . . . . . . . . . Lt. Col. P. Cranfield
Officer Commanding, Administrative Wing . . . . . . . . . . . Lt. Col. J. O'Brien
Officer Commanding, Training Wing . . . . . . . . . . . . . . . Lt. Col. M. O'Malley
Officer Commanding, No. 1 Support Wing . . . . . . . . . . . . Lt. Col. K. Hogan
Officer Commanding, No. 2 Support Wing . . . . . . . . . . . Lt. Col. M. Hipwell
Chief, Aeronautical Engineer . . . . . . . . . . . . . . . . . . . . . . . . Lt. Col. U. Lyons
Officer Commanding, Engineering Wing . . . . . . . . . . . . . . Lt. Col. J. Moore
Chief, Air Traffic Controller . . . . . . . . . . . . . . . . . . . . . . . . Lt. Col. G. Kerwin

**Procurement Office**

Staff Officer, Administration
 and Supply  . . . . . . . . . . . . . . . . . . . . . . . . . . . . . . . . . Cdt. J. Saunderson

\* \* \* \* \*

## GENERAL DEFENCE DATA

**Manpower**
  Total Armed Forces . . . . . . . . . . . . . . . . . . . . . . . . . . . . . . . . . . . . . . . . . . 16,390
   (See Page 267)
  Population  . . . . . . . . . . . . . . . . . . . . . . . . . . . . . . . . . . . . . . . . . . . . . . . 3,533,000

**Spending**
  Military Expenditures . . . . . . . . . . . . . . . . . . . . . . . . . . . . . . . . . . . . . . . $291 million
  Gross National Product . . . . . . . . . . . . . . . . . . . . . . . . . . . . . . . . . . . . . . $16.3 billion
  Military Expenditure as a Percentage of
   Gross National Product . . . . . . . . . . . . . . . . . . . . . . . . . . . . . . . . . . . . 1.8%
  Military Expenditure as a Percentage of
   Central Government Expenditure . . . . . . . . . . . . . . . . . . . . . . . . . . . . . 3.3%

**Defence Treaties** *(See Part II for Additional Detail)*

   Bilateral:    None

   Multilateral:  Biological Weapons Convention
           Environmental Modification Convention
           Limited Test Ban Treaty
           Treaty on the Control of Arms on the Seabed
           Treaty on the Non-Proliferation of Nuclear Weapons

# ISRAEL
## State of Israel
### *Medinat Israel*

## Defence Establishment Command Structure and Force Organization

The Prime Minister is Commander-in-Chief of the Israel Defence Forces and exercises his authority through the Minister of Defence. All branches of the military are subject to the authority of the Chief of the General Staff of the Army. In practice, the Air Force and Navy enjoy considerable autonomy.

**Total armed forces:** 174,000 (Army: 135,000; Navy: 9,000; Air Force: 30,000). **Paramilitary forces:** 4,500 (Border Guards). **Total armed forces after mobilization:** 500,000 (100,000 in 24 hours).

## HEAD OF STATE

H. E. Chaim Herzog

**OFFICE OF THE PRESIDENT**
*Beit Hanasi*
*3 Hakeset Street*
*Jerusalem 92188*
*Telephone:  (2) 668231*

President .............................................Chaim Herzog

**OFFICE OF THE PRIME MINISTER**
*3 Kaplan Street*
*Hakirya*
*Jerusalem 91919*
*Telephone:  (2) 639211*

Prime Minister and Commander-in-Chief ..............Menachem Begin
Deputy Prime Minister ....................................(Vacant)
Deputy Prime Minister ..................................David Levy
Manager, Prime Minister's Bureau ..................Yechiel Kadishai
Director-General ..........................Matityahu Shumulevitz

**MINISTRY OF DEFENCE**
*7 "A" Street*
*Hakirya*
*Tel Aviv 67659*
*Telephone:  (3) 212219-20*
*Telex:  33719 misit il*

Minister ...............................................Moshe Arens
Assistant Minister.......................................(Vacant)
Assistant to the Minister, Deputy
    Director-General, General Affairs ......................Haim Israeli
Military Secretary to the Minister .................Brig. Gen. Dan Yatom
Senior Advisor, Strategic Policy ..........................Avraham Lif
Chief Censor ....................................Yehoshua Bar David

**Head Office**

Director-General ................................Menachem Meron
Deputy Director-General ..................................(Vacant)
Deputy Director-General, Defence Sales ..............Ya'akov Shapira
Deputy Director-General,
    Organization and Administration ....................Yehuda Moron
Assistant to the Director-General .........................Meir Kedmi
Assistant to the Deputy Director-General,
    Defence Sales ........................................(Vacant)
Spokesman.........................................Dan Weinreich
Information Officer .................................Meir Shenkar
Chief, Defence Exports
    to Special Countries ...........................Yahezkel Ben-Sira

| | |
|---|---|
| **Headquarter Units** | Military Ombudsman .............................Maj. Gen. Dani Matt |
| | Chief Scientist ...................................Dr. Manes Pratt |
| | Assistant Chief Scientist ................................Shmuel Aviad |
| **Coordination of Government Operations in the Administered Territories** | Coordinator ............................Brig. Gen. (Ret.) Eliezer Fuad |
| | Deputy Coordinator.............................Col. Arie Bekenstein |
| **Procurement and Production Administration** | Director ......................................................Haim Golan |
| | Deputy Director and Head of Supplies Group ............Shalom Aharoni |
| | Deputy Director and Head, Industrial and Planning Centre ......................Avraham Oren |
| | Deputy Director, Operational Supervision and Emergency Arrangements ......................Pinhas Barne'a |
| | Economic Advisor ......................................Ya'akov Gnizi |
| | Manager, Aircraft Project ..........................Shmuel Bentov |
| | Head, Air Force Group ...............................Gary Brovisky |
| | Head, Ground Forces Group .........................Michael Snir |
| | Head, Navy Group .......................................Arye Laor |
| | Head, Aircraft .................................Gershon Goldenberg |
| | Head, Vehicles and Machinery ..........................Haim Elroy |
| | Head, Ground Forces Weapons ........................Hanan Moked |
| | Head, Import and Transport ...........................David Schief |
| | Head, Supplies .....................................Yoram Malchy |
| | Head, Stores and Sewing Plants.....................Pinhas Hirschberg |
| | Head, Sales Unit ......................................Dan Kohen |
| | Head, Electronics and Control Devices..................Yitzhak Aloni |
| | Internal Auditor ...................................Zvi Tennenbaum |
| **Construction and Property Department** | Director ...............................................Dr. Nafali Gurel |
| | Deputy Director, Construction ........................Ya'akov Yaniv |
| | Deputy Director, Engineering and Planning ...........Dr. Leah Kaplan |
| | Head, Costing and Contracts ...........................Moshe Doron |
| | Head, Contracts Unit ..................................Leon Brandt |
| | Construction Manager, Negev District ...................Yitzhak Raviv |
| | Construction Manager, Northern District ................Yair Gottlieb |
| | Construction Manager, Central District ................Arie Goldbard |
| | Construction Manager, Southern District.................Yona Goresnic |
| | Construction Manager, Eilat ............................Nissim Assa |
| | Senior Engineer, Planning ..........................Ephraim Perry |
| | Head, Planning ......................................Haim Peleg |
| | Head, Services and Maintenance ..................Mordechai Savitzky |
| | Auditor .........................................Yossef Luxembourg |
| **Research and Development Department** | Head of Department...............................Dr. Benzion Nave |
| | Deputy.................................................Mr. Ilan Lev |
| **Defence Establishment Comptroller** | Military Advisor .................................Brig. Gen. Ami Ayalon |
| | Internal Auditor .....................................Aharon Bar-Niv |
| | Assistant Internal Auditor ..........................Ya'akov Gansel |
| | Assistant Auditor, IDF.........................Col. Binyamin Meitiv |
| | Advisor, Internal Audit Units .........................Nahman Barak |
| **Finance Department** | Director ..............................................Dov Hochman |
| | Assistant Head of Department ..........................Meir Zemach |
| **Budget Department** | Director ...............................Brig. Gen. Reuven Herschco |
| | Assistant Director and Head of Scientific Industries Division ...........................Yossef Gat |
| | Head, Ground Forces Budget .................Aluf-Michne Shimon Ziv |
| | Head, Planning and Systems ...................................... |
| | Head, Air Force and GHQ Budget .................Col. Baruch Merum |

| | | |
|---|---|---|
| **Rehabilitation Department** | Head of Department | Arye Fink |
| | Assistant Head, In Charge of Employment and Professional Training | Ya'acov Patt |
| | Director, Commemoration of the Fallen | Na'aman Schayek |
| | Director, Medical Services | Dr. Alfred Cimchy |
| | Director, Rehabilitation Office, Tel-Aviv | Yitzhak Erel |
| | Director, Rehabilitation Office, Dan Area | Yehudit Ravitch |
| | Director, Rehabilitation Office, Jerusalem | Moshe Cohen |
| | Director, Rehabilitation Office, Be'er Sheva | Shalom Halevy |
| | National Supervisor, Field Services | Arye Issaroff |
| **Legal Adviser's Bureau** | Legal Adviser | Moshe Kochanovsky |
| | Senior Assistant Legal Adviser | Haim Bazurha |
| | Assistant Legal Adviser | Moshe Kuperstein |
| | Assistant Legal Adviser | Haim Katz |
| | Assistant Legal Adviser | Nava Rashba |
| **Economic Adviser** | Economic Adviser | (Vacant) |
| | Assistant Economic Adviser (Micro-Economics) | Zvi Tropp |
| **Personnel Administration** | Director | Shlomo Hayat |
| | Deputy Director, Supplies and Services Unit | Moshe Tabo |
| **Organization, Control and Information Department** | Director | Shimshon Zelnir |
| | Deputy Director, Special Projects | Dr. Shahar Gershom |
| | Head, EDP Centre | Gideon Malbitzky |
| | Head, Organization | Natan Gershtansky |
| | Head, Control and Information Unit | Kalman Ronen |
| **National Emergency Board** | Chairman | Moshe Gat |
| | Permanent Deputy to Chairman and Chairman, Southern Region (Acting) | Moshe Gat |
| | Chairman, Northern Region | Eitan Shimshoni |
| | Chairman, Central Region | Yitzhak Zeid |
| **IDF and Defence Establishment Archives** | Director | Chaim Sarid |
| | Deputy Director | Zahav Ostfeld |
| **Youth and Nahal Department** | Director | Raphael Shefer |
| | Deputy Director | Yair Doar |
| | Editor-in-Chief, "Bamahane Nahal" and "Bamahane Gadna" | Yoram Tehar-Lev |
| **Spokesman and Public Relations** | Spokesman | Dan Weinreich |
| | Information Officer | Meir Shenkar |
| **Ministry of Defence Missions Abroad** | Head of Mission, United States and Canada | Mr. Avraham Ben Yossef |
| | Head of Mission, Federal Republic of Germany | |
| | Head of European Mission | Brig. Gen. Amir Reuveni |
| | Representative in Venezuela, Santo Domingo and Haiti | Brig. Gen. Avraham Ahmog |
| | Representative in Brazil | Col. Yechiel Yesha'ayahu Sharaby |
| | Representative in Columbia, Panama and Costa Rica | Ram Bar |
| **Israel Military Industries** | Director-General | Michael Schor |
| | Deputy Director-General, Ammunition Plants | Asher Peleg |

Director, Production Coordination . . . . . . . . . . . . . . . . Dr. Gavriel Komissar
Deputy Director-General,
    Administration and Manpower . . . . . . . . . . . . . . . . . . . . . Yossef Dromi
Deputy Director-General,
    Exports and Local Sales . . . . . . . . . . . . . . . . . . . . . . . . . . . Manes Danan
Director, Central Laboratory . . . . . . . . . . . . . . . . . . . . . . . . . Ze'ev Zalmon
Director, Arms Plants . . . . . . . . . . . . . . . . . . . . . . . . . . . . . . . . . Tzvi Yarom
Director, Chemical Plants . . . . . . . . . . . . . . . . . . . . . . . . . . . . . Israel Arad
Director, "Ashot Ashkelon" Industries, Ltd. . . . . . . . . . . . . . Ezra Yesody
Director, Jerusalem Plants (Acting) . . . . . . . . . . . . . . . . . . . Moshe Paltiel
Director, Haifa Plants . . . . . . . . . . . . . . . . . . . . . . . . . . Binyamin Karmon
Director, Systems Division . . . . . . . . . . . . . . . . . . . . . . . Hanoch Fenikel
Central Area Combined Industries . . . . . . . . . . . . . . . . . . . Shmuel Elad
Director, Engineering Systems . . . . . . . . . . . . . . . . . . . Ya'acov Lapidoth
Director, Industrial Services . . . . . . . . . . . . . . . . . . . . . . . Yona Margalir
Director, Supplies . . . . . . . . . . . . . . . . . . . . . . . . . . . . . . . . . Zeev Yorval
Director, Internal Audit . . . . . . . . . . . . . . . . . . . . . . . . . . . . Hayim Zayf
Director, Finance and Economy . . . . . . . . . . . . . . . . . . Avraham Sheintal
Chief Accountant . . . . . . . . . . . . . . . . . . . . . . . . . . . . . . Reuven Einhorn
Director, Research and Development . . . . . . . . . . . . . . . . . Dr. Arye Levy
Director, Planning and Control Division . . . . . . . . . . . . . . David Levonai
Head, Safety Department . . . . . . . . . . . . . . . . . . . . . . . . Dr. Yosef Sway
Legal Adviser . . . . . . . . . . . . . . . . . . . . . . . . . . . . . . . . (Mrs.) Margalit Nof

**Armament Development
Authority**

Director . . . . . . . . . . . . . . . . . . . . . . . . . . . . . . . . . . . . . . Dr. Ze'ev Bonan
Deputy Director, Research and Development . . . . . . . . . . . Dr. Eliezer Gon
Senior Assistant to the Director . . . . . . . . . . . . . . . . . . . . . . . David Harel
Deputy Director, Finance and Procurement . . . . . . . . . . . . . Shalom Drori
Deputy Director, Special Assignments . . . . . . . . . . . . . . . . . . . . Tzvi Ever

# DEFENCE FORCES

**ARMY**
**Israeli Defence Force—IDF**
*c/o Ministry of Defence*
*7 "A" Street*
*Tel Aviv 61070*

*Telephone:  (3) 212220*
*Telex:  33719 misbit il*

Chief of the General Staff and
    Chief of Staff of the Army . . . . . . . . . . . . . . . . . . . . Lt. Gen. Moshe Levy
Deputy Chief of Staff, Chief,
    "G" Branch . . . . . . . . . . . . . . . . . . . . . . . . . . . . Maj. Gen. David Ivri
Director, Military Intelligence . . . . . . . . . . . . . . . . . Maj. Gen. Ehud Barak
Chief, "Q" Branch . . . . . . . . . . . . . . . . . . . . . . . Maj. Gen. Yohanan Gur
Chief, "A" Branch . . . . . . . . . . . . . . . . . . . . . . . . Brig. Gen. Yoron Amoss
Chief, Planning Branch . . . . . . . . . . . . . . . . . Maj. Gen. Menachem Einan
Chief, Planning Branch . . . . . . . . . . . . . . . . . . . . . . . . . . . . . Maj. Gen.
Commander, Armored Corps . . . . . . . . . . . . . . Maj. Gen. Moshe Bar-Kocha
Commander, Northern Command . . . . . . . . . . . . . . . Maj. Gen. Amir Drori
Commander, Central Command . . . . . . . . . . . . . . . . . . Maj. Gen. Uri Or
Commander, Southern Command . . . . . . . . . . . . . . . Maj. Gen. Chaim Erez
Coordinator, Government Operations in
    the Administered Territories . . . . . . . . . . . . Brig. Gen. (Ret.) Eliezin Fuad
Spokesman, IDF . . . . . . . . . . . . . . . . . . . . . . . . . Brig. Gen. Ya'akov Even
Director, Military Training . . . . . . . . . . . . . . . . . . . Maj. Gen. Yosef Peled
Director, National Defence College . . . . . . . . . . . Maj. Gen. Yehoshua Sagi

**NAVY**
*c/o Ministry of Defence*
*7 Kaplan Street*
*Tel Aviv 64734*

*Telephone:  (2) 212144*
*Telex:  33719 misbit il*

Commander . . . . . . . . . . . . . . . . . . . . . . . . . . . . . . . Rear Adm. Ze'ev Almog

**AIR FORCE**
*c/o Ministry of Defence*
*7 Kaplan Street*
*Tel Aviv 64734*

*Telephone: (2) 212144*
*Telex: 33719 misbit il*

Commander.................................Maj. Gen. Amos Lapidot
Deputy Commander, Training and Operations........................
Deputy Commander, Intelligence ...................................
Deputy Commander, Manpower.....................................
Deputy Commander, Equipment ....................................

**PARA MILITARY FORCES**
**Fighting Pioneer Youth**
*(NAHAL)*
*Tel Aviv*

Commander..............................Brig. Gen. Amnon Eshkol

\* \* \* \* \*

# GENERAL DEFENCE DATA

**Manpower**
    Total Armed Forces..............................................174,000
      (See Page 271)
    Population ...................................................3,916,000

**Spending**
    Military Expenditures ...........................................$5 billion
    Gross National Product ..........................................$17 billion
    Military Expenditure as a Percentage of
      Gross National Product ..........................................29.1%
    Military Expenditure as a Percentage of
      Central Government Expenditure ................................34.2%

**Defence Treaties** *(See Part II for Additional Detail)*

    Bilateral:     Egypt
                Lebanon
                United States

    Multilateral:   Limited Test Ban Treaty

# ITALY
## Italian Republic
*Repubblica Italiana*

### Defense Establishment Command Structure and Force Organization

The President of the Republic is the nominal Commander-in-Chief of the armed forces and presides over the Supreme Defense Council, an appointed, policy-making body. Actual control and authority for the armed forces rests with the Minister of Defense, who is advised by the Defense Committee.

Directly responsible to the Minister of Defense and in charge of the entire defense establishment is the Defense General Secretary. He heads the administrative chain of command, consisting of five Central Offices. With the help of the Chiefs of Staff Committee, he also heads the military command through 19 General Directorates. The executive counterpart to the Chiefs of Staff Committee is the Armed Forces Supreme Board. The four Chiefs of Staff (Army, Navy, Air Force, Carabinieri) are all responsible to the Defense General Secretary.

**Total armed forces:** 370,000 (Army: 257,000; Navy: 44,000; Air Force: 69,000). **Paramilitary forces:** 136,780 (90,000 Carabinieri; 46,780 Finance Guards).

## HEAD OF STATE

H. E. dott. Sandro Pertini

**OFFICE OF THE PRESIDENT**
*Palazzo del Quirinale*
*00100, Rome*

*Telephone: (16) 46 99*
*Telex: 611440 sgpri*

President of the Republic and Commander-in-Chief ...dott. Sandro Pertini
Secretary-General .............................. Antonio Maccanico
Head, Press Office .......................... Michelangelo Iacobucci

**Supreme Defense Council**
*(Consiglio Suprema de Difesa)*

Chairman................................ Sandro Pertini (President)
Member ...........................Bettino Craxi (Prime Minister)
Member................... Giutio Andreotti (Minister of Foreign Affairs)
Member ...................Oscar Luigi Sealfers (Minister of the Interior)
Member .....................Giovanni Goria (Minister of Treasury)
Member ...................Giovanni Spadolini (Minister of Defense)
Member ................................Gen. Vittorio Santini
(Chief of the Defense Staff)
Member ..........................Pietro Lungo (Minister of Budget)
Member...........Meato Altissino (Minister of Industry and Commerce)

**OFFICE OF THE PRIME MINISTER**
*Piazza Colonna 370*
*Palazzo Chigi*
*00100, Rome*

*Telephone: (6) 67 79*
*Telex: 612476 pemsi i*

Prime Minister .................................Amintore Fanfani
Under Secretary ............................Francesco Compagnoli

## MINISTRY OF DEFENSE
*(Ministerio Della Difesa)*
*Via XX Settembre 8*
*Palazzo Baracchini*
*00100, Rome*

*Telephone: (6) 47 57 697 i 47 57 703,*
*47 59 841*
*Telex: 611438 amati*

| | |
|---|---|
| Minister | Giovanni Spadolini |
| Under Secretary | Tommaso Bisagno |
| Under Secretary | Bartolo Ciccardini |
| Under Secretary | Vittorio Olcese |
| Under Secretary | Silvano Signori |
| General Secretary | Lt. Gen. Giuseppe Piovano |
| Chief of the Cabinet, Defense Ministry | Lt. Gen. Mario De Paolis |
| Vice Chief of the Cabinet, Defense Ministry | Col. Bonifacio Incisa Di Camerana |
| Vice Chief of the Cabinet, Defense Ministry | Brig. Gen. Francesco Pugliese |
| Military Advisor to the President | Gen. Mario Parisio |
| Chief of Security Service for the Cabinet, Defense Ministry | Col. Domenico Bonazzoli |
| Chief, Public Information Service | Col. Rinaldo Rinaldi |

### Defense Committee

| | |
|---|---|
| Chairman | Giovanni Spadolini (Minister of Defense) |
| Member *(ex Officio)* | Lt. Gen. Giuseppe Piovano (General Secretary, Defense) |
| Member *(ex officio)* | Gen. Vittorio Santini (Chief, Defense Staff) |
| Member *(ex officio)* | Gen. Umberto Capuzzo (Chief of Staff, Army) |
| Member *(ex officio)* | Adm. Angelo Monassi (Chief of Staff, Navy) |
| Member *(ex officio)* | Gen. Lamberto Bartolucci (Chief of Staff, Air Force) |
| Member *(ex officio)* | Gen. Lorenzo Valditara (Chief of Carabinieri) |

# DEFENSE FORCES

## ARMED FORCES
*c/o Ministry of Defense*
*Via XX Settembre 8*
*00100, Rome*

*Telephone: (6) 47 59 841*
*Telex: 611438 smd i*

| | |
|---|---|
| Defense General Secretary | Lt. Gen. Giuseppe Piovano |
| Chief of Defense Staff | Gen. Vittorio Santini |
| Deputy Chief of Staff | Gen. Franco Pisano |
| President, Superior Council of Armed Forces | Lt. Gen. Giuseppe Calamani |
| Commanding General, Carabinieri | Lt. Gen. Lorenzo Valditara |
| Commanding General, Finance Guard | Lt. Gen. Nicola Chiari |
| Director, SISMI (Military Intelligence) | Lt. Gen. Ninetto Lugaresi |
| Vice Director, SISMI | Maj. Gen. Abelardo Mei |
| | Maj. Gen. Giuseppe D'Ambrosio |

### Armed Forces Supreme Board

| | |
|---|---|
| Chairman | Lt. Gen. Giuseppe Piovano (Defense General Secretary) |
| Member | Gen. Umberto Capuzzo (Chief of Staff, Army) |
| Member | Gen. Adm. Angelo Monassi (Chief of Staff, Navy) |
| Member | Lamberto Bartolucci (Chief of Staff, Air Force) |
| Member | Gen. Lorenzo Valditara (Chief of Carabinieri) |

## ARMY
*(Esercito Italiano)*
*Palazzo Esercito*
*Via XX Settembre 123*
*00187, Rome*

*Telephone: (6) 47 35 1*
*Telex: 611438 smd i*

| | |
|---|---|
| Chief of Staff | Gen. Umberto Capuzzo |
| Deputy Chief of Staff | Gen. Mario Fausto Fortunato |
| Chief, Army S.I.O.S. | Brig. Gen. Benito Gavazza |
| Chief of Office, Chief of Staff | Col. Biagio Rizzo |
| Chief, Army Attaché Office | Col. Paolo Cavanenghi |

### Territorial Army
*(Force per la Difesa Interna del Territorio)*

| | |
|---|---|
| Commander, First Territorial Military Command (Torin) | Gen. Renato Lodi |
| Commander, Fifth Territorial Military Command (Padua) | Gen. Giorgio Donati |
| Commander, Seventh Territorial Military Command (Florence) | Gen. Franco Barbolini |

|  | Commander, Eighth Territorial Military Command (Rome) .......................Gen. Salvator Coniglio |
|---|---|
|  | Commander, Tenth Territorial Military Command (Naples) .......................Gen. Giacinto Antonelli |
|  | Commander, Eleventh Territorial Military Command (Palermo) .....................Gen. Vittorio Monastra |

**Field Army**
*(Esercito di Campagna)*

Commander, Third Army Corps (Milan) ........Gen. Riccardo Bisogniero
Commander, Fourth Army Corps (Bolzano) .............Gen. Luigi Poli
Commander, Fifth Army Corps
(Vittorio Veneto) ......................Gen. Michele Santaniello
Commander, Sardinian Autonomous Command
(Cagliari) ..........................................Gen. Neri Loi

**NAVY**
*(Marina Militare Italiano)*
*Palazzo Marina*
*Piazza della Marina, Via F. Corridoni*
*00196, Rome*

*Telephone:   (6) 36 80 1*
*Telex:   611438 smd i*
*Cable:   MARISTAT ROMA*

Chief of Staff ...............................Adm. Angelo Monassi
Deputy Chief of Staff .......................Vice Adm. Cesare Pellini
Chief, Navy S.I.O.S. ..........................Rear Adm. Aldo Gallo
Vice Chief, Navy S.I.O.S. ...................Capt. Gianfranco Battelli
Chief, General Affairs ........................Capt. Luciano Monego
Chief, Navy Attache Office ......................Cdr. Tullio Dequal
Commander-in-Chief, Fleet ................Vice Adm. Vittorio Marulli
Chief, Navy Personnel ...................Vice Adm. Giasone Piccioni
Head, First Department (Personnel) ........Rear Adm. Giuseppe Arena
Head, Second Department (Intelligence) .........Rear Adm. Aldo Gallo
Head, Third Department (Plans
and Operations) ......................Rear Adm. Guido Venturoni
Head, Fourth Department (Weapons
and Means Studies) ........................Rear Adm. Mario Augell
Head, Fifth Department
(Communications) .........................Rear Adm. Mario Saliu
Head, Sixth Department (Helicopters) ...............Capt. Giorgio Ghe
Head, Naval Aviation Office .................Gen. Div. A. Zeno Tascio
Head, General Affairs Office ..............Rear Adm. Luciano Monego
Head, General Financial
Planning Office ...........................Capt. Mario Castelletti
Head, Documentation and Promotional
Activities Office ..........................Capt. Massimo Benedetti

**Allied Naval Forces Southern Europe/
Lower Tyrrhenian Naval District
(Naples)**
*Maridipart*
*Naples*

Commander in Chief .....................Adm. Giuseppe Di Giovanni

**Northern Tyrrhenian Naval District**
*Maridipart*
*La Spezia*

Commander-in-Chief ....................Vice Adm. Vittorio Gioncada

**Ancona Naval District**
*Maridipart*
*Ancona*

Commander-in-Chief ...................Vice Adm. Sergio Agostinelli

**Ionian/Strait of Otranto Naval District**
*Maridipart*
*Taranto*

Commander-in-Chief ......................Vice Adm. Antonio Fedele

**Sicily Naval District**
*Marisicilia*
*Messina*

Commander-in-Chief ......................Rear Adm. Reuzo Rosso

**Sardinia Naval District**
*Marisardegna*
*La Maddalena*

Commander-in-Chief .................... Rear Adm. Narciso Tonarelli

**First Naval Division**
*Comdinav 1*
*La Spezia*

Commander ............................. Rear Adm. Filippo Ruggiero

**Second Naval Division**
*Comdinav 2*
*Taranto*

Commander ................................ Rear Adm. Franco Papili

**Third Naval Division**
*Comdinav 3*
*Brindisi*

Commander ........................... Rear Adm. Gianfranco Nasini

**Fourth Naval Division**
*Comdinav 4*
*Taranto*

Commander ............................ Rear Adm. Antonino Gerací

**Submarine Operations**
*Maricosom*
*Taranto*

Commander ................................ Rear Adm. Diego Grotti

**Underwater Demolition Teams**
*Comsubin*
*La Spezia*

Commander .......................... Rear Adm. Cataldo Gigantesco

**Navy Logistic Inspectorate**
*Marispelog*
*00100 Rome*

Commander ........................... Rear Adm. Antonino Geraci

**Navy Air Maritime Training Centre**
*Maricentadd*
*74100 Taranto*

Commander ............................... Rear Adm. Giulio Benini

**AIR FORCE**
*(Aeronautica Militare)*
*Palazza Aeronautica*
*Viale dell'Universita 4*
*00185, Rome*

*Telephone: (6) 49 86*
*Telex: 611438 smd i*

Chief of Staff ......................... Gen. Lamberto Bartolucci
Deputy Chief of Staff .......................... Gen. Franco Ferri
Chief, Air S.I.O.S. ........................ Brig. Gen. Zeno Tascio
Vice Chief, Air S.I.O.S. ....................... Col. Vinicio Salvi
Chief, Air Attache Office ........................... Col. Sergio Sala
Inspector, Air Traffic and
    Communications ...................... Maj. Gen. Carmelo Mure
Aviation Inspector, Navy ................... Maj. Gen. Zeno Tascio
Logistic Inspector ...................... Maj. Gen. Ciro Berarducci
Chief, First Division ................... Brig. Gen. Luciano Casarsa
Chief, Second Division ................. Brig. Gen. Giorgio Santucci
Chief, Third Division .................. Brig. Gen. Adelchi Pillinini
Chief, Fourth Division ................. Brig. Gen. Luciano Meloni
Chief, Fifth Division ................... Brig. Gen. Romolo Mangani

**First Air Region**
*Piazza Novelli 1*
*Milan*

Commander ........................... Lt. Gen. Claudio Venturini

**Second Air Region**
*Via Lepanto 4*
*Rome*

Commander ............................. Lt. Gen. Michele Sicoli

**Third Air Region**
*Via Dalmazia 70/D*
*Bari*

Commander .........................Lt. Gen. Gioacchino Papacchini

**General Command School**
*(Comando Generale Scuole)*
*Guidonia Airport*
*Rome*

Commander .............................Maj. Gen. Cesare Fazzino

## GENERAL DEFENSE DATA

**Manpower**

 Total Armed Forces ............................................370,000
  (See Page 277)
 Population ...............................................57,353,000

**Spending**

 Military Expenditures.........................................$8.9 billion
 Gross National Product ........................................$368 billion
 Military Expenditure as a Percentage of
  Gross National Product ..........................................2.4%
 Military Expenditure as a Percentage of
  Central Government Expenditure ................................10.1%

**Defense Treaties** *(See Part II for Additional Detail)*

  Bilateral:  Malta
       United States

  Multilateral: Biological Weapons Convention
       Environmental Modification Convention
       Limited Test Ban Treaty
       Multinational Force and Observers in the Sinai
       North Atlantic Treaty Organization
       Observer group in India and Palistan
       Treaty on the Control of Arms on the Seabed
       Treaty on the Non-Proliferation of Nuclear Weapons
       United Nations Interim Force in Lebanon
       United Nations Military Observer Group in India and
        Pakistan
       United Nations Truce Supervision Organization

# IVORY COAST
## Republic of the Ivory Coast
### *République de la Côte de'Ivoire*

## Defence Establishment Command Structure and Force Organization

The President serves as Commander-in-Chief of the armed forces. Administrative matters relating to the military are the responsibility of the Ministers of Defence, Marine, and National Security. The Army functions as the joint staff for all services.

**Total armed forces:** 5,070 (Army: 4,000; Navy: 500; Air Force: 570). **Para-military forces:** 3,000.

## HEAD OF STATE

H. E. Felix Houphouët-Boigny

**OFFICE OF THE PRESIDENT**
*Boulevard Clozel*
*B.P. 1354*
*Abidjan*

*Telephone: 32 02 22*
*Telex: 3754 cotivoir abidjan,*
*3311 cotivoir abidjan*

President of the Republic and
Commander-in-Chief . . . . . . . . . . . . . . . . . . . . . .Felix Houphouët-Boigny

**MINISTRY OF DEFENCE AND CIVIC SERVICE**
*(Ministère de la Défence et du Service Civique)*
*B.P. V-11*
*Route d'Ajame*
*Abidjan*

*Telephone: 32 02 88*

Minister . . . . . . . . . . . . . . . . . . . . . . . . . . . . . . . . . . .Jean Konan Banny
Director, Civic Service . . . . . . . . . . . . . . . . . . . . . . . . .Moussa Diarra
Director of Cabinet . . . . . . . . . . . . . . . . . . . . . . . . . . . . . .N'zi David
Inspector-General . . . . . . . . . . . . . . . . . . . . . .Lt. Gen. Ibrahima Coulibaly
Director, Military Administration
and Legislative Affairs . . . . . . . . . . . . . . . . . . . . . . . . . . . .Lt. Col. Cohen

**MINISTRY OF NAVY AND MERCHANT MARINE**
*Tour A de la Cité Administrative*
*B.P. V-67*
*Abidjan*

*Telephone: 32 06 88*
*Telex: 3399 mimimar*

Minister of Marine . . . . . . . . . . . . . . . . . . . .Capt. Lamine Mohamed Fadika
Director of Cabinet . . . . . . . . . . . . . . . . . . . . . . . . . . .Mema Soumahoro
Secretary-General, Marines . . . . . . . . . . . . . . . . . . . .Boniface Pegawagnaba
Director, Maritime Affairs . . . . . . . . . . . . . . . . . . . . . . . . .Robert Guehi
Director, Maritime Transport . . . . . . . . . . . . . . . . . . . .Daniel Douloure
Commander, National Navy . . . . . . . . . . . . . . . . . . . .Capt. Lassana Timité

**MINISTRY OF NATIONAL SECURITY**
*(In charge of police force)*
*B.P. V121-6*
*Boulevard Angailvant*
*Abidjan*

*Telephone: 32 23 00, 32 30 69*

Minister . . . . . . . . . . . . . . . . . . . .Gén. de Div. M. Gaston Quassenan Kone
Charge de Mission . . . . . . . . . . . . . . . . . . . . . . . .Lt. Col. Gnahore Guibero

# DEFENCE FORCES

## ARMED FORCES
*(Forces Armées Nationales—FANCI)*
*Telephone: 32 03 66*

| | |
|---|---|
| Chief of Staff | Gén. de Brig. Bertin Zéné |
| Deputy Chief of Staff | Col. Roger Zinzou |
| Director, Defence | Lt. Col. Louis Tehodore Anga |
| Director, Medical Services | Col. Dramene Coulibaly |
| Director, Financial Affairs and Programs (AFP) | Col. Lasana Palenfo |
| Chief, G-1 | Lt. Col. Dembele Sory |
| Chief, G-3 | Col. Marcel Dey |
| Chief, G-4 | Cdt. Joseph Konakpo |
| Chief, Military Athletic Service | Capt. Agro Amouya |
| Chief, Medical Service | Lt. Col. Abina Yao |
| Inspector-General | Gén. de Corps d'Armée Ibrahama Coublibaly |
| Director, Bingerville Military Technical Preparatory School | Cdt. Fanny Bouchbur |
| Director, Boueke Military Preparatory School | Lt. Col. Pierre Ruggieri |

### Regional Commands

| | |
|---|---|
| 1st Military Region (South and West), Akouédo | Col. Felix Ory |
| 2nd Military Region (West), Daloa | Col. Raoul Loba |
| 3rd Military Region (Central and North), Bouake | |

## NAVY
*Tour A de la Cité Administrative*
*B.P. V-67*
*Abidjan*
*Telephone: 32 06 88*

| | |
|---|---|
| Commander | Cdt. Lassana Timité |
| Deputy Commander | Lt. Cdt. Fako Koné |

## AIR FORCE
*B.P. 10*
*Abidjan*
*Telephone: 36 84 74*
*Telex: avafan 727*

| | |
|---|---|
| Commander | Lt. Col. Abdoulaye Coulibaly |
| Deputy Commander | Lt. Col. Vassanoussi Bamba |
| Chief, Maintenance | Cdt. Bourgoin Hacques Fofana |
| Chief, Administration | Cdt. Etienne Koye |
| Chief, Logistical/Finance | Cdt. Niamien N'Cho |

## NATIONAL POLICE
*(Gendarmerie Nationale)*
*c/o Ministry of Armed*
*  Forces and Civic Service*
*B.P. V-11*
*Route d'Ajame*
*Abidjan*
*Telephone: 32 02 88*

| | |
|---|---|
| Commander | Gén. de Div. Oumar N'Daw |
| Adjoint | Col. Kraidy |

\* \* \* \* \*

# GENERAL DEFENCE DATA

### Manpower
| | |
|---|---|
| Total Armed Forces | 5,070 |
| (See Page 283) | |
| Population | 8,569,000 |

**Spending**
    Military Expenditures . . . . . . . . . . . . . . . . . . . . . . . . . . . . . . . . . . . . .$116 million
    Gross National Product . . . . . . . . . . . . . . . . . . . . . . . . . . . . . . . . . . . .$10 billion
    Military Expenditure as a Percentage of
        Gross National Product . . . . . . . . . . . . . . . . . . . . . . . . . . . . . . . . . .1.2%
    Military Expenditure as a Percentage of
        Central Government Expenditure . . . . . . . . . . . . . . . . . . . . . . . . . . .3.6%

**Defence Treaties** *(See Part II for Additional Detail)*

    Bilateral:        France

    Multilateral:     Economic Community of West African States
                      Limited Test Ban Treaty
                      Organization of African Unity
                      Treaty on the Control of Arms on the Seabed
                      Treaty on the Non-Proliferation of Nuclear Weapons

**Military Rank Comparisons**
    See Appendix A.

# JAMAICA

## Defence Establishment Command Structure and Force Organization

Constitutionally, the Governor-General is Minister of Defence and Commander-in-Chief of the Jamaican Defence Force (JDF). In practice, the elected government controls the JDF. The Prime Minister appoints the Minister of National Security and Justice, who exercises his authority over the military through the Chief of Staff.

The JDF is composed of a Regular Force and a Reserve Force, both of which are tri-service organizations.

**Total armed forces:** 1,700 (Army: 1,520;   Navy: 100;   Air Force: 80). **Para-military forces:** 8,200 (5,900 Police).

## HEAD OF STATE

H. M. Queen Elizabeth II

## GOVERNOR-GENERAL

H. E. The Most Hon. Florizel Glasspole, O.N., C.D., G.C.M.G.

**OFFICE OF THE GOVERNOR-GENERAL**
*King's House*
*Hope Road*
*Kingston 10*
*Telephone:   92-76424, 92-76143*

Governor-General . . . . . . . . Sir Florizel Glasspole, O.N., C.D., G.C.M.G.
Secretary to the Governor-General . . . . . . . Neville H. Smith, O.D., M.V.O.

**OFFICE OF THE PRIME MINISTER**
*P.O. Box 205*
*Jamaica House*
*Hope Road*
*Kingston 10*
*Telephone:   92-79941*

Prime Minister and Minister,
  Finance and Planning, and
  Mining and Natural Resources . . . . . . . . . . . . Edward Seaga, M.P., P.C.

**MINISTRY OF NATIONAL SECURITY AND JUSTICE, AND OFFICE OF THE ATTORNEY GENERAL**
*P.O. Box 472*
*Office Center*
*12 Ocean Boulevard*
*Kingston Mall*
*Telephone:   92-20080*

Minister and Attorney General . . . . . . . . . . Winston Spaulding, Q.C., M.P.
Parliamentary Secretary . . . . . . . . . . . . . . . . . . . . . Cap. Glen Webley, M.P.
Permanent Secretary, National Security . . . . . . . . . . . . . . . Donald Rainford

# DEFENCE FORCES

**ARMED FORCES**
**Jamaica Defence Force—JDF**
*Headquarters J.D.F.*
*Up Park Camp*
*Kingston 5*

*Telephone:  926-6482, 926-8121*
*Telex:  2359 minjedef ja*
*Cable:  JADEF Kingstonja*

Chief of Staff . . . . . . . . . . . . . . . . . . . . . . . . . . . . . Maj. Gen. Robert J. Neish
C.D., A.F.C., A.D.C.
Colonel Adjutant/Quartermaster
   (In charge of procurement) . . . . . . . . . . . . . . . Col. Trevor N. N. MacMillan
General Staff Officer In Charge of Training . . . . . . . . . . Col. R. Ken Barnes

### Regular Force

Commander, First Battalion
   Jamaica Regiment (I JR) . . . . . . . . . . . . . . . . . . . Lt. Col. D. C. M. Ormsby
Commander, Second Battalion,
   Jamaica Regiment (II JR) . . . . . . . . . . . . . . . . . . . Lt. Col. N. A. Ogilvie
Commander, Support and Service . . . . . . . . . . . . . . . Lt. Col. T. G. D. Lewis
Commander, Coast Guard . . . . . . . . . . . . . . . . . . . . . . . . Cdr. P. L. Brady
Commander, Air Wing . . . . . . . . . . . . . . . . . . . . . . . Lt. Cdr. J. A. McFarlane

### Reserve Force

Commander, Third Battalion
   Jamaica Regiment . . . . . . . . . . . . . . . . . . . . . . . . N.R. Lt. Col. G. M. Henry

**JAMAICA CONSTABLULARY FORCE**
*Police Headquarters*
*101-103 Old Hope Road*
*Kingston 6*

*Telephone:  927-4421, 927-9817, 927-9802*
*Telex:  2388 compol ja*

Commissioner of Police . . . . . . . . . . . . . . . . . . . . . . . . . . . . . Joseph Williams
Deputy Commissioner, Services . . . . . . . . . . . . . . . . . . . . . Herman Ricketts

\* \* \* \* \*

# GENERAL DEFENCE DATA

**Manpower**
   Total Armed Forces. . . . . . . . . . . . . . . . . . . . . . . . . . . . . . . . . . . . . . . . 1,700
      (See Page 287)
   Population . . . . . . . . . . . . . . . . . . . . . . . . . . . . . . . . . . . . . . . . . . . 2,295,000

**Spending**
   Military Expenditures . . . . . . . . . . . . . . . . . . . . . . . . . . . . . . . . . . . $17 million
   Gross National Product . . . . . . . . . . . . . . . . . . . . . . . . . . . . . . . . . . . $2 billion
   Military Expenditure as a Percentage of
      Gross National Product . . . . . . . . . . . . . . . . . . . . . . . . . . . . . . . . . 0.8%
   Military Expenditure as a Percentage of
      Central Government Expenditure . . . . . . . . . . . . . . . . . . . . . . . . . . . 2%

**Defence Treaties** *(See Part II for Additional Detail)*

   Bilateral:     United States

   Multilateral:  Biological Weapons Convention
                  Treaty for the Prohibition of Nuclear Weapons in
                     Latin America
                  Treaty on the Non-Proliferation of Nuclear Weapons

# JAPAN

## *Nippon*

### Defense Establishment Command Structure and Force Organization

The Prime Minister commands the armed forces of Japan. He is advised on important matters of national security by a National Defense Council. Operational control of the military is exercised through the Director General of the Defense Agency, who functions as Minister of Defense. He seeks guidance from a Joint Staff Council, which consists of the Chiefs of Staff of the three services and other military personnel.

**Total armed forces:** 245,000 (Army: 155,000;   Navy: 45,000;   Air Force: 45,000).

## SYMBOL OF STATE

H. I. M. Hirohito, Emperor of Japan

**IMPERIAL HOUSEHOLD AGENCY**
*1-1 Chiyoda*
*Chiyoda-ku*
*Tokyo 100*
Telephone:   *(3) 213-1111, 213-2111*

Emperor of Japan . . . . . . . . . . . . . . . . . . . . . . . . . . . . . . . . . . . H. I. M. Hirohito

**OFFICE OF THE PRIME MINISTER**
*1-6 Nagata-cho*
*Chiyoda-ku*
*Tokyo 100*
*Official Residence:*
  *2-3 Nagata-cho*
  *Chiyoda-ku*
*Tokyo 100*
Telephone:   *(3) 581-0101, 581-0241*

Prime Minister . . . . . . . . . . . . . . . . . . . . . . . . . . . . . . . Yasuhiro Nakasone
Director-General . . . . . . . . . . . . . . . . . . . . . . . . . . . . . . . . . . Hyosuke Niwa
State Minister and
    Chief Cabinet Secretary . . . . . . . . . . . . . . . . . . . . . . . Masahura Gotoda

#### National Defense Council
*1-6 Nagata-cho*
*Chiyoda-ku*
*Tokyo 100*
Telephone:   *(3) 581-2361*

Member *(ex officio)* . . . . . . . . . . . . . . . . . . . . . . . . . . . . . Yasuhiro Nakasone
(Prime Minister)
Member *(ex officio)* . . . . . . . . . . . . . . . . . . . . . . . . . . . . . . . . Shintaro Abe
(Minister of Foreign Affairs)
Member *(ex officio)* . . . . . . . . . . . . . . . . . . . . . . . . . . . . . Noboru Takeshita
(Minister of Finance)
Member *(ex officio)* . . . . . . . . . . . . . . . . . . . . . . . . . . . . . . Kazuo Tanikawa
(Director-General, Defense Agency
and Minister of State)
Member *(ex officio)* . . . . . . . . . . . . . . . . . . . . . . . . . . . . . . . Zyun Shiozaki
(Director-General, Economic Planning Agency
and Minister of State)

**JAPAN DEFENSE AGENCY**
*9-7-45 Akasaka*
*Minato-ku*
*Tokyo 107*
Telephone:   *(3) 408-5211*

Director-General and Minister of State . . . . . . . . . . . . . . . . Kazuo Tanikawa
Parliamentary Vice Minister . . . . . . . . . . . . . . . . . . . . . . . . Taikan Hayashi
Administrative Vice Minister . . . . . . . . . . . . . . . . . . . . . . . . Haruo Natsune

**Director-General's Secretariat**

Director of the Secretariat of the Director-
General of the Japan Defense Agency
(Deputy Vice Minister) . . . . . . . . . . . . . . . . . . . . . . . . . . . .Atsuyuki Sassa
Chief, Administration Division . . . . . . . . . . . . . . . . . . . . .Masami Yamashita
Chief, Public Information Division . . . . . . . . . . . . . . . . . .Tatsufumi Tsuboi
Special Assistant, Legal Affairs . . . . . . . . . . . . . . . . . . . .Sadaaki Furukawa

**Bureau of Defense Policy**

Director-General . . . . . . . . . . . . . . . . . . . . . . . . . . . . . . . . .Shinji Yazaki
Special Assistant, Defense Build-up Program . . . . . . . . . . .Nasuo Morotomi
Chief, Defense Planning Division . . . . . . . . . . . . . . . . . . . . . . .Kazuo Fujii
Chief, First Defense Operations Division . . . . . . . . . . . . . . . . . .Seiji Ema
Chief, Second Defense Operations Division . . . . . . . . . . . . .Shojiro Imanishi
Chief, First Defense Intelligence Division . . . . . . . . . . . . . . .Ryuji Mtsumura
Chief, Second Defense Intelligence Division . . . . . . . . . . . .Yasutomo Mitsui

**Bureau of Equipment**

Director-General . . . . . . . . . . . . . . . . . . . . . . . . . . . . . . . . .Hiroo Kinoshita
Special Assistant, Research and Development . . . . . . . . . . . .Sachio Uehara
Chief, Coordination Division . . . . . . . . . . . . . . . . . . . . .Yoshihiko Numakura
Chief, Procurement and Supply Division . . . . . . . . . . . . . .Tatsuo Kusatsu
Chief, Weapons and Materials Division . . . . . . . . . . . . . . . . .Teruo Suzuki
Chief, Communication Division . . . . . . . . . . . . . . . . . . . . .Masatuka Suzuki
Chief, Ships Division . . . . . . . . . . . . . . . . . . . . . . . . . . . .Tadshi Ichiriki
Chief, Aircraft Division . . . . . . . . . . . . . . . . . . . . . . . . . . .Naoaki Murata

**Bureau of Finance**

Director-General . . . . . . . . . . . . . . . . . . . . . . . . . . . . . .Muneo Shishikura

**Bureau of Personnel
and Education**

Director-General . . . . . . . . . . . . . . . . . . . . . . . . . . . . . . . .Takafumi Ueno

**Foreign Relations Bureau**

Director-General . . . . . . . . . . . . . . . . . . . . . . . . . . . . . . . . .Hirokazu Arai

**Health and Medical Bureau**

Director-General . . . . . . . . . . . . . . . . . . . . . . . . . . . . . . .Susumu Shimada
Chief, Health and Medical Division . . . . . . . . . . . . . . . . . . .Michio Obata

**Central Procurement Office**
*9-7-45 Akasaka*
*Minato-ku*
*Tokyo 107*
*Telephone: (3) 408-5211*

Dirctor-General . . . . . . . . . . . . . . . . . . . . . . . . . . . . . .Takeshi Moriyama
Deputy Director-General, Administration . . . . . . . . . . . . . . .Hisashi Kotani
Deputy Director-General, First Contract
and Cost Estimate . . . . . . . . . . . . . . . . . . . . . . . . . . . . . .Hiroshi Awaya
Deputy Director-General, Second
Contract and Cost Estimate . . . . . . . . . . . . . . . . . . . . . .Tadashi Kobodo
Deputy Director-General, Third
Contract and Cost Estimate . . . . . . . . . . . . . . . . . . . . . . . .Zenji Ooura
Deputy Director-General,
First Procurement Control . . . . . . . . . . . . . . . . . . . . . . . . .Ichiro Honda
Deputy Director-General,
Second Procurement Control . . . . . . . . . . . . . . . . . . . . . .Takaaki Ukita

**National Defense College**
*2-1 Makameguro*
*2-Chome*
*Meguro-ku*
*Tokyo 153*
*Telephone: (3) 713-6111*

President . . . . . . . . . . . . . . . . . . . . . . . . . . . . . . . . . . . .Fumio Miyoshi
Vice President . . . . . . . . . . . . . . . . . . . . . . . . .Lt. Gen. Atsuhiro Okamura

**National Defense Academy**
*10-20 Hashirimizu*
*1-Chome*
*Yokosuka-shi*
*Kanagawa 239*
*Telephone: (0468) 41-3810*

President . . . . . . . . . . . . . . . . . . . . . . . . . . . . . . . . . . .Kuniyasu Tsuchida
Vice President . . . . . . . . . . . . . . . . . . . . . . . . . . . . . . . . . . . .Koji Ono
Vice President, Training . . . . . . . . . . . . . . . . . . .Lt. Gen. Misao Matsumoto

**National Defense Medical College**
*2 Namiki 3-Chome*
*Tokorozawa-shi*
*Saitama-ken 359*
*Telephone:   (0429) -1211*

President . . . . . . . . . . . . . . . . . . . . . . . . . . . . . . . . . . . . .Dr. Yasuyuki Kano
Vice President, Administration . . . . . . . . . . . . . . . . .Masami Nakanomyo
Vice President, Education. . . . . . . . . . . . . . . . . . . . . . . . . . . . . . . .(Vacant)
Vice President, Medical Practice . . . . . . . . . . . . . . . . . .Dr. Kiyoshi Hosono

**Technical Research and**
**    Development Institute**
*2-24 Ikejiri*
*1-Chome*
*Setagaya-ku*
*Tokyo 154*
*Telephone:   (3) 411-0151*

Director-General . . . . . . . . . . . . . . . . . . . . . . . . . . . . . . . . .Dr. Yukie Omori
Deputy Director-General . . . . . . . . . . . . . . . . . . . . . . . . . . .Fusao Yokoyama
Assistant Director-General,
    Ground Development . . . . . . . . . . . . . . . . . . . . . . .Lt. Gen. Hirotake Yabe
Assistant Director-General,
    Naval Development . . . . . . . . . . . . . . . . . . . . . . .Rear Adm. Shunji Sakura
Assistant Director-General,
    Air Development . . . . . . . . . . . . . . . . . . . . . . .Lt. Gen. Naotake Tateyama
Assistant Director-General,
    GM Development . . . . . . . . . . . . . . . . . . . . . . . . . . . . .Katsumi Kindaichi

**Defense Facilities**
**    Administration Agency**
*9-7-45 Akasaka*
*Minato-ku*
*Tokyo 107*
*Telephone:   (3) 408-5211*

Director-General . . . . . . . . . . . . . . . . . . . . . . . . . . . . . . . . . . . .Akira Shiota
Deputy Director-General . . . . . . . . . . . . . . . . . . . . . . .Takeshi Moriyama
Director-General, General
    Affairs Department . . . . . . . . . . . . . . . . . . . . . . . . . . . . . . . . .Shingo Ito
Director-General, Facilities
    Department . . . . . . . . . . . . . . . . . . . . . . . . . . . . . .Takeshi Senshu
Director-General, Construction
    Department . . . . . . . . . . . . . . . . . . . . . . . . . . . . . . . .Shu Asakuma
Director-General, Labour
    Department . . . . . . . . . . . . . . . . . . . . . . . . . . . . . . . .Kazuo Kinashi

## DEFENSE FORCES

**ARMED FORCES**
**Self-Defense Forces—SDF**
*Joint Staff Council*
*9-7-45 Akasaka*
*Minato-ku*
*Tokyo 107*
*Telephone:   (3) 408-5211*

Chairman . . . . . . . . . . . . . . . . . . . . . . . . . . . . . .Gen. Sumio Murai, GSDF
Director, Joint Staff Office . . . . . . . . . .Lt. Gen. Mayuki Ichinomiya, ASDF
Chief, J1 . . . . . . . . . . . . . . . . . . . . . . . . . . . . .Maj. Gen. Hideki Suzuki, GSDF
Chief, J2 . . . . . . . . . . . . . . . . . . . . . . . . .Maj. Gen. Ryuzo Yabunaka, ASDF
Chief, J3 . . . . . . . . . . . . . . . . . . . . . . . . . . . .Rear Adm. Seiko Obata, MSDF
Chief, J4 . . . . . . . . . . . . . . . . . . . . . . .Rear Adm. Masao Hamanaka, ASDF
Chief, J5 . . . . . . . . . . . . . . . . . . . . . . . . . . .Maj. Gen. Masao Ishii, GSDF

**ARMY**
**Ground Self-Defense Force—GSDF**
*9-7-45 Akasaka*
*Minato-ku*
*Tokyo 107*
*Telephone:   (3) 408-5211*

Chief of Staff. . . . . . . . . . . . . . . . . . . . . . . . . . . . . . .Gen. Keitaro Watanabe
Vice Chief of Staff . . . . . . . . . . . . . . . . . . . . . . . . . . .Lt. Gen. Michio Magori
Director, Comptroller Department . . . . . . . . . . . . . .Maj. Gen. Takashi Ohta
Director, Personnel Department . . . . . . . . . . . . . .Maj. Gen. Yukio Shimizu
Director, Intelligence Department . . . . . . . . . .Maj. Gen. Yasushi Kinoshita
Director, Operations Department . . . . . . . . . . . .Maj. Gen. Hiroshi Takeda
Director, Logistics Department . . . . . . . . . . . . . . .Maj. Gen. Kenji Tagagi
Director, Training Department . . . . . . . . . . . . . .Maj. Gen. Toshihiro Inoue
Surgeon General . . . . . . . . . . . . . . . . . . . . . . . . . . . .Lt. Gen. Tatsuo Ishizaki

**Northern Army**
*Hokkaido*

Commander, Northern Army . . . . . . . . . . . . . . . .Lt. Gen. Morio Nakamura
Commander, 2nd Division . . . . . . . . . . . . . . . . . . . .Lt. Gen. Hiroshi Mizusawa
Commander, 5th Division . . . . . . . . . . . . . . . . . . . .Lt. Gen. Hiroshi Hiratsuka
Commander, 7th Division . . . . . . . . . . . . . . . . . . . . .Lt. Gen. Naohiko Arai
Commander, 11th Division . . . . . . . . . . . . . .Lt. Gen. Tatsuharu Hisayama
Commander, 1st
    Artillery Brigade . . . . . . . . . . . . . . . . . . . . . . .Maj. Gen. Hiromi Gohara
Commander, 1st Anti-aircraft
    Artillery Brigade . . . . . . . . . . . . . . . . . . . . . . .Col. Michiharu Sekiya
Commander, 3rd
    Engineering Brigade . . . . . . . . . . . . . . . . . . . . . . .Maj. Gen. Tokihisa Nakao
Commander, 1st Tank Group . . . . . . . . . . . . . . . . . . . .Col. Hiroshi Kuniya

**Eastern Army**

Commander, Eastern Army . . . . . . . . . . . . . . .Lt. Gen. Tsutomu Matsunaga
Commander, 1st Division . . . . . . . . . . . . . . . . . . . . . .Lt. Gen. Teruo Kamei
Commander, 12th Division . . . . . . . . . . . . . . . .Lt. Gen. Toshihiko Kondo
Commander, 1st Airborne Brigade . . . . . . . . .Maj. Gen. Tomoyuki Mizuno
Commander, 1st Engineering Brigade . . . . . .Maj. Gen. Masaharu Mishima
Commander, 1st Training Brigade . . . . . . . . . . . . . .Lt. Gen. Kunihiro Joei
Commander, 1st Helicopter Brigade . . . . . . . .Maj. Gen. Hiroshige Tamura
Commander, 1st Signal Brigade . . . . . . . . . .Maj. Gen. Yoshiaki Nakamoto
Commander, 2nd Anti-aircraft
    Artillery Group . . . . . . . . . . . . . . . . . . . . . . . . . . . . . . . .Col. Kenji Dou

**Northeastern Army**

Commander, Northeastern Army . . . . . . . . . . . . . .Lt. Gen. Noboru Matsuura
Commander, 6th Division . . . . . . . . . . . . . . . . . . . . . .Lt. Gen. Satoshi Aoto
Commander, 9th Division . . . . . . . . . . . . . . . . . . . .Lt. Gen. Kanae Masuoka
Commander, 5th Engineer Birgade . . . . . . . . . . . .Maj. Gen. Takeo Ohashi
Commander, 2nd Artillery Group . . . . . . . . . . . . . . .Col. Junichi Oshima
Commander, 5th Anti-aircraft Artillery . . . . . . . . .Col. Tadakatsu Daitoku

**Middle Army**

Commander, Middle Army . . . . . . . . . . . . . . . . . . . .Lt. Gen. Wataru Osawa
Commander, 3rd Division . . . . . . . . . . . . .Lt. Gen. Tomozaburo Inamori
Commander, Division 10 . . . . . . . . . . . . . . . .Lt. Gen. Isao Wakatsuki
Commander, Division 13 . . . . . . . . . . . . . . . .Lt. Gen. Ichiro Tsuchiya
Commander, 2nd Combined Brigade . . . . . . . . . .Maj. Gen. Mizuo Otsuka
Commander, 4th Engineer Brigade . . . . . . . . . . . .Maj. Gen. Akiro Hagino
Commander, 2nd Training Brigade . . . . . . . . . . .Maj. Gen. Kazuo Sakurai
Commander, 8th Anti-aircraft
    Artillery Group . . . . . . . . . . . . . . . . . . . . . .Col. Akihisa Kuroyanagi

**Western Army**
*Kyushu*

Commander, Western Army . . . . . . . . . . . . . . . . . . . .Lt. Gen. Nobuo Saito
Commander, 4th Division . . . . . . . . . . . . . . . . . . . . . .Lt. Gen. Teruo Sone
Commander, 8th Division . . . . . . . . . . . . . . . . . .Lt. Gen. Akira Igarashi
Commander, 1st Combined Brigade . . . . . . . . . . . . .Maj. Gen. Sho Kuroda
Commander, 2nd Anti-aircraft
    Artillery Brigade . . . . . . . . . . . . . . . . . . . . . .Maj. Gen. Mitsuru Yatabe
Commander, 5th Engineer Brigade . . . . . . . . . . . . . . .Maj. Gen. Toru Isaji
Commander, 3rd Training Brigade . . . . . . . . . . .Maj. Gen. Kenji Taniwaki
Commander, 3rd Artillery Group . . . . . . . . . . . . . .Col. Satoru Uchikado

**NAVY**
**Maritime Self-Defense Force—MSDF**
*9-7-45 Akasaka*
*Minato-ku*
*Tokyo 107*
*Telephone:    (3) 408-5211*

Chief of Staff . . . . . . . . . . . . . . . . . . . . . . . . . . . .Adm. Manabu Yoshida
Deputy Chief of Staff . . . . . . . . . . . . . . . . . . . . .Vice Adm. Yoshiteru Yamada

**Administration Department**

Director . . . . . . . . . . . . . . . . . . . . . . . . . . . . . . . .Rear Adm. Ikuo Takasaki

**Operations and**
    **Plans Department**

Director . . . . . . . . . . . . . . . . . . . . . . . . . . . . .Rear Adm. Mitsuo Kanasaki
Deputy Director . . . . . . . . . . . . . . . . . . . . . . . .Rear Adm. Makoto Sakuma

**Intelligence Department**

Director . . . . . . . . . . . . . . . . . . . . . . . . . . . . . . . .Rear Adm. Sadaomi Sue
Head, First Intelligence Division . . . . . . . . . . . . . . . .Capt. Toshiyasu Arai
Head, Second Intelligence Division . . . . . . . . . . . . .Capt. Snuta Imamichi

**Self-Defense Fleet**

Commander-in-Chief . . . . . . . . . . . . . . . . . . . . . . .Vice Adm. Tsuro Koga
Commander, Fleet Escort Force . . . . . . . . . . . . . .Vice Adm. Ousuke Fukai
Commander, Fleet Air Force . . . . . . . . . . . . . . . .Vice Adm. Masao Shigeno
Commander, Fleet Submarine Force . . . . . . . . .Vice Adm. Tsuneo Fujikawa
Commander, Escort Flotilla 1 . . . . . . . . . . . . . . . .Rear Adm. Mineo Konishi
Commander, Escort Flotilla 2 . . . . . . . . . . . . . . . .Rear Adm. Osamu Goto

Commander, Escort Flotilla 3 . . . . . . . . . . . . . . . Rear Adm. Masami Ogawa
Commander, Escort Flotilla 4 . . . . . . . . . . . . . . Rear Adm. Kimio Kanazaki
Commander, Submarine Flotilla 1 . . . . . . . . . . . . . Capt. Takeo Shinmachi
Commander, Submarine Flotilla 2 . . . . . . . . . . . . . Capt. Sugao Hasegawa
Commander, Minesweeper Flotilla 1 . . . . . . . . . . . . . Capt. Kouji Kawai
Commander, Minesweeper Flotilla 2 . . . . . . . . . . . . Capt. Yoshiharu Ashida
Commander, Fleet Training
    and Development Command . . . . . . . . . . . . . . . . Rear Adm. Tazuo Sone
Commander, Air Training Command . . . . . . . . . Vice Adm. Kenichiro Koga
Commander, Training Squadron . . . . . . . . . . . . . Rear Adm. Satoshi Okada
Commander, Fleet Air Wing 1 . . . . . . . . . . . . . . Rear Adm. Makoto Suzuki
Commander, Fleet Air Wing 2 . . . . . . . . . . . . . . . Rear Adm. Atago Terai
Commander, Fleet Air Wing 4 . . . . . . . . Rear Adm. Syuichiro Higashiyama
Commander, Fleet Air Wing 5 . . . . . . . . Rear Adm. Katsuhiko Matsumoto
Commander, Fleet Air Wing 21 . . . . . . . . . . . . . . Rear Adm. Yoichi Tazaki
Commander, Fleet Air Wing 31 . . . . . . . . . . . . . . . Rear Adm. Toru Matsuo
Commandant, Yokosuka District . . . . . . . . . . . . . Vice Adm. Kohei Katagiri
Commandant, Kure District . . . . . . . . . . . . . . . . Vice Adm. Hiroshi Nagata
Commandant, Sasebo District . . . . . . . . . . . . . . . . . Vice Adm. Yuzo Abe
Commandant, Maizuru District . . . . . . . . . . Vice Adm. Takanori Inoyama
Commandant, Ominato District . . . . . . . . . . . . . Vice Adm. Kaneo Yasuoka

**Maritime Safety Agency**

Commander . . . . . . . . . . . . . . . . . . . . . . . . . . . . . . . . . . . . . . . Hiroshi Nagai
Deputy Commander . . . . . . . . . . . . . . . . . . . . . . . . . . Fumitoshi Yamashita

**AIR FORCE**
**Air Self-Defense Force—ASDF**
*9-7-45 Akasaka*
*Minato-ku*
*Tokyo 107*

*Telephone:    (3) 408-5211*

Chief of Staff . . . . . . . . . . . . . . . . . . . . . . . . . . . . . . . . Gen. Shigehiro Mori
Deputy Chief of Staff . . . . . . . . . . . . . . . . . . . . . . . . Lt. Gen. Taro Katsuya

**General Affairs Department**

Director . . . . . . . . . . . . . . . . . . . . . . . . . . . . . . . Lt. Gen. Makoto Nakazawa

**Defense Department**

Director . . . . . . . . . . . . . . . . . . . . . . . . . . . . Maj. Gen. Yoshitoyo Soejima
Deputy Director
    (Director, Intelligence) . . . . . . . . . . . . . . . . . . . . . Maj. Gen. Itaru Suzuki

**Air Defense Command**

Commander . . . . . . . . . . . . . . . . . . . . . . . . . . . . . . . . Lt. Gen. Ichiro Shima

**Northern Air Defense Force**
Commander . . . . . . . . . . . . . . . . . . . . . . . . . . . . . Lt. Gen. Jyoichi Kigure
Commanding Officer,
    2nd Air Wing . . . . . . . . . . . . . . . . . . . . . . . . . Maj. Gen. Minoru Tanaka
Commanding Officer,
    3rd Air Wing . . . . . . . . . . . . . . . . . . . . . . . . Maj. Gen. Sekinori Kanegae
Commanding Officer, Northern
    Aircraft Control and Warning Wing . . . . . . . . . . Maj. Gen. Tsutomu Fujii
Commanding Officer, 3rd Air
    Defense Missile Group . . . . . . . . . . . . . . . . . . . . . . . Col. Akira Mizukami
Commanding Officer, 6th Air
    Defense Missile Group . . . . . . . . . . . . . . . . . . . . . Col. Takashi Ichikawa

**Central Air Defense Force**
Commander . . . . . . . . . . . . . . . . . . . . . . . . . . . . . . . . Lt. Gen. Akinori Koga
Commanding Officer, 6th Air Wing . . . . . . . . . Maj. Gen. Kazuyoshi Takei
Commanding Officer, 7th Air Wing . . . . . . . . . . . . . Maj. Gen. Akio Suzuki
Commanding Officer, Central
    Aircraft Control and Warning Wing . . . . . . . . . . Maj. Gen. Yuichi Shirai
Commanding Officer, 1st Air
    Defense Missile Group . . . . . . . . . . . . . . . . . . . . Maj. Gen. Seizo Yajima
Commanding Officer, 4th Air
    Defense Missile Group . . . . . . . . . . . . . . . . . . . . . Col. Tatsuyuki Ogura

**Western Air Defense Force**

Commander ...................................Lt. Gen. Yasuhiro Itano
Commanding Officer,
   5th Air Wing .........................Maj. Gen. Hiroshi Hossho
Commanding Officer,
   8th Air Wing .............................Maj. Gen. Hiroo Abe
Commanding Officer, Western
   Aircraft Control and Warning Wing .........Maj. Gen. Junzo Motono
Commanding Officer, 2nd Air
   Defense Missile Group........................Col. Katsumi Tanaka

**Southwestern Composit Air Division**

Commander ...................................Lt. Gen. Toru Shimizu
Commanding Officer, 83rd
   Air Squadron ............................Col. Yoshihisa Nomura
Commanding Officer, Southwestern
   Aircraft Control and Warning Wing ...........Col. Akihiko Shinozaki
Commanding Officer, 5th Air
   Defense Missile Group ....................Col. Norinobu Takeuchi

**Flying Training Wing**

Commander.................................Lt. Gen. Noboru Fujioka
Commanding Officer,
   1st Air Wing.........................Maj. Gen. Teruo Kawarazaki
Commanding Officer,
   4th Air Wing ..........................Maj. Gen. Fusao Murayama
Commanding Officer, 11th
   Flying Training Wing ......................Maj. Gen. Masao Hara
Commanding Officer, 12th
   Flying Training Wing.......................Maj. Gen. Atsushi Tani
Commanding Officer, 13th
   Flying Training Wing ....................Col. Hiroyuki Nakabayashi

**Other Commands**

Commanding Officer,
   Tactical Airlift Wing ......................Lt. Gen. Ichiro Funakoshi
Commanding Officer, Air Traffic
   Control and Weather Wing ..................Maj. Gen. Hiroshi Syoji
Commanding Officer, Air
   Rescue Wing..........................Maj. Gen. Kimio Yoshimura
Commanding Officer, Air
   Proving Wing ...........................Maj. Gen. Taira Omura
Commanding Officer, Air Material
   Command Headquarters......................Lt. Gen. Akira Goto
Commanding Officer, Technical
   Training Command Headquarters ..........Lt. Gen. Hirotaka Kondo

* * * * *

# GENERAL DEFENSE DATA

**Manpower**
   Total Armed Forces.............................................245,000
     (See Page 289)
   Population ................................................118,519,000

**Spending**
   Military Expenditures.......................................$10.8 billion
   Gross National Product ..................................$1,153 billion

Military Expenditure as a Percentage of
Gross National Product .............................................0.9%
Military Expenditure as a Percentage of
Central Government Expenditure ....................................5%

**Defense Treaties** *(See Part II for Additional Detail)*

Bilateral:      China
                United States

Multilateral:   Biological Weapons Convention
                Environmental Modifications Convention
                Limited Test Ban Treaty
                Treaty on the Control of Arms on the Seabed
                Treaty on the Non-Proliferation of Nuclear Weapons

# JORDAN

## Hashemite Kingdom of Jordan
### *al-Mamlaka al-Urdunniyah al-Hashimiyah*

## Defense Establishment Command Structure and Force Organization

The King is Supreme Commander-in-Chief of the armed forces. He is assisted by the Commander-in-Chief who supervises the administration and operation of the Army through the General Headquarters Chief of Staff. The main functions of the Ministry of Defense are administrative and logistical, including preparation of the military budget. The Ministry does not participate in the operational control of the armed forces.

The Royal Jordanian Air Force has its own Commander and Chief of Staff who are responsible for administration and operations. They are subordinate to the General Headquarters Commander-in-Chief and his Chief of Staff. The Navy is organizationally part of the Army.

Internal security is the responsibility of the Public Security Force, which is under the direction of the Ministry of the Interior.

**Total armed forces:** 72,800 (Army: 65,000; Navy: 300; Air Force: 7,500). **Para-military forces:** 11,050 (Public Security Force).

## HEAD OF STATE

H. M. King Hussein Ibn Talal

**OFFICE OF H. M. THE KING**
*The Royal Palace*
*Amman*
*Telephone: 37341*
*Telex: 21332/3*

King of Jordan and
    Supreme Commander-in-Chief . . . . . . . . . . . . . . H. M. Hussein Ibn Talal

**OFFICE OF THE PRIME MINISTER**
*P.O. Box 80*
*Amman*
*Telephone: 41111-5*
*Telex: 21444 pm jo*

Prime Minister and Minister of Defense . . . . . . . . . . . . . . . . . Mudar Badran
Minister of State for Prime Ministry Affairs
    and Minister of Transportation . . . . . . . . . . . . . . . . . . . Hikmat Al-Saket
Minister of State for Prime Ministry Affairs . . . . . . . . . . . . . . . . Ali Suheimat

**MINISTRY OF DEFENSE**
*P.O. Box 79*
*Amman*
*Telephone: 22131, 6219/5, 62101, 44782*
*Telex: 21200*
*Cable: 6HQ(JAF)*

Prime Minister and Minister of Defense . . . . . . . . . . . . . . . . . Mudar Badran
Military Secretary and Senior Advisor to The King . . . . . . . . . . . . . (Vacant)

**MINISTRY OF INTERIOR**
*P.O. Box 100*
*Amman*
*Telephone: 38849, 63111*

Minister . . . . . . . . . . . . . . . . . . . . . . . . . . . . . . . . . . . . . . . . . . . . . Ahmad Obeidat

# DEFENSE FORCES

**ARMY**
**Jordanian Armed Forces**
*General Headquarters*
*Amman*

*Telephone:    22132, 44782*
*Telex:    21200*

Commander-in-Chief,
    Jordanian Armed Forces . . . . . . . . . . . . . . Lt. Gen. Sharif-Zaid Bin Shaker
Chief of Staff, Jordanian
    Armed Forces . . . . . . . . . . . . . . . . . . . . . . . Maj. Gen. Fathi Abu Talib
Director of Finance . . . . . . . . . . . . . . . . . . . . . Maj. Gen. Jalal Ali Khutat
Assistant Chief of Staff,
    Plans and Organization . . . . . . . . . . . . . . . . . . Maj. Gen. Tayseer Za'rour
Assistant Chief of Staff,
    Manpower . . . . . . . . . . . . . . . . . . . . . . . Maj. Gen. Ahmad Aladdin Arslan
Director, Special
    Communications . . . . . . . . . . . . . . . . . . . . . Col. Salah ad-Din Hamdukh
Inspector General . . . . . . . . . . . . . . . . . . . . . . . . Maj. Gen. Bassam Kakish
Director, Medical
    Service . . . . . . . . . . . . . . . . . . . . . Maj. Gen. General Da'ud Hannaniyah

**NAVY**
**Jordan Sea Force**
*Amman*

Chief of Staff . . . . . . . . . . . . . . . . . . . . . . . . . . . . . . . . . . Lt. Col. A. Rashid

**AIR FORCE**
**Royal Jordanian Air Force**
*Amman*

*Telephone:    55919*

Commander . . . . . . . . . . . . . . . . . . . . . . . . . . . . . Brig. Gen. Ihsan Shurdon
Assistant Commander, Operations and
    Air Defense . . . . . . . . . . . . . . . . . . . . . . . . . . . . . . . . . . . . . (Vacant)
Assistant Commander, Logistics . . . . . . . . . . . . . . . . . . . . . . . . . . (Vacant)

    **King Abdullah Air Base**
    *Amman*

Commander . . . . . . . . . . . . . . . . . . . . . . . . . . . . . Lt. Col. Suleiman Obedat

    **Prince Hassan Air Base**
    *Aqaba*

Commander . . . . . . . . . . . . . . . . . . . . . . . . . . . . . . Lt. Col. Awnee Belal

    **King Hussein Air College**

Commander . . . . . . . . . . . . . . . . . . . . . . . . . . . . Lt. Col. Mohammed Oudah

**PUBLIC SECURITY FORCE**
*(Under Ministry of Interior)*
*Amman*

Commander . . . . . . . . . . . . . . . . . . . . . . . . . . . . Lt. Gen. Mohamad Idris
Deputy Commander . . . . . . . . . . . . . . . . . . . . . Maj. Gen. Mohamad Ali Amin

\* \* \* \* \*

# GENERAL DEFENSE DATA

**Manpower**
    Total Armed Forces . . . . . . . . . . . . . . . . . . . . . . . . . . . . . . . . . . . . . 72,800
        (See Page 297)
    Population . . . . . . . . . . . . . . . . . . . . . . . . . . . . . . . . . . . . . . . . 3,246,000

**Spending**
    Military Expenditures . . . . . . . . . . . . . . . . . . . . . . . . . . . . . . . . . . $399 million
    Gross National Product . . . . . . . . . . . . . . . . . . . . . . . . . . . . . . . . . $3.3 billion

Military Expenditure as a Percentage of
Gross National Product ...............................................12%
Military Expenditure as a Percentage of
Central Government Expenditure ...............................23.4%

**Defense Treaties** *(See Part II for Additional Detail)*

Bilateral:    Iraq
Saudi Arabia
United States

Multilateral:    Biological Weapons Convention
League of Arab States
Limited Test Ban Treaty
Treaty on the Control of Arms on the Seabed
Treaty on the Non-Proliferation of Nuclear Weapons

# KAMPUCHEA
## People's Republic of Kampuchea
*Sathearanakrath Pracheameanit Kampuchea*

### Defense Establishment Command Structure and Force Organization

The President is Commander-in-Chief of the armed forces of Kampuchea. The Minister of Defense has responsibility for administration of the military.

**Total armed forces:** 20,000.

### HEAD OF STATE

Heng Samrin

### NATIONAL ASSEMBLY

| | |
|---|---|
| **NATIONAL ASSEMBLY**<br>*Phnom Penh* | Chairman . . . . . . . . . . . . . . . . . . . . . . . . . . . . . . . . . . . . . . . . . . . Chea Sim<br>Vice-Chairman . . . . . . . . . . . . . . . . . . . . . . . . . . . . . . . . . . . . . . . Mat Ly<br>Vice-Chairman . . . . . . . . . . . . . . . . . . . . . . . . . . . . . . . . . . . . . . . Tep Vong<br>Vice-Chairman . . . . . . . . . . . . . . . . . . . . . . . . . . . . . . . . . . . . . . . Nu Beng<br>Secretary-General . . . . . . . . . . . . . . . . . . . . . . . . . . . . . . . . . . (Mrs.) Phelk Piroun |
| **COUNCIL OF STATE**<br>*Phnom Penh* | President . . . . . . . . . . . . . . . . . . . . . . . . . . . . . . . . . . . . . . . . . . Heng Samrin<br>Vice-President . . . . . . . . . . . . . . . . . . . . . . . . . . . . . . . . . . . . . . Say Phouthand<br>Secretary-General . . . . . . . . . . . . . . . . . . . . . . . . . . . . . . . . . . . Chan Ven<br>Member . . . . . . . . . . . . . . . . . . . . . . . . . . . . . . . . . . . . . . . . . . . . Men Chan<br>Member . . . . . . . . . . . . . . . . . . . . . . . . . . . . . . . . . . . . . . . . . . . . Kham Len<br>Member . . . . . . . . . . . . . . . . . . . . . . . . . . . . . . . . . . . . . . . . . . . . Heng Teav<br>Member . . . . . . . . . . . . . . . . . . . . . . . . . . . . . . . . . . . . . . . . . . . . Vandy Kaon |
| **OFFICE OF THE CHAIRMAN OF THE COUNCIL OF MINISTERS**<br>*Phnom Penh* | Chairman of the Council of Ministers . . . . . . . . . . . . . . . . . . . . . . . . Chan Si |
| **OFFICE OF THE VICE-CHAIRMAN OF THE COUNCIL OF MINISTERS AND MINISTRY OF FOREIGN AFFAIRS**<br>*Phenom Phenh* | Vice-Chairman of the Council of Ministers<br>and Minister of Foreign Affairs . . . . . . . . . . . . . . . . . . . . . . . . . Hun Sen<br>Vice-Minister of Foreign Affairs . . . . . . . . . . . . . . . . . . . Hor Nam Hong |
| **OFFICE OF THE VICE-CHAIRMAN OF THE COUNCIL OF MINISTERS AND MINISTRY OF PLANNING**<br>*Phnom Penh* | Vice-Chairman of the Council of Ministers and<br>Minister of Planning . . . . . . . . . . . . . . . . . . . . . . . . . . . . . . Chea Soth |
| **OFFICE OF THE VICE-CHAIRMAN OF THE COUNCIL OF MINISTERS AND MINISTRY OF DEFENSE**<br>*Phnom Penh* | Vice-Chairman of the Council of Ministers and<br>Minister of Defense . . . . . . . . . . . . . . . . . . . . . . . . . . . . . . . . Bou Thong |

# DEFENSE FORCES

**ARMED FORCES**
**People's Revolutionary Forces**
*(Forces Populaires Revolutionnaires)*
*Phenom Penh*

Vice Minister of Defense and Chief of Staff . . . . . . . . . . . . . . . . . . .Seuy Keo
Vice Minister of Defense and Director-General,
   Political Department . . . . . . . . . . . . . . . . . . . . . . . . . . . . . . . . . .Meas Kroch
Vice Minister of Defense and Director-General
   of Supplies . . . . . . . . . . . . . . . . . . . . . . . . . . . . . . . . . . . . . . . . . . .Dy Phinn

\* \* \* \* \*

# GENERAL DEFENSE DATA

**Manpower**
   Total Armed Forces . . . . . . . . . . . . . . . . . . . . . . . . . . . . . . . . . . . . . . . .20,000
      (See Page 301)
   Population . . . . . . . . . . . . . . . . . . . . . . . . . . . . . . . . . . . . . . . . . . . . .5,882,000

**Spending**
   Military Expenditures . . . . . . . . . . . . . . . . . . . . . . . . . . . . . . . . . . . . . . . . . . . .
   Gross National Product . . . . . . . . . . . . . . . . . . . . . . . . . . . . . . . . . . . .$500 million
   Military Expenditure as a Percentage of
      Gross National Product . . . . . . . . . . . . . . . . . . . . . . . . . . . . . . . . . . . . . . . . . .
   Military Expenditure as a Percentage of
      Central Government Expenditure . . . . . . . . . . . . . . . . . . . . . . . . . . . . . . . . . . .

**Defense Treaties** *(See Part II for Additional Detail)*

   Bilateral:      German Democratic
                      Republic
                   Vietnam

   Multilateral:   Treaty on the Non-Proliferation of Nuclear Weapons

# KENYA
## Republic of Kenya
### *Djumhuri ya Kenya*

## Defence Establishment Command Structure and Force Organization

The President exercises his authority as Commander-in-Chief of the Armed Forces through the Permanent Secretary of Defence. Reporting directly to the Minister is the Chief of the General Staff, who is responsible for operational control of the military. All services form part of the Army.

**Total armed forces:** 16,650 (Army: 13,000; Navy: 650; Air Force: 3,000). **Para-military forces:** 1,800 (Police).

## HEAD OF STATE

H. E. The Hon. Daniel T. Arap Moi, C.G.H., M.P.

**OFFICE OF THE PRESIDENT**
*Harambee House*
*Harambee Avenue*
*P.O. Box 30510*
*Nairobi*

*Telephone: (2) 27411*
*Cable: RAIS*

President of the Republic and
Commander-in-Chief of the
Armed Forces .................... Daniel T. Arap Moi, C.G.H., M.P.
Minister of State ....................... James Samuel Gichuru, M.P.
Assistant Minister ................................. J. Ole Tipis, M.P.
Assistant Minister ............................... D. N. Kuguru, M.P.
Assistant Minister ............................... I. K. A. Salat, M.P.
Assistant Minister ....................................... John Keen

**DEPARTMENT OF DEFENCE**
*Ulinzi House*
*P.O. Box 40668*
*Nairobi*

*Telephone: (2) 721100*
*Cable: DEFENCE*

Permanent Secretary .................................... A. Githinji
Deputy ............................................. I. M. M'Imathiu

## DEFENCE FORCES

**ARMED FORCES**
**Defence Headquarters**
*Uliniz House*
*P.O. Box 40668*
*Nairobi*

*Telephone: (2) 331100*
*Cable: DEFENCE*

Chief of General Staff ....Lt. Gen. Jackson K. Mulinge, M.B.S., M.G.H.
Chief of Staff ........................................ Brig. Musamba

**ARMY**
**Kenya Army**
*P.O. Box 30503*
*Nairobi*

*Telephone: (2) 331100*
*Cable: ARMY*

Commander, Kenya Army .......................... Maj. Gen. J. Sawe
Deputy Commander and Army Chief of Staff ........ Brig. M. Mohamed

**NAVY**
**Kenya Navy**
*P.O. Box 95350*
*Mombasa*
*Telephone:   451351*
*Cable:   NAVY*

Commander, Kenya Navy .........................Brig. E. S. Mbilu
Deputy Commander ..........................Lt. Col. N. D. Gatonye

**AIR FORCE**
**Kenya Air Force**
*Eastleigh*
*P.O. Box 48888*
*Nairobi*
*Telephone:   (2) 64401*
*Cable:   KAF*

Commander, Kenya Air Force ..........Maj. Gen. Mahmoud Mohamed

**POLICE**
**Kenya Police**
*Nairobi*

Commissioner ...............................................Njiinu

\* \* \* \* \*

# GENERAL DEFENCE DATA

**Manpower**
   Total Armed Forces ...............................................16,650
     (See Page 303)
   Population ..................................................17,832,000

**Spending**
   Military Expenditures.........................................$253 million
   Gross National Product .......................................$6.637 billion
   Military Expenditure as a Percentage of
     Gross National Product ...........................................3.8%
   Military Expenditure as a Percentage of
     Central Government Expenditure ...............................12.9%

**Defence Treaties** *(See Part II for Additional Detail)*

    Bilateral:     Ethiopia
               United Kingdom
               United States

    Multilateral:   Biological Weapons Convention
               Limited Test Ban Treaty
               Organization of African Unity
               Treaty on the Non-Proliferation of Nuclear Weapons

# KIRIBATI
## Republic of Kiribati

### Defense Establishment Command Structure and Force Organization

The President of the Republic of Kiribati commands the country's police force, which is responsible for internal security.

**Police:** 188.

## HEAD OF STATE

Hon. Ieremia T. Tabai, G.C.M.G.

**OFFICE OF THE PRESIDENT**
*P.O. Box 68*
*Bairiki*
*Tarawa*
*Telephone: 210*
*Cable: TAUTAEKA TARAWA*

President of the Republic and
Minister of Foreign Affairs . . . . . . . . . . . . . . Ieremia T. Tabai, G.C.M.G.

**OFFICE OF THE VICE PRESIDENT**
*P.O. Box 75*
*Bairiki*
*Tarawa*
*Telephone: 233*
*Cable: MINHOM TARAWA*

Vice President and Minister of
Home Affairs and Decentralization . . . . . . . . . . . . Hon. Teatae Teannaki

## DEFENSE FORCES

**POLICE**
**Kiribati Police**
*Police Headquarters*
*P.O. Box 497*
*Betia*
*Tarawa*
*Telephone: 684*
*Cable: COMPOL TARAWA*

Commissioner of Police . . . . . . . . . . . . . . . . . . . . . . . . . . . . . . . P. J. Somerville
Assistant Commissioner . . . . . . . . . . . . . . . . . . . . . . . . . . . Temaua Tenano

\* \* \* \* \*

## GENERAL DEFENSE DATA

**Manpower**
   Total Armed Forces . . . . . . . . . . . . . . . . . . . . . . . . . . . . . . . . . . . . . . . . 188
      (See Page 305)
   Population . . . . . . . . . . . . . . . . . . . . . . . . . . . . . . . . . . . . . . . . . . . . 59,000

**Spending**

Military Expenditures .....................................................

Gross National Product .....................................................

Military Expenditure as a Percentage of
  Gross National Product .................................................

Military Expenditure as a Percentage of
  Central Government Expenditure ......................................

**Defense Treaties** *(See Part II for Additional Detail)*

Bilateral:     None

Multilateral:  None

# DEMOCRATIC PEOPLE'S REPUBLIC OF KOREA
## (North Korea)
### *Choson Minchu-Chui Inmin Konghwa-Guk*

## Defense Establishment Command Structure
## and Force Organization

The President is the Chairman of the Military Committee and Supreme Commander of the armed forces. The Minister of the People's Armed Forces has responsibility for administrative matters relating to the military.

**Total armed forces:** 784,000 (Army: 700,000; Navy: 33,000; Air Force: 51,000). **Paramilitary forces:** 798,000 (Workers-Farmers Red Guard: 760,000; Security and Border Guards: 38,000).

## HEAD OF STATE

H. E. Marshal Kim Il-sŏng

| | | |
|---|---|---|
| **OFFICE OF THE PRESIDENT** *Pyongyang* | President of the Democratic People's Republic and Supreme Commander | Kim Il-sŏng |
| | Vice President | Kim Il |
| | Vice President | Yim Ch'un-ch'u |
| | Vice President | Pak Sŏng-ch'ŏl |
| **Military Committee** | Chairman | Kim Il-sŏng |
| | Member | O Chin-u |
| | Member | Kim Chong-il |
| | Member | Choe Hyon |
| | Member | O Paek-yong |
| | Member | Chon Mun-sop |
| | Member | O Kuk-yol |
| | Member | Paek Had-im |
| | Member | Kim Chol-man |
| | Member | Kim Kang-Hwan |
| | Member | Tae Pyong-yol |
| | Member | Yi Ul-sol |
| | Member | Chu To-il |
| | Member | Yi Tu-ik |
| | Member | Cho Myong-nok |
| | Member | Kim Il-chol |
| | Member | Choe Sang-uk |
| | Member | Yi Pong-won |
| | Member | O Yong-pang |
| **STATE ADMINISTRATION COUNCIL** *Pyongyang* | Premier | Yi Chong-ŏk |
| | First Vice Premier | Kang Song-san |
| | Vice Premier | Kye Ŭng-t'ae |
| | Vice Premier | Hŏ Tam |
| | Vice Premier | Chŏng Chun-ki |
| | Vice Premier | Choe Chae-u |
| | Vice Premier | Kong Chin-t'ae |
| | Vice Premier | Kim Tu-yŏng |
| | Vice Premier | Kim Chang-chu |

Vice Premier . . . . . . . . . . . . . . . . . . . . . . . . . . . . . . . . . . . . . . . Kim Pok-sin
Vice Premier . . . . . . . . . . . . . . . . . . . . . . . . . . . . . . . . . . Hong Song-yŏng
Vice Premier . . . . . . . . . . . . . . . . . . . . . . . . . . . . . . . . . . . . Choe Kwang
Vice Premier . . . . . . . . . . . . . . . . . . . . . . . . . . . . . . . . . . . . . Hong Si-hak
Vice Premier . . . . . . . . . . . . . . . . . . . . . . . . . . . . . . . . . . . . . . Kim Hoe-il

**MINISTRY OF PEOPLE'S**
**ARMED FORCES**
*Pyongyang*

Minister . . . . . . . . . . . . . . . . . . . . . . . . . . . . . . . . . . . . . Gen. O. Chin-u
Vice Minister . . . . . . . . . . . . . . . . . . . . . . . . . . . . . . . . Lt. Gen. Im Ch'ol
Vice Minister . . . . . . . . . . . . . . . . . . . . . . . . . . . . . Lt. Gen. Kim Ik-hyon
Vice Minister . . . . . . . . . . . . . . . . . . . . . . . . . . . . . Col. Gen. Kim Pong-yul
Vice Minister . . . . . . . . . . . . . . . . . . . . . . . . . . . Col. Gen. Kim T'ae-hong
Vice Minister . . . . . . . . . . . . . . . . . . . . . . . . . . . . . Lt. Gen. Paek Hak-im
Vice Minister . . . . . . . . . . . . . . . . . . . . . . . . . . . Lt. Gen. Pak Chung-kuk
Director, Communications Bureau . . . . . . . . . . . Maj. Gen. Chan Pong-chan
Director, Foreign Liaison Bureau . . . . . . . . . . . . . Sr. Col. Kang Chong-ch'ol
Director, General Rear Services Bureau . . . . . . . . . . . . . Lt. Gen. Yi P'il-song
Director, Military Training Bureau . . . . . . . . . . . . . . Sr. Col. Chong Hyon-son
Director, Operations Bureau . . . . . . . . . . . . . . . . Maj. Gen. Wi Chang-chin

**General Political Administration**

Director . . . . . . . . . . . . . . . . . . . . . . . . . . . . . . . . . . . . . . . . Gen. So Ch'ol
Deputy Director . . . . . . . . . . . . . . . . . . . . . . . . . . . . Lt. Gen. Chon Si-ho
Deputy Director . . . . . . . . . . . . . . . . . . . . . . . . . . Maj. Gen. Kim Ung-to
Deputy Director . . . . . . . . . . . . . . . . . . . . . . . . . . . . Maj. Gen. Yi Si-won
Deputy Director . . . . . . . . . . . . . . . . . . . . . . . . . . . . Lt. Gen. Yun Ch'i-ho

**Military Armistice Commission**

Senior Member . . . . . . . . . . . . . . . . . . . . . . . . . . . Maj. Gen. Han Chu-kyong
Secretary . . . . . . . . . . . . . . . . . . . . . . . . . . . . . . . . . . . Ch'oe Won-ch ol
Assistant Secretary . . . . . . . . . . . . . . . . . . . . . . . . . . . . . . . . Kim Yon-ki
Assistant Secretary . . . . . . . . . . . . . . . . . . . . . . . . . . . . . . . . . . Pak Il-su
Member . . . . . . . . . . . . . . . . . . . . . . . . . . . . . . . . . . . . . . Cho Pok-yong
Member . . . . . . . . . . . . . . . . . . . . . . . . . . . . . . . . . . . . . Chu Won-chin
Member . . . . . . . . . . . . . . . . . . . . . . . . . . . . . . . . . . . . . . Col. Ho Hon
Member . . . . . . . . . . . . . . . . . . . . . . . . . . . . . . . . . . . . . Kim Tu-hwan
Member . . . . . . . . . . . . . . . . . . . . . . . . . . . . . . . . . . . . . . Kim Un-hak
Member . . . . . . . . . . . . . . . . . . . . . . . . . . . . . . . . . . . . . . Yi Chan-pok
Member . . . . . . . . . . . . . . . . . . . . . . . . . . . . . . . . . . . . . . . . Yi Yong-il

# DEFENSE FORCES

**ARMED FORCES**
*Pyongyang*

Chief . . . . . . . . . . . . . . . . . . . . . . . . . . . . . . . . . . . . Lt. Gen. O Kuk-yol
First Deputy Chief . . . . . . . . . . . . . . . . . . . . . . . . . Col. Gen. Kim Ch'ol-man
Deputy Chief . . . . . . . . . . . . . . . . . . . . . . . . . . . . Lt. Gen. Cho Myong-son
Deputy Chief . . . . . . . . . . . . . . . . . . . . . . . . . . . . Lt. Gen. Hwang Ch'ol-san
Deputy Chief . . . . . . . . . . . . . . . . . . . . . . . . . . . . . . . Kim Kang-hwan
Deputy Chief . . . . . . . . . . . . . . . . . . . . . . . . . . . . . Maj. Gen. Kim Sang-ho

**ARMY**
*Pyongyang*

Commander (Artillery) . . . . . . . . . . . . . . . . . . . . . Lt. Gen. Kim Kwang-chin

**NAVY**
*Pyongyang*

Commander . . . . . . . . . . . . . . . . . . . . . . . . . . . . . . Vice Adm. Pang Ch'ol-kap

**AIR FORCE**
*Pyongyang*

Commander . . . . . . . . . . . . . . . . . . . . . . . . . . . . . . Lt. Gen. Cho Myong-nok

\* \* \* \* \*

## GENERAL DEFENSE DATA

**Manpower**

    Total Armed Forces.............................................784,000
      (See Page 307)
    Population ................................................20,586,000

**Spending**

    Military Expenditures.......................................$1.3 billion
    Gross National Product......................................$15.9 billion
    Military Expenditure as a Percentage of
      Gross National Product .........................................8.2%
    Military Expenditure as a Percentage of
      Central Government Expenditure ...............................10.4%

**Defense Treaties** *(See Part II for Additional Detail)*

    Bilateral:      Soviet Union
                  Togo

    Multilateral:  None

# REPUBLIC OF KOREA
## (South Korea)
### *Daehan Minguk*

### Defense Establishment Command Structure and Force Organization

The President is Commander-in-Chief. He is advised on defense policy by the National Security Council. Operational control of the Armed Forces is exercised by the Chairman of the Joint Chiefs of Staff. Administration of the military is the responsibility of the Minister of National Defense.

**Total armed forces:** 601,600 (Army: 520,000;    Navy: 49,000;    Air Force: 32,600). **Reserves:** 3,300,000;    **Homeland Reserve Defense Force:** 4,400,000. **Civilian Defense Corps:** 1,820,000.

### HEAD OF STATE

H. E. Chun Doo-Hwan

| | |
|---|---|
| **OFFICE OF THE PRESIDENT** *Chong Wa Dae (The Blue House) 1 Sejong-ro, Chongro-gu Seoul* | President of the Republic and Commander-in-Chief ...........................Chun Doo-Hwan <br> Chief Secretary.................................Hahm Byung-Choon |
| **National Security Council—NSC** | Chairman .......................................Chun Doo-Hwan <br> (President of the Republic) <br> Member ..........................................Kim Sang-Hyup <br> (Prime Minister) <br> Member ..........................................Kim Joon-Sung <br> (Deputy Prime Minister and Minister of Economic Planning) <br> Member.........................................Yoon Sung-Min <br> (Minister of National Defense) <br> Member .........................................Lee Bum-Suk <br> (Minister of Foreign Affairs) <br> Member ..........................................Rho Tae-Woo <br> (Minister of Home Affairs) <br> Member.........................................Kang Kyong-Shik <br> (Minister of Finance) <br> Member ..........................................Rho Shin-Young <br> (Director, Agency for National Security Planning) |
| **Agency for National Security Planning** | Director ...........................................Rho Shin-Young |
| **OFFICE OF THE PRIME MINISTER** *1 Sejong-ro, Chongro-gu Seoul* | Prime Minister...................................Kim Sang-Hyup |

**OFFICE OF THE DEPUTY PRIME MINISTER**
*82-1 Sejong-ro, Chongro-gu*
*Seoul*

Deputy Prime Minister and
Minister of the Economic
Planning Board . . . . . . . . . . . . . . . . . . . . . . . . . . . . . . . . Kim Joon-Sung

**MINISTRY OF NATIONAL DEFENSE**
*101 Huam Dong*
*Yongsan-gu*
*Seoul*
*Telex:    23402 jpamnd k*
*(Procurement Agency)*

Minister . . . . . . . . . . . . . . . . . . . . . . . . . . . . . . . . . . . . . . . . Yoon Sung-Min
Deputy Minister . . . . . . . . . . . . . . . . . . . . . . . . . . . . . . . Kwon Yung-Kag

**National Defense College**

Commandant . . . . . . . . . . . . . . . . . . . . . . . . . . . . Maj. Gen. Kim Ki-Taek

## DEFENSE FORCES

**ARMED FORCES**
**Joint Chiefs of Staff—JCS**
*Yongsan-gu*
*Seoul*

Chairman, JCS . . . . . . . . . . . . . . . . . . . . . . . . . . . . . Gen. Kin Yoon-Ho
Chief of Staff,, Army . . . . . . . . . . . . . . . . . . . . . Gen. Hwang Yung-Si
Chief, Naval Operations . . . . . . . . . . . . . . . . . . . Adm. Oh Kyung-Hwan
Chief of Staff, Air Force . . . . . . . . . . . . . . . . . . . . Gen. Kim Sang-Tae

**ARMY**
**Republic of Korea Army—ROKA**
*Yongsan-gu*
*Seoul*

Chief of Staff . . . . . . . . . . . . . . . . . . . . . . . . . . . . Gen. Hwang Young-Si
Deputy Chief of Staff . . . . . . . . . . . . . . . . . . . . Lt. Gen. Kim Hong-Han
Commander, First ROK Army . . . . . . . . . . . . . . . . . . Gen. So Joon-Yul
Commander, Second ROK Army . . . . . . . . . . . . . . . Gen. Lee Ki-Back
Commander, Third ROK Army . . . . . . . . . . . . . . . Gen. Chung Ho-Yong
Commandant, Command and
General Staff College . . . . . . . . . . . . . . . . . . . Maj. Gen. Yoon Jong-Hwa

**NAVY**
**Republic of Korea Navy—ROKN**
*Daebang-dong, Yongdungpo-gu*
*Seoul*

Chief, Naval Operations . . . . . . . . . . . . . . . . . . . Adm. Oh Kyung-Hwan
1st Vice Chief, Operations . . . . . . . . . . . . . . . . . . . Vice Adm. Kim Tae-Yong
2nd Vice Chief, Operations and
Commander, Marines . . . . . . . . . . . . . . . . . . . Lt. Gen. Park Heejae
Superintendent, Naval Academy . . . . . . . . . . . Rear Adm. Paek Seung-Hun

**AIR FORCE**
**Republic of Korea Air Force—ROKAF**
*Daebang-dong, Yongdungpo-gu*
*Seoul*

Chief of Staff . . . . . . . . . . . . . . . . . . . . . . . . . . . . . Gen. Kim Sang-Tae
Vice Chief of Staff . . . . . . . . . . . . . . . . . . . . . . . . . Lt. Gen. Kim In-Ki
Superintendent, Air Force Academy . . . . . . . . . . Maj. Gen. Han Young-Kyu

\* \* \* \* \*

## GENERAL DEFENSE DATA

**Manpower**
Total Armed Forces . . . . . . . . . . . . . . . . . . . . . . . . . . . . . . . . . . . 601,600
(See Page 311)
Population . . . . . . . . . . . . . . . . . . . . . . . . . . . . . . . . . . . . . . . . . 41,092,000

**Spending**
Military Expenditures . . . . . . . . . . . . . . . . . . . . . . . . . . . . . . . $3.8 billion
Gross National Product . . . . . . . . . . . . . . . . . . . . . . . . . . . . . $62.5 billion
Military Expenditure as a Percentage of
Gross National Product . . . . . . . . . . . . . . . . . . . . . . . . . . . . . . . 6.2%
Military Expenditure as a Percentage of
Central Government Expenditure . . . . . . . . . . . . . . . . . . . . . . . . 28.4%

**Defense Treaties** *(See Part II for Additional Detail)*

Bilateral:      United States

Multilateral:   Limited Test Ban Treaty
Treaty on the Non-Proliferation of Nuclear Weapons

# KUWAIT
## State of Kuwait
### *Dawlat Kuwait*

## Defence Establishment Command Structure
## and Force Organization

The Amir is the Commander-in-Chief and exercises his command through the Minister of Defence.

**Total armed forces:** 12,400 (Army: 10,000;  Navy: 500 (Coastguard);  Air Force: 1,900).
**Para-military forces:** 18,000 (National Guard).

## HEAD OF STATE

H. H. Sheikh Jaber Al-Ahmed Al-Sabah

**OFFICE OF H. H. THE AMIR**
*P.O. Box 799*
*Safat*
*Telephone: 439021*
*Telex: 2700*

Amir of Kuwait and
    Commander-in-Chief ........H. H. Sheikh Jaber Al-Ahmad Al-Sabah
Special Adviser.....................Sheikh Abdullah Al-Jaber Al-Sabah
Minister, Office Affairs .............Sheikh Khalid Al-Ahmed Al-Sabah
Under Secretary ...........................Mohammad D. Al-Aradi
Director ..........................................Ibrahim M. Al-Shatti
Assistant Under Secretary......................Tawfeeq A. Al-Nassar
Assistant Under Secretary,
    Political and Legal Affairs .............Sheikh Ibrahim D. I. Al-Sabah
Assistant Under Secretary, Administrative
    and Financial Affairs ...................Sheikh Duaij J. A. Al-Sabah
Assistant Under Secretary........................Khalid Abu Al-Saud
Director, Protocol Department ............Abdul Aziz Al-Abdul-Razzak

**OFFICE OF H. H. THE CROWN
    PRINCE, HEIR APPARENT AND
    PRIME MINISTER**
*c/o Council of Ministers*
*P.O. Box 1397*
*Safat*
*Telephone: 431901*
*Telex: 22796 kt*

Crown Prince, Heir Apparent and
    Prime Minister ........H. H. Sheikh Sa'ad Abdullah Al Salem Al-Sabah
Deputy Prime Minister and Minister
    of Foreign Affairs .........Sheikh Sabah Al-Ahmad Al-Jaber Al-Sabah
Director, Office of H. H. Heir
    Apparent and Prime Minister ..................Abdul Latif Al-Bahar

**MINISTRY OF DEFENCE**
*P.O. Box 1170*
*Safat*
*Telephone: 819288*
*Telex: 22784 mod kt*

Minister .....................Sheikh Salem Sabah Al-Salem Al-Sabah
Under Secretary........................Abdul-Razzak Y. Al-Khamis
Assistant Under Secretary,
    Administrative Affairs .............................Sa'ad S. Al-Salem
Assistant Under Secretary,
    Chief Military Affairs Office .................Mohammad Al-Khalaf
Assistant Under Secretary, Logistics Affairs ..........Faisal A. Al-Dauod
Chief, Military Medical Administration ...........Dr. Ali F. Al-Atawnah

# DEFENCE FORCES

**ARMED FORCES**
*c/o Ministry of Defence*
*P.O. Box 1170*
*Safat*
*Telephone:   819288*
*Telex:   22784 kt*

Chief of Staff . . . . . . . . . . . . . . . . . . . . . .Lt. Gen. Abdullah Farad Al-Ganan

**ARMY**
*c/o Ministry of Defence*
*P.O. Box 1170*
*Safat*
*Telephone:   819288*
*Telex:   22784 kt*

Commander . . . . . . . . . . . . . . . . . . . . .Lt. Gen. Abdullah Farad Al-Ganan

**NAVY**
*c/o Ministry of Defence*
*P.O. Box 1170*
*Safat*
*Telephone:   819288*
*Telex:   22784 kt*

Commander . . . . . . . . . . . . . . . . . . . . . . . . . . . . . . . . . .Col. Habib Al-Meel

**AIR FORCE**
*c/o Ministry of Defence*
*P.O. Box 1170*
*Safat*
*Telephone:   819288*
*Telex:   22784 kt*

Commander . . . . . . . . . . . . . . . . . . . . .Lt. Gen. Abdullah Farad Al-Ganan

**NATIONAL GUARD**
*c/o Ministry of Defence*
*P.O. Box 1170*
*Safat*
*Telephone:   819288*
*Telex:   22784 kt*

Commander . . . . . . . . . . . . . . . . . . . . . . . . . . . . .Sheikh Salem A. S. Al-Sabah
Deputy Commander . . . . . . . . . . . . . . . . . . . . . . . . . . . . . . . . . . . . . . . . . . . . . .
Director, Military Committee . . . . . . . . . . . . . .Lt. Col. Khadid A. J. Boodai

\* \* \* \* \*

# GENERAL DEFENCE DATA

**Manpower**
Total Armed Forces. . . . . . . . . . . . . . . . . . . . . . . . . . . . . . . . . . . . . . . . . . . . .12,400
(See Page 313)
Population . . . . . . . . . . . . . . . . . . . . . . . . . . . . . . . . . . . . . . . . . . . . . .1,553,000

**Spending**
Military Expenditures. . . . . . . . . . . . . . . . . . . . . . . . . . . . . . . . . . . . . . . .$1.3 billion
Gross National Product . . . . . . . . . . . . . . . . . . . . . . . . . . . . . . . . . . . . . .$31 billion
Military Expenditure as a Percentage of
Gross National Product . . . . . . . . . . . . . . . . . . . . . . . . . . . . . . . . . . . . . . .4.2%

Military Expenditure as a Percentage of
Central Government Expenditure ...............................14.1%

**Defence Treaties** *(See Part II for Additional Detail)*

Bilateral:     United States

Multilateral:  Biological Weapons Convention
Cooperation Council for the Arab States of the Gulf
Environmental Modification Convention
League of Arab States
Limited Test Ban Treaty

# LAOS
## Lao People's Democratic Republic
*Saatharanarat Prachhathippatay Prachhachhon Lao*

### Defense Establishment Command Structure and Force Organization

The President is Commander-in-Chief, but operational contol of armed forces is vested in the Prime Minister and exercised by the Minister of Defense.

**Total armed forces:** 48,700 (Army: 46,000;    Navy: 1,700;    Air Force: 1,000).

### HEAD OF STATE

H. E. Souphanouvong

**OFFICE OF THE PRESIDENT**
*Vientiane*
*Telephone: 2315, 2181*

President of the Lao People's Democratic Republic
and Commander-in-Chief ........................Souphanouvong

**PEOPLE'S SUPREME COUNCIL**
*Vientiane*

Chairman .........................................Souphanouvong
Deputy Chairman .............................Sisomphone Lovansay
Deputy Chairman ..............................Faydang Lobliayao
Deputy Chairman and Secretary General ..............Khamsouk Keola

**OFFICE OF THE COUNCIL OF MINISTERS**
*Vientiane*
*Telephone: 3171*

Chairman .....................................Kaysone Phomvihane
First Deputy Chairman ........................Nouhak Phoumsavanh
Deputy Chairman...............................Phoumi Vongvichit
Deputy Chairman and Minister
of Foreign Affairs ...............................Phoun Sipaseuth
Deputy Chairman and Minister of Defense .........Khamtay Siphandone
Deputy Chairman and Chief
of State Planning Committee......................Saly Vongkhamsao
Minister ........................Thongsavath Khaykhamphithoune
Minister .................................Ma Khaykhamphithoune
Minister ................................Khamsouk Xaignaseng
Minister ....................................Souli Nanthavong
Minister ...............................Thongchanh Ouparavanh
Minister .......................................Soth Phethlasy
Minister ................................Thammasinh Xaikhamphane
Adviser to the Government ......................Souvanna Phoumma

**MINISTRY OF NATIONAL DEFENSE**
*Vientiane*
*Telephone: 2046*

Minister of Defense, Deputy Chairman
of the Council of Ministers and
Commander-in-Chief, Lao People's
Liberation Army (LPA) ..................Gen. Khamtay Siphandone
Secretary of State and Deputy Defense
Minister, LPA Politburo....................Gen. Siphone Phalikhan
Secretary of State and Deputy
Chief of Staff, LPA ...........................Somsak Saisongkham
Deputy Chief of Staff, LPA ...........Brig. Gen. Choummali Saignakone

Deputy Minister of
National Defense . . . . . . . . . . . . . . . . . .Brig. Gen. Osakan Thammatheva
Director, Office of National Defense . . . . . . . . . . . . . . . .Padit Thiangtham
Director, Administrative Affairs . . . . . . . . . . . . . . . . . . .Cheng Saignavong
Member, Directorate of the General
Political Department of the LPA . . . . . . . . . . . . . . . . . . . . . . . . .Chanko
Deputy Secretary of the Party Central
Military Commission and Chief
of Staff, LPA . . . . . . . . . . . . . . . . . . . . .Gen. Sisavath Keobounphanh
Cabinet Chief of Defense Ministry . . . . . . . . . . . . . . . .Col. Savay Sayaksena

## DEFENSE FORCES

**ARMED FORCES**
*Vientiane*
*Telephone:   3151, 3360*

Commander-in-Chief, Deputy Prime Minister,
and Minister of National Defense . . . . . . . . . . . . . . .Khamtai Siphandone
Chief, General Political Bureau
of the Armed Forces . . . . . . . . . . . . . . . . . . .Maj. Gen. Siphone Phalikhan
Director General Logistics Department . . . . . . . . . . . . . . . . . . . .Gen. Lakhon

**ARMY**
**Lao People's Liberation Army—LPA**
*Vientiane*

Chief of Staff . . . . . . . . . . . . . . . . . . . . . . . .Gen. Sisavath Keobounphanh
Deputy Chief, Army Political
Department . . . . . . . . . . . . . . . . . . . . . .Brig. Gen. Osaken Thammatheva
Chief, Army Logistics Department . . . . .Brig. Gen. Bounnian Kham-Ouane

**AIR FORCE**
**The Air Force of the Lao People's Army**
*Vientiane*

Chief of Staff . . . . . . . . . . . . . . . . . . . . . . . . . . . . . . . . . . . . .Col. Phonsai
Vice Commander . . . . . . . . . . . . . . . . . . . . . . .Lt. Col. Khamkong Soulivong

**NATIONAL POLICE DEPARTMENT**
*Vientiane*
*Telephone:   2059*

Police Commander . . . . . . . . . . . . . . . . . . . . . . . . . . . . .Phosay Sayphannha
Attache to the National Police Department . . . . . . . . . . . . . . .Phan Savanvilai
Director, Immigration
Department . . . . . . . . . . . . . . . . . . .Bounthanh Vilaisa Vanh Phetsamone

\* \* \* \* \*

## GENERAL DEFENSE DATA

**Manpower**
Total Armed Forces . . . . . . . . . . . . . . . . . . . . . . . . . . . . . . . . . . . . . . . . . .48,700
(See Page 317)
Population . . . . . . . . . . . . . . . . . . . . . . . . . . . . . . . . . . . . . . . . . . . . .3,577,000

**Spending**
Military Expenditures . . . . . . . . . . . . . . . . . . . . . . . . . . . . . . . . . . . .$21 million
Gross National Product . . . . . . . . . . . . . . . . . . . . . . . . . . . . . . . . . . .$300 million
Military Expenditure as a Percentage of
Gross National Product . . . . . . . . . . . . . . . . . . . . . . . . . . . . . . . . . . . . . . . .7%
Military Expenditure as a Percentage of
Central Government Expenditure . . . . . . . . . . . . . . . . . . . . . . . . . . . . . . . . .

**Defense Treaties** *(See Part II for Additional Detail)*

Bilateral:      Bulgaria
Czechoslovakia
Vietnam

Multilateral:   Biological Weapons Convention
Environment Modification Convention
Limited Test Ban Treaty
Treaty on the Non-Proliferation of Nuclear Weapons

# LEBANON
## Republic of Lebanon
### *Jumhuriyat Lubnan*

### Defense Establishment Command Structure and Force Organization

All military authority in Lebanon is centralized in the person of the Commander-in-Chief, who is directly responsible to the President.

**Total armed forces:** 11,000.

## HEAD OF STATE

H. E. Amin Gemayel

**OFFICE OF THE PRESIDENT**
*Ba'abda*
*Telephone: 220000*
*Telex: 21000 prl le*

| | |
|---|---|
| President of the Republic | Amin Gemayel |
| Chief of Protocol of the Republic | Nael El-Assaad |
| Director-General | Boutros Germani |
| Director-General, Chief of Section | Mahmoud Osman |
| Director-General, Chief of Section | Joseph Saadallah El-Khoury |
| Advisor | Wadih Haddad |
| Advisor | Alfre Madi |

**OFFICE OF THE PRIME MINISTER**
*Sanayeh*
*Beirut*
*Telephone: 221000*

| | |
|---|---|
| Prime Minister | Shafik Wazzan |
| Deputy Prime Minister and Minister of Foreign Affairs | Elie Salem |
| Director-General | Shafic Mnaymneh |
| Director-General, Chief of Section | Youssef Stephane |
| Chief of Protocol to the Prime Minister | Abdel Rahman Sheikha |

**MINISTRY OF NATIONAL DEFENSE, EDUCATION, AND FINE ARTS**
*Yarze*
*Telephone: 452400, 420400*
*Telex: 20901 armlib*

| | |
|---|---|
| Minister | Issam Khuri |
| Chief of Military Cabinet | Col. Emile Lahoud |
| Chief, Office of Information and Public Relations | Milad El-Kareh |
| Director-General, Public Security | Zahi Bustani |
| Director-General, Internal Security | Brig. Gen. Osman Osman |
| Secretary General, Higher Defense Council | Brig. Gen. Nabil Quraytem |

## DEFENSE FORCES

**ARMED FORCES**
*c/o Ministry of Defense*
*Yarze*
*Telephone: 420400*

| | |
|---|---|
| Commander-in-Chief | Gen. Ibrahim Tannous |

**ARMY**
*c/o Ministry of Defense*
*Yarze*
*Telephone: 420400*

| | |
|---|---|
| Chief of Staff | Brig. Gen. Nadim Al-Hakim |
| Commander, 1st Armored Battalion | |
| Commander, 2nd Armored Battalion | |
| Commander, 1st Infantry Battalion | Gen. Ibrahim Shahin |

Commander, 2nd Infantry Battalion . . . . . . . . . . . . . . Col. Issam Aboujamra
Commander, 3rd Infantry Battalion . . . . . . . . . . . . . . . . . Col. Said Kaakour
Commander, 4th Infantry Battalion . . . . . . . . . . . . . . Col. Georges Harouk
Commander, 5th Infantry Battalion . . . . . . . . . . . . . Col. Gabriel Karsony
Commander, 6th Infantry Battalion . . . . . . . . . . . . . . . . . Col. Louth Jaber
Commander, 8th Infantry Battalion . . . . . . . . . . . . . . . Col. Michael Aoun
Commander, 1st Artillery Battalion . . . . . . . . . . . . . . . Maj. Adel Sassine
Commander, 2nd Artillery Battalion . . . . . . . . . . . . . . . Maj. Michel Faysal
Commander, 3rd Artillery Battalion . . . . . . . . . . . . . . . . Maj. Naji Hassan
Commander, 4th Artillery Battalion . . . . . . . . . . . . . . . . . . . . . . . . . . . . . . .

**AIR FORCE**
*c/o Ministry of Defense*
*Yarze*
*Telephone:  420400*

Commander . . . . . . . . . . . . . . . . . . . . . . . . . . . . . . . . . . . Col. Fahim Al-Hag
Commander, Helicopter Squadron . . . . . . . . . . . Lt. Col. Sleiman Mazloum

**NAVY**
*c/o Ministry of Defense*
*Yarze*
*Telephone:  420400*

Commander . . . . . . . . . . . . . . . . . . . . . . . . . . . . . . . . . . Col. Antoine Kreidy

\* \* \* \* \*

## GENERAL DEFENSE DATA

**Manpower**
    Total Armed Forces . . . . . . . . . . . . . . . . . . . . . . . . . . . . . . . . . . . . . . 11,000
      (See Page 319)
    Population . . . . . . . . . . . . . . . . . . . . . . . . . . . . . . . . . . . . . . . . . 3,177,000

**Spending**
    Military Expenditures . . . . . . . . . . . . . . . . . . . . . . . . . . . . . . . . . $272 million
    Gross National Product . . . . . . . . . . . . . . . . . . . . . . . . . . . . . . . . $3 billion
    Military Expenditure as a Percentage of
      Gross National Product . . . . . . . . . . . . . . . . . . . . . . . . . . . . . . . . . 9%
    Military Expenditure as a Percentage of
      Central Government Expenditure . . . . . . . . . . . . . . . . . . . . . . . . . 26%

**Defense Treaties** *(See Part II for Additional Detail)*

    Bilateral:     France
                    Israel
                    United States

    Multilateral:   Biological Weapons Convention
                    League of Arab States
                    Limited Test Ban Treaty
                    Treaty on the Non-Proliferation of Nuclear Weapons

# LESOTHO
## Kingdom of Lesotho

### Defence Establishment Command Structure and Force Organization

The King of Lesotho is by tradition Commander-in-Chief of the armed forces. Actual control of the military is exercised by the Prime Minister who also holds the portfolio of Minister of Defence and Internal Security. Administration of the armed forces is the responsibility of the Commander of the Lesotho Para-military Force.

**Para-military forces:** 1,500 (Army). **Police:** 400.

### HEAD OF STATE

H. M. King Moshoeshoe II

**OFFICE OF H. M. THE KING**
*Maseru 100*

*Telephone:* 22170
*Telex:* 330 bb

King of Lesotho ................................. H. M. Moshoeshoe II

**OFFICE OF THE PRIME MINISTER AND MINISTRY OF DEFENCE AND INTERNAL SECURITY**
*P.O. Box 527*
*Maseru 100*

*Telephone:* 23861
*Telex:* 330 bb

Prime Minister and Minister of Defence
    and Internal Security......................... Chief Leabua Jonathan
Minister to the Prime Minister ................ Evaristus R. Sekhonyana
Minister of State.................................... Julius Khasoane
Minister of State ............................. Ignatius Tlake Mokone
Minister of State ...................................... John Mothepu

### DEFENCE FORCES

**ARMY**
**Lesotho Para-military Force**
*P.O. Box MS 13*
*Maseru 100*

*Telephone:* 23004

Commander ............................... Maj. Gen. J. M. Lekhanya

**POLICE**
**Lesotho Mounted Police**
*Headquarters*
*P.O. Box MS 13*
*Maseru 100*

*Telephone:* 23061
*Telex:* 331 bb

Commissioner ................................. Maj. Gen. S. R. Matela
Chief, Criminal Investigation Department................. Maj. Motsoari
Deputy Chief.......................................... Col. T. Nomo
Deputy Chief......................................... Lt. Col. T. Pinda
Deputy Chief....................................... Col. B. S. Mollse
Deputy Chief....................................... Lt. Col. B. Tsasanyane
Deputy Chief ................................... Maj. A. S. Raditapole
Deputy Chief ................................. Lt. Col. J. M. Lehloenya
Deputy Chief ................................... Maj. Ramoseeka S. P.
Deputy Chief................................... Maj. B. T. Thakalekoala
Deputy Chief.................................... Maj. G. L. Makepe

**National Security Service**

Chief . . . . . . . . . . . . . . . . . . . . . . . . . . . . . . . . . . . . . . . . . . . . . . .Maj. Gen. S. J. Molapo
Deputy Chief . . . . . . . . . . . . . . . . . . . . . . . . . . . . . . . . . . .Capt. Lephele E. M.
Deputy Chief . . . . . . . . . . . . . . . . . . . . . . . . . . . . . . . . . . . . . .Maj. Maloi E. M.
Deputy Chief. . . . . . . . . . . . . . . . . . . . . . . . . . . . . . . . . . . . . . . . . . . . . . .C. T. Chen
Deputy Chief . . . . . . . . . . . . . . . . . . . . . . . . . . . . . . . . . . . . . .Lt. Col. J. Khojane
Deputy Chief . . . . . . . . . . . . . . . . . . . . . . . . . . . . . . . . . . . . . . . .Brig. S. E. Ts'iu
Deputy Chief . . . . . . . . . . . . . . . . . . . . . . . . . . . . . . . . . . . . . .Maj. S. P. Pebane
Deputy Chief . . . . . . . . . . . . . . . . . . . . . . . . . . . . . . . . . . . . .Lt. Col. E. M. Thene
Deputy Chief . . . . . . . . . . . . . . . . . . . . . . . . . . . . . . . . . . . .Capt. Hlohlomi I. M.

\* \* \* \* \*

# GENERAL DEFENCE DATA

## Manpower

Total Armed Forces. . . . . . . . . . . . . . . . . . . . . . . . . . . . . . . . . . . . . . . . . . . . . .1,500
    (See Page 321)
Population . . . . . . . . . . . . . . . . . . . . . . . . . . . . . . . . . . . . . . . . . . . . .1,395,000

## Spending

Military Expenditures . . . . . . . . . . . . . . . . . . . . . . . . . . . . . . . . . . . . . . . . . . . .
Gross National Product . . . . . . . . . . . . . . . . . . . . . . . . . . . . . . . . . . . . . . . .$564 million
Military Expenditure as a Percentage of
    Gross National Product . . . . . . . . . . . . . . . . . . . . . . . . . . . . . . . . . . . . . . . . .
Military Expenditure as a Percentage of
    Central Government Expenditure . . . . . . . . . . . . . . . . . . . . . . . . . . . . . . . . .

## Defence Treaties *(See Part II for Additional Detail)*

Bilateral:     None

Multilateral:  Organization of African Unity
               Treaty on the Control of Arms on the Seabed
               Treaty on the Non-Proliferation of Nuclear Weapons

# LIBERIA
## Republic of Liberia

### Defense Establishment Command Structure and Force Organization

The Chairman of the People's Redemption Council is Commander-in-Chief of the Liberian armed forces. He is advised by the Council and exercises his command through the Minister of National Defense. The Ministry of Security controls the Police.

**Total armed forces:** 5,400 (Army: 4,900; Navy: 250; Air Force: 250). **Para-military forces:** 1,750.

## HEAD OF STATE

General Samuel K. Doe

**PEOPLE'S REDEMPTION COUNCIL**
*P.O. Box 9014*
*Capitol Hill*
*Monrovia*
*Telephone: 224836, 224736, 224668*

| | |
|---|---|
| Chairman and Commander-in-Chief | Gen. Samuel K. Doe |
| Co-Chairman | Maj. Gen. J. Nicholas Podier, Jr. |
| Speaker | Brig. Gen. Jeffred S. S. Gbatu |
| Secretary-General | Col. Abraham D. Kollie |
| Senior Member | Col. Jerry C. Jorwley, Jr. |
| Senior Member | Brig. Gen. Thomas Quiwonkpa |
| Head, National Security Committee | Col. Larry W. Borteh |
| Member | Lt. Col. Kionshe Gonyor |
| Member | Lt. Col. William Gould |
| Member | Lt. Col. Jacob Swen |
| Member | Lt. Col. Albert Toe |
| Member | Lt. Col. Alfred Y. Zeh |
| Co-member | Maj. Swen Dixon |
| Co-member | Col. David Karmai |
| Co-member | Maj. Yellah Kebbeh |
| Co-member | Maj. Robert B. Nowoku |
| Co-member | Maj. John Nyumah |
| Co-member | Col. Harrison Pennue |
| Co-member | Lt. Col. Joseph K. Sampson |
| Co-member | Maj. Stanley C. Tarwuo |
| Co-member | Maj. Joseph Tubman |
| Co-member | Maj. Robert Zuo |

**MINISTRY OF NATIONAL DEFENSE**
*P.O. Box 9007*
*Monrovia*
*Telephone: 222303, 222601*
*Telex: 4351 mnd li (Benson St.)*

| | |
|---|---|
| Minister | Col. Gray D. Allison |
| Deputy Minister, Administration | Capt. Anthony Togba |
| Assistant Minister, Public Affairs | Col. Tommy Raynes |

**MINISTRY OF SECURITY**
*Monrovia*

| | |
|---|---|
| Minister | Capt. Patrick Minikon |

323

# DEFENSE FORCES

**ARMED FORCES**
*c/o Ministry of Defense*
*P.O. Box 9007*
*Monrovia*
*Telephone:    222366, 222601*

Chief of Staff, Armed Forces . . . . . . . . . . . . . . . . . . .Lt. Gen. Henry Dunbar
Commander, Logistics . . . . . . . . . . . . . . . . . . . . . . . . . . .Col. John Nuewen
Concillor to Controller, Armed Forces . . . . . . . . . . . . . . .Maj. George Dunye
Commander . . . . . . . . . . . . . . . . . . . . . . . . . . .Gen. Thomas Quiwonkja
Commander, Logistics . . . . . . . . . . . . . . . . . . . . . . . . .Capt. Samuel Dokie

**NAVY**
*c/o Ministry of Defense*
*P.O. Box 9007*
*Monrovia*

Commander. . . . . . . . . . . . . . . . . . . . . . . . . . . . .Cdr. W. Kelly Garnett

**POLICE**
*Monrovia*

Director . . . . . . . . . . . . . . . . . . . . . . . . . . . . . . . . . . . . .M. Joe Mayers

\* \* \* \* \*

# GENERAL DEFENSE DATA

**Manpower**
Total Armed Forces. . . . . . . . . . . . . . . . . . . . . . . . . . . . . . . . . . . . . . . . . .5,400
(See Page 323)
Population . . . . . . . . . . . . . . . . . . . . . . . . . . . . . . . . . . . . . . . . . .2,024,000

**Spending**
Military Expenditures . . . . . . . . . . . . . . . . . . . . . . . . . . . . . . . . . .$15 million
Gross National Product . . . . . . . . . . . . . . . . . . . . . . . . . . . . . . . .$1.2 billion
Military Expenditure as a Percentage of
Gross National Product . . . . . . . . . . . . . . . . . . . . . . . . . . . . . . . . . .1.5%
Military Expenditure as a Percentage of
Central Government Expenditure . . . . . . . . . . . . . . . . . . . . . . . . . . . .5.1%

**Defense Treaties** *(See Part II for Additional Detail)*

Bilateral:     Guinea
United States

Multilateral:  Economic Community of West African States
Limited Test Ban Treaty
Organization of African Unity
Treaty on the Non-Proliferation of Nuclear Weapons

# LIBYA
## Socialist People's Libyan Arab Jamahiriya
### *al-Jamahiriyah al-Arabiya al-Libya al-Shabiya al-Ishtirakiya*

## Defense Establishment Command Structure
## and Force Organization

The Leader of the Revolution is Chairman of the Revolution Command Council, Minister of Defense, and Supreme Commander of the Armed Forces of Libya. His authority is exercised through the Commander-in-Chief.

**Total armed forces:** 65,000 (Army: 55,000; Navy: 5,000; Air Force: 5,000). **Para-military forces:** 5,000.

**OFFICE OF THE LEADER
OF THE REVOLUTION**
*c/o Secretariat of the General
People's Committee*
*Tripoli*
*Telephone: (21) 48210-14, 30777*
*Telex: 20032*

Leader of the Revolution,
General Secretary of the
General Secretariat of the
General People's Congress and Supreme
Commander of the Armed Forces . . . . . . . . . . Col. Mu'ammar al-Qathafy
Staff Major . . . . . . . . . . . . . . . . . . . . . . . . . . . . . Maj. Abdel Salam Jalloud

**GENERAL SECRETARIAT OF THE
GENERAL PEOPLE'S CONGRESS**
*Tripoli*
*Telephone: (21) 30777*
*Telex: 20032*

Secretary . . . . . . . . . . . . . . . . . . . . . . . . . . . . . Muhammad Al-Zrouk Rajab
Assistant Secretary . . . . . . . . . . . . . . . . . . . . . . . . . . . . . Ali Abu al-Khayir
Secretary, People's Congresses Affairs . . . . . . . . . . Muhammad Ali Bawash
Secretary, People's Committees Affairs . . . . . . . . . . . . . . Abdullah Zahmoul
Secretary, Trade Unions and Associations
and Guilds Affairs . . . . . . . . . . . . . . . . . . . . . . . . . . . . . . Makhtar Qurbu

**SECRETARIAT OF THE GENERAL
PEOPLE'S COMMITTEE**
*Tripoli*
*Telephone: (21) 48210-14, 30777*
*Telex: 20032*

Secretary of the General
People's Committee . . . . . . . . . . . . . . . . . . Eng. Jadallah Azouz Al-Talhi

## DEFENSE FORCES

**ARMED FORCES**
**Armed Forces of the Libyan Arab Jamahiriya**
*Tripoli*
*Telephone: 30001*
*Telex: 20032*

Leader of the Revolution and
Supreme Commander of the
Armed Forces . . . . . . . . . . . . . . . . . . . . . . . . Col. Mu'ammar al-Qathafy
Commander-in-Chief of the
Armed Forces . . . . . . . . . . . . . . . . . . . . . . . . Gen. Abu Bakar Yunis Jaber
Chief of General Staff . . . . . . . . . . . . . . . . . . . . . Maj. Khweildi al-Humaidi
Commander of Jamahariya Security Group
(Intelligence and Counter Intelligence) . . . . . . Gen. Mustafa al-Kharrobi
Commander, Information Service . . . . . . . . . . . . . . . . Col. Yunis Bulgasim
Head, Security and Military
Intelligence Service . . . . . . . . . . . . . . . . . . Capt. Abdul Majid al-Khweildi
Commander, General Organization
for Military Industry . . . . . . . . . . . . . . . . . . . . . . . . . . . . . . . . . . . . . . .
Commander, Military Academy . . . . . . . . . . . . . . . . . . . . . . . . . . . . . . . . .

**ARMY**
**Arab Army**
*Tripoli*

Commander . . . . . . . . . . . . . . . . . . . . . . . . . . . . .Lt. Col. Mustafa Al Kharrobi

**NAVY**
**Arab Navy**
*Tripoli*

Commander . . . . . . . . . . . . . . . . . . . . . . . . . . . . . .Al Khoueidi Al Hamidi
Commandante, Naval Academy
    Khoms, Tripoli . . . . . . . . . . . . . . . . . . . . . . . . . . . . . . .

**AIR FORCE**
**Arab Air Force and Air Defense Command**
*Tripoli*

Commander . . . . . . . . . . . . . . . . . . . . . . . . . . . . .Lt. Col. Salah Farjani
Deputy Commander . . . . . . . . . . . . . . . . . . . . . . . . . . . .Col. Salah Abdullah
Chief of Operations . . . . . . . . . . . . . . . . . . . . . . . . . . . .Col. Jabril Khadiki

**POPULAR RESISTANCE FORCES**
*(Militia)*
*Tripoli*

Commander . . . . . . . . . . . . . . . . . . . . . . . . . . . .Maj. Khweildi al-Humaidi

**JAMAHIRIYA GUARDS**
*Tripoli*

Commander . . . . . . . . . . . . . . . . . . . . . . . . . . . . . . . . .Khalifa Hunaysh

**ISLAMIC CORPS**
*Tripoli*

Leader of the Revolution and
    Supreme Commander . . . . . . . . . . . . . . . . . . .Col. Mu'ammar al-Qathafy
Commander . . . . . . . . . . . . . . . . . . . . . . . . . . . . . . .Masoud Abdel Aziz

\* \* \* \* \*

## GENERAL DEFENSE DATA

**Manpower**
    Total Armed Forces . . . . . . . . . . . . . . . . . . . . . . . . . . . . . . . . . . . . . . .65,000
        (See Page 325)
    Population . . . . . . . . . . . . . . . . . . . . . . . . . . . . . . . . . . . . . . . . . .3,425,000

**Spending**
    Military Expenditures . . . . . . . . . . . . . . . . . . . . . . . . . . . . . . . . . .$523 million
    Gross National Product . . . . . . . . . . . . . . . . . . . . . . . . . . . . . . . . .$30.5 billion
    Military Expenditure as a Percentage of
        Gross National Product . . . . . . . . . . . . . . . . . . . . . . . . . . . . . . . . . . .1.7%
    Military Expenditure as a Percentage of
        Central Government Expenditure . . . . . . . . . . . . . . . . . . . . . . . . . . . . .4.5%

**Defense Treaties** *(See Part II for Additional Detail)*

    Bilateral:    Algeria
                  France
                  Niger
                  Togo

    Multilateral: Aden Tripartite Alliance
                  Biological Weapons Convention
                  League of Arab States
                  Limited Test Ban Treaty
                  Organization of African Unity
                  Treaty on the Non-Proliferation of Nuclear Weapons

# LIECHTENSTEIN
## Principality of Liechtenstein

### Defense Establishment Command Structure
### and Force Organization

Switzerland is responsible for the security of Liechtenstein. There is no standing army; internal security is handled by the police.

**Police Force:** 38. Auxiliaries: 22.

## HEAD OF STATE

H. S. H. Prince Franz Josef II

**OFFICE OF H. S. H. THE REIGNING PRINCE**
*Schloss Vaduz*
*FL-9490 Vaduz*

*Telephone: (75) 2 12 12*
*Telex: 77999*

Reigning Prince .......................... H. S. H. Prince Franz Josef II
Secretary of H. S. H. The Reigning Prince and
    Director of the Cabinet ........................... Robert Allgaeuer

**OFFICE OF THE CHIEF OF GOVERNMENT (PRIME MINISTER)**
*(Internal Affairs, Education, Finances, Foreign Affairs, Culture and Building Industry)*
*National Administration*
*FL-9490 Vaduz*

*Telephone: (75) 66111*
*Telex: 77755 repi fl*

Chief of Government (Prime Minister) .................. Hans Brunhart
Deputy Chief of the Government ....................... Hilmar Ospelt

## DEFENSE FORCE

**POLICE DEPARTMENT**
**Princely Liechtenstein Security Corps**
*National Administration*
*FL-9490 Vaduz*

*Telephone: (75) 66111*
*Telex: 77755 repi fl*

Chief of Police ...................................... Vinzenz Batliner

\* \* \* \* \*

# GENERAL DEFENSE DATA

**Manpower**
Total Armed Forces ...................................................38
  (See Page 327)
Population ....................................................26,000

**Spending**
Military Expenditures .....................................................
Gross National Product .....................................................
Military Expenditure as a Percentage of
  Gross National Product .................................................
Military Expenditure as a Percentage of
  Central Government Expenditure ........................................

**Defense Treaties** *(See Part II for Additional Detail)*

  Bilateral:     None

  Multilateral:  Treaty on the Non-Proliferation of Nuclear Weapons

# LUXEMBOURG
## Grand Duchy of Luxembourg
### *Grand-Duché de Luxembourg*

## Defense Establishment Command Structure
## and Force Organization

The President is Commander-in-Chief. He is advised by the High Commission for National Protection and exercises his authority through the Ministry of the Armed Forces.

**Total armed forces:** 690 (Army). **Para-military forces:** 500 (Gendarmerie).

## HEAD OF STATE

H. R. H. Grand Duc Jean Benôit Guillaume Marie Robert Antoine Louis Adolphe Marc d'Aviano

**GRAND DUCAL COURT**
*Palais Grand-Ducal*
*2, Rue du Rost*
*L-2447 Luxembourg*
*Telephone: 2 26 01*
*Telex: 1871 palais lu*

Grand Duke . . . . . . . . . . H. R. H. Grand Duc Jean Benôit Guillaume Marie Robert Antoine Louis Adolphe Marc d'Aviano
Marshal of the Court . . . . . . . . . . . . . . . . . . . . . . . . . . . . . Christian Calmes

**OFFICE OF THE PRESIDENT OF THE GOVERNMENT (PRIME MINISTER)**
*Hotel de Bourgogne*
*4, rue de la Congrégation*
*Luxembourg-Ville, L-1352*
*Telephone: 478-1*

President (Prime Minister) and Minister of Cultural Affairs, Religion, Press and Information, Territorial Development, Sector of Finances dealing with Credit, the International Financial Center of Luxembourg, and the Treasury . . . . . . . . . . . . . . . . . . . . Pierre Werner

**High Commission for National Protection**
*(Haut-Commissariat de la Protection Nationale)*
*5, rue Auguste Lumiére*
*L-1950 Luxembourg-Ville*
*Telephone: 478 229*
*Telex: 1414 or 3404*
*Cable: PRONAT LU*

High Commissioner . . . . . . . . . . . . . . . . . . . . . . . . . . . . . Col. Albert Lucas

**OFFICE OF THE VICE PRESIDENT OF THE GOVERNMENT**
*5, rue Notre-Dame*
*L-2910 Luxembourg-Ville*
*Telephone: 478-1*

Vice President and Minister of Foreign Affairs, Foreign Trade, National Economy, Middle Classes and Justice . . . . . . . . . . . . . . . . . . . . . . . Colette Flesch
Secretary of State . . . . . . . . . . . . . . . . . . . . . . . . . . . . . . Paul Helminger

**MINISTRY OF THE ARMED FORCES**
*Plateau du St.-Esprit*
*L-1475 Luxembourg-Ville*
*Telephone: 40803*

Minister . . . . . . . . . . . . . . . . . . . . . . . . . . . . . . . . . . . . Emile Krieps
Management Counselor . . . . . . . . . . . . . . . . . . . . . . . . . . . . Joseph Berg
Assistant Management Counselor . . . . . . . . . . . . . . . . . . . . . Fernand Kirch
Military Counselor . . . . . . . . . . . . . . . . . . . . . . . . . . . . . Col. Armand Boden

Telex: 3404 or 1414
Cable: PRONAT

| Military Counselor | Lt. Col. Rodolphe Lutty |
| Special Attaché | Lt. Col. Camille Biver |
| Head Inspector | Robert Mahr |
| Head Inspector, First Class | Raymond Cloos |
| Head Inspector, First Class | Camille Kirschten |
| Head Inspector, First Class | René Ollinger |

## DEFENSE FORCES

**ARMY**
*(Armée Luxembourgeoisie)*
*5, rue Auguste Lumiere*
*P.O. Box 1873*
*L-1018 Luxembourg-Ville*

Telephone: 48 88 36
Telex: 2912
Cable: COMDTA LU

| Commander | Col. François Welfring |
| Deputy Commander | Lt. Col. Gaston Williere |
| Instruction Officer | Lt. Col. Roger Michaelis |
| Personnel Officer | Lt. Col. Nicolas Ley |
| Logistics Officer | Maj. Jean-Paul Heck |

**Military Instruction Center**
*(Centre d'Instruction Militaire)*
*Caserne du Herzenberg*
*L-9330 Diekirch*

Telephone: 808844-1
Telex: 2913
Cable: CIMDK LU

| Commander | Lt. Col. Armand Bruck |
| Battalion Commander | Lt. Col. René Alzin |

\* \* \* \* \*

## GENERAL DEFENSE DATA

**Manpower**

| Total Armed Forces | 690 |
| (See Page 329) | |
| Population | 366,000 |

**Spending**

| Military Expenditures | $55 million |
| Gross National Product | $5.3 billion |
| Military Expenditure as a Percentage of Gross National Product | 1% |
| Military Expenditure as a Percentage of Central Government Expenditure | 2.3% |

**Defense Treaties** *(See Part II for Additional Detail)*

Bilateral: United States

Multilateral: Biological Weapons Convention
Limited Test Ban Treaty
North Atlantic Treaty Organization
Treaty on the Control of Arms on the Seabed
Treaty on the Non-Proliferation of Nuclear Weapons
Western European Union

# MADAGASCAR
## Democratic Republic of Madagascar
### *Repoblika Demokratika Malagasy*

## Defense Establishment Command Structure and Force Organization

The President, who chairs the Supreme Council of Revolution, commands the armed forces of Madagascar. He is counseled on all projects relating to national defense by The Military Committee for Development. The Minister of Defense has responsibility for administration of the military.

**Total armed forces:** 20,900 (Army: 20,000;   Navy: 400;   Air Force: 500). **Para-military forces:** 8,000 (Gendarmerie).

## HEAD OF STATE

H. E. Didier Ratsiraka

**OFFICE OF THE PRESIDENT**
*Ambohitsorohitra*
*Antananarivo*
*Telephone: 27474*
*Telex: 22339*

President of the Democratic Republic, President of the Supreme Council of the Revolution and Secretary-General of the Vanguard of the Malagasy Revolution ........................ Didier Ratsiraka
Civil Cabinet Director ............................. Jean Bemananjara
Deputy Civil Cabinet Director ......... Laurent Radaody Rakotondravao
Secretary-General ................................ Joseph Adrien Dahy
Military Cabinet Director ............................ Com. Manjary
Military Counselor .......................... Col. Romy Ratfimbazyfay

**MILITARY COMMITTEE FOR DEVELOPMENT**
*Antananarivo*
*Telephone: 22564, 22091*
*Telex: 22339*

President ........................ Gen. de Brigade Edouard Rabeony

## SUPREME COUNCIL OF THE REVOLUTION

**SUPREME COUNCIL OF THE REVOLUTION**
*Ambohitsorohitra*
*Antananarivo*
*Telephone: 27474*
*Telex: 22339*

President ......................................... Didier Rastsiraka
Secretary-General ....................... Francois de Paul Rabotoson
Member ............................... Désiré Rakatoarijaona
Member ................................. Arsêne Ratsifehera
Member ......................................... Etienne Mora
Member .............................. Richard Andriamanjato
Member .......................... Marojama Razanabahiny
Member ............................. Rakotovao-Razakaboana
Member ............................................. Célestin Radio
Member ..................................... Justin Rakotoniaina
Member ...................... Jean-Baptiste Ramanantsalama
Member ............................. Solo N. Andriamorasata
Member ................... Jean de Dieu Randriantanany
Member ........................ Georges Thomas Indianjafy

| | |
|---|---|
| Member | Jean Ferlin Fiakara |
| Member | Ferdinand Jaotombo |
| Member | Simon Pierre |
| Member | Rakotonirina Manandafy |
| Member | Désiré Rakotonanahary |
| Member | Max Marson |

**OFFICE OF THE PRIME MINISTER**
*Mahazoarivo*
*Antananarivo*
*Telephone: 25258*
*Telex: 22339*

| | |
|---|---|
| Prime Minister | Col. Désiré Rakotoarijaona |
| Secretary-General of the Government | Samuel Ramaroson |
| Civil Cabinet Director | Prosper Voriandro |
| Counselor | Norbert Rakotoarisoa |

**MINISTRY OF DEFENSE**
*Antananarivo*
*Telephone: 22091, 22211*
*Telex: 22339*

| | |
|---|---|
| Minister | Contre-Amr. Guy Sibon |
| General Secretary | Col. Jean-Jacques Rasolomalala |
| Director, Economic Affairs | Lt. Col. Ravelomitsanga |
| Director, Social Affairs | Médécin-Col. Gilbert Ramahandry |

### Office of Military and Ideological Affairs
*(Direction des Affaires Militaires et Ideologiques)*
*Telephone: 22211*

| | |
|---|---|
| Director | Col. Ralaikoa |
| Chief, Military Personnel Service | Lt. Col. Rabesahala |

### Office of Logistical Affairs
*(Direction des Affaires Logistiques)*
*Telephone: 22211*

| | |
|---|---|
| Director | Col. Soja |

### National Military Office for the Strategic Industries
*(Office Militaire National pour les Industries Stratégiques)*
*21 rue Razanakombana*
*P.O. Box 1 bis*
*Antananarivo*
*Telephone: 24283*
*Telex: 22370*

| | |
|---|---|
| Director-General | Col. Hubert Andrianasolo |
| Chief, Economic Study Division | Andrianarijaona |
| Chief, Management Division | Rakotondrainibe Aimé |
| Chief, Finance and Treasury Division | Ramaholison Teau |

## DEFENSE FORCES

**ARMED FORCES**
*Antananarivo*
*Telephone: 21414*
*Telex: 22339*

| | |
|---|---|
| Chief of Staff | Gen. de Brigade Jean Rakotoharison |
| Deputy Chief of Staff | Col. Rabibisoa |

**ARMY**
*(Armée Populaire)*
*Antananarivo*
*Telephone: 21414*
*Telex: 22339*

| | |
|---|---|
| Commander | Col. Philippe Jean |
| Inspector General | Gen. de Div. Rabepasika |

**NAVY**
*(Aero Naval Forces)*
*Antananarivo*
*Telephone: 21414*
*Telex: 22339*

| | |
|---|---|
| Commander | Capt. de Fregate Roland Ratsimandresy |
| Aeronautical Command | Col. Michel Rakotobe |

**AIR FORCE**
*(Armée de l'Air)*
*Antananarivo*
Telephone:  21414
Telex:  22339

Commander . . . . . . . . . . . . . . . . . . . . . . . . . . . . . . . . . . . .Col. Rabemanantsoa

**NATIONAL CONSTABULARY**
*(Gendarmerie Nationale)*
*Antananarivo*

Commander . . . . . . . . . . . . . . . . . . . . . . . . . . . . . . . . . . . .Col. Jean Phillipe

\* \* \* \* \*

## GENERAL DEFENSE DATA

**Manpower**
    Total Armed Forces. . . . . . . . . . . . . . . . . . . . . . . . . . . . . . . . . . . . . . . . . .20,900
       (See Page 331)
    Population . . . . . . . . . . . . . . . . . . . . . . . . . . . . . . . . . . . . . . . . . . .8,992,000

**Spending**
    Military Expenditures . . . . . . . . . . . . . . . . . . . . . . . . . . . . . . . . . . . .$125 million
    Gross National Product . . . . . . . . . . . . . . . . . . . . . . . . . . . . . . . . . . .$3.102 billion
    Military Expenditure as a Percentage of
       Gross National Product . . . . . . . . . . . . . . . . . . . . . . . . . . . . . . . . .4.1%
    Military Expenditure as a Percentage of
       Central Government Expenditure . . . . . . . . . . . . . . . . . . . . . . . . . . . .13.5%

**Defense Treaties** *(See Part II for Additional Detail)*

    Bilateral:     France

    Multilateral:   Organization of African Unity
                  Limited Test Ban Treaty
                  Treaty on the Non-Proliferation of Nuclear Weapons

**Military Rank Comparisons**
    See Appendix A.

# MALAWI
## Republic of Malawi

### Defense Establishment Command Structure and Force Organization

The President, as Commander-in-Chief and Minister of Defense and Internal Affairs, is in direct command of the armed forces. All services are part of the Army.

**Total armed forces:** 4,700 (Army: 4,550; Navy: 100; Air Force: 50). **Para-military forces:** 1,750. Police: 3,000.

### HEAD OF STATE

H. E. The Life President Dr. Hastings Kamuzu Banda, PH.B., M.D., L.R.V.P., L.R.C.S., L.R.F.P.S.

**OFFICE OF THE PRESIDENT AND CABINET**
*Private Bag 301*
*Capital City*
*Lilongwe 3*
*Telephone: Lilongwe 611, 731 199*
*Telex: 4115*
*Cable: PRESMIN*

President, Minister of Defense and Internal Affairs, and Commander-in-Chief ......Dr. Hastings Kamuzu Banda, PH.B., M.D. L.R.V.P., L.R.C.S., L.R.F.P.S.
Secretary to the President and Head of the Department of Information and Tourism.........................John Ngwiri

**MINISTRY OF DEFENSE AND INTERNAL AFFAIRS**
*Private Bag 301*
*Lilongwe 3*
*Telephone: Lilongwe 611, 731 199*

Minister..........Dr. Hastings Kamuzu Banda, PH.B., M.D., L.R.V.P., L.R.C.S., L.R.F.P.S.

### DEFENSE FORCES

**ARMY**
*Kamuzu Barracks*
*P.O. Lilongwe*
*Lilongwe*
*Telephone: 732 900*

Commander ....................................Gen. M. M. Khanga
Deputy Commander.......................Maj. Gen. John Mponela
Chief of Staff, Intelligence.............................Brig. Manlana
Chief, Training ...................................Brig. Dzimadzi

**POLICE**
*Police Headquarters*
*Private Bag 305*
*Capital City*
*Lilongwe 3*
*Telephone: 731 999*

Inspector General...................................M. J. Kamwana
Special Branch .............................................B. J. Itima

\* \* \* \* \*

335

# GENERAL DEFENSE DATA

**Manpower**

Total Armed Forces...............................................4,700
    (See Page 335)
Population ....................................................6,000,000

**Spending**

Military Expenditures.........................................$25,000,000
Gross National Product .....................................$1.385,000,000
Military Expenditure as a Percentage of
    Gross National Product ...........................................1.8%
Military Expenditure as a Percentage of
    Central Government Expenditure ..................................6.0%

**Defense Treaties** *(See Part II for Additional Detail)*

Bilateral:      United States

Multilateral:   Environmental Modification Convention
                Limited Test Ban Treaty
                Organization of African Unity

# MALAYSIA

## Defence Establishment Command Structure and Force Organization

The King and Supreme Head of State is Commander-in-Chief of the Malaysian Armed Forces. The National Security Council, chaired by the Prime Minister, coordinates the country's defence and internal security efforts. The Armed Forces Council, headed by the Minister of Defence, has responsibility for administrative, command, and disciplinary matters within the military.

**Total armed forces:** 99,100 (Army: 80,000; Navy: 8,100; Air Force: 11,000). **Paramilitary forces:** 90,000 (Police Field Force).

## SUPREME HEAD OF STATE

*Yang di-Pertuan Agong*
H. M. Sultan Haji Ahmad Shah Ibni Al-Marhum Sultan Abu Bakar

**OFFICE OF H. M. THE KING**
*Istana Negara*
*Kuala Lumpur 08 03*
*Telephone:* (3) 88381

King of Malaysia and
Commander-in-Chief ............H. M. Sultan Haji Ahmad Shah Ibni Al-Marhum Sultan Abu Bakar
Deputy King of Malaysia ................H. R. H. Tuanku Jaafar Ibni Al-Mourhum Tuanku Abdul Rahman

**PRIME MINISTER'S DEPARTMENT**
*Jalan Dato Onn*
*Kuala Lumpur 1101*
*Telephone:* (3) 105333, 203722

Prime Minister and
Minister of Defence ..........Dato[+] Seri Dr. Mahathir Bin Mohamad
Deputy Prime Minister and
Minister of Home Affairs ........................Dato Hitam Musa

**National Security Council**

Chairman ......................Dato Seri Dr. Mahathir bin Mohamad
(Prime Minister and Minister of Defence)
Member ......................Gen. Tan Sri Dato' Mohamad Ghazali bin Dato Mohamad Seth
(Chief of Defence Forces)
Member ..........................Gen. Tan Sri Dato' Zain Hashim
(Chief of Army)
Member ......................Vice Adm. Dato' Zain bin Dato Salleh
(Chief of Navy)
Member ..........................Lt. Gen. Datuk Mohamed bin Taib
(Chief of Air Force)
Member ......................Tan Sri Mohammad Haniss bin Omar
(Inspector-General, Police)
Member .................................Dato Hitam Musa
(Deputy Prime Minister and Minister of Home Affairs)

**MINISTRY OF DEFENCE**
*(Kementerian Pertahanan)*
*Jalan Padang Tembak*
*Kuala Lumpur 15 03*
*Telephone:* (3) 921333, 201033
*Telex:* 30289 kemtah ma
*Cable:* Kementah Kualalumpur

Prime Minister and
Minister of Defence ............Dato Seri Dr. Mahathir Bin Mohamad
Deputy Minister ...................Abang Abu Bakar Bin Datu Bandar Abang Haji Mustapha
Secretary General ................Tan Sri Dato' Mohammed Yusof bin Abd. Rehman
Chief, Public Relations Division ..............Maj. R. Sachithananthan

---

[+]Dato', Tan Sri, and Datuk are awards bestowed by the Government of Malaysia.

**Armed Forces Council**

Chairman ......................Dato Seri Dr. Mahathir bin Mohamad
(Minister of Defence)

Member ............Tan Sri Dato' Mohammed Yusof bin Abd. Rehman
(Secretary-General, Ministry of Defence)

Member ....................Gen. Tan Sri Dato' Mohamad Ghazali
bin Dato Mohamad Seth
(Chief of Defence Forces)

Member ...........................Gen. Tan Sri Dato' Zain Hashim
(Chief of Army)

Member .........................Vice Adm. Dato' Zain bin Dato Salleh
(Chief of Navy)

Member ..........................Lt. Gen. Datuk Mohamed bin Taib
(Chief of Air Force)

Member............................Maj. Gen. Dato Osman bin Zain
(Chief of Personnel Services)

Member ............Maj. Gen. Dato' Hj Mohamed Daud bin Abu Bakar
(Chief of Logistics Services)

## MILITARY TRAINING
## INSTITUTIONS

**Armed Forces Defence College—MPAT**
*Jalan Padang Tembak*
*Kuala Lumpur 15-03*

Commandant ......................Brig. Gen. Dato Leong Siew Meng

**Armed Forces Staff College—MTAT**
*Jalan Padang Tembak*
*Kuala Lumpur 15-03*

Commandant ....................Brig. Gen.  Haji Mustaffa bin Awang

**Royal Military College—RMC**
*Sg Besi*

Commandant ............................Col. Mohamed bin Munip

# DEFENCE FORCES

**ARMED FORCES**
**Malaysian Armed Forces—General Staff**
*Jalan Padang Tembak*
*Kuala Lumpur 15 03*

*Telephone:   (3) 921333, 201033*
*Telex:   30289 kemtah ma*
*Cable:   Kementah Kualalumpur*

Chief, Defence Forces .............Gen. Tan Sri Dato' Mohamad Ghazali
bin Dato Mohamad Seth

**Joint Services Staff**

Chief, Staff Operations .........Maj. Gen. Hj Admad bin Hj Abdul Kadir
Head, Joint Operations/Exercises
    Planning Staff ...................................Cdr. M. W. Alvisse
Head, Defence Planning
    Staff ...................Brig. Gen. Hj Abdul Ghani bin Hj Mahluddin
Head, Strategic Planning Staff ..................Col. Othman bin Harun
Head, Development Planning Staff ............Col. (Air) Anim bin Harun
Head, Joint Secretariat .....................Col. Mohamad Kalam Azad

**Defence Intelligence Services**

Chief, Defence Intelligence
    Services.......................Lt. Gen. Dato Ghazali bin Hj Che Mat
Deputy Chief ...............Brig. Gen. Abdul Rahman bin abd Hamid

**Personnel Services**

Chief, Personnel Services ..............Maj. Gen. Dato Osman bin Zain
Deputy Chief ...............Brig. Gen. Dato Mohamed Shah bin Yahya
Director, Medical and
    Dental Services ............Brig. Gen. (Dr.) Shamsuddin bin Hussein

Director, Manpower ...............Col. Wan Nordin bin Wan Mohamed
Director, Records and Pensions ..........Col. Mohamed Ismail bin Omar
Director, Pay Services ...............................Col. Loo Yew Pin
Provost Marshall .....................Col. Hamid Khan bin Karamdin
Director, Education .......................Lt. Col. Salleh bin Ranting

**Logistics Services**

Chief, Logistics
    Services ..........Maj. Gen. Dato' Hj Mohamed Daud bin Abu Bakar
Deputy Chief .............Brig. Gen. Nik Mahmood Fakharuddin Kamil
Director, Management ..............................Col. Cheng Wah
Director, Supply and
    Transport ....................Col. Mohamed Kassim bin Ahmad
Director, Electrical and
    Mechanical Engineers .......................Col. Tang Siew Kuan
Director, Ordnance Services ...................Col. Ghafar bin Osman
Director, Accommodation
    and Works ...........................Col. Ibrahim bin Hj Abdullah

**ARMY**
**Royal Malaysian Army—RMA**
*c/o Ministry of Defence*
*Jalan Pandang Tembak*
*Kuala Lumpur 15-03*

Chief of Army .....................Gen. Tan Sri Dato' Zain Hashim
Deputy Chief .......................Lt. Gen. Dato Jaafar Onn
Chief of Staff .........................Brig. Gen. Mohamed Yusof Din
Chief, Logistics ..........................Brig. Gen. Kong How Weng
Chief, General Staff..............................Col. R. Mahendran
Director, Training ............................Col. Ismail bin Omar
Director, Equipment.................Col. Aboo Samah bin Aboo Bakar
Chief, Administration ......................Col. Sulaiman bin Kudus
Chief, Logistics ......................Col. Abdul Ghani bin Abdullah
Director, Infantry .....................Col. Abdul Manaf bin Ibrahim
Director, Directorate of
    Special Forces ......................Lt. Col. Shamsuddin bin Abbas
Director, Calvary .........................Col. Mohamad Arif bin Ali
Chief Signals Officer .....................Brig. Gen. Idris bin Ahmad
Chief Engineer .....................Brig. Gen. Dato Chen Kwee Fong
Director, Artillery.................Col. Abu Bakar bin Mohamad Salleh
Director, Intelligence
    Directorate .......................Lt. Col. Maaulud bin Maamin
Director, Directorate of
    Reserve Force..........................Brig. Gen. Dato Mohamad
                                                      Dahalan bin Sulaiman
Chief of Staff, Administration
    Army Corps Headquarters ....Brig. Gen. Abdul Rahman bin Hj Khamis
Chief of Staff, Army Corps
    Headquarters ...................Brig. Gen. Dato Chong Thean Bok

**Commands**

Commander, Army Corps .......Lt. Gen. Dato Abdul Jamil bin Hj Ahmad
Commander, I Division
    (GOC) ..............Maj. Gen. Dato Hassan bin Hj Mohamad Salleh
Commander, II Division
    (GOC) ..................Maj. Gen. Dato Hashim bin Mohomad Ali
Commander, III Division
    (GOC) ......................Maj. Gen. Dato Hj Esa bin Ahmad
Commander, IV Division
    (GOC) ..............................Maj. Gen. Dato N. Selvarajah
Commander, XI Division (GOC)
    (Reserve Force).....Maj. Gen. Dato Hj Wan Ismail bin Mohamad Salleh
Director, Task Force VII ..........Maj. Gen. Dato Abdullah bin Samsudin
Commander, 1 Brigade ........................Brig. Gen. Baljit Singh
Commander, 2 Brigade .............Brig. Gen. Mohamad Ali bin Dollah
Commander, 3 Brigade ............Brig. Gen. Dato Abul'As bin Ismail
Commander,
    4 Brigade........Brig. Gen. Shah Mohamad Amin bin Mohamad Salleh
Commander, 5 Brigade .........Brig. Gen. Mansor bin Mohamad Yunus
Commander, 6 Brigade .................Brig. Gen. Zainal bin Hj Jawati

Commander, 7 Brigade ....................Brig. Gen. Tahir bin Ismail
Commander, 8 Brigade ..................Brig. Gen. Yahaya bin Yusoff
Commander, 9 Brigade ..................Brig. Gen. Mahmud bin Yusof
Commander, 10 Brigade ...........................................
Commander, 11 Brigade ...............Brig. Gen. Adam bin Abu Bakar
Commander, 12 Brigade ........Brig. Gen. Hj Mohamad Isa bin Che Kak
Commander, 13 Brigade ....................Brig. Gen. Lai Chung Wah
Commander, Special
    Service Group .....................Brig. Gen. Dato Harun bin Taib
Commander, 51 Brigade
    (Reserve)..............................Brig. Gen. N. Stevenson
Commander, Task Force VII .........Brig. Gen. Zakaria bin Hj Dahalan
Commander, RASCOM................Brig. Gen. Jaafar bin Mohamed

## NAVY
### Royal Malaysian Navy—RMN
*c/o Ministry of Defence*
*Jalan Padang Tembak*
*Kuala Lumpur 15 03*

Chief of Navy .....................Vice Adm. Dato' Mohamad Zain bin
                                                Dato Mohamad Salleh
Deputy Chief ..............Rear Adm. Dato Abdul Wahab bin Nawawi
Assistant Chief, Plans ...........................Cdr. P. K. Nettur
Assistant Chief, Technical ...................Cdr. Albert Thong Hon Sin
Director, Operations........................Capt. K. Araseratnam
Director, Personnel ..........Capt. Abdul Khalid bin Hj Mohamad Said
Director, Hydrography ......................Capt. Goh Siew Chong
Director, Training ..............................Capt. Ahmad Haron
Director, Development and Plans ...............Capt. Ahmad Ramli Nor
Director Technical.............................Capt. Lim Soy Kiang
Director, Supply and Finance .............Capt. Mohamad Ramli Samjis
Project Officer, Corvette .............Capt. Abu Bakar bin Abdul Jamal

### Commands

Commander, Fleet
    Operational Command ................Cdr. Haron bin Dato Dr. Salleh
Commander, Navy Region I .....................Cdr. Yaakob Hj Duad
Commander, Navy Region II..............Cdr. Tuan Hashim Mohamad
Chief of Staff, Evaluation
    and Examinations (Fleet
    Operational Command) .........Capt. Khairuddin bin Abdul Rahman
Chief of Staff, Fleet
    Operational Command .....................Capt. Cheah Chee Peng
Chief of Staff, Equipment
    (Fleet Operational Command) ................Capt. Selvarajah Arasu
Commanding Officer, RMN Ship
    *Kd Sri Indera Sakti* ....................Capt. Abdul Halim Zakaria
Commanding Officer, RMN Ship
    *Kd Hang Tuah* ...........................Capt. Nik Aris Abdullah
Commanding Officer, Naval
    Garrison LUMUT ....................Capt. Abdul Wahid Awang
Fleet Material Command .....................Capt. Khoo Tee Chuan
Commanding Officer, Naval
    Training Centre KD PELANDOK ...............Capt. N. E. Peterson

## AIR FORCE
### Royal Malaysian Air Force—RMAF
*c/o Ministry of Defence*
*Jalan Padang Tembak*
*Kuala Lumpur 15 03*

Chief of Air Force ..................Lt. Gen. Datuk Mohamed bin Taib
Deputy Chief ...............Maj. Gen. Dato' Mohamed bin Ngah Said
Assistant Chief,
    Operations .....................Brig. Gen. Mohamad Yunus bin Tasi
Assistant Chief,
    Engineering ..........Brig. Gen. Mohamad Tahir bin Abdul Rahman
Assistant Chief,
    Administration ..........Brig. Gen. Abdul Kadir bin Datuk Abu Bakar
Commander, Air Support
    Command...........................Brig. Gen. Muslin bin Ayub
Senior Air Staff Officer,
    Air Support Command .............................Col. Thesetra
Commander, Headquarters
    Air Operations Command ..............Brig. Gen. Fauzi bin Hussein

Director, Air Operations ......................... Col. Nawi bin Alias
Director, Aircraft Engineers ....................... Col. Lau Chong See

**Commands**

Commanding Officer,
    RMAF Base Kuala Lumpur ...................... Col. Lim Way Aun
Commanding Officer,
    RMAF Base Butterworth ...... Col. Abdul Ghani bin Tan Sri Abdul Aziz
Commanding Officer,
    RMAF Base Kuantan .......................... Col. Tengku Jaafar
Commanding Officer, RMAF
    Aircraft Overhaul Depot ................ Col. Kamaruddin bin Shariff
Commanding Officer, RMAF
    Base Alor Star .............. Col. Mustaffar Bakri bin Mohamad Raus

* * * * *

## GENERAL DEFENCE DATA

**Manpower**
    Total Armed Forces.............................................. 99,100
        (See Page 337)
    Population ................................................. 14,661,000

**Spending**
    Military Expenditures ....................................... $1.1 billion
    Gross National Product ..................................... $23.2 billion
    Military Expenditure as a Percentage of
        Gross National Product ..................................... 4.8%
    Military Expenditure as a Percentage of
        Central Government Expenditure .............................. 13.5%

**Defense Treaties** *(See Part II for Additional Detail)*

Bilateral:    United States

Multilateral: Five-Power Defence Arrangements
              Limited Test Ban Treaty
              Treaty on the Control of Arms on the Seabed
              Treaty on the Non-Proliferation of Nuclear Weapons

# MALDIVES
## Republic of Maldives
### *Divehi Jumhuriyah*

### Defense Establishment Command Structure and Force Organization

The President is Commander-in-Chief of the National Security Service, a combined army, navy and police force responsible for the security of the Republic.

**Total armed forces:** 400.

## HEAD OF STATE

H. E. Maumoon Abdul Gayoom

**OFFICE OF THE PRESIDENT**
*Male*

Telephone:  3701
Telex:   66013 radhun mf
         77001 theem mf

| | |
|---|---|
| President of the Republic and Commander-in-Chief | Maumoon Abdul Gayoom |
| Minister of State for Presidential Affairs | Hon. Abdullah Jameel |
| Executive Secretary to the President | Abbas Ibrahim |
| Senior Presidential Aide | Mohamed Sadiq Abdul |
| Senior Presidential Aide | Gayoom Hassan |

**NATIONAL SECURITY SERVICE**
*Male*

Telephone:  2606
Telex:   66056 aman mf (Code: 0896)

| | |
|---|---|
| Commander-in-Chief and President | Maumoon Abdul Gayoom |
| Chief of Staff | Hon. Ilyas Ibrahim |
| Assistant to the Chief of Staff | Anbaree Abdul Sattar |
| High Ranking Officer | Maj. H. Moosa |
| High Ranking Officer | Capt. Abbas Ibrahim |
| High Ranking Officer | Capt. Adam Zahir |
| High Ranking Officer | Capt. Mohamed Zahir |
| High Ranking Officer | Capt. Hussain Ibrahim Fulu |
| High Ranking Officer | Capt. Shoukath Ibrahim |

\* \* \* \* \*

## GENERAL DEFENSE DATA

**Manpower**
Total Armed Forces .............................................. 400
Population ..................................................... 163,000

**Spending**
Military Expenditures ...........................................
Gross National Product ......................................... $30 million
Military Expenditure as a Percentage of
Gross National Product ......................................
Military Expenditure as a Percentage of
Central Government Expenditure ..............................

**Defense Treaties** *(See Part II for Additional Detail)*

Bilateral:     None

Multilateral:  Treaty on the Non-Proliferation of Nuclear Weapons

# MALI
## Republic of Mali
*République du Mali*

### Defense Establishment Command Structure and Force Organization

The President is Minister of Defense and commands the armed forces of Mali.

**Total armed forces:** 4,950 (Army: 4,600;  Navy: 50;  Air Force: 300). **Para-military forces:** 5,000.

## HEAD OF STATE

H. E. Gén. d'Armée Moussa Traore

**OFFICE OF THE PRESIDENT**
*B. P. 1463*
*Bamako*
*Telephone:   22 24 71, 22 37 72*

President of the Republic, General
  Secretary of the Democratic Union
  of the Malian People (UDPM)
  and Minister of Defense . . . . . . . . . . . . . . . .Gén. d'Armée Moussa Traore

**MINISTRY OF DEFENSE**
*B. P. 215*
*Bamako*
*Telephone:   22 26 17, 22 23 03*

Minister of Defense and President . . . . . . . . . .Gén. d'Armée Moussa Traore
President, Veterans Affairs . . . . . . . . . . . . . . . . . . . . . . .M. Daouda Traore
Defense Councillor . . . . . . . . . . . . . . . . . . . . . . . . . . . . .Col. Sangare Bongari

**MINISTRY OF INTERIOR**
*Bamako*
*Telephone:*

Minister . . . . . . . . . . . . . . . . . . . . . . . . . . . . . . .Lt. Col. Abdrhamane Maiga

## DEFENSE FORCES

**ARMY**
*B. P. 10*
*Bamako*

Chief of Staff . . . . . . . . . . . . . . . . . . . . . . . . . . . . . . .Lt. Col. Koke Jembele

**AIR FORCE**
*B. P. 56*
*Bamako*
*Telephone:   22 57 38*

Chief of Staff . . . . . . . . . . . . . . . . . . . . . . . . . . . . .Lt. Col. Mamadou Coulibaly

**SECURITY FORCES**
*Bamako*

Commander . . . . . . . . . . . . . . . . . . . . . . . . . . . . . . .Lt. Col. Amara Janfaga

**GENDARMERIE NATIONALE**
*Bamako*

Chief of Staff . . . . . . . . . . . . . . . . . . . . . . . . . . . . . . .Lt. Col. Mohamed Keita

\* \* \* \* \*

# GENERAL DEFENSE DATA

**Manpower**

Total Armed Forces................................................4,950
    (See Page 345)
Population ................................................7,015,000

**Spending**

Military Expenditures ..........................................$33 million
Gross National Product..........................................$1.3 billion
Military Expenditure as a Percentage of
    Gross National Product ..........................................2.5%
Military Expenditure as a Percentage of
    Central Government Expenditure ..............................20.5%

**Defense Treaties** *(See Part II for Additional Detail)*

Bilateral:    China
              Nigeria
              Soviet Union
              United States

Multilateral:    Limited Test Ban Treaty
                 Treaty on the Non-Proliferation of Nuclear Weapons

**Military Rank Comparisons**

See Appendix A.

# MALTA
## Republic of Malta

### Defence Establishment Command Structure and Force Organization

The President is Supreme Commander of the Armed Forces and his authority is exercised by the Prime Minister. The Commander of the Armed Forces has administrative responsibility for the military. A Task Force is responsible for armed public safety duties.

**Total armed forces:** 1,700 (Army: 1,540;    Coastal Patrol force: 120;    Air Wing: 40). **Paramilitary forces:** 310 (Pioneer Corps).

## HEAD OF STATE

H. E. Agatha Barbara

**OFFICE OF THE PRESIDENT**
*The Palace*
*Valletta*

*Telephone:   21221*
*Telex:   100 mod mlt*

President of the Republic and
  Supreme Commander . . . . . . . . . . . . . . . . . . . . . . . . . . . .Agatha Barbara
Secretary . . . . . . . . . . . . . . . . . . . . . . . . . . . . . . . . . . . . . . . .Saviour Demarco

**OFFICE OF THE PRIME MINISTER**
*Auberge de Castille*
*Castille Place*
*Valletta*

*Telephone:   25231, 22407*

Prime Minister . . . . . . . . . . . . . . . . . . . . . . . . .Dominic (Dom) Mintoff, M.P.
Senior Deputy Prime Minister . . . . . . . . . . . . . . . . . . . . . . . . .Joseph Cassar
Deputy Prime Minister . . . . . . . . . . . . . . . . . . . . . . . . . . . . . . .Wistin Abela
Administrative Secretary . . . . . . . . . . . . . . . . . . . . . . .Edmond W. Micallef
Secretary, Office of the Prime Minister . . . . . . . . . . .Maurice Abela, M.B.E.

**MINISTRY OF THE INTERIOR**
*Auberge de Castille*
*Valletta*

*Telephone:   25231*
*Telex:   692, 700 or 471*
*Cable:   PRIMIN*

Minister . . . . . . . . . . . . . . . . . . . . . . . . . . . . . . . . . . . . . . . . . .Lorry Sant, M.P.

## DEFENCE FORCES

**ARMED FORCES**
**Armed Forces of Malta**
*Headquarters*
*Luqa Barracks*

*Telephone:   824220*
*Telex:   489 armfor mw*

Commander, Armed Forces. . . . . . . . . . . . . . . . . . . . . . . . . .Col. John Spiteri
Deputy Commander,
  Armed Forces . . . . . . . . . . . . . . . . .Maj. Stephen Samut-Tagliaferro
Commanding Officer, Second
  Regiment, St. Patrick's Barracks . . . . . . . . . . . . . . . .Maj. Peter Ripard
Commander, Task Force . . . . . . . . . . . . . . . . . . . . . . . .Col. John N. Cachia

**POLICE**
*Police General Headquarters*
*Floriana*

*Telephone:   24002, 20451*
*Telex:   333 mw*

Commisioner of Police . . . . . . . . . . . . . . . . . .Dr. Lawrence Pullicino, LL.D.

\* \* \* \* \*

# GENERAL DEFENCE DATA

**Manpower**

Total Armed Forces...............................................1,700
   (See Page 347)
Population ....................................................376,000

**Spending**

Military Expenditures .........................................$6 million
Gross National Product ........................................$1.2 billion
Military Expenditure as a Percentage of
   Gross National Product .........................................0.5%
Military Expenditure as a Percentage of
   Central Government Expenditure .................................1.4%

**Defence Treaties** *(See Part II for Additional Detail)*

   Bilateral:      Italy
                   United Kingdom

   Multilateral:   Biological Weapons Convention
                   Limited Test Ban Treaty
                   Treaty on the Control of Arms on the Seabed
                   Treaty on the Non-Proliferation of Nuclear Weapons

# MAURITANIA
## Islamic Republic of Mauritania
*Jumhuriyat Muritaniyah al-Islamiyah*

### Defence Establishment Command Structure and Force Organization

The President is the Commander-in-Chief and exercises control of the armed forces through the Ministry of Defense.

**Total armed forces:** 8,470 (Army: 8,000;    Navy: 320;    Air Force: 150). **Para-military forces:** 2,500.

## HEAD OF STATE

H. E. Lt. Col. Mohamed Khouna Ould Haidalla

**OFFICE OF THE PRESIDENT AND MILITARY COMMITTEE FOR NATIONAL SALVATION**
La Présidence de la République
*B.P. 184*
*Nouakchott*
*Telephone: 523 17*
*Telex: 580 prim*

President of the Islamic Republic,
President of the Military Committee
for National Salvation and
Commander-in-Chief........Lt. Col. Mohamed Khouna Ould Haidalla

**OFFICE OF THE PRIME MINISTER**
*Nouakchott*
*Telephone: 523 17*
*Telex: 580 prim*

Prime Minister and
Minister of Defense.........Ould Taya Col. Maouiya Ould Sidi Ahmed

**MINISTRY OF DEFENSE**
*B.P. 184*
*Nouakchott*
*Telephone: 520 20*
*Telex: 566 mitra*

Minister of Defense and
Prime Minister.............Ould Taya Col. Maouiya Ould Sidi Ahmed

## DEFENSE FORCES

**ARMED FORCES**
*c/o Ministry of Defense*
*B.P. 184*
*Nouakchott*
*Telephone:   520 20*

Chief of Staff................................Lt. Col. Yall Abdoulaye
Chief of Staff, National Guard .................Cdt. Ahmed Ould Aide

**ARMY**
*c/o Ministry of Defense*
*B.P. 184*
*Nouakchott*

Chief of Staff, National Army ..................Lt. Col. Yall Abdoulaye
Deputy Chief of Staff ..............Lt. Col. Moulaye Ould Boukhareiss

**Regional Commands**

Commander, First Military Region . . . . . . . . . .Cdt. Mohamed Ould Lekhal
Commander, Second Military Region . . . . . . . . .Capt. Salem Ould Memou
Commander, Third Military
  Region . . . . . . . . . . . . . . . . . . . . . . . . . .Cdt. Sidya Ould Mohamed Yahya
Commander, Fourth Military Region . . . . . . . . . . . . . . . . . . . . . . . . . . . . . . . . .
Commander, Fifth Military Region . . . . . . . . . . . . . . . . . .Capt. Diop Djibril
Commander, Sixth Military Region . . . . . . . . . .Capt. Braika Ould M'Barek
Commander, Seventh Military
  Region . . . . . . . . . . . . . . . . . . . . . . . . . . . .Capt. Ely Ould Mohamed Fall

**National Constabulary**
*(Gendarmerie Nationale)*

Commander . . . . . . . . . . . . . . . . . . . . . .Capt. Mohamed Lemine Ould Zeine

**NAVY**
*c/o Ministry of Defense*
*B.P. 184*
*Nouakchott*

Commander . . . . . . . . . . . . . . . . . . . . . . . . . . . . . . . .Lt. de Vaisseau Sy Bocar

**AIR FORCE**
**Air Wing**
*(Groupement Aérien de la Republique*
  *Islamique de Mauritanie)*
*c/o Ministry of Defense*
*B.P. 184*
*Nouakchott*

Commander . . . . . . . . . . . . . . . . . . . . . . . . . . . . . . . . . . . . . . . . . . . .Cdt. Sidibe

\* \* \* \* \*

# GENERAL DEFENSE DATA

**Manpower**
  Total Armed Forces . . . . . . . . . . . . . . . . . . . . . . . . . . . . . . . . . . . . . . . . .8,470
    (See Page 349)
  Population . . . . . . . . . . . . . . . . . . . . . . . . . . . . . . . . . . . . . . . . . . . . . .1,561,000

**Spending**
  Military Expenditures . . . . . . . . . . . . . . . . . . . . . . . . . . . . . . . . . . . . . .$86 million
  Gross National Product . . . . . . . . . . . . . . . . . . . . . . . . . . . . . . . . . . . . .$547 million
  Military Expenditure as a Percentage of
    Gross National Product . . . . . . . . . . . . . . . . . . . . . . . . . . . . . . . . . . . .15.8%
  Military Expenditure as a Percentage of
    Central Government Expenditure . . . . . . . . . . . . . . . . . . . . . . . . . . . . .25.9%

**Defense Treaties** (*See Part II for Additional Detail*)

  Bilateral:     France

  Multilateral:  Economic Community of West African States
                 Limited Test Ban Treaty
                 Organization of African Unity

**Military Rank Comparisons**
  See Appendix A.

# MAURITIUS

## Defence Establishment Command Structure
## and Force Organization

Mauritius does not have a formal defence force. Internal security is the responsibility of the Police which operate under the authority of the Minister of Defence and Internal Security.

**Police Force:** 4,274.

## HEAD OF STATE

H. M. Queen Elizabeth II

## GOVERNOR-GENERAL

H. E. Sir Dayendranath Burrenchobay, K.B.E., C.M.G., C.V.O.

**OFFICE OF THE GOVERNOR-GENERAL**
*Le Reduit*
*Telephone: 543021*
*Telex: 4249 extern iw*

Governor-General .................. Sir Dayendranath Burrenchobay, K.B.E., C.M.G., C.V.O.

**OFFICE OF THE PRIME MINISTER AND MINISTRIES OF DEFENCE AND INTERNAL SECURITY, AND REFORM INSTITUTIONS**
*Government House*
*Port Luis*
*Telephone: 011001*
*Telex: 4249 extern iw*

Prime Minister, Minister of Defence and Internal Security, and Minister of Reform Institutions .......... Hon. Aneerood Jugnauth, Q.C., M.L.A.

**OFFICE OF THE DEPUTY PRIME MINISTER AND MINISTRIES OF INFORMATION AND COOPERATIVES**
*Government House*
*Port Luis*

Deputy Prime Minister and Minister of Information and Cooperatives ...................... Harishun Boodhoo, M.L.A.

## DEFENCE FORCES

**POLICE DEPARTMENT**
*Line Barracks*
*Port Luis*
*Telephone: 08-1212*
*Telex: 4249 extern iw*

Commissioner of Police ............... Mr. A. Rajarai, Q.P.M., M.P.M.
Deputy Commissioner of Police ............. Mr. B. Juggernauth, M.P.M.
Assistant Commissioner of Police (South) Curepipe ......................... Mr. C. Nicolas, M.P.M.
Assistant Commissioner, Criminal Investigation Division ..................... Mr. E. Marcel, M.P.M.

\* \* \* \* \*

351

# GENERAL DEFENCE DATA

**Manpower**

Total Armed Forces . . . . . . . . . . . . . . . . . . . . . . . . . . . . . . . . . . . . . . . . . . . . . . 4,274
   (See Page 351)
Population . . . . . . . . . . . . . . . . . . . . . . . . . . . . . . . . . . . . . . . . . . . . . . . . . . . 990,000

**Spending**

Military Expenditures . . . . . . . . . . . . . . . . . . . . . . . . . . . . . . . . . . . . . . . . . . $2 million
Gross National Product . . . . . . . . . . . . . . . . . . . . . . . . . . . . . . . . . . . . . . . . . $1 billion
Military Expenditure as a Percentage of
   Gross National Product . . . . . . . . . . . . . . . . . . . . . . . . . . . . . . . . . . . . . . . . 0.2%
Military Expenditure as a Percentage of
   Central Government Expenditure . . . . . . . . . . . . . . . . . . . . . . . . . . . . . . . . . 0.6%

**Defense Treaties** *(See Part II for Additional Detail)*

Bilateral:      United Kingdom

Multilateral:   Biological Weapons Convention
                Limited Test Ban Treaty
                Treaty on the Control of Arms on the Seabed
                Treaty on the Non-Proliferation of Nuclear Weapons

# MEXICO
## The United States of Mexico
### *Los Estados Unidos Mexicanos*

## Defense Establishment Command Structure and Force Organization

The President is the Commander-in-Chief of the Armed Forces. Day-to-day control of the military is charged to the Secretary of Defense. The Army and Air Force commanders answer directly to the Secretary of Defense, while the Navy comes under the control of the Secretary of the Navy.

The country is divided into 35 military zones which correspond to the 31 States and the Mexico City Federal District. The President appoints the zones' commanding generals.

**Total armed forces:** 144,000 (Army: 119,500 regular; Navy: 20,000; Air Force: 4,500).
**Para-military forces:** 392,000 (National Police: 22,000; Rural Militia: 120,000 Part-time conscripts: 250,000).

## HEAD OF STATE

H. E. Lic. Miguel de la Madrid Hurtado

**OFFICE OF THE PRESIDENT**
*(Oficina del Presidente)*
*Los Pinos*
*Mexico, D.F.*

*Telephone: 515-3717*
*Telex: 170985 (Los Pinos),*
*177-4500, 177-7519 (Palacio Nacional)*

President and Commander-in-Chief of the Armed Forces ......... Lic. Miguel de la Madrid Hurtado
Private Secretary ........................ Roberto Casillas Hernández
Chief of Presidential Staff ................. Gral. Brig. Carlos Humberto Bermudez Dávila
Deputy Chief of Presidential Staff, Operations ................ Gral. Brig. Arturo Cardona Marino
Deputy Chief of Presidential Administration ................ Gral. Brig. Eliud Ángel Casiano Bello
Comptroller and General Assistant, Presidential Staff .............. Cnel. Ignacio Sánchez Ortíz

**NATIONAL DEFENSE SECRETARIAT**
*(Edificio Secretaría de la Defensa Nacional)*
*Ávila Camacho e Industria Militar*
*Lomas de Sotelo*
*11640 Mexico 10, D.F.*

*Telephone: 557-4500, 557-0959, 557-3555*

Secretary ............................... Gral. Juan Arévalo Gardoqui
Under Secretary ............... Gral. Marco Antonio Guerrero Mendoza
Chief, Joint Chiefs of Staff ................ Gral. Venicio Sontoyo Ferria
Personal Secretary to the Secretary of National Defense ................ Cnel. José Ángel García Elizarde
Personal Secretary to the Under Secretary of National Defense ...... Tte. Cnel. Humberto Bravo Sánchez
Chief Official ........................... Gral. José Miguel Cal y Mayor
Aid to the Chief Official ........................... May. Proal Medina
Commander, Armed Forces ............. Gral. Miguel Mendoza Márquez
Director-General, War Materials .............. Ing. Gonzalo Ortiz Segura
Director-General, Military Education and the University of the Army and Armed Forces ...................... Gral. Alfredo Ochoa Toledo
Director-General, Military Justice .............. Gral. José Espejel Flores

**SECRETARY OF THE NAVY**
*(Secretaría de la Marina)*
*José Azueta 9*
*068088 Mexico 1,*
*D.F. Mexico*
*Telephone:   512-2457, 510-4423, 512-1184*

Secretary . . . . . . . . . . . . . . . . . . . . . . . . Alm. Miguel Ángel Gómez Ortega
Under Secretary . . . . . . . . . . . . Vice Alm. Humberto Martínez Najara
Chief Official . . . . . . . . . . . . . . . . . . . . . . . . . . . Alm. Fernando Piarra Lara

# DEFENSE FORCES

**ARMY**
*(El Ejército Mexicano)*
*Secretaría del Ejército*
*Ávila Camacho e Industria Militar*
*Lomas de Sotelo*
*Mexico 10, D.F.*
*Telephone:   557-4500*
*(Under National Defense Secretariat)*

Commander . . . . . . . . . . . . . . . . . . . . . . . . . . Gral. Juan Arévalo Gardoqui
Under Secretary . . . . . . . . . . . . . . Gral. Marco Antonio Guerrero Mendoza
Inspector-General, Army and Air Force . . . . . . . Gral. Antonio Rivielo Bazan
Director-General, Infantry . . . . . . . . . . . . . . Gral. Alberto Quintanar López
Director-General, Cavalry  . . . . . . . . Gral. Brig. Jorge G. Grajales Velásquez
Director-General, Artillery . . . . . . . . . . Gral. Brig. Mario Oliver Bustamante
Director-General, Engineers . . . . . . . . . . . Gral. Brig. José María Alva Valles
Director of General Transmissions . . . . . . . . Gral. Brig. José Ventura Duarte
Director-General, Comptrol
   and Intendance . . . . . . . . . . . . . . . . Gral. Brig. Thomas Mancerra Segura
Director-General, Health  . . . . . . . . . . . . . . Gral. Brig. Alger León Moreno

**AIR FORCE**
*(La Fuerza Aérea Mexicana)*
*Ávila Comacho e Industria Militar*
*Lomas de Sotelo*
*Mexico 10, D.F.*
*Telephone:   557-3310*

Commander . . . . . . . . . . . . . . . . . . . . . . . . Gral. Miguel Mendoza Márquez
Chief of Staff . . . . . . . . . . . . . . . . . . . . . . . Brig. Gral. Vicente Ahuja Fuster
Inspector-General . . . . . . . . . . . . . . . . . . . . . . Gral. Antonio Rivielo Bazan
Deputy Chief of Staff . . . . . . . . . . . . . . . Brig. Humberto Lucero Nevarez
Deputy Chief, First Section . . . . . . . . . . . . . . . . . . . . . Cnel. Oscar Bernal
Deputy Chief, Second Section . . . . . . . . . . . . . Tte. Cnel. Cornado Armenta
Deputy Chief, Third Section . . . . . . . . . . . . . . . Cnel. Manuel Victor Estrada
Deputy Chief, Fourth Section . . . . . . . . . . . . . May. Miguel Basurto Hidalgo
Deputy Chief, Fifth Section . . . . . . . . . . . . . . May. Victor Manuel Cancino

**NAVY**
*(Marina Nacionale)*
*Commandancia General de l'Armada*

Commander General . . . . . . . . . . . . . . . . . . . . . Hector Ramirez de Arillano
Chief of Staff . . . . . . . . . . . . . . . . . . . . . . Vice Alm. Héctor Argudin Estrada
Deputy Chief of Staff . . . . . . . . . . . . . . Contra Alm. Felix Jaime Pérez Elías
Inspector General . . . . . . . . . . . . . . . . . . . Alm. Manuel Hernández Obregon
Director-General, Services . . . . . . . . . . . . . Vice Alm. Enrique Amado Ávila
Gulf Commander (H.Q. Veracruz) . . . . Contra Alm. Pablo Severino Portela
Pacific Commander
   (H.Q. Acalpulco) . . . . . . . . . . . . . . Contra Alm. Jorge Oricaga Amernana
Director, Navy Shipyard No. 8
   (Salina Cruz, Oaxaca)  . . . . . . . . . . . . . . Vice Alm. Enrique Baltanas Hope

**Zone Commands**

Commander, Zone 1 (Madero) . . . . . . . . . . Vice Alm. David Zepeda Torres
Sector Commander . . . . . . . . . . . . . . . . . Vice Alm. Alvaro Sandoval Peralta

Commander, Zone 2 (Ensenada) . . . . Vice Alm. Mauricio Schleske Sanchez

Commander, Zone 3 (Veracruz) . . . . . . . . . . Vice Alm. Miguel Portela Cruz
Sector Commander . . . . . . . . . . . . . . . . Contra Alm. Luis Olguin Fernandez
Sector Commander . . . . . . . . . . . . . . . . . . . Contra Alm. Ambrosi Ariza Lopez

Commander, Zone 4 (La Paz) . . . . . . . . . . . . . Vice Alm. Carlos Lopez Sotelo
Sector Commander . . . . . . . . . . . . . . . . . . . . . . . . Cap. Jorge Lagos Kuntzy
Sector Commander . . . . . . . . . . . . . . . Contra Alm. Fernando Magaña Gayau

Commander, Zone 5 (Frontera) . . . . . . . . Vice Alm. Luis Hernandez Baeza

Commander, Zone 6 (Guaymas) . . . . . . . . . Vice Alm. Pedro Toledo Astorga
Sector Commander . . . . . . . . . . . . . . . Contra Alm. Mario Rodriguez Esperon

Commander, Zone 7
(Carmen) ................ Vice Alm. Armando Abaroa Schaufelberger
Sector Commander ............. Contra Alm. Federico Romero Godinez
Sector Commander ................. Contra Alm. Mario Gonzalez Laine

Commander, Zone 8 (Mazatlan) ......... Alm. Armando Martinez Flores

Commander, Zone 9 (Yucalpeten) ....... Vice Alm. Jose A. Sierra Reynaud
Sector Commander ................... Contra Alm. Gandhi Zilli Viveros

Commander, Zone 10 (San Blas)........ Vice Alm. Marcial l'Eglisse Muttio

Commander, Zone 11 (Chetumal) ........ Vice Alm. Carlos Vorrath Ponce
Sector Commander ................. Contra Alm. Enrique Arce Suarez
Sector Commander ................ Contra Alm. Sergio Loperena Garcia

Commander, Zone 12 (Vallanta) ....... Vice Alm. Tomas Ortega Bertrand

Commander, Zone 14 (Manzanillo) ........ Vice Alm. Vidal Preciado Ruiz
Sector Commander ................. Contra Alm. Eduardo Luna Roma

Commander, Zone 16 (L. Cardenas) ... Vice Alm. Salvador Gomez Bernard

Commander, Zone 18 (Acapulco) ....... Vice Alm. Roberto Maufome Ruiz
Sector Commander.............. Contra Alm. Jose M. Monroy Gutierrez

Commander, Zone 20 (S. Crux) ........ Vice Alm. Enrique Baltanas Hope
Sector Commander ............. Contra Alm. Augusto Esparza Rodriguez

Commander, Zone 22 (Madero) ....... Vice Alm. Alvaro Arzamendi Garcia

**Naval Aviation School**

Director ........................ Contra Alm. Ruben Miranda Cordova
Deputy Director ...................... Cap. Eduardo B. Gordillo Flores
Director of Studies ..................... Cap. Gabriel Pelaez Andrade
Flight Director ................... Cap. Domingo H. M. Campos Moran

\* \* \* \* \*

## GENERAL DEFENSE DATA

**Manpower**
Total Armed Forces.............................................144,000
(See Page 353)
Population ................................................71,330,000

**Spending**
Military Expenditures .......................................$627 million
Gross National Product .......................................$142 billion
Military Expenditure as a Percentage of
Gross National Product ......................................0.4%
Military Expenditure as a Percentage of
Central Government Expenditure ................................2.4%

**Defense Treaties** *(See Part II for Additional Detail)*

Bilateral: United States

Multilateral: Act of Chapultepec
Biological Weapons Convention
Inter-American Defense Board
Inter-American Treaty of Reciprocal Assistance
Limited Test Ban Treaty
Treaty for the Prohibition of Nuclear Weapons in Latin
America
Treaty on the Non-Proliferation of Nuclear Weapons

**Military Rank Comparisons**
See Appendix A.

# MONACO
## Principality of Monaco
### *Principauté de Monaco*

### Defense Establishment Command Structure
### and Force Organization

France is responsible for the defense of the sovereignty and independence of Monaco. The Principality maintains a palace guard and a police force.

### HEAD OF STATE

H. S. H. Prince Rainier III

**OFFICE OF H.S.H. THE PRINCE**
*Palais de Monaco*
*B.P. 518*
*MC 98015 Monaco-ville*

Telephone:   *(93) 30 18 31*
Telex:   *469920 palamon carlo*

Ruler of Monaco . . . . . . . . . . . . . . . . . . . . . . . . . . . . H.S.H. Prince Rainier III

**OFFICE OF THE MINISTER
  OF STATE**
*(Ministere d'Etat)*
*B.P. 522*
*MC 98015 Monaco-ville*

Telephone:   *(93) 30 19 21*
Telex:   *469942 govermo carlo*

Minister of State . . . . . . . . . . . . . . . . . . . . . . . . . . . . . . . . . . . . . . . Jean Herly

**GOVERNMENT COUNCILLOR FOR
  INTERNAL AFFAIRS**
*(Conseiller de Gouvernement pour l'Interieur)*
*Ministere d'Etat*
*Place de la Visitation*
*Monaco-ville*

Telephone:   *(93) 30 19 21*
Telex:   *469942 govermo carlo*

Councillor . . . . . . . . . . . . . . . . . . . . . . . . . . . . . . . . . . . Michel Desmet

**POLICE**
*(Force Publique)*
*Heracles Building*
*Rue Suffren Reymond*
Telephone:   *30 42 46*

General Inspector of the French National Police . . . . . Robert Cassoudessalle
Chief Commander . . . . . . . . . . . . . . . . . . . . . . . . . . Col. Jean Paul Soutiras

**THE PRINCE'S RIFLEMEN**
*(Carabiniers du Prince)*
*5 Place de Palais*
*5 Boulevard de Belgique*
Telephone:   *30 71 85*

Commander . . . . . . . . . . . . . . . . . . . . . . . . . . . . . . . . . Capt. Maurice Allent

\* \* \* \* \*

# GENERAL DEFENSE DATA

**Manpower**
  Total Armed Forces ..................................................
  Population ....................................................26,000

**Spending**
  Military Expenditures ................................................
  Gross National Produce ..............................................
  Military Expenditure as a Percentage of Gross National Product ................
  Military Expenditure as a Percentage of Central Government Expenditure .......

**Defense Treaties** *(See Part II for Additional Detail)*

  Bilateral:      France

  Multilateral:   None

# MONGOLIA
## Mongolian People's Republic
### *Bugd Nayramdakh Mongol Ard Uls*

### Defense Establishment Command Structure
### and Force Organization

The Minister of Defense is Commander-in-Chief of the Mongolian People's Army. The Council of Ministers provide general guidance and policy direction.

**Total armed forces:** 34,600 (Army: 31,500;    Air Force: 3,100). **Para-military forces:** 10,000.

## HEAD OF STATE

H. E. Yumjaagiyn Tsedenbal

**PRESIDIUM OF THE GREAT PEOPLE'S HURAL**
*Ulan Bator*

| | |
|---|---|
| Chairman of the Presidium | Yumjaagiyn Tsedenbal |
| Deputy Chairman | Sampilyn Jalan-Aajav |
| Deputy Chairman | Nyamyn Tagyaral |
| Deputy Chairman | Tsedendambyn Gotou |
| Deputy Chairman | Gombojavyn Ochirbat |
| Deputy Chairman | Sonomyn Udval |
| Deputy Chairman | Lodonglln Tudev |
| Deputy Chairman | Banzragehiin Lamjav |

**COUNCIL OF MINISTERS**
*Ulan Bator*

| | |
|---|---|
| Chairman | Jambyn Batmönh |
| First Deputy Chairman | Damdinjavyn Maydar |
| First Deputy Chairman | Tümenbayaryn Ragchaa |
| Deputy Chairman | Tsendiim Molom |
| Deputy Chairman | Myatavyn Peljee |
| Deputy Chairman | Dumaagyn Sodnom |
| Deputy Chairman | Choinoryn Suren |
| Deputy Chairman | Dondogyn Tsevgmid |
| Director of Administration | Baldangiyn Badarch |

**MINISTRY OF DEFENSE**
*Ulan Bator*

| | |
|---|---|
| Minister and Commander-in-Chief of the Mongolian People's Army | Col. Gen. Jarantain Avhia |

**MINISTRY OF PUBLIC SECURITY**
*Ulan Bator*

| | |
|---|---|
| Minister | O. Choijilsuren |

\* \* \* \* \*

## GENERAL DEFENSE DATA

**Manpower**
Total Armed Forces . . . . . . . . . . . . . . . . . . . . . . . . . . . . . . . . . . . . . . . . . . . .34,600
Population . . . . . . . . . . . . . . . . . . . . . . . . . . . . . . . . . . . . . . . . . . . . . . . . . .1,759,000

359

**Spending**

Military Expenditures . . . . . . . . . . . . . . . . . . . . . . . . . . . . . . . . . . . . . . . . . . . . $239.6 million
Gross National Product . . . . . . . . . . . . . . . . . . . . . . . . . . . . . . . . . . . . . . . . . . . . $2.8 billion
Military Expenditure as a Percentage of
    Gross National Product . . . . . . . . . . . . . . . . . . . . . . . . . . . . . . . . . . . . . . . . . . 1.4%
Military Expenditure as a Percentage of
    Central Government Expenditure . . . . . . . . . . . . . . . . . . . . . . . . . . . . . . . . . . . .

**Defense Treaties** *(See Part II for Additional Detail)*

Bilateral:     Bulgaria
               Soviet Union

Multilateral:  Biological Weapons Convention
               Environmental Modification Convention
               Limited Test Ban Treaty
               Treaty on the Control of Arms on the Seabed
               Treaty on the Non-Proliferation of Nuclear Weapons

# MOROCCO
## Kingdom of Morocco
### *al-Mamlaka al-Maghribiya*

### Defense Establishment Command Structure and Force Organization

The King is Commander-in-Chief of the General Staff of the Royal Armed Forces and has direct control of each of the separate services. Policy and planning functions for the armed forces are performed by the Co-ordinator of Offices and Services of the General Staff, who acts as day-to-day commander of the armed forces during the King's absence. The Secretary-General for National Defense Administration is responsible for the administrative affairs of the armed forces.

**Total armed forces:** 141,000 (Army: 125,000;  Navy: 6,000;  Air Force: 10,000). **Paramilitary forces:** 30,000.

### HEAD OF STATE

H. M. King Hassan II

**OFFICE OF H. M. THE KING**
*Palais Royal*
*Rabat*
*Telephone: 601 22, 656 57, 601 24*

King of Morocco, Commander-in-Chief,
    and Chief of the Armed Forces General Staff ..........H. M. Hassan II
Advisor .........................................Ahmed Reda Guedira
Advisor .............................................Mohamed Aouad
Advisor .............................................Ahmed Bensouda
Director, Personal Secretariat .......................Abdelfattah Frej
Director, Office of Aides-de-Camp ........Col. Maj. Mohamed Cherkaoui
Minister of the Royal House, Chief
    of Protocol and of the Chancery,
    Co-ordinator of Offices and
    Services of the General Staff
    of the Royal Armed Forces ...........Gen. Moulay Abdelhafid Alaoui
Commander, Royal Guard ..............Col. Maj. Mohamed Cherkaoui

**ADMINISTRATION OF NATIONAL DEFENSE**
*(Administration de la Defense Nationale)*
*6 Bis, rue Patrice Lumumba*
*Rabat*
*Telephone: 627 31, 601 50, 608 05*
*Telex: 31987*

Secretary-General, National
    Defense Administration ...............Col. Maj. Mohamed Achahbar
High Commissioner for Veterans
    and Members of the Liberation Army ............Mohamed Benjelloun

**General Office of National Security**
*Zankat Soekarno*
*Rabat*
*Telephone: 240 11/16*

Director-General ............................Col. Abdelhak El Kadiri
Controller General, Internal Security ..........Hadj. Mohamed Tadlaoui

**Rabat Security Office**
*Avenue Trabless*
*Rabat*
*Telephone: 202 31*

Director .........................................Abdeslam M'Zaiti
Personal Secretary ................................Ben Omar Soussi

# DEFENSE FORCES

**ARMED FORCES**
**Royal Armed Forces**
*(Forces Armées Royales)*
*Avenue Mohamed V*
*Rabat*

*Telephone: 645 11, 607 54, 603 75, 602 76*
*Telex: 31887*

| | |
|---|---|
| Chief, General Staff of the Armed Forces | H. M. King Hassan II |
| Inspector-General | Gen. Driss Ben Aissa Fakir |
| Co-ordinator of Offices and Services, General Staff | Gen. Moulay Abdelhafid Alaoui |
| Inspector, Communications (Signals) | Col. Ziriab Mostapha |
| Inspector, Engineering | Col. Kamili Mahfoud |

**ARMY**
**Royal Army**
*Telephone: 607 10*
*Telex: 32977*

| | |
|---|---|
| Commander | H. M. Hassan II |
| Inspector-General | Gen. Driss Ben Aissa Fakir |
| Inspector, Infantry | Col. Maj. Mohamed Abrouk |
| Commander, Southern Zone | Col. Maj. Abdelaziz Bennani |

**Group Commands**

| | |
|---|---|
| Commander, Ohoud Group, Southern Zone | Col. Maj. Abrouk |
| Commander, Zellaka Group, Southern Zone | |
| Commander, El Arak Group, Southern Zone | |

**Frontier Sector Commands**

| | |
|---|---|
| Commander, North Frontier Command (Oujda) | |
| Commander, East Frontier Command (Errachidia) | |
| Commander, South Frontier Command (Ouarzazate) | |

**South Operational Sectors, Southern Zone**

| | |
|---|---|
| Commander, Oued Draa | |
| Commander, Saguiet El Hamra | |
| Commander, Oued ad Dakar | |

**Headquarters Southern Zone**

| | |
|---|---|
| Commander, Bouizakara | |

**Royal Military Academy of Meknes**
*(Academie Royale Militaire de Meknes)*

| | |
|---|---|
| Commander | Col. Maj. Abdenbi Britel |

**NAVY**
**Royal Navy**
*Boulevard Sour Jdid*
*Casablanca*

*Telephone: 27 84 51*

| | |
|---|---|
| Commander | H. M. Hassan II |
| Inspector-General, Royal Navy | Capt. de Corvette Lahcen Ouhira |
| Inspector, Royal Navy | Capt. Aghnaj |
| Inspector, Royal Navy | Capt. Oumghari |
| Inspector, Royal Navy | Capt. Abdelkader Boubker |
| Commander, First Landing Battalion, Royal Marines | Lt. Col. Hadj Amar Oumghain |
| Commandante, Naval Academy (Casablanca) | Capt. de Corvette Triki |

**AIR FORCE**
**Royal Air Force**
*(Forces Royales Aeriennes—FRA)*
*Des Far*
*Rabat*

*Telephone: 607 10*
*Telex: 32977*

| | |
|---|---|
| Commander | H. M. Hassan II |
| Inspector-General, Royal Air Force | Col. Maj. Mohamed Kabbaj |
| Commander, Royal Air Academy—Marrakesh | Lt. Col. El Mouch Salah |

**Royal Constabulary**
*(Gendarmerie Royale)*
*Telephone: 22519*

| | |
|---|---|
| Commander | Col. Maj. Housni Benslimane |
| Commandante, Rabat Sale Air Base | Cdt. Azelmad |

* * * * *

## GENERAL DEFENSE DATA

**Manpower**

Total Armed Forces...............................................141,000
(See Page 361)
Population ................................................22,230,000

**Spending**

Military Expenditures.........................................$1.1 billion
Gross National Product.......................................$18.7 billion
Military Expenditure as a Percentage of
    Gross National Product ...........................................6.1%
Military Expenditure as a Percentage of
    Central Government Expenditure ................................17.8%

**Defense Treaties** *(See Part II for Additional Detail)*

Bilateral:      France
                United States

Multilateral:   League of Arab States
                Limited Test Ban Treaty
                Organization of African Unity
                Treaty on the Control of Arms on the Seabed
                Treaty on the Non-Proliferation of Nuclear Weapons

**Military Rank Comparisons**

See Appendix A.

# MOZAMBIQUE
## People's Republic of Mozambique
### *Republic Popular de Mocambique*

## Defense Establishment Command Structure and Force Organization

The President is Commander-in-Chief of the armed forces. His authority is exercised through the Minister of National Defense.

**Total armed forces:** 21,600 (Army, 20,000; Navy: 600; Air Force: 1,000). **Para-military forces:** 6,000 (Border Guard).

## HEAD OF STATE

H. E. Samora Moises Machel

**OFFICE OF THE PRESIDENT**
*1780 Avenida Julius Nyerere*
*Maputo*
*Telephone: 741121*
*Telex: 6243 prpm mo*

President of the People's Republic and
Commander-in-Chief of the Armed Forces . . . . . . . . . . . . . . Field Marshal
Samora Moises Machel

**MINISTRY OF NATIONAL DEFENSE**
*(Ministerio da Defesa Nacional)*
*Avenida Martires de Mueda*
*Maputo*
*Telephone: 742081*
*Telex: 6331 mdn mo*

Minister . . . . . . . . . . . . . . . . . . . . . . . . . . . Lt. Gen. Alberto Joaquim Chipande
Vice Minister and Chief of the
General Staff, People's Forces for
the Liberation of Mozambique . . . . . . Lt. Gen. Sebastiao Marcos Mabote
National Political Commissar, People's Forces
for the Liberation of Mozambique . . . Lt. Gen. Armando Emilio Guebuza

**MINISTRY OF SECURITY**
*Maputo*

Minister . . . . . . . . . . . . . . . . . . . . . . . . . . . . Maj. Gen. Jacinto Soares Veloso

## DEFENSE FORCES

**ARMED FORCES**
**People's Forces for the Liberation of Mozambique—FPLM**
*Avenida Martires de Mueda*
*Maputo*
*Telephone: 742081*
*Telex: 6331 mdn mo*

Chief of the General Staff, FPLM, and
Vice Minister of Defense . . . . . . . . . . . Lt. Gen. Sebastiao Marcos Mabote

**ARMY**
*Avenida Martires de Mueda*
*Maputo*
*Telephone: 742081*
*Telex: 6331 mdn mo*

Commander, Zambezia Province . . . . . . . . . . . Maj. Gen. Bonifacio Gruvete
Commander, Nampula Province . . . . . . . . . . . . . Maj. Gen. Eduardo Nihia
Commander, Gaza Province . . . . . . . . . . . . . . Maj. Gen. Fernando Matavele
Commander, Inhambane Province . . . . . . . . Maj. Gen. António Hama Thai
Commander, Sofala Province . . . . . . . . . . . . . Maj. Gen. Joaquim Munhepe
Commander, Manica Province . . . . . . . . . . . . . . . . . . Maj. Gen. Tobias Dai
Commander, Tete Province . . . . . . . . . . . . . . . . . . . . . . . . Col. Matias Juma

**NAVY**
*(Marinha de Guerra)*
*Avenida Martires de Mueda*
*Maputo*
*Telephone:   742081*
*Telex:   6331 mdm mo*

Commander (Acting) . . . . . . . . . . . . . . . . . . . . . . . . . . . Capt. António Miringe

**AIR FORCE**
*(Force Aerea)*
*Avendia Martires de Mueda*
*Maputo*
*Telephone:   742081*
*Telex:   6331 mdm mo*

Commander . . . . . . . . . . . . . . . . . . . . . . . . . . . Maj. Gen. Americo Mpfumo

\* \* \* \* \*

# GENERAL DEFENSE DATA

**Manpower**

Total Armed Forces. . . . . . . . . . . . . . . . . . . . . . . . . . . . . . . . . . . . . . . . . . . . .21,600
  (See Page 365)
Population . . . . . . . . . . . . . . . . . . . . . . . . . . . . . . . . . . . . . . . . . . . .12,695,000

**Spending**

Military Expenditures . . . . . . . . . . . . . . . . . . . . . . . . . . . . . . . . . . . . . .$191.85 million
Gross National Product . . . . . . . . . . . . . . . . . . . . . . . . . . . . . . . . . . . . . . . . .$2.76 billion
Military Expenditure as a Percentage of
  Gross National Product . . . . . . . . . . . . . . . . . . . . . . . . . . . . . . . . . . . . . . .6.9%
Military Expenditure as a Percentage of
  Central Government Expenditure . . . . . . . . . . . . . . . . . . . . . . . . . . . . . . . .62%

**Defense Treaties** *(See Part II for Additional Detail)*

Bilateral:      Soviet Union
                Tanzania
                Zimbabwe

Multilateral:   Organization of African Unity
                *Mozambique-Angola-Tanzania-Zambia:* Agreement concern-
                  ing joint defense strategy against external attack (1976)

# NAURU
## Republic of Nauru
### *Naoero*

#### Defense Establishment Command Structure
#### and Force Organization

Nauru does not maintian military forces and has no formal defense structure.

### HEAD OF STATE

H. E. The Hon. Hammer DeRoburt, O.B.E., M.P.

**OFFICE OF THE PRESIDENT**
*Government Offices*
*Yaren*
*Telephone: 3100*
*Telex: 33100 oagiteb zv*

President .........................Hammer DeRoburt, O.B.E., M.P.
Minister Assisting the President ................R. B. Detudamo, M.P.

**DEPARTMENT OF INTERNAL AFFAIRS**
*c/o Chief Secretary's Department*
*Government Offices*
*Yaren*
*Telephone: 3300*
*Telex: 33081 govnaru zv*

President and Minister for
    Internal Affairs ..................Hammer DeRoburt, O.B.E., M.P.

### DEFENSE FORCES

**POLICE**
Yaren

Director ...........................................D. A. Daniel

\* \* \* \* \*

### GENERAL DEFENSE DATA

**Manpower**
    Total Armed Forces .....................................................
    Population .......................................................9,000

**Spending**
    Military Expenditures ..............................................
    Gross National Product.......................................$155 million
    Military Expenditure as a Percentage of
        Gross National Product .......................................
    Military Expenditure as a Percentage of
        Central Government Expenditure ...................................

**Defense Treaties** *(See Part II for Additional Detail)*

Bilateral:    None

Multilateral:    Treaty on the Non-Proliferation of Nuclear Weapons

# NEPAL
## Kingdom of Nepal
### *Nepal Alhirajya*

## Defence Establishment Command Structure
## and Force Organization

The King is Supreme Commander of the Royal Nepalese Army, exercising his authority through the Prime Minister who is also Minister of Defence. Constitutionally, the King would command the Army only during emergencies. In practice, he maintains control over the Army at all times.

**Total armed forces:** 25,000 (Army). **Para-military forces:** 15,000 (Police).

## HEAD OF STATE

H. M. King Birendra Bir Bikram Shah Dev

**OFFICE OF THE KING**
*Narayanhity Royal Palace*
*Durbar Marg*
*Kathmandu*
*Telephone: 12396, 12796*
*Cable: REX KATHMANDU*

King of Nepal and Supreme Commander
of the Royal Nepalese Army . . . . . . . H. M. Birendra Bir Bikram Shah Dev
Aide, Foreign Affairs . . . . . . . . . . . . . . . . . . Meer Subba Ishwar Man Singh
Aide, Home and Military
Affairs . . . . . . . . . . . . . . . . . . . . . . Lt. Gen. Dan Gambir Singh Rayamajhi
Aide, Press . . . . . . . . . . . . . . . . . . . . . . . . . . . . . . . . . . . . . Chiran S. Thapa

**OFFICE OF THE PRIME MINISTER**
*Cabinet Secretariat*
*Singha Durbar*
*Kathmandu*
*Telephone: 15733, 11555*

Prime Minister, Defence and
Royal Palace Affairs . . . . . . . . . . . . . . . . . . . . . . Lokendra Bahadur Chand
Chief Secretary . . . . . . . . . . . . . . . . . . . . . . . . . . . . . Bhogendra Nath Rimal
Deputy Secretary . . . . . . . . . . . . . . . . . . . . . Devendra Bahadur Pradhan
Press Secretary . . . . . . . . . . . . . . . . . . . . . . . . . . . . . Surentra Raj Sharma

**MINISTRY OF DEFENCE**
*Cabinet Secretariat*
*Singha Durbar*
*Kathmandu*
*Telephone: 16089, 16207*

Minister of Defence and Prime Minister . . . . . . . . Lokendra Bahadur Chand
Secretary . . . . . . . . . . . . . . . . . . . . . . . . . . . . . . . . . . Nara Kanta Adhikari

## DEFENCE FORCES

**ARMY**
**Royal Nepali Army**
*Tundikhel*
*Kathmandu*
*Telephone: 11173, 11622*

Chief of the Army Staff . . . . . . . . . . . . . . . . Maj. Gen. Arjun Narsingh Rana
Chief of the General Staff . . . . . . . . . . . . . Maj. Gen. Bharat Keshari Simha
Quartermaster General . . . . . . . . . . . . . . . Maj. Gen. Prabhu Narsingh Rana
Adjutant General . . . . . . . . . . . . . . . . . . . . . . Maj. Gen. Satchit Shumsher
Chief Engineer . . . . . . . . . . . . . . . . . . . . . . Brig. Gen. Madan Bickram Rana
Director, Medical Services . . . . . . . . . . . . . Brig. Gen. Thakur Nath Bhattarai
Director, Ordnance Factories . . . . . . . . . . . . . . . Brig. Gen. Raghu Raj Dali
Director, Military Operations . . . . . . . . . . . . . . . . Brig. Gen. Gadul S. J. B.
Master General, Ordnance . . . . . . . . . . . . Brig. Gen. Human Singh Basnyat
Commanding Officer, Tribhuban Chandra
Military Hospital . . . . . . . . . . . . . . . Brig. Gen. (Dr.) Birendra B. Basnyat

Commanding Officer, Royal Palace Brigade
(Kathmandu) ..................................Col. Y. P. J. Rana
Commanding Officer, No. 1 Brigade
(Kathmandu)..............................Brig. Gen. M. B. Basnet
Commanding Officer, No. 2 Brigade
(Dharan) ..................................Brig. Gen. R. B. Rana
Commanding Officer, No. 3 Brigade
(Biratnagur) ..............................Brig. Gen. G. P. Mehara
Commanding Officer, No. 4 Brigade
(Nepalganj)..............................Brig. Gen. L. C. B. Singha
Commander, Air Wing .....................Col. Tejendra Jung Thapa
Deputy Commander, Air Wing ................Lt. Col. Sudarsan Malla

**POLICE**
*Police Headquarters*
*Naxal*
*Kathmandu*
*Telephone:   11110, 11725*

Inspector-General of Police ........................Dil Bahadur Lama
Inspector-General of Police, Intelligence ..............Chad Bahadur Rai

\* \* \* \* \*

# GENERAL DEFENCE DATA

**Manpower**
Total Armed Forces...............................................25,000
  (See Page 369)
Population .................................................15,715,000

**Spending**
Military Expenditures .........................................$17 million
Gross National Product .........................................$2 billion
Military Expenditure as a Percentage of
  Gross National Product ...........................................0.9%
Military Expenditure as a Percentage of
  Central Government Expenditure ..................................6.4%

**Defence Treaties** *(See Part II for Additional Detail)*

Bilateral:    None

Multilateral:  Limited Test Ban Treaty
          Treaty on the Control of Arms on the Seabed
          Treaty on the Non-Proliferation of Nuclear Weapons

# NETHERLANDS
## Kingdom of the Netherlands
### *Koninkrijk der Nederlanden*

### Defence Establishment Command Structure and Force Organization

The Sovereign is nominal Commander-in-Chief of the armed forces. Executive authority over the military is exercised by the Prime Minister. The Minister of Defence has administrative responsibility for defence matters and is advised by the Council of Ministers.

**Total armed forces:** 102,850 (Army: 67,000; Navy: 16,850; Air Force: 19,000). **Paramilitary forces:** 13,000 (Royal Military Constabulary: 8,700; Border Guards: 4,300).

## HEAD OF STATE

H. M. Beatrix Wilhelmina Armgard

**OFFICE OF THE QUEEN**
*Paleis Lange Voorhout*
*2514 EH The Hague*
*Telephone: (70) 63 89 23, 65 92 37*

Queen of the Netherlands and
  Commander-in-Chief ............ H. M. Beatrix Wilhelmina Armgard

**OFFICE OF THE PRIME MINISTER**
*Plein 1813, No. 4*
*The Hague*
*Telephone: (70) 61 40 31*

Prime Minister ....................................... Ruud Lubbers
Vice Prime Minister .............................. Gijsvan Aardenne

**MINISTRY OF DEFENCE**
*(Ministerie van Defensie)*
*Plein 4*
*P.O. Box 20701*
*2500 ES The Hague*
*Telephone: (70) 72 27 22*
*Telex: 31337 mvdgv nl*

Minister of Defence ................................... dr. J. de Ruiter
State Secretary for Defence, Personnel .............. dr. W. K. Hoekzema
State Secretary of Defence, Material ................ J. van Houwelingen
Secretary-General ........................ dr. G. H. J. M. Peijnenburg
1st Deputy Secretary-General ........................... J. L. Cusell
2nd Deputy Secretary-General ............... dr. Ch. L. M. Schaepman

**Defence Council**

Chairman .............................................. dr. J. de Ruiter
  (Minister of Defence)
Member ................................... dr. W. K. Hoekzema
  (State-Secretary of Defence, Personnel)
Member .................................... J. van Houwelingen
  (State Secretary of Defence, Material)
Member ........................... dr. G. H. J. M. Peijnenburg
  (Secretary-General)
Member ...................................... G. L. J. Huyser
  (Chief, Netherlands Defence Staff)
Member ............................................ dr. B. Buiten
  (Director-General of Personnel)
Member .............................. Lt. Gen. G. W. Boerman
  (Director-General of Materiel)
Member .......................... C. M. E. de Laat de Kanter
  (Director-General, Economic and Financial Affairs)

Member . . . . . . . . . . . . . . . . . . . . . . . . . . . . . . . . . . . . . . . Vice Adm. J. H. B. Hulshof
(Chief of Navy Staff and Commander-in-Chief, Navy)
Member . . . . . . . . . . . . . . . . . . . . . . . . . . . . . . . . . . . . . . . . . . . Lt. Gen. C. Roos
(Chief of Army Staff and Commander-in-Chief, Army)
Member . . . . . . . . . . . . . . . . . . . . . . . . . . . . . . . . . . . . . . . . . . . . Lt. Gen. C. Baas
(Chief of Air Force Staff and Commander-in-Chief, Air Force)
Member . . . . . . . . . . . . . . . . . . . . . . . . . . . . . . . . . . . . . . . . L. van der Put
(Director of General Policy Affairs)
Member . . . . . . . . . . . . . . . . . . . . . . . . . . . . . . . . . . . . . . . . . . A. J. Sligting
(Director, Information)
Member . . . . . . . . . . . . . . . . . . M. J. P. O. Baron van Harinxma thoe Slooten
(Director, Legal Services)
Member . . . . . . . . . . . . . . . . . . . . . . . . . . . . . . . . . . . . . . . . . . . . . . . . . . .
(Representative of the Minister of Foreign Affairs)

**Directorate-General of Personnel**

Director-General . . . . . . . . . . . . . . . . . . . . . . . . . . . . . . . . . . . . . dr. B. Buiten
Director, Plans and Policy . . . . . . . . . . . . . . . . . . . . . . . . . . . . . . . . W. Drees
Director, Military . . . . . . . . . . . . . . . . . . Commodore drs. F. J. van Doorn
Director, Civilian . . . . . . . . . . . . . . . . . . . . . . . . . . P. J. G. van der Mark
Director, Medical Services . . . . . . . . . . . . . . . . Maj. Gen. dr. R. G. Nypels
Director, Conscription . . . . . . . . . . . . . . . . . . . . . . . . . . . . G. J. de Lange

**Directorate-General of Materiel**

Director-General . . . . . . . . . . . . . . . . . . . . . . . . . . . . . Lt. Gen. G. W. Boerman
Director, Plans . . . . . . . . . . . . . . . . . . . . . . . . . . . Rear Adm. H. J. Betman
Director, Support . . . . . . . . . . . . . . . . . . . . . . . . . . . drs. ing. M. Vermaas
Director, Infrastructure . . . . . . . . . . . . . . . . . . . . . Maj. Gen. J. Zielhuis

**Directorate-General of Economic and Financial Affairs**

Director-General . . . . . . . . . . . . . . . . . . . . . . C. M. E. de Laat de Kanter
Director, Plans and Policy . . . . . . . . . . . . . . . . . . . . . . . . . . D. van den Berg
Director, Administration . . . . . . . . . . . . . . . . . . . . . . Brig. Gen. H. Breimer
Director, Automation . . . . . . . . . . . . . . . . . . . . . Brig. Gen. H. J. Koenen
Director, Organization . . . . . . . . . . . . . . . . . . . . . . . . . drs. F. J. B. Teerink

**Directorate of Legal Services**

Director . . . . . . . . . . . . . . . . . . M. J. P. D. Baron van Harinxma thoe Slooten
Deputy Director . . . . . . . . . . . . . . . . . . . . . . . . . . . . . . . . Th. J. Barentsen

**Directorate of General Policy Affairs**

Director . . . . . . . . . . . . . . . . . . . . . . . . . . . . . . . . . . . . . . . . L. van der Put
Deputy Director . . . . . . . . . . . . . . . . . . . . . . . . . . . . . . . . . . . . D. J. Barth

**Directorate of Information**

Director. . . . . . . . . . . . . . . . . . . . . . . . . . . . . . . . . . . . . . . . . A. J. Sligting
Deputy Director . . . . . . . . . . . . . . . . . . . . . . . . . . . . . . . . . . . J. Querens
Chief of Navy Information . . . . . . . . . . . . . . . . . Commander J. D. Doorman
Chief of Army Information . . . . . . . . . . . . . . Maj. G. A. Struijker Boudier
Chief of Air Force Information . . . . . . . . . . . . . . . . . Lt. Col. D. van Muirlwik

**Directorate of Internal Affairs**

Director . . . . . . . . . . . . . . . . . . . . . . . . . . . . . . . . . . . . . . . . . . . L. van Eijk

**The Ministry of Defence Audit Board**

Director . . . . . . . . . . . . . . . . . . . . . . . . . . . . . . . . . . . . . . drs. J. F. d'Hondt

**Directorate of the Joint Services Audit Board**

Director. . . . . . . . . . . . . . . . . . . . . . . . . . . . . . Brig. Gen. H. H. G. Koolen

**Personnel Committee**

Director-General of Personnel . . . . . . . . . . . . . . . . . . . . . . . . . dr. B. Buiten
Director of Personnel, Navy . . . . . . . . . . . . . . . . . . . Rear Adm. R. H. Post
Director of Personnel, Army . . . . . . . . . . . . . . . . . . . . . . . . . . . . . . . . . . . . .
Director of Personnel, Air Force . . . . . . . . . . . . . . . . . . . Maj. Gen. H. Tros
Director of Personnel, Plans and Policy . . . . . . . . . . . . . . . . . . . . . . W. Drees
Director of Personnel, Military . . . . . . . . . . . . . . Comdr. drs. F. J. van Doorn
Director of Personnel, Civilian . . . . . . . . . . . . . . . . . . P. J. G. van der Mark
Director of Personnel, Medical Services . . . . . . . Maj. Gen. dr. R. G. Nypels

Director of Personnel, Conscription . . . . . . . . . . . . . . . . . . . . .G. J. de Lange
Adjoint: Representative of
    Directorate of Information . . . . . . . . . . . . . . . . . . . . . . . . . . . . . . . . . . .

**Materiel Committee**

Director-General of Materiel . . . . . . . . . . . . . . . . .Lt. Gen. G. W. Boerman
Director of Materiel, Navy . . . . . . . . . . . . . . . . . . . . . . . .Rear Adm. W. Kool
Director of Materiel, Army. . . . . . . . . . . . . . . . . . .Maj. Gen. A. J. Beersma
Director of Materiel, Air Force . . . . . . . . . . . . . . .Maj. Gen. E. van der Kaa
Director of Materiel, Plans. . . . . . . . . . . . . . . . . . . .Rear Adm. H. J. Betman
Director of Materiel, Support . . . . . . . . . . . . . . . . . . .drs. ing. M. Vermaas
Director of Materiel, Infrastructure . . . . . . . . . . . . . . .Maj. Gen. J. Zielhuis

**Economic and Finance Committee**

Director-General of Economic
    and Financial Affairs . . . . . . . . . . . . . . . . . . . .C. M. E. de Laat de Kanter
Director of Economic Management, Navy . . . . . . . . . . . . . . . . . . . . .M. Kool
Director of Economic Management, Army . . . . . . .Maj. Gen. J. A. Hartman
Director of Economic Management, Air Force . . . . . . . . . .drs. H. J. Busman

# DEFENCE FORCES

**ARMED FORCES**
**Defence Staff**
*Ministry of Defence*
*Plein 4*
*P.O. Box 20701*
*2500 ES The Hague*

*Telephone: (70) 72 27 22*
*Telex: 31337 mvdgv nl*

Chief, Defence Staff . . . . . . . . . . . . . . . . . . . . . . . . . . . .Gen. G. L. J. Huyser
Director, Defence Staff . . . . . . . . . . . . . . . . . . . . . . .Commodore R. de Boeft

**Chiefs of Staff/Commanders-in-Chief Committee**

Chairman . . . . . . . . . . . . . . . . . . . . . . . . . . . . . . . . . . .Gen. G. L. J. Huyser
                                                         (Chief, Defence Staff)
Member. . . . . . . . . . . . . . . . . . . . . . . . . . . . . . . . . . .Vice Adm. J. H. B. Hulshor
             (Chief, Naval Staff and Commander-in-Chief, Navy)
Member . . . . . . . . . . . . . . . . . . . . . . . . . . . . . . . . . . . . . . . . . .Lt. Gen. J. G. Roos
             (Chief, Army Staff and Commander-in-Chief, Army)
Member . . . . . . . . . . . . . . . . . . . . . . . . . . . . . . . . . . . . . . . . . . . .Lt. Gen. C. Baas
             (Chief, Air Staff and Commander-in-Chief, Air Force)
Member. . . . . . . . . . . . . . . . . . . . . . . . . . . . . . . . . . . . . . . .Comdr. R. de Boeft
                                     (Director of the Defence Staff)
Member . . . . . . . . . . . . . . . . . . . . . . . . . . . . . . . . . . . . . . . . . . . . . . . . . . . . . .
           (Adjoint: Representative of the Directorate of Information)

**ARMY**
**The Royal Netherlands Army—RNLA**
*Army Staff*
*Ministry of Defence*
*Therese Schwartzestraat 15*
*P.O. Box 90701*
*2509 LS The Hague*

*Telephone: (70) 73 57 35*
*Telex: 31347 klgv nl*

Chief, Army Staff and Commander-in-Chief,
    Army . . . . . . . . . . . . . . . . . . . . . . . . . . . . . . . . . . . . . .Lt. Gen. J. G. Roos
Vice Chief . . . . . . . . . . . . . . . . . . . . . . . . . . . . . . . . . .Maj. Gen. J. Shaberg

**Army Board**

Chairman . . . . . . . . . . . . . . . . . . . . . . . . . . . . . . . . . . . .Lt. Gen. J. G. Roos
             (Chief, Army Staff and Commander-in-Chief, Army)
Member . . . . . . . . . . . . . . . . . . . . . . . . . . . . . . . . . . . . . . . . . . . . . . . . . . . . . .
                                    (Director of Personnel, Army)
Member . . . . . . . . . . Maj. Gen. A. J. Beersma (Director of Materiel, Army)

Member..................................Maj. Gen. J. A. Hartman
(Director of Economic Management)
Member..............................Maj. G. A. Struijker Boudier
(Adjoint: Chief of Army Information)

**Directorate of Personnel**
*Van der Burchlaan 31*
*P.O. Box 90701*
*2509 LS The Hague*
*Telephone: (70) 73 37 35*
*Telex: 31347 klgv nl*

Director ...................................................(Vacant)

**Directorate of Materiel**

Director ...................................Maj. Gen. A. J. Beersma

**Directorate of Economic Management
RNLA**

Director ...................................Maj. Gen. J. A. Hartman

**COMMANDS**

**First Army Corps**
*P.O. Box 9019*
*7300 EA Apeldoorn*
*Telephone: (55) 77 54 33*

Commander ....................................Lt. Gen. W. J. Loos

**Royal Netherlands Army Training
Command**
*Barchman Wuytierslaan 198*
*P.O. Box 3010*
*3800 DA Amersfoort*
*Telephone: (33) 63 86 22*

Commander...................................Maj. Gen. W. J. Poot

**National Territorial Command**
*Groen van Prinsterersingel 44*
*P.O. Box 1081*
*2800 BB Gouda*
*Telephone: (1820) 18 44 4*

Commander ................................Maj. Gen. C. E. Cohen

**National Logistics Command**
*Houtmarkt 5*
*P.O. Box 5010*
*7400 GC Deventer*
*Telephone: (5700) 16 34 1*

Commander ...........................Brig. Gen. A. A. v.d. Wakker

**Netherlands Army Staff College**
*Van der Burchlaan 31*
*P.O. Box 90701*
*2509 LS The Hague*
*Telephone: (70) 73 57 35*

Director ...................................Brig. Gen. J. C. M. Knol

**Royal Military Academy**
*Kasteelplein 10*
*P.O. Box 90154*
*4800 RG Breda*
*Telephone: (76) 22 39 11*

Governor .........................................Comdr. D. Klik

## NAVY
**Royal Netherlands Navy (RNLN)**
*Navy Staff*
*Ministry of Defence*
*Koningin Marialaan 17*
*P.O. Box 20702*
*2500 ES The Hague*

*Telephone: (70) 81 42 61*
*Telex: 31335 rnavy nl*

Chief, Naval Staff and Commander-in-
Chief, Navy .............................Vice Adm. J. H. B. Hulshof
Vice Chief............Rear Adm. P. M. van Alderwerelt van Rosenburgh

**Admiralty Board**

Chairman ................................Vice Adm. J. H. B. Hulshof
(Chief, Naval Staff and Commander-in-Chief, Navy)
Member ...................................Rear Adm. R. H. Post
(Director of Personnel, Navy)
Member ....................................Rear Adm. W. Kool
(Director of Materiel, Navy)
Member .............................................M. Kool
(Director of Economic Management)
Member ....................................Comdr. J. D. Doorman
(Adjoint: Chief of Navy Information)

**Directorate of Personnel**
*Lange Voorhout 7*
*P.O. Box 20702*
*2500 ES The Hague*

*Telephone: (70) 81 42 61*
*Telex: 31335 rnavy nl*

Director.....................................Rear Adm. R. H. Post

**Directorate of Materiel**
*Torenstraat 172*
*P.O. Box 20701*
*2500 ES The Hague*

*Telephone: (70) 81 42 61*
*Telex: 31335 rnavy*

Director .......................................Rear Adm. W. Kool

**Royal Netherlands Naval College**
*Marine Postkamer*
*Nieuwe Haven*
*1780 CA Den Helder*

*Telephone: (2230) 11 23 4*

Commander....................................Comdr. J. Rietman

**Netherlands Naval Staff College**
*Violenweg 10*
*2597 KL The Hague*

*Telephone: (70) 81 42 61*

Director...........................................Capt. A. Pruijs

**Hydrographer of the Royal Navy**
*Badhuisweg 169-171*
*2597 JN Den Haag*

*Telephone: (70) 814261*

Hydrographer ..........................Rear Adm. L. H. van Opstal

**Directorate of Economic Management**
*Koningin Marialaan 17*
*P.O. Box 20702*
*2500 ES The Hague*

*Telephone: (70) 81 42 61*
*Telex: 31335 kmgv nl*

Director ...............................................M. Kool

## COMMANDS

**Netherlands Home Command**
*c/o Marine Postkamer*
*Nieuwe Haven*
*1780 CA Den Helder*
*Telephone:    (2230) 11 23 4*

Commander . . . . . . . . . . . . . . . . . . . . . . . . . . . . . . . . . Rear Adm. R. Krijger

**Netherlands Antilles Command**
*Marinebasis Parera*
*Willemstaf*
*Curacao*
*Telex:    611230 rnlnavy na*

Commander. . . . . . . . . . . . . . . . . . . . . . . . . . . . . Commodore P. W. Schelrers

**Royal Netherlands Marine Corps**
*Headquarters Netherlands*
*Marine Corps*
*Westplein 12*
*3016 BM Rotterdam*
*Telephone:    (10) 36 37 00*

Commander . . . . . . . . . . . . . . . . . . . . . . . . . . Maj. Gen. RNMC T. Rudolphie

## AIR FORCE
**Royal Netherlands Air Force—RNAF**
*Air Force Staff*
*P.O. Box 20703*
*Binckhorstlaan 135*
*2516 BA The Hague*
*Telephone:    (70) 49 35 91*

Chief, Air Staff, Commander-in-Chief,
  Air Force . . . . . . . . . . . . . . . . . . . . . . . . . . . . . . . . . Lt. Gen. C. Baas
Vice Chief . . . . . . . . . . . . . . . . . . . . . . . . . . . . . . . . . Maj. Gen. M. C. Visser
Deputy Chief, Plans . . . . . . . . . . . . . . . . . . . . . . Comdr. ing. A. Adriaens
Deputy Chief, Operations . . . . . . . . . . . Comdr. J. A. K. van Mossevelde
Chief Cabinet . . . . . . . . . . . . . . . . . . . . . . . . . . . . . Col. W. H. Timmermans
Assistant Chief, Plans . . . . . . . . . . . . . . . . . . . . . . Col. H. J. M. Vendrig
Assistant Chief, Operational Requirements . . . . . . . . . . . . . Col. W. Oldhoff
Assistant Chief, Organization. . . . . . . . . . . . . . . . . . . . . . . Col. M. Paauwe
Assistant Chief, Operational Management . . . . . . . . . . . Col. J. M. Petersen
Assistant Chief, Intelligence . . . . . . . . . . . . . . . . . . . . . . Col. H. F. Enkelaar
Assistant Chief, Communications. . . . . . . . . . . . . . . Col. J. P. den Engelsman
Assistant Chief, Flight Ground Safety . . . . . . . . . . . . . Col. W. P. H. Bezemer

**Air Force Board**

Chairman. . . . . . . . . . . . . . . . . . . . . . . . . . . . . . . . . . . . . Lt. Gen. C. Baas
                    (Chief, Air Staff and Commander-in-Chief, Air Force)
Member. . . . . . . . . . . . . . . . . . . . . . . . . . . . . . . . . . . . Maj. Gen. H. I. Tros
                    (Director of Personnel, Air Force)
Member . . . . . . . . . . . . . . . . . . . . . . . . . . . . . Maj. Gen. ir. E. van der Kaa
                    (Director of Material, Air Force)
Member . . . . . . . . . . . . . . . . . . . . . . . . . . . . . . . . . . . drs. H. J. Busman
                    (Director of Economic Management, Air Force)

**Directorate of Personnel**
*P.O. Box 90519*
*Spui 47*
*2509 LM The Hague*
*Telephone:    (70) 7227 22*

Director. . . . . . . . . . . . . . . . . . . . . . . . . . . . . . . . . . Maj. Gen. H. I. Tros
Deputy Director, Plans and Policy . . . . . . . . . . . . . Col. C. F. A. van Swieten
Deputy Director, Recruitment
  Planning and Management . . . . . . . . . . . . . . . . . . . . . . Comdr. R. Witke

**Directorate of Materiel**
*P.O. Box 20703*
*Binckhorstlaan 135*
*2516 BA The Hague*
*Telephone:    (70) 49 35 91*

Director . . . . . . . . . . . . . . . . . . . . . . . . . . . . . . . Maj. Gen. ir. E. van der Kaa
Deputy Director, Plans and
  Management . . . . . . . . . . . . . . . . . . . . . . . . . . . Comdr. ir. H. Boekenoogen
Deputy Director, Engineering and Supply . . . . . . . . . . Comdr. ir. A. Hidma
Deputy Director, Procurement . . . . . . . . . . . . . Comdr. ir. R. R. Pelsmaeker
Chief, Aircraft Division . . . . . . . . . . . . . . . . . . . . . . Col. ir. J. J. P. Kimmel
Chief, Scientific Research Division . . . . . . . . . . . . . . Col. ir. M. H. Knoch
Chief, Plans and Policy Division . . . . . . . . . . . . . . . . Col. J. C. Weststrate
Chief, Contracts Division . . . . . . . . . . . . . . . . . . . . . . Col. mr. J. Harms

Chief, Support Systems Division . . . . . . . . . . . . . . . . . . . Col. ir. C. C. Bakker
Chief, Procurement Division . . . . . . . . . . . . . . . . . . . . . . . . . . . . . . Col. J. Duin
Chief, Management Systems Division . . . . . . . . . . Col. ir. A. J. R. Westbroek
Chief, Quality Assurance Branch . . . . . . . . . . . . . . . . . . Col. ir. J. J. Wolters
Chief, Ground Systems . . . . . . . . . . . . . . . . . . . . . . . . . . . . . . . . Col. P. Smit

**Directorate of Economic Management**
*P.O. Box 20703*
*Binckhorstlaan 135*
*2516 BA The Hague*

*Telephone: (70) 49 35 91*

Director . . . . . . . . . . . . . . . . . . . . . . . . . . . . . . . . . . . . . . . . . drs. H. J. Busman
Deputy Director, Finance . . . . . . . . . . . . . . . . . . . . . . Col. drs. D. W. Dee
Deputy Director, Management
    Info Systems . . . . . . . . . . . . . . . . . . . . . . . . . . . . Col. ir. C. G. M. Konings
Deputy Director, Organization . . . . . . . . . . . . . . . . . . . . . Mr. D. B. Salverda

## COMMANDS

**Logistic and Training Command (CLO)**
*P.O. Box 460*
*Blikkenburgerlaan 2a*
*3700 AL Zeist*

*Telephone: (3404) 14811*

Commander . . . . . . . . . . . . . . . . . . . . . . . . . . . . . . . . Maj. Gen. F. M. van Pul

**Tactical Air Command (CTL)**
*P.O. Box 516*
*Tiendweg 5*
*3700 AM Zeist*

*Telephone: (3404) 14811*

Commander . . . . . . . . . . . . . . . . . . . . . . . . . . . . Maj. Gen. A. J. Meulenbroek

**Public Information Service**
*Spui 32*
*2511 BS The Hague*

*Telephone: (70) 72 27 22*

Chief . . . . . . . . . . . . . . . . . . . . . . . . . . . . . . . . . . . . . . . . . . Col. A. P. de Jong

**Air Force Staff College**
*P.O. Box 5953*
*Rotterdamseweg 35*
*2280 HZ Rijswijk*

*Telephone: (70) 46 93 35*

Commandant . . . . . . . . . . . . . . . . . . . . . . . . . . . . . . . . . . . Col. W. Kasteleijn

## CONSTABULARY
**The Royal Marechaussée**
*The Marechaussée Staff*
*Ministry of Defence*
*Raamweg 4*
*P.O. Box 90615*
*2509 LP The Hague*

*Telephone: (70) 73 57 35*
*Telex: 31550 kmar nl*

Chief of Staff and Commander of
    the Royal Marechaussée . . . . . . . . . . . . . . . . . . . . Maj. Gen. F. J. van Lier

**The Marechaussée Board**

Chairman . . . . . . . . . . . . . . . . . . . . . . . . . . . . . . dr. G. H. J. M. Peijnenburg
        (Secretary-General of the Ministry of Defence)
Member . . . . . . . . . . . . . . mr. M. J. P. D. Baron van Harinxma thoe Slooten
        (Director of Legal Services)
Member . . . . . . . . . . . . . . . . . . . . . . . . . . . . . . . . . . . Brig. Gen. H. Breimer
    (Director of Economic and Financial Affairs, Administration)
Member . . . . . . . . . . . . . . . . . . . . . . . . . . . . . . . . . Maj. Gen. J. Schaberg
        (Vice Chief of the Army Staff)
Member . . . . . . . . . . . . . . . . . . . . . . . . . . . . . . . . . . . . . . . . . . . . . . . . . . . .
        (Director of Personnel, Army)
Member . . . . . . . . . . . . . . . . . . . . . . . . . . . . . . . . . Maj. Gen. A. J. Beersma
        (Director of Material, Army)

Member . . . . . . . . . . . . . . . . . . . . . . . . . . . . . . . . . . . Maj. Gen. F. J. van Lier
(Commander of the Royal Marechaussée)
Member . . . . . . . . . . . . . . . . . . . . . . . . . . . . . Maj. G. A. Struijker Boudier
(Adjoint: Chief of Army Information)

\* \* \* \* \*

# GENERAL DEFENCE DATA

**Manpower**
Total Armed Forces . . . . . . . . . . . . . . . . . . . . . . . . . . . . . . . . . . . . . . . . . . . . 102,850
(See Page 371)
Population . . . . . . . . . . . . . . . . . . . . . . . . . . . . . . . . . . . . . . . . . . . . . . . . 14,349,000

**Spending**
Military Expenditures . . . . . . . . . . . . . . . . . . . . . . . . . . . . . . . . . . . . . . . . . $5.4 billion
Gross National Product . . . . . . . . . . . . . . . . . . . . . . . . . . . . . . . . . . . . . . . . $173 billion
Military Expenditure as a Percentage of
Gross National Product . . . . . . . . . . . . . . . . . . . . . . . . . . . . . . . . . . . . . . . . 3.2%
Military Expenditure as a Percentage of
Central Government Expenditure . . . . . . . . . . . . . . . . . . . . . . . . . . . . . . . 9.2%

**Defence Treaties** *(See Part II for Additional Detail)*

Bilateral:      United States

Multilateral:   Biological Weapons Convention
Limited Test Ban Treaty
Multinational Force and Observers in Sinai
North Atlantic Treaty Organization
Protocol I of Treaty of Tlatelolco
Treaty on the Control of Arms on the Seabed
Treaty on the Non-Proliferation of Nuclear Weapons
United Nations Interim Force in Lebanon
United Nations Truce Supervision Organization
Western European Union

# THE NETHERLANDS ANTILLES
*Nederlandse Antillen*

### Defence Establishment Command Structure
### and Force Organization

The Netherlands is responsible for the defence of the Netherlands Antilles. All defence personnel are Royal Dutch military. The Prime Minister is also Minister of General Affairs, a position that combines defence and foreign affairs duties, and is therefore the highest local defence official. The Marines, Air Force and National Guard are under Navy command.

**Total armed forces:** 600. **Police:** 644 (including ship on station).

### HEAD OF STATE

H. M. Queen Beatrix of The Netherlands

### GOVERNOR

H. E. drs. Bernardito (Ben) M. Leito

**OFFICE OF THE GOVERNOR**
*Fort Amsterdam 1*
*Curacao*
*Telephone:  (9) 611289*
*Telex:   1119 gna na*
*Cable:   612000*

Governor ..............................drs. Bernardito (Ben) M. Leito
Acting Governor (in absence of Governor Leito) ..............J. Beaujon
Adjutant to Governor ..................Maj. T. A. Breedveld, RNLMC
Chef du Cabinet ........................................C. A. Kramer

**OFFICE OF THE PRIME MINISTER**
*Fort Amsterdam 17*
*Curacao*
*Telephone:  (9) 613988*
*Telex:  1079 alsec na*

Prime Minister and Minister of
    General Affairs...................Ing. Domenico (Don) Felip Martina
Director, Government Information Service..............G. A. A. Lasten

**OFFICE OF THE VICE PRIME MINISTER**
*Fort Amsterdam 17*
*Curacao*
*Telephone:  (9) 613988*
*Telex:  1079 alsec na*

First Vice Prime Minister, Minister of General Affairs,
    and Minister of Finance ..........................Gilbert de Paula
Second Vice Prime Minister and Minister of
    Public Health and Environment .............Marcolina (Margo) Croes

### DEFENCE FORCES

**NAVY**
**Royal Nederlands Marine—RNLM**
*Parera, Curacao*
*Telephone:   (9) 614222 (Central)*
*           (9) 614021 (Fonlantilles)*

Flag Officer, Netherlands Antilles (Fonlantilles) ....Comdr. P. W. Schelres
Chief of Staff ........................Col. Pieter Hiemstra, RNLMC

**Marine Corps**

*Telephone:   (9) 641222 (Central)*
*           614021 (Fonlantilles)*

Commander and Chief of Staff ............Col. Pieter Hiemstra, RNLMC
Deputy Commander .......................Lt. Col. Dik Grote, RNLMC
Commandant, Aruba Contingent,
    Savaneta Camp (8-47100) ...................Lt. Col. M. Heinemann

**Air Force**
*Curacao*
*Telephone:   81622*
*           (Central):   81628*

Commander ........................Maj. G. W. G. F. (Fritz) Rijnders

**Curacao National Guard**
*(Vrijwilligerskorps Curacao—VKC)*
*van Leeuwenhoekstraat 11*
*Willemstad, Curacao*
*Telephone:   (9) 23262, 23401*

Commander .......................................Col. G. H. Raven
Deputy Commander ..............................Maj. J. Kraayeveld

* * * * *

# GENERAL DEFENCE DATA

**Manpower**
    Total Armed Forces .................................................600
        (See Page 379)
    Population .................................................247,000

**Spending**
    Military Expenditures ...............................................
    Gross National Product ........................................$652 million
    Military Expenditure as a Percentage of
        Gross National Product ...........................................
    Military Expenditure as a Percentage of
        Central Government Expenditure .....................................

**Defence Treaties** *(See Part II for Additional Detail)*

    Bilateral:     None

    Multilateral:   Limited Test Ban Treaty
                   Treaty on the Non-Proliferation of Nuclear Weapons

# NEW ZEALAND

### Defence Establishment Command Structure
### and Force Organization

The Governor-General, as representative of the Queen, is the nominal Commander-in-Chief. Actual executive authority for the armed forces is vested with the Prime Minister, who acts through the Minister of Defence. The latter is aided by a Secretary of Defence, responsible for financial matters and administration of the civilian element of the Ministry of Defence, and a Chief of Defence Staff, whose authority is exercised through the three service Chiefs. The Minister of Defence is also advised by a Defence Council, which coordinates defence matters and overall policy.

**Total armed forces:** 12,961 (Army: 5,723; Navy: 2,843; Air Force: 4,395). **Total reserves:** 11,265 (Army: 8,361; Navy: 1,361; Air Force: 1,543).

## HEAD OF STATE

H. M. Queen Elizabeth II

## GOVERNOR-GENERAL

H. E. The Hon. Sir David Beattie, G.C.M.G., Q.C., G.C.V.O.

**OFFICE OF THE GOVERNOR-GENERAL**
*Private Bag*
*Government House*
*Wellington*

*Telephone:* *(4) 898 055 (Wellington)*
*(9) 686 015 (Auckland)*

Governor-General and
    Commander-in-Chief ...Sir David Beattie, G.C.M.G., Q.C., G.C.V.O.
Official Secretary ..............................Col. James Brown (Ret.)
Comptroller of the Household .........................Col. F. B. Bath
Aide-de-Camp .............................Capt. G. Sean Trengrove
Aide-de-Camp ................................Flt. Lt. J. McWilliam

**PRIME MINISTER'S DEPARTMENT**
*Third Floor*
*Parliament Building*
*Wellington*

*Telephone:* *(4) 749 137*

Prime Minister, Minister of Finance,
    Minister in Charge of the Legislative
    Department, Minister in Charge of the
    Audit Department, and Minister in
    Charge of the New Zealand Security
    Intelligence Service ......................Robert D. Muldoon, C.H.
Principal Private Secretary...............................D. S. S. Kerr
Press Secretary .........................................B. Lockstone
Director, External Intelligence Bureau .....................R. B. Atkins

**MINISTRY OF DEFENCE**
*Private Bag*
*Wellington*

*Telephone:* *(4) 726 499, (4) 749 299*
*Telex:* *3513 defcom nz*

Minister of Defence (and Minister
    of State, Leader of the House
    of Representatives, Minister
    of State Services, and Minister
    in Charge of War Pensions
    and Rehabilitation) ............David Spence Thompson, M.C., E.D.
Secretary of Defence .......................Denis B. G. McLean, Esq.
Deputy Secretary of Defence .........................Roger L. Green
Assistant Secretary, Policy .............................Douglas Law
Assistant Secretary, Finance .........................Alan J. Twohill
Assistant Secretary, Science and EDP .............Dr. Donald J. Barnes

Assistant Secretary, Management and
   Administration .......................... Mr. Graeme C. Freeman
Director, Government Communications
   Security Bureau................................... C. M. Hanson
Director, Public Relations ................. Wing Cdr. Geoff T. Clarke

**Defence Council**

Chairman ..................... David Spence Thompson, M.C., E.D.
                                        (Minister of Defence)
Member *(ex officio)* ..... Air Marshall David Ewan Jamieson, C.B., O.B.E.
                                 (Chief of Defence Staff)
Member *(ex officio)* ........................... Denis B. G. McLean
                                 (Secretary of Defence)
Member *(ex officio)* ........ Maj. Gen. Robin G. Williams, C.B., M.B.E.
                                    (Chief, Army Staff)
Member *(ex officio)*........................... Rear Adm. C. J. Steward
                                    (Chief, Naval Staff)
Member *(ex officio)* ...... Air Vice-Marshal David Manson Crooks, O.B.E.
                                   (Chief, Air Staff)
Associate Member .............................. Mr. B. V. J. Galvin
                            (Secretary to the Treasury)
Associate Member.................................. Mr. M. Norrish
                          (Secretary of Foreign Affairs)

# DEFENCE FORCES

**ARMED FORCES**
**Defence Headquarters**
*New Zealand Army*
*c/o Ministry of Defence*
*Private Bag*
*Wellington*

*Telephone:  (4) 726 499, (4) 749 299*
*Telex:  3513 defcom nz*

Chief of Defence Staff ...... Air Marshall David E. Jamieson, C.B., O.B.E.
Deputy Chief, Defence Staff ................... Brig. J. A. Mace, O.B.E.
Assistant Chief, Defence
   Staff—Operations and Plans .............. Air Comdr. Patrick Neville,
                                     O.B.E., RNZAF, A.F.C.
Assistant Chief, Defence
   Staff—Personnel ........................... Comdr. D. B. Domett
Assistant Chief, Defence
   Staff—Support (In Charge
   of Procurement) ............. Air Comdr. S. McIntyre, O.B.E., D.F.C.

**ARMY**
**New Zealand Army**
*c/o Ministry of Defence*
*Private Bag*
*Wellington*

*Telephone:  (4) 726 499, (4) 749 299*
*Telex:  3513 defcom nz*

Chief, General Staff .................... Maj. Gen. Robin G. Williams,
                                        M.B.E, C.B.
Deputy Chief, General Staff ........... Brig. Alfred C. Hamilton, O.B.E.
Director-General, Operations
   and Training ................... Brig. I. H. Burrows, O.B.E., M.C.
Army Public Relations Officer ............. Maj. M. R. Wicksteed, RNZA

    **Land Force Headquarters**
    *Private Bag*
    *Takapuna*
    *Auckland*

    *Telephone:  (9) 491466*

Commander, Land Operations ....... Brig. Geoffrey A. Hitchings, M.B.E.
Director-General, Personnel
   and Logistics ...................... Brig. Roy T. V. Taylor, M.B.E.

**NAVY**
**Royal New Zealand Navy**
*c/o Ministry of Defence*
*Private Bag*
*Wellington*

*Telephone:  (4) 726 499, (4) 749 299*
*Telex:  3513 defcom nz*

Chief, Naval Staff ............................ Rear Adm. C. J. Steward
Deputy Chief, Naval Staff....................... Comdr. D. B. Domett
Chief, Naval Technical Services.......... Capt. Neill Mck Walker, O.B.E.
Director, Naval Operations and Plans ................ Cdr. J. G. Leonard
Director, Organization and Staff Duties ................ Cdr. David Bell
Director, Officer Postings and Appointments......... Cdr. John G. Peddie
Hydrographer ............................ Cdr. W. F. Jacques, O.B.E.

**HMNZS Naval Base**
*Devonport*
*Auckland*
*Telephone:* *(9) 454000*

Commodore, Auckland .........................Comdr. L. J. Tempero
Commander, 11th Frigate Squadron ..............Cdr. John E. N. Welch
Commander, 1st New Zealand
    Patrol Craft Squadron ..................Lt. Cdr. N. T. Byrne, M.B.E.
Captain Superintendent .............Capt. Geoffrey F. Hopkins, O.B.E.
Superintendent, Naval Supply Depot ......................J. M. Ryan
Captain, Naval Training..........Capt. Lindsay A. W. Urquhart, RNZN
Captain, Fleet Support ...........................Capt. J. A. B. Lewis

**AIR FORCE**
**Royal New Zealand Air Force—RNZAF**
*c/o Ministry of Defence*
*Private Bag*
*Wellington*
*Telephone:* *(4) 726 499, (4) 728 111*
        *(after hours)*
*Telex:* *3513 defcom nz*

Chief, Air Staff..........Air Vice-Marshal David Manson Crooks, O.B.E.
Deputy Chief, Air Staff ......Air Comdr. Michael F. NcD. Palmer, C.B.E.
Chief, RNZAF Public Relations .................Sqd. Ldr. Chris D. Cole

**Support Group Headquarters**
**RNZAF Base Wigram**
*Private Bag*
*Christchurch*
*Telephone:* *482049*

Air Officer Commanding ...........Air Comdr. John J. Gordon, O.B.E.

**Operations Group Headquarters**
**RNZAF Base, Auckland**
*Private Bag*
*Auckland*
*Telephone:* *AK (9) 4163000*

Air Officer Commanding ..............Air Comdr. Bernard J. O'Connor,
                         O.B.E., A.F.C.

**NEW ZEALAND FORCE, SOUTH**
   **EAST ASIA**
*Headquarters*
*NZ FP05*
*c/o GPO*
*Singapore*
*Telephone:* *2576505 (Singapore)*

Commander ......................Brig. I. H. Burrows, O.B.E., M.C.
Deputy Commander ...........Group Capt. Donald W. Pawson, A.F.C.
Commander, First Battalion, Royal
   New Zealand Infantry Regiment ..........Lt. Col. Michael R. Farland

\* \* \* \* \*

# GENERAL DEFENCE DATA

**Manpower**
   Total Armed Forces............................................12,961
      (See Page 381)
   Population ..................................................3,120,000

**Spending**
   Military Expenditures ......................................$455 million
   Gross National Product ....................................$23.5 billion
   Military Expenditure as a Percentage of
      Gross National Product .........................................1.9%
   Military Expenditure as a Percentage of
      Central Government Expenditure ................................4.8%

**Defence Treaties** *(See Part II for Additional Detail)*

Bilateral:    Australia
United States

Multilateral:   ANZUS
Biological Weapons Convention
Five-Power Defence Arrangement
Limited Test Ban Treaty
Multinational Force and Observers in Sinai
South-East Asia Collective Defence Treaty
Treaty on the Control of Arms on the Seabed
Treaty on the Non-Proliferation of Nuclear Weapons
United Nations Military Observer Group in India and
   Pakistan
United Nations Truce Supervision Organization

# NICARAGUA
## Republic of Nicaragua
### *República de Nicaragua*

## Defense Establishment Command Structure and Force Organization

The Coordinator of the Junta of National Reconstruction and Commander of the Revolution exercises his authority over the armed forces through the Minister of Defense. The latter retains operational control of the three services and the People's Militia. The Minister of Interior is responsible for the administration of the national intelligence agency.

**Total armed forces:** 21,700 (Army: 20,000 Plus Border Guard;  Navy: 200;  Air Force: 1,500). **Para-military forces:** Up to 50,000 (Civilian Militia).

## HEAD OF STATE

Cdr. Daniel Ortega Saavedra

**JUNTA OF THE NATIONAL RECONSTRUCTION GOVERNMENT**
*(Junta del Gobierno de Reconstruccion Nacional)*
*Casa de Gobierno*
*Apartado No. 2398*
*Managua*
*Telephone:    (2) 2738-4, 22551-4*

Commander of the Revolution
  and Coordinator of the Junta . . . . . . . . . . . Cdte. Daniel Ortega Saavedra
Member . . . . . . . . . . . . . . . . . . . . . . . . . . . . . Dr. Sergio Ramírez Mercado
Member . . . . . . . . . . . . . . . . . . . . . . . . . . . . . Dr. Rafael Córdova Rivas
Minister-General Secretary of the Junta . . . . . . . . . Rodrigo Reyes Portcarro

**SANDINISTA NATIONAL LIBERATION FRONT**
*(Frente Sandinista de Liberacion Nacional— FSLN)*
*Apartado No. 2324*
*Managua*
*Telephone:    (2) 66628, 66674*

Head of State and Coordinator,
  National Board of Directors . . . . . . . . . . . . . Cdte. Daniel Ortega Saavedra
Member . . . . . . . . . . . . . . . . . . . . . . . . . . . . . . . Tomás Borge Martínez
Member . . . . . . . . . . . . . . . . . . . . . . Cdte. Humberto Ortega Saavedra
Member . . . . . . . . . . . . . . . . . . . . . . . . . . . . . . Henry Ruíz Hernańdez
Member . . . . . . . . . . . . . . . . . . . . . . Cdte. Jaime Wheelock Roman
Member . . . . . . . . . . . . . . . . . . . . . . . . . . . . . . . . Victor Tirado Lopez
Member . . . . . . . . . . . . . . . . . . . . . . . . Cdte. Carlos Nunez Tellez
Member . . . . . . . . . . . . . . . . . . . . . . . . . . . . . . . . . Luis Carrion Cruz
Member . . . . . . . . . . . . . . . . . . . . . . . . . . . . . . Bayardo Arce Castano

**MINISTRY OF DEFENSE**
*(Ministerio de Defensa)*
*"El Chipote"*
*Complejo German Pomares*
*Managua*
*Telephone:    (2) 27201-9*
*Telex:    1369 m def nic*

Minister . . . . . . . . . . . . . . . . . . . . . . . . . Cdte. Humberto Ortega Saavedra

**MINISTRY OF INTERIOR**
*(Ministerio de Gobernacion)*
*Apartado No. 68*
*Managua*
*Telephone:    (2) 275317, 22035, 22060*

Minister . . . . . . . . . . . . . . . . . . . . . . . . . . . . . Cdte. Tomás Borges Martínez

**General Directorate for State Security**
*(Direccion General de la Seguridad
   del Estado)*

Director . . . . . . . . . . . . . . . . . . . . . . . . . . . . . . . . . . . . . . . . . . . . Lenín Cerna

## DEFENSE FORCES

**ARMY**
**Sandinista People's Army**
*(El Ejército Popular Sandinista)*
*Complejo Militar*
*"German Pomares"*
*Managua*
*Telephone:    (2) 272019*

Minister of Defense and Chief of Staff  . . . Cdte. Humberto Ortega Saavedra
Vice Minister . . . . . . . . . . . . . . . . . . . . . . . . Cdte. Joaquín Cuadra Lacaya
Vice Minister . . . . . . . . . . . . . . . . . . . . . . . . . Cdte. Leopoldo Rivas Alfara

**AIR FORCE**
**Sandinista Air Force**
*(La Fuerza Aerea Sandinista)*
*Km. 10½ Carretera Norte*
*Managua*
*Telephone:    (2) 3601*

Chief of Staff . . . . . . . . . . . . . . . . . . . . . . . . . . . . . . . . . . Cdte. Raul Venerio

**NAVY**
**Sandinista Navy**
*(La Armada Sandinista)*

Commander . . . . . . . . . . . . . . . . . . . . . . . . . . . . . . . . . . . . . . . Richard Lugo

**MILITIA**
**Sandinista People's Militia**
*(Militia Popular Sandinista—MPS)*

Chief . . . . . . . . . . . . . . . . . . . . . . . . . . . . . . Cdte. Humberto Ortega Saavedra
Inspector-General . . . . . . . . . . . . . . . . . . . . . . . . . . . . . . Francísco Ramirez

\* \* \* \* \*

## GENERAL DEFENSE DATA

**Manpower**
   Total Armed Forces . . . . . . . . . . . . . . . . . . . . . . . . . . . . . . . . . . . . . . . . . . 21,700
      (See Page 385)
   Population  . . . . . . . . . . . . . . . . . . . . . . . . . . . . . . . . . . . . . . . . . . 2,643,000

**Spending**
   Military Expenditures . . . . . . . . . . . . . . . . . . . . . . . . . . . . . . . . . . . . . $49 million
   Gross National Product . . . . . . . . . . . . . . . . . . . . . . . . . . . . . . . . . . . $1.8 billion
   Military Expenditure as a Percentage of
      Gross National Product  . . . . . . . . . . . . . . . . . . . . . . . . . . . . . . . . . 2.7%
   Military Expenditure as a Percentage of
      Central Government Expenditure . . . . . . . . . . . . . . . . . . . . . . . . . . 9.1%

**Defense Treaties** *(See Part II for Additional Detail)*

   Bilateral:      France
                United States

   Multilateral:   Act of Chapultepec
                Biological Weapons Convention
                Inter-American Defense Board
                Inter-American Treaty of Reciprocal Assistance
                Limited Test Ban Treaty
                Treaty on the Control of Arms on the Seabed
                Treaty on the Non-Proliferation of Nuclear Weapons
                Treaty for the Prohibition of Nuclear Weapons in Latin
                   America

   **Military Rank Comparisons**
      See Appendix A.

# NIGER
## Republic of Niger
### *Republique du Niger*

## Defense Establishment Command Structure
## and Force Organization

The President is Commander-in-Chief and Minister of Defense. He is advised on defense matters by the Supreme Military Council. Operational control of the military is the responsibility of the Chief of the General Staff. The country is divided into three military regions; all Army units are attached to one of the three battalions in these regions.

**Total armed forces:** 2,220 (Army: 2,150;   Air Force: 70). **Para-military forces:** 2,060 (Presidential Guard, 200; Republican Guard, 1,500).

## HEAD OF STATE

H. E. Gen. Seyni Kountche

**OFFICE OF THE PRESIDENT,**
**SUPREME MILITARY COUNCIL**
*Niamey*

Telephone:   72 23 81
Telex:   5214 presirep

President of the Supreme Military Council,
   Chief of State, Minister of National
   Defense and Minister of Interior . . . . . . . . . . . . . . . .Gen. Seyni Kountche
Director, Cabinet. . . . . . . . . . . . . . . . . . . . . . . . . . . . .Mahamane Sani Bako
Secretary-General . . . . . . . . . . . . . . . . . . . . . . . . . . . . .Aboubacar Abdou
Head, General Secretariat of the Presidency . . . . . . . . .Madou Mahomadou
Head, Grand Chancellery . . . . . . . . . . . . . . . . .Gen. Dupuis Henry Yacouba
Counselor for National Security . . . . . . . . . . . . . . .Capt. Oumarou Amadou

**MINISTRY OF INTERIOR**
*Niamey*

Telephone:   72 21 76, 72 32 10
Telex:   5214 presirep

Minister . . . . . . . . . . . . . . . . . . . . . . . . . . . . . . . . . . . .Gen. Seyni Kountche
Minister Delegate . . . . . . . . . . . . . . . . . . . . . . . . . . . . . . .Amadou Fity Maiga
Commander, Presidential Guard . . . . . . . . . . . . . . . . . . . .Lt. Idrissa Amadou
Commander, Republican Guard . . . . . . . . . . . . . . . .Capt. Moussa Hassane

**MINISTRY OF NATIONAL DEFENSE**
*(Ministere de la Defense Nationale)*
*Escadrille Nationale*
*P.O. Box 626*
*Niamey*

Telephone:   72 28 40, 72 26 50
Telex:   5214 presirep

Minister . . . . . . . . . . . . . . . . . . . . . . . . . . . . . . . . . . . .Gen. Seyni Kountche
Secretary-General . . . . . . . . . . . . . . . . . . . . . . .Chef d'Escadron Pierre Houa
Grand Chancellor, National
   Order (Responsible for awarding
   military grades and awards) . . . . . . . . . . . . . .Gen. Depuis Henry Yacouba

## DEFENSE FORCES

**ARMED FORCES**
**Forces Armees Nigeriennes—FAN**
*Niamey*

Telephone:   72 25 11, 72 25 14

Chief of the General Staff . . . . . . . . . . . . . . . . . . . . . . . . .Lt. Col. Ali Seibou
Deputy Chief . . . . . . . . . . . . . . . . . . . . . . . . . . . . .Cdt. Toumba Aboubacar
Inspector General . . . . . . . . . . . . . . . . . . . . . . . . . . . . . .Lt. Col. Musa Sala

**Regional Commands**
Commander, First Battalion (Niamey). . . . . . . . . . . .Capt. Amadou Seydou
Chief, Military Commissariat
   (In charge of Procurement) . . . . . . . . . . . . . . . . . . . . . . .Intendant Ferrero

**AIR FORCE**
**Escadrille Nationale Nigerienne**
*Niamey*
*Telephone:*   *72 21 77, 73 24 02*
*Telex:*   *5214 presirep*

Chief . . . . . . . . . . . . . . . . . . . . . . . . . . . . . . . . . . . . . . . . . . Maj. Francois Wright

**NATIONAL CONSTABULARY**
**Gendarmerie Nationale**
*Niamey*
*Telephone:*   *72 28 40, 72 34 51*
*Telex:*   *5214 presirep*

Commander . . . . . . . . . . . . . . . . . . . . . . . . . . . . . . . . . . Cdt. Youssoufa Maiga

\* \* \* \* \*

# GENERAL DEFENSE DATA

**Manpower**
Total Armed Forces . . . . . . . . . . . . . . . . . . . . . . . . . . . . . . . . . . . . . . . . . 2,220
   (See Page 387)
Population  . . . . . . . . . . . . . . . . . . . . . . . . . . . . . . . . . . . . . . . . . . . 5,833,000

**Spending**
Military Expenditures . . . . . . . . . . . . . . . . . . . . . . . . . . . . . . . . . . . . $17 million
Gross National Product . . . . . . . . . . . . . . . . . . . . . . . . . . . . . . . . . . . $1.8 billion
Military Expenditure as a Percentage of
   Gross National Product . . . . . . . . . . . . . . . . . . . . . . . . . . . . . . . . . . . . 1%
Military Expenditure as a Percentage of
   Central Government Expenditure  . . . . . . . . . . . . . . . . . . . . . . . . . . . . . 4.8%

**Defense Treaties** *(See Part II for Additional Detail)*

   Bilateral:       France
                    Libya
                    United States

   Multilateral:    Biological Weapons Convention
                    Economic Community of West African States
                    Limited Test Ban Treaty
                    Organization of African Unity
                    Treaty on the Control of Arms on the Seabed

**Military Rank Comparisons**
   See Appendix A.

# NIGERIA
## Federal Republic of Nigeria

### Defence Establishment Command Structure and Force Organization

The Executive President is Commander-in-Chief of the Armed Forces of Nigeria. The Minister of Defence has administrative and operational control over the military.

**Total armed forces:** 187,000 (Army: 173,000; Navy: 6,000; Air Force: 8,000). **Paramilitary forces:** 200,000 (Police).

### EXECUTIVE PRESIDENT

H. E. Alhaji Sheju Shagari

**OFFICE OF THE EXECUTIVE PRESIDENT**
*State House*
*Rabadu Road*
*Ikoyi Island, Lagos*
*Telephone: (1) 684401, 681987, 684400*

Executive President and Commander-in-Chief of the Armed Forces ...................................... Alhaji Shehu Shagari
Minister of State, Special Duties ......................... Olu Awotesu
Special Advisor, National Assembly Liaison ........... Dr. K. O. Mbadiwe
Special Advisor, National Security ..................... Dr. Bukar Shaib
Minister of Police Affairs in the Presidency ........ Alhaji Ndagi Mamudu

**OFFICE OF THE VICE PRESIDENT**
*State House*
*Ribadu Road*
*Ikoyi Island, Lagos*
*Telephone: (1) 681987, 684400/1*

Vice President ..................................... Dr. Alex Ekwueme

**MINISTRY OF DEFENCE**
*Independence Building*
*Tafawa Balewa Square*
*Lagos*
*Telephone: (1) 633994*
*Telex: 22610 deptry ng*

President and Minister (Acting) of Defence .......... Alhaji Shehu Shagari
Federal Permanent Secretary ...................... Alhaji Aminu Saleh
Secretary for Defence ............................... E. O. Obayan
Principal Secretary, Services ...................... R. A. Bamboye
Principal Secretary, DP ............................. J. A. Akinyemi
Under-Secretary, Administration ..................... M. I. Nwagwu
Controller of Finance ............................... F. N. Esenwa
Project Manager ..................................... Col. B. K. Larola
Principal Technical Officer, Armed Forces Projects Division ...................................... Alhaji M. Babatunde
Project Manager, Electrical Engineering ................... S. C. Khana
Project Manager, Hydrology ......................... Dr. S. N. Singh
Project Manager, Architecture ....................... O. D. Olutimayin
Principal Engineer and Civil Engineer ..................... F. J. Olaofe

### DEFENCE FORCES

**ARMED FORCES**
*c/o Ministry of Defence*
*Independence Building*
*Tafawa Balewa Square*
*Lagos*
*Telephone: (1) 631056*
*Telex: 22610 deptry ng, 21535*

Chief of the Defence Staff ........................... Lt. Gen. I. S. Jalo
Deputy Chief of Staff .................... Vice Adm. Husseini Abdulahi
Adjutant-General ....................... Maj. Gen. David Jemibewon
Director-General, Recruitment ................ Maj. Gen. R. M. Dumuje

## ARMY
**Army of the Federal Republic of Nigeria**
*c/o Ministry of Defence*
*Independence Building*
*Tafawa Balewa Square*
*Lagos*

*Telephone:   (1) 632204*
*Telex:   22609, 22628, 22630*

Chief of Staff . . . . . . . . . . . . . . . . . . . .Maj. Gen. Mohammed Inna Wuhishi
Principal General Staff Officer . . . . . . . . . . . . . .Brig. Mohammed Remawa
Director, Ordnance . . . . . . . . . . . . . . . . . . . . . . . . . . . . . . . . . . . . . . . . . . . . .
Director, Logistics . . . . . . . . . . . . . . . . . . . . . . . . . . . . . . . .Brig. Gen. Ifere
Director, Material . . . . . . . . . . . . . . . . . . . . . . . . . . . . . . . . . .Brig. Gen. Toki
Director, Supply and Transport . . . . . . . . . . . . . .Col. Saidu Ayodele Balogun
Director, Military Intelligence . . . . . . . . . . . . . . . . . . . . . . . . . . . . . . . . . . . . .
Director, Military Education . . . . . . . . . . . . . . . . . . . . . .Brig. S. N. Omojokun
Director, Health Services . . . . . . . . . . . . . . . . . . . . . . .Maj. Gen. J. U. Ekong
Director, Military Pensions . . . . . . . . . . . . . . . . . . . . . .Lt. Col. P. Onyekweli
Quartermaster-General . . . . . . . . . . . . . . . . . . . . . . . . . . . .Brig. M. J. Vatsa
Commander, Signals . . . . . . . . . . . . . . . . . . . . . . . . . . . . . . . . . . . . . . . . . . . .
Commander, Artillery . . . . . . . . . . . . . . . . . . . . . . .Brig. Gen. M. G. Nasko
Commander, Infantry . . . . . . . . . . . . . . . . . . . . . . . . . . . .Brig. M. D. Jega
Commander of the Guards . . . . . . . . . . . . . . . . . . . . . . . .Col. M. B. Kaliel
Commander, Army Police . . . . . . . .Provost Marshal, Col. I. O. Nwachukum
Commandant, Nigerian Defence Academy . . . . . . .Brig. Abdullahi Shelleng

### Infantry Commands

Commander, 1st Division, Divisional Headquarters
   (Kaduna) . . . . . . . . . . . . . . . . . . . . . . . . . . . . . . . . . . . . . . . . .Maj. Gen. Innih
Commander, 2nd Division (Ibadan) . . . . . . . . . . . . .Maj. Gen. Joseph Garba
Commander, 3rd Division (Jos) . . . . . . . . . . . . . . . . . . .Maj. Gen. Ejiga
Commander, 4th Division (Ikeja) . . . . . . . . . . . . . . . . . . . . . .Maj. Gen. Bali

### Other Commands

Commander, 3rd Armoured Division . . . . . . . . . . . . . . . . . .Brig. M. Buhari
Commander, 2nd Mechanized Division . . . . . . . . . . .Brig. H. A. Haananyia
Commander, 1st Mechanized Division . . . . . . . . . . . . . .Brig. A. O. Aduloju
Commander, 4th Air-Lift Battalion . . . . . . . . . . . . . . . . . . .Lt. Col. Fagbire
Commander, 3rd Mechanized Infantry Brigade . . . . . . .Lt. Col. S. Z. Karau

## NAVY
**Navy of the Federal Republic of Nigeria**
*c/o Ministry of Defence*
*Independence Building*
*Tafawa Balewa Square*
*Lagos*

*Telephone:   (1) 635664*
*Telex:   65140 etnctex ng,*
*        61164 navale ng (Port Harcourt)*

Commander of the Navy . . . . . . . . . . . . . . . .Rear Adm. Benson-Okudawo
Chief of Staff . . . . . . . . . . . . . . . . . . . . . . . . . . . . .Vice Adm. Aksin Aduwo
Flag Officer Commanding, Western Naval
   Command . . . . . . . . . . . . . . . . . . . . . . . . . . . .Rear Adm. Denson Okujaga
Flag Officer Commanding, Eastern Naval
   Command . . . . . . . . . . . . . . . . . . . . . . . . . . . . . . .Commodore A. Ajanaku
Chief, Logistics . . . . . . . . . . . . . . . . . . . . . . . . . .Rear Adm. V. L. Oduwaiye
Chief, Operations . . . . . . . . . . . . . . . . . . . . . . . .Commodore A. A. Aikhomu
Chief, Materials . . . . . . . . . . . . . . . . . . . . . . . . . . .Commodore S. J. Uguna
Chief, Personnel . . . . . . . . . . . . . . . . . . . . . . . . .Commodore O. P. Fingesi
Superintendent, Naval Dockyard . . . . . . . . . . . . . . . . . . . .Captain C. O. Kaja
Commandant, Nigerian Naval College
   (Port Harcourt) . . . . . . . . . . . . . . . . . . . . . . . . . . . . . . .Capt. F. I. Nesiama

## AIR FORCE
**Air Force of the Federal Republic of Nigeria**
*c/o Ministry of Defence*
*Independence Building*
*Tafawa Balewa Square*
*Lagos*

*Telephone:   (1) 635557*
*Telex:   22613 naf ng, 22614 (Chief of*
*   Air Staff)*

Chief of Staff . . . . . . . . . . . . . . . . . . . . . . . . . . . . . .Air Vice Marshal A. D. Bello
Director, Operations . . . . . . . . . . . . . . . . . . . . . . . . .Air Comdr. A. Okpere
Air Officer, Operations . . . . . . . . . . . . . . . . . . . . . .Air Comdr. G. A. Osho
Air Officer, Logistics . . . . . . . . . . . . . . . . . . . . . . . . . . . . . . . .M. Yahaya
Director, Engineering . . . . . . . . . . . . . . . . . . . . .Group Capt. M. O. David
Director, Supply . . . . . . . . . . . . . . . . . . . . . . . . . . .Group Capt. I. Alkali
Air Officer, Administration . . . . . . . . . . . . . . . . .Air Comdr. M. Mohammed
Director, Administration . . . . . . . . . . . . . . . . . . .Group Capt. S. A. Mudasiru
Director, Personnel . . . . . . . . . . . . . . . . . . . . . . .Group Capt. S. Omeruah
Director, Works . . . . . . . . . . . . . . . . . . . . . . . . . .Group Capt. A. Daggash
Director, Plans . . . . . . . . . . . . . . . . . . . . . . . . . . . .Group Capt. J. Ehigie
Director, Training . . . . . . . . . . . . . . . . . . . . . . . . . . .Group Capt. J. Femi
Air Officer, Inspection . . . . . . . . . . . . . . . . . . . . .Air Comdr. L. O. Uwayzor
Director, Inspection . . . . . . . . . . . . . . . . . . . . . . .Group Capt. Z. N. Adama
Director, Manuals . . . . . . . . . . . . . . . . . . . . . . . . .Group Capt. A. U. Emaiku
Information Officer . . . . . . . . . . . . . . . . . . . . . . . .Wing Comdr. M. A. Adediji
Director, Pay and Finance . . . . . . . . . . . . . . .Group Capt. E. A. Ogunmiloro
Commander, Support Command . . . . . . . . . . . . . . .Group Capt. A. Imam

Commander, Tactical Command . . . . . . . . . . . . . . . . . . . . Air Comdr. I. Alfa
Commander, Training Command . . . . . . . . . . . . . . . Air Comdr. M. Muazu
Commander, Transport Group . . . . . . . . . . . . . . Group Capt. J. O. Atanda
Commander, Logistics Group . . . . . . . . . . . . . . . . . . Group Capt. F. S. Awe
Commander, Pay and Records . . . . . . . . . . . . . . . . Group Capt. U. Abbas
Commander, Communications . . . . . . . . . . . . . . . Group Capt. D. Ikpeme
Commander, Medical Services . . . . . . . . . . . . . . . . . . . Group Capt. Odeh
Commander, Air Traffic . . . . . . . . . . . . . . . . . . . Group Capt. N. B. Banfa
Commander, Ground Training . . . . . . . . . . . . . . . . Group Capt. Abdullahi
Commander, Flying Training Group . . . . . . . . . . . . . . . . . . . . . . . . . . . . . .
Commander, Strike Group . . . . . . . . . . . . . . . . . . . . . . . . . . . . . . . . . . . . . . .
Commander, Air Force Military School . . . . . . . Wing Comdr. M. N. Umaru

**POLICE**
**Police Force of the Republic of Nigeria**
*Headquarters*
*Maloney Street*
*Lagos*

*Telephone:*
*Telex:   71142 sigpole ng*

Inspector-General of Police . . . . . . . . . . . . . . . . . . . . . . M. Sunday Adewusi
Deputy Inspector-General . . . . . . . . . . . . . . . . . . . . . . . . . . . . . . . . . . . . . .
Commissioner, "A" Dept. . . . . . . . . . . . . . . . . . . . . . . . . . . . B. E. Eyitene
Commissioner, "B" Dept. . . . . . . . . . . . . . . . . . . . . . . . . . . . E. O. Ugowe
Assistant Commissioner, Railway Police . . . . . . . . . . . . . . P. B. O. Osayande
Assistant Commissioner, Federal Highway Patrol . . . . . . . . . . . O. A. Olowu
Force Public Relations Officer . . . . . . . . . . . . . . . . . . . . . . R. E. Ezekiel-Hart
Force Medical Officer . . . . . . . . . . . . . . . . . . . . . . . . . . . . Dr. P. C. Nwanze
Force Marine Officer . . . . . . . . . . . . . . . . . . . . . . . . . . . . . . . . . D. A. Alliu
Force Signal Officer . . . . . . . . . . . . . . . . . . . . . . . . . . . . . . . . H. K. Palmer
Force Transport Officer . . . . . . . . . . . . . . . . . . . . . . . . . . . A. O. Ogunewu
Commandant, Police College, Ikeja . . . . . . . . . . . . . . . . . . . . J. O. Akhigbe

\* \* \* \* \*

# GENERAL DEFENCE DATA

**Manpower**
Total Armed Forces . . . . . . . . . . . . . . . . . . . . . . . . . . . . . . . . . . . . 187,000
  (See Page 389)
Population . . . . . . . . . . . . . . . . . . . . . . . . . . . . . . . . . . . . . . . . 82,396,000

**Spending**
Military Expenditures . . . . . . . . . . . . . . . . . . . . . . . . . . . . . . . . . $2.2 billion
Gross National Product . . . . . . . . . . . . . . . . . . . . . . . . . . . . . . . . $87.8 billion
Military Expenditure as a Percentage of
  Gross National Product . . . . . . . . . . . . . . . . . . . . . . . . . . . . . . . . . . 2.6%
Military Expenditure as a Percentage of
  Central Government Expenditure . . . . . . . . . . . . . . . . . . . . . . . . . . . 9.3%

**Defence Treaties** *(See Part II for Additional Detail)*

Bilateral:      Chad
                Mali
                Soviet Union
                United States

Multilateral:   Biological Weapons Convention
                Economic Community of West African States
                Limited Test Ban Treaty
                Organization of African Unity
                Treaty on the Non-Proliferation of Nuclear Weapons

# NORWAY

## Kingdom of Norway
### *Kongeriket Norge*

## Defense Establishment Command Structure and Force Organization

The King is Commander-in-Chief of the armed forces. However, actual responsibility for military affairs lies with the government, which delegates its authority in these matters to the Minister of Defense.

The Defense Council acts as a policy forum. It also coordinates military and civilian activities in the area of defense.

The Chief of Defense is Norway's highest military officer. He commands the three services and the Home Guard. The Inspector-General of each service is primarily concerned with matters of administration and strategy. The heads of the two regional Defense Commands are Norway's top operational commanders.

**Total armed forces:** 42,100 (Army: 24,400; Navy: 9,400; Air Force: 8,300). **Paramilitary forces:** 85,000 (Home Guard).

## HEAD OF STATE

H. M. King Olav V

**OFFICE OF H. M. THE KING**
*Det Kgl. Slott*
Oslo 1

*Telephone: (2) 44 19 20*

King of Norway and Commander-in-Chief ................H. M. Olav V
Principal Private Secretary ............................Magne Hagen

**OFFICE OF THE PRIME MINISTER**
*Akersgaten 42*
*P.O. Box 8001, Dep*
Oslo 1

*Telephone: (2) 11 90 90*
*Telex: 19183 stm n*

Prime Minister ........................................Kare Willoch
State Secretary .......................................Erling Norvik
State Secretary .......................................Kjell Colding
State Secretary .......................................Erik Naesheim

**Defense Council**
*(Forsvarsradet)*

Chairman ...........................Kare Willoch (Prime Minister)
Member (*ex officio*) ...........Anders C. Sjaastad (Minister of Defense)
Member (*ex officio*) ...........Svenn Stray (Minister of Foreign Affairs)
Member (*ex officio*) ........Mona Røkke (Minister of Justice and Police)
Member (*ex officio*)..............Rolf Preshus (Minister of Finance)
Member (*ex officio*) ...............Arne Skauge (Minister of Commerce)
Member (*ex officio*) ........Inger Koppernes (Minister of Transportation)
Member (*ex officio*) ...............Kjell Eliassen (Foreign Councillor,
Ministry of Foreign Affairs
Member (*ex officio*) .............Casper Stephansen (Secretary General,
Ministry of Defense)
Member (*ex officio*) ........Gen. Sven Aage Hauge (Chief, Defense Staff)
Member (*ex officio*) ..........Genlt. Ulf Berg (Chief, Defense Command
North Norway)
Member (*ex officio*) ................Carsten A. Lutken (Chief, Defense
Command South Norway)

Member (*ex officio*) . . . . . . . . . . . . . . Tor R. Bryntesen (Director General of Civil Defense)

Member (*ex officio*) . . . . . . Finn Lied (Director, Defense Research Institute)

## MINISTRY OF DEFENSE
*(Forsvarsdepartementet)*
*Sørkedalsveien 148*
*P.O. Box 8126, Dep.*
*Oslo 1*

*Telephone: (2) 11 90 90*
*Telex: 11240 mildp n*

Minister . . . . . . . . . . . . . . . . . . . . . . . . . . . . . . . . . . . . Anders C. Sjaastad
State Secretary . . . . . . . . . . . . . . . . . . . . . Oddmund H. Hammerstad
Secretary General . . . . . . . . . . . . . . . . . . . . . . . . . . . Casper Stephansen
Director General, Administration Department . . . . . . Kristian Heidenstrøm
Director General, Personnel and Organization
    Department . . . . . . . . . . . . . . . . . . . . . . . . . . . . . . . . . . . . Arne Jokstad
Director General, Wages and Negotiations
    Department . . . . . . . . . . . . . . . . . . . . . . . . . . . . . . . . . . Aage Andersen
Director General, Material and Procurement
    Department . . . . . . . . . . . . . . . . . . . . . . . . . . . . Bernhard J. Eggesbø
Director General, Construction and Properties
    Department . . . . . . . . . . . . . . . . . . . . . . . . . . . . . . Johannes O. Leine
Director General, Policy, Planning and Budget
    Department . . . . . . . . . . . . . . . . . . . . . . . . . . . . . . . . Per Johannesen
Director General, Press and Information
    Department . . . . . . . . . . . . . . . . . . . . . . . . . . . . . . . . Chris F. Prebensen

### Defense Joint Materiel Service

Chief . . . . . . . . . . . . . . . . . . . . . . . . . . . . . . . . . . . Kom. II John Eid
Assistant Chief . . . . . . . . . . . . . . . . . . . . . . . . . . . Tom-Helmer Hexeberg

### Chaplain Corps

Chief . . . . . . . . . . . . . . . . . . . . . . . . . . . . . . . . . . . Ob. II Olav Tysnes

### Norwegian Defense Research Institute
*P.O. Box 25*
*N-2007 Kjeller*

*Telephone: (2) 12660*
*Telex: 76581 elect n*

Director . . . . . . . . . . . . . . . . . . . . . . . . . . . . . . . . . . . . . . . Finn Lied
Deputy Director . . . . . . . . . . . . . . . . . . . . . . . . . . . . . . Thomas Krog

### Defense Communications Administration
*Oslo Mil/Akershus*
*Oslo 1*

*Telephone: (2) 424546*

Director . . . . . . . . . . . . . . . . . . . . . . . . . . . . . . . . . . . . Birger Soma
Technical Director . . . . . . . . . . . . . . . . . . . . . . . . Andreas Stenseth

### Joint Medical Service
*Oslo Mil/Akershus*
*Oslo 1*

*Telephone: (2) 246590*

Director General . . . . . . . . . . . . . . . . . . . . . . Genmaj. Dr. Trond Kluge
Chief of Staff . . . . . . . . . . . . . . . . . . . . . . . . . . . Kom. II P. H. Lauritzen
Chief, Personnel . . . . . . . . . . . . . . . . . . . . . . . . . . . . . Oblt. A. Stark
Chief, Medical Branch . . . . . . . . . . . . . . . . . . . . . Ob. I. M. Tidemann

### Defense Construction Service
*Oslo Mil/Akershus*
*Oslo 1*

*Telephone: (2) 403030*

Director . . . . . . . . . . . . . . . . . . . . . . . . . . . . . . . . . . . Alf Bergesen
Technical Director . . . . . . . . . . . . . . . . . . . . . . . . . . . . . Finn Carlsen

## DEFENSE FORCES

### ARMED FORCES
### Headquarters Defense Command
*(Forsvarets overkommando)*
*Oslo Mil/Huseby*
*Oslo 1*

*Telephone: (2) 17 80 80*
*Telex: 11240*
*Cable: HQDEFCOMNOR*

Chief of Defense . . . . . . . . . . . . . . . . . . . . . . . . . . Gen. Sven Aage Hauge
Chief of Staff . . . . . . . . . . . . . . . . . . . . . . . . . . . . . . . Genlt. Rolf Eios

**Joint Staff**
Chief, Personnel Division . . . . . . . . . . . . . . . . . . . . . Ob. I Henning Synnevåg
Chief, Intelligence Division . . . . . . . . . . . . . . . . . . Kom. I Jan Ingebrigtsen
Chief, Security Division . . . . . . . . . . . . . . . . . . . . . . Ob. I Inge Torhaug
Chief, Operations Division . . . . . . . . . . . . . . . . . . Kadm. Sivert Farstad
Chief, Logistics Division
    (In charge of procurement) . . . . . . . . . . . . . . . . . Kom. I Egil Halvorsen

Chief, Plans and Budget Division ................Ob. I Cato B. Gravdal
Chief, Administration Division .............................(Vacant)
Chief, Liaison Section ..............................Ob. I Egil Lund
Chief, Communications and Electronics Branch ......Ob. I Konrad Spilde
Chief, Press and Information Branch .............Bjarne P. Lundgaard
Public Information Officer, Army.....................K. Haakenstad
Public Information Officer, Navy .....................J. Gundersen
Public Information Officer, Air Force ..................O. R. Bollmann
Public Information Officer, Home Guard ...............O. S. Knutsen

**Defense Command South Norway**
*(Forsvarskommando Sor-Norge)*
*Oslo Mil/Holmenkollen*
*Oslo 1*

*Telephone:  (2) 14 73 90*

Commander ..............................Vadm. Carten A. Lütken
Chief of Staff............................Ob. I Rolf J. Kvaerness
Commander, Land Forces ...............Genmaj. Bjørn Frantzen
Commander, Naval Forces ....................Kadm. Rolf E. Pedersen
Commander, Air Forces ...............Genmaj. Eyvind B. Schibbye
Chief, Tactical Evaluation ............................Ob. I E. Herud
Chief, Personnel Staff....................Oblt. Gunnar Sandsbraaten
Chief, Operations Staff ...............................(Vacant)
Chief, Operations Center ......................Ob. II Gunnar Berge
Chief, Land Operations ..................Oblt. Jørund Skåmedal
Chief, Air Operations ......................Oblt. Reidar K. Efraimsen
Chief, Maritime Operations ..............KK. Lauritz G. Karvel
Chief, Supply Staff (Logistics) ...........KK. Kjell B. Nielsen
Chief, Communications Staff....................Oblt. Agnar Sandvik
Chief, Engineering Staff .......................Oblt. Magne K. Nesset
Chief, Medical Staff............................Oblt. Ove J. Hjort
Chief, Administration Division ...............Maj. Aage S. Frenning
Chief, Intelligence and Security Staff ........................(Vacant)
Chief, Press and Information .....................Maj. Odd Lågstad

**Defense Command North Norway**
*(Forsvarskommando Nord-Norge)*
*P.O. Box 357*
*8001 Bodö*

*Telephone:   (2) 32 300*
*Telex:   64073 fkn n*

Commander.........................................Genlt. Ulf Berg
Chief of Staff.............................Kom. Olav F. Aamoth
Commander, Land Forces .............Genmaj. Martin Vadset
Commander, Naval Forces.........................Kadm. Torolf Rein
Commander, Air Forces .............Genmaj. Alf Granviken
Chief, Personnel Staff .....................Oblt. Gunnar J. Jervås
Chief, Operations Staff ...............................Ob. II A. Vik
Chief, Operations Center ..................Ob. II P. K. Heiervang
Chief, Land Operations .....................Oblt. Arild O. R. Wik
Chief, Air Operations ...............................
Chief, Maritime Operations .....................KK. Kjell A. Prytz
Chief, Communications Staff ...............Oblt. Thorbjørn Andreassen
Chief, Engineering Staff .......................Oblt. Arne Broberg
Chief, Medical Staff .......................Oblt. Kjell S. Aarnes
Chief, Administration Division .....................Oblt. Ola Grottland
Chief, Intelligence and Security Staff ......................(Vacant)
Chief, Press and Information ...................Maj. Terje Øvergard

## ARMY
**Royal Norwegian Army**
*(Haeren)*
*Oslo Mil/Huseby*
*Oslo 1*

*Telephone:  (2) 17 80 80*
*Telex:  11240*
*Cable:  HQDEFCOMNOR*

Inspector-General .........................Genmaj. Egil Ingebrigtsen

**Army Staff**
*(Haerstaben)*

Chief of Staff ....................................Ob. I Vigleik Eide
Chief, Personnel Branch ..........................Ob. II Alf Hammer
Chief, Army Supply Command (Procurement) .................(Vacant)
Chief, Organization Branch .............................(Vacant)
Inspector, Infantry ................................Ob. I Helge Faret

Inspector, Cavalry .................................... Ob. I Kjell Østli
Inspector, Artillery ........................... Ob. I Stein Langebråten
Inspector, Engineers ........................... Ob. I Ole Chr Englund
Inspector, Signals............................ Ob. I Bjørn Veie Rosvoll
Inspector, Army Transport ................... Ob. I Johannes Aarsand
Inspector, Medical Services....................... Ob. I Jan G. Narup
Inspector, Education .......................... Steinar Johannessen

**Land Command, East Norway**
*Hamar*
*Telephone:* *(65) 21660*

Commander ............................... Genmaj. Olav Breidlid
Chief of Staff ...................................... Ob. II Per Holm

**Land Command, South Norway**
*Kristiansand*
*Telephone:* *(42) 24067*

Commander ............................... Genmaj. Kjell O. Hope
Chief of Staff ............................. Oblt. Olav A. Haaland

**Land Command, West Norway**
*Bergen*
*Telephone:* *(5) 213640*

Commander .............................. Genmaj. Olav Litlleskare
Chief of Staff ..................................... Oblt. T. J. Fure

**Land Command, Trøndelag**
*Trondheim*
*Telephone:* *(7) 530530*

Commander .................... Genmaj. Thorbjørn B. Bergersen
Chief of Staff ............................. Oblt. Knut Bekkevahr

**Division 6**
*Harstad*
*Telephone:* *(82) 63520*

Commander ................................. Genmaj. A. Rosnes
Chief of Staff ............................. Ob. II Gullow Gjeseth

**Army Quartermaster Corps**
*(Haerens Intendantur)*
*Oslo Mil/Akershus*
*Oslo 1*
*Telephone:* *(2) 403030*

Quartermaster General .......................... Ob. I Olav R. Nagell

**Army Materiel Command**
*(Haerens Forsyningskommando)*
*Oslo Mil/Loeren*
*Oslo 1*
*Telephone:* *(2) 157590*

Commander......................... Genmaj. Karstein A. Kristiansen
Chief of Staff .............................................. (Vacant)

**Army War College**
*(Haerens Krigskolen)*
*P.O. Box 42 Linderud*
*Oslo 5*
*Telephone:* *(47-02) 403252*

Director.......................................... Oblt. Arne Pran

**NAVY**
**Royal Norwegian Navy**
*(Sjøforsvaret)*
*Oslo Mil/Huseby*
*Oslo 1*
*Telephone:* *(2) 17 80 80*
*Telex:* *11240*
*Cable:* *HQDEFCOMNOR*

Inspector-General ....................... Kadm. Bjarne M. Grimstvedt

**Navy Staff**
*(Sjøforsvarsstaben)*

Chief of Staff ............................... Kom. I J. Herman Hegstad
Inspector General ............................... Kadm. Roy Breivik

Chief, Personnel Branch . . . . . . . . . . . . . . . . . . . . . . . . . Kom. II Olar Kjetun
Chief, Organization Branch . . . . . . . . . . . . . . . . . Kom. II Ole Kr Thomesen
Inspector, Coast Guard . . . . . . . . . . . . . . . . . . . . . . Kom. I Magnus A. Stene
Inspector, Coastal Artillery . . . . . . . . . . . . . . . . . . . . . . . . . . . . . . . . . . (Vacant)
Inspector, Coastal Artillery (Air & Ground Defense) . . . . . . . KK. Per Sollien
Inspector, Coastal Artillery (Underwater Defense) . . . . . . KK. Kare Ilebekk
Inspector, Coastal Artillery (Weapons & Tactics) . . . . . . . KK. Terje Solvang

**East Norway Naval District**
*P.O. Box 21*
*3191 Horten*
*Telephone:　(33) 42081*

Commander . . . . . . . . . . . . . . . . . . . . . . . . . . . . . . . . . Kadm. Ivar A. Nielsen
Chief of Staff . . . . . . . . . . . . . . . . . . . . . . . . . . . . . . . . . . Kom. I T. Tofteberg

**South Norway Naval District**
*4600 Kristiansand*
*Telephone:　(42) 24067*

Commander . . . . . . . . . . . . . . . . . . . . . . . . . . . . . . . . . . Kom. I A. Danielsen
Chief of Staff . . . . . . . . . . . . . . . . . . . . . . . . . . . . . . . . . . KK. Johan Amundsen

**Rogaland Naval District**
*P.O. Box 9008*
*4020 Hundvaag*
*Telephone:　(4) 575000*

Commander . . . . . . . . . . . . . . . . . . . . . . . . . . . Kom. I Torbjørn Johannessen
Chief of Staff . . . . . . . . . . . . . . . . . . . . . . . . . . . . . . . . . . . KK. Einar Iversen

**West Norway Naval District**
*P.O. Box 1*
*5078 Haakonsvern*
*Telephone:　(5) 322000*

Commander . . . . . . . . . . . . . . . . . . . . . . . . . . . . . . . . . . . Kadm. Bård Helle
Chief of Staff . . . . . . . . . . . . . . . . . . . . . . . . . . . . . . . Kom. I Hans I. Hensen

**Trøndelag Naval District**
*7000 Trondheim*
*Telephone:　(7) 530530*

Commander . . . . . . . . . . . . . . . . . . . . . . . . . . . . . . . Kom. I Henning Grasmo
Chief of Staff . . . . . . . . . . . . . . . . . . . . . . . . . . . . . KK. R. Chr. K. Hansen

**Narvik Naval District**
*P.O. Box 8*
*8551 Lødingen*
*Telephone:　(82) 41560*

Commander . . . . . . . . . . . . . . . . . . . . . . . . . . . Kom. II Magne S. Sølvberg
Chief of Staff . . . . . . . . . . . . . . . . . . . . . . . . . . . . . . . . . . . . . . . . . . (Vacant)

**Harstad Naval District**
*P.O. Box 50*
*9401 Harstad*
*Telephone:　(82) 63520*

Commander . . . . . . . . . . . . . . . . . . . . . . . . . . . . . . . . . Kom. II K. O. Hegstad
Chief of Staff . . . . . . . . . . . . . . . . . . . . . . . . . . . . . . . . . . . . KK. K. Blakstad

**Tromsø Naval District**
*P.O. Box 5113*
*9021 Tromsdalen*
*Telephone:　(83) 84072*

Commander . . . . . . . . . . . . . . . . . . . . . . . . . . . . . . . . . Kom. II Finn Moseng
Chief of Staff . . . . . . . . . . . . . . . . . . . . . . . . . . . . . . . . . KK. Arne Sperbund

**Sea Training Command**
*(Kysteskadren)*
*P.O. Box 24*
*5078 Haakonsvern*
*Telephone:　(5) 323000*

Commodore . . . . . . . . . . . . . . . . . . . . . . . . . . . . . . . . . . . Kom. II Arne Utne
Commander, Training MTB's . . . . . . . . . . . . . . . . . . . . . . . . . . . KK. J. Moen
Commander, Training Submarines . . . . . . . . . . . . . . Kom. II Reidar Skarlo
Commander, Training Escorts . . . . . . . . . . . . . . . . . . . . . KK. K. N. Ritland
Commander, Training Mine Forces . . . . . . . . . . . . . . . . . . KK. H. Mallaug

**Naval Materiel Command**
*(Sjøforsvarets Forsyningskommando)*
*P.O. Box 3*
*5078 Haakonsvern*
*Telephone:　(5) 322000*

Commander . . . . . . . . . . . . . . . . . . . . . . . . . . . . . . . . . Kadm. Julius J. Meyer
Chief of Staff . . . . . . . . . . . . . . . . . . . . . . . . . . . . . . . . . Kom. II Ørnulf Daeli

**NAVAL WAR COLLEGE**
*(Sjøkrigsskolen)*
*P.O. Box 25*
*5034 YTRE LAKSEVAAG*
*Telephone: (5) 260530*

Director . . . . . . . . . . . . . . . . . . . . . . . . . . . . . . . . . . . . Kom. II Kåre J. Granmar

**AIR FORCE**
**Royal Norwegian Air Force**
*(Luftforsvaret)*
*Oslo Mil/Huseby*
*Oslo 1*
*Telephone: (2) 178080*
*Telex: 11240*
*Cable: HQDEFCOMNOR*

Inspector-General . . . . . . . . . . . . . . . . . . . . . . . Genmaj. Magne T. Sørensen

**Air Force Staff**
*(Luftforsvarsstaben)*

Chief of Staff . . . . . . . . . . . . . . . . . . . . . . . . . . . . . . Ob. I Eivind Tjensvoll
Chief, Personnel Branch . . . . . . . . . . . . . . . . . . . . . . Ob. II B. T. Helland
Chief, Organization Branch . . . . . . . . . . . . . . . . Ob. II Carl A. Bjurstedt
Inspector, Flying (Air Service) . . . . . . . . . . . . . . . . . Ob. II Nils Chr. Astrup
Inspector, Anti-Aircraft Defense . . . . . . . . . . . . . . . . . Ob. I Inge Tvedten
Inspector, Control & Warning . . . . . . . . . . . . . . . . . . . Ob. I J. Bakken
Inspector, Air Medical Institute . . . . . . . . . . . . . . . . . . . H. T. Andersen

**Rygge Main Air Base**
*1590 Rygge*
*Telephone: (32) 53520*

Commander . . . . . . . . . . . . . . . . . . . . . . . . . . . . . . . . . Ob. I Ørnulf L. Thune

**Gardermoen Air Base**
*2062 Gardermoen*
*Telephone: (2) 978110*

Commander . . . . . . . . . . . . . . . . . . . . . . . . . . . . . . . . . . . Ob. II Tore Engh

**Sola Main Air Base**
*4050 Sola*
*Telephone: (4) 651555*

Commander . . . . . . . . . . . . . . . . . . . . . . . . . . . . . . . . Ob. I Birger M. Strand

**Ørland Main Air Base**
*7130 Brekstad*
*Telephone: (76) 24100*

Commander . . . . . . . . . . . . . . . . . . . . . . . . . . . . . . . Ob. I Jens P. Andersen

**Bodø Main Air Base**
*8001 Bodø*
*Telephone: (81) 23040*

Commander . . . . . . . . . . . . . . . . . . . . . . . . . . . . . . . . Ob. I Olav F. Aamoth

**Andøya Air Base**
*8480 Andenes*
*Telephone: (88) 47011*

Commander . . . . . . . . . . . . . . . . . . . . . . . . . . . . . . . . . Ob. II Realf Ottesen

**Torp Air Base**
*3200 Sandefjord*
*Telephone: (34) 66456*

Commander . . . . . . . . . . . . . . . . . . . . . . . . . . . . Oblt. Karl F. J. Honningsvåg

**Lista Air Base**
*4560 Vanse*
*Telephone: (43) 93600*

Commander . . . . . . . . . . . . . . . . . . . . . . . . . . . . . . . Oblt. Fredrik J. Iversen

**Flesland Air Base**
*5069 Bergen*
*Telephone: (5) 226110*

Commander ................................... Ob. II Reidar Isaksen

**Vaernes Air Base**
*7500 Stjørdal*
*Telephone: (76) 94811*

Commander ................................... Oblt. Gunnar Wergeland

**Bardufoss Air Base**
*9201 Bardnfoss*
*Telephone: (89) 33011*

Commander ................................... Ob. II Per I. Utgård

**Banak Air Base**
*9701 Laskelr*
*Telephone: (84) 61344*

Commander ................................... Oblt. Arne M. Holden

**Fornebu Air Base**
*1330 Oslo*
*Telephone: (2) 533980*

Commander ................................... Oblt. John O. Spiel

**Linnerud Air Base**
*(Nike Battalion)*
*Oslo*
*Telephone: (2) 214250*

Commander ................................... Ob. II Oddvar A. Espås

**Air Force War College**
*(Luftkrigsskolen)*
*7000 Trondheim*
*Telephone: (7) 28834*

Director ....................................... Oblt. Hans Dramstad

**Air Force Materiel Command**
*(Luftforsvarets Forsyningskommando)*
*P.O. Box 10*
*7007 Kjeller*
*Telephone: (2) 717701*

Commander ................................... Genmaj. Arne Sejnaes
Chief of Staff ................................. Ob. I I. H. Jacobsen
Head, Organization and Planning Section ............... Ob. I Per Klemp
Head, Inspection Section ................................ (Vacant)
Head, Technical Section ........................ Ob. II Erik A. Tangen
Head, Materiel Section ........................ Ob. II B. Padøy
Head, Depot Maintenance Section ...................... Anders Lunde
Head, Economic Section ......................... Ob. II Ole Dokke
Head, Base Division ........................... Oblt. Eirik Sandberg
Head, Quartermaster Section (Supply) .............. Oblt. Sigurd Opland

**HOME GUARD**
*(Heimevernet)*
*Oslo Mil/Huseby*
*Oslo 1*
*Telephone: (2) 17 80 80*
*Telex: 11240*

Inspector-General ............................... Genmaj. Ola Berg

**National Council for the Home Guard**

Chairman ..................................... Jan T. Berg-Knutsen
Vice Chairman ................................. Herluf Nygaard
Secretary ..................................... Trond K. Tollerud

**Home Guard Staff**
*(Heimevernsstaben)*

Chief of Staff ................................. (Vacant)
Chief, Personnel Branch ............... Ob. II Sigmund Amundsen
Chief, Organization Branch .............. Ob. II Sverre Simonsen
Chief, Naval Home Guard ....................... Arne Knudtsen
Chief, Air Defense Home Guard ................ Oblt. Kåre O. Tofte

* * * * *

# GENERAL DEFENSE DATA

**Manpower**

Total Armed Forces . . . . . . . . . . . . . . . . . . . . . . . . . . . . . . . . . . . . . . . . . . . . . . 42,100
   (See Page 393)
Population . . . . . . . . . . . . . . . . . . . . . . . . . . . . . . . . . . . . . . . . . . . . . . . . . . . . 4,113,000

**Spending**

Military Expenditures . . . . . . . . . . . . . . . . . . . . . . . . . . . . . . . . . . . . . . . . . . . . . $1.5 billion
Gross National Product . . . . . . . . . . . . . . . . . . . . . . . . . . . . . . . . . . . . . . . . . . . $51.7 billion
Military Expenditure as a Percentage of
   Gross National Product . . . . . . . . . . . . . . . . . . . . . . . . . . . . . . . . . . . . . . . . . . . 3%
Military Expenditure as a Percentage of
   Central Government Expenditure . . . . . . . . . . . . . . . . . . . . . . . . . . . . . . . . . . . 6.7%

**Defense Treaties** *(See Part II for Additional Detail)*

Bilateral:     United States

Multilateral:    Biological Weapons Convention
               Environmental Modification Convention
               Limited Test Ban Treaty
               North Atlantic Treaty Organization
               Treaty on the Control of Arms on the Seabed
               Treaty on the Non-Proliferation of Nuclear Weapons
               United Nations Interim Face in Lebanon
               United Nations Military Observer Group in India and
                  Pakistan
               United Nations Truce Supervision Organization

# OMAN

## Sultanate of Oman
### *Sultanat 'Uman*

## Defence Establishment Command Structure and Force Organization

The Sultan is Commander-in-Chief of the armed forces of Oman. The three service commanders have responsibility for administrative matters relating to defence.

**Total armed forces:** 18,000 (Army: 15,000;  Navy: 1,000;  Air Force: 2,000). **Paramilitary forces:** 3,300.

## HEAD OF STATE

H. M. Sultan Qaboos bin Said

**OFFICE OF H.M. THE SULTAN, PRIME MINISTER, MINISTER OF DEFENCE, FINANCE AND FOREIGN AFFAIRS**
*The Royal Palace*
*Muscat*
*Telephone:  745 550, 600 631*
*Telex:  3445-9, 3385*

Sultan, Prime Minister, Minister of Defence, Finance and Foreign Affairs and Commander-in-Chief . . . . . . . . . . . . . . . . . . . . . . .H. M. Qaboos bin Said

**Advisor for National Security to H. M. The Sultan**
*P.O. Box 747*
*Muscat*
*Telephone:  722 857*

Advisor, National Security . . . . . . . . . . . . . . . . . . . . . . .Ali Majid a-Mamari

**OFFICE OF THE DEPUTY PRIME MINISTER FOR LEGAL AFFAIRS**
*c/o Ministry of Diwan Affairs*
*P.O. Box 5227*
*Ruwi, Muscat*
*Telephone:  722 841-3*

Deputy Prime Minister for Legal Affairs . . . . .Fahad bin Mahmoud al-Said
Undersecretary . . . . . . . . . . . . . . . . . . . . . . . . . .Hassan Saeed Mohammed

**OFFICE OF THE DEPUTY PRIME MINISTER FOR SECURITY AND DEFENCE AFFAIRS**
*(Located at Bait Al Falaj)*
*P.O. Box 602*
*Muscat*
*Telephone:  702 824*

Deputy Prime Minister for National Security and Defence Affairs. . . . . . . . .Sayyid Faher bin Taimur al-Said

**MINISTRY OF DEFENCE**
*(Headquarters: Bait al-ralaj, Ruwi)*
*P.O. Box 113*
*Muscat*

*Telephone:   701 109, 702 195, 702 963*
*Telex:   3228 defence mb*

Minister of Defence and
    Prime Minister ....................... H. M. Sultan Qaboos bin Said
Deputy Prime Minister for Security
    and Defence ...................... Sayyid Faher bin Taimur al-Said
Under Secretary of Defence and
    Assistant Chief, Defence Staff ....... Brig. Gen. Hassan Ehsan Nazeeb,
                                           WSH., WKhm., Bmv.
Director, Financial Affairs ................ Rashid Ali Ahmed al-Riyami
Director, Personnel .............. Sayyid Taimur bion Khalifa al Busaidi
Chief Engineer, Engineering Division ..................... John Flinton

**Procurement Offices**
*(Ministry of Defence Purchasing
    Agent: Charles Kendall and
    Partners, Ltd. 7 Albert Court
    Prince Consort Road,
    London, SW 2 England)*

Director of Purchasing ................... Abdul Aziz Sabir al Oremi

## DEFENCE FORCES

**ARMED FORCES**
**Office of the Chief of the Defence Staff**
*c/o Ministry of Defence*
*P.O. Box 113*
*Muscat*

*Telephone:   618 600, 702 290*
*Telex:   3228 defence mb*

Chief, Defence Staff ....................... Gen. Sir Timothy Creasey
Assistant Chief, Defence
    Staff and Under Secretary of
    Defence ...................... Brig. Gen. Hassan Ehsan Naseeb,
                                   Wsh., WKhm., Bmv.
Commander, Land Forces ..... Maj. Gen. J. P. B. C. Watts, C.B.E., M.C.
Commander, Air Force ............... Air Vice Marshall Erik P. Bennett
Commander, Navy ............................... Cdr. John Gunning

**ARMY**
**Sultan of Oman's Land Forces—SOLF**
*Headquarters*
*P.O. Box 897*
*Muscat*

*Telephone:   618 600, 618 601*
*Telex:   3228 defence mb*

Commander ............... Maj. Gen. J. P. B. C. Watts, C.B.E., M.C.
Deputy Commander ...................... Brig. Gen. Hamad Manah
Commander, Southern Oman BDE ....... Brig. Gen. Al Mutassim Hamad
Commander, Northern Oman BDE ........... Brig. Gen. Naseeb Hamad

**NAVY**
**Sultan of Oman's Navy—SON**
*Headquarters, SON*
*P.O. Box 897*
*Muscat*

*Telephone:   618 060*
*Telex:   3228 defence mb*

Commander ..................................... Cdr. John Gunning

**AIR FORCE**
**Sultan of Oman's Air Force—SOAF**
*Headquarters, SOAF*
*P.O. Box 897*
*Muscat*

*Telephone:   681 645*
*Telex:   3228 defence mb*

Commander ...................... Air Vice Marshal Erik P. Bennett

**ROYAL OMAN POLICE**
*(Headquarters in Qurum)*
*P.O. Box 2*
*Muscat*

*Telephone:   600 099*
*Telex:   3377 compol mb*

Inspector General ........................... Brig. Said Al-Kalbani

\* \* \* \* \*

# GENERAL DEFENCE DATA

**Manpower**
Total Armed Forces .............................................18,000
  (See Page 401)
Population ...................................................948,000

**Spending**
Military Expenditures.......................................$1.2 billion
Gross National Product .....................................$4.8 billion
Military Expenditure as a Percentage of
  Gross National Product .......................................24.6%
Military Expenditure as a Percentage of
  Central Government Expenditure .................................44%

**Defence Treaties** *(See Part II for Additional Details)*

    Bilateral:    United States

    Multilateral:   Cooperation Council for the Arab States of the Gulf
                League of Arab States

# PAKISTAN
## Islamic Republic of Pakistan
### *Islami Jumhuria-e-Pakistan*

## Defence Establishment Command Structure and Force Organization

The President is Commander-in-Chief and Chief of Staff of the Army. Operational and administrative control of the military is the responsibility of the Minister of Defence, who is advised by the Chairman of the Joint Chiefs of Staff.

**Total armed forces:** 478,600 (Army: 450,000; Navy: 11,000; Air Force: 17,600). **Paramilitary forces:** 109,100 (National Guard: 22,000; Frontier Corps: 65,000; Pakistan Rangers: 15,000; Coast Guard: 2,000; Frontier Constabulary: 5,100).

## HEAD OF STATE

H. E. Gen. Mohammad Zia-ul-Haq

### OFFICE OF THE PRESIDENT

**Secretariat (Public)**
*Murree Brewery Road*
*Rawalpindi*
*Telephone: 63600, 64533, 65717*

President of the Islamic Republic, Chief Martial Law Administrator (CMLA), Commander-in-Chief, Army Chief of Staff, Minister of Cabinet Affairs, Secretariat and Establishment Division, Planning and Development, Science and Technology, States and Frontier Regions ............................Gen. Mohammad Zia-ul-Haq
Chief of Staff to the President......................Lt. Gen. K. M. Arif

**Secretariat (Personal)**
*Mall-Mayo Road Crossing*
*Rawalpindi*
*Telephone: 65971*
*Telex: 5742 omlas pk*
  *(President's Residence)*

Military Secretary to the President.....................Lt. Col. Mohammad Zaheer Malik
Aide-de-Camp to the President ....................Maj. Qamar Zaman

**Cabinet Division**
*Pak Secretariat No. 1*
*Rawalpindi*
*Telephone: 63205, 23562*
*Telex: 791*

Secretary ...........................................Zahur Azar
Chief Martial Law Administrator and Army Chief of Staff ................Gen. Mohammad Zia-ul-Haq
Martial Law Administrator and Navy Chief of Staff ....................Adm. Karamat Rahman Njazi
Martial Law Administrator and Air Force Chief of Staff ...............Air Chief Marshal Mohammad Anwar Shamim
Martial Law Administrator, Governor of Punjab Province .........Lt. Gen. Mohammad Jilani Khan
Martial Law Administrator, Governor of Sind Province .....................Lt. Gen. S. M. Abbasi
Martial Law Administrator, Governor of North-West Frontier Province ............Lt. Gen. Fazle Haq Khan
Martial Law Administrator, Governor of Baluchistan Province .................Lt. Gen. Rahimuddin Khan

## MINISTRY OF DEFENCE
*Pak Secretariat Block 2*
*Rawalpindi*

*Telephone:   65819, 68709, 614891*
*Telex:    5779 DEFDV PK*

| | |
|---|---|
| Minister | Ali Ahmad Talpur |
| Secretary-General | Maj. Gen. (Ret.) M. Rahim Khan |
| Personal Secretary to the Secretary-General | Abdul Ghafoor |
| Assistant Personal Secretary to the Secretary-General | Ahmed Ali Dard |
| Secretary of Defence and Aviation | Asif Rahim |
| Additional Secretary of Defence | Air Vice Marshal A. Rashid Sheikh |
| Personal Secretary to the Additional Secretary of Defence | Nasrullah Khan |
| Additional Secretary-I | Rasheed-ud-Din Arshad |
| Additional Secretary-II | Air Vice Marshal (Ret.) S. A. Yusaf |
| Personal Secretary to Additional Secretary-II | Mahmood-ul-Hassan |
| Joint Secretary | Chief Abdul Qadir |
| Joint Secretary | A. S. Qureshi |
| Joint Secretary | Muzaffar Hussain |
| Chief Inspector, Armaments | Brig. Zewer Hassain |
| Joint Director, Defence Audit Department | Muhammad Saleem Siddiqi |
| Secretary, Defence Science Laboratories (Karachi) | |
| Secretary, Armed Services Board | Brig. A. Qadir Khan |
| Surveyor-General | Mian Muhammad Sharif |
| Director, Field Surveys | M. Rafique |
| Director, Military Lands and Cantonments Department | Abdul Jalil Khan |
| Director, Office of the CAO | Mohammad Latif |

### Defence Production Division
*Pak Secretariat*
*No. 11, Block 1*
*Rawalpindi*

*Telephone:   68316*
*Cable:   DEFENCE*

| | |
|---|---|
| Secretary | Vice Adm. A. Zamir |
| Director-General, Defence Purchases | Maj. Gen. Abdullah Khan |
| Director, Purchase Coordination | Brig. S. E. Jivanandham |
| Director, Purchase Coordination (Army) | Col. Muhammad Afzal |
| Director, Purchase Coordination (Navy) | Cdr. S. Z. Sultan |
| Director, Purchase Coordination (Air Force) | Wing Cdr. M. Bashir Ahmed |
| Chief Scientist and Scientific Advisor, Defence Science and Technology Organization | Dr. M. Aslam Khan |
| Chairman, Pakistan Ordnance Board | Maj. Gen. Talat Masood |
| Chairman, Defence Production Board (Secretariat) | Maj. Gen. (Ret.) Ihsan ul Haq Malik |
| Directorate of Works and Chief Engineer | Col. Faiz Muhammad |
| Director-General, Project-Directorate | Maj. Gen. Shabbir Hussain |

### Directorate General of Procurement (Army)
*8 Liaquat Barracks*
*Islamabad*

| | |
|---|---|
| Director-General of Procurement | Maj. Gen. Ch. Abdul Rahman |
| Deputy Director of Procurement | Col Dildar Ahmad |
| Deputy Director of Procurement | Col. Asghar Ali |
| Deputy Director of Procurement | Col. Mahmood Ahmad |
| Deputy Director, (A&C) | Lt. Col. Muhammad Idris |
| Deputy Director, Engineers | Lt. Col. Muzamil Ullah |
| Deputy Director, Supply | Lt. Col. Muhammad Bashir |
| Deputy Director, Medical | Lt. Col. Amin Ahmed |
| Deputy Director, Material | Lt. Col. Muhammad Irfan |
| Director Director, Signals | Lt. Col. Ansar Ahmad Zuberi |

### Directorate of Procurement (Navy)
*6 Liaquat Barracks*
*Islamabad*

*Telephone:   511535*

| | |
|---|---|
| Director of Procurement | Capt. M. E. Alam |
| Personal Assistant to Director of Procurement | S. H. Naqvi |
| Deputy Director of Procurement | Cdr. M. S. Ahmed |
| Assistant Director of Procurement | Lt. Cdr. A. L. Puri |
| Chief, Security | Ikram R. Siddiqui |

**Directorate of Procurement (Air Force)**
*No. 1, Liaquat Barracks*
*Islamabad*
*Telephone: 516547, 516585*

Director of Procurement ............................................

# DEFENCE FORCES

**ARMED FORCES**
**Joint Staff Headquarters**
*Chaklala*
*Rawalpindi*
*Telephone: 63350*

President, Commander-in-Chief
    and Chief of Staff of the Army ............Gen. Mohammad Zia-ul-Haq
Director-General of Plans .....................Maj. Gen. Syed Rafaqat
Staff Officer (Coordinator) to the
    Director-General of Plans .............Maj. Mansoor-ul-Haque Khan
Director-General of Logistics ........Rear Adm. Mohammad Fazil Janjua
Director, Joint Plans Group ...................Air Comdr. K. A. Mirza
Director, Operations and Intelligence
    Directorate..............................Brig. Khawaja Javed Elias
Director, Training Directorate ...............Comdr. Hamid Rab, P.N.
Director, Logistics Plans Directorate ..........Brig. Khaliq Ahmed Khan
Director, Administrative and Manpower
    and Materiel Directorate ...............................
Director, Inter-Services Public Relations
    Directorate ..................................Brig. T. H. Siddiqui
Director, Inter-Services
    Intelligence Directorate .........Lt. Gen. Akhtar Abdul Rahman Khan
Commandant, Pakistan
    Military Academy ...............................................
Commandant, Command and
    General Staff College ..........................................

**Joint Chiefs of Staff Committee**

Chairman .............................Gen. Muhammad Iqbal Khan
Member .......................................Gen. Sawar Khan
                                        (Deputy Chief of Staff, Army)
Member..........................Vice Adm. Tariq K. Khan, HI(M)
                                        (Chief of Staff, Navy)
Member .....................Air Chief Marshal Mohammad Shamim
                                        (Chief of Staff, Air Force)
Personal Staff Officer to Chairman .............Brig. Munib-ur-Rahman
Aid to Chairman ...........................Capt. Majeed Ismat Ch.
Officiating Director-General..............Maj. Gen. Kamal Matinuddin

**ARMY**
**Pakistan Army**
*General Headquarters*
*Rawalpindi*
*Telephone: 61600/2, 61404*
*Telex: 623*

Chief of Staff and President...............Gen. Mohammad Zia-ul-Haq
Deputy Chief of Staff .............................Gen. Sawar Khan
Adjutant-General.....................Maj. Gen. Zahid Ali Akbar Khan
Quartermaster-General ......................Lt. Gen. Saeed Qadir
Master-General, Ordnance .............Maj. Gen. M. Islan-ullah Khan
Embarkation Commandant,
    Embarkation Headquarters............Lt. Col. Mussod Ahmad Khan
Commander, Station Headquarters (Karachi) ..........Col. Syed Ahmad
Managing Director, Canteen
    Stores Department ....................Brig. (Ret.) Z. D. Ahmad
Commander, Karachi Fixed
    Communications Signal
    Company ........................Maj. Khurshid Alam Naz, PSC
Sector Commander, Headquarters,
    Karachi National Guards
    (Acting) ....................Brig. Iftikhar Ahmad Khan S. I. (M)

General Staff Officer (Training),
  Headquarters, National Cadet
  Corps., & Women Guards ...............Lt. Col. Habib Ahmed, S.J.
Commandant, Central Ordanance
  Wing (*Shahrah-e-Faisal*) ...................Lt. Col. Amanullah Khan
Commander, Headquarters,
  Karachi Logistics Area ................Brig. Mohammad Khan Malik

**NAVY**
**Pakistan Navy**
*Naval Headquarters*
*Liaquat Barracks*
*Islamabad*
*Telephone: 25831, 516781*

Chief of Staff.......................Vice Adm. Tariq K. Khan, HI (M)
Vice Chief of Staff ............................Rear Adm. M. Saeed
Director, Naval Intelligence ................Comdr. M. Siddiq Choudhry
Commander (Fleet) ............................Comdr. Y. H. Malik
Commander (Karachi) ........................Rear Adm. I. A. Sirohey
Director, Pakistan Naval Staff College ................Comdr. A. Tasnim
Director-General, Pakistan Coast Guards ......Brig. Shamim Yasis Manto

**AIR FORCE**
**Pakistan Air Force**
*Headquarters Peshawar*
*Telephone: 76430-9*

Chief of Staff .............Air Chief Marshal Mohammad Anwar Shamim
Vice Chief of Staff ..................Air Marshal Abdul Rashid Sheikh
Deputy Chief of Staff, Operations ........Air Vice Marshal Jamal A. Khan
Deputy Chief of Staff,
  Administration ........Air Vice Marshal Muhammad Ashraf Choudhry
Deputy Chief of Staff,
  Maintenance ......................Air Vice Marshal Atta Ilahi Sheik
Assistant Chief of Staff, Plans ...............Air Comdr. Amjad H. Khan
Director of Air Intelligence .................Group Capt. S.T.I. Piracha
Assistant Provost Marshal,
  Air Force Police........................Sqn. Ldr. S. Feroze Ali Rizvi

\* \* \* \* \*

## GENERAL DEFENCE DATA

**Manpower**
  Total Armed Forces.............................................478,600
    (See Page 405)
  Population ................................................93,106,000

**Spending**
  Military Expenditures.....................................$1.265 billion
  Gross National Product...................................$25.054 billion
  Military Expenditure as a Percentage of
    Gross National Product ..................................5.0%
  Military Expenditure as a Percentage of
    Central Government Expenditure ..........................23.2%

**Defence Treaties** *(See Part II for Additional Detail)*

    Bilateral:     China
                   India
                   Turkey
                   United States

    Multilateral:  Biological Weapons Convention

# PANAMA
## Republic of Panama
### *República de Panama*

## Defense Establishment Command Structure and Force Organization

The Commander-in-Chief of the National Guard controls the armed forces of Panama. Panama and the United States share responsibility for the security and defense of the canal, and the protection of its permanent neutrality.

**Para-military forces:** 11,000 (National Guard).

## HEAD OF STATE

H. E. Ricardo de la Espriella

**OFFICE OF THE PRESIDENT**
*(Oficina de la Presidencia)*
*Palacio Presidencial*
*Panama 1*

*Telephone: 221748, 228566, 222320*
*Telex: 2770 presipa pg, 2123 prescia pa*

President of the Republic . . . . . . . . . . . . . . . . . . . . . .Ricardo de la Espriella

**OFFICE OF THE VICE PRESIDENT**
*(Oficina de la Vice Presidencia)*
*Palacio Presidencial*
*Panama 1*

*Telephone: 229401, 228384*

Vice President . . . . . . . . . . . . . . . . . . . . . . . . . . . . . . . . .Jorge Illuecca

## DEFENSE FORCES

**ARMED FORCES**
**National Guard**
*(Guardia Nacional)*
*Apartado 3434*
*Panama 1*

*Telephone: 282802*
*Telex: 3145 gda-nal pg*
*(Cuartel Central Chorillo)*

Commander-in-Chief . . . . . . . . . . . . . .Gral. Brig. Manuel Antonio Noreiga
Aide to Commander-in-Chief . . . . . . . . . . . . . . . . . . . .May. Juan B. Cambra
Chief of Communications . . . . . . . . . . . . . . . . . . . . . .May. Arnulfo Castrejón
Chief, Panama Police . . . . . . . . . . . . . . . . . . .Tte. Cnel. Julian Melo Borbua
Chief, Presidential Guard . . . . . . . . . . . . . . . . . . . . .May. Nivaldo Madrinan
Chief, Maritime Operations . . . . . . . . . . . . . . . . . . . .May. Jorge M. Correa
Supervisor, Military Zones . . . . . . . . . . . . . . . . . .Tte. Cnel. Julio O. Young
Chief, 1st Military Zone . . . . . . . . . . . . . . . . . . . . . . . .Tte. Cnel. Macias
Chief, 4th Military Zone . . . . . . . . . . . . . . . . . . . . . . .May. Virgilio Mirones
Chief, 5th Military Zone . . . . . . . . . . . . . . . . . . . . . . . .Tte. Lorenzo Purcel
Chief, 6th Military Zone . . . . . . . . . . . . . . . .May. Carlos Arosemeña King
Chief, 11th Military Zone . . . . . . . . . . . . . . . . . . . . . .May. Gerardo García

**General Staff of the National Guard**
*(Estado Mayor General de la Guardia Nacional)*
*Apartado 3434*
*Panama 1*

Chief of General Staff . . . . . . . . . . . . . . . . . . . . .Cnel. Roberto Díaz Herrera
Deputy, Chief of Staff . . . . . . . . . . . . . . . . . . . . . . . . . .Cap. Arce Trujillo
Executive Secretary, Command and
    General Staff . . . . . . . . . . . . . . . . . . . . . . . . . . .May. Eduardo Herrera
Chief, G-1 Headquarters . . . . . . . . . . . . . . . . . . . . . .Tte. Cnel. Angel Mina

*Telephone: 227913*

Chief, G-2 Headquarters ...............Tte. Cnel. Roberto Díaz Herrera
Chief, G-3 Headquarters...........................Tte. Cnel. Castillo
Chief, G-4 Headquarters.....................Tte. Cnel. Marcos Justini
Chief, G-5 Headquarters.....................Tte. Cnel. Alberto Purcel

**Navy**
*(Marina Nacional)*
*Apartado 3434*
*Panama 1*
*Telephone: 221397*

Chief ........................................May. Juan B. Cambra
Deputy Chief ................................May. Moises Gomez

**Air Force**
*(Fuerza Aérea Panameña)*
*Apartado 3434*
*Panama 1*
*Telephone: 662000*

Commander-in-Chief .........................May. Augusto Villalaz

**National Department of Investigation—**
**DENI**
*(Departamento Nacional de*
*Investigación)*

Director-General ...........................May. Ricardo Garibaldo

\* \* \* \* \*

# GENERAL DEFENSE DATA

**Manpower**
    Total Armed Forces...............................................11,000
        (See Page 409)
    Population ...................................................2,011,000

**Spending**
    Military Expenditures ........................................$24 million
    Gross National Product .......................................$3.2 billion
    Military Expenditure as a Percentage of
        Gross National Product .........................................0.8%
    Military Expenditure as a Percentage of
        Central Government Expenditure .................................2.9%

**Defense Treaties** *(See Part II for Additional Detail)*

    Bilateral:      United States

    Multilateral:   Act of Chapultepec
                    Biological Weapons Convention
                    Inter-American Defense Board
                    Inter-American Treaty of Reciprocal Assistance
                    Limited Test Ban Treaty
                    Treaty on the Control of Arms on the Seabed
                    Treaty on the Non-Proliferation of Nuclear Weapons
                    Treaty for the Prohibition of Nuclear Weapons in Latin
                        America

    **Military Rank Comparisons**
        See Appendix A.

# PAPUA NEW GUINEA

## Defence Establishment Command Structure
## and Force Organization

The Papua New Guinea Constitution states that there shall be no Commander-in-Chief of the armed forces. The Minister of Defence, acting on the advice of the Commander of the Defence Force and on the authority of the principal legislative body, the National Executive Council, exercises control over the country's military forces.

**Total armed forces:** 3,775 (Army: 3,400; Navy: 300; Air Force: 75). **Police:** 400.

## HEAD OF STATE

H. M. Queen Elizabeth II

## GOVERNOR-GENERAL

H. E. Sir Tore Lokoloko, G.C.M.G.

**OFFICE OF THE GOVERNOR-GENERAL**
*Government House Konedobu*
*P.O. Box 79*
*Port Moresby*
*Telephone:  21 4466*
*Telex:  22275*
*Cable:  GOVGEN PORT MORESBY*

Governor-General ...................... Sir Tore Lokoloko, G.C.M.G.

**DEPARTMENT OF THE PRIME MINISTER**
*Central Government Offices*
*P.O. Box 6605*
*Boroko*
*Telephone:  27 1211*
*Telex:  23055*
*Cable:  SENTROFF FOR PRIMIN*

Prime Minister ............................... Michael Somare, M.P.
Deputy Prime Minister ............................... Paias Wingti

**Ministry for Media**
*(Government Information)*

Minister ........................................... Boyamo Sali

**DEPARTMENT OF DEFENCE**
*Central Government Offices, Waigani*
*P.O. Wards Strip*
*Telephone:  25 6166, 27 1329*
*Telex:  22194*
*Cable:  DEFENCE PORT MORESBY*

Minister .............................................. Epel Tito

**Office of the Secretary for Defence**
*Telephone:  24 2358*

Secretary for Defence.............................. Balthazer Maketu
Executive Officer....................................... Paul Tukan

**411**

Assistant Secretary, Finance and Programming . . . . . . . . . . . . John Kokinai
Secretary, National Assessment . . . . . . . . . . . . . . . . . . . . . . . . . . . K. Rigg
Assistant Secretary, Policy and Planning . . . . . . . . . . . . . . . Stephen Mokis

**MINISTER FOR POLICE**
*P.O. Box 2085*
*Konedobu*

*Telephone:  21 1222*
*Telex:  22113*

Minister . . . . . . . . . . . . . . . . . . . . . . . . . . . . . . . . . . . . . . John Giheno

# DEFENCE FORCES

**ARMED FORCES**
**Papua New Guinea Defence Force—PNGDF**
*H.Q. PNGDF, Murray Barracks*
*Free Mail Bag*
*Boroko*

*Telephone:  25 6166*
*Telex:  22157*
*Cable:  DEFENCE PORT MORESBY*

Commander . . . . . . . . . . . . . . . . . . . . . . . . Brig. Gen. G. Maipaka Mamae
Chief of Staff . . . . . . . . . . . . . . . . . . . . . . . . . . . . . . . . . . Col. L. Dotauna

**Operations Branch**
Chief of Operations . . . . . . . . . . . . . . . . . . . . . . . . . . . . . . Col. T. Huai
Director, Land Operations . . . . . . . . . . . . . . . . . . . . . Lt. Col. R. Lokinap
Director, Air Operations . . . . . . . . . . . . . . . . . . . . . Wing. Cdr. G. Barker
Director, Maritime Operations . . . . . . . . . . . . . . . . . . . Lt. Col. B. Manoi
Director, Intelligence . . . . . . . . . . . . . . . . . . . . . . . . . . Maj. A. Trongat
Director, Communications . . . . . . . . . . . . . . . . . . . . . . . Maj. J. Eayrs
Director, Force Operations . . . . . . . . . . . . . . . . . . . . . . . . . . Maj. Ani

**Personnel Branch**
Chief of Personnel . . . . . . . . . . . . . . . . . . . . . . . . . . . . Col. I. Glanville
Director, Health Services . . . . . . . . . . . . . . . . . . . . Lt. Col. A. P. Loscombe
Director, Personnel Services . . . . . . . . . . . . . . . . . . . . Lt. Col. D. Josiah
Director, Training and Education . . . . . . . . . . . . . . . . . Lt. Col. K. Frank

**Logistics Branch**
Chief of Logistics . . . . . . . . . . . . . . . . . . . . . . . . . . . . Col. B. Dademo
Director, Transport and Movement . . . . . . . . . . . . . . . . . Lt. Col. J. Bau
Director, Supply . . . . . . . . . . . . . . . . . . . . . . . . . . . Lt. Col. D. Takendu
Director, Engineers . . . . . . . . . . . . . . . . . . . . . . . . . . . Lt. Col. J. Tuat
Director, Technical Services . . . . . . . . . . . . . . . . . . . Lt. Col. J. Haurama

**Pacific Islands Regiment**

Commander, 1st Battalion . . . . . . . . . . . . . . . . . . . . . . . Lt. Col. L. Nuia
Commander, 2nd Battalion . . . . . . . . . . . . . . . . . . . . Lt. Col. R. Lokinap

**Other Commands**

Commanding Officer, Igam Barracks . . . . . . . . . . . . . . Lt. Col. K. W. Guria
Commanding Officer, Moem Barracks . . . . . . . . . . . . . . Lt. Col. L. Dotaona
Commanding Officer, Murray Barracks . . . . . . . . . . . . . Lt. Col. J. Sanawe
Commanding Officer, Taurama Barracks . . . . . . . . . . . . . Lt. Col. D. Josiah

**NATIONAL POLICE**
**Royal Papua New Guinea Constabulary**
*P.O. Box 2085*

*Telephone:  21 1222*
*Telex:  22113*

Commissioner . . . . . . . . . . . . . . . . . . . . . . . . . . . . . . . . . . Henry Toham
Head (Acting) . . . . . . . . . . . . . . . . . . . . . . . . . . . . . . . . . . . . T. W. Selva
Chief, Legal Section . . . . . . . . . . . . . . . . . . . . . . . . . . . . . . . . R. Tiden
Chief, Public Relations Section . . . . . . . . . . . . . . . . . . . . . . . G. Waranner

**Office of the Deputy Commissioner,**
**Chief of Administration**

Deputy Commissioner and Chief, Administration . . . . . . . . . . . . . . L. Dion
Assistant Commissioner, Personnel . . . . . . . . . . . . . . . . . . R. P. Symonds
Assistant Commissioner, Logistics . . . . . . . . . . . . . . . . . . . . . T. Samai
Chief, Stores and Equipment Section . . . . . . . . . . . . . . . . . . . . G. Hone
Chief, Transport Section . . . . . . . . . . . . . . . . . . . . . . . . . . . . J. Taylor
Chief, Works and Lands Section . . . . . . . . . . . . . . . . . . . P. Kamanabe
Chief, Research and Development (Acting) . . . . . . . . . . . . . . . J. Jakapan

**Office of the Deputy Commissioner, Chief of Operations**

*Telephone:   21 1222*

Deputy Commissioner and Chief, Operations (Acting) . . . . . . . . . .D. Tasion
Assistant Commissioner, General Operations . . . . . . . . . . . . . . . . .J. Napkai
Divisional Superintendent, "A" Division—
 Papua Region. . . . . . . . . . . . . . . . . . . . . . . . . . . . . . . . . . . . . . . . .J. Gamea
Divisional Superintendent, "B" Division—
 Highlands Region . . . . . . . . . . . . . . . . . . . . . . . . . . . . . . . . . . . . . .G. Ainui
Divisional Superintendent, "C" Division—
 New Guinea Coastal Region . . . . . . . . . . . . . . . . . . . . . . . . . . . .F. Mugugia
Divisional Superintendent, "D" Division—
 New Guinea Islands Region . . . . . . . . . . . . . . . . . . . . . . . . . . . . . .C. Pulai
Divisional Superintendent, National Capital Division . . . . . . . . . . . .G. Ora
Assistant Commissioner, Central Intelligence . . . . . . . . . . . . . . . . . .I. Geno
Chief, Narcotics . . . . . . . . . . . . . . . . . . . . . . . . . . . . . . . . . . . . . . .G. Tuka
Chief, Fraud. . . . . . . . . . . . . . . . . . . . . . . . . . . . . . . . . . . . . . .R. A. Howard
Chief, Interpol . . . . . . . . . . . . . . . . . . . . . . . . . . . . . . . . . . . . . . . . . . . . . .
Chief, Criminal Records . . . . . . . . . . . . . . . . . . . . . . . . . . . . . . .T. Hendley
Chief, Special Operations . . . . . . . . . . . . . . . . . . . . . . . . . . . . . . .P. Tohian
Chief, Communications . . . . . . . . . . . . . . . . . . . . . . . . . . . . . . .Maj. Brown

\* \* \* \* \*

# GENERAL DEFENCE DATA

**Manpower**

Total Armed Forces. . . . . . . . . . . . . . . . . . . . . . . . . . . . . . . . . . . . .3,775
 (See Page 411)
Population . . . . . . . . . . . . . . . . . . . . . . . . . . . . . . . . . . . . . . . .3,126,000

**Spending**

Military Expenditures . . . . . . . . . . . . . . . . . . . . . . . . . . . . . . . . .$30 million
Gross National Product. . . . . . . . . . . . . . . . . . . . . . . . . . . . . . . .$2.4 billion
Military Expenditure as a Percentage of
 Gross National Product . . . . . . . . . . . . . . . . . . . . . . . . . . . . . . . .1.3%
Military Expenditure as a Percentage of
 Central Government Expenditure . . . . . . . . . . . . . . . . . . . . . . . . . .3.5%

**Defense Treaties** *(See Part II for Additional Detail)*

Bilateral:     None

Multilateral:     Biological Weapons Convention
        Environmental Modification Convention
        Limited Test Ban Treaty
        Treaty on the Non-Proliferation of Nuclear Weapons

# PARAGUAY

## Republic of Paraguay
## *República del Paraguay*

### Defense Establishment Command Structure and Force Organization

The President is Commander-in-Chief of the Armed Forces of Paraguay. He has direct control over the Armed Forces General Staff, to which the staffs of the three services are subordinate. He also controls the National Police through the Ministry of the Interior.

**Total armed forces:** 16,000 (Army: 12,500; Navy: 2,500; Air Force: 1,000). **Para-military forces:** 4,000 (Civil Guard).

## HEAD OF STATE

H. E. General of the Army Alfredo Stroessner

**OFFICE OF THE PRESIDENT**
*(Oficina de la Presidencia)*
*Avda. El Paraguayo Independiente y O'Leary*
*Asunción*

*Telephone:    (21) 44 387*

| | |
|---|---|
| President of the Republic and Commander-in-Chief of the Armed Forces | Gral. de Ejército Alfredo Stroessner |
| Chief of the Military Cabinet | Gral. Div. Guillermo F. Clebsch |
| Military Aid | (Vacant) |
| Naval Aid | Cap. Ignacio Catalino Moreno C. |
| Air Force Aid | Cnel. Alcibiades Ramón Soto V. |

**MINISTRY OF NATIONAL DEFENSE**
*(Ministério de Defensa Nacional)*
*Avda. Mariscal López y Vice Presidente Sanchez*
*Asunción*

*Telephone:    (21) 204 771, 772, 773, 774, 775, 776*

| | |
|---|---|
| Minister | Gral. Div. (S.R.) Marcial Samaniego |
| Under-Secretary | Gral. Brig. Raul E. Calvet Torres |
| Military Assistant | Cnel. Aquiles García de Zuniga |
| Naval Assistant | Cap. Raul Fernández Coronel |
| Air Force Assistant | (Vacant) |
| Inspector, Administrative Services of the Army | Cnel. Pedro Vicente Gaete G. |
| Inspector, Administrative Services of the Navy | (Vacant) |
| Financial Director | Cnel. Geronimo Osvaldo Ventre |
| President, Supreme Military Court and of Appeals | Gral. Brig. Otello C. Carpinelli Yegros |
| President, Council of the ANAC | Tte. Cnel. Julio C. Zarza |
| Director-General, Civil Aeronautics | Cnel. Víctor Rafael Basualdo Fornells |
| Director, Military Industries | Gral. Brig. Juan Vicente Rabito |

**National War College**
*(Escuela Nacional de Guerra)*
*Tte. Fariña y Tte. Jiménez*
*Asunción*

*Telephone:    (21) 65 602, 61 140*

| | |
|---|---|
| Commandant | Gral. Div. Gustavo Prieto Busto |
| Deputy Commander | (Vacant) |
| General Assistant | Cnel. Daniel Lorenzo Arguello |
| Chief of Studies | Cnel. Hugo Christian Martínez |

415

**Paraguay-Brazil Joint Air Lane Commission**
*(Comisión Mixta Paraguaya-Brasileña de Ruta)*
*Asunción*
*Telephone:* *(21) 204 689*

Chief Member, Paraguay ................Cnel. Venancio Morinigo Britez
Chief Member, Brazil .............Cnel. Qema Alvaro Duarte de Oliveira

## MINISTRY OF INTERIOR
*Estrella y Montevideo*
*Asunción*
*Telephone:* *(21) 47 196*

Minister ...........................Dr. Sabino Augusto Mantanaro
Under-Secretary .........................Dr. Miguel Faustino Lamas

## DEFENSE FORCES

## ARMED FORCES
**Armed Forces General Staff**
*(Estado Mayor General de las Fuerzas Armadas)*
*Avda. Mariscal López y Vice Presidente Sanchez*
*Asunción*
*Telephone:* *(21) 22 370, 22 586*

Commander-in-Chief and President
   of the Republic ..................Gral. de Ejército Alfredo Stroessner
General Assistant ................................Cnel. Alfredo Zelaya
Commander, General Headquarters.......Gral. Brig. Francísco Ruiz Díaz
Chief, Armed Forces General Staff ....Gral. Div. Alejandro Fretes Davakos
Deputy Chief of Staff ..................Gral. Brig. Francísco Ruiz Díaz
Assistant to the Chief of Staff ................Tte. Cnel. Luis González R.
Assistant to the Deputy
   Chief of Staff ................Tte. Cnel. Miguel Angel Ocampos Roux
Chief, Personnel Department (D-1) ...........Cap. Nav. Pedro Rivas Jara
Chief, Intelligence Department (D-2) .....Cnel. Pedro Gómez de la Fuente
Chief, Operations Department (D-3) .........Cnel. Prisco Antonio Nunez
Chief, Logistics Department (D-4) .................Cnel. Roberto Orella
Chief, Mobilization and Planning
   Department ....................Cnel. Domingo A. Cabañas Vásquez
Chief, Transmissions Department (D-6) .....Cnel. Teofilo Oviedo Palacios
Chief, Economic and Finance
   Department (D-7)......................Cnel. Ramón R. Rodríguez
Chief, Public Relations and Military
   Ceremony Department (D-8) .........Cnel. Martín Marcial Brasa Pérez
Chief, Information Department (D-9).......Cnel. Martín Ubaldo Delgado
Quartermaster, General Headquarters ........Cnel. Panfilo Mora Escobar
Director of Publications .................Cnel. Eleuterio Servin Ramírez

**Presidential Escort Regiment**
*(Regimento de Escolta Presidencial)*
*Avda. Mariscal López y Gral. Santos*
*Asunción*
*Telephone:* *(21) 204 895*

Commander ..........................Gral. Brig. Francísco Ruiz Díaz
Deputy Commander .......................Cnel. Pedro Julian Miers
General Assistant to the Commander .........Cap. Expedito A. Garrigoza
Battalion Commander ....................Tte. Cnel. Juan Bautista Pistilli

## ARMY
*(Ejército de Paraguay)*
*Avda. Mariscal López y Vice Presidente Sanchez*
*Asunción*
*Telephone:* *(21) 22 370*

Commander of the Army ....................................(Vacant)

**First Army Corps**
*(Cuerpo I del Ejército)*
*Campo Grande—Km. 9 Via Verrea*
*Asunción*
*Telephone:* *(21) 290 992, 290 211–13*

Commander ...........................Gral. Div. Andres Rodríguez
Chief of Staff ..................Gral. Brig. Francísco Sanchez González
Assistant to the Commander................Tte. Cnel. Lino César Oviedo

**1st Cavalry Division**
Commander .....................Gral. Brig. Orlando Machuca Vargas
Chief of Staff ...............................Cnel. Ruben Adolfo
Assistant to the Commander .................Tte. Cnel. Oscar Saucedo

Commander, R.C. 1 "Valois Rivarola" . . . . . . .Cnel. Isidro Caballero López
Commander, R.C. 2 "Cnel. Toledo" . . . . . .Cnel. Victor A. Aguilera Torres
Commander, R.C. 3 "Cnel. Mongelos" . . . . . . .Cnel. Trifon G. López Prado
Commander, R.C. 4 "Aca Caraya" . . . . . . . . . . . . . .Cnel. Pablo Feschenko

### 1st Infantry Division
Commander. . . . . . . . . . . . . . . . . . . . . . . . . . . . . .Gral. Brig. Eumelio Bernal
Chief of Staff. . . . . . . . . . . . . . . . . . . .Cnel. Anibal Gabriel Acevedo Paredes
General Assistant to the Commander . . . . . . . .Cnel. Mario Aguirre Escobar
Commander, R.I. 14
    "Cerro Cora" . . . . . . . . . . . . . . . . . .Cnel. Lisandro Nery Caballero Vargas
Deputy Commander, R.I. 14 . . . . . . . . . . . . . . . . . .Cnel. Eustaquio Guillen
Assistant to the Commander, R.I. 14 . . . . . . . .Tte. Eugenio Alcaraz Adorno

### 3rd Infantry Division
Commander . . . . . . . . . . . . . . . . . . . . . .Gral. Brig. Victor Manuel Florentín
Chief of Staff . . . . . . . . . . . . . . . . . . . . . . .Cnel. Julian Aguilera Segovia
Assistant to the Commander . . . . . . . . . . . . . . . . . . . . .Cap. Lorenzo Bernal
Commander, R.I. 8 "Piribebuy" . . . . .Cnel. Floro Antonio Maciel Guerrero

**Second Army Corps**
*(Cuerpo II Ejército)*
*Villarrica*

*Telephone:    (21) 292*

Commander. . . . . . . . . . . . . . . . . . . . . . .Gral. Div. Pedro R. Floren Florentín
Chief of Staff . . . . . . . . . . . . . . . . . . . . .Gral. Brig. Bernardino Valoy Arza
Assistant to the Commander . . . . . . . . . . . . .Cnel. Jorgeliño Santacruz Feliu

### 2nd Infantry Division
Commander . . . . . . . . . . . . . . . . . . . . . . . .Gral. Brig. Miguel Ángel Berino
Chief of Staff . . . . . . . . . . . . . . . . . . . . .Cnel. Agustín Sánchez Rodríguez
Assistant to the Commander . . . . . . . . . . . . . . . .May. Cirilo Velásquez S.
Commander, R.I. 27 "Gral. Garay" . . . . . .Cnel. Ladislao Alfonso Martínez

### 4th Infantry Division
Commander. . . . . . . . . . . . . . . . . . . . . . . . . . .Gral. Brig. Juan de Dios Garbet
Chief of Staff . . . . . . . . . . . . . . . . . . . . .Cnel. Gregorio Manuel Delgado A.
Assistant to the Commander . . . . . . . . . . . . . . .Cnel. Miguel Ángel Salinas
Commander, R. I. 5 "Gral. Diaz" . . . .Cnel. Evelio Fabio Benítez Santacruz

### 5th Infantry Division
Commander . . . . . . . . . . . . . . . . . . . . . . . . . . . .Gral. Brig. José Roa Benítez
Chief of Staff . . . . . . . . . . . . . . . . . . . . . . . . . . . .Cnel. Justo Pastor Segovia
General Assistant to the Commander . . . . . . . . .Cnel. Armindo Jiménez Flor
Commander, R.I. 15
    "Lomas Valentinas" . . . . . . . . . . . . . .Tte. Cnel. Fernando Bejarano Mario

**Third Army Corps**
*(Cuerpo III del Ejército)*
*Mariscal Estigarribia*
*Chaco*

Commander . . . . . . . . . . . . . . . . . . . . . . . . . . . . .Gral. Div. Eduardo Sánchez
Chief of Staff . . . . . . . . . . . . . . . .Gral. Brig. César José Maria Bazan García

### 6th Infantry Division
Commander . . . . . . . . . . . . . . . . . . . . . . . . .Gral. Brig. Ricardo Bogado Silva
Chief of Staff . . . . . . . . . . . . . . . . . . . . . . . . .Cnel. Arsenio Echague Orlando
Commander, R.I. 6 "Boqueron" . . . . . . . . . . . . .Cnel. Aladino M. Enciso O.

### 7th Infantry Division
Commander . . . . . . . . . . . . . . . . . . . . . . . . .Gral. Brig. Alberto Aníbal Nizza
Chief of Staff . . . . . . . . . . . . . . . . . . . . . . . . . . . . . . . . . . . . . . . . . . . .(Vacant)
Commander, R.I. 10, "Sauce" . . . . . . . . .Cnel. Adalberto Fleitas Martínez

### 8th Infantry Division
Commander. . . . . . . . . . . . . . . . . .Gral. Brig. Juan Manuel Campos Guillen
Chief of Staff . . . . . . . . . . . . . . . . . . . .Cnel. Manuel Luis Santacruz Méndez
Commander, R.I. 4 "Curupayty" . . . . . . .Cnel. Juan Simon Paredes Bareiro

**Combat Support Command**
*(Comando de Apoyo de Combate)*

Commander. . . . . . . . . . . . . . . . . . . . . . .Gral. Div. Gaspar German Martínez
Chief of Staff . . . . . . . . . . . . . . . . . . . .Gral. Brig. Rogelio Bartolome Argana

**Military Guard of Paraguay**
*(Guardia Militar de Paraguay)*

Commander . . . . . . . . . . . . . . . . . . . . . . . .Gral. Brig. Enrique Duarte Alder
Chief of Staff . . . . . . . . . . . . . . . . . . . . . . . . . . . . .Cnel. Crispulo Peña Rojas

Assistant to the Commander ..................May. Felix H. Saldivar O.
Commander, R.I. 16, "Mariscal Lopez" ..............Cnel. Teofilo Bento
Commander, Artillery Group No. 1 ...........................(Vacant)
Commander, Artillery Group No. 2 ............Cnel. Tomás A. Aquino A.
Commander, Artillery Group No. 3 ................Cnel. Reinaldo Frigola
Commander, First Battalion of R.I. 16
    "Mariscal Lopez"...................Tte. Cnel. Eduardo Ramón Sosa

**Engineering Command**
*(Comando de Ingeniería)*
*4 de Mayo y 24 Pytda.*
*Asunción*

*Telephone:    (21) 80 463, 70 669*

Commander ..........................Gral. Brig. Alejandro Schreiber
Chief of Staff ..............................Cnel. Silvio Rafael Noguera
General Assistant to the Commander.....Cnel. Fructuoso Emilse Mendoza

**Transmissions Command**
*(Comando de Transmisiones)*
*Ayolas y 24 Pytda.*
*Asunción*

*Telephone:    (21) 72 708, 72 941*

Commander ..........................Cnel. Eladio Iriarte Domínguez
Chief of Staff ...............................Cnel. Luis Valiente Flor
Assistant to the Commander ................Tte. Cnel. Virgilio A. Lovera
Commander, Communications
    Batallion ...........................Tte. Cnel. Jorge Mendoza Gaete

**Logistical Command**
*(Comando de Logísticas)*
*Chiefs of Staff of the Armed Forces*
*Planta Baja*
*Asunción*

*Telephone:    (21) 206 181/9*

Commander ........................Gral. Div. César Machuca Vargas
Chief of Staff ...............Gral. Brig. Rafael Benito J. Guenes Serrano

**Office of Recruitment and Mobilization**
    **Services**
*(Dirección de Reclutamiento y Servicios*
    *de Mobilización)*
*Avda. Eusebio Ayala y Tte. Jiménez*
*Asunción*

*Telephone:    (21) 60 305, 61 206*

Director..........................Gral. Brig. Bernardino Peralta Baez
Deputy Director ......................Cnel. José E. Carballo Jiménez
General Assistant to the Director ........Cnel. Cristóbal Rodríguez Zarate

**Office of Services, Military Geography**
    **Institute**
*(Ofic. de Servicios, Instituto de*
    *Geografía Militar)*
*Asunción*

Director ................................Gral. Brig. Abraham Abed

**Office of Army Supply Services**
*(Dirección de Servicios de Provisiones*
    *del Ejército)*
*5 de Diciembre esq. Chile*
*Asunción*

*Telephone:    (21) 44 702, 45 218*

Director .........................................Gral. Joaquín Molas
Deputy Director, Materials .....................Cnel. Vicente Olmedo
Deputy Director, Subsistence ................Cnel. Elvio Alonso Martino
Assistant to the Director .....................Col. Aníbal Medina Godoy

**Office of Health Services, Armed Forces**
*(Dirección de Servicios de de Salud,*
    *Fuerzas Armadas)*
*Gral. Santos y Manuel Domínguez*
*Asunción*

*Telephone:    (21) 44 044*

Director ...............Gral. (Gral. de San Med) Dr. Tito Efigenio Velilla
Director, Central Hospital of the
    Armed Forces ...........Cnel. (Cnel. San Med) Dr. Víctor D. Olmedo
Commander, School of Military
    Sanitation ...................................Cnel. Lorenzo Morel
Director, Odontological Service of the
    Armed Forces ...................Cnel. Dr. Antonio N. Pangrazio C.

**Office of Training Services**
*(Dirección del Servicio de Entrenemiento)*
*Avda. Choferes del Chaco y Pacheco*
*Asunción*
*Telephone: (21) 60 405*

Director . . . . . . . . . . . . . . . . . . . . . . . . . . . . . . . .Cap. Jaime E. Grau P.
Commander, Training Batallion . . . . . . . . . . . May. Odalio Palacios Oviedo

**Office of Land and Cattle Farms, Armed Forces**
*(Dirección del Servicio Agropecuario de las Fuerzas Armadas)*
*Madame Lynch y Oberaba*
*Asunción*
*Telephone: (21) 29 886*

Director . . . . . . . . . . . . . . . . . . . . . . . . . . . . . . . . .Cnel. Eduardo Allende

**Office of War Materials**
*(Dirección del Servicio de Material de Guerra)*
*Campo Grande*
*Km. 9 Via Ferrea*
*Asunción*
*Telephone: (21) 60 234*

Director . . . . . . . . . . . . . . . . . . . . . . . . . . . .Cnel. Solano Ignacio Gamarra

**Military Institutes of Instruction Command**
*(Comando de Institutos Militares de Enseñanza) C.I.M.E.*
*5 Piso*
*Asunción*
*Telephone: (21) 206 181/9*

Commander . . . . . . . . . . . . . . . . . . . . . Gral. Div. Gerardo Alberto Johannsen
Chief of Staff . . . . . . . . . . . . . . . . . . . . . Gral. Brig. Ramón Humberto Garcete

**Francisco Lopez Military College**
*Capiata*
*Telephone: 23 723*

Commander . . . . . . . . . . . . . . . . . . . . . . .Gral. Brig. Luis Esteban Olmedo O.
Commander of the Corps of Cadets . . . . . . . . . . . . Cnel. Rogelio Levy Acuña
Assistant to the Commander . . . . . . . . . . . . . . .Tte. Cnel. Arsenio Caballero

**Acosta Nu Military Primary School**
*3a. Pytda. Ntra Sra de la Asunción y Chile*
*Asunción*
*Telephone: (21) 43247*

Commander . . . . . . . . . . . . . . . . . . . . . . . . . . . . . . . .Cnel. Dario A. Franco
Commander of the Corps of Cadets . . . . Tte. Cnel. Garlindo Felix Guaragna
Assistant to the Commander . . . . . . . . . . . . . . . .May. Francísco Ortíz Leiva

**Encarnacion Military Primary School**

Commander . . . . . . . . . . . . . . . . . . . . . .Cnel. Ramiro Manuel Benítez Velilla

**Military Instruction Center for Students and Reserve Officials**
*(Centro de Instrucción Militar para Estudiantes y Oficiales de Reserva)*
*Mariano Roque Alonso*
*Ruta Transchaco*
*Asunción*
*Telephone: (21) 290 440*

Commander . . . . . . . . . . . . . . . . . . . . . . . . . . .Cnel. Alfredo Diosnel Zelaya
Commander of the Instruction Center No. 1 . . . . . . . . . . . . . . . . . . (Vacant)

**Paraguayan Military Sports Federation**
*(Fedemipar)*
*Avda. Uruguay 258*
*Asunción*
*Telephone: (21) 26 900*

President . . . . . . . . . . . . . . . . . . . . . . . . Gral. Brig. Bernardino Peralta Baez

**Command and Staff School**
*(Escuela de Comando y Estado Mayor)*
*Avda. Gral. Santos y Buenos Aires*
*Asunción*
*Telephone:    (21) 204 958, 22 256*

Commander . . . . . . . . . . . . . . . . . . . . . .Gral. Brig. Luis Rolando Tomassone
Deputy Commander . . . . . . . . . . . . . . . . . . . . .Cnel. Isidro Gauto Caballero
Assistant to the Commander . . . . . . . . . . . . . . . . . . . . .Cap. Domingo Gaona

**Armed Forces Officer Training School**
*Avda. Eusebio Ayala y Tte. Jiménez*
*Asunción*
*Telephone:    (21) 61 737*

Commander . . . . . . . . . . . . . . . . . . . . . . . . .Cnel. Ramon Rivas Martínez
Assistant to the Commander . . . . . . . . . . . . . . .May. Luis A. Ferreira Garbini

**Armed Forces School Fiscal Education**
*(Escuela de Educación Física de las*
    *FF.AA.)*
*Avda. Uruguay 258*
*Asunción*
*Telephone:    (21) 204 950*

Commander . . . . . . . . . . . . . . . . . . . . . . . . .Cnel. Benito Morales Reichert

**NAVY**
*(Armada Nacional)*
*Hernandarías, e/Pdte. Franco y Palma*
*Asunción*
*Telephone:    (21) 93 707, 93 752*

Commander . . . . . . . . . . . . . . . . . . . . . . . . . . . .Vice Alm. César E. Cortese
Chief of Staff . . . . . . . . . . . . . . . . . . . .Contra Alm. Eduardo Gonzalez Petit
Assistant to the Commander . . . . . . . . . . . . . . . . . .Cap. Manuel Fernández
Commander, Coast Defense Corps . . . . . . . . . .Cap. Luis B. Davalos Bogado
Prefect General of the Ports . . . . . . . . . . . . .Cap. Óscar A. Brizuela Perdomo
Commander, War Fleet . . . . . . . . . . . . . . . . . .Cap. Carlos A. Royg Trujíllo
Commander, B.C. 1 "Boqueron"    . . . . . . . . . .Cap. Carlos G. Lopez Moreira
Commander, "Humaita" . . . . . . . . . . . . . . .Cap. Lucas Adolfo Sosa Salinas
Commander, Naval Aviation . . . . . . . . . . . . . .Cap. José R. Ocampos Alfaro
Director, Naval Materiel and Shipyards . . . . . . . .Cap. Carlos Andrés Cubas
Director, Naval Supply Service . . . . . . . . . . . .Cap. Luis Schroeder Martínez
Commander, Naval Command and
    Staff School . . . . . . . . . . . . . . . . . . . . . . . . . . . . . .Cap. Flavio A. Abadie
Commander, Training School of the Fleet . . . . . . . . . . . . .Cap. Luis Daponte
Commander, Center of Naval Instruction
    and Special Studies . . . . . . . . . . . . . . . . . . . .Cap. Luis Augusto Rojas Ortíz
Commander, Encarnacion Naval Base . . . . . .Cap. Sergio R. Yegros Viveros
Commander, Pdte. Stroessner
    Naval Base . . . . . . . . . . . . . . . . . . . . . . . . .Cap. Justo A. Rolon Maldonado
Director, Public Relations of the Navy . . . . . . . .Cap. Osvaldo José Corvalán

**AIR FORCE**
*(Aeronaútica Militar)*
*Campo Grande—Nu Guazu*
*Asunción*
*Telephone:    (21) 291 317*

Commander . . . . . . . . . . . . . . .Gral. Div. Luis Alberto González Ravetti
Chief of Staff . . . . . . . . . . . . . . . . . . . . .Gral. Brig. Ángel *Souto* Hernández
General Assistant to the Commander . . . . . . . . . . . . . . . .Cnel. Pablo Romero
Commander, Regiment "Silvio
    Pettirossi" . . . . . . . . . . . . . . . . . . . . . . . . .Cnel. Ismael Otazu Insaurralde
Commander, Military Air Transport . . . . . . .Cnel. Marcial Vargas Martinez

**Aeronautic and Naval Military Center**
*(Centro Militar, Naval y Aeronautico)*
*Estigarribia*
*Asunción*
*Telephone:    (21) 47 602*

President . . . . . . . . . . . . . . . . . . . . . . . . .Gral. Brig. Alejandro Schreiber
Vice President . . . . . . . . . . . . . . . . . . . . .Gral. Brig. Bernardino Peralta Baez

**Office of Aeroneutic and Naval Military**
    **Cooperation**
*Benjamin Constant egq. 14 Moyo 1*

President . . . . . . . . . . . . . . . . . . . . . . .Gral. Brig. Ramon Humberto Garcete
Vice President . . . . . . . . . . . . . . . .Gral. Brig. Francísco Sánchez González

\* \* \* \* \*

# GENERAL DEFENSE DATA

**Manpower**
Total Armed Forces................................................16,000
  (See Page 415)
Population ......................................................3,347,000

**Spending**
Military Expenditures ..........................................$49 million
Gross National Product ........................................$4.1 billion
Military Expenditure as a Percentage of
  Gross National Product ......................................1.2%
Military Expenditure as a Percentage of
  Central Government Expenditure ..............................11.4%

**Defense Treaties** *(See Part II for Additional Detail)*

    Bilateral:     United States

    Multilateral:  Act of Chapultepec
                  Biological Weapons Convention
                  Inter-American Defense Board
                  Inter-American Treaty of Reciprocal Assistance
                  Treaty on the Non-Proliferation of Nuclear Weapons
                  Treaty for the Prohibition of Nuclear Weapons in Latin
                    America

**Military Rank Comparisons**
See Appendix A.

# PERU

## Republic of Peru
### *República del Perú*

### Defense Establishment Command Structure and Force Organization

The President is Commander-in-Chief of the armed forces. Administration of the three services is handled by their respective cabinet ministers. Operational control and coordination of the military is the responsibility of the Chief of the Joint Command of the Armed Forces. Peru is divided into five military districts.

**Total armed forces:** 135,500 (Army: 75,000; Navy: 20,500; Air Force: 40,000). **Paramilitary forces:** 25,000 (Guardia Civil).

## HEAD OF STATE

H. E. Arq. Fernando Belaunde Terry

**OFFICE OF THE PRESIDENT**
*Palacio de Gobierno s/n.*
*Lima 1*

*Telephone:  (14) 27-1366*
*Telex:  20167 pe palacio*

President of the Republic and
   Commander-in-Chief .................Arq. Fernando Belaunde Terry
First Vice President ..................Fernando Schwalb López-Aldaña
Second Vice President .........................Javier Alva Orlandini
Secretary-General .......................Oscar Maurtua de Romana

**OFFICE OF THE PRIME MINISTER**
*(Oficina del Primer Ministro)*
*Avenida Abancay Cdra. 5*
*Lima 1*

*Telephone:  (14) 28-9590*
*Telex:  20187 pe*

Prime Minister and Chancellor .........Fernando Schwalb López-Aldaña
Secretary-General for the Prime Minister ..........Jorge Trelles Montero

## DEFENSE FORCES

**ARMED FORCES**
**Joint Command of the Armed Forces**
*(Comando Conjunto de la Fuerza Armada—*
*CCFA)*
*291 Avenida Arequipa*
*Lima 1*

*Telephone:  (14) 23-7351, 36-9778/2491*

Chief, Joint Command ..............Gral. Div. Arnaldo Briceño Zevallos
Chief of Staff .................................Gral. Div. Julian Julia
Assistant Chief of Staff.....................Gral. Div. Victor Pedraglio
Chief, District 1........................Contra Alm. Carlos Egúsquiza
Chief, District 2...........................Contra Alm. Carlos Saez
Chief, District 3 ............................Gral. Brig. Cesar Yanez
Chief, District 4 ...........................Gral. Div. Carlos Manucci
Chief, District 5 ................................................

**ARMY**
**Army of Peru**
*(Ejército del Perú)*
*Ministerio de Guerra*
*Avenida Boulevar S/n.*
*Lima*

Minister of War .........................Gral. Div. Oscar Brush Noel
Commander-in-Chief .............................Gral. Div. Briceño
Secretary-General of the Ministry of War ....Gral. Brig. Eduardo Chirinos
Inspector-General, Army .......................Gral. Div. José Balta
Commander, Region I..........................Gral. Div. H. Rejas
Commander, Region II (Lima)............Gral. Div. Guillermo Monzón

*Telephone:  (14) 35-9567*
*Telex:  25438 pe congregi*
    *(Ministerio de Guerra*
      *Comandancia, Monterrico)*

Director, Central Academy . . . . . . . . . . . . . . . . . . . .Gral. Div. Jorge Torres
Director, Personnel. . . . . . . . . . . . . . . . . . . . . . . . .Gral. Div. Hernan Romero

**Army Logistics Command**
*(Comando de Logisticas del Ejército)*
*(In charge of procurement)*
*Telephone:  (14) 36-1629*

Director . . . . . . . . . . . . . . . . . . . . . . . . . . . . . . . .Gral. Div. Francisco Mauri

**Military Industries of Peru**
*(Industrias Militarias del Perú)*
*3008 Avenida Benavides*
*Telephone:  (14) 52-8503*

Manager . . . . . . . . . . . . . . . . . . . . . . . . . . . . . . . .Gral. Div. German Parra

**NAVY**
**Navy of Peru**
*(Marina de Guerra del Perú)*
*Ministério de Marina*
*Avenida Salaverry*
*Cuadra 24 S/n.*
*Lima*
*Telephone:  (14) 31-4620*

Minister of the Navy . . . . . . . . . . . . . . . . . . .Vice Alm. Jorge Dubois Gervasi
Commander-in-Chief, Navy . . . . . . . . . . . . . . .Vice Alm. Ricardo Zevallos
Commander, Naval Operations . . . . . . . . . . .Vice Alm. Geronimo Cafferata
Inspector-General . . . . . . . . . . . . . . . . . . . . . . .Vice Alm. Victor Nicolini
Commander, Naval Zone II
   and Callao Naval Base . . . . . . . . . . . . . . . . . . .Vice Alm. José Carcelan
Commander, Surface Forces . . . . . . . . . . . . . . .Contra Alm. Ciro Saravia
Commander, Submarine Force . . . . . . . . . . . . .Contra Alm. Alfonso Panizo
Commander, Naval Aviation Forces . . . . . .Contra Alm. Raúl Vargas-Fuller
Commander, Amazon Naval Zone
   and Naval Forces . . . . . . . . . . . . . . . . . . . . . . .Contra Alm. Jaime Navach
Director-General, Maritime Interests . . . . .Contra Alm. António Forcelledo
Director, Personnel. . . . . . . . . . . . . . . . . . . . . .Vice Alm. Javier Llerena Pérez
Director, Engineers . . . . . . . . . . . . . . . . . . . . . .Contra Alm. Cesar Villaran
Director, Communications . . . . . . . . . . . . . . . .Contra Alm. Julio de los Rios
Director, Commercial Shipping . . . . . . . . . . . .Contra Alm. Andres Ferrari

**General Staff, Navy**
*Telephone:  31-4620*

Chief of Staff . . . . . . . . . . . . . . . . . . . . . . . . . .Vice Alm. Carlos Garrido Lecca
Deputy Chief . . . . . . . . . . . . . . . . . . . . . . . . . . . . .Alm. Alberto Trigoso

**Marine Corps**
*(Cuerpo Maritimo)*

Commander . . . . . . . . . . . . . . . . . . . . . . . . . . . .Contra Alm. Enrique Brian

**Hydrolic & Navigation Department**
*(Dirección de Hidrografia*
  *y Navegación)*

Director . . . . . . . . . . . . . . . . . . . . . . .Contra Alm. Jorge del Aguila Sanchez

**Naval War College**
*(Escuela Naval de Guerra)*
*590 Ave. S. Peña*
*La Punta*
*Telephone:  65-3565*

Director . . . . . . . . . . . . . . . . . . . . . . . . . . . . . .Contra Alm. Daniel Mariscal

**Navy Logistics Command**
*(Comando Naval de Logistica)*
*(In charge of procurement)*

Director . . . . . . . . . . . . . . . . . . . . . . . . . . . . . . .Vice Alm. Julio Pacheco

**AIR FORCE**
**Air Force of Peru**
*(Fuerza Area Del Peru-FAP)*
*Ministério de Aeronautica*

Minister of Aeronautics . . . . . . .Tte. Gral. Hernán Boularte Ponce de León
Secretary-General of Aeronautics . . . . . . .May. Gral. Luis Nicho Fernandez
Commander. . . . . . . . . . . . . . . . . . . . . . . . . . . . . . . .Tte. Gral. José Zlatar
Commander, Operations . . . . . . . . . . . .Tte. Gral. Hardy Montoya Alvarez

Campo de Marte
Jesús Marí
Lima

Telephone: (14) 32-5540
Telex: 20125 pe minear

**General Staff, Air Force**
(Estado Mayor General, Fuerza Aerea)

Telephone: (14) 32-5540

**Air Force War College**
(Escuela Superior de Guerra de la
  Fuerza Aerea)
488 M de Pino
Lima

Telephone: (14) 71-9419

**Air Force Material Command**
(Comando de Materiales de la Fuerza
  Aerea)
(In charge of procurement)
Telephone: (14) 23-0507

**Civil Guard**
(Guardia Civil)

**Investigative Police**
(Policia Investigativa)

Commander, Air Defense............May. Gral. Luis Vizcardo Vizcarra
Commander, Personnel.............May. Gral. Cesar Olivera Fernandez
Commander, Instruction...............May. Gral. Pablo Verela Novella
Chief, Public Relations..................Cdr. Oscar Granthon Stagnaro
Commander, Las Palmas Air Base........May. Gral. Cesar Gonzalo Luza
Commander, Collique Air Base........Cnel. Apolinario Figueroa Gutarra

Chief of Staff ..........................Tte. Gral. Cesar Enrico Praeli
Deputy Chief ......................May. Gral. Alfredo Lema Miranda

Director........................May. Gral. Arnaldo Velar de Ramirez
Deputy Director........................Cnel. Carlos Bernales Parodi

Director..........................Tte. Gral. Juan Vernal Castagnino
Deputy Director ..................May. Gral. Percy Belarde de Vargas

Chief .........................................Gral. Rodolfo Graham

Chief .........................................Romulo Alayza Tejada

\* \* \* \* \*

# GENERAL DEFENSE DATA

**Manpower**
    Total Armed Forces .............................................135,500
        (See Page 423)
    Population ................................................18,631,000

**Spending**
    Military Expenditures.........................................$900 million
    Gross National Product ....................................$19.5 billion
    Military Expenditure as a Percentage of
        Gross National Product .........................................4.6%
    Military Expenditure as a Percentage of
        Central Government Expenditure ..............................24.4%

**Defense Treaties** (See Part II for Additional Detail)

    Bilateral:      United States

    Multilateral:   Act of Chapultepec
                    Inter-American Defense Board
                    Inter-American Treaty of Reciprocal Assistance
                    Limited Test Ban Treaty
                    Treaty on the Non-Proliferation of Nuclear Weapons
                    Treaty for the Prohibition of Nuclear Weapons in Latin
                        America

# PHILIPPINES
## Republic of the Philippines
*Republika ñg Pilipinas* (Pilipino)
*República de Filipinas* (Spanish)

## Defense Establishment Command Structure and Force Organization

The President is Commander-in-Chief of the Armed Forces of the Philippines (AFP), which are comprised of four seperate services (Army, Navy, Air Force, and Constabulary) administered by a joint headquarters. The President is advised on defense matters by the National Intelligence Security Authority and the National Security Council.

Administrative control of the military is exercised by the Minister of Defense, and operational command by the Chief of Staff of the Armed Forces. The Chief of Staff is advised by a General Military Council, whose members include the four service commanders.

The AFP are organized into five regional commands: NORTHCOM, SOUTHCOM, WESTCOM, CEMCOM, and EASTCOM. Logistics are the responsibility of an inter-service Logistics Center.

**Total armed forces:** 112,800 (Army: 70,000; Navy: 26,000; Air Force: 16,800). **Paramilitary forces:** 110,500 (Constabulary: 43,500; Civil Home Defence Force: 65,000; Coastguard: 2,000).

## HEAD OF STATE

H. E. Ferdinand Edralin Marcos

**OFFICE OF THE PRESIDENT**
*Malacanang*
*Metro Manila*
*Telephone:  47 21 31, 47 96 61*

President of the Republic and
Commander-in-Chief ....................Ferdinand Edralin Marcos
Presidential Executive Assistant ......................Juan C. Tuvera
Presidential Security Command/
Commanding General ................Brig. Gen. Santiago Barangan

**OFFICE OF THE PRIME MINISTER**
*Room 518, Central Bank Building*
*Mabini Corner Vito Cruz*
*Metro Manila*
*Telephone:  (2) 05 70 51*
*Telex:  0268 cbc onf*

Prime Minister .....................................Cesar E. A. Virata
Deputy Prime Minister ...............................Jose A. Rono

**National Security Council**

Chairman .........................................Cesar E. A. Virata
(Prime Minister and Minister of Finance)
Member *(ex officio)* ...............................Carlos P. Romulo
(Minister of Foreign Affairs)
Member *(ex officio)* ..............................Juan Ponce Enrile
(Minister of National Defense)
Member *(ex officio)* ...............................Ricardo C. Puno
(Minister of Justice)
Member *(ex officio)* ..........................Gregorio S. Cendana
(Minister of Public Information)

**National Intelligence Security Agency**

Director-General .................................Gen. Fabian C. Ver

427

**MINISTRY OF NATIONAL DEFENSE**
*Camp General Emilio Aguinaldo*
*Quezon City*
*Metro Manila*
*Telephone: (2) 78 97 26, 78 69 11, 78 29 61*
*Telex: 22471 dnd ph*

Minister of National Defense . . . . . . . . . . . . . . . . . . . . . .Juan Ponce Enrile
Deputy Minister for Home Defense and
   Officer-in-Charge, National Police Commission . . . . . . . . . .Jose M. Crisol
Senior Military Assistant to the Deputy
   Minister for Home Defense . . . . . . .Col. Conrado G. Samarista, PA, GSC
Deputy Minister for Defense for Munitions . . . . . . . . . . . .Isabelo R. Castro
Senior Military Assistant to the
   Deputy Minister for Munitions . . . . . . . . .Col. Danilo C. Lazo, PA, GSC
Deputy Minister for Civilian Relations and Chief,
   Office of Detainee Affairs . . . . . . . . . . . . . . . . . . . . . . . . . . . . . . .(Vacant)
Senior Military Assistant to the Deputy
   Minister for Civilian Relations . . . . . . .Col. Eduardo R. Ermita, PA, GSC
Senior Assistant Secretary of
   National Defense and Senior
   Military Assistant . . . . . . . . . . . . . . . . . . . . . .Brig. Gen. Jaime M. Alfonso
Assistant Secretary for Legal
   Affairs . . . . . . . . . . . . . . .Brig. Gen. Samuel M. Soriano, JAGS, MNSA
Deputy Assistant Secretary for Legal
   Affairs . . . . . . . . . . . . . . . . . . . . . . . . . . .Atty. Ramon F. Nieva, MNSA
Chief, Action Center . . . . . . . . . . . . . . . . . .Atty. Diosdado M. Cervantes
Assistant Secretary for Plans and
   Programs . . . . . . . . . . . . . . . . . . . . . . .Brig. Gen. Victor C. Lizardo (Ret.)
Deputy Assistant Secretary for Plans and
   Programs . . . . . . . . . . . . . . . . . . . . . . . . . . .Capt. Virgilio O. Bartolome, PN
Assistant Secretary for Administration . . . .Atty. Marcelino C. De Guzman
Deputy Assistant Secretary for Administration . . .Atty. Rodrigo D. Dandoy
Assistant Secretary for Installations and
   Logistics . . . . . . . . . . . . . . . . . . . . . . . . . .Brig. Gen. Mario C. Espina (Ret.)
Assistant Secretary for Comptrollership . . . . . . . . . .Brig. Gen. Teruel (Ret.)
Chief, Public Information Service . . . . . . . . . . . . . . .Atty. Jose T. Flores, Jr.
Deputy Chief, Public Information Service . . . . .Mr. Silvestre C. Afable, Jr.
Chief, Protocol . . . . . . . . . . . . . . . . . . . . . . . . . . . .Col. Tito C. Robles (Ret.)
Special Assistant, Veterans Affairs . . . . . . . . . . . . . .Col. Oaias E. Labao, PC
Officer-in-Charge, Special Assistance
   Unit . . . . . . . . . . . . . . . . . . . . . . . . . . . . .Mr. Gregorio R. Florencio, Jr.
Director, Government Arsenal . . . . .Col. Florante M. Buenaventura (Ret.)
Public Relations Officer,
   Government Arsenal . . . . . . . . . . . . . . . . . . . .Capt. Artemio C. Bahia, PC
Administrator, Office of
   Civil Defense (OCD) . . . . . . . . . . . . . .Col. Victor R. Pagulayan, Jr. (Ret.)
Public Relations Officer, OCD . . . . . . . . . . . . . . . . .Atty. Priscilla P. Duque
Director, Bureau of Coast and
   Geodetic Survey (BSGS) . . . . . . . . . . . . . . . .Comdr. Antonio P. Ventura
Public Relations Officer, BCGS . . . . . . . . . . . . . . . .Miss Erlinda M. Cadano
Director, Philippine Atmospheric,
   Geophysical, and Astronomical
   Services Administration (PAGASA) . . . . . . . . . . .Dr. Roman L. Kintanar
Public Relations Officer, PAGASA . . . . . . . . . . . . . . .Mr. Juanito E. Lucas
Administrator, Philippine Veterans
   Affairs Office (PVAO) . . . . . . . . . . . . . . . . . . . . . . .Atty. Juan L. Gacad
Public Relations Officer, PVAO . . . . . . . . . . . .Mr. Leodegario D. Salvador
President, National Defense College
   of the Philippines . . . . . . . . . . . . . . . . . . . . . . .Capt. Jose C. Lansangan

## DEFENSE FORCES

**ARMED FORCES**
**Armed Forces of the Philippines—AFP**
*Headquarters Camp General Emilio*
   *Aguninaldo*
*Quezon City*
*Metro Manila*

Chief of Staff, Armed Forces of the Philippines . . . . . . .Gen. Fabian C. Ver
Vice Chief of Staff . . . . . . . . . . . . . . . . . . . . . . . . . . . .Lt. Gen. Fidel Ramos
Public Relations Officer, Chief of Staff . . . . . . . . . . .Col. Emiliano Templo
Judge Advocate General . . . . . . . . . . . . . . .Brig. Gen. Hamilton B. Dimaya
Deputy Judge Advocate General . . . . . . . .Col. Leon O. Ridad, JAGS, GSC

<table>
<tr><td>Telephone:    (2) 78 69 11<br>Telex:    42029 afaho pm<br>42004 dcslog pm</td><td></td><td></td></tr>
</table>

Telephone:    (2) 78 69 11
Telex:    42029 afaho pm
42004 dcslog pm

Commanding General, Civil
Relations Service . . . . . . . . . . . . . . . . .Brig. Gen. Pacifico Lopez de Leon
Deputy, Civil Relations Service . . . . . . . . . . . . . .Col. Honesto M. Isleta, PA
Commanding General, AFP
Medical Center . . . . . . . . . . . . . . . . . . . .Brig. Gen. Evaristo N. Sanchez
Public Relations Officer, AFP
Medical Center . . . . . . . . . . . . . . . . . . . .Lt. Cdr. Manuel R. Tuazon, PN
Director, Veterans Memorial Medical
Center . . . . . . . . . . . . . . . . . . . . . . . . . . . . . . .Dr. William M. Valdez
Public Relations Officer, VMMC . . . . . . . . . . . . . .Mr. Reynaldo R. Reyes

**General Military Council**

Chairman . . . . . . . . . . . . . . . . . . . . . . . . . . . . . . . . . . .Gen. Fabian C. Ver
(Chief of Staff, Armed Forces of the Philippines)
Member (ex officio) . . . . . . . . . . . . . . . . . . . . . . . . .Lt. Gen. Fidel V. Ramos
(Vice Chief of Staff, AFP, and Chief,
Philippine Constabulary)
Member (ex officio) . . . . . . . . . . . . . . . . . . .Maj. Gen. Josephus Q. Ramas
(Commanding General, Army)
Member (ex officio) . . . . . . . . . . . . . . . . . . .Maj. Gen. Vicente Piccio, Jr.
(Commanding General, Air Force)
Member (ex officio) . . . . . . . . . . . . . . . . . .Rear Adm. Simeon Alejandro
(Flag Officer-in-Command, Navy)
Member . . . . . . . . . . . . . . . . . . . . . . . .Brig. Gen. Catalino Villanueva
Member . . . . . . . . . . . . . . . . . . . . . . . . .Brig. Gen. Roland Pattugalan
Member . . . . . . . . . . . . . . . . . . . . . .Brig. Gen. Fortunato C. Corrachea
Member . . . . . . . . . . . . . . . . . . . . . . . . . .Comdr. Serapio Martillano
Member . . . . . . . . . . . . . . . . . . . . . . . . .Brig. Gen. Abraham Baladad
Member . . . . . . . . . . . . . . . . . . . . . . . . . . . .Comdr. Juanito Veridiano
Member . . . . . . . . . . . . . . . . . . . . . . . . .Brig. Gen. Alexander L. Felix
Member . . . . . . . . . . . . . . . . . . . . . . . . .Brig. Gen. Sinforoso L. Duque
Member . . . . . . . . . . . . . . . . . . . . . . . . .Brig. Gen. Hamilton B. Dimaya
Member . . . . . . . . . . . . . . . . . . . . . . . . . .Brig. Gen. Evaristo Sanchez
Member . . . . . . . . . . . . . . . . . . . . . . . . . .Brig. Gen. Recaredo Albano
Member . . . . . . . . . . . . . . . . . . . . . . . . . .Brig. Gen. Pedro Balbanero
Member . . . . . . . . . . . . . . . . . . . . . . . . . . . .Brig. Gen. Leo Santos
Member . . . . . . . . . . . . . . . . . . . . . . . . . . .Col. Elvigia R. Mendoza
Member . . . . . . . . . . . . . . . . . . . . . . . . . . .Col. Tranquilino C. Cruz

**Regional Commands**

Commander, NORTHCOM . . . . . . . . . . . . . .Brig. Gen. Alexander L. Felix
Commander, SOUTHCOM . . . . . . . . . . . . . . .Maj. Gen. Delfin C. Castro
Commander, WESTCOM . . . . . . . . . . . . . . . . . .Comdr. Gil Fernandez
Commander, CEMCOM . . . . . . . . . . . . . . . . . .Grig. Gen. Jose P. Magno
Commander, EASTCOM . . . . . . . . . . . . . . .Brig. Gen. Salvador M. Mison

**ARMY**
**Philippine Army—PA**
*Headquarters Philippine Army*
*Fort Bonifacio*
*Metro Manila*

*Telephone: (2) 85 26 90, 85 54 55,*
*85 19 65, 85 19 21*

Commanding General, Philippine Army . . . . . . .Maj. Gen. Josephus Ramas
Chief of Staff . . . . . . . . . . . . . . . . . . . . . .Brig. Gen. Cirilo O. Oropesa
Deputy Chief, Operations . . . . . . . . . . . . . . .Brig. Gen. Ramon L. Cannu
Secretary, General Staff . . . . . . . . . . . . . . . .Lt. Col. Cornelio C. Aldea, Jr.
Public Relations Officer . . . . . . . . . . . . . . . . . .Col. Herminio T. Salas
Army Procurement Officer . . . . . . . . . . . . . .Lt. Col. Hermoso C. Tabangay
Assistant Chief of Staff for Personnel, G-1 . . . . . . .Col. Mariano P. Adalem
Assistant Chief of Staff for Intelligence, G-2 . . . . .Col. Victor B. Mamawag
Assistant Chief of Staff for Operations, G-3 . . . . .Col. Franklin V. Samonte
Assistant Chief of Staff for Logistics, G-4 . . . . . . . . . . .Col. Fidel C. Samson
Assistant Chief for Staff for Plans, G-5 . . . . . . . . . . . .Col. Pedro Y. Villalon
Assistant Chief of Staff for
Comptrollership, G-6 . . . . . . . . . . . . . . . .Col. Dalmacio G. Pizana, Jr.
Assistant Chief of Staff for
Home Defense, G-7 . . . . . . . . . . . . . . . . . .Brig. Gen. Cirilo O. Oropesa
Assistant Chief of Staff for
Materiel Development, G-8 . . . . . . . . . . . . . . .Col. Ascencion V. Barcelo
Army Inspector General . . . . . . . . . . . . . . . . . . . . .Col. Angel L. Sadang

Army Chief Engineer/CG. 51st
    Engineering Brigade ..................... Brig. Gen. Simeon B. Ver
Army Chief of Ordnance and Chemical
    Services.................................... Col. Joven G. Villanos
Army Quartermaster ........................ Col. Napoleon G. Basco
Army Chief Surgeon ........................ Col. Damaso C. Salvador
Army Dental Surgeon ..................... Col. Gregorio P. Alona, Jr.
Army Chief Chaplain........................ Col. Neopolo P. Arsitio
Army Judge Advocate .................. Col. Dominiador V. dela Cruz
Chief, Communications/Electronics ................ Col. Jose P. Gomez
Army Provost Marshal .......................... Col. Juan C. Resma
Army Adjutant ............................... Col. Conrado B. Sadsad
Chief, Army Special Services Division .......... Maj. Filemon S. Juat, Jr.
Army Chief Nurse .......................... Col. Agustina A. Duque
Chief, Army Historical Division ............. Lt. Col. Wilfredo Laganzon
Commanding General, 1st
    Infantry Division ..................... Brig. Gen. Mariano Miranda
Commanding General, 2nd
    Infrantry Division ..................... Brig. Gen. Zosimo C. Carlos
Commanding General, 3rd
    Infantry Division ..................... Brig. Gen. Cesar D. Templo
Commanding General, 4th
    Infantry Division ..................... Brig. Gen. Madrino Muñoz
Commanding General, 5th
    Infantry Division .................... Brig. Gen. Benjamin G. Santos

## NAVY
**Philippine Navy—PN**
*Headquarters Philippine Navy*
*Roxas Boulevard*
*Manila*

*Telephone: (2) 59 63 48, 50 43 22*
*Telex: 23804 nsd ph (Naval Supply,*
*    Zambales)*

Flag Officer in Command,
    Philippine Navy ..................... Rear Adm. Simeon Alejandro
Flag Secretary ........................... Cdr. Julito M. Cassillan, II
Vice Commander/Commandant
    Philippine Coast Guard ................. Comdr. Brillante C. Ochoco
Chief of Naval Staff ...................... Comdr. Ponciano T. Bautista
Secretary of Naval Staff..................... Cdr. Napoleon C. Baylon
Naval Inspector............................ Cdr. Generoso O. Lintag
Chief, Naval History ..................... Capt. Antonio A. Empedrad
Naval Public Relations Officer ........... Lt. Col. Venancio R. Tumibay
Naval Procurement Officer.................. Cdr. Rodolfo M. Guanzon
Assistant Chief of Naval Staff for
    Personnel, N-1 ..................... Capt. Armando Q. Madamba
Assistant Chief of Naval Staff for
    Intelligence, N-2.......................... Capt. Danilo E. Pizarro
Assistant Chief of Naval Staff for
    Operations, N-3.................. Capt. Emerson C. Tangan, GSC
Assistant Chief of Naval Staff for
    Logistics, N-4 .......................... Capt. Domingo Salipsip
Assistant Chief of Naval Staff for
    Plans and Programs, N-5 ............... Capt. Bayani T. Matic, GSC
Assistant Chief of Naval Staff for
    Comptrollership, N-6 ..................... Cdr. Rodlfo T. Javier
Assistant Chief of Naval Staff for
    Home Defense, N-7 ...................... Cdr. Juan De Leon, GSC
Assistant Chief of Naval Staff for
    Ships and Yards, N-8 .............. Capt. Domingo H. Calajate, GSC
Assistant Chief of Naval Staff
    for Communications and
    Electronics, N-9 ................... Capt. Marino P. Panes Jr., GSC
Chief, Office of Civil Relations............... Capt. Delfin M. dela Cruz
The Naval Adjutant .......................... Cdr. Samuel T. Cortez
Naval Provost Marshall ...................... Cdr. Nestor R. Raynes
Director, Naval Reserve Center................ Capt. Edgardo B. Gallos
Chief, Research and Development Office .......... Cdr. Romeo H. Bruce
Naval Public Works Officer ............... Lt. Cdr. Wenifredo R. Suarez
Naval Special Service Officer ..................... Capt. Escala

Director, Office for Special Studies ..........Cdr. Eduardo L. Tolentino
Director, Petroleum and Energy Conservation.....Cdr. Antonio R. Siapno
Director, Naval Information Systems
    Office....................................Cdr. Armando B. Heredia
Commander, Fleet Support Command .......Comdr. Alfredo C. Protacio
Commander, Naval Shipyard ................Capt. Antonio G. Suratos
Commander, Naval Combat Systems
    Facilities ................................Cdr. Francis T. Mallillin
Commander, Naval Supply Center.................Cdr. Manuel M. Ison
Commanding Officer, Naval Research
    and Development Center ....................Cdr. Simeon Q. Aquino
Commanding Officer, Naval Station
    Hospital ...............................Lt. Cdr. Antonio S. Morga
Commandant, Philippine Marines ......Brig. Gen. Rodolfo M. Punsalang
Deputy Commandant, Philippine Marines....Brig. Gen. Artemino Dadiar
Deputy Commandant, Philippine
    Coast Guard ...........................Capt. Benjamin R. Suarez
Commander, Sealift Amphibious
    Command ...............................Comdr. Roberto Ampig
Commander, Naval Defense Forces ........Comdr. Dante Q. de Guzman
Commander, Bonifacio Naval Station.............Capt. Isidro O. Codera
Commander, Naval Forces Southern
    Philippines ............................Comdr. Alfredo V. Divino
Commander, Naval Base Cavite ...........................(Vacant)
Commander, Naval Intelligence
    Security Force ...........................Capt. Danilo E. Pizarro
Commander, Naval Air Group .............Cdr. Romeo F. Villanueva
The Naval Chaplain ..........................Col. Jose P. Cadusale
Chief Surgeon, Navy..........................Col. Luis V. Vizcarra
Chief Nurse Navy ...............................Col. Pacita Bunoan
Chief Dental Surgeon .........................Col. Romulo F. Reyes
Naval Judge Advocate .......................Col. Higino E. Dacanay
Commander, Naval Training
    Command ..................Capt. Tagumpay R. Jardiniano, GSC

**AIR FORCE**
**Philippine Air Force—PAF**
*Headquarters Philippine Air Force*
*Nichols Air Base*
*Pasay City*
*Metro Manila*

*Telephone: (2) 828 4415*

Commanding General......................Maj. Gen. Vincente Piccio
Commander, 1st Air Division
    (Acting) .............................Brig. Gen. Ismael A. Sabarre
Chief of Air Staff ....................Brig. Gen. Godofredo C. Sta Ana
Chief of Air Staff .......................Brig. Gen. Jaime Mugurgas
Secretary of Air Staff/Director of Portocol/
    Director, Information Services .................Col. Francisco Atayde
Air Inspector General...........................Col. Erasmo A. Rivera
Public Relations Officer ..............................Pablo Gonzales
Air Force Procurement Officer .....................Lt. Col. Benedicto
Director, OREFS ...........................Col. Dominico L. Casas
Assistant Chief of Air Staff for Personnel..............Col. Alfredo Reyes
Assistant Chief of Air Staff for Operations
    (Acting) ..................................Col. Antonio E. Sotelo
Assistant Chief of Air Staff for Materiel
    (Acting)..................................Col. Eladio V. Gonzalez
Assistant Chief of Air Staff for Plans and
    Programs .......................................Col. Jose De Leon
Assistant Chief of Air Staff for Comptrollership ......Col. Rodolfo Hanten
Assistant Chief of Air Staff for Home Defense.........Col. Erasmo Rivera
Air Adjutant .................................Col. Caesar A. Soriano
Director, Air Communication Electronics.......Col. Carmelito G. Beltran
Air Judge Advocate .....................Col. Norberto P. Furagganan
Director, Civil Engineers .....................Col. Alfredo SJ Bayani
Chief Air Staff .........................Col. Apolonio F. de Jesus, Jr.
Chief Nurse ..............................Col. Teresita D. Iway
Chief, Air Dental Surgeon ...............Col. Petrocinio D. Lansangan
Chief Air Chaplain .........................Col. Jose A. Canaveral, Jr.

Chief, Historical Activities . . . . . . . . . . . . . . . . . . . .Col. Hilario M. Villaflor
Director, Special Services . . . . . . . . . . . . . . . .Col. Rodolfo V. Purugganan
Director, Special Studies . . . . . . . . . . . . . . . .Col. Nicasio P. Rodriguez, Jr.
Air Provost Marshall . . . . . . . . . . . . . . . . . . . . .Col. Vidal S. Evangelista
Director, Headquarters
     Administration Services . . . . . . . . . . . . . . . . . . . . . .Maj. Tereso C. Pelias
Chief, Accounting (Acting) . . . . . . . . . . .Lt. Col. Laureano P. Lacambacal

**PARA-MILITARY FORCES**
**Philippine Constabulary-Integrated National**
   **Police—PC**
*Camp Crame*
*Quezon City*
*Metro Manila*
*Telephone:   (2) 78 79 61, 78 69 81*

Chief, Philippine Constabulary, Deputy Chief
  of Staff and Director-General,
  Integrated National Police . . . . . . . . . . . . . . . .Lt. Gen. Fidel. V. Ramos
Deputy Chief . . . . . . . . . . . . . . . . . . . . . . . . . . . .Maj. Gen. Prospero Olivas
Chief, Constabulary Staff . . . . . . . . . . . . . . . . . . . . . . . . . . .Col. Jack Galang

\* \* \* \* \*

# GENERAL DEFENSE DATA

**Manpower**
  Total Armed Forces . . . . . . . . . . . . . . . . . . . . . . . . . . . . . . . . . . . . . . . .112,800
     (See Page 427)
  Population . . . . . . . . . . . . . . . . . . . . . . . . . . . . . . . . . . . . . . . . . . . . .51,574,000

**Spending**
  Military Expenditures . . . . . . . . . . . . . . . . . . . . . . . . . . . . . . . . . . . . .$808 million
  Gross National Product . . . . . . . . . . . . . . . . . . . . . . . . . . . . . . . . . .$34.208 billion
  Military Expenditure as a Percentage of
    Gross National Product . . . . . . . . . . . . . . . . . . . . . . . . . . . . . . . . . . . . . . .2.4%
  Military Expenditure as a Percentage of
    Central Government Expenditure . . . . . . . . . . . . . . . . . . . . . . . . . . . . . . .16.0%

**Defense Treaties** *(See Part II for Additional Detail)*

    Bilateral:    United States

    Multilateral:  Biological Weapons Convention
                Limited Test Ban Treaty
                South-East Asia Collective Defense Treaty
                Treaty on the Non-Proliferation of Nuclear Weapons

# POLAND
## Polish People's Republic
*Polska Rzeczpospolita Ludowa*

### Defense Establishment Command Structure
### and Force Organization

The Premier is Minister of National Defense and Commander-in-Chief of the armed forces. He is advised by the Ruling Armed Forces Council (Council of National Salvation). Poland is divided into three military districts with headquarters in Warsaw, Wroclaw and Bydgoszcz, respectively.

**Total armed forces:** 317,000 (Army: 207,000;   Navy: 22,000;   Air Force: 88,000). **Paramilitary forces:** 85,000 (border and internal defense troops).

## COUNCIL OF STATE

**OFFICE OF THE CHAIRMAN**
*ul. Wiejska 4/6/8*
*00-902 Warsaw*

*Telephone:  28 70 01, 28 40 01*
*Telex:   816256*

Chairman .......................................... Henryk Jabloński

**MINISTRY OF NATIONAL DEFENSE**
*(Ministerstwo Obrony Narodowej)*
*ul. Klonowa*
*00-591 Warsaw*

*Telephone:   Centrala 21006*

Minister ...................................... Gen. Wojciech Jaruzelski
Vice Minister, General Affairs ................. Lt. Gen. Józef Urbanowicz
Chief, General Staff .......................... Lt. Gen. Florian Siwicki
Chief Inspector, Territorial Defense .......... Lt. Gen. Tadeusz Tuczapski
Chief Inspector, Training .................... Lt. Gen. Eugeniusz Molczyk
Chief, Main Political Administration,
   Polish Armed Forces ......................... Maj. Gen. Józef Baryla
Quartermaster-General,
   Polish Army ....................... Lt. Gen. Mieczyslaw Obiedziński
Chief Technical Inspector,
   Polish Armed Forces, and
   Vice Minister of National Defense ............. Lt. Gen. Zbigniew Nowak
Chief, Main Administration
   for Combat Training .................... Maj. Gen. Wojciech Barański
Director, Cadre Department ................. Maj. Gen. Zygmunt Zieliński
Chief, Military Internal Service ............... Brig. Gen. Edward Poradko
Chief, Foreign Liaison Office ......................... Col. Marian Bugaj

## DEFENSE FORCES

**ARMY**
**Polish People's Army**
*(Wojska Ladowe)*
*ul. Radowiecka 4*
*02-519 Warsaw*

*Telephone:   21 00 6*

Chief of General Staff ........................ Lt. Gen. Florian Siwicki
Commander, Warsaw Military
   District ..................................... Maj. Gen. Jerzy Skalski
Commander, Wroclaw Military
   District (Silesia) .................... Maj. Gen. Henryk Rapacewicz
Commander, Bydgoszcz Military
   District (Pomerania) ..................... Maj. Zbigniew Blechman
Commander, Border Guards .............. Maj. Gen. Czeslaw Stopiński

**NAVY**
**Polish Navy**
*(Marynarka Wojenna)*
*Skwer Kosciuszki*
*81-370 Gdynia 19*

Commander . . . . . . . . . . . . . . . . . . . . . . . . . . . . . . . . . . .Adm. Ludwik Janczyszyn
Chief of Staff, Navy . . . . . . . . . . . . . . . . . . . . . . .Rear Adm. Kazimierz Bossy

**AIR FORCE**
**Polish Air Force**
*(Wojska Lotincze)*
*ul. Kościuszki 92-98*
*60-928 Poznan*

*Telephone:    25 04 41, 25 64 09*

Commander . . . . . . . . . . . . . . . . . . . . . . . . . . . . . .Maj. Gen. Tytus Krawczyc
Chief of Staff, Air Force . . . . . . . . . . . . . . . . . . . . . . . .Brig. Gen. Jerzy Zych

**NATIONAL AIR DEFENSE FORCES**
*(Dowodztwo Wojsk Obrony Powietrznej*
   *Kraju)*
*ul. Wawelska 7a*
*02-034 Warsaw*

Commander . . . . . . . . . . . . . . . . . . . . . . . . . . . .Maj. Gen. Longin Lozowicki

\* \* \* \* \*

# GENERAL DEFENSE DATA

**Manpower**
   Total Armed Forces . . . . . . . . . . . . . . . . . . . . . . . . . . . . . . . . . . . . . . . . . . .317,000
      (See Page 433)
   Population . . . . . . . . . . . . . . . . . . . . . . . . . . . . . . . . . . . . . . . . . . . . .36,229,000

**Spending**
   Military Expenditures . . . . . . . . . . . . . . . . . . . . . . . . . . . . . . . . . . . . . . .$9.5 billion
   Gross National Product . . . . . . . . . . . . . . . . . . . . . . . . . . . . . . . . . . . . . .$176 billion
   Military Expenditure as a Percentage of
      Gross National Product . . . . . . . . . . . . . . . . . . . . . . . . . . . . . . . . . . . . . .5.4%
   Military Expenditure as a Percentage of
      Central Government Expenditure . . . . . . . . . . . . . . . . . . . . . . . . . . . . .13.8%

**Defense Treaties** *(See Part II for Additional Detail)*

   Bilateral:      Bulgaria              Hungary
               Czechoslovakia        Romania
               Ethiopia              Soviet Union
               German Democratic
                  Republic

   Multilateral:  Biological Weapons Convention
               Environmental Modification Convention
               Limited Test Ban Treaty
               Treaty on the Control of Arms on the Seabed
               Treaty on the Non-Proliferation of Nuclear Weapons
               United Nations Disengagement Observer Force
               Warsaw Treaty Organization

# PORTUGAL
## Republic of Portugal
### *República Portuguesa*

## Defense Establishment Command Structure and Force Organization

The President is the Supreme Commander of the armed forces of Portugal. He is advised by the Superior Council of National Defense on defense policy and on the organization, operation and discipline of the armed forces. The Ministry of National Defense has political responsibility for military policy and the administration of the armed forces.

**Total armed forces:** 66,500 (Army: 41,500; Navy: 13,300; Air Force: 11,700). **Paramilitary forces:** 18,300 (National Republican Guard: 14,600; Public Security Police: 16,100; Fiscal Guard: 7,600).

## HEAD OF STATE

H. E. Gen. António dos Santos Ramalho Eanes

**OFFICE OF THE PRESIDENT**
*Praça Afonso Albuquerque*
*1300 Lisbon*

*Telephone: (1) 637141, 637147, 660141*
*Telex: 16733 prerep p*

President of the Republic
and Supreme Commander . . . . . Gen. António dos Santos Ramalho Eanes

**Superior Council of National Defense**

Chairman . . . . . . . . . . . . . . . . . . . Gen. António dos Santos Ramalho Eanes
(President of the Republic)
Member . . . . . . . . . . . . . . . . . . . . . . Dr. Francisco José Pinto Balsemão
(Prime Minister)
Member . . . . . . . . . . . . . . . . . . . . . . Eng. Ricardo Manuel Baião Horta
(Minister of National Defense)
Member . . . . . . . . . . . . . . . . . . . . . . Amb. Vasco Futscher Pereira
(Minister of Foreign Affairs)
Member . . . . . . . . . . . . . . . . . . . . . . . . . . . . . Eng. Angelo Correia
(Minister of Internal Administration)
Member . . . . . . . . . . . . . . . . . . . . . . Eng. Ricardo Manuel Baião Horta
(Minister of Industry)
Member . . . . . . . . . . . . . . . . . . . . . . Eng. José Carlos Viana Baptista
(Minister of Transports and Communications)
Member . . . . . . . . . . . . . . . . . . . . . . Gen. Nuno Viriato de Melo Egídio
(Chief of General Staff)
Member . . . . . . . . . . . . . . . . . . . . Adm. António Egídio de Sousa Leitão
(Chief of Staff, Navy)
Member . . . . . . . . . . . . . . . . . . . . . . Gen. Amadeu García dos Santos
(Chief of Staff, Army)
Member . . . . . . . . . . . . . . . . . . . . . . . . Gen. José Lemos Ferreira
(Chief of Staff, Air Force)
Member . . . . . . . . . . . . . . . . . . . . . . Lt. Gen. Tomás Conceição Silva
(Minister of the Republic to Azores)
Member . . . . . . . . . . . . . . . . . . . . . . Maj. Gen. Lino Días Miguel
(Minister of the Republic to Madeira)

Member ............................... Dr. João Bosco Mota Amaral
(President of Regional Government, Azores)
Member .................................. Dr. Alberto João Jardim
(President of Regional Government, Medeira)
Secretary ............................ Gen. Joaquim Lopes Cavalheiro

**MINISTRY OF NATIONAL DEFENSE**
*(Ministério de Defesa Nacional)*
*Rua Professor Gomes Teixeira*
*1300 Lisbon*

*Telephone:　(1) 676202*
*Telex:　42530 fefnac*

Minister of National Defense ................. Eng. Ricardo Baião Horta
Secretary of State for
　National Defense .............. Eng. Carlos José Sanchez Vaz Pardal
Chief, Office of the Minister ............. Lt. Col. António Chiado Caçote
Chief, Office of the Secretary
　of State .............................. Cdr. Jorge Duarte Meira
Assistant to the Minister ..................... Dr. Luis Afonso Queiro
Assistant to the Secretary
　of State ............................... Dr. Vitor Manuel Lourenço
Assistant to the Secretary
　of State ........................... Dr. Isabel Frausto de Azevdeo

## DEFENSE FORCES

**ARMED FORCES**
*Avenida Ilha da Madeira*
*1400 Lisbon*

*Telephone:　(1) 610001*

Chief, General Staff of the
　Armed Forces (CEMGFA) .......... Gen. Nuno Viriato de Melo Egídio
Chief, Office of the General
　Staff ............................... Co. António Rodrígues de Areia

**ARMY**
*(Exercito Português)*
*Rua Museu da Artilharia*
*1100 Lisbon*

*Telephone:　(1) 867131, 872232, 873670*
*Telex:　222223*

Chief of Staff ........................ Gen. Amadeu Garcia dos Santos
Vice Chief of Staff ........................ Lt. Gen. José Lopes Alves
Inspector General ................. Lt. Gen. Armenio Ramires de Oliveira
Adjutant General, Personnel ............. Lt. Gen. Mário Firmino Miguel
Director, Operational
　Department .............. Maj. Gen. José Alberto Loureiro dos Santos
Director, Finance
　Department ....................... Maj. Gen. Julio Simões da Silva
Director, Department of Army
　Instruction ........... Maj. Gen. José do Nascimento de Sousa Lucena

**Office of the Quartermaster General**

Quartermaster General ..................... Lt. Gen. Jorge Salaza Barga

**Regional Commands**

Commander, Lisbon Military
　Region ............................. Lt. Gen. Artur Baptista Beirão
Commander, Center Military
　Region (Coimbra) .................... Lt. Gen. Domingos P. Tavares
Commander, North Military
　Region (Porto) ............. Lt. Gen. Mário Avelino Sardoeira Delgado
Commander, South Military
　Region (Evora) .......... Lt. Gen. José Fernando Lopes Gomes Marques
Commander, Azores Military
　Zone ............................... Maj. Gen. Abel Cabral Couto
Commander, Medeira Military
　Zone ............................ Maj. Gen. Luis D. Correia da Cruz

**NAVY**
*(Marinha de Guerra Portuguesa)*
*Praça do Comercio*
*1100 Lisbon*

*Telephone:　(1) 368961, 365392, 325350*
*Telex:　12587 cencop*

Chief of Staff .................... Adm. António Egídio de Sousa Leitão
Vice Chief of Staff ................. Vice Adm. Gabor Ziegler Patkoczy
Commander, Naval Forces
　Land ............................... Vice Adm. Ilídio Elias da Costa
Commander, Azores Naval
　Zone ....................... Capt. Adelino Lima Martins (Interim)
Commander, Madeira Naval
　Zone ..................... Capt. Adriano Gonçcalvves da Chunha
Commander, Marine
　Corps ................ Capt. POMC Francisco I. M. Oliveira Monteiro

**Office of the Superintendent of Materiel Services**
*Base Naval do Alfeite*
*2800 Alfeite*

Superintendent . . . . . . . . . . . . . . . . . . . Vice Adm. Rui do Carmo Fernandes
Director for Supplying . . . . . . . . . . . . . . . . . . . . . Capt. João María Contente

**AIR FORCE**
*(Força Aérea Portuguesa)*
*Avenida Leite de Vasconcelos*
*Alfagide*
*2700 Amadora*
*Lisbon*

*Telephone:   (1) 972383, 974264, 971852*
*Telex:   12110 seafa p*

Chief of Staff . . . . . . . . . . . . . . . . . . . . . . . . . . . . . Gen. José Lemos Ferreira
Vice Chief . . . . . . . . . . . . . . . . . . . . . . . Lt. Gen. Jorge M. Brochado Miranda
Inspector General . . . . . . . . . . . Lt. Gen. Fernando L. P. De Moura Carvalho
Commander, Operations . . . . . . . . . Lt. Gen. Francisco Días da Costa Gomes
Commander, Personnel . . . . Lt. Gen. Helder de Andrade Pinheiro de Freitas
Commander, Paratrooper
    Brigade . . . . . . . . . . . . . . . . . . . . . Maj. Gen. Heitor Hamilton Almendra
Commander, Maintenance
    Depot . . . . . . . . . . . . . . . . . . . . . . . Lt. Gen. Rui C. Conceição Espadinha
Commander, Supply Depot . . . . . . . . . . . . . . Col. Carlos J. da Costa Pereira
Commander, Azores Aerial
    Zone . . . . . . . . . . . . . . . . . . . . . . . . . . . Maj. Gen. Manuel J. Brou Ramos
Director, Training
    Department . . . . . . . . . . . . . . . . . Maj. Gen. Evandro Botelho de Amaral

**Logistics and Administration Command**
*(In charge of procurement)*
*Av. Leite Vasconcelos*
*Alfragide*
*2700 Amadora*
*Lisbon*

Commander . . . . . . . . . . . . . . . . . . . . Lt. Gen. Casimiro J. P. Abreu Proença

\* \* \* \* \*

# GENERAL DEFENSE DATA

**Manpower**
    Total Armed Forces. . . . . . . . . . . . . . . . . . . . . . . . . . . . . . . . . . . . . 66,500
        (See Page 435)
    Population . . . . . . . . . . . . . . . . . . . . . . . . . . . . . . . . . . . . . . . . 10,056,000

**Spending**
    Military Expenditures . . . . . . . . . . . . . . . . . . . . . . . . . . . . . . . $852 million
    Gross National Product . . . . . . . . . . . . . . . . . . . . . . . . . . . . . . . $23 billion
    Military Expenditure as a Percentage of
        Gross National Product . . . . . . . . . . . . . . . . . . . . . . . . . . . . . . 3.7%
    Military Expenditure as a Percentage of
        Central Government Expenditure . . . . . . . . . . . . . . . . . . . . . . . 12.9%

**Defense Treaties** *(See Part II for Additional Detail)*

    Bilateral:      Guinea-Bissau
                    United States

    Multilateral:   Biological Weapons Convention
                    Limited Test Ban Treaty
                    Treaty on the Control of Arms on the Seabed
                    Treaty on the Non-Proliferation of Nuclear Weapons

# QATAR
## State of Qatar
### *Dawlat Qatar*

## Defense Establishment Command Structure and Force Organization

The Amir is Supreme Commander of the Qatar Armed Forces. Operational control of the military is the responsibility of the Heir Apparent, who is Minister of Defense and Commander-in-Chief.

**Total armed forces:** 6,000 (Army: 5,000;    Navy: 700;    Air Force: 300).

## HEAD OF STATE

H. H. Sheikh Khalifa bin Hamad al-Thani

**OFFICE OF H. H. THE AMIR AND PRIME MINISTER**
*P.O. Box 923*
*Doha*

*Telephone:  415888*
*Telex:  4297 amiri dh*

Amir of Qatar,
Prime Minister and
Supreme Commander of the
Qatar Armed Forces . . . . . . . . H. H. Sheikh Khalifa bin Hamad al-Thani
Director . . . . . . . . . . . . . . . . . . . . . . . . . . . . . . . . . . . . . . . . . . Issa al-Kawari
Technical Advisor . . . . . . . . . . . . . . . . . . . . . . . . . . . . . . . . . . Hisham Oaddumi
Political Advisor . . . . . . . . . . . . . . . . . . . . . . . . . . . . . . . . . Dr. Hasan Kamel

**MINISTRY OF DEFENSE AND OFFICE OF H. H. THE HEIR APPARENT**
*P.O. Box 37*
*Doha*

*Telephone:  325572, 320797*

Heir Apparent, Minister of Defense,
and Commander-in-Chief . . . . . . . . . . . . . . . . . . . . . . . H. H. Maj. Gen.
Sheikh Hamad bin Khalifa al-Thani
Aide to Minister . . . . . . . . . . . . . . . . . . . . . . . Maj. Abdullah Said Abu Saleh
Deputy Commander-in-Chief . . . . . . . . . . . . . . Brig. Mohammad al-Attiyah

## DEFENSE FORCES

**ARMED FORCES**
**Qatar Armed Forces—QAF**
*General Headquarters*
*P.O. Box 37*
*Doha*

*Telephone:  334111*

Commander-in-Chief, Minister of
Defense and Heir Apparent . . . . . . . . . . . . . . . . . . . . . . H. H. Maj. Gen.
Sheikh Hamad bin Khalifa al-Thani
Deputy Commander-in-Chief . . . . . . . . . . . . . . Brig. Muhammad al-Attiyah
Assistant to Deputy
Commander-in-Chief . . . . . . . . . . Sheikh Abdullah bin Khalifa al-Thani
Advisor . . . . . . . . . . . . . . . . . . . . . . . Maj. Gen. Muhammuad Mahmoud
Chief of Staff . . . . . . . . . . . . . Sheikh Mubareh bin Abdel Rahman al-Thani
Commander of Internal
Security Organizations . . . . . . . . . Sheikh Abdullah bin Hamad al-Thani

**NAVY**
**Qatar Sea Arm—QSA**
*General Headquarters*
*P.O. Box 37*
*Doha*

*Telephone:  22088*

Commander . . . . . . . . . . . . . . . . . . . . . . . . . . . . . . . . . . . . Col. Saiah Azab
Chief, Operations . . . . . . . . . . . . . . . . . . . . Maj. Saif Ahmad al-Mannai
Chief, Administration . . . . . . . . . . . . . . . . . . Maj. Sultan Ahmad al-Ojan
Chief, Supply . . . . . . . . . . . . . . . . . . . . . . . Maj. Abd al-Rahim al-Zijara
Chief, Coast Guard . . . . . . . . . . . . . . . . . . . . Maj. Rabia Fadel al-Kaabi

**AIR FORCE**
**Qatari Amiri Air Force—QAAF**
*General Headquarters*
*P.O. Box 37*
*Doha*
*Telephone:    851389*

Commander  . . . . . . . . . . . . . . Lt. Col. Sheikh Hamad bin Abdulla al-Thani
Commander, Helicopter Wing  . . . . . . . . . . Lt. Col. Ahmad Salih al Mannai

**POLICE**
**Qatar State Police Force**
*Police Headquarters*
*Doha*
*Telephone:    321111*

Chief . . . . . . . . . . . . . . . . . . . . . . . . . . . . . . Brig. Hamad bin Jassim al-Thani

\* \* \* \* \*

# GENERAL DEFENSE DATA

**Manpower**
    Total Armed Forces. . . . . . . . . . . . . . . . . . . . . . . . . . . . . . . . . . . . . . . . . .6,000
      (See Page 439)
    Population . . . . . . . . . . . . . . . . . . . . . . . . . . . . . . . . . . . . . . . . . . . . .258,000

**Spending**
    Military Expenditures . . . . . . . . . . . . . . . . . . . . . . . . . . . . . . . . . . . . . .$555 million
    Gross National Product . . . . . . . . . . . . . . . . . . . . . . . . . . . . . . . . . . . . .$6.6 billion
    Military Expenditure as a Percentage of
      Gross National Product . . . . . . . . . . . . . . . . . . . . . . . . . . . . . . . . . . . . .8.4%
    Military Expenditure as a Percentage of
      Central Government Expenditure . . . . . . . . . . . . . . . . . . . . . . . . . . . . . .20.1%

**Defense Treaties** *(See Part II for Additional Detail)*

      Bilateral:      United Kingdom

      Multilateral:    Biological Weapons Convention
                 Cooperation Council for the Arab States of the Gulf
                 League of Arab States
                 Treaty on the Control of Arms on the Seabed

# ROMANIA
## Socialist Republic of Romania
### *República Socialista Romania*

### Defense Establishment Command Structure
### and Force Organization

The President is Supreme Commander of the armed forces. He is advised by the Defense Council. Operational control of the military is the responsibility of the Minister of National Defense.

**Total armed forces:** 181,000 (Army: 140,000;   Navy: 7,000;   Air Force: 34,000). **Paramilitary forces:** 37,000 (Border Guards: 17,000;   Ministry of Defense Security Troops: 20,000).

## HEAD OF STATE

H. E. Nicolae Ceausescu

**STATE COUNCIL**
*Calea Victoriei 49-53*
*Bucharest*
*Telephone:   (40-0) 14 81 10*

President and Supreme Commander ................Nicolae Ceaușescu
Vice President ........................................Ștefan Voitec
Vice President ..................................Gheorghe Rădulescu
Vice President ..........................................Iosif Kovacs
Vice President .......................................Maria Ciocan
Vice President.......................................Petru Enache

**Defense Council**

Chairman .......................................Nicolae Ceaușescu
(President)
Secretary ....................................Col. Gen. Vasile Milea
(Chief of General Staff)
Member *(ex officio)* ..........................Constantin Dăscălescu
(Prime Minister)
Member *(ex officio)* ..................................Ștefan Andrei
(Minister of Foreign Affairs)
Member *(ex officio)* ..........................George Homoștean
(Minister of Interior)
Member *(ex officio)* .....................Lt. Gen. Constantin Olteanu
(Minister of National Defense)
Member *(ex officio)* ...............................Emilian Dobrescu
(Chief of the State Planning Committee)
Member ...................................Col. Gen. Ion Coman
Member...............................Lt. Gen. Gheorghe Gomoiu
Member...............................Col. Gen. Marin Nicolescu

**MINISTRY OF NATIONAL DEFENSE**
*Intrarea Drumul Taberei 9*
*Bucharest*
*Telephone:   (40-0) 31 70 10, 46 01 11*

Minister.................................Lt. Gen. Constantin Olteanu
First Deputy Minister and Chief,
   General Staff .................................Col. Gen. Vasile Milea
Deputy Minister, Political Council...........Lt. Gen. Gheorghe Gomoiu
Deputy Minister .........................Col. Gen. Marin Nicolescu
Deputy Minister .........................Lt. Col. Victor Stănculescu
Chief of Protocol.........................Col. Gheorghe Gherăsoiu
Director of Secretariat .........................Col. Costache Lozeanu

Director, Military Publishing House
(Bucharest) . . . . . . . . . . . . . . . . . . . . . . . . . . . . . . . .Col. Gen. Vasile Alexe
Director, Military Design and Research
Institute (Clinceni). . . . . . . . . . . . . . . . . . .Maj. Gen. Dumitru Andrescu
Deputy Director . . . . . . . . . . . . . . . . . . . . . .Rear Adm. Marcel Diaconescu

**Higher Political Council**

Secretary . . . . . . . . . . . . . . . . . . . . . . . . . . . . . .Lt. Gen. Gheorghe Gomoiu
Deputy Secretary, Party Organization . . . . . . . . . .Maj. Gen. Ilie Ceaušescu
Deputy Secretary . . . . . . . . . . . . . . . . . . . . . . . .Col. Gheorghe Găinuse
Deputy for Culture . . . . . . . . . . . . . . . . . . . . . .Rear Adm. Iosif Pricop
Deputy for Propaganda . . . . . . . . . . . . . . . . . .Maj. Gen. George Popescu

# DEFENSE FORCES

**ARMED FORCES**
**General Staff**
*Intrarea Drumul Taberei 9*
*Bucharest*
*Telephone:    (40-0) 31 70 10, 46 01 11*

Chief, General Staff . . . . . . . . . . . . . . . . . . . . . . .Col. Gen. Vasile Milea
First Deputy Chief . . . . . . . . . . . . . . . . . . . . . . . . . . . . .Lt. Gen. Ion Sută
Deputy Chief, Counterintelligence and
Coding (International Affairs) . . . . . . . . . .Lt. Gen. Emil Constantin Popa
Deputy Chief . . . . . . . . . . . . . . . . . . . . . . . . . . .Rear Adm. Gheorghe Sandu
Deputy Chief, Rear Services . . . . . . . . . . . . . . . . . .Lt. Gen. Emil Ştefănescu
Chief, Artillery Section . . . . . . . . . . . . . . . . . . . . . .Col. Gen. Ion Popescu
Deputy Chief, Artillery Section . . . . . . . . . . . . . . . .Lt. Gen. Vasile Bărboi
Chief, Aviation/Air Defense Section. . . . . . . . . . .Maj. Gen. George Popescu
Chief, Chemical Troops Section . . . . . . . . . . . . . . . .Maj. Gen. Mihai Chitac
Chief, Engineering Troops Section . . . . . . . . . . . .Maj. Gen. Emil Andriescu
Chief, Foreign Liaison Section . . . . . . . . . . . . . . . . . .Col. Aurica Guinea
Chief, Infantry and Land Forces Section . . . . . . . . . . .Lt. Gen. Ion Hortopan
Chief, Intelligence Section . . . . . . . . . . . . . . . . . . . .Rear Adm. Ştefan Dinu
Deputy Chief, Intelligence Section . . . . . . . . . . . . .Maj. Gen. Nicolae Cucu
Chief, Medical Services Section . . . . . . . . . . .Maj. Gen. Alexandru Popescu
Chief, Navy Section . . . . . . . . . . . . . . . . . . . . . . . . . . . . . .Cpt. Ion Boian
Chief, Personnel/Education (Cadre) . . . . . . . . . .Lt. Gen. Constantin Opriță
Chief, Signal Troops . . . . . . . . . . . . . . . . . . . . . . .Lt. Gen. Gheorghe Enciu
Chief, Topography . . . . . . . . . . . . . . . . . . . . . . . . . . . . .Vasile Dragomir
Chief, Transportation Troops . . . . . . . . . . . . . . .Maj. Gen. Zaharia Cristache

**ARMY**
**Romanian People's Army**
*Intrarea Drumul Taberei 9*
*Bucharest*
*Telephone:    (40-0) 31 70 10*

Commander, First Army (Bucharest) . . . . . . . . . .Maj. Gen. Lucian Tonescu
Chief of Staff . . . . . . . . . . . . . . . . . . . . . . . . . . .Lt. Gen. Dumitru Fotescu
Deputy, Bucharest Garrison . . . . . . . . . . . . . . .Maj. Gen. Alexandru Turcu
Commander, Second Army (Buzau) . . . . . . . . . . .Maj. Gen. Ion Dindăreanu
Commander, Third Army (Craiova) . . . . . . . . . . . .Maj. Gen. Dumitru Rŏsu
Commander, Fourth Army (Cluj) . . . . . . . . . . . . .Lt. Gen. Iulian Topliceanu
Deputy Chief, Political Council . . . . . . . . . . .Maj. Gen. Ioan Panlimonescu

**NAVY**
**Romanian Navy**
*Naval Command*
*Intrarea Drumul Taberei 9*
*Bucharest*
*Telephone:    (40-0) 31 70 10, 46 01 11*

Commander . . . . . . . . . . . . . . . . . . . . . . . . . . . .Vice Adm. Vasile Musat
First Deputy and Chief of Staff . . . . . . . . . . . . . . . . .Rear Adm. Mihai Aron
Assistant Deputy Chief of Staff,
Political Matters. . . . . . . . . . . . . . . . . . . . . . . . .Rear Adm. Tudor Baciu
Deputy . . . . . . . . . . . . . . . . . . . . . . .Rear Adm. Alexnadru Constantinescu
Deputy, Training (Commander,
Mangalia) . . . . . . . . . . . . . . . . . . . . . . . . . . . .Rear Adm. Aurelian Ionescu

**AIR FORCE**
*Intrarea Drumul Tagerei 9*
*Bucharest*

**Military Aviation Command**

Commander . . . . . . . . . . . . . . . . . . . . . . . . . . .Lt. Gen. Gheorghe Zărnescu
First Deputy and Chief of Staff . . . . . . . . . . . . .Maj. Gen. Gheorghe Ionescu
Deputy, Air Traffic Control . . . . . . . . . . . . . . . . . . . .Maj. Gen. Vasile Bucur
Deputy, Political Matters . . . . . . . . . . . . . . . . . . . . . .Col. Dimitru Bulacu

Deputy, Transport Aircraft ...............Maj. Gen. Gheorghe Cristian
Deputy, Special Assistant for
    Pilot Training .....................Maj. Gen. Gheorghe Gherghina
Deputy, Fighter Aircraft ...........................Col. Horia Opruta

**Territorial Air Defense Command**

Commander.................................Lt. Gen. Mircea Mocanu
First Deputy and Chief of Staff ............Lt. Gen. Constantin Drăghici
Deputy, Political Matters ..................Maj. Gen. Floria Cirneanu
Deputy, Surface to Air Missiles .............Maj. Gen. Laurențiu Cupša
Deputy, Radar Forces .....................Lt. Gen. Pompiliu Ionescu
Deputy, Air Defense Aircraft ................Maj. Gen. Aurel Niculescu
Deputy, Anti-Aircraft Artillery Troops .........Maj. Gen. Romulus Ularu
Commander, Eastern Air Defense Region
    (Ploiesti) ....................................Maj. Gen. Dumitru Popa
Commander, Western Air Defense Region
    (Timisoara) ................................Maj. Gen. Virgil Manta

## PARA-MILITARY FORCES

**Border Guards**
*Intrarea Drumul Taberei 9*
*Bucharest*
*Telephone:   (40-0) 31 70 10, 46 01 11*

Commander.................................Col. Gen. Vasile Petruti
Chief of Staff .......................................Col. Victor Călina
Deputy Secretary, Political Council .....................Col. Ion Lucan
Deputy ...................................Maj. Gen. Ştefan Onofrei

**Patriotic Guards**
*Intrarea Drumul Taberei 9*
*Bucharest*
*Telephone:   (40-0) 31 70 10, 46 01 11*

Chief of Staff.........................................Col. Gen. Milea
Deputy Chief of Staff..........................Alexandru Petriceanu

**Civil Defense**
*Intrarea Drumul Taberei 9*
*Bucharest*
*Telephone:   (40-0) 31 70 10, 46 01 11*

Commander ..............................Maj. Gen. Ioan Geoanu
Chief of Staff .....................Maj. Gen. Constantin Cegavirdici
Deputy (Bucharest Commander) ............Maj. Gen. Constantin Ioana

\* \* \* \* \*

# GENERAL DEFENSE DATA

**Manpower**
    Total Armed Forces...............................................181,000
        (See Page 441)
    Population ...............................................22,510,000

**Spending**
    Military Expenditures.......................................$3.7 billion
    Gross National Product.....................................$85.8 billion
    Military Expenditure as a Percentage of
        Gross National Product ......................................4.4%
    Military Expenditure as a Percentage of
        Central Government Expenditure ...............................11.2%

**Defense Treaties** *(See Part II for Additional Detail)*

Bilateral:

| | |
|---|---|
| Angola | Kampuchea |
| Bulgaria | Mozambique |
| Burundi | Poland |
| Czechoslovakia | Soviet Union |
| Gabon | Sudan |
| German Democratic | Vietnam |
| Republic | Zaire |
| Hungary | Zambia |

Multilateral:  Biological Weapons Convention
Limited Test Ban Treaty
Treaty on the Control of Arms on the Seabed
Treaty on the Non-Proliferation of Nuclear Weapons
Warsaw Treaty Organization

# RWANDA

## Republic of Rwanda
*République Rwandaise* (French)
*Republika Y' U Rwanda* (Kinyarwanda)

## Defense Establishment Command Structure and Force Organization

The President is Minister of National Defense and Chief of Staff of the Army. All services are part of the Army. The National Police are under the jurisdiction of the Ministry of the Interior.

**Total armed forces:** 5,150 (Army: 5,000;     Air Force: 150). **Para-military forces:** 1,200.

## HEAD OF STATE

H. E. Maj. Gen. Juvenal Habyarimana

**OFFICE OF THE PRESIDENT AND MINISTRY OF NATIONAL DEFENSE**
*B.P. 15*
*Kigali*
*Telephone: 5160*
*Telex: 517 presirep rw*

President of the Republic, President of the Council of Ministers, Minister of National Defense, and Chief of Staff of the Army . . . . . . . . . . . . . . . . . . . . . . . . . . Maj. Gen. Juvenal Habyarimana

**MINISTRY OF NATIONAL DEFENSE**
*(Ministère de la Defense Nationale)*
*B.P. 85*
*Kigali*
*Telephone: 5160*

Minister and President of the Republic . . . . Maj. Gen. Juvenal Habyarimana
Private Secretary . . . . . . . . . . . . . . . . . . . . . . . . . . . . . Maj. Leonidas Rusatira
Assistant Secretary . . . . . . . . . . . . . . . . . . . . . . . . . . . . . . . . . . Maj. Bagosora

**MINISTRY OF THE INTERIOR**
*B.P. 446*
*Kigali*
*Telephone: 5477*

Minister . . . . . . . . . . . . . . . . . . . . . . . . . . . . . . . . . Thomas Habanabakize

## DEFENSE FORCES

**ARMY**
*(Forces Armees Rwandaises—FAR)*
*B.P. 85*
*Kigali*
*Telephone: 5158, 5751*

Chief of Staff and President of the Republic . . . . . . . . . . . . . . . . . . . . . . . . . Maj. Gen. Juvenal Habyarimana
Deputy Chief of Staff, Army . . . . . . . . . . . . . . . . . Lt. Col. Laurent Serubuga
Deputy Chief of Staff, Gendarmerie . . . . . . . Maj. Pierre Celestin Rwagafilita
Director, War College . . . . . . . . . . . . . . . . . . . . . . Lt. Col. Fabien Gahimano

**NATIONAL POLICE**
*(Gendarmerie Nationale)*
*Kimihurura*
*Telephone: 6817, 6818*

Chief . . . . . . . . . . . . . . . . . . . . . . . . . . . . . . Maj. Pierre Celestin Rwagafilita

\* \* \* \* \*

445

# GENERAL DEFENSE DATA

**Manpower**

Total Armed Forces . . . . . . . . . . . . . . . . . . . . . . . . . . . . . . . . . . . . . . . . . . . . . 5,150
(See Page 445)
Population . . . . . . . . . . . . . . . . . . . . . . . . . . . . . . . . . . . . . . . . . . . . . . 5,451,000

**Spending**

Military Expenditures . . . . . . . . . . . . . . . . . . . . . . . . . . . . . . . . . . . . . . . . $21 million
Gross National Product . . . . . . . . . . . . . . . . . . . . . . . . . . . . . . . . . . . . . . . . $1 billion
Military Expenditure as a Percentage of
Gross National Product . . . . . . . . . . . . . . . . . . . . . . . . . . . . . . . . . . . . . . . 2%
Military Expenditure as a Percentage of
Central Government Expenditure . . . . . . . . . . . . . . . . . . . . . . . . . . . . . . 15.3%

**Defense Treaties** *(See Part II for Additional Detail)*

Bilateral:      United States

Multilateral:   Biological Weapons Convention
                Limited Test Ban Treaty
                Organization of African Unity
                *Rwanda—Burundi—Zaire*:
                   Mutual Security Pact (1966, 1974)
                Treaty on the Control of Arms on the Seabed
                Treaty on the Non-Proliferation of Nuclear Weapons

# ST. CHRISTOPHER-NEVIS*
## State of St. Christopher-Nevis

### Defence Establishment Command Structure and Force Organization

The Governor commands the police force of St. Christopher-Nevis. External defence is the responsibility of the United Kingdom.

**Police:** 300.

## HEAD OF STATE

H. M. Queen Elizabeth II

## GOVERNOR

H. E. Clement Athelston Arrindell

**OFFICE OF THE GOVERNOR**
*Government House*
*Basseterre*
*St. Christopher*
*Telephone:  2315*

Governor ...............................Clement Athelston Arrindell

**OFFICE OF THE PRIME MINISTER**
*Government Headquarters*
*P.O. Box 186*
*Basseterre*
*St. Christopher*
*Telephone:  2521, ext. 57*
*Telex:  6820 extnlskb kc*

Prime Minister and Minister of
    Home and External Affairs ..........Dr. Kennedy Alphonse Simmonds

## DEFENCE FORCES

**ARMED FORCES**
*Defence Force Headquarters*
*Springfield*
*Telephone:  2154*

Commandant ..............................Stanley Valentine Franks
Commander.........................................Errell Maynard
Deputy Commander ..................................Aubrey York

**POLICE FORCE**
**Royal St. Christopher—Nevis**
**Police Force**
*St. Kitts*

Commander ..............................Stanley Valentine Franks
Deputy Commander ................................Edward Hughes

* * * * *

---

*The island of St. Christopher is popularly referred to as St. Kitts.

447

# GENERAL DEFENCE DATA

**Manpower**

Total Armed Forces . . . . . . . . . . . . . . . . . . . . . . . . . . . . . . . . . . . . . . . . . . . . . . . . .300
(See Page 447)
Population . . . . . . . . . . . . . . . . . . . . . . . . . . . . . . . . . . . . . . . . . . . . . . . . . .52,000

**Spending**

Military Expenditures . . . . . . . . . . . . . . . . . . . . . . . . . . . . . . . . . . . . . . . . . . . .
Gross National Product . . . . . . . . . . . . . . . . . . . . . . . . . . . . . . . . . . . . . . . . .$40 million
Military Expenditure as a Percentage of
    Gross National Product . . . . . . . . . . . . . . . . . . . . . . . . . . . . . . . . . . . . . . . . . .
Military Expenditure as a Percentage of
    Central Government Expenditure . . . . . . . . . . . . . . . . . . . . . . . . . . . . . . . . . . .

**Defence Treaties** *(See Part II for Additional Detail)*

Bilateral:      None

Multilateral:   None

# ST. LUCIA

## Defence Establishment Command Structure and Force Organization

The Governor-General has executive authority over the police force of St. Lucia. The United Kingdom is responsible for the island's external defence.

**Police:** 300.

## HEAD OF STATE

H. M. Queen Elizabeth II

## GOVERNOR-GENERAL

H. E. Sir Allen M. Lewis, G.C.M.G., Q.C.

**OFFICE OF THE GOVERNOR-GENERAL**
*Government House*
*The Morne*
*Castries*
*Telephone: 22481*

Governor-General . . . . . . . . . . . . . . . . . . Sir Allen Lewis, G.C.M.G., Q.C.

**OFFICE OF THE PRIME MINISTER**
*Government Building*
*Laborie Street*
*Castries*
*Telephone: 2611, ext. 110*

Prime Minister and Minister
  of Finance, Planning, Foreign
  and Home Affairs . . . . . . . . . . . . . . . . . . . . . . . . . . . John G. M. Compton
Secretary to the Cabinet . . . . . . . . . . . . . . . . . . . . . . . . . . . Victor Girard
Director of Finance . . . . . . . . . . . . . . . . . . . . . . . . . . . . . Dwight Venner
Permanent Secretary . . . . . . . . . . . . . . . . . . . . . . . . . . . . . Earl Huntley
Parliamentary Secretary . . . . . . . . . . . . . . . . . . . . . . . . . . . John Bristol

**ROYAL SAINT LUCIA POLICE FORCE**
*Telephone: 22855*

Commander and Governor-
  General . . . . . . . . . . . . . . . . . . . . . . Sir Allen M. Lewis, G.C.M.G., Q.C.

* * * * *

## GENERAL DEFENCE DATA

**Manpower**
  Total Armed Forces . . . . . . . . . . . . . . . . . . . . . . . . . . . . . . . . . . . . . . . .300
  Population . . . . . . . . . . . . . . . . . . . . . . . . . . . . . . . . . . . . . . . . . . .119,000

449

**Spending**
Military Expenditures . . . . . . . . . . . . . . . . . . . . . . . . . . . . . . . . . . . . . . . . . . . . . . . . . . . .
Gross National Product . . . . . . . . . . . . . . . . . . . . . . . . . . . . . . . . . . . . . . . . . . . . . . . . . . .
Military Expenditure as a Percentage of
   Gross National Product . . . . . . . . . . . . . . . . . . . . . . . . . . . . . . . . . . . . . . . . . . . . . . . . .
Military Expenditure as a Percentage of
   Central Government Expenditure . . . . . . . . . . . . . . . . . . . . . . . . . . . . . . . . . . . . . . . . .

**Defence Treaties** *(See Part II for Additional Detail)*

Bilateral:      United States

Multilateral:   Regional Security System
                Treaty on the Control of Arms on the Seabed
                Treaty on the Non-Proliferation of Nuclear Weapons

# ST. VINCENT AND THE GRENADINES

## Defence Establishment Command Structure and Force Organization

The Governor-General commands the police force of St. Vincent and the Grenadines. There is no formal military structure, and the United Kingdom has responsibility for defence in the event of an emergency.

**Police:** 473.

## HEAD OF STATE

H. M. Queen Elizabeth II

## GOVERNOR-GENERAL

H. E. Dr. Sir Sydney Douglas Gunn-Munro

**OFFICE OF THE GOVERNOR-GENERAL**
*Kingstown*
*Telephone: 456-1401*

Governor-General . . . . . . . . . . . . . . . . Dr. Sir Sydney Douglas Gunn-Munro

**OFFICE OF THE PRIME MINISTER**
*Kingstown*
*Telephone: 457-1637, 456-1703*

Prime Minister . . . . . . . . . . . . . . . . . . . . . . . . . . . . . . Robert Milton Cato
Cabinet Secretary and Permanent Secretary
   to the Prime Minister . . . . . . . . . . . . . . . . . . . . . . . . . . . . J. A. Pompey
Deputy Prime Minister . . . . . . . . . . . . . . . . . . . . . . . . . . Hudson K. Tannis

**MINISTRY OF FOREIGN AFFAIRS, INTERNAL SECURITY AND TOURISM**
*Kingstown*
*Telephone: 457 1632*

Deputy Prime Minister and
   Minister of Foreign Affairs,
   Internal Security and Tourism . . . . . . . . . . . . . . . . . . . Hudson K. Tannis
Permanent Secretary (Acting) . . . . . . . . . . . . . . . . . . . . . Myron Dellimore
Port Officer . . . . . . . . . . . . . . . . . . . . . . . . . . . . . . . . . D. E. N. Byron-Cox

## DEFENCE FORCE

**POLICE FORCE**
*Kingstown*

Commissioner (Acting) . . . . . . . . . . . . . . . . . . . . . . . . . . . F. B. Constantine
Deputy Commissioner . . . . . . . . . . . . . . . . . . . . . . . . . . . . . . D. C. Bobb
Assistant Superintendent (Acting) . . . . . . . . . . . . . . . . . . . . . . A. T. Jackson

\* \* \* \* \*

## GENERAL DEFENCE DATA

**Manpower**
   Total Armed Forces . . . . . . . . . . . . . . . . . . . . . . . . . . . . . . . . . . . . . . 473
   Population . . . . . . . . . . . . . . . . . . . . . . . . . . . . . . . . . . . . . . . . . 121,000

**Spending**
  Military Expenditures . . . . . . . . . . . . . . . . . . . . . . . . . . . . . . . . . . . . . . . . . . . . . . . . .
  Gross National Product . . . . . . . . . . . . . . . . . . . . . . . . . . . . . . . . . . . . . . . . . . . . .$47 million
  Military Expenditure as a Percentage of
    Gross National Product . . . . . . . . . . . . . . . . . . . . . . . . . . . . . . . . . . . . . . . . . . . . . .
  Military Expenditure as a Percentage of
    Central Government Expenditure . . . . . . . . . . . . . . . . . . . . . . . . . . . . . . . . . . . . .

**Defence Treaties** *(See Part II for Additional Detail)*

  Bilateral:     United States

  Multilateral:  Regional Security System

# SÃO TOMÉ AND PRÍNCIPE
## Democratic Republic of São Tomé and Príncipe
### *Republica Democratica de São Tomé e Príncipe*

### Defense Establishment Command Structure and Force Organization

The President is Commander-in-Chief of the Armed Forces of São Tomé and Principé and exercises his authority through the Minister of Defense.

**Total armed forces:** 800.

## HEAD OF STATE

H. E. Dr. Manuel Pinto da Costa

**OFFICE OF THE PRESIDENT**
*Praça do Pouo*
*São Tomé*
*Telephone: 21020*
*Telex: 209*

President of the MLSTP,
President of the Democratic
Republic, and Commander-in-
Chief of the Armed Forces ................Dr. Manuel Pinto da Costa

**MINISTRY OF NATIONAL DEFENSE**
*8 Avenida 12 de Julho*
*São Tomé*
*Telephone: 21092*
*Telex: 210*

Minister ........................Oscar Aguiar do Sacramento é Sousa
Director, Military Cabinet ............................João Luís Mota

## DEFENSE FORCES

**ARMED FORCES**
*Bairro Militar*
*São Tomé*
*Telephone: 21092*

Commander-in-Chief ......................Dr. Manuel Pinto da Costa
Chief of Staff ...........................................João Bixigas

**POLICE NATIONAL DEPARTMENT**
*R. Ex-João De Deus*
*São Tomé*
*Telephone:*

Commander ................................Romão Pereira de Couto

**Internal Security Direction**

Director ...........................................Amado Vaz

\* \* \* \* \*

453

## GENERAL DEFENSE DATA

**Manpower**
Total Armed Forces . . . . . . . . . . . . . . . . . . . . . . . . . . . . . . . . . . . . . . . . . . . .800
  (See Page 453)
Population . . . . . . . . . . . . . . . . . . . . . . . . . . . . . . . . . . . . . . . . . . . . . . . .85,000

**Spending**
Military Expenditures . . . . . . . . . . . . . . . . . . . . . . . . . . . . . . . . . . . . . . . .$1 million
Gross National Product . . . . . . . . . . . . . . . . . . . . . . . . . . . . . . . . . . . . .$80 million
Military Expenditure as a Percentage of
  Gross National Product . . . . . . . . . . . . . . . . . . . . . . . . . . . . . . . . . . . . .1.3%
Military Expenditure as a Percentage of
  Central Government Expenditure . . . . . . . . . . . . . . . . . . . . . . . . . . . . . . .2.5%

**Defense Treaties** *(See Part II for Additional Detail)*

Bilateral:  None

Multilateral:  Biological Weapons Convention
Environmental Modification Convention
Treaty on the Non-Proliferation of Nuclear Weapons

# SAUDI ARABIA
## Kingdom of Saudi Arabia
### al-Mamlaka al-'Arabiyah al-Sa'udiyah

## Defense Establishment Command Structure and Force Organization

The King is Commander-in-Chief of the Armed Forces, but operational control of the military is exercised by the Second Deputy Prime Minister, who is also Minister of Defense and Aviation. Security policy is formulated by the High Defense Council. The Army, Navy and Air Force are under the direction of the Ministry of Defense and Aviation. The Chief of Staff is directly responsible to the Minister for the supervision of the activities of the three services.

The country is divided into nine area commands, which serve as intermediate headquarters between the Ministry of Defense and Aviation and units in the field.

The National Guard is under the personal control of the King through a commander appointed by him. The current Commander of the National Guard, Crown Prince Abdullah bin Abdul Aziz, also holds an appointment within the Ministry of Defense and Aviation as Controller of Militia Reserves (whether these reserves would be added to the National Guard or the regular army upon mobilization is not clear). The Frontier Force, the Coast Guard and the internal security forces are controlled by the Minister of the Interior.

**Total armed forces:** 77,200 (Army: 35,000; Navy: 2,200; Air Force: 15,000; National Guard: 25,000). **Para-military forces:** 6,500 (Frontier Force and Guard).

## HEAD OF STATE

H. M. King Fahd bin Abdul Aziz Al-Saud

**OFFICE OF H. M. THE KING AND PRIME MINISTER**
*Riyadh*
Telephone:   (1) 402-0245, 402-1264

*Jeddah*
Telephone:   (2) 665-4232, 665-4233

*Taif*
Telephone:   (2) 732-2157, 732-2355, 732-2757

King of Saudi Arabia,
   Prime Minister and Commander-
   in-Chief of the Armed Forces . . . . . . . H. M. Fahd bin Abdul Aziz Al-Saud
Military Adviser . . . . . . . . . . . . . . . . . . . . . . . Gen. Mohammad Al-Esheikh

**High Defense Council**

Chairman . . . . . . . . . . . . . . . . . . . . . . . H. M. Fahd bin Abdul Aziz Al-Saud
                                         (King and Prime Minister)
Member *(ex officio)* . . . . . . . H. R. H. Prince Sultan bin Abdul Aziz Al-Saud
                                         (Second Deputy Prime Minister and
                                         Minister of Defense and Aviation)
Member *(ex officio)* . . . . . . . . H. R. H. Prince Naif bin Abdul Aziz Al-Saud
                                         (Minister of Interior)
Member *(ex officio)* . . . . . . . . . . . . . . . . . Sheikh Mohammad Ali Ahalkhail
                                         (Minister of Finance and National Economy)
Member *(ex officio)* . . . . . . . . . . . . . . Sheikh Hussein Ibrahim Al-Mansouri
                                         (Minister of Communications)

Member *(ex officio)* .................................H. R. H. Prince
Saud Al-Faisal bin Abdul Aziz Al-Saud
(Minister of Foreign Affairs)

Member *(ex officio)* ...............Gen. Mohammad Saleh Al-Hammad
(Chief of the General Staff,
Saudi Arabian Armed Forces)

## OFFICE OF H. R. H. THE CROWN PRINCE, DEPUTY PRIME MINSTER, AND HEAD OF THE NATIONAL GUARD

*Riyadh*

*Telephone:*    *(1) 402-2489, 402-9727*
*Telex:*    *450020*

*Jeddah*

*Telephone:*    *(2) 665-4223, 665-4297*

*Taif*

*Telephone:*    *(2) 732-2730, 732-2755*
*Telex:*    *450047*

Crown Prince and Deputy
Prime Minister .....................................H. R. H. Prince
Abdullah bin Abdul Aziz Al-Saud

Director, Office of the Crown Prince .............Sheikh Nasser Al-Rajihi

Advisor to the Crown Prince ....................Sheikh Al-Mussallam

## OFFICE OF H. R. H. THE SECOND DEPUTY PRIME MINISTER AND MINISTER OF DEFENSE AND AVIATION

*Riyadh*

*Telephone:*    *(1) 403-0517, 403-0111*
*(Cabinet Secretariat)*

*Jeddah*

*Telephone:*    *(2) 642-4044, 642-4149,*
*643-2455*

*Taif*

*Telephone:*    *(2) 732-2730, 732-2755*

Second Deputy Prime Minister and
Minister of Defense and Aviation ....................H. R. H. Prince
Sultan bin Abdul Aziz Al-Saud

## MINISTRY OF DEFENSE AND AVIATION

*Riyadh (Main Ministry)*

*Telephone:*    *(1) 402-1115, 402-9220*
*Telex:*    *200191 modas sj*

Minister and Second Deputy
Prime Minister .........H. R. H. Prince Sultan bin Abdul Aziz Al-Saud

Assistant to the Minister ...................Gen. Othman Al-Homayyed
Chief of General Staff ..............Gen. Mohammed Saleh Al-Hammad
Controller of Militia
Reserves ..............Crown Prince Abdullah bin Abdul Aziz Al-Saud
Director-General,
Military Factories..........Prince Bandar bin Fahd bin Khalid Al-Saud
Director-General, Military Works ............Maj. Nasser Fahd Al-Faisal
Director, Medical Services ..........................Gen. Rida Khalifa
Director-General, Technical
Medical Services.............................Col. Abdulaziz Mirda
Director, Procurement Contracts ..............Lt. Col. Fahd I. Al-Jarbou

## MINISTRY OF INTERIOR

*Riyadh (Main Ministry)*

*Telephone:*    *(1) 403-0955*
*Telex:*    *201159*

Minister ..................H. R. H. Prince Naif bin Abdul Aziz Al-Saud

Vice President ..........H. R. H. Prince Ahmed bin Abdul Aziz Al-Saud
Deputy Minster, Security ..........Mohammad bin Abdulaziz Al-Duraibi

# DEFENSE FORCES

**ARMY**
**Saudi Arabian Land Forces—SALF**
*c/o Ministry of Defense*
*Riyadh*
*Telephone: (1) 402-3106*
*Telex: 201621*

Commander, SALF . . . . . . . . . . . . . .Lt. Gen. Abdul Mohsen Ali Al-Omran

**NAVY**
**Royal Saudi Naval Forces—RSNF**
*Dammam (Eastern Province)*
*Telephone: (383) 2500, Ext. 832-5000*

Commander, RSNF. . . . . . . . . . .Brig. Mohammad Oun Sharaf Al-Barakat

**AIR FORCE**
**Royal Saudi Air Force—RSAF**
*Riyadh*
*Telephone: (1) 402-7966, 402-1140*
*Telex: 201661 jawiah sj*

Commander, RSAF. . . . . . . . . . . . . . .Lt. Gen. Mohammad Suleiman Sabri

**SAUDI ARABIAN**
**NATIONAL GUARD—SANG**
*Riyadh*
*Telephone: (1) 402-4600, 402-4077*
*Telex: 201064 natgrd sj*

Commander . . . . . . . . .H. R. H. Prince Abdullah bin Abdul Aziz Al-Saud
Deputy Commander . . . . . . .H. R. H. Prince Badh bin Abdul Aziz Al-Saud
Assistant Deputy
   Commander . . . . . . . .Sheikh Abdul Aziz bin Abdul Mohsin Al-Tuwaijiri
Deputy of the National Guard . . . . .Sheikh Abdul Aziz bin Ali Al-Tuwaijiri
Senior British Advisor . . . . . . . . . . . . . . . . . . . . . .Brig. Gen. John Hooper
PM, SANG . . . . . . . . . . . . . . . . . . . . . . .Brig. Gen. John J. H. Yeosock

**Deputy for Technical Affairs**

Deputy . . . . . . . . . . . . . . . . . . . . . .Sheikh Abdul Rahman Abu Haimed
Assistant Deputy . . . . . . . . . . . . . . . . . . .Mohammed Kanaan Al-Muyasser
Chief Engineer . . . . . . . . . . . . . . . . . . . . . . . . . . . . . .Khaled Al-Askar
Engineer. . . . . . . . . . . . . . . . . . . . . . . . . . . . . .Abdul Rahman Al-Abdaan
Engineer . . . . . . . . . . . . . . . . . . . . . . . . . . . . . . . . . . .Aadil Al-Mandil
Engineer . . . . . . . . . . . . . . . . . . . . . . . . . . . . . . . . . . . .Sa'ad Al-Own

**Department of Financial and**
**Administrative Affairs**

Director . . . . . . . . . . . . . . . . . . . . . .Sheikh Abdul Aziz bin Ali Al-Tuwaijiri
Legal Director . . . . . . . . . . . . . . . . . . . . . . . . . . . . . . . . .Qusai Al-Azzai
Assistant Legal Director . . . . . . . . . . . . . . . . . . . . . . .Najim Al-Tuwaijiri
Director of Finance . . . . . . . . . . . . . . . . . . . . . . . . . . . .Nasir Al-Omair
Director of Public Relations. . . . . . . . . . . . . . . . . .Abdul Rahman Al-Shithri
Office Manager and
   Procurement Specialist . . . . . . . . . . . . . . . . . . . . . .Othman Abu Haimad
Chief of Procurement . . . . . . . . . . . . . . . . . . . . . . . .Suleiman Al-Ghanem
Technical Supervisory Office . . . . . . . . . . . . . . . . . . . . . .B'dah Al-Qahtani
Organization Office . . . . . . . . . . . . . . . . . . . . . . . . . . . .Suleiman Sa'eed

**Deputy for Military Affairs (Logistics)**

Deputy . . . . . . . . . . . . . . . . . . . . . . . . . . . .Sheikh Abdul Aziz bin Ayyaf
Director, Ordnance and
   Transportation . . . . . . . . . . . . . . . . . . . . . . . . . .Col. Hammad Al-Huraishi
Director, Military Personnel . . . . . . . . . . . . . .Col. Abdul Aziz Al-Shalhoub
Director, Supply . . . . . . . . . . . . . . . . . . . . . . . . .Abdul Karim Al-Mushaiqa
Director, Weapons and Ammunition . . . . . . . . . . . . . . .Mohammad Jarboa
Ammunition Specialist . . . . . . . . . . . . . . . . . . . . . . . . . . . .Geoffrey Holden
Ammunition Specialist . . . . . . . . . . . . . . . . . . . . . . . . .Ibrahim Al-Tuwaijiri
Chief Inspector, Auto
   Maintainence and Transportation . . . . . . . . . . . . . .Hammad Al-Hamlan

**Military Organization**

Chief . . . . . . . . . . . . . . . . . . . . . . . . Gen. Mohammad bin Abdullah Al-Amr
Advisor . . . . . . . . . . . . . . . . Brig. Gen. (Ret.) Mohsin bin Mohammad Al-Ali
Director, Military
    Training Department . . . . . . . . . . . . . . . . Maj. Bandar bin Nahl Al-Harbi
Director, Plans and Operations . . . . . . . . . . . . . . Maj. Shaakir Al-Ghushyan
Director, Armament and
    Organization Department . . . . . . . . . . . . . . . . . . . Maj. Bandar Al-Orair

**Commanders**

Commander, Imam Mohammad
    bin Saud 1st Mechanized
    Brigade . . . . . . . . . . . . . . . . . . . . . . Brig. Gen. Oweidh bin Ali Al-Koud
Commander, 1st Combined
    Arms Battalion . . . . . . . . . . . . . . . . . . . . . Maj. Mutaib Tafoor Al-Onaizi
Commander, 2nd Combined
    Arms Battalion . . . . . . . . . . . . . . . Maj. Abdul Rahman Nuar Al-Mutairi
Commander, 3rd Combined
    Arms Battalion . . . . . . . . . . . . . . . . . . . . . . . . . Maj. Suleiman Al-Za'air
Commander, 4th Combined
    Arms Battalion . . . . . . . . . . . . . . . . . . . . . . . . . . . Maj. Firhan Al-Milhim
Commander, 5th Combined
    Arms Battalion . . . . . . . . . . . . . . . . . . . . . Maj. Mutieb Jallah Al-Onaizi
Commander, 1st Logistics
    Support Battalion . . . . . . . . . . . . . . . . . . . . . . . . . Maj. Salam Al-Subaiee
Commander, 2nd Logsitics
    Support Battalion . . . . . . . . . . . . . . . . Capt. Abdul Rahman Al-Muqhem
Commander, 1st Artillery
    Battalion . . . . . . . . . . . . . . . . . . . . . Maj. Mohammad Omar Al-Qahtani

**PUBLIC SECURITY FORCES**
*c/o Ministry of Interior*
*Riyadh*

*Telephone:   (1) 403-6100*
*Telex:   201167 amenam sj*

Director-General . . . . . . . . . . Gen. Abdullah bin Abdul Rahman Al-Esheikh

**COAST GUARD**
*c/o Ministry of Interior*
*Riyadh*
*Telephone:   (1) 402-0222, 402-0538*

Chief . . . . . . . . . . . . . . . . . . . . . . . . . . . . . . . . . . . . . . . . . . . . . . . . . . . . . . .

**FRONTIER FORCE**
*c/o Ministry of Interior*
*Riyadh*
*Telephone:   (1) 402-0222, 402-0538*
*Telex:   201625*

Director-General . . . . . . . . . . . . . . . . . . . . . Lt. Gen. Mohammed bin Hallal

* * * * *

# GENERAL DEFENSE DATA

**Manpower**
    Total Armed Forces . . . . . . . . . . . . . . . . . . . . . . . . . . . . . . . . . . . . . . . . 77,200
       (See Page 455)
    Population . . . . . . . . . . . . . . . . . . . . . . . . . . . . . . . . . . . . . . . . . . . 19,795,000

**Spending**

Military Expenditures . . . . . . . . . . . . . . . . . . . . . . . . . . . . . . . . . . . . . . . $16.7 billion
Gross National Product . . . . . . . . . . . . . . . . . . . . . . . . . . . . . . . . . . . . . . $117 billion
Military Expenditure as a Percentage of
  Gross National Product . . . . . . . . . . . . . . . . . . . . . . . . . . . . . . . . . . . . 14.4%
Military Expenditure as a Percentage of
  Central Government Expenditure . . . . . . . . . . . . . . . . . . . . . . . . . . . . 26.7%

**Defense Treaties** *(See Part II for Additional Detail)*

Bilateral:        United States

Multilateral:   Biological Weapons Convention
                    Cooperation Council for the Arab States of the Gulf
                    League of Arab States
                    Treaty on the Control of Arms on the Seabed

# SENEGAL
## Republic of Senegal
### *Republique du Senegal*

### Defense Establishment Command Structure and Force Organization

The President is Commander-in-Chief and exercises his command through the Minister of Armed Forces.

**Total armed forces:** 9,800 (Army: 8,500;     Navy: 500;     Air Force: 400;     Constabulary: 6,800).

## HEAD OF STATE

H. E. Abdou Diouf

**OFFICE OF THE PRESIDENT**
*Avenue Roume*
*B.P. 168*
*Dakar*
*Telephone:   23 10 88, 21 50 75*
*Telex:   258, 537 presid sg*

President of the Republic and Commander-in-Chief . . . . . . . . Abdou Diouf
Attache to Cabinet . . . . . . . . . . . . . . . . . . . . . . . . . . . . . . . . . . . . Magatte Ba
Commandant of the Military House . . . . . . . . . . . . . . . . Cdt. Francois Gomis
Aide-de-Camp . . . . . . . . . . . . . . . . . . . . . . . . . . . . Capt. Abdel Kader Gueye

**OFFICE OF THE PRIME MINISTER**
*Administrative Building*
*B.P. 140*
*Dakar*
*Telephone:   23 10 88, 21 50 75*
*Telex:   258, 537*

Prime Minister . . . . . . . . . . . . . . . . . . . . . . . . . . . . . . . . . . . . Habib Thiam

**General Secretariat of the Government**
*Dakar*
*Telephone:   2256 15*

Secretary-General . . . . . . . . . . . . . . . . . . . . . . . . . . . . . . . . . . Andre Sonko

**MINISTRY OF ARMED FORCES**
*(Ministre des Forces Armees)*
*B.P. 176*
*Telephone:   23 10 88, 22 56 13, 22 12 16*
*Telex:   482, 483, 485*

Minister . . . . . . . . . . . . . . . . . . . . . . . . . . . . . . . . . . . . . . . . . . . Daouda Sow
Special Secretary . . . . . . . . . . . . . . . . . . . . . . . . . . . (Mrs.) Oulimata Mbaye
Staff Director . . . . . . . . . . . . . . . . . . . . . . . . . . . . . . . . . . Mohamed Sonko
Staff Chief . . . . . . . . . . . . . . . . . . . . . . . . . . . . . . . . . . Samba Aissata Ka
Chief, Military Cabinet . . . . . . . . . . . . . . . . . . . . . . . . Lt. Col. Amadou Fall
Director, Constabulary and
     Military Justice . . . . . . . . . . . . . . . . . . . . Gen. de Brigade Wally Faye
Attache . . . . . . . . . . . . . . . . . . . . . . . . . . . . . . . . . . . . . . E. H. Laba Sow
Counsellor . . . . . . . . . . . . . . . . . . . . . . . . . . . . . . . . Col. Claude Bakuiet
Counsellor . . . . . . . . . . . . . . . . . . . . . . . . . . . . . . . . Lt. Col. Henri Burger

# DEFENSE FORCES

**ARMED FORCES**
**Armed Forces General Staff**
*Immeuble Administratif*
*Dakar*

*Telephone: 23 10 76*
*Telex: 482, 483, 485*

| | |
|---|---|
| Chief of Staff | Gen. de Div. Idrissa Fall |
| Deputy Chief of Staff | Lt. Col. Mamadou M. Seck |
| Director of Staff | Cdt. Mamadou Niang |
| Director, Plans and Operations | Cdt. Abdourahmane Gueye |
| Director, Military Personnel and Mobilization | Col. Badara Konte |

**ARMY**
*(Armee de Terre)*
*Quartier Dial-Diop*
*Dakar*

*Telephone: 23 10 88*
*Telex: 482, 483 485*

| | |
|---|---|
| Commander | Col. Victor Barry |
| Commander, Western Military Zone (Dakar) | Lt. Col. Abdourahmane Ngom |
| Commander, Northern Military Zone (Saint Louis) | Lt. Col. Almamy Tamba |
| Commander, Eastern Military Zone (Tambacounda) | |
| Commander, Southern Military Zone (Ziguinchor) | Lt. Col. Saliou Niang |
| Commander, Central Military Zone (attached to Southern Zone) | |

**NAVY**
*(Armee de Mer)*
*Quartier Dial-Diop*
*Dakar*

*Telephone: 21 71 40*
*Telex: 482, 483, 485*

| | |
|---|---|
| Commander | Capt. Faye Gassama |
| Commander of the Naval Base | Cdt. Abdoulaye Thiaw |

**AIR FORCE**
*(Armee de l'Air)*
*Quartier Dial-Diop*
*B.P. 4042*
*Dakar*

*Telephone: 22 44 68*
*Telex: 482, 483, 485*

| | |
|---|---|
| Commander | Cdt. Amadou Lam |

**CONSTABULARY**
*(Gendarmerie Nationale)*
*Dakar*

*Telephone:*

| | |
|---|---|
| Commander | Col. Victor Barry |

\* \* \* \* \*

# GENERAL DEFENSE DATA

**Manpower**

| | |
|---|---|
| Total Armed Forces | 9,800 |
| (See Page 461) | |
| Population | 5,990,000 |

**Spending**

| | |
|---|---|
| Military Expenditures | $66 million |
| Gross National Product | $2.6 billion |
| Military Expenditure as a Percentage of Gross National Product | 2.6% |
| Military Expenditure as a Percentage of Central Government Expenditure | 11.4% |

**Defense Treaties** *(See Part II for Additional Detail)*

Bilateral:       France
Gambia
United States

Multilateral:    Biological Weapons Convention
Economic Community of West African States
Limited Test Ban Treaty
Organization of African Unity
Treaty on the Non-Proliferation of Nuclear Weapons
United Nations Interim Force in Lebanon

*Note: The Confederation of Senegambia was formed on Feb. 1, 1982, to bring about the integration of Senegal and Gambia's security services, armed forces, and economic and monetary systems.*

*There is a government of the Confederation, composed of members of the two individual governments. The President of Senegal serves as the President of the Confederation, and the President of the Gambia is the Vice-President. A Council of Ministers has also been formed.*

# SEYCHELLES
## Republic of Seychelles

### Defense Establishment Command Structure and Force Organization

The President is Commander-in-Chief and exercises his authority through the Minister of Youth and Defense, who is also Chief of the Armed Forces.

**Total armed forces:** 1,000 (Army: 750;  Naval Service: 150;  Air Wing: 100). **Paramilitary forces:** 900 (Police: 450;  People's Militia: 450).

## HEAD OF STATE

H. E. France Albert René

**OFFICE OF THE PRESIDENT**
*State House*
*Box 55*
*Victoria, Mahe*

*Telephone: 23911*
*Telex: 2217 state sz*

President and Commander-in-Chief ................France Albert René
Principal Secretary ....................................David Thomas
Personal Secretary ........................(Mrs.) Bernadette Barrado

**SEYCHELLES PEOPLE'S PROGRESSIVE FRONT—SPPF**
*Maison du Peuple*
*Victoria, Mahe*

*Telephone: 21041*
*Telex: 2260 seygov sz*

Secretary-General ........................................Guy Sinon

**MINISTRY OF YOUTH AND DEFENSE**
*State House*
*P.O. Box 55*
*Victoria, Mahe*

*Telephone: 22321, 23991, 23937*
*Telex: 2217 state sz*

Minister and Chief of the Armed Forces .................Ogilvy Berlouis
Chief, Presidential Security .......................Maj. Roland Marie
Principal Secretary ....................................Ralph Adam

## DEFENSE FORCES

**ARMED FORCES**
**Seychelles People's Liberation Army**
*Box 154*
*Victoria, Mahe*
*Telephone: 2618, 22520*

Commander-in-Chief of the Armed Forces ...........France Albert René
Chief of Armed Forces and Minister of Youth and
    Defense...............................................Ogilvy Berlouis
Chief of Staff, Defense Forces (People's Militia)............James Michel
Commander, Union Vale Military Camp..............Maj. Phillipe Lucas
Commander, Coetivy Training Camp ..........Maj. McDonald Marengo

**NAVY**
*Box 154*
*Victoria, Mahe*
*Telephone: 2618, 22520*

Commander .......................................Capt. P. Hodoul

**POLICE DEPARTMENT**
**Police Headquarters**
*Box 46*
*Revolution Avenue*
*Victoria, Mahe*

*Telephone:    22011, 22591*
*Telex:    2298 compol 52*

| | |
|---|---|
| Commissioner | J. Pillay |
| Deputy Commissioner | M. Fontaine |
| C.I.D. Officer | J. Larue |
| Chief, Interpol Office | J. Pillay |
| Chief, Special Force Unit, Mont Fleuri | A. Kilindo |
| Chief, Mobile Unit | A. Kilindo |
| Chief, Special Branch | A. Camille |
| Chief, Police Mobile Unit, Petit Paris | A. Kilindo |
| Director, Police Training School, Praslin | S. Radegonde |

* * * * *

# GENERAL DEFENSE DATA

**Manpower**
Total Armed Forces . . . . . . . . . . . . . . . . . . . . . . . . . . . . . . . . . . . . . . . . . . . . . . . . . . . 1,000
    (See Page 465)
Population . . . . . . . . . . . . . . . . . . . . . . . . . . . . . . . . . . . . . . . . . . . . . . . . . . . . . . . . 66,000

**Spending**
Military Expenditures . . . . . . . . . . . . . . . . . . . . . . . . . . . . . . . . . . . . . . . . . . . . . . . .
Gross National Product . . . . . . . . . . . . . . . . . . . . . . . . . . . . . . . . . . . . . . . . . . . . . . . .
Military Expenditure as a Percentage of
    Gross National Product . . . . . . . . . . . . . . . . . . . . . . . . . . . . . . . . . . . . . . . . . . . . . .
Military Expenditure as a Percentage of
    Central Government Expenditure . . . . . . . . . . . . . . . . . . . . . . . . . . . . . . . . . . . . . . .

**Defense Treaties** *(See Part II for Additional Detail)*

Bilateral:        None

Multilateral:    Biological Weapons Convention
                Organization of African Unity
                Treaty on the Control of Arms on the Seabed

# SIERRA LEONE
## Republic of Sierra Leone

### Defense Establishment Command Structure
### and Force Organization

The President of the Republic is Commander-in-Chief of the Armed Forces and Minister of Defense.

**Total armed forces:** 2,650 (Army: 2,500;     Navy: 150). **Para-military forces:** 2,300 (Police).

## HEAD OF STATE

H. E. Siaka Probyn Stevens

**OFFICE OF THE PRESIDENT**
**State House**
*Independence Avenue*
*Freetown*
*Telephone: 22287*
*Telex: 3230 presec sl*

President of the Republic, Minister of Defense,
    Commander-in-Chief of the Armed Forces,
    and Commander of Internal Security Units ....Dr. Siaka Probyn Stevens
Secretary to the President ............................Abdul Karime
Minister of State ...................................Edward Karebo
Minister of State ..................................Philipson Kamara
Minister of State .......................................Tamba Juana

**STATE MINISTRY, POLICE**
*Freetown*

Minister of State for Police ............................John A. Grant
Adjunct .............................................P. M. Johnson

**MINISTRY OF DEFENSE**
**Tower Hill**
*Freetown*
*Telephone: 23884*
*Telex: 3218 extrnl sl*
*(Ministry of Foreign Affairs)*

President and Minister of Defense ..............Dr. Siaka Probyn Stevens
Secretary General of Defense,
    Navy and Aviation......................Christina A. Kamara-Taylor

## DEFENSE FORCE

**ARMED FORCES**
**Sierra Leone Military Forces—SLMF**
*Headquarters*
*Murraytown Barracks*
*Freetown*
*Telephone: 31481*
*Telex: 3218 extrnl sl*
*Cable: COMMAND FREETOWN*

Commander, SLMF, Chief of Staff,
    and Minister of State .......................Brig. Joseph S. Momoh
Deputy Commander, SLMF ..........................Col. S. H. King
Commander, First Battalion ......................Col. M. S. Tarawalli
Commander, Second Battalion ...................Lt. Col. A. O. Kamara
Commander, Signals ..........................Lt. Col. A. B. Toronka
Camp Commandant, HQ ........................Lt. Col. J. R. Macarthy
Senior Medical Officer ............................Lt. Col. I. A. Sheriff
Commander, Engineering Corps .................Maj. Gandy Williams

\* \* \* \* \*

467

## GENERAL DEFENSE DATA

**Manpower**
    Total Armed Forces . . . . . . . . . . . . . . . . . . . . . . . . . . . . . . . . . . . . . . . . . . . . . . .2,650
        (See Page 467)
    Population . . . . . . . . . . . . . . . . . . . . . . . . . . . . . . . . . . . . . . . . . . . . . . . . .3,535,000

**Spending**
    Military Expenditures . . . . . . . . . . . . . . . . . . . . . . . . . . . . . . . . . . . . . . . . .$11 million
    Gross National Product . . . . . . . . . . . . . . . . . . . . . . . . . . . . . . . . . . . . . . .$963 million
    Military Expenditure as a Percentage of
        Gross National Product . . . . . . . . . . . . . . . . . . . . . . . . . . . . . . . . . . . . . . . .1.1%
    Military Expenditure as a Percentage of
        Central Government Expenditure . . . . . . . . . . . . . . . . . . . . . . . . . . . . . . . .3.8%

**Defense Treaties** *(See Part II for Additional Detail)*

    Bilateral:      Guinea
                    United States

    Multilateral:   Biological Weapons Convention
                    Economic Community of West African States
                    Limited Test Ban Treaty
                    Organization of African Unity
                    Treaty on the Non-Proliferation of Nuclear Weapons

# SINGAPORE

## Republic of Singapore
*Hsing-chia p'o Kung-ho Kuo* (Chinese)
*Republik Singapura* (Malay)

### Defence Establishment Command Structure
and Force Organization

The President is Commander-in-Chief of the armed forces of Singapore. The Minister of Defence, with the Armed Forces Council, has responsibility for the administration and operation of the military.

**Total armed forces:** 57,200 (Army: 50,000; Navy: 3,200; Air Force: 4,000). **Paramilitary forces:** 7,500 (Police and Marine Police). **Reserves:** 130,000 (Home Guards and Gurkhas).

### HEAD OF STATE

H. E. C. V. Devan Nair

**OFFICE OF THE PRESIDENT**
*Istana*
*Orchard Road*
*Singapore 0922*
*Telephone: 7375522*
*Cable: PRESIDENT SINGAPORE*

President of the Republic and
    Commander-in-Chief . . . . . . . . . . . . . . . . . . . . . . . . . . . . .C. V. Devan Nair

**OFFICE OF THE PRIME MINISTER**
*Istana Annexe*
*Orchard Road*
*Singapore 0922*
*Telephone: 7375133*
*Cable: PRIMIN SINGAPORE*

Prime Minister . . . . . . . . . . . . . . . . . . . . . . . . . . . . . . . . . . .Lee Kuan Yew
First Deputy Prime Minister, Education . . . . . . . . . . . . .Dr. Goh Keng Swee
Second Deputy Prime Minister, Foreign Affairs . . . . . . . . . . .S. Rajaratnam

**MINISTRY OF DEFENCE**
*Tanglin Road*
*Singapore 1024*
*Telephone: 637744*
*Telex: 21373 sindef rs*
*Cable: SINGDEF SINGAPORE*

First Minister for Defence . . . . . . . . . . . . . . . . . . . . . . . . . . .Goh Chok Tong
Second Minister for Defence . . . . . . . . . . . . . . . . . . . . . . .Howe Yoon Chong
Minister of State for Defence . . . . . . . . . . . . . . . . . . . . . .Dr. Yeo Ning Hong
Senior Parliamentary Secretary . . . . . . . . . . . . . . . . . . . . . . . . .Phua Bah Lee
First Permanent Secretary . . . . . . . . . . . . . . . . . . . . . . . . . . .Lim Siong Guan
Second Permanent Secretary . . . . . . . . . . . . . . . . . . . . .Phillip Yeo Liat Kok
Deputy Secretary, Personnel and Policy . . . . . . . . . .Richard Lau Boon Teow
Deputy Secretary, Development (and
    Deputy Secretary, Air Force) . . . . . . . . . . . . . . . . . . . . . .Lim Ming Seong
Deputy Secretary, Resource Management . . . . . . . . . . . . . . . .Tan Yang Kai
Director, Manpower Division . . . . . . . . . . . . . . . . . . . . . . . .Low Puk Yeong
Director, Logistics Division . . . . . . . . . . . . . . . . . . . . . . . . . .Teo Ming Kian
Director, Security and Intelligence Division . . . . . . . .Eddie Teo Chan Sang
Director, Finance Division . . . . . . . . . . . . . . . . . . . . . . . . . . .Low Cher Kiah
Director, Systems and Computers Division (Acting) . . . . . . . .William Chan
Director, Defence Science Organization . . . . . . . . . . . . . . .Tham Choon Tat

Director, Lands and Estates Division .................... Goh Song How
Commander, Central Manpower Base .......... Lt. Col. Ling Woo Leong
Director, Special Projects Office
   (Research and Development) ..................... Col. Lui Pao Chan
Commander, Military Security Department ....... Lt. Col. Tan Hong Huat
Commandant, Singapore Command
   and General Staff College ............. Col. K. P. Ramchandon Menon

**Armed Forces Council**

Chairman .......................................... Goh Chok Tong
                                           (Minister of Defence)
Member......................... Maj. Gen. Winston Choo Wee Leong
     (Chief of the General Staff and Commander of the Army)
Member....................................... Col. Khoo Eng An
                                   (Commander of the Navy)
Member................................ Col. Michael Teo Eng Cheng
                          (Commander of the Air Force)

# DEFENCE FORCES

**ARMY**
**Republic of Singapore Armed Forces**
*c/o Ministry of Defence*
*Tanglin Road*
*Singapore 1024*

*Telephone: 637744*
*Telex: 21373 sindef rs*
*Cable: SINGDEF SINGAPORE*

Commander and Chief of the
   General Staff ................... Maj. Gen. Winston Choo Wee Leong
Deputy Chief of the General Staff ................ Col. Manchuvan S. Gill
Chief of Staff, General Staff ..................... Col. Lee Hsien Loong
Commander, 3rd Division ...................... Col. Kwan Yue Yeong
Commander, 6th Division ...................... Col. Chan Jwee Kay
Commander, 9th Division ....................... Col. Charles Chew
Commander, People's Defence Force ........ Col. Edward Yong Men Win
Chief of Infantry ................................ Col. Chin Chow Yoon
Chief of Armour................................. Col. Colin G. Theseira
Chief of Artillery................................ Lt. Col. Govrinde Rasu
Chief of Signal ................................. Lt. Col. Lai Seck Khui

**NAVY**
**Republic of Singapore Navy**
*c/o Ministry of Defence*
*Tanglin Road*
*Singapore 1024*

*Telephone: 637744*
*Telex: 21373 sindef rs*
*Cable: SINGDEF SINGAPORE*

Commander ...................................... Col. Khoo Eng An
Chief of Staff ............................ Col. James Leo Chian An
Fleet Commander (on Study Leave)................. Col. Lee Seng Kong
Deputy Fleet Commander (Acting) ................. Lt. Col. Peter Chen
Commander, Naval Schools ................... Lt. Col. Lim Kuong Hoon

**AIR FORCE**
**Republic of Singapore Air Force**
*c/o Ministry of Defence*
*Tanglin Road*
*Singapore 1024*

*Telephone: 637744*
*Telex: 21373 sindef rs*
*Cable: SINGDEF SINGAPORE*

Commander (on Study Leave) ............. Col. Michael Teo Eng Cheng
Commander (Acting) and
   Deputy Commander ...................... Col. Gary Yeo Peng Yong
Commander of the Singapore Air Defence .......... Lt. Col. Tan Jer Meng
Senior Staff Officer to IADS—Butterworth ............ Col. T. J. Desouza
Chief of Operations ........................... Lt. Col. Soon Eng Boon
Chief of Logistics .............................. Lt. Col. Richard Liao
Chief of Purchasing ................................ Chiu Hock Peng

**POLICE**
**Republic of Singapore Police**
*Phoenix Park, Tanglin Road*
*Singapore 1024*

Commissioner of Police ............................. Goh Yong Hong
Deputy Commissioner ................................ Michael Chai
Head, Public Relations Division............................ Teo Wue

\* \* \* \* \*

# GENERAL DEFENCE DATA

**Manpower**
Total Armed Forces............................................57,200
(See Page 469)
Population ..................................................2,472,000

**Spending**
Military Expenditures .......................................$620 million
Gross National Product......................................$10.8 billion
Military Expenditure as a Percentage of
    Gross National Product .........................................5.7%
Military Expenditure as a Percentage of
    Central Government Expenditure ...............................20.6%

**Defense Treaties** *(See Part II for Additional Detail)*

Bilateral:      United States

Multilateral:   Biological Weapons Convention
                Five-Power Defence Arrangements
                Limited Test Ban Treaty
                Treaty on the Control of Arms on the Seabed
                Treaty on the Non-Proliferation of Nuclear Weapons

# SOLOMON ISLANDS

## Defence Establishment Command Structure and Force Organization

The Solomon Islands does not maintain a military force and has no formal defence structure. The United Kingdom is responsible for the country's external defence, and the police force maintains internal security.

## HEAD OF STATE

H. H. Queen Elizabeth II

## GOVERNOR-GENERAL

H. E. Sir Baddeley Devesi

**OFFICE OF THE GOVERNOR-GENERAL**
*Government House*
*Honiara*
*Telephone:  222*
*Telex:  66201 governor hq*

Governor-General . . . . . . . . . . . . . . . . . . . . . . . . . . . . .Sir Baddeley Devesi

**OFFICE OF THE PRIME MINISTER**
*P.O. Box 61*
*Honiara*
*Telephone:  202*
*Telex:  66311 primus hq*
*Cable:  PRIMUS HONIARA*

Prime Minister . . . . . . . . . . . . . . . . . . . . . . . . . . . . . . .Soloman Mamaloni
Deputy Prime Minister . . . . . . . . . . . . . . . . . . . . . . . . . . .Kamilio Teke

**MINISTRY OF JUSTICE AND POLICE**
*P.O. Box 404*
*Honiara*
*Telephone:  915*
*Telex:  66311 primus hq*

Minister . . . . . . . . . . . . . . . . . . . . . . . . . . . . . . . . . . . . . . .P. Keyaumi
Commissioner of Police . . . . . . . . . . . . . . . . . . . . . . . . . . .J. P. Holloway

\* \* \* \* \*

## GENERAL DEFENCE DATA

**Manpower**
Total Armed Forces . . . . . . . . . . . . . . . . . . . . . . . . . . . . . . . . . . . . . . . . . . .
Population . . . . . . . . . . . . . . . . . . . . . . . . . . . . . . . . . . . . . . . . . . . .245,000

**Spending**
Military Expenditures . . . . . . . . . . . . . . . . . . . . . . . . . . . . . . . . . . . . . . . . . . . . . .
Gross National Product . . . . . . . . . . . . . . . . . . . . . . . . . . . . . . . . . . . . . . . 93.9 million
Military Expenditure as a Percentage of
   Gross National Product . . . . . . . . . . . . . . . . . . . . . . . . . . . . . . . . . . . . . . . . . . . . . .
Military Expenditure as a Percentage of
   Central Government Expenditure . . . . . . . . . . . . . . . . . . . . . . . . . . . . . . . . . . . . .

**Defence Treaties** *(See Part II for Additional Detail)*

Bilateral:    None

Multilateral:    Environmental Modification Convention
                 Treaty on the Control of Arms on the Seabed

# SOMALIA
## Somali Democratic Republic
### *al-Jumhurriyah al-Sumaliyah al-Dimuqratiyah*

## Defense Establishment Command Structure and Force Organization

The President is Commander-in-Chief of the armed forces of Somalia. He is advised on security policy by a National Defense Council, and exercises his authority through the Minister of Defense.

**Total armed forces:** 62,550 (Army: 60,000; Navy: 550; Air Force: 2,000). **Para-military forces:** 29,500.

## HEAD OF STATE

H. E. Maj. Gen. Mohamed Siad Barre

**POLTIBURO**
*People's Palace*
*Mogadishu*
*Telephone: 723*

President Commander-in-Chief, Chairman of the Socialist Revolutionary Council, and Secretary General of the Somali Revolutionary Socialist Party (SRSP) ..................... Maj. Gen. Mohamed Siad Barre
First Vice President and Minister of Defense ................ Lt. Gen. Mohamed Ali Samantar
Second Vice President and Minister of Government Affairs ...... Maj. Gen. Hussein Kulmia Afrah
Third Vice President and Chairman of the People's Assembly ........................ (Vacant)
Minister of Planning and National Security Advisor ........ Brig. Gen. Ahmed Suleyman Abdulle

**OFFICE OF THE PRESIDENT**
*People's Palace*
*Mogadishu*
*Telephone: 723*

President ............................ Maj. Gen. Mohamed Siad Barre
Minister at the Presidency ..................... Col. Musa Rabile Ghod
Assistant to the President ............. Maj. Gen. Hussein Kulmie Afrah

**MINISTRY OF DEFENSE**
*Mogadishu*
*Telephone: 710*

Minister .............................. Lt. Gen. Mohamed Ali Samatar
Assistant Minister ........................ Brig. Gen. Ahmed Sahal Ali
Chief, Directorate of Logistics ........... Brig. Gen. Ali Ismael Mohamed
Chief, Directorate of Support ....... Brig. Gen. Mohamed Sheikh Aduleh
Chief, Directorate of Technical Services ......................... Brig. Gen. Mohamed Ali Abokor
Director of Staff ............................ Col. Said Abdullah Omar
Commander, National Security Service ......................... Brig. Gen. Mohamed Jabril Musa
Commander, Custodial Corps ...... Cdr. Maj. Gen. Ismael Ahmed Ismael
Commander, People's Militia .......... Brig. Gen. Abduahman Hussein

# DEFENSE FORCES

**ARMY**
**Somali National Army**
*c/o Ministry of Defense*
*Mogadisha*

Commander, National Army ............Lt. Gen. Mohamed Ali Samatar
Commander, Northern Sector ..............Gen. Mohamed Hashi Gani
Commander, Southern Sector ................Brig. Said Farah Logeisai
Commander, Central Sector ...............................Col. Jama Ali
Commander of the Military Regions ......Col. Mahmud Abr Ar. Rahman
Commander, Northwest Region .............Lt. Col. Mahmud Abdi Ran
Commander, Togdher Region ......................Col. Abokor Nur
Commander, Snaag Region ..........Lt. Col. Hashim Muhammad Guled
Commander, Bari Region...................Ahmad Muhammad Isaaq
Commander, Nogul Region.......................Ahmad Sugule Hirsi
Commander, Mudugh Region .....Lt. Col. Ibrahim Muhamed Sharmarke
Commander, Galgudud Region.....................Col. Said Ali Fadil
Commander, Hiran Region ..........Ahmad Mahmud Farah Ali Hashim
Commander, Bokol Region .................Col. Muhamed Ali Hashim
Commander, Gedo Region ..................Col. Abshir Kahiye Farah
Commander, Bai Region...................Col. Husan Abshir Farah
Commander, Central Shebel Region ...................Col. Said Bileh
Commander, Lower Shebel Region ..................Ahmad Abdi Said
Commander, Central Juba Region ...........Col. Muhammad Egey Elmi
Commander, Lower Juba Juda Region ..............................

**Military Academy**

Director ...............................................Col. Nagui

**NAVY**
**Somali National Navy**
*c/o Ministry of Defense*
*Mogadishu*

Commander ......................Brig. Gen. Mohamed Omar Osman
Deputy Commander ........................Col. Farah Ahmed Omer

**AIR FORCE**
**Somali National Army Air Force**
*c/o Ministry of Defense*
*Mogadishu*

Commander ......................Brig. Gen. Abdi Osman Mohamed
Chief of Staff ......................Gen. Mohamed Adul Kadir Elmi
Director, Operations ......................Lt. Col. Ismael Moaline
Commander, Somali Air Defense Force....Col. Ahmed Mohammed Cheik

**NATIONAL POLICE**

Commander ..........................Maj. Gen. Adan Abdi Dualeh

\* \* \* \* \*

# GENERAL DEFENSE DATA

**Manpower**
Total Armed Forces ...............................................62,550
    (See Page 475)
Population ...................................................6,124,000

**Spending**
Military Expenditures.........................................$93 million
Gross National Product .......................................$1.5 billion
Military Expenditure as a Percentage of
    Gross National Product .........................................6.2%
Military Expenditure as a Percentage of
    Central Government Expenditure ..............................18.4%

**Defense Treaties** *(See Part II for Additional Detail)*

Bilateral:      Soviet Union
                United States

Multilateral:   League of Arab States
                Limited Test Ban Treaty
                Organization of African Unity

# SOUTH AFRICA
## Republic of South Africa
### *Republiek Van Suid-Afrika*

## Defence Establishment Command Structure and Force Organization

The President is the Commander-in-Chief of the armed forces. Constitutional responsibility for the defence of South Africa lies with the Minister of Defence, a Member of Parliament appointed to the Cabinet by the Prime Minister. Operational and administrative control of the armed forces is exercised by the Chief of the South African Defence Force (SADF), who heads the Department of Defence. The three service chiefs have considerable command autonomy, but report directly to the Chief of the SADF.

The South African Defence Force is composed of the Permanent Forces (Army, Navy, Air Force, Medical Corps), the Citizen Force and the Commandos. The Citizen Force includes reserves and other non-career members of the armed forces who are semi-active and who would augment the Permanent Forces in time of war in their home areas. The Commandos, also non-careerists, would also be used for the defence of their home areas.

**Total armed forces:** 92,700 (Army: 76,000; Navy: 6,400; Air Force: 10,300). **Reserves:** 232,300 (Commandos: 90,000; Citizen Force: 142,300).

## HEAD OF STATE

H. E. Marais Viljoen

**OFFICE OF THE STATE PRESIDENT**
*Bryntirion, Pretoria 0002*
*Telephone: (12) 743131*
*Telex: 3-0433 sa*

State President of the Republic .......................... Marais Viljoen
State Vice President ............................ Alwyn L. Schlebusch

**OFFICE OF THE PRIME MINISTER**
*Union Buildings*
*Private Bag X213*
*Pretoria 0001*

*Telephone: (12) 211211*
*Telex: 3-0397 sa*

Prime Minister and Minister
  of State Security ............................. Pieter Willem Botha
Director-General ................................. Dr. J. E. du Plessis
Minister of Defence ............................. Gen. Magnus Malan

**State Security Council**

Chairman .......................................... Pieter Willem Botha
  (Prime Minister and Minister of State Security)
Member ....................................... Gen. Magnus Malan
  (Minister of Defence)
Member ....................................... Louis le Grange
  (Minister of Police and Prisons)
Member ....................................... Roelof F. Botha
  (Minister of Foreign Affairs and Information)

**National Intelligence Service**
*Private Bag X87*
*Pretoria 0001*

*Telephone: (12) 39761*

Chief, Prime Minister and
  Minister of State Security ..................... Pieter Willem Botha
Director-General ................................. Dr. L. D. Barnard

**DEPARTMENT OF DEFENCE**
*(Department Van Verdediging)*
*Defence Forces Headquarters*
*Potgieter Street*
*Private Bag X414*
*Pretoria 0001*
*Telephone: (12) 26954*
*Telex: 3-721 sa*

Department Chief and
   Chief of the SADF . . . . . . . . . . Gen. Constand L. Viljoen, SSA, SM, SOE

     **ARMSCORS**
     *(Armament Development
      and Production Corporation)*

Chairman . . . . . . . . . . . . . . . . . . . . . . . . . . . . . . . . . . . . . . . Cdt. P. Marais

# DEFENCE FORCES

**ARMED FORCES**
**South African Defence
  Force—SADF**
*Defence Forces Headquarters*
*Potgieter Street*
*Private Bag X414*
*Pretoria 0001*
*Telephone: (12) 26954*
*Telex: 3-721 sa*

Chief, SADF . . . . . . . . . . . . . . . Gen. Constand L. Viljoen, SSA, SM, SOE

     **Defence Staff Council**

Chairman . . . . . . . . . . . . . . . . . . Gen. Constand L. Viljoen, SSA, SM, SOE
                                 (Chief SADF)
Member . . . . . . . . . . . . . . . . . . Lt. Gen. R. F. Holtzhausen, SSAS, SD, SM
                               (Chief of Staff, Personnel)
Member . . . . . . . . . . . . . . . . Lt. Gen. P. W. Van der Westhuizen, SSA, SM
                               (Chief of Staff, Intelligence)
Member . . . . . . . . . . . . . . . . . . . . Lt. Gen. I. R. Gleeson, SSAS, SD, SM
                               (Chief of Staff, Operations)
Member . . . . . . . . . . . . . . . . . . . . . . . . . . Lt. Gen. I. Lemmer, SD, SM
                               (Chief of Staff, Logistics)
Member . . . . . . . . . . . . . . . . . . . . . . . . . . Lt. Gen. W. J. Bergh, SD, SM
                               (Chief of Staff, Finance)
Member . . . . . . . . . . . . . . . . . . . . . . . . . . Maj Gen. C. P. Naude
                               (Chaplain General)

     **Defence Command Council**

Chairman . . . . . . . . . . . . . . . . . . Gen. Constand L. Viljoen, SSA, SM, SOE
                                 (Chief, SADF)
Member . . . . . . . . . . . . . . . . . Lt. Gen. Jannie J. Geldenhuys, SSA, SD, SM
                                 (Chief, Army)
Member . . . . . . . . . . . . . . . . . . . . . . . . . . . . Vice Adm. A. P. Putter
                                 (Chief, Navy)
Member . . . . . . . . . . . . . . . . . . . . . . Lt. Gen. A. Mike Muller, SSA, SD
                                 (Chief, Air Force)
Member . . . . . . . . . . . . . . . . . . . . . . . . . Lt. Gen. N. J. Nieuwoudt, SD, SM
                                 (Surgeon General)
Member . . . . . . . . . . . . . . . . . . . . . . . . . Maj. Gen. K. M. Pickersgill
                                 (Quartermaster General)

      **South African Military Academy**
      *Saldanha Bay*

Officer Commanding . . . . . . . . . . . . . . . . . . . . . . . Brig. S. W. J. Kotze, SM

      **South African Defence College**
      *Pretoria*

Officer Commanding . . . . . . . . . . . . . . . . . . . . . . . . . . Brig. D. J. Mortimer

## ARMY
*Private Bag X172*
*Pretoria 0001*

*Telephone: (12) 269721*
*Telex: 3-721 sa*

Chief of the Army ......................Lt. Gen. Jannie J. Geldenhuys
SSA, SD, SM
Chief of Army Staff, Personnel ................Maj. Gen. G. L. Meiring
Chief of Army Staff, Intelligence....................Brig. D. R. Verbeek
Chief of Army Staff, Operations .................Maj. Gen. D. R. Marais
Chief of Army Staff, Logistics ............Maj. Gen. R. Badenhorst, SD
Chief of Army Staff, Finance ..................Brig. W. J. Badenhorst
General Officer Commanding,
   Northern Transvaal Command ........Maj. Gen. F. E. C. Vandenberg,
SD, SM
Officer Commanding, Western
   Province Command .......................Brig. S. J. Van der Spuy
Officer Commanding, Eastern
   Province Command...................Brig. C. P. Van der Westhuizen
Officer Commanding, Natal
   Command .............................Brig. P. E. K. Bosman, SM
Officer Commanding, Orange
   Free State Command ......................Brig. W. C. Meyer, SD
Officer Commanding, Northwest
   Transvaal Command ...........................Brig. J. J. Bischoff
Officer Commanding,
   Witwatersrand Command ...............Brig. J. J. Van Heerden, SM
Officer Commanding,
   Southern Cape Command .................Brig. P. M. Lombard, SM
Officer Commanding, South
   West Africa Command .........................Maj. Gen. Lloyd
Officer Commanding, Army
   Staff College ...............................Col. W. G. Kritzinger
Officer Commanding, South
   African Battle School...........................Brig. C. Van Rooyen

## NAVY
*Private Bag X104*
*Pretoria 0001*

*Telephone: (12) 214911*
*Telex: 57-7946 sa*

Chief of the Navy .............................Vice Adm. A. P. Putter
Chief of Naval Staff, Operations .............Adm. G. Syndercombe, SM
Chief of Naval Staff, Finance ....................Comdr. C. Herselman
Chief of Naval Staff, Logistics.........................Comdr. N. Wise
Chief of Naval Staff, Personnel .....................Comdr. R. Eberlein
Chief of Naval Staff, Intelligence .....................Comdr. J. de Kock
Inspector-General of the Navy..............Rear Adm. J. Weideman, SM
Officer Commanding, Naval
   Operations Command ...................Comdr. D. Silberbaur, SM
Officer Commanding, Naval
   Training Command .................Comdr. C. Sanderhoff, SD, SM
Officer Commanding, Naval
   Logistics Command ..................Capt. J. Kleynschmid, SD, SM
Officer Commanding, Naval
   Natal Command .........................Comdr. P. Wijnberg, SM
Officer Commanding, Naval
   Cape Command...............................Comdr. T. Beddy
Officer Commanding, Naval
   Staff College ............................Capt. Simpson-Anderson

## AIR FORCE
*Private Bag X199*
*Pretoria 0001*

*Telephone: (12) 269941*
*Telex: 3-761 sa*

Chief of the Air Force ...................Lt. Gen. A. Mike Muller, SD
Chief of Air Force Staff,
   Operations ...........Maj. Gen. J. P. B. Van Loggerenberg, SD
Chief of Air Force Staff,
   Logistics ...........................Maj. Gen. H. G. du Plessis, SM
Chief of Air Force Staff, Finance.....................Brig. D. Haarholt
Chief of Air Force Staff, Personnel .....................Brig. J. Coetzee
Chief of Air Force Staff, Intelligence ...........Brig. A. J. S. Van der Lith
Inspector-General of the Air Force ............Maj. Gen. E. A. C. Pienaar
Officer Commanding, Transport Command ..........Brig. R. H. Repsold
Officer Commanding, Southern Air Command .........Brig. C. Lombard
Officer Commanding, Western Air Command ...........Brig. B. Huyser

Officer Commanding, Training Command . . . . . . . . . . . . . Brig. J. Moolman
Officer Commanding, Airspace Control
  Command . . . . . . . . . . . . . . . . . . . . . . . . . . . . . . . Brig. H. E. Lehman
Officer Commanding, Tactical Support
  Command . . . . . . . . . . . . . . . . . . . . . . . . . . . . . Brig. J. J. Koekemoer
Officer Commanding, Air Logistics
  Command . . . . . . . . . . . . . . . . . . . . . . . . . . . . . . Brig. A. J. Henning
Officer Commanding, Air
  Force Staff College. . . . . . . . . . . . . . . . . . . . . . . . . . . . . . . . . . . . . . .

**MEDICAL CORPS**
*Pretoria*

Surgeon General. . . . . . . . . . . . . . . . . . . . Lt. Gen. N. J. Nieuwoudt, SD, SM
Chief of Medical Staff, Personnel . . . . . . . . . . . . . . . . . . Brig. O. du Toit, SD
Chief of Medical Staff, Operations . . . . . . . . . . . . . Maj. Gen. D. P. Kuobel
Chief of Medical Staff, Logistics . . . . . . . . . . Maj. Gen. Scheepers, SD, SM
Chief of Medical Staff, Finance . . . . . . . . . . . . . . . . . . Brig. P. Pousegrouw

**POLICE**
*Pretoria*
*Schoeman Street*
*Telex:   3-0349 sa*

Chief of Police. . . . . . . . . . . . . . . . . . . . . . . . . . . . . Maj. Gen. Johann Coetzee

\* \* \* \* \*

# GENERAL DEFENCE DATA

**Manpower**
  Total Armed Forces. . . . . . . . . . . . . . . . . . . . . . . . . . . . . . . . . . . . . . . . 92,700
    (See Page 477)
  Population . . . . . . . . . . . . . . . . . . . . . . . . . . . . . . . . . . . . . . . . 30,021,000

**Spending**
  Military Expenditures. . . . . . . . . . . . . . . . . . . . . . . . . . . . . . . . . . . . $2.043 billion
  Gross National Product. . . . . . . . . . . . . . . . . . . . . . . . . . . . . . . . . . $64.497 billion
  Military Expenditure as a Percentage of
    Gross National Product . . . . . . . . . . . . . . . . . . . . . . . . . . . . . . . . . . . 3.2%
  Military Expenditure as a Percentage of
    Central Government Expenditure . . . . . . . . . . . . . . . . . . . . . . . . . . . 13.9%

**Defence Treaties** *(See Part II for Additional Detail)*

  Bilateral:     United States

  Multilateral:  Biological Weapons Convention
                 Limited Test Ban Treaty
                 Treaty on the Control of Arms on the Seabed

# SPAIN
## Spanish State
### Estado Español

### Defense Establishment Command Structure and Force Organization

The King is Head of the Supreme Council of Defense and Commander-in-Chief of the armed forces. The Army is the main military planning and supervisory agency, while the Ministry of Defense handles administrative policy. The Home Office (Governacion) exercises command over the State security forces which are composed of the General Police Corps, the Armed and Traffic Police, the Civil Guard Corps and other units.

**Total armed forces:** 347,000 (Army: 255,000; Navy: 54,000; Air Force: 38,000). **Para-military forces:** 105,000 (Guardia Civil: 65,000; Policia Nacional: 40,000).

### HEAD OF STATE

H. M. King Juan Carlos I

**OFFICE OF THE KING**
*(Oficina del Rey)*
*Palacio de la Zarazuela*
*Madrid*
*Telephone: (1) 222-9075*

King of Spain and Commander-in-Chief ............. King Juan Carlos I

**Superior Council of Defense**
*(Consejo Superior de Defensa)*

Head ......................................... King Juan Carlos I
Member *(ex officio)* ............. Narciso Serra Serra (Minister of Defense)
Member *(ex officio)* ...................... Gral. Alvaro de Lacalle Leloup
(Chairman of the Joint Chiefs of Staff)
Member *(ex officio)* .................. Gral. Ramón de Ascanio y Togores
(Chief, General Staff of Army)
Member *(ex officio)* .............. Alm. Saturnino Saunzes de la Hidalga
(Chief, Navy Staff)
Member *(ex officio)* .............. Tte. Gral. Emilio García—Conde Ceña
(Chief, Air Force Staff)

**OFFICE OF THE PRIME MINISTER AND PRESIDENT OF THE COUNCIL**
*Palacio de la Moncloa*
*Madrid 3*
*Telephone: (1) 449-1700, 449-0900, 244-4848*
*Telex: 22083 pego e, RCA 24845, ITI 44061*

Prime Minister and President of Government .... Felipe González Márquez
Deputy Prime Minister ...................... Alfonso Guerra González
Secretary to the Deputy Prime Minister ............. Rafael Delgado Rojas
Minister of the Presidency ............. Javier Moscoso del Prado y Muñoz

**MINISTRY OF DEFENSE**
*(Ministério de Defensa)*
*c/o Romero Robledo, 8,*
*Madrid - 8*
*Telephone: (1) 449-7000, 449-0700*

Minister of Defense ............................... Narciso Serra Serra
Deputy Secretary, Defense Policy ....... Gral. José Santos Peralba Giraldez
Deputy Secretary, Defense ..................... Eduardo Serra Rexach
Chief, Ministerial Cabinet .................. Gral. Manuel Alonso Aguilar
Chief, Information and Public Relations Office ..... Luis Reverter Gelabert
Secretary-General, Economic Affairs ............. Jesus Palacios Rodrigo
Secretary-General, Technical Affairs ...................... Vice Alm.
Mauricio Hermida Guerra-Mondragon

Director, Supreme Council for Military Justice . . . . . . . . . . . . . . . . . Tte. Gral.
Manuel Esquivias Franco
Inspector, Supreme Council of
the Ministry . . . . . . . . . . . . . . . . . . . . . . . . . . . . . Gral. Carlos Ibañez Muñoz
General Secretary, Defense Policy Affairs . . . . . . . . . . . . . . . . . . . Gral. Brig.
Eduardo Munilla Gómez

## DEFENSE FORCES

**ARMED FORCES**
*(Las Fuerzas Armadas)*
*Vitruvo 1*
*Madrid 6*
*Telephone:    (1) 261-2800*

Commander-in-Chief and King of Spain . . . . . . . . . . . . . . King Juan Carlos I

### Joint Chiefs of Staff, General Staff
*(Junta de Jefes de Estado Mayor)*
*Vitruvio 1*
*Madrid 6*
*Telephone:    (1) 261-2800*

Chairman . . . . . . . . . . . . . . . . . . . . . . . . . . . Gral. Alvaro de Lacalle Leloup
Member *(ex officio)* . . . . . . . . . . . Gral. Ramón de Ascanio y Togores (Army)
Member *(ex officio)* . . . . . . . . . Alm. Saturnino Saunzes de la Hidalga (Navy)
Member *(ex officio)* . . . . . . Tte. Gral. Emilio García-Conde Ceñal (Air Force)
Chief, Organization . . . . . . . . . . . . . . . . . . . . . . . . . . . . . . . . . . . (Vacant)
Chief, Intelligence . . . . . . . . . . . . . . . . . . . . Gral. Brig. Jaime Barbeito Louro
Chief, Strategy . . . . . . . . . . . . . . . . . . . . . . . . . . . . . . . . . . . . . . (Vacant)
Chief, Coordination and Planning . . . . . . . . . . . . . . . . . . . . . . Gral. Brig.
Eduardo Gómez-Acebo Rodil
Chief, Telecommunications and Electronics. . . . . . . . . . . . . . . . Contra Alm.
Eliseo Alvarez-Arenas Pacheco
Chief, Mobilization . . . . . . . . . . . . . . . . . . . . . . . . . . . . . . . . . . . (Vacant)
Technical Secretary-General,
General Technical Secretariat . . . . . . . . . . . . . . Cnel. Diego Jayme Biondi
Governor, General
Headquarters . . . . . . . . . . . . . . . . . Cnel. Rodrigo Alonso y Ponce de Leon
Chief, Aquisitions. . . . . . . . . . . . . . . . . . . . . . . . . . . . . . . . . . . . (Vacant)
Deputy Chief, Aquisitions . . . . . . . . . . . . . . . . . Antonio Urcelay Rodríguez

### Center for National Defense Studies
*(Centro de Estudios Nacionales*
*de Defensa)*
*Po de las Castellana 71*
*Telephone: (1) 441-7500, 441-7143*

Director . . . . . . . . . . . . . . . . . . . . . . . . . Alm. Fautino Rubalcaba Troncoso
Director,
Military Studies College . . . . . . . . . . . . . . . . . . . . . Gral. Juan Cano Hevia
Director, Joint Chiefs of Staff School . . . . . . . . . . . . . . . . . . . . . . . (Vacant)

**ARMY**
*(Ejército de Tierra)*
*c/o Prim 8y6*
*Madrid 4*
*Telephone:    (1) 232-7571*

Chief, Army Staff . . . . . . . . . . . . . . . . . . . Gral. Ramón de Ascanio y Togores
Deputy Chief, Army Staff . . . . . . . . . . . Gral. Div. Gustavo Urrutia Gracia
Chief, Organization . . . . . . . . . . . . . . . Gral. Brig. Ricardo Escriban Igarza
Chief, Intelligence . . . . . . . . . . . . . . . . . . . . . . . . . . . . . . . . . . . (Vacant)
Chief, Operations. . . . . . . . . . . . . . . Gral. Brig. Fernándo Rodriguez Ventosa
Chief, Logistics . . . . . . . . . . . . . . . Gral. Brig. Francísco Arnaiz Torres
Inspector General of the Army . . . . . . . . . . . . . . . . . . . . . Luis Roson Prez
Commander, Army Artillery
Headquarters (JART) . . . . . . . . Gral. Manuel Fernández Manrique Sainz
Chief, Coordination & Planning . . . . . . . . . . . . . . . . . . . . . . . . . . (Vacant)
Director, Office of Army General
Services (DISG) . . . . . . . . . . . . . . . . . . . . . . . . . . . . . . . . . . . . (Vacant)
Quartermaster General,
Office of Army Economic Affairs . . . . . . . . . . . . . . . . Juan Yañez Gómez
Director General, National Guard . . . . . . . . . . Gral. José Aramburu Topete
Head, Office of Judicial Matters . . . . . . . . . . Gral. Eugenio Miñon Ferreiro
Commander, Army Engineer
Headquarters (JING) . . . . . . . . Gral. Octávio García de Castro y Barceló
Chief, Office of Information and Public
Relations of the General Staff . . . . . . . . . . . . . Mariano Aguilar Olivencia

**Military Regions**
*(Zonas Militares)*

Captain General, Region I
(Madrid) . . . . . . . . . . . . . . . . . .Tte. Gral. Rafael Allende Salazar y Urbina
Captain General, Region II
(Seville) . . . . . . . . . . . . . . . . . . . . . .Tte. Gral. Manuel Saavedra Palmeiro
Captain General, Region III
(Valencia) . . . . . . . . . . . . . .Tte. Gral. Manuel Vallespín González Valdés
Captain General, Region IV
(Barcelona) . . . . . . . . . . . . .Tte. Gral. José Sáenz de Santa María Tinture
Captain General, Region V
(Zaragoza) . . . . . . . . . . . . . .Tte. Gral. Luis Caruana y Gómez de Barreda
Captain General, Region VI
(Burgos) . . . . . . . . . . . . . . . . . .Tte. Gral. Joaquín Ruiz de Oña González
Captain General, Region VII
(Valladolid) . . . . . . . . . . . . . . . .Tte. Gral. Fernándo Soteras Casamayor
Captain General, Region VIII
(La Coruna) . . . . . . . . . . . . . . . . . . .Tte. Gral. Fermín Casado Cepeda
Captain General, Region IX
(Granada) . . . . . . . . . . . . . . . . . . . . .Tte. Gral. Ricardo Oñate de Pedro
Captain General, Region X
(Canary Islands) . . . . . . . . . . . . . .Tte. Gral. Miguel Fontenla Fernández
Captain General, Region XI
(Baleares Islands) . . . . . . . . . . . . . . . .Tte. Gral. Antonio Pascual Galmes

**Army Support and Logistics Command**
*(Dirección General de Armamento y*
*Material)*
*(in charge of procurement)*

Chief . . . . . . . . . . . . . . . . . . . . . . . . . . . . . . . . .Gral. Manuel Álvarez Zalba
Director, Support and Personnel (DIAP) . . . . . . . . . .Gral. Juan García Siso
Director, Infrastructure (DIIN) . . . . . . . . . . . . . .Gral. Pedro Amaya de Torre
Director, Materials (DIMA) . . . . . . . . . . . .Gral. Fernando Esquivias Franco
Chief, Industrial Inspection . . . . . . . . . . .Gral. Mariano de Paramo Velasco
Chief, Industrial Programs . . . . . . . . . . . . . . . .Gral. Tomás Júarez Redondo
Chief, Research and Development . . . . . .Gral. Máximo Solano Campuzano
Chief, Aerospace Technical Industries . . . . . . . . .Gral. José Rodríguez Baltar

**NAVY**
*(Armada Espanola)*
*Cuartel General de la Armada*
*Montalban, 2*
*Madrid - 14*

*Telephone:   (1) 222-6510*
*Telex:   27416 macom-e*

Chief of Staff . . . . . . . . . . . . . . . . . . . .Alm. Saturnino Saunzes de la Hidalga
Deputy Chief of Staff . . . . . . . . . . . . .Vice Alm. Guillermo de Salas Cardenal
Chief, Office of Information and
    Public Relations . . . . . . . . . . . . . . . . . . . . . . . . .Eduardo Montero Romero
Personal Secretary . . . . . . . . . . . . . . . . . . . . . . . . .C. N. Ramón Bravo Nuche
Chief, Logistics . . . . . . . . . . . . . . . .Contra Alm. Ricardo Álvarez Maldonado
Chief, Organization . . . . . . . . . . . .Contra Alm. Ricardo Alvarez Maldonado
Chief, Strategy . . . . . . . . . . . . . . . .Contra Alm. Guillermo de Salas Cardenal
Chief, Tactics . . . . . . . . . . . . .Contra Alma. Ángel L. Díaz del Rio Martínez
Chief, Air Arm . . . . . . . . . . . . . . . .Contra Alm. Guillermo de Salas Cardenal
Chief, Personnel . . . . . . . . . . . . . . . . . . . . .Alm. Juan António Moreno Aznar
Director, Naval Construction
    Administration . . . . . . . . . . . . . . . . . . . . .Vice Alm. Ricardo Cruz Requejo

**Naval Zones**

Captain General,
    Cantabrian Zone . . . . . . . . . . . . . . . . . . . . . . .Alm. José Lorenzo Rey Díaz
Captain General,
    Straits Zone . . . . . . . . . . . . . .Alm. Hermenegildo Franco González-Llanos
Commandant General,
    Canarian Zone . . . . . . . . . . . . . . . . . . . . .Vice Alm. Tomás Clavijo Navarro
Captain General,
    Mediterranean Zone . . . . . . . . . . . . . . . . . . . . . .Alm. Ángel Liberal Lucini

**Support and Logistics Headquarters**
*(Sede de Apoyo y Logística)*
*Avenida de Pio XII*
*83 Madrid - 16*

Chief . . . . . . . . . . . . . . . . . . . . . . . . . . . . . . . . . . . . .Alm. Jaime Díaz-Deus
Deputy Chief . . . . . . . . . . . . . . . . . . . . . .Contra Alm. Luis Abad Vicente

**Office of Naval Instruction**
*(Dirección de Instrucción Naval)*
*Cuartel General de la Armada*

Comptroller General . . . . . . . . . . . . . . . . . . . . . Alm. Tomás Valdes Ibañez
Director, Naval War College . . . . . . . . . . . . . . . . . . . . . . . . . . . . . Vice Alm.
Salvador Moreno de Alboran y Reyna
Deputy Director,
    Naval War College . . . . . . . . . . . . Cap. Federico F. de Bordeje y Morencos
Director, Naval Academy . . . . . . . . . . Cap. José T. Sánchez de Ocana y Erice
Deputy Director, Naval Academy . . . . . . . . . . Cap. José María Pérez Antelo

**Spanish Fleet**
*(Flota Española)*

Commander General . . . . . . . . . . . . . . . Vice Alm. Joaquín Contreras Franco
Assistant Secretary . . . . . . . . . . . . . . . . . . . . . . . . . . . . . . . . . . . . . . . (Vacant)
Commander, Amphibious Command . . . . . . . . . . . . . . . . . . . . . Contra Alm.
Joaquín Rodriguez Guerra y Alvarez Osorio
Chief of Staff, Amphibious Command . . . . . Cap. José A. Jimenez-Guiterrez
Commander,
    Naval Aeronautic Group . . . . . . . . . . Contra Alm. Manuel Elena Manzano
Chief of Staff,
    Naval Aeronautic Group . . . . . . . . Cap. José Enrique Delgado Manzanares
Commander,
    Naval Escort Command . . . . . . . . . . . . . . Contra Alm. Juan Reyna Carvajal
Chief of Staff,
    Naval Escort Command . . . . . . . . . . . . . . Cap. Carlos González-Cela Pardo
Chief of Staff, Fleet . . . . . . . . . . . . . . . . . . . . . . . . . . . . Eduardo Vila Corpas

**Marine Corps**
*(Cuerpo Marítimo)*
*General Command of the Marines*

Commandant General . . . . . . . . . . . . . . . . . . . . Gral. José María Costa Furtía
Second in Command . . . . . . . . . . . . . . . . . Gral. Vicente Bisbal Amengual
Third in Command . . . . . . . . . . . . . . . . . . . Gral. Pedro Galiana Garmilla

**AIR FORCE**
*(Ejército del Ejército)*
*c/o Romero Robledo,*
*8 Madrid - 8*

*Telephone (1) 243-6817*

Chief of Staff . . . . . . . . . . . . . . . . . . . . . Tte. Gral. Emilio García-Conde Ceñal
Deputy Chief of Staff . . . . . . . . . . . . . . . Gral. Div. Gabriel de Cruz Jiménez
Chief, Aircraft Division . . . . . . . . . . . . . . . Gral. Brig. Pedro Gomez Esteban
Chief, Organization Division . . . . . . . . . . . . . . . . . . . . . . . . . . . . . . . . (Vacant)
Chief, Operations Division . . . . . . . . . . . . . . Gral. Brig. Luis Fernández Roca
Chief, Logistics Division . . . . . . . . . . . Gral. Brig. Federico Michavila Pallares
Chief, Air Force Headquarters Staff . . . . . . . . . . . . . . . . . . . . . . . . (Vacant)
Deputy Chief, Air Force
    Headquarters Staff . . . . . . . . . . . . . . . . . . . . Gral. Ignacio Martínez Eiroa
Chief, Albacete Air Sector . . . . . . . . . . . . Cnel. Ramón Fernández Sequeiro
Chief, Badajoz Air Sector . . . . . . . . . . . . . . . . . . Cnel. Ángel Salom Ferrer
Chief, Baleares Air Sector . . . . . . . . . . . . Gral. Brig. Enrique Tapias Curbera
Chief, Cadiz Air Sector . . . . . . . . . . . . . . . . . . . . . Cnel. Vicente Pérez Rayo
Chief, Cataluna Air Sector . . . . . . . . . . . Gral. Brig. Fernándo Alcázar Sotoca
Chief, Galicia Air Sector . . . . . . . . . . . . . . . . Cnel. Antonio Fernández García
Chief, Granada Air Sector . . . . . . . . . . . . . . . . Cnel. Ángel Jerez Manzanero
Chief, La Rioja Air Sector . . . . . . . . . . . . . . . Cnel. Álvaro Martínez Munaiz
Chief, Leon Air Sector . . . . . . . . . . . . . . . . . . . . Cnel. Cristóbal García Lisón
Chief, Malaga Air Sector . . . . . . . . . . . . . . . . . . Cnel. Julio Sancho González
Chief, Murcia Air Sector . . . . . . . . . . . . . Cnel. Antonio Vara de Rey Izarduy
Chief, Salamanca Air Sector . . . . . . . . . . . . . . . . Cnel. Enrique Pagé Larraz
Chief, Tenerife Air Sector . . . . . . . . . . . . . Cnel. Tomás González Ferreiro
Chief, Valencia Air Sector . . . . . . . . . . . . . . Cnel. Ricardo Garrido Jiménez
Chief, Valladolid Air Sector . . . . . . . . . . Cnel. Alfonso Carrillo Ruíz Martínez
Chief, Vascongadas Air Sector . . . . . . . . . . . . . . . . . . . . . . . . . . . . (Vacant)
Military Secretary of the Air Force . . . . . . . . . Gral. Abundio Cesteros García
Inspector-General of the Air Force . . . . . . . . . . . . . Gral. Domingo Prats Vila
Chief, Aerial Combat Command and
    Air Region I (Madrid) . . . . Tte. Gral. Miguel Martínes Vara de Rey y Teus
Chief, Aerial Tactics Command and
    Air Region II (Seville) . . . . . . . . . . . Tte. Gral. Fernando de Queral Muller
Chief, Aerial Transport Command and
    Air Region III (Zaragoza) . . . . . . . Tte. Gral. Emiliano Barañano Martínez
Chief, Canary Islands
    Aerial Command . . . . . . . . . . . . . . . . . . . . Gral. Gonzalo Puigcerver Roma

**Material Command**
*(Mando de Material del Ejército del Aire)*

Chief . . . . . . . . . . . . . . . . . . . . . . . . . . . . . Tte. Gral. Gregorio Martín Olmedo
Field Assistant . . . . . . . . . . . . . . . . . . . . . . Tte. Cnel. Jesús María Alia Munoz
Deputy Chief and Director of
   Materiel Services . . . . . . . . . . . . . . . . Gral. Div. Andres Santos Rodríguez
Director, Office of Maintenance . . . . . . . . . . . . . . . . . . . . . . . . . . . . . (Vacant)
Director, Office of Supplies . . . . . . . . . . . . . . . . . . . . . . . . . . . . . . . . (Vacant)
Director, Office of Adquisitions . . . . . . . . . . Gral. Brig. Estében Martínez Gil
Secretary-General . . . . . . . . . . . . . . . . . . . . . . . . . . . Cnel. Luis Noval Camelo

**Air Force College**
*(Colégio de la Fuerza Aerea)*
*Telephone:   (1) 24-4022*

Director . . . . . . . . . . . . . . . . . . . . . . . . . . Gral. Jesús Bengoechea Baamanda
Deputy Director . . . . . . . . . . . . . . . . . . . . . . . . . . . . . . . . . . . . . . . . (Vacant)

**GENERAL DIRECTORATE OF THE
NATIONAL GUARD**
*(Dirección General de la Guardia Civil)*
*Guzman el Bueno 110*
*Telephone:   (1) 234-0200*

Director-General . . . . . . . . . . . . . . . . . . . . Tte. Gral. José Aramburu Topete
Field Assistant . . . . . . . . . . . . . . . . . . . . Cdnte. Guillermo Ostos Mate Cañero
Field Assistant . . . . . . . . . . . . . . . . . . . . . . . . . . Cdnte. José Moreno Wirtz
Private Secretary . . . . . . . . . . . . . . . . . . . . . . . Cnel. Joaquín Vásquez García
Deputy-General, General . . . . . . . . . Gral. Div. Antonio Hermosil Bernardín
Field Assistant . . . . . . . . . . . . . . . . . . . . . . . . . . . Tte. Cnel. Luis Marín Díaz
Chief, Personnel Section . . . . . . . . . . . . . . . . Cnel. Guillermo Amengual Mir
Chief, General Affairs . . . . . . . . . . . . . . Cnel. G. C. Juan Barrientos Labrador
Chief, Social Action . . . . . . . . . . . . . . . . . . . . . . . . . . . . . . . . . . . . . . (Vacant)

**National Guard Zones**
*(Zonas de la Guardia Civil)*

Chief, Zone 1 (Madrid) . . . . . . . . . . Gral. Brig. Constantino Gómez González
Chief, Zone II (Seville) . . . . . . . . . . Alejandro de la Mata y García de la Rosa
Chief, Zone III (Valencia) . . . . . . . . . . Gral. Brig. Buenventura López Ruano
Chief, Zone IV (Barcelona) . . . . . . . . . . . Gral. Brig. Miguel Pérez Hernández
Chief, Zone V (La Rioja) . . . . . . . . . . . . . . . José Rodríquez-Medel Carmon
Chief, Zone VI (Leon) . . . . . . . . . . . . . . . . . . . . . . . . Álvaro Casado Mestre

\* \* \* \* \*

## GENERAL DEFENSE DATA

**Manpower**
   Total Armed Forces . . . . . . . . . . . . . . . . . . . . . . . . . . . . . . . . . . . . 347,000
     (See Page 481)
   Population . . . . . . . . . . . . . . . . . . . . . . . . . . . . . . . . . . . . . . . . . 37,940,000

**Spending**
   Military Expenditures . . . . . . . . . . . . . . . . . . . . . . . . . . . . . . . . . . $3.6 billion
   Gross National Product . . . . . . . . . . . . . . . . . . . . . . . . . . . . . . . . $217 billion
   Military Expenditure as a Percentage of
     Gross National Product . . . . . . . . . . . . . . . . . . . . . . . . . . . . . . . . . 1.7%
   Military Expenditure as a Percentage of
     Central Government Expenditure . . . . . . . . . . . . . . . . . . . . . . . . . . 10.1%

**Defense Treaties** *(See Part II for Additional Detail)*

   Bilateral:    United States

   Multilateral:    Biological Weapons Convention
                Environmental Modification Convention
                Limited Test Ban Treaty
                North Atlantic Treaty Organization

# SRI LANKA

## Democratic Socialist Republic of Sri Lanka
### Sri Lanka Prajatantrika Samajawadi Janarajaya

## Defence Establishment Command Structure and Force Organization

The President is Commander-in-Chief of the armed forces. He also holds the portfolio of Minister of Defence.

**Total armed forces**: 16,500 (Army: 11,000; Navy: 2,900; Air Force: 2,600). **Paramilitary forces**: 22,000 (17,000 Police; 5,000 Volunteer Militia).

## HEAD OF STATE

H. E. Junius Richard Jayewardene

**PRESIDENTIAL SECRETARIAT**
*Republic Square*
*Colombo 1*
*Telephone: 24801, 26309, 25306, 29010*

President of the Democratic Socialist Republic, Minister of Defence, Higher Education, Plan Implementation, Janatha Estate Development, State Plantations, and Power and Energy, and Commander-in-Chief ................... Junius Richard Jayewardene
Secretary ..................................... W. M. P. B. Menikdiwela

**MINISTRY OF DEFENCE**
*Janadipathi Mawatha*
*Republic Building*
*Colombo 1*
*Telephone: 25371*
*Telex: 21139 forinsec ce*

Minister of Defence and President of the Republic ........................... Junius Richard Jayewardene
Deputy Minister and Internal Security ........... T. B. Werapitiya, M.P.
Secretary ...................................... Col. C. A. Dharmapa'a
Chief, Coordinating Authority ..................... Gen. D. S. Attygalle
Coordinating Officer for Parliamentary Affairs ............. Mrs. S. Ebert
Private Secretary to the Deputy Minister ............. S. B. Karaliyadde

## DEFENCE FORCES

**ARMY**
**Sri Lanka Army**
*Army Headquarters*
*Baladaksha Mawatha*
*Colombo 3*
*Telephone: 32681, 31704*
*Cable: ARMY*

Commander of the Army ................... Maj. Gen. T. I. Weeratunga
Chief of Staff .............................. Brig. S. C. Ranatunga
Secretary ........................................ Col. Thambiraja
Director, Operations and Training ............... Brig. Mano Madawela
Director, Personnel Administration ......... Brig. George Thevanayasajni
Director, Logistics ............................. Brig. P. K. B. Pereira
Director, Army Medical Services ................ Col. H. I. K. Fernando
Director, Engineer Services ................ Col. G. D. G. N. Seneviratne
Judge Advocate General ......................... Lt. Col. W. H. Niriella
Legal Staff Officer ................................... Col. Buhary
Paymaster and Officer in Charge, Records ........ Lt. Col. G. V. Elapatha
Civilian Administrative Officer ......................... S. Medawewa

**Commands**

Commander, Sri Lanka Volunteer Force .......... Brig. H. V. Athukorale
Commander, Support Force ........................ Brig. Senevivalni
Commander, Task Force 1, Southern Command ..... Col. H. Wanasinghe

Commander, Task Force 2, Central Command ................(Vacant)
Commander, Task Force 3, North Central
    Command ...................................Col. M. H. Gunaratne
Commander, Task Force 4, Northern Command .....Col. C. H. Fernando
Commander, Log Command .......................Col. Dharmasiri
Commander, Task Force 5, Western Command .........Col. H. G. Silva
Commander, Garrison, Diyatalawa ..................Col. J. Jayaratne
Commandant, Sri Lanka Defense Academy ............Col. P. Wijchoon
Commandant, Army Training Center ...............Y. Balaratnarajah

**NAVY**
**Sri Lanka Navy—SLN**
*Naval Headquarters*
*P.O. Box 593*
*Flagstaff Street,*
*Colombo 1*

*Telephone:  21151, 23278*
*Cable: CEYNAVY*

Commander of the Navy ..................Rear Adm. A. H. A. de Silva
Secretary .....................................Lt. N. Chandradeva
Director, Naval Operations ...................Capt. G. M. F. Marshall
Director, Naval Personnel and Administration ........Capt. M. L. Mendis
Director, Naval Support and Systems .........Capt. (S) R. P. Abeysinghe
Director, Naval Engineering.....................Capt. K. R. L. Perera
Director, Naval Health Services ..........Surgeon Capt. M. Amarasingte
Director, Naval Electrical and Electronic
    Engineering .........................Cdr. U. L. J. S. K. R. Perera
Staff Officer, Naval Operations .............Lt. Cdr. D. K. Dassanayake
Staff Officer, Training .....................Lt. Cdr. K. Sri Kantha
Staff Officer, Stores and Administration .........Lt. Cdr. Lawt Carthelis
Staff Officer, Communications .............Lt. Cdr. H. R. Amaraweera

**Commands**

Commanding Officer, Sri Lanka Volunteer
    Naval Force ..............................Cdr. V. A. J. Mendis
Commandant, Naval and Maritime
    Academy ...............................Cdr. G. D. A. Wirasekera
Commanding Officer, SLNS *Tissa* ...................Cdr. A. Wijetilleke
Commanding Officer, SLNS *Elara* ..........Cdr. W. W. E. C. Fernando
Commanding Officer, SLNS *Parakrama* .........Capt. G. M. F. Marshall
Commanding Officer, SLNS *Gemunu* ......Cdr. F. N. Q. Wickramaratna
Commanding Officer, SLNS *Rangalla* ...........Cdr. A. R. C. Fernando
Commanding Officer, SLNS *Vijaya* ..............Lt. S. P. F. Wijeratne
Commanding Officer, SLNS *Ruhuna* ............Lt. Cdr. N. W. Musafer
Commanding Officer, SLNS *Samudra Devi* .......Cdr. A. I. Jayawardena

**AIR FORCE**
**Sri Lanka Air Force—SLAF**
*"Rifle Green House"*
*Sir Chittampalam Gardiner Mawatha*
*Colombo 2*

*Telephone:  33184, 32171*
*Cable:  AIRFORCE*

Commander of the Air Force ..............Air Vice Marshal D. C. Perera
Chief of Staff ..........................Group Capt. A. W. Fernando
Director, Aeronautical Engineering.........Wing Cdr. B. E. S. Fernando
Director, Electrical Engineering .......Group Capt. H. A. D. Ranasinghe
Director, Logistics .................Group Capt. V. D. A. Dissanayake
Director, Administration ..................Wing Cdr. G. M. U. de Silva
Director, Health Services .....................Air Cdr. Puvimanasinghe
Director, Civil Engineering ..............Sq. Leader D. N. Harischandra
Command Intelligence Officer.............Wing Cdr. H. M. Seneviratne
System Analysis Research and
    Evaluation Officer ....................Sq. Leader M. P. Wijesuriya
Chief Purchasing Officer..............Wing Cdr. R. N. Wicramasinghe

**Commands**

Commander, SLAF Base Kutunayake .........Group Capt. N. R. Rahim
Commandant, Air Force
    Academy China Bay .........Wing Cdr. M. J. T. De S. Gunawardana
Commander, Headquarters
    Unit SLAF, Colombo....................Wing Cdr. D. S. G. Vithana
Commander, Sir Lanka Volunteer
    Air Force Headquarters ........Wing Cdr. J. L. R. Goonetileke, P.S.C.

**POLICE**
*Police Headquarters*
*Fort Colombo*

*Telephone:  21111*

Inspector-General...................................R. Rajasngham
Senior Deputy Inspectors-General..............S. D. E. S. Gunawaadena
Senior Deputy Inspectors-General....................S. Vamadeva
Crimes and Operations ..........................R. Sunderalingam

Personnel and Training . . . . . . . . . . . . . . . . . . . . . . . . . . . . .A. Navaratnam
C.I.D . . . . . . . . . . . . . . . . . . . . . . . . . . . . . . . . . . . . . .S. W. H. Weerasinghe
Director, Headquarters Administration . . . . . . . . . . . . . . . .U. D. Senarath
Director, Research and Development . . . . . . . . . . . . . . . . . .M. Selvaratnam
Superintendant, Public Relations . . . . . . . . . . . . . .K. A. D. C. Wijenayake

\* \* \* \* \*

# GENERAL DEFENCE DATA

**Manpower**

Total Armed Forces . . . . . . . . . . . . . . . . . . . . . . . . . . . . . . . . . . . . . . . .16,500
   (See Page 487)
Population . . . . . . . . . . . . . . . . . . . . . . . . . . . . . . . . . . . . . . . . . . .15,398,000

**Spending**

Military Expenditures . . . . . . . . . . . . . . . . . . . . . . . . . . . . . . . . . . .$27 million
Gross National Product . . . . . . . . . . . . . . . . . . . . . . . . . . . . . . . .$4.080 billion
Military Expenditure as a Percentage of
   Gross National Product . . . . . . . . . . . . . . . . . . . . . . . . . . . . . . . . . . . .0.7%
Military Expenditure as a Percentage of
   Central Government Expenditure . . . . . . . . . . . . . . . . . . . . . . . . . . . . .1.7%

**Defence Treaties** *(See Part II for Additional Detail)*

   Bilateral:       United Kingdom
                    United States

   Multilateral:    Environmental Modification Convention
                    Limited Test Ban Treaty
                    Treaty on the Non-Proliferation of Nuclear Weapons

# SUDAN
## Democratic Republic of the Sudan
### *Jumhuriyat al-Sudan al-Dimuqratiya*

## Defense Establishment Command Structure and Force Organization

The President is Minister of Defense and Supreme Commander of the People's Armed Forces of Sudan. He exercises control over the military through the Minister of Defense.

**Total armed forces:** 58,000 (Army: 53,000; Navy: 2,000; Air Force: 3,000). **Paramilitary forces:** 3,500 (National Guard: 500; Republican Guard: 500; Border Guard 2,500).

## HEAD OF STATE

H. E. Field Marshal Gaafar Mohamed Nimeiry

**OFFICE OF THE PRESIDENT**
*Khartoum*
*Telephone: 75300, 70726*

President of the Democratic Republic, Minister of Defense and Supreme Commander of the People's Armed Forces . . . . . . . . Field Marshal Gaafar Mohamed Nimeiry
Advisor to the President, Decentralization . . . . . . . . . . . . . . . . . . . . . Al-Shiekh Bashir Al-Shiekh
Advisor to the President, Laws Reform . . . . . . . Dr. Yousif Michael Bakhiet
Advisor to the President, Press . . . . . . . . . . . . . . . . . . . Col. (Ret.) Mohammad Mahgoub Suliman
Minister in the President's Office . . . . . . . . . . . . . . . . Khalid al Khayr Umar

**OFFICE OF THE FIRST VICE PRESIDENT**
*Khartoum*
*Telephone: 79775*

First Vice President and Chief of State Security . . Maj. Gen. Omer Mohammad El-Tayeb al-Tayyib
Minister of State in the Ministry of State Security . . . . . . . . . . . . . . Kamal Hasan Ahmad Utman

**MINISTRY OF DEFENSE**
*Khartoum*
*Telephone: 7074, 2771*
*Telex: 411 prokaid km*

Minister of Defense and President of the Republic . . . . . . Field Marshal Gaafar Mohamed Nimeiry
Minister of State for Defense . . . . . . . . . . . . . . Maj. Gen. (Ret.) Fathi Omer Abul Hassan

## DEFENSE FORCES

**ARMY**
*Khartoum*
*Telephone: 72771, 79910*
*Telex: 22411 prokaid sd*
  *(Khartoum-Airport)*

Commander . . . . . . . . . . . . . . . . . . . . . . . . . . . . . . . . Gen. Izz Eddin Ali Malie
Deputy Commander-in-Chief . . . . . . Gen. Abdul Rahman Mohamed Hassan Suwar El Dahab
Chief, Operations . . . . . . . . . . . . . . . . . . . . . Maj. Gen. Akif Yassin Khatir
Chief, Logistics . . . . . . . . . . . . . . . . . . . Maj. Gen. Mohamed Tawfik Khalil
Chief, Administration . . . . . . . . . . . . . . . . . . Maj. Gen. Tag Eldin Abdalla

491

**NAVY**
*Port Sudan*
*Telephone: PS 3016*

Commander . . . . . . . . . . . . . . . . . . . . . . .Lt. Gen. Yousif Houssein Ahmed
Deputy Commander . . . . . . . . . .Maj. Gen. Mubarak Al Rahman Unballa
Chief of Staff . . . . . . . . . . . . . . . . . . . . . . . .Brig. Bushra Ahmed Rahman
Liaison Officer, General
 Headquarters, Khartoum . . . . . . . . . . . . . . . .Maj. Majoob Hassan Adam

**AIR FORCE**
*al Quwwat al-Jawwiya al-Sudaniya*
*Telephone: 79101*
*Telex: 22411 prokaid sd*
 *(Khartoum-Airport)*

Commander . . . . . . . . . . . . . . . . . . . .Lt. Gen. Mohamed Mirghani El Tahir

 **Air Defense Command**
 *Port Sudan*
 *Telephone: 3947*

Commander . . . . . . . . . . . . . . . . . . . . . . . . . .Maj. Gen. Fuad Ahmed Saleh
Chief of Staff . . . . . . . . . . . . . . . .Brig. Mohamed Osman Mohamed El Fadl

\* \* \* \* \*

# GENERAL DEFENSE DATA

**Manpower**
 Total Armed Forces . . . . . . . . . . . . . . . . . . . . . . . . . . . . . . . . . . . . . . . . . .58,000
  (See Page 491)
 Population . . . . . . . . . . . . . . . . . . . . . . . . . . . . . . . . . . . . . . . . . . .19,868,000

**Spending**
 Military Expenditures . . . . . . . . . . . . . . . . . . . . . . . . . . . . . . . . . . . . .$260 million
 Gross National Product . . . . . . . . . . . . . . . . . . . . . . . . . . . . . . . . . . . .$8.6 billion
 Military Expenditure as a Percentage of
  Gross National Product . . . . . . . . . . . . . . . . . . . . . . . . . . . . . . . . . . . . .3.0%
 Military Expenditure as a Percentage of
  Central Government Expenditure . . . . . . . . . . . . . . . . . . . . . . . . . . . . . .12.2%

**Defense Treaties** (*See Part II for Additional Detail*)

 Bilateral:    China
        Egypt
        Uganda
        United States

 Multilateral:  League of Arab States
        Limited Test Ban Treaty
        Organization of African Unity
        Treaty on the Non-Proliferation of Nuclear Weapons

# SURINAME
## Republic of Suriname
### *Republiek Suriname*

## Defense Establishment Command Structure and Force Organization

The President of the Republic is nominally the Commander-in-Chief. Operational authority over the military, however, rests with the Chairman of the Policy Center, who is also the Commander of the National Army.

**Total armed forces:** 1,000.

## HEAD OF STATE (Acting)

H. E. L. mr. Lachmipersad F. Ramdat-Misier

**OFFICE OF THE PRESIDENT**
*Kleine Combeweg 1*
*Paramaribo*
*Telephone: 72841*

President of the Republic and
Commander-in-Chief (Acting) ........Lachmipersad F. Ramdat-Misier

**OFFICE OF THE PRIME MINISTER**
*Gravenstraat 6*
*Paramaribo*
*Telephone: 74600*

Prime Minister of the Republic and Minister
for General and Foreign Affairs ............dr. Errol (Likat Ali) Alibux

**MINISTRY OF ARMED FORCES AND POLICE**
*Gravenstraat 52-54*
*Paramaribo*
*Telephone: 73444, 74244*

Minister ......................................Capt. Wilfred Maynard
Permanent Secretary.......................................P. Haime

**POLICY CENTER**
*Paramaribo*

Chairman .................................Lt. Col. Desiré Bouterse

## DEFENSE FORCES

**ARMY**
**National Army**
*Memre Boekoe Kazerne*
*Paramaribo*
*Telephone: 71515, 76254, 98325, 99566*

Commander, National Army....................Lt. Col. Desiré Bouterse
Chief of Staff .............................Capt. Ivan Graanoogst
Chief, People's Mobilization .......................Capt. Boereuveen
Battalion Commander ...............................P. Bhagwandas

\* \* \* \* \*

# GENERAL DEFENSE DATA

**Manpower**

Total Armed Forces.................................................1,000
   (See Page 493)
Population ......................................................356,000

**Spending**

Military Expenditures .................................................
Gross National Product .........................................$1 billion
Military Expenditure as a Percentage of
   Gross National Product .............................................
Military Expenditure as a Percentage of
   Central Government Expenditure ......................................

**Defense Treaties** *(See Part II for Additional Detail)*

Bilateral:      United States

Multilateral:   Treaty on the Non-Proliferation of Nuclear Weapons
                Treaty for the Prohibition of Nuclear Weaspon in
                   Latin America

# SWAZILAND
## Kingdom of Swaziland

### Defence Establishment Command Structure and Force Organization

The Queen Regent is Supreme Commander of the armed forces. Her authority is exercised by the Prime Minister. The Commander of the Defence Force is responsible for operational and administrative matters relating to the military.

**Total armed forces:** 5,000. **Police:** 500.

## HEAD OF STATE

H. M. Queen Dzeliwe Shongwe

**OFFICE OF H. M. THE QUEEN**
*P.O. Box 1*
*Lobamba*

*Telephone: 61271 (Embo State House),*
*53161 (Lozitha State House),*
*61980 (Queen's Office,*
*Lobamba)*

*Telex: 2134 wd*

Queen Regent and Supreme Commander . . . . . . . . Queen Dzeliwe Shongwe

**OFFICE OF THE PRIME MINISTER**
*P.O. Box 395*
*Mbabane*

*Telephone: 42971 (Deputy Prime Minister)*

Prime Minister . . . . . . . . . . . . . . . . . . . . . . . . . . . . . . Prince Bhekimpi Dlamini
Minister of Home Affairs . . . . . . . . . . . . . . . . . . . . . . . Prince Nqaba Dlamini

## DEFENCE FORCES

**ARMED FORCES**
**Swaziland Umbufto Defence Force**
*Private Bag 3*
*Kwaluseni*

*Telephone: 42251, 53111*
*Telex: 2189 wd*

Commander . . . . . . . . . . . . . . . . . . . . . . . . . Col. Mangomeni M. Ndzimandze
Deputy Commander and Chief
    (Acting) of the Army . . . . . . . . . . . . . . . . . . . . . . . . . . Lt. Col. G. F. Dubee

**POLICE**
*P.O. Box 49*
*Mbabane*

*Telephone: 42501*
*Telex: 2017 wd*

Commissioner . . . . . . . . . . . . . . . . . . . . . . . . . . . . . . . . . . . . . . . . . Titus Msibi
Deputy Commissioner . . . . . . . . . . . . . . . . . . . . . . . . . . . . . . . . . Edgar Hillary

\* \* \* \* \*

495

# GENERAL DEFENCE DATA

**Manpower**

Total Armed Forces . . . . . . . . . . . . . . . . . . . . . . . . . . . . . . . . . . . . . . . . . . . . . . .5,000
  (See Page 495)
Population . . . . . . . . . . . . . . . . . . . . . . . . . . . . . . . . . . . . . . . . . . . . . . . . . . .589,000

**Spending**

Military Expenditures . . . . . . . . . . . . . . . . . . . . . . . . . . . . . . . . . . . . . . . . . .$9 million
Gross National Product . . . . . . . . . . . . . . . . . . . . . . . . . . . . . . . . . . . . . . . .$365 million
Military Expenditure as a Percentage of
  Gross National Product . . . . . . . . . . . . . . . . . . . . . . . . . . . . . . . . . . . . . . . .2.5%
Military Expenditure as a Percentage of
  Central Government Expenditure . . . . . . . . . . . . . . . . . . . . . . . . . . . . . . . . .6.2%

**Defence Treaties** *(See Part II for Additional Detail)*

    Bilateral:    None

    Multilateral:    Limited Test Ban Treaty
                Organization of African Unity
                Treaty on the Control of Arms on the Seabed
                Treaty on the Non-Proliferation of Nuclear Weapons

# SWEDEN
## Kingdom of Sweden
### *Konungariket Sverige*

## Defense Establishment Command Structure and Force Organization

The King is nominal Commander-in-Chief of the Swedish armed forces. Civilian control is exercised in peacetime by the Defense Minister; in case of war, it is exercised by the Prime Minister. Operational control is vested with the Supreme Commander, who is under the direction of the Minister of Defense. The Supreme Commander is assisted in matters of central military planning by the integrated Defense Staff.

Overall military planning is carried out by the National Defense Council, which may include any member of Parliament summoned by the Prime Minister. The Defense Head Committee, comprised of the heads of all government agencies relevant to defense and, on the military side, by the Supreme Commander, implements the Council's recommendations.

Sweden is divided into six Military Command Areas, each of which is headed by a commanding general, supported by an integrated staff.

The armed forces are not fully integrated. The individual service commanders are responsible for the organization (including procurement) and training of their respective units. The country's defense is based on the principle of national service for all men and rapid mobilization of all trained conscripts.

**Total armed forces:** 64,500 (Army: 45,000;  Navy: 10,000;  Air Force: 9,500). **Para-military forces:** 550 (Coast Guard). **Total armed forces after mobilization:** 850,000 (in 72 hours).

## HEAD OF STATE

H. M. King Carl XVI Gustaf

**OFFICE OF H. M. THE KING**
*Kungl. Slottet*
*Slottsbacken*
*S-111 30 Stockholm*

*Telephone: (8) 10 09 63*

| | |
|---|---|
| King of Sweden and Commander-in-Chief | H. M. Carl XVI Gustaf |
| Marshal of the Realm | Sten Rudholm |
| First Marshal of the Royal Court | Lennart Ahrén |
| Public Affairs Officer | Elisabeth Tarras-Wahlberg |

**OFFICE OF THE PRIME MINISTER**
*S-103 33 Stockholm*

*Telephone: (8) 763 1000*
*Telex: 17820 premier s*

| | |
|---|---|
| Prime Minister | Olof Palme |
| Under Secretary | Odd Engström |
| Undersecretary of State | Ulf Larsson |
| Undersecretary of State | Kjell Larsson |

**National Defense Council**

| | |
|---|---|
| Chairman | Olof Palme (Prime Minister) |
| Member | Gen. Lennart Ljung (Supreme Commander, Armed Forces) |
| Member | Vam. Bror Stefenson (Chief, Defense Staff) |
| Member | Holger Romander (Chief, National Police Board) |

497

Member ..................................Gunnar Gustafsson
(Chief, Civil Defense Administration)
Member ...................................Barbro Westerholm
(Chief, Board of Social Affairs)
Member...................................Anthony Hagström
(Chief, Telecommunications Administration)
Member ....................................Ingvar Lindström
(Chief, Agricultural Marketing Administration)
Member.....................................Gunnar Nordbeck
(Chief, Board for Economic Defense)
Member.......................................Bertil Rehnberg
(Chief, Labor Market Board)
Member ..................................Claes-Eric Norrbom
(Chief, Board of Transportation)
Member ...................................Per-Axel Landahl
(Chairman, Psychological Defense Planning Committee)
Member .........................Civilian Commissioner of one of the
six Military Command Areas

**DEPARTMENT OF DEFENSE**
*S-103 33 Stockholm*

*Telephone:   (8) 763 1000*
*Cable:   Försvarskansli*

Minister of Defense................................Anders Thunborg
Under Secretary ......................................Per Olof Borg
Chief, Planning and Budget...................Öv. 1 Bengt Gustafsson
Chief, Legal Affairs ...............................Olof Forssberg
Chief, Military Installations Division ................Övlt. Ingvar Ehrling
Chief, Materiel Division ..............................Hans Palm
Chief, Organization ..............................Hans Albrektson
Chief, Personnel.................................Alice Nilsson
Chief, Conscription Division ..........................Jan Olson
Chief, International Division ....................Gmj. Nils Landergren
Chief, Security Policy and
Long-Term Planning Division ..........................Nils Gyldén
Chief, Advisory Committee to the
Military Command ............................Gen. Lennart Ljung

**Operations Command**

Head ..........................................Vam. Bror Stefenson
Chief, Section 1 (Strategic/
Operative Studies and Planning) ...................Öv. Lennart Frick
Chief, Section 2 (Executive and
Training Divisions) ............................Öv. 1 Gunnar Unell
Chief, Section 3 (Staff Division,
Information Security) ...........................Öv. Bertil Lövdahl
Chief, Section 4 (Quartermaster/
Communications/Field Work/
Volunteer Division) ..........................Öv. Lars-Erik Widman
Chief, Section 5 (Guidance/
Intelligence/Security Division) .................Kmd. Ulf Samuelson
Chief, Section 6 ..............................Öv. 1 Bertil Runnberg

**Planning Command**

Head ..............................................Gmj. Lars Persson
Chief, Section I (Studies;
Programs; Analysis) .........................Kmd. Peter Nordbeck
Chief, Section II (Organization;
Grounds and Buildings) ...........................Öv. Eric Jansson
Chief, Section III (Personnel;
Codetermination) .............................Öv. 1 Roland Grahn
Chief, Section IV (Social Services) .........................Ulf Karlsson
Chief, Administration Section ...............Övlt. Karl-Gunnar Siggebo
Chief, Information Section ........................Övlt. Jan-Åke Berg

**Civil Administration**
*Karolinen*
*651 80 Karlstad*

Director General .........................................Alf Resare
Chief, Wage Bureau ...............................David Andersson
Chief, Financial Bureau ...............................Owe Stenberg

*Telephone: (54) 10 30 00*

Chief, Audit Bureau . . . . . . . . . . . . . . . . . . . . . . . . . . . . . . . . . . . . . Kurt Edman
Chief, Juridical Bureau . . . . . . . . . . . . . . . . . . . . . . . . . . . . . . . . . . Hans Tillberg
Chief, Central Unit . . . . . . . . . . . . . . . . . . . . . . . . . . . . . . . . . . Johan Tobieson
Chief, Patent Unit . . . . . . . . . . . . . . . . . . . . . . . . . . . . . . . . . . . . Lennart Sjöö

**Defense Medical Office**
*Karolinen*
*651 80 Karlstad*
*Telephone: (54) 10 30 00*

Director and Chief of Medical Corps . . . . . . . . . . . . . . . . . . . . . . Bo Rybeck
Chief, Unit for Health and
    Medical Care in War . . . . . . . . . . . . . . . . . . . . . . . . . . . Björn Zetteström
Chief, Unit for Health and
    Medical Care in Peacetime . . . . . . . . . . . . . . . . . . . . . . Göran Lagerholm
Chief, Personnel . . . . . . . . . . . . . . . . . . . . . . . . . . . . . . . . . . . . Bengt Sjölund
Chief, Supply . . . . . . . . . . . . . . . . . . . . . . . . . . . . . . . . . . . . . Georg Hellström
Chief, Administration . . . . . . . . . . . . . . . . . . . . . . . . . . . . . . . Bengt Kjellberg

**Fortifications Office**
*631 89 Eskilstuna*
*Telephone: (16) 15 40 00*

Director General . . . . . . . . . . . . . . . . . . . . . . . . . . . . . . . . . . . . Stig Swanstein
Chief, Central Planning . . . . . . . . . . . . . . . . . . . . . . . . Öv. 1 Sven Karevik
Chief, Fortifications . . . . . . . . . . . . . . . . . . . . . . . . . . Öv. 1 Bengt Persson
Chief, Barracks . . . . . . . . . . . . . . . . . . . . . . . . . . . . . . . . . . Öv. Sture Hägg
Chief, Construction . . . . . . . . . . . . . . . . . . . . . . . . . . . . . . . Dick Lindholm
Chief, Emergency Construction
    and Repairs . . . . . . . . . . . . . . . . . . . . . . . . Öv. Harald Alexanderson

**Defence Materiel Administration**
*104 50 Stockholm*
*Telephone: (8) 23 77 00*

Director General . . . . . . . . . . . . . . . . . . . . . . . . . . . . . . Carl-Olof Ternryd
Chief, Central Planning . . . . . . . . . . . . . . . . . . . . . Gmj. Ragnar Persson
Chief, Army Materiel . . . . . . . . . . . . . . . . . . . . . . . . . . . . Gmj. Helge Gard
Chief, Navy Materiel . . . . . . . . . . . . . . . . . . . . . . . . R. Adm. Ola Backman
Chief, Air Force Materiel . . . . . . . . . . . . . . . . . . . . Gmj. Gunnar Lindquist

**Conscription Office**
*Karolinen*
*651 80 Karlstad*
*Telephone: (54) 10 30 00*

Director . . . . . . . . . . . . . . . . . . . . . . . . . . . . . . . . . . . . Gmj. Ingvar Rittsél
Chief, Planning . . . . . . . . . . . . . . . . . . . . . . . . . . . . . Mj. Stellan Jansson
Chief, Accounting . . . . . . . . . . . . . . . . . . . . . . . . . . Övlt. Eilert Helander
Chief, Registration . . . . . . . . . . . . . . . . . . . . . . . . . . Övlt. Hans Klinthof
Chief, Administration . . . . . . . . . . . . . . . . . . . . . . . . . . . . Lars Skoglund

**Defense Research Agency**
*Fack*
*104 50 Stockholm*
*Telephone: (8) 63 15 00*

Director General . . . . . . . . . . . . . . . . . . . . . . . . . . . Nils-Henrik Lundquist
Chief, Central Administration . . . . . . . . . . . . . . . . . . . . Karl-Gustaf Mattson
Chief, Division I (Defense Studies and
    Information Systems) . . . . . . . . . . . . . . . . . . . . . . . . . . . Göran Franzen
Chief, Division II (Weapons and
    Technology Research; Effects Studies) . . . . . . . . . . . . . . Gunnar Blomqvist
Chief, Division III (Data Handling;
    Optical Technology; Electronics;
    Reliability Technology) . . . . . . . . . . . . . . . . . . . . . . . . . . Torsten Linell
Chief, Division IV (Biomedical Section;
    Microbiology; Chemistry) . . . . . . . . . . . . . . . . . . . . . . . . Stig Jacksen
Chief, Division V (Behavioral Science;
    Biotechnology; Medical Division) . . . . . . . . . . . . . . . . Charles Strömblad

**Civil Defense Administration**
*Karolinen*
*651 80 Karlstad*
*Telephone: (54) 10 30 00*

Director General . . . . . . . . . . . . . . . . . . . . . . . . . . . . . Gunnar Gustafsson
Chief, Planning . . . . . . . . . . . . . . . . . . . . . . . . . . . . . . Övlt. Erik Thyberg
Chief, Production . . . . . . . . . . . . . . . . . . . . . . . . . . . . . . . John Tjörneryd
Chief, Administration . . . . . . . . . . . . . . . . . . . . . . . . . Roland Lundqvist

**Board for Psychological Defense**
*Birger Jarlsg. 9*
*111 45 Stockholm*
*Telephone: (8) 23 02 60*

Chief . . . . . . . . . . . . . . . . . . . . . . . . . . . . . . . . . . . . . . . Per-Axel Landahl

**Military Broadcasting Service**
*Box 301*
*161 26 Bromma*
*Telephone:   (8) 759 00 20*

Chief . . . . . . . . . . . . . . . . . . . . . . . . . . . . . . . . . . . . . . . . . Lars Ljunggren

**Aeronautical Research Institute**
*Box 11021*
*161 11 Bromma*
*Telephone:   (8) 26 28 40*

Chief . . . . . . . . . . . . . . . . . . . . . . . . . . . . . . . . . Gmj. Sven-Olof Olin
Chief, Aerodynamics Division . . . . . . . . . . . . . . . . . . . . . . . Georg Drougge
Chief, Mechanics Division . . . . . . . . . . . . . . . . . . . . . . . . . Stig Lundgren
Chief, Technical Division . . . . . . . . . . . . . . . . . . . . . . . . . Curt Nelander

## DEFENSE FORCES

**ARMED FORCES**
**Swedish Defense Forces**
*(Försvaret)*
*Lindingövägen 24*
*P.O. Box 800 01*
*104 50 Stockholm*
*Telephone:   (8) 22 15 60*

Supreme Commander, Defense Forces . . . . . . . . . . . . . . Gen. Lennart Ljung
Chief, Defense Staff . . . . . . . . . . . . . . . . . . . . . . . . . Vam. Bror Stefenson

**Defense Head Committee**
*Försvarsdepartmentet*
*103 33 Stockholm*
*Telephone:   (8) 763 0000*

Chairman . . . . . . . . . . . . . . . . . . . . . . . . . . . . . . . . . . . . Gen. Lennart Ljung
Vice Chairman . . . . . . . . . . . . . . . . Eric Holmqvist, Member of the Riksdag
Secretary . . . . . . . . . . . . . . . . . . . . . . . . . . . . . . . . . . . . . . . . . Jan Nilsson
Member . . . . . . . . . . . . . . . . . . . . . . . . . . . . . . . . . . . . . . Glt. Nils Sköld
(Commander, Army)
Member . . . . . . . . . . . . . . . . . . . . . . . . . . . . . . . . . Glt. Sven-Olof Olson
(Commander, Air Force)
Member . . . . . . . . . . . . . . . . . . . . . . . . . . . . . . . . . . Vam. Per Rudberg
(Commander, Navy)

**Southern Military Command**
*P.O. Box 514*
*291 25 Kristianstad*
*Telephone:   (44) 11 50 80*

Commander . . . . . . . . . . . . . . . . . . . . . . . . . . . . . . . . . Vam. Bengt Schuback

**Western Military Command**
*P.O. Box 601*
*541 29 Skövde*
*Telephone:   (500) 650 00*

Commander . . . . . . . . . . . . . . . . . . . . . . . . . . . . . . . . Gmj. Kjell Nordström

**Eastern Military Command**
*P.O. Box 1004*
*152 01 Strängnäs*
*Telephone:   (152) 129 00*

Commander . . . . . . . . . . . . . . . . . . . . . . . . . . . . . . . . . Glt. Bengt Lehander

**Berglagens Command**
*P.O. Box 1023*
*651 15 Karlstad*
*Telephone:   (54) 11 54 80*

Commander . . . . . . . . . . . . . . . . . . . . . . . . . . . . . . . . Gmj. Bengt Tamfeldt

**Lower Norrlands Command**
*P.O. Box 370*
*831 25 Östersund*
*Telephone:   (63) 11 70 40*

Commander . . . . . . . . . . . . . . . . . . . . . . . . . . . . . . . . . . Gmj. Rolf Wigur

**Upper Norrlands Command**
*P.O. Box 9101*
*961 19 Boden*
*Telephone:    (921) 114 70; 118 20*

Commander . . . . . . . . . . . . . . . . . . . . . . . . . . . . . . . . . . . . . Glt. Erik Bengtsson

**Gotland Military Command**
*(under Eastern Military Command)*
*Fack*
*621 01 Visby*
*Telephone:    (498) 119 50*

Commander . . . . . . . . . . . . . . . . . . . . . . . . . . . . . . Gmj. Lars-Erik Wanlgren

**Stockholm Command**
*P.O. Box 2026*
*103 11 Stockholm*
*Telephone:    (8) 10 19 95*

Commander-in-Chief . . . . . . . . . . . . . . . . . . . . . . . . . . Glt. Bengt Lehander

## INTEGRATED MILITARY ACADEMIES

**Defense Academy**
*Fack*
*100 45 Stockholm*
*Telephone:    (8) 67 96 20*

Commanding Officer . . . . . . . . . . . . . . . . . . . . . . . . . . Gmj. Bengt Liljestrand

**Military Academy**
*Fack*
*100 45 Stockholm*
*Telephone:    (8) 24 25 60*

Commanding Officer . . . . . . . . . . . . . . . . . . . Gmj. Nils-Fredrik Palmstierna

**ARMY**
**Swedish Army**
*(Svenska Armen)*
*104 50 Stockholm*

Commander . . . . . . . . . . . . . . . . . . . . . . . . . . . . . . . . . . . . . . . . Glt. Nils Sköld
Chief of Staff . . . . . . . . . . . . . . . . . . . . . . . . . . . . . . . . . . Gmj. Krister Larsson
Chief, Section I (Planning; Studies;
    Tactics and Intelligence) . . . . . . . . . . . . . . . . . . . . . . . Öv. 1 Jörn Beckman
Chief, Section II (Equipment; Organization) . . . . . . . . Öv. 1 Bengt Sjöberg
Chief, Section III (Personnel; Information) . . . . . . . . Öv. 1 Johan Palmgren
Chief, Section IV (Training;
    Regulations and Education) . . . . . . . . . . . . . . . . . . . . Öv. 1 Åke Lundin

**Southern Command**

Commander, *Kronoberg* Infantry
    Regiment (Växjö) . . . . . . . . . . . . . . . . . . . . . . . . . . . . Öv. 1 Finn Werner
Commander, *Norra Smålands* Infantry
    Regiment (Eksjö) . . . . . . . . . . . . . . . . . . . . . . . . . . . Öv. 1 Lars Andersson
Commander, *Skånska Dragonregementet* Armored
    Regiment (Hässleholm) . . . . . . . . . . . . . . . . . . . . . . . . . . Öv. Hans Nilsson
Commander, *Södra skånska* Armored
    Regiment (Ystad and Revingehed) . . . . . . . . . . . . . . . Öv. 1 Bertil Green
Commander, *Norra skånska* Armored
    Regiment (Kristianstad) . . . . . . . . . . . . . . . . . . . . . Öv. 1 Curt Hasselgren
Commander, *Wendes* Artillery
    Regiment (Kristianstad) . . . . . . . . . . . . . . . . . . . . . . . . Öv. Hans Richter
Commander, *Smålands* Artillery
    Regiment (Jönköping) . . . . . . . . . . . . . . . . . . . . . . . . Öv. Lars Carlsson
Commander, *Skånska* Air Defense
    Regiment (Ystad) . . . . . . . . . . . . . . . . . . . . . . . . . Öv. Lars Mårtensson
Commander, *Gota* Engineer
    Regiment (Eksjö) . . . . . . . . . . . . . . . . . . . . . . . . Öv. Lars-Åke Persson
Commander, *Skånska* Maintenance
    Regiment (Hässleholm) . . . . . . . . . . . . . . . . . . . . Öv. Góran Wéllerlund

**Western Command**

Commander, *Älvsborgs* Infantry
Regiment (Borås) . . . . . . . . . . . . . . . . . . . . . . . . . .Öv. 1 Henry Magnusson
Commander, *Halland* Infantry
Regiment (Halmstad) . . . . . . . . . . . . . . . . . . . . . . . .Öv. 1 Raland Morell
Commander, *Skaraborgs* Armored
Regiment (Skövde) . . . . . . . . . . . . . . . . . . . . . . . . .Öv. 1 Carl-Gösta Norderup
Commander, *Bohusläns* Infantry
Regiment (Uddevalla) . . . . . . . . . . . . . . . . . . . . . . . . . .Öv. Arne Rolff
Commander, *Livregementets husarer* Ranger
Cavalry Regiment (Skövde) . . . . . . . . . . . . . . . . . . . . .Öv. Lars Andersson
Commander, *Göta* Air Defense
Regiment (Göteborg) . . . . . . . . . . . . . . . . . . . . . . . . . .Öv. Sven Platerud
Commander, *Göta* Signal
Regiment (Karlsborg) . . . . . . . . . . . . . . . . . . . . . . . . .Öv. Kurt Olofsson
Commander, *Göta* Maintenance
Regiment (Skövde) . . . . . . . . . . . . . . . . . . . . . . . . . . .Öv. Yngve Ekman

**Eastern Command**

Commander, *Livgrenadjärerregementet* Infantry
Regiment (Linköping) . . . . . . . . . . . . . . . . . . . . . . .Öv. 1 Per-Arne Ringh
Commander, *Hälsinge* Infantry
Regiment (Gävle) . . . . . . . . . . . . . . . . . . . . . . . . . . .Öv. 1 Ingemar Arnhall
Commander, *Livgardets dragoner* Armored
Cavalry Regiment (Stockholm) . . . . . . . . . . . . . .Öv. 1 Hodder Stjernswärd
Commander, *Södermanlands* Armored
Regiment (Strängnäs) . . . . . . . . . . . . . . . . . . . . . . . .Öv. 1 Åke Eriksson
Commander, *Upplands* Signal
Regiment (Uppsala) . . . . . . . . . . . . . . . . . . . . . . .Öv. 1 Fredrik Lilliecreutz
Commander, *Svea livgarde* Infantry
Regiment (Kungsängen) . . . . . . . . . . . . . . . . . . . . .Öv. Rolf Frykhammar
Commander, *Svea* Artillery
Regiment (Linköping) . . . . . . . . . . . . . . . . . . . . . . . .Öv. Rune Eriksson
Commander, *Roslagens* Air Defense
Regiment (Norrtälje) . . . . . . . . . . . . . . . . . . . . . . . . . .Öv. Stig Prinzell
Commander, *Svea* Engineer
Regiment (Almnäs, Södertälje) . . . . . . . . . . . . . . .Öv. Sven-Erik Nilsson
Commander, *Svea* Maintenance
Regiment (Linköping) . . . . . . . . . . . . . . . . . . . . . . . .Öv. Claës Tamm

**Berglagens Command**

Commander, *Värmlands* Infantry
Regiment (Karlstad) . . . . . . . . . . . . . . . . . . . . . . .Öv. 1 Ulf Ling-Vannerus
Commander, *Livregementets grenadjärer* Infantry
Regiment (Örebro) . . . . . . . . . . . . . . . . . . . . . . . . . .Öv. 1 John Petersson
Commander, *Dalregementet* Infantry
Regiment (Falun) . . . . . . . . . . . . . . . . . . . . . . . . . .Öv. 1 Fredrik Gyllenram
Commander, *Berglagens* Artillery
Regiment (Kristinehamn) . . . . . . . . . . . . . . . . . . . . .Öv. Carl Carlsson

**Lower Norrlands Command**

Commander, *Jämtlands fältjägerregemente*
Infantry Regiment (Östersund) . . . . . . . . . . . . . . . .Öv. 1 Jan Liedgren
Commander, *Västernorrlands* Infantry
Regiment . . . . . . . . . . . . . . . . . . . . . . . . . . . . . . . . . . .Öv. 1 Åke Sagren
Commander, *Norrlands* Artillery
Regiment (Östersund) . . . . . . . . . . . . . . . . . . . . .Öv. Lars-Olof Strandberg
Commander, *Norrlands* Maintenance
Regiment (Sollefteå) . . . . . . . . . . . . . . . . . . . . .Öv. Per-Anders Lindespång

**Upper Norrlands Command**

Commander, *Västerbottens* Infantry
Regiment (Umeå) . . . . . . . . . . . . . . . . . . . . . . . . . .Öv. 1 Olof Dackenberg
Commander, *Lapplands jägar* Infantry
Regiment (Kiruna) . . . . . . . . . . . . . . . . . . . . . . . . . . .Öv. Leif Nillson
Commander, *Bodens* Artillery
Regiment (Boden) . . . . . . . . . . . . . . . . . . . . . . . . .Öv. 1 Thure Wadenholt

Commander, *Norbottens* Mechanized
Regiment (Boden) .......................Öv. Jan Wickbom
Commander, *Norrlands dragoner* Ranger
Cavalry Regiment (Arvidsjaur) ...................Öv. Lars Wallén
Commander, *Lulea* Air Defense
Regiment (Luleå) ........................Öv. Lars Brunnberg
Commander, *Bodens* Engineer
Regiment (Boden) .........................Öv. Bertil Alm
Commander, *Norrlands* Signal
Battalion (Boden).....................Övlt. Carl-Henrik Bengtsson
Commander, *Norbottens* Army Air
Battalion (Boden) ..........................Övlt. Folke Estedt

**Fortifications Corps**
*100 45 Stockholm*
*Telephone: (8) 22 15 60*

Commanding Officer ..........................Öv. 1 Bertil Runnberg

**Weapons Technology Corps**
*Fack*
*104 50 Stockholm*
*Telephone: (8) 63 55 80*

Commanding Officer...........................Öv. 1 Börje Gahnberg

**Roads and Bridge Construction Corps**
*Fack*
*104 50 Stockholm*
*Telephone: (8) 22 15 60*

Commanding Officer ...................Öv. 1 Harald Alexandersson

**Army Academies**

**Artillery and Engineer Regiments
Officers' School**
*Box 10078*
*100 55 Stockholm*
*Telephone: (8) 67 08 40*

Commanding Officer ..........................Öv. Ingvar Marklund

**Army Combat School**
*Box 21008*
*100 31 Stockholm*
*Telephone: (8) 736 08 20*

Commanding Officer...........................Öv. Matts Liljegren

**Imperial Home Guard**
*P.O. Box 3528*
*103 69 Stockholm*
*Telephone: (8) 67 95 20*

Commanding Officer.............................Gmj. Robert Lugn
Chief of Staff........................Öv. Åke von Scheele
Chief, Administration ..............................Mj. Jan Sjören

**Troop Inspectorate**
*Östermalmsgatan 87*
*104 50 Stockholm*
*Telephone: (8) 67 96 20*

Inspector, Infantry and Cavalry ...................Öv. 1 Lennart Tollerz
Inspector, Armored Units ...............Öv. 1 Bjorn Henrik Zickerman
Inspector, Artillery.........................Öv. 1 Gösta Gärdin
Inspector, Air Defense .........................Öv. 1 Sven Sjölander
Inspector, Engineer and Signal Units ..................Öv. 1 Owe Dahl
Inspector, Maintenance and Supply Units...............Öv. 1 Curt Sjöö

**NAVY**
**Swedish Navy**
*(Marinen)*
*P.O. Box 800 03*
*104 50 Stockholm*
*Telephone: (8) 22 15 60*

Commander ...........................Vam Per Rudberg
Chief of Staff ...........................Gmj. Bo Varenius
Chief, Section I (Planning; Studies;
Tactics and Intelligence) ......................Kmd. Claës Tornberg
Chief, Section II (Organization;
Material and Equipment; Staff and
Coordination; Navigation; Medical) ..............Öv. Ingvar Johansson

Chief, Section III (Personnel;
  Security; Information; Volunteers) ..............Kmd. Gösta Sunberg
Chief, Section IV (Production
  Management; Training; Conscription) ........Kmd. 1 Bengt O'Konor
Chief, Section V (Coast Artillery
  Affairs, Publications and Educational
  Materials; Legal; Administration) ..........Öv. 1 Per-Erik Bergstrand

**Overall Command of Fleet and
Coast Artillery**

Commanding Officer ...............................Kam. Jan Enquist
Chief of Staff .......................................Kmd. Jan Bring
(See below for commanders of individual coast artillery regiments.)

**Southern Command**

Commander, Southern Coast Navy
  Base (Karlskrona) .................Kmd. 1 Lennart Jedeur-Palmgren
Commander, Malmö Patrol
  District (Malmö) ..........................KK. Christer Fredholm
Commander, *Blekinge* Coast Defense
  Headquarters (Karlskrona) ...................Öv. 1 Stefan Furenius
Commander, *Karlskrona* Coast Artillery
  Regiment (Karlskrona)...........................Öv. Kjell Lodenius

**Western Command**

Chief, West Coast Military
  Command (Västra Frölunda).................Öv. 1 Torbjorn Ottoson
Commander, *Gotlands* Coast Defense
  Headquarters and Artillery
  Regiment (Fårösund) ...........................Öv. Urban Sobeus
Commander, *Älvsborgs* Coast Artillery
  Regiment (Göteborg) .......................Öv. Svante Kristenson

**Lower Norrlands Command**

Commander, *Norrlands* Coast Defense
  Headquarters and Härnösand Coast Artillery
  Regiment (Härnösand) ..........................Öv. Lars Persson

**Upper Norrlands Command**

Commander, *Lulea* Patrol District (Luleå) ..............Örlkn. Eric Haal

**Stockholm Coast Defense Headquarters**

Commander .......................................Öv. 1 Lars Hanson
Chief of Staff ...................................Övlt. Jan Svenhager

**Marine Engineers Corps**
*Fack*
*130 61 Hårsfjärden*
*Telephone:  (750) 630 00*

Commander .........................................Olof Bergelin

**NAVAL ACADEMIES**

**Berga Naval Academy**
*Fack*
*130 61 Hårsfjärden*
*Telephone:  (750) 630 00*

Commanding Officer ...........................Kmd. Cay Holmberg

**Karlskrona Naval Academy**
*P.O. Box 1029*
*371 24 Karlskrona*
*Telephone:  (455) 800 20*

Commanding Officer ..............................Kmd. Lars Norrsell

**Naval Combat Academy**
*P.O. Box 3535*
*183 03 Täby*
*Telephone:  (8) 756 02 40*

Commanding Officer......................Kmd. Gustaf Hammarskiöld

## AIR FORCE
**Swedish Air Force**
*(Flygvapet)*
*P.O. Box 800 04*
*104 50 Stockholm*
*Telephone:   (8) 22 15 60*

| | |
|---|---|
| Commander | Glt. Sven-Olof Olson |
| Chief of Staff | Gmj. Evert Bage |
| Chief, Section I (Studies; Planning; Intelligence and Security; ADB) | Öv. Rolf Clementson |
| Chief, Section II (Aviation; Bases; Coordination; Air Traffic) | Öv. 1 Carl Norberg |
| Chief, Section III (Personnel; Organization) | Öv. 1 Jan-Henrik Torselius |
| Chief, Section IV (Training) | Öv. 1 Sven Kamsén |
| Chief, Troop Inspection | Öv. 1 Tore Persson |
| Chief, Air Safety Inspection | Öv. 1 Åke Sjögren |
| Chief, Weather Service | Bengt Bengtsson |
| Chief, Air Force Engineer Corps | Anders Kågström |

**Southern Command**

Commander, *Skånska* Air Wing
(Ängelholm) .......... Öv. 1 Anders Sjöberg
Commander, *Blekinge* Air Wing
(Ronneby) .......... Öv. Erik Spångberg

**Western Command**

Commander, *Västgöta* Air Wing
(Karlsborg) .......... Öv. Gunnar Hovgard
Commander, *Skaraborgs* Air Wing
(Satenäs) .......... Öv. Björn Amelin

**Eastern Command**

Commander, *Västmanlands* Air Wing
(Västerås) .......... Öv. Börje Bjorkholm
Commander, *Bråvalla* Air Wing
(Norrköping) .......... Öv. 1 Kurt Hagerström
Commander, *Hälsinge* Air Wing
(Söderhamn) .......... Öv. Roland Magndahl
Commander, *Upplands* Air Wing
(Uppsala) .......... Öv. 1 Karl-Eric Fernander

**Lower Norrlands Command**

Commander, *Jämtlands* Air Wing
(Frösön) .......... Öv. 1 Rolf Gustafsson

**Upper Norrlands Command**

Commander, *Norrbottens* Air Wing
(Luleå) .......... Öv. 1 Bert Stenfeldt

## AIR FORCE ACADEMIES

**Air Force Combat School**
*P.O. Box 645*
*751 27 Uppsala*
*Telephone:   (18) 13 95 00*

Commanding Officer .......... Öv. Gillis Weingarth

**Air Force Academy**
*P.O. Box 100*
*146 00 Tullinge*
*Telephone:   (8) 778 00 20*

Commanding Officer .......... Öv. Bernt Östh

\* \* \* \* \*

## GENERAL DEFENSE DATA

**Manpower**
Total Armed Forces .......... 64,500
(See Page 497)
Population .......... 8,331,000

**Spending**

Military Expenditures . . . . . . . . . . . . . . . . . . . . . . . . . . . . . . . . . . . . . . . $3.710 billion
Gross National Product . . . . . . . . . . . . . . . . . . . . . . . . . . . . . . . . . . . . . . $119.310 billion
Military Expenditure as a Percentage of
    Gross National Product . . . . . . . . . . . . . . . . . . . . . . . . . . . . . . . . . . . . . . . . . 3.2%
Military Expenditure as a Percentage of
    Central Government Expenditure . . . . . . . . . . . . . . . . . . . . . . . . . . . . . . 7.2%

**Defense Treaties** *(See Part II for Additional Detail)*

Bilateral:    United States

Multilateral:    Biological Weapons Convention
                Limited Test Ban Treaty
                Treaty on the Control of Arms on the Seabed
                Treaty on the Non-Proliferation of Nuclear Weapons
                United Nations Force in Cyprus
                United Nations Interim Force in Lebanon
                United Nations Military Observer Group in India and
                   Pakistan
                United Nations Truce Supervision Organization

# SWITZERLAND

## Swiss Confederation

*Schweizerische Eidgenossenschaft* (German)
*Confederation Suisse* (French)
*Confederazione Svizzera* (Italian)

## Defense Establishment Command Structure and Force Organization

Supreme command of the armed forces is exercised by the Federal Council, Switzerland's seven-man collective executive. Operational control is vested in the Chief of the Federal Military Department (the defense minister).

The Swiss armed forces have no commander-in-chief in peacetime. In case of war, parliament would appoint a general as commander-in-chief.

Switzerland does not maintain a standing (regular) army. The Swiss defense system is based on a general draft and a militia-type (reserve) service. Following initial training the troops are committed to yearly training courses with their assigned units. In wartime, Switzerland's defense depends on the mobilization of its national militia. The Air Force is an integral part of the Army.

The Commission for National Defense is the most important of several defense-related councils. It has an advisory and planning role. The Command Staff comprises the defense minister's closest advisers. The Armaments Committee coordinates procurement and procurement planning.

**Total armed forces: 21,000. Total armed forces after mobilization: 625,000 (in 48 hours).**

## HEAD OF STATE

Pierre Aubert

**OFFICE OF THE PRESIDENT**
*Department of Foreign Affairs*
*Bundeshaus West*
*3003 Bern*

*Telephone: (31) 61 21 11*
*Telex: 33330 helv ch*
*Cable: BUNDESHAUS, BERN CH.*

President of the Swiss Confederation ..................... Pierre Aubert

**OFFICE OF THE VICE PRESIDENT**
*Bernerhof*
*Bundesg. 3*
*3003 Bern*

*Telephone: (31) 61 21 11*
*Telex: 33330 helv ch*
*Cable: BUNDESHAUS, BERN CH.*

Vice President ........................................ Willy Ritschard

**Federal Council**

Chief, Finance Department ........................... Willi Ritschard
Chief, Foreign Affairs Department ...................... Pierre Aubert

Chief, Interior Department .............................Alphons Egli
Chief, Justice and Police Department ..............Rudolph Friedrich
Chief, Military Department ..................Georges-André Chevallaz
Chief, Public Economy Department......................Kurt Furgler
Chief, Transportation, Communications and
   Energy Department ...............................Léon Schlumpf

**FEDERAL MILITARY DEPARTMENT**
*(Eidgenössisches Militärdepartement)*
*Bundeshaus Ost*
*3003 Bern*

*Telephone:  (31) 67 12 11*
*Telex:  33572*
*Cable:  BUNDESHAUS, BERN CH.*

Chief of Department .........................Georges-André Chevallaz
Director of Military Administration .................Hans-Ulrich Ernst
Director, Information and Documentation Service .........Daniel Margot
Director, Organization and Personnel ..............Dr. Walter Tschanz
Director, Computer Center ............................Rudolf Peter
Director, Legal Division .............................François Godet
Director, Military Affairs Division .................Enis Georg Haeberli
Director, Military Real Estate
   Division .........................................François Briod
Director, Financial Division..........................Dr. Paul Erne

**Commission for National Defense**

Chairman ...............................Georges-André Chevallaz
   (Chief, Military Department)
Member ...............................KorpsKdt Jörg Zumstein
   (Chief, General Staff)
Member ...............................KorpsKdt Roger Mabillard
   (Chief, Training Group)
Member .............................Charles Grossenbacher
   (Chief, Armaments Group)
Member...............................KorpsKdt Edwin Stettler
   (Commander, Field Army Corps 1)
Member...............................KorpsKdt Eugen Lüthy
   (Commander, Field Army Corps 2)
Member ...............................KorpsKdt Roberto Moccetti
   (Commander, Mountain Army Corps 3)
Member...............................KorpsKdt Josef Feldmann
   (Commander, Field Army Corps 4)

**Command Staff**

Chairman ...............................Georges-André Chevallaz
   (Chief, Military Department)
Member ...............................Hans-Ulrich Ernst
   (Director, Military Administration)
Member ...............................KorpsKdt Jörg Zumstein
   (Chief, General Staff)
Member ...............................KorpsKdt Roger Mabillard
   (Chief, Training Group)
Member ...............................Charles Grossenbacher
   (Chief, Armaments Group)
Member...............................KorpsKdt Ernst Wyler
   (Commander, Air and Air Defense Troops)

**Armaments Committee**

Chairman...............................KorpsKdt Jörg Zumstein
   (Chief, General Staff)
Member ...............................KorpsKdt Roger Mabillard
   (Chief, Training Group)
Member ...............................Charles Grossenbacher
   (Chief, Armaments Group)
Member...............................KorpsKdt Ernst Wyler
   (Commander, Air and Air Defense Troops)

**Armaments Group**
*(Gruppe für Rüstungsdienste)*
*Kasernenstr. 19*
*3000 Bern 25*

Chief .........................................Charles Grossenbacher
Chief, Information Service ......................Dr. Hugo Wermelinger
Chief, Organization and Personnel .................Dr. Rolf Z'graggen

*Telephone:    (31) 67 57 01*

**Office of Defense Technology**
Director .............................................Ulrich Lanz
Chief, Systems Analysis Division ........................Heinz Hoh
Chief, Ordnance, and Combat Vehicles Division ........Heinrich Würgler
Chief, Electronics and Guided Missiles Division ..............Cuno Lüthi
Chief, Munitions and Anti-ABC Division ..............Heinrich Schaerer
Chief, Aviation .................................Rolf Immenhauser
Chief, Transport Vehicles/Engineers and
    Civil Defense Supplies Division .......................Heinz Gisiger
Chief, Munitions and Quality Control ................Hansjörg Huggler
Chief, Artillery Testing Division .......................Fritz Gilomen
Chief, AC Laboratory (Spiez) .......................Dr. Roger Amman
Chief, Specialized Electronics Division .................Peter Bachofner

**Procurement Office**
Director .............................................René Huber
Chief, Equipment Division.............................Alfred Henny
Chief, Electronics and Guided Missiles Division ............Thomas Hess
Chief, Ordnance/Combat and Transport Vehicles/
    Engineers Supplies Division............................Ruedi Kropf
Chief, Munitions/Anti-NBC/General Supplies
    Division .................................................Willy Keusen
Chief, Aviation Division ................................Peter Lyoth

**Arms Production Office**
Director .........................................Fritz Dannecker
Director, Construction Laboratory .....................Heinz Stücklin
Director, Munitions Factory (Thun)...............Dr. Friedrich Blatter
Director, Munitions Factory (Altdorf)...........Dr. Albert Sommerauer
Director, Weapons Factory (Bern) ..........................(Vacant)
Director, Gunpowder Factory (Wimmis) ..........Dr. Hansulrich Reich
Director, Airplane Factory (Emmen) .............Lucien Othenin-Girard

**Training Group**
*(Gruppe für Ausbildung)*
*Papiermühlestr. 14*
*3003 Bern*

*Telephone:    (31) 672332*

Chief.....................................KorpsKdt Roger Mabillard

**Staff**
Chief, Planning and General Affairs Divison ........Obst. Jacques Michel
Chief, Training Division ...........................Divr. Hans Dürig
Chief, Organization and Training Division ............Obst. Josef Bührer
Chief, Training Camps Division ........................Walter Haab
Commander, Federal Military Schools .............Divr. Hans Bachofner

**Adjutancy Office**
Director .....................................Divr. Emanuel Stettler
Chief, Army Chaplaincy Office .......................Gottfried Kuert
Chief, Troop Information Service..............Bgdr. Stefan Sonderegger
Chief, Women's Auxiliary ...........................Johanna Hurni
Chief, Central Office of Army
    Social Services...........................Bgdr. Bernhard Fellman
Chief, Military Service/International Law/
    Organization Division ...............................Rolf Sprenger

## OTHER OFFICES OF FEDERAL MILITARY DEPARTMENT

**Field Commissariat**
*Effingerstr. 19*
*3008 Bern*

*Telephone:    (31) 67 51 12*

Director ...............................................Rudolf Buri

**Military Attorney General's Office**
*Amtshausgasse 4*
*3003 Bern*

*Telephone:    (31) 67 33 03*

Director......................................Bgdr. Raphael Barras

**Federal Topography Office**
*Seftigenstr. 264*
*3084 Wabern*
*Telephone:  (31) 54 13 31*

Director . . . . . . . . . . . . . . . . . . . . . . . . . . . . . . . . . . . . Francis Jeanrichard

**Central Office for Coordinated Defense**
*Wildhainweg 9*
*3003 Bern*
*Telephone:  (31) 67 40 02*

Director . . . . . . . . . . . . . . . . . . . . . . . . . . . . . . . . . . . . Dr. Alfred Wyser

## DEFENSE FORCES

**ARMED FORCES**
**General Staff**
*(Gruppe für Generalstabsdienste)*
*3003 Bern*
*Telephone:  (31) 67 52 76*
*Telex:  33 572*

Chief of General Staff . . . . . . . . . . . . . . . . . . . . . . . KorpsKdt Jörg Zumstein
Chief, Staff Division . . . . . . . . . . . . . . . . . . . . . . . . . . . Werner Gantenbein

**Operations Subgroup**
Chief . . . . . . . . . . . . . . . . . . . . . . . . . . . . . . . . . . . . Divr. Gérard de Loes
Chief, Mobilization Division . . . . . . . . . . . . . . . . . . . Obst. Crivelli Giuliano
Chief, NC Protection Division . . . . . . . . . . . . . . . . . Obst. Ulrich Imobersteg

**Information and Security Subgroup**
Chief . . . . . . . . . . . . . . . . . . . . . . . . . . . . . . . . . . . Divr. Mario Petitpierre
Chief, Intelligence Division . . . . . . . . . . . . . . . . . . . . . . Obst. Peter Kistler
Chief, Military Security Division . . . . . . . . . . . . . . . . . . . . Dr. Peter Huber

**Logistics Subgroup**
Chief . . . . . . . . . . . . . . . . . . . . . . . . . . . . . . . . . . . . . . . Divr. Urs Bender
Chief, Territorial Service Division . . . . . . . . . . . . . . . . . . . Dr. Jean Rossier

**Planning Subgroup**
Chief . . . . . . . . . . . . . . . . . . . . . . . . . . . . . . . . . . . . . . Divr. Heinz Hasler
Chief, Materiel Division . . . . . . . . . . . . . . . . . . . . . . . . . Obst. Willy Krebs
Chief, Operative Training . . . . . . . . . . . . . . . . . . . . . Divr. Gustav Däniker

**Office of Engineering and**
**Fortifications**

Director . . . . . . . . . . . . . . . . . . . . . . . . . . . . . . . . . . . Divr. Bruno Hirzel
Chief, Engineer Corps Division . . . . . . . . . . . . . . . . . Obst. André Cheneval
Chief, Fortifications Division . . . . . . . . . . . . . . . . . . Obst. Francis Lambert
Chief, Fortifications Corps Division . . . . . . . . . . . . . . . . . Obst. Willi Bär
Chief, Military Construction Division . . . . . . . . . . . . . . . . . René Bretscher

**Medical Office**

Director . . . . . . . . . . . . . . . . . . . . . . . . . . . . . . . . . Divr. Dr. André Huber
Chief, Medical Services . . . . . . . . . . . . . . . . . . . . . . . . . . Dr. Willy Kauer
Chief, Administration and Operations,
  Medical Corps . . . . . . . . . . . . . . . . . . . . . . . . . . . . . Obst. Rolf Fischer
Chief, Pharmaceutical Staff . . . . . . . . . . . . . . . . . . . . Obst. Dr. Kurt Beutl

**Central War Commissary**
*Wylerstr. 52*
*3000 Bern 52*

Director . . . . . . . . . . . . . . . . . . . . . . . . . . . . . . Bgdr. Jean-Pierre Ehrsam
Chief, Supply and Accounting Division . . . . . . . . . . . . . . Fabio Pfaffhauser
Chief, Munitions Division . . . . . . . . . . . . . . . . . . . . . . . Wolfgang Lennartz
Chief of Instruction, Supply Troops . . . . . . . . . . . . . Obst. Franz Kesselring

**Materiel Administration**
*Viktoriastr. 85*
*3000 Bern 25*

Director . . . . . . . . . . . . . . . . . . . . . . . . . . . . . . . . Bgdr. Heinrich Staedeli
Chief, Central Services and Cantonal Affairs . . . . . . . . . . . . . . . Even Gollut

**Depot Operations**
Director . . . . . . . . . . . . . . . . . . . . . . . . . . . . . . . . . . . . . . . . Max Lüthi
Chief, Troop Equipment Division . . . . . . . . . . . . . . . . . . . . Louis Margot
Chief, Motorized Vehicles Division . . . . . . . . . . . . . . . . . . . Paul Surbeck
Chief, Electronics Division . . . . . . . . . . . . . . . . . . . . . Dr. Jürg Wettstein
Chief, Supply Troops Division . . . . . . . . . . . . . . . . . . . Obst. Hans Straub
Chief, Personnel and Accounting Division . . . . . . . . . . . . . . . Fritz Schmutz

**Federal Signal Troops Office**
*3003 Bern*

*Telephone:   (31) 67 36 28*

Director/Commanding Officer .................Divr. Josef Biedermann
Chief, Planning and Electronics Division ..............Charles Scherrer
Chief, Operations/Equipment/Administration............Rudolf Ritter

**Federal Transport Troops Office**
*Blumenbergstr. 39*
*3000 Bern 25*

*Telephone:   (31) 67 28 80*

Director.........................................Bgdr. Hermann Stocker
Chief, Motorized Vehicles Division ......................Alain Nicati
Chief, Training Division ...................Maj. Hans-Ulrich Wieland
Chief, Other Services (Accounting, Personnel,
   Military Police) .......................................Albert Siegrist

**Federal Office of Civil Defense Troops**
*Wylerstr. 52*
*3000 Bern 25*

*Telephone:   (31) 67 33 37*

Director .......................................Bgdr. René Ziegler
Chief, Training.........................Maj. Ulrich Brandenberger
Chief, Equipment and Construction ......................Roland Ryff
Chief, Administration and Personnel ..................André Wiedmer

**Federal Artillery Office**
*Papiermühlestr. 14*
*3003 Bern*

*Telephone:   (31) 67 25 91*

Director/Commanding Officer .................Divr. Fritz Wermelinger
Chief, Organization and Equipment ......................Heinz Weber
Chief, Personnel ...................................Roland Chevalley
Chief, Administration ...................................Max Rebetez

**Federal Infantry Office**
*Papiermühlestr. 14*
*3003 Bern*

*Telephone:   (31) 67 44 24*

Director/Commanding Officer...................Divr. Robert Treichler
Chief, Artillery Ranges/Transport/Education .........Obst. Adrien Stoll
Chief, Training ...........................Obst. Hansueli Tschanz
Chief, Equipment and Organization...................Hans Schweizer
Chief, Personnel.....................................Fortunat Buchli
Chief, Administration .................................René Simon

**Federal Office of Mechanized and**
**Light Troops**
*Papiermühlestr. 14*
*3003 Bern*

*Telephone:   (31) 67 26 29*

Director/Commanding Officer ............Divr. Jean-Rodolphe Christen
Chief, Administration ...........................Jean-Michel Zosso
Chief, Planning .............................Maj. Ernst Stettler
Chief, Organization and Equipment ......................Olivier Bron
Chief, Training.......................................Theodor Riesen
Chief, Personnel .................................Heinz Krähenbühl

# ARMY
*3003 Bern*

## ARMY UNIT COMMANDERS

**Field Army Corps 1**
*1012 Lausanne 12*
*Telephone: (21) 22 77 74*

Commander .................................KorpsKdt Edwin Stettler
Commander, Mechanized Division 1
   (Lausanne) .................................Divr. Bernard Chatelan
Commander, Field Division 2 (Colombier) .........Divr. Michel Montfort
Commander, Field Division 3 (Bern) ...............Divr. Paul Ritschard
Commander, Territorial Zone 1 (Lausanne) ...........Divr. Henri Butty

**Field Army Corps 2**
*6010 Kriens*

*Telephone:   (41) 41 77 67*

Commander .................................KorpsKdt Eugen Lüthy
Commander, Mechanized Division 4 (Solothurn) ....Divr. Friedrich Suter
Commander, Field Division 5 (Aarau) ..........Divr. Pierre-Marie Halter
Commander, Field Division 8 (Kriens) ............Divr. Edmund Mueller
Commander, Territorial Zone 2 (Kriens) ...........Divr. Rudolf Bucheli

**Mountain Army Corps 3**
*6301 Zug*

*Telephone:   (42) 31 67 44*

Commander..............................KorpsKdt Roberto Moccetti
Commander, Mountain Division 9
   (Bellinzona)...........................Divr. Walter Zimmermann
Commander, Mountain Division 10
   (St.-Maurice) .............................Divr. Adrien Tschumy
Commander, Mountain Division 12 (Chur) ............Divr. Ernst Riedi

Commander, Territorial Zone 9
(Bellinzona) ............................Bgdr. Alessandro Torriani
Commander, Territorial Zone 10
(St.-Maurice) ..........................Bgdr. Jean-Gabriel Digier
Commander, Territorial Zone 12 (Chur) .........Bgdr. Jon Andri Tgetgel

**Field Army Corps 4**
*8021 Zurich*
*Telephone: (1) 242-3820*

Commander ...............................KorpsKdt Josef Feldmann
Commander, Field Division 6 (Zurich).................Divr. Rolf Binder
Commander, Field Division 7 (St. Gallen) ...............Divr. Kurt Lipp
Commander, Mechanized Division 11
(Winterthur) .............................Divr. Andreas Gadient
Commander, Territorial Zone 4 (Zurich) ...............Bgdr. Hans Ruh

**AIR FORCE**
*(Kommando der Flieger-und*
*Fliegerabwehrtruppen)*
*3000 Bern 25*
*Telephone: (31) 67 38 02*

Commander of Air and Air Defense Troops ........KorpsKdt Ernst Wyler
Chief of Staff and Chief, Coordination and
Planning Division .........................Bgdr. Jean-Claude Kunz
Chief, Operations and Combat Division .............Divr. Walter Duerig
Commander, Aviation Brigade (Payerne) ............Bgdr. Paul Leuthold
Commander, Airbase Brigade (Duβendorf) .....Bgdr. Werner Glanzmann
Commander, Anti-Aircraft Brigade (Bern) ...........Bgdr. Henri Criblez

**Office of Military Aviation**
**and Air Defense**

Director/Commanding Officer .....................Divr. René Gurtner
Chief, Corps of Instructors, Aviation (Payerne) .....Obst. Athos Taminelli
Chief, Corps of Instructors, AAA (Emmen).......Obst. Leopold Amacker
Chief, Military Aviation...........................Obst. Ernst Kuster
Chief, Air Defense................................Max Baehler
Chief, Communications and Electronics ..................Hans Würgler
Chief, Personnel ...................................Iwan Felber
Chief, Training .........................Obst. Hansruedi Rollin
Chief, Personnel and Accounting ......................Erich Frutiger
Director, Aviation Medical Institute
(Dübendorf)...................................Dr. Alfred Gubser
Commander, Surveillance Squadron ...........Obst. Hans Ruedi Ruesch

**Office of Military Airfields**

Director...................................Bgdr. Werner Glanzmann
Chief, Technical Division ..............................Hans Surber
Chief, Construction and Installations Division .................Emil Lee
Chief, Operations and Procurement Division ......Hanspeter Fankhauser

✲ ✲ ✲ ✲ ✲

## GENERAL DEFENSE DATA

**Manpower**
Total Armed Forces .............................................21,000
(See Page 507)
Population ..................................................6,407,000

**Spending**
Military Expenditures.......................................$2.28 billion
Gross National Product ...................................$114.43 billion
Military Expenditure as a Percentage of
Gross National Product .........................................2.0%
Military Expenditure as a Percentage of
Central Government Expenditure ...............................22.1%

**Defense Treaties** *(See Part II for Additional Detail)*

Bilateral:     None

Multilateral:  Biological Weapons Convention
Limited Test Ban Treaty
Treaty on the Control of Arms on the Seabed
Treaty on the Non-Proliferation of Nuclear Weapons

# SYRIA
## Syrian Arab Republic
### *al-Jamhouriya al-Arabia al-Souriya*

## Defense Establishment Command Structure and Force Organization

The President is Commander-in-Chief of the armed forces of Syria. His authority is exercised through the Minister of Defense. The Air Force and the Air Defense Command each has its own commander and staff; they are subordinate to the Chief of Staff of the Armed Forces. The Navy is subordinate to the local army commander responsible for the coastal region. Syria has at least five major internal security and intelligence services, some of which fall under the Interior Ministry, while others are answerable to the Chief of Military Intelligence. The National Security Council coordinates all the security and intelligence services.

**Total armed forces:** 222,500 (Army: 170,000; Navy: 2,500; Air Force: 50,000). **Paramilitary forces:** 9,800 (Gendarmerie: 8,000; Desert Guard: 1,800).

## HEAD OF STATE

H. E. Lt. Gen. Hafez al-Assad

**OFFICE OF THE PRESIDENCY**
*Muhajreen*
*Presidential Palace*
*Abu Rumaneh*
*Al-Rashid Street*
*Damascus*
*Telephone: 331112*

President and Commander-in-Chief .............Lt. Gen. Hafez al-Assad
Political Advisor ...............................................
Economic Affairs Advisor ......................Dr. Bashshar Kabbara
Chief, Press Office .......................................As'ad Elias
Chief, Protocol .......................................Khalil Saadawi
Minister of State for Presidential Affairs ..............Abdul-Karim Adi

**OFFICE OF THE PRIME MINISTRY**
*Shahbandar Street*
*Damascus*
*Telephone: 226000*

Prime Minister ......................Dr. Eng. Abdul-Ra'ouf al-Kassem
Deputy Prime Minister and
    Minister of Foreign Affairs ..................Abdul-Halim Khaddam
Deputy Prime Minister for
    Public Services ....................................Walid Hamdoun
Deputy Prime Minister for
    Economic Affairs.........................Abdul-Kader Kaddourah

**MINISTRY OF DEFENSE**
*Ommayad Square*
*Damascus*
*Telephone: 112101-5*
*Telex: 411371 fermod sy*

Minister and Deputy
    Commander-in-Chief.................Lt. Gen. al-Imad Mustafa Talas
Deputy Defense Minister ..........................Gen. Moukayyed
Deputy Minister, Administration ....Maj. Gen. Awad bin Ali Rashid Bagh
Deputy Minister,
    Ground Forces .................Maj. Gen. Yusef bin Ragheh Shakur
Director, Political Department ................Gen. Tamereddine Nasser
Chairman, National Security Council ............Gen. Muhammad Kholi
Deputy Minister, Air and Air
    Defense Forces..........................Maj. Gen. Subhi Haddad

**MINISTRY OF INTERIOR**
*Merjeh Circle*
*Damascus*
*Telephone: 220100, 227541, 111001*

Minister ...................................Gen. Nasir Al-din Nasir

# DEFENSE FORCES

**ARMED FORCES**
**Syrian Arab Army**
*c/o Ministry of Defense*
*Ommayad Square*
*Damascus*

*Telephone:   229100, 112100-4*
*Telex:   11371 fermod*

**General Staff**
Chief of Staff . . . . . . . . . . . . . . . . . . . . . . . . . . . . . . . . . Lt. Gen. Hikmat Shihabi
Chief, Army Protocol . . . . . . . . . . . . . . . . . . . . . . . . . . . . . Haytham Sabouni
Chief, Foreign Liaison . . . . . . . . . . . . . . . . . . . . . . . . . Brig. Gen. Talat Jamil
Deputy Chief of Staff . . . . . . . . . . . . . . . . . . . . . . . . . . . Maj. Gen. Ali Aslan
Chief, Military Intelligence . . . . . . . . . . . . . . . . . . . . . . . Maj. Gen. Ali Duba
Chief, Personnel and Administration . . . . . . . . . . . . . . . . . . . . . . . . . . . . .
Chief, Operations . . . . . . . . . . . . . . . . . . . . . . . . . . . . . . . . . . . . . . . . . . .
Chief, Training and Logistics . . . . . . . . . . . . . . . . . . . . . . . . . . . . . . . . . . .

**Commands**

Commander, 5th Infantry Division  . . . . . . . . . . . . . . . . . Brig. Omar Abrash
Commander, 7th Infantry Division . . . . . . . . . . . . . . . . . . Brig. Ali al-Salem
Commander, 9th Infantry Division . . . . . . . . . . . . . . . . . . . Brig. Yunis Yunis
Commander, 1st Armored Division . . . . . . . . . . . . . . . . . . . . . . . . . . . . . . . .
Commander, 3rd Armored Division  . . . . . . . . . . . . . . . . . . . . . . . . . . . . . . .
Commander, Popular Army . . . . . . . . . . . . . . . . . . . . . . . . . . . . . . . . . . . . .
Commander, Palestine Liberation Army Brigade . . . . . . . . . . . . . . . . . . . . .

**NAVY**
**Syrian Arab Navy**
*c/o Ministry of Defense*
*Ommayad Square*
*Damascus*

*Telephone:   229100, 112100-4*
*Telex:   11371 fermod*

Commander, Navy . . . . . . . . . . . . . . . . . . . . . . . Maj. Gen. Fadhaah Hussein

**AIR FORCE**
**Syrian Arab Air Force**
*P.O. Box 90*
*Al-Mihdi ibn Barakeh Street*
*Damascus*

*Telephone:   339191/2, 339205, 339200*
*Telex:   11900 safcon sy*

Commander, Air and Air
    Defense Forces . . . . . . . . . . . . . . . . . . . . . . . . . . . Maj. Gen. Subhi Haddad
Assistant Commander . . . . . . . . . . . . . . . . . . . . . . . . Maj. Gen. Adnan Jabi
Chief of Staff . . . . . . . . . . . . . . . . . . . . . . . . . . . . Maj. Gen. Ibrahim Hassan
Chief, Air Force Protocol . . . . . . . . . . . . . . . . . . . . . . . . Col. Anwar Saqbani
Chief Engineer . . . . . . . . . . . . . . . . . . . . . . . . . . . . . . . Zouheir Sharabati
Chief, Air Force Academy . . . . . . . . . . . . . . . . . . . . . . . . . . . . . . . . . . . . .

**AIR DEFENSE COMMAND**
*Damascus*

Commander . . . . . . . . . . . . . . . . . . . . . . . . . . . . . . . . . . . Maj. Gen Ali Salih

**SPECIAL FORCES**
*Damascus*

Commander . . . . . . . . . . . . . . . . . . . . . . . . . . . . . . . . . . . . . . . . Gen. Haydar

**DETACHMENTS FOR THE DEFENSE**
  **OF THE REGIME**
*Damascus*

Commander . . . . . . . . . . . . . . . . . . . . . . . . . . . . . . . . Lt. Col. Rifat al-Assad

\* \* \* \* \*

# GENERAL DEFENSE DATA

**Manpower**
   Total Armed Forces . . . . . . . . . . . . . . . . . . . . . . . . . . . . . . . . . . . . . . . . 222,500
      (See Page 513)
   Population  . . . . . . . . . . . . . . . . . . . . . . . . . . . . . . . . . . . . . . . . . . 9,423,000

**Spending**
Military Expenditures . . . . . . . . . . . . . . . . . . . . . . . . . . . . . . . . . . . . . . . . . $2.2 billion
Gross National Product . . . . . . . . . . . . . . . . . . . . . . . . . . . . . . . . . . . . . . . $12 billion
Military Expenditure as a Percentage of
    Gross National Product . . . . . . . . . . . . . . . . . . . . . . . . . . . . . . . . . . . . . . 18.1%
Military Expenditure as a Percentage of
    Central Government Expenditure . . . . . . . . . . . . . . . . . . . . . . . . . . . . . . 35.4%

**Defense Treaties** *(See Part II for Additional Detail)*

Bilateral:      Soviet Union

Multilateral:   League of Arab States
                Limited Test Ban Treaty
                Treaty on the Non-Proliferation of Nuclear Weapons

# TAIWAN
## Republic of China
### Chung-hwa Min-Kuo

## Defense Establishment Command Structure and Force Organization

The President is Commander-in-Chief of the armed forces. He exercises command through the Ministry of National Defense and the Armed Forces General Staff. The National Security Council advises the President on defense policy.

**Total armed forces:** 464,000 (Army: 310,000; Navy: 38,000; Marines: 39,000; Air Force: 77,000). **Para-military forces:** 25,000 (Taiwan Garrison Command).

## HEAD OF STATE

H. E. Chiang Ching-Kuo

**OFFICE OF THE PRESIDENT**
*Chiehshou Hall*
*Chungking S. Road*
*Taipei, 100*
*Telephone: (2) 311-3731*

President and Commander-in-Chief ................Chiang Ching-Kuo
Vice President .........................................Hsieh Tung-min
Secretary-General ......................................Ma Chi-chuang
Deputy Secretary-General ..............................Chang Tsu-yi
Chief of Staff to the President .......................Gen. Ma An-Lan
Chief, Protocol Section ..............................Chan Te-Kuei

**National Security Council**
*Chiehshou Hall*
*Chungking S. Road*
*Taipei, 100*
*Telephone: (2) 311-5687*

Chairman ...........................................Chiang Ching-kuo
Secretary-General ....................................Shen Chang-huan

**MINISTRY OF NATIONAL DEFENSE**
*Chiehshou Hall*
*Chungking S. Road*
*Telephone: (2) 311-7001*

Minister ...........................................Soong Chang-chih
Vice Minister ....................................Gen. Chang Kuo-ying
Administrative Vice Minister ................Vice Adm. Cheng Pen-chi
Administrative Vice Minister ..................Lt. Gen. Jung Cheng-en
Administrative Vice Minister ................Lt. Gen. Ku Chuan-hsing

## DEFENSE FORCES

**ARMED FORCES**
**General Staff**
*Chungking S. Road*
*Taipei, 100*
*Telephone: (2) 311-7001*

Chief of the General Staff .......................Gen. Hao Pei-tsun
Director, Liaison Office ...................Maj. Gen. Ma Chung-yao

**Military Spokesman Office**
*2nd Floor, 164 Po Ai Road*
*(Po Ai Building)*
*Taipei*
*Telephone: (2) 311-9108*

Director ......................................Maj. Gen. Wang Miao

**Combined Service Forces**
*General Headquarters*
*Yung Chi Road*
*P.O. Box 7230*
*Taipei, 100*
*Telephone:    (2) 761-4121*

Commander . . . . . . . . . . . . . . . . . . . . . . . . . . . . . . . . . . Gen. Chiang Wei-kuo
Director, Foreign Affairs Service . . . . . . . . . . . . . . . Maj. Gen. Yang Shih-fa

**ARMY**
*General Headquarters*
*c/o Ministry of National Defense*
*Chiehshou Hall*
*Chungking S. Road*
*Taipei, 100*
*Telephone:    (2) 321-4911*

Commander . . . . . . . . . . . . . . . . . . . . . . . . . . . . . . . . . Gen. Chiang Chung-ling
Director, Army General Headquarters Office . . . Maj. Gen. Kang Kao-hsin

**NAVY**
*General Headquarters*
*c/o Ministry of National Defense*
*Chiehshou Hall*
*Chungking S. Road*
*Taipei, 100*
*Telephone:    (2) 594-3811*

Commander . . . . . . . . . . . . . . . . . . . . . . . . . . . . . . . . . . . Adm. Tsou Chien
Director, Navy General Headquarters Office  . . . . . Rear Adm. Shih Po-hua

**AIR FORCE**
*General Headquarters*
*c/o Ministry of National Defense*
*Chiehshou Hall*
*Chunking S. Road*
*Taipei, 100*
*Telephone:    (2) 711-1121*

Commander . . . . . . . . . . . . . . . . . . . . . . . . . . . . . . . . . . . . Gen. Kuo Ju-lin
Director, Air Force General Headquarters Office . . . . Col. Chen Yuan-shen

**TAIWAN GARRISON**
*General Headquarters*
*172 Po Ai Road*
*Taipei, 100*
*Telephone:    (2) 311-1501*

Commander . . . . . . . . . . . . . . . . . . . . . . . . . . . . . . . . . Gen. Chen Shou-shan
Spokesman . . . . . . . . . . . . . . . . . . . . . . . . . . . . . . Maj. Gen. Wang Kao-shen
Chief, Liaison Office . . . . . . . . . . . . . . . . . . . . . . . . Col. Warren K. J. Sung

\* \* \* \* \*

## GENERAL DEFENSE DATA

**Manpower**
    Total Armed Forces . . . . . . . . . . . . . . . . . . . . . . . . . . . . . . . . . . . . . . . . 464,000
      (See Page 517)
    Population . . . . . . . . . . . . . . . . . . . . . . . . . . . . . . . . . . . . . . . . . . 18,456,000

**Spending**
    Military Expenditures . . . . . . . . . . . . . . . . . . . . . . . . . . . . . . . . . . . . . . $3.2 billion
    Gross National Product . . . . . . . . . . . . . . . . . . . . . . . . . . . . . . . . . . . $38 billion
    Military Expenditure as a Percentage of
        Gross National Product . . . . . . . . . . . . . . . . . . . . . . . . . . . . . . . . . 8.4%
    Military Expenditure as a Percentage of
        Central Government Expenditure . . . . . . . . . . . . . . . . . . . . . . . . . . . . . 47.7%

**Defense Treaties** *(See Part II for Additional Detail)*

    Bilateral:      None
    Multilateral:  None

# TANZANIA
## United Republic of Tanzania
### *Jumhuri Ya Muungano Wa Tanzania*

## Defence Establishment Command Structure and Force Organization

The President of the Republic is Commander-in-Chief of the Tanzanian People's Defence Forces (TPDF). Operational and administrative control of the military is the responsibility of the Chief of the TPDF. Zanzibar has its own constitution and, technically, its own defence forces. Operationally, however, they are fully integrated into the TPDF. The Vice President of Tanzania is the Chief Executive of Zanzibar and is the commander of defence forces on the island.

**Total armed forces:** 44,850 (Army: 43,000; Navy: 850; Air Force: 1,000). **Para-military forces:** 36,400 (Police Field Force: 1,400; Citizen's Militia: 35,000).

## HEAD OF STATE

H. E. Mwalimu Dr. Julius K. Nyerere

**OFFICE OF THE PRESIDENT**
*The State House*
*P.O. Box 9120*
*Dar-es-Salaam*
*Telephone: 23261, 23266, 21085*
*(Principal Secretary)*
*Telex: 41192 msasani*

President of the United Republic and Commander-in-Chief of the Tanzanian People's Defence Forces . . . . . Mwalimu Dr. Julius K. Nyerere
Principal Secretary to the President and Secretary to the Cabinet . . . . . . . . . . . . . . . . . . . . . . . . . . . . . T. Apiyo
Private Secretary . . . . . . . . . . . . . . . . . . . . . . . . . . . . . . . . . . . . . J. W. Butiku
Press Secretary . . . . . . . . . . . . . . . . . . . . . . . . . . . . . . . . . . . . . . H. Halahala
Minister of State . . . . . . . . . . . . . . . . . . . . . . . . . . . . . . . . . . . . . . Amir Jamal
Minister of State . . . . . . . . . . . . . . . . . . . . . . . . . . . . . . Lt. Gen. A. Twalipo

**OFFICE OF THE VICE PRESIDENT**
*P.O. Box 776*
*Zanzibar*
*Telephone: 20511*

Vice President and Chairman of the Revolutionary Council . . . . . . . . . . . . . . . . . . Aboud Jumbe Mwinyi
Principal Secretary . . . . . . . . . . . . . . . . . . . . . . . . . . . . . . . . . . . T. Machume
Minister of State, Zanzibar Affairs . . . . . . . . . . . . . . . . Aboud Talib Aboud

**OFFICE OF THE PRIME MINISTER**
*P.O. Box 980*
*Dodoma*
*Telephone: 20511*

Prime Minister . . . . . . . . . . . . . . . . . . . . . . . . . . . . . . . . . . . . . Edward Sokoine

**MINISTRY OF DEFENCE AND NATIONAL SERVICE**
*(Wizara ya Ulinzi na Jesha la Kajehga Kaifa)*
*Dar-es-Salaam*
*P.O. Box 9544*
*Telephone: 28291, 23385*
*Telex: 41051 ngome*

Minister . . . . . . . . . . . . . . . . . . . . . . . . . . Brig. Gen. Muhidine Kimario
Deputy Minister . . . . . . . . . . . . . . . . . . . . . . . . . . . . . . . . . . . Seif Bakari
Deputy Minister . . . . . . . . . . . . . . . . . . . . . . . . . . . . . . Stephen Kibona
Principal Secretary . . . . . . . . . . . . . . . . . . . . . . . . . . . . . . . . . C. Masanja

# DEFENCE FORCES

**ARMED FORCES**
**Tanzanian People's Defence Forces—TPDF**
*Dar-es-Salaam*
*P.O. Box 9000*

Chief of Defence Force ........................Lt. Gen. David Msuguri
Chief of Staff ...............................Maj. Gen. I. H. Kombe
Commander of the Popular Militia ........................Brig. Shiaro

\* \* \* \* \*

# GENERAL DEFENCE DATA

**Manpower**
Total Armed Forces...............................................44,850
(See Page 519)
Population ...............................................19,868,000

**Spending**
Military Expenditures ........................................$248 million
Gross National Product ......................................$4.952 billion
Military Expenditure as a Percentage of
Gross National Product ..........................................5.0%
Military Expenditure as a Percentage of
Central Government Expenditure ...............................16.3%

**Defence Treaties** *(See Part II for Additional Detail)*

Bilateral:    China
Mozambique
Uganda

Multilateral:    Limited Test Ban Treaty
Organization of African Unity
*Tanzania—Angola—Mozambique—Zambia*: Agreement
concerning joint defence strategy against external attack
(1976)

# THAILAND
## Kingdom of Thailand
*Prasthes Thai*

### Defense Establishment Command Structure and Force Organization

The King is Commander-in-Chief of the Royal Thai Armed Forces. Administration of the military is coordinated by the Prime Minister who is also the Minister of Defense. He is advised by the Defense Council. Operational control of the military is exercised by the Supreme Commander of the armed forces. The Royal Thai Army, organized into divisions and combat regiments, is deployed in four armies headquartered at Bangkok, Korat, Phitsanulok, and Nakhon Si Thammarat.

**Total armed forces:** 238,000 (Army: 160,000;  Navy: 35,000;  Air Force: 43,000). **Paramilitary forces:** (Provincial Police: 40,000;  Border Police: 14,000;  Volunteer Defense Corps: 52,000).

### HEAD OF STATE

H. M. King Bhumibol Adulyadej

**OFFICE OF THE KING**
*Grand Palace*
*Na Phra Lan Road*
*Bangkok 10200*
*Telephone: (2) 221-1151*

King of Thailand . . . . . . . . . . . . . . . . . . . . . . . . . H. M. Bhumibol Adulyadej
President, Privy Council . . . . . . . . . . . . . . . . . . . . Prof. Sanya Dharmasakdi
His Majesty's Principal Private
    Secretary . . . . . . . . . . . . . . . . . . . . . . . . . . Mom Luang Thawisan Ladawan

**OFFICE OF THE PRIME MINISTER**
*Government House*
*Nakhon Pathom Road*
*Bangkok 10300*
*Telephone: (2) 282 3762/3*

Prime Minister . . . . . . . . . . . . . . . . . . . . . . . . . . . Gen. Prem Tinsulanonda
Deputy Prime Minister . . . . . . . . . . . . . . . . . . . . . Boontheng Thongsawasdi
Deputy Prime Minister . . . . . . . . . . . . . . . . . . . . . . . . . Bhicnai Rattakul
Deputy Prime Minister . . . . . . . . . . . . . . . . . . . . . Adm. Sontni Boonyadnai
Deputy Prime Minister . . . . . . . . . . . . . . . . Gen. Prachuap Suntharangkun
Minister to the Office of the Prime Minister . . . . . . . . . . Meechai Ruchpan
Minister . . . . . . . . . . . . . . . . . . . . . . . . . . . . . Kamol Thongstnammachaut
Minister . . . . . . . . . . . . . . . . . . . . . . . . . . . . . . . . . . Swasdi Kamprakorb
Minister . . . . . . . . . . . . . . . . . . . . . . . . Flying Officer Suri Mahasanthana
Minister . . . . . . . . . . . . . . . . . . . . . . . . . . . . Pol Lt. Cham Manootnam
Minister . . . . . . . . . . . . . . . . . . . . . . . . . . Chaisiri Ruanguanchanqses
Minister . . . . . . . . . . . . . . . . . . . . . . . . . . . . . . . . . . Banyat Bantadtan

**MINISTRY OF DEFENSE**
*Sanamachai Road*
*Bangkok 10200*
*Telephone: (2) 222 3121/2*

Minister of Defense and Prime Minister . . . . . . . . Gen. Prem Tinsulanonda
Deputy Minister . . . . . . . . . . . . . . . . . . Air Chief Marshal Panieng Kantarat
Secretary to the Minister . . . . . . . . . . . . . . . Air Marshal Chinda Ram-indra
Under Secretary for Defense . . . . . . . . . . . . . . Gen. Thuantnong Suvanadat
Deputy Under Secretary for Defense . . . . . . . . . . Gen. Chamnaun Nilvisase
Deputy Under Secretary for Defense . . . . . . . . . Adm. Surapol Saengchote
Deputy Under Secretary for Defense . . . Air Chief Marshal Sansern Vanich

**Defense Council**

Chairman . . . . . . . . . . . . . . . . . . . . . . . . . . . . . . Gen. Prem Tinsulanonda
(Prime Minister and Minister of Defense)

Member . . . . . . . . . . . . . . . . . . . . . . . . . . . . . . . . . . . . Gen. Sithi Chiraroj
(Undersecretary for Defense)
Member . . . . . . . . . . . . . . . . . . . . . . . . . . . . . . Gen. Chao Sawatsongkhram
(Deputy Undersecretary for Defense)
Member . . . . . . . . . . . . . . . . . . . . . . . . . . . . . . . . . . Gen. Saiyd Kerdphol
(Supreme Commander of the Armed Forces)
Member . . . . . . . . . . . . . . . . . . . . . . . . . . . . . Gen. Rien Disthabanchong
(Chief of Staff of the Supreme Command and the Army)
Member . . . . . . . . . . . . . . . . . . . . . . . . . . . . . . Gen. Athit Kamlang-Ek
(Commander-in-Chief of the Army)
Member . . . . . . . . . . . . . . . . . . . . . . . . . . . . . . . Gen. Sak Boontarakul
(Deputy Commander-in-Chief of the Army)
Member . . . . . . . . . . . . . . . . . . . . . . . . . . . Adm. Somboon Chuapibul
(Commander-in-Chief of the Navy)
Member . . . . . . . . . . . . . . . . . . . . . . . . . . Adm. Prabnat Chandvirach
(Deputy Commander-in-Chief of the Navy)
Member . . . . . . . . . . . . . . . . . . . . . . . . . . . . . . Adm. Samak Saiwong
(Chief of Staff of the Navy)
Member . . . . . . . . . . . . . . . . . . . . Air Chief Marshal Prapan Dhupatemiya
(Commander-in-Chief of the Air Force)
Member . . . . . . . . . . . . . . . . Air Chief Marshal Sompal Burusratanaphan
(Deputy Commander-in-Chief of the Air Force)
Member . . . . . . . . . . . . . . . . . . . . . . . . Air Chief Marshal Arun Promdep
(Chief of Staff of the Air Force)

## DEFENSE FORCES

**ARMED FORCES**
**Royal Thai Armed Forces**
*Supreme Command Headquarters*
*Rachinee Road*
*Bangkok 10200*

*Telephone: (2) 222 1121/31*

Supreme Commander . . . . . . . . . . . . . . . . . . . . . . . . Gen. Saiyud Kerdphol
Chief of Staff . . . . . . . . . . . . . . . . . . . . . . . . . . Gen. Rien Disthabanchong
Chief of Security . . . . . . . . . . . . . . . . . . . . . . . . . . . Gen. Sermna Nakhon

**ARMY**
**Royal Thai Army**
*Sanamchai Road*
*Bangkok 10200*

*Telephone: (2) 221 2131/40*

Commander-in-Chief . . . . . . . . . . . . . . . . . . . . . . . Gen. Arthit Kamlang-Ek
Deputy Commander-in-Chief . . . . . . . . . . . . . . . . . . . . . . . . . . . . . . . . . .
Chief of Staff . . . . . . . . . . . . . . . . . . . . . . . . . . Gen. Rien Disthabanchong

**First Army**
*Bangkok*

Commander . . . . . . . . . . . . . . . . . . . . . . . . . . . . . . . Lt. Gen. Pin Thammasri

**Royal Guards**
*Bangkok*

Commander . . . . . . . . . . . . . . . . . . . . . . . . . . Maj. Gen. Arthit Kumlungaek

**Second Army**
*Korat*

Commander . . . . . . . . . . . . . . . . . . . . . . . . . . . . . Lt. Gen. Pak Meenakanit

**Third Army**
*Phitsanulok*

Commander . . . . . . . . . . . . . . . . . . . . . . . . . . . . . Lt. Gen. Prom Priwnuan

**Fourth Army**
*Nakhon Si Thammarat*

Commander . . . . . . . . . . . . . . . . . . . . . . . . . . . . . Lt. Gen. Chuan Wannarat
Commander, Harn Suk Motorcycle Team . . . . . . . . . . . . . . . . . Col. Tanapol

**Special Forces**
*Lopburi*

Commander . . . . . . . . . . . . . . . . . . . . . . . . . . . Maj. Gen. Asnee Smuttrasen

**Army Field Forces**

Commander . . . . . . . . . . . . . . . . . . . . . . . Lt. Gen. Wisitniporn Wongtnai

**Chulachomklao Royal Military**
**Academy**

Commander ..................... Maj. Gen. Yuthasak Klongtruetrok

**NAVY**
**Royal Thai Navy**
*Aroon-Amarin Road*
*Bangkok 10600*

*Telephone:   (2) 446 1180*
*Telex:   84142 navdock th (Dock Yard)*

Commander-in-Chief ....................... Adm. Somboon Chuapibul
Commander-in-Chief of the Fleet ........ Adm. Prasert Taenkam Prabhat
Deputy Commander-in-Chief ..................... Adm. Chandvirach
Chief of Staff ................................ Adm. Samak Saiwong
Director, Logistics .................... Rear Adm. Yongyudt Supakalin
Director, Operations ................. Rear Adm. Komut Kamolanavin
Director, Ordnance .................... Rear Adm. Samarng Kresopon
Chief, Education ...................... Vice Adm. Chua Ketustiarn
Commander, Royal Thai
    Marines ................... Vice Adm. Yutnaya Cherdboonmuango
Commander, Sattahip Naval Base ........ Vice Adm. Tarit Bungaratapan
Director, Naval Dockyard ......... Vice Adm. Ura Snidvangs na Ayudhya
Commandant, Naval Officers College ......... Vice Adm. Supa Gajasenj

**AIR FORCE**
**Thoyal Thai Air Force**
*Vibhavadi Road*
*Bangkhen, Don Muang*
*Bangkok 10210*

*Telephone:   (2) 523 6151*
*Telex:   84 288*

Commander-in-Chief ........... Air Chief Marshal Prapan Dhupatemiya
Deputy Commander-in-Chief ......................................
Chief of Staff .............. Air Chief Marshal Sompol Burusratanaphan

**PROVINCIAL POLICE**
*Bangkok*

Commissioner........................... Lt. Gen. Amphon Chitpatima

\* \* \* \* \*

## GENERAL DEFENSE DATA

**Manpower**
   Total Armed Forces .............................................. 238,000
     (See Page 521)
   Population .................................................. 49,823,000

**Spending**
   Military Expenditures ......................................... $1 billion
   Gross National Product ....................................... $31 billion
   Military Expenditure as a Percentage of
     Gross National Product ........................................ 3.2%
   Military Expenditure as a Percentage of
     Central Government Expenditure ............................... 16.9%

**Defense Treaties** *(See Part II for Additional Detail)*

    Bilateral:    United States

    Multilateral:    Biological Weapons Convention
                Limited Test Ban Treaty
                South-East Asia Collective Defense Treaty
                Treaty on the Non-Proliferation of Nuclear Weapons

# TOGO
## Republic of Togo
### *République Togolaise*

## Defense Establishment Command Structure and Force Organization

The President is Commander-in-Chief and Minister of National Defense. He controls all aspects of the national defense and the Togolaise Armed Forces. The Army Staff functions as a joint staff of the entire military organization. French officers serve the military in an advisory capacity.

**Total armed forces:** 3,600 (Army: 3,400; Navy: 100; Air Force: 100). **Para-military forces:** 1,500.

## HEAD OF STATE

H. E. Général d'Armée Gnassingbé Eyadéma

**OFFICE OF THE PRESIDENT**
*Palais Presidentiel*
*Avenue de la Marina*
*Lomé*

*Telephone:  21 31 85*
*Telex:  5201 prestigo*

President of the Republic, Minister
of National Defense and
Commander-in-Chief . . . . . . . . . . . . Gén. d'Armée Gnassingbé Eyedéma

**MINISTRY OF NATIONAL DEFENSE**
*Lomé*

*Telephone:  21 28 91, 21 28 92, 21 35 23*
*Telex:  5321 mindef to*

Minister of National Defense
and President of the
Republic . . . . . . . . . . . . . . . . . . . . . . Gen. d'Armée Gnassingbé Eyedéma
Senior Advisor to the President . . . . . . . . . . . . . . . . . . . Col. Patrick Pacaud
Director of Services . . . . . . . . . . . . . . Lt. Col. Cartier (French Army Advisor)
Director of Veterans Affairs . . . . . . . . . . . . . . . . . . . . Col. Bawabadi Chango

## DEFENSE FORCES

**ARMED FORCES**
**Toglaise Armed Forces**
*(Forces Armées Togolaises)*
*Route d'Atakpame*
*Agoenyive*

*Telephone:  21 28 91, 21 28 92, 21 35 23*
*Telex:  5201 prestigo*

Chief of Staff and
Second-in-Command . . . . . . . . . . . . . . . . . . Lt. Col. Amégée Mawulikplimi
Deputy Chief of Staff . . . . . . . . . . . . . . . . . . . . . . . . . . . . . Col. Yao Amégée
Chief, G-1 . . . . . . . . . . . . . . . . . . . . . . . . . . . . . . . . . . . . . . . Maj. Kossi Tepe
Deputy Chief, G-1 . . . . . . . . . . . . . . . . . . . . . . . . . . . . . . . . . 1st Lt. Djelema
Chief, G-2 . . . . . . . . . . . . . . . . . . . . . . . . . . . . . . . . . . . . . Capt. Mama Douti
Deputy Chief, G-2 (Advisor) . . . . . . . . . . . . . . . . . . . . . . . . . . . . Capt. Marrot
(French Officer)
Chief, G-3 . . . . . . . . . . . . . . . . . . . . . . . . . . . . . . . . . . . . . . . Capt. Ribeyron
(French Officer)
Deputy Chief, G-3 . . . . . . . . . . . . . . . . . . . . . . . . . . . . . . Capt. Late Lawson
Chief, G-4 . . . . . . . . . . . . . . . . . . . . . . . . . . . . . . . . . . . . . Capt. Komlan Fiaty
Deputy Chief, G-4 (Advisor) . . . . . . . . . . . . . . . . . . . . . Adjt. Chef Richard
(French Officer)
Inspector General . . . . . . . . . . . . . . . . . . . . . . . . . . . . . . . Col. Koffi Kongo
Commander, Presidential Guard . . . . . . . . . . . . . . . . . . . . . . . . Capt. Tchapo

Commander, Parachute
Commando Regiment .........................Col. Bonton Bassabi

**NAVY**
*(Marine Nationale Togolaise)*
*EM/FAT, B.P. 938*
*Base Navale*
*Lomé Port*

Commander...................................Capt. Christian Matton
(French Naval Officer)
Commander, Patrol Boat *Kara* ...............Lt. Adegnon Kodjo Fogan
Commander, Patrol Boat *Mono* .......................Lt. Akollor Efoué

**AIR FORCE**
*(Escadrille Nationale)*
*c/o Ministry of National Defense*
*Lomé*

*Telephone:  21 29 79, 21 31 82, 21 33 65*

Commander .....................................Lt. Cdt. Florent
(French Air Force Officer)
Commander, Niamtougou
Air Base.........................Lt. Cdt. Jacques Berthonneau
(French Air Force Officer)
Commander, Tokoin Air Base ...........................Cdt. Popular
(French Air Force Officer)

**CONSTABULARY**
*(Gendarmerie Nationale)*
*Lomé*

*Telephone:  21 32 40*

Commander..................................Maj. Agosseye Assih

\* \* \* \* \*

# GENERAL DEFENSE DATA

**Manpower**
Total Armed Forces...............................................3,600
(See Page 525)
Population ...................................................2,783,000

**Spending**
Military Expenditures ..........................................$25 million
Gross National Product .......................................$1.048 billion
Military Expenditure as a Percentage of
Gross National Product ...........................................2.4%
Military Expenditure as a Percentage of
Central Government Expenditure ..................................7.0%

**Defense Treaties** *(See Part II for Additional Detail)*

Bilateral:    France
People's Democratic Republic of Korea
Libya
United States

Multilateral:    Biological Weapons Convention
Environmental Modification Convention
Limited Test Ban Treaty
Organization of African Unity
Treaty on the Control of Arms on the Seabed
Treaty on the Non-Proliferation of Nuclear Weapons

**Military Rank Comparisons**
See Appendix A.

# TONGA
## Kingdom of Tonga
*Pule'anga Fakatu'i 'o Tonga*

### Defense Establishment Command Structure and Force Organization

The King is Commander-in-Chief of the armed forces and exercises his authority through the Minister of Defense.

**Total armed forces:** Approximately 500. **Para-military forces:** 50 (Royal Guards).

## THE SOVEREIGN

H. M. King Taufa'ahau Tupou IV, G.C.M.G., G.C.V.O., K.B.E.

**OFFICE OF THE KING**
*P.O. Box 6*
*Nuku'alofa*
*Telephone: 21-000*

King of Tonga and
   Commander-in-Chief . . . . . . . . . . . . . . . . . . H. M. Taufa'ahau Tupou IV,
                            G.C.M.G., G.C.V.O., K.B.E.
Private Secretary . . . . . . . . . . . . . . . . . . . . . . . . . . . . F. Maketi Tongilava
Master of the Household . . . . . . . . . . . . . . . . . . . . . . . . . . A. Fielakepa

**OFFICE OF THE PRIME MINISTER**
*P.O. Box 62*
*Nuku'alofa*
*Telephone: 21-300*
*Telex: 66235 minofa ts*

Prime Minister . . . . . . . . . . . . . . . . . . H. R. H. Prince Fatafehi Tu'ipelehake
Deputy Prime Minister . . . . . . . . . . . . . . . . . . . . . . . . . Baron Fuita C.B.E.
Secretary to the Government . . . . . . . . . . . . . . . . . . . . . . . . . Dan Tufui

**MINISTRY OF DEFENSE**
*P.O. Box 72*
*Nuku'alofa*
*Telephone: 21-300/301*
*Telex: 66235 minofa ts*

Minister of Defense . . . . . . . . . . . . . . . . . . H. R. H. Crown Prince Tupouto'a

## DEFENSE FORCES

**ARMED FORCES**
**Tonga Defense Services**
*Headquarters*
*P.O. Box 72*
*Nuku'alofa*
*Telephone: 21-099*
*Telex: 66235 minofa ts*

Chief of Staff . . . . . . . . . . . . . . . . . . . . . . . . . . . . Maj. Fetu'utolo Tupou
Commanding Officer, Land Force . . . . . . . . . . . . . . . . . . . . Capt. Finau Tolu
Commanding Officer,
   Tonga Royal Guard . . . . . . . . . . . . . . . . . . . . . . . Lt. 'Etuini Faleara
Commanding Officer,
   Royal Tongan Marines . . . . . . . . . . . . . . . . Lt. Tevita Tauaika 'Uta'atu
Commanding Officer, Technical
   Logistics Support Group . . . . . . . . . . . . . . . . . . . . . . . Lt. Sione Petelo
Commanding Officer, Tonga
   Defense Services Training Depot . . . . . . . . . . Lt. Tevita Tauaiki 'Uta'atu

\* \* \* \* \*

## GENERAL DEFENSE DATA

**Manpower**
  Total Armed Forces ...............................................500
    (See Page 527)
  Population ...................................................102,000

**Spending**
  Military Expenditures ................................................
  Gross National Product ......................................$34.2 million
  Military Expenditure as a Percentage of
    Gross National Product .............................................
  Military Expenditure as a Percentage of
    Central Government Expenditure .....................................

**Defense Treaties** *(See Part II for Additional Detail)*

  Bilateral:     None

  Multilateral:  Biological Weapons Convention
                 Limited Test Ban Treaty
                 Treaty on the Non-Proliferation of Nuclear Weapons

# TRINIDAD AND TOBAGO
## Republic of Trinidad and Tobago

### Defence Establishment Command Structure and Force Organization

The President is Commander-in-Chief of the armed forces. Operational control is vested with the Prime Minister, and administrative matters are the responsibility of the Minister of National Security.

**Total armed forces:** 1,950 (Army: 1,400; Coast Guard: 500; Air Wing: 50).

## HEAD OF STATE

H. E. Ellis Emmanuel Innocent Clarke, T.C.

**OFFICE OF THE PRESIDENT**
*Circular Road*
*St. Ann's*
*Port-au-Spain*
*Telephone: 624-2161*

President of the Republic
   and Commander-in-Chief ....... Ellis Emmanuel Innocent Clarke, T.C.
Aide-de-Camp ................................... Lt. Col. I. E. Faustin

**MINISTRY OF THE PRIME MINISTER**
*Whitehall*
*Maraval Road*
*Port-au-Spain*
*Telephone: 622-3141*
*Telex: 3254*

Prime Minister and Minister
   of Finance............................. George M. Chambers, M.P.
Permanent Secretary to
   Prime Minister .......................................... (Vacant)
Permanent Secretary in the
   Office of the Prime Minister ............................. (Vacant)

**MINISTRY OF NATIONAL SECURITY**
*Government Building*
*Knox Street*
*Port-of-Spain*
*Telephone: 623-2441, 623-2461, 623-2466*

Minister .............................. John Stanley Donaldson, M.P.
Permanent Secretary ................................. Leo Seebaran
Chief Executive Officer,
   National Security Officer ........................ Louis J. Rodriquez

## DEFENCE FORCES

**ARMED FORCES**
**Trinidad and Tobago Defence Force**
*Defence Force Headquarters*
*Chaguaramas*
*Telephone: 625-1021*

Commander ............................. Cdr. Mervyn O. Williams
Deputy Commander ..................... Col. Joseph Theodore (acting
   Cdr. in absence of Cdr. Williams)

**ARMY**
**Trinidad and Tobago Regiment**
*Teteron Barracks*
*Chaguaramas*
*Telephone: 625-2211*

Commander ................................. Col. Joseph Theodore

529

**NAVY**
**Trinidad and Tobago Coast Guard**
*Stauble's Bay*
*Chaguaramas*
*Telephone:  625-4939*

Commander . . . . . . . . . . . . . . . . . . . . . . . . . . . . . . . . .Cdr. Jack E. Williams
Second-in-Command . . . . . . . . . . . . . . . . . . . . . . . .Lt. Cdr. Richard Kelshall

**AIR FORCE**
**Air Wing**
*Heliport Hangar*
*Chaguaramas*
*Telephone:  625-1021, ext. 242*

Commander . . . . . . . . . . . . . . . . . . . . . . . . . . . . . . . . . . . . . . . . . .Philip Rugg

**TRINIDAD AND TOBAGO**
   **CADET FORCE**
*General Office*
   *3rd Floor*
*76 Duke*
*Telephone:  623-4995*

Commander. . . . . . . . . . . . . . . . . . . . . . . . . . . . . . . . . . . . . . .Cdt. Hugh Walke
Second in Command . . . . . . . . . . . . . . . . . . . . . . . . . . . . . . . . . .Neil Alexis

\* \* \* \* \*

# GENERAL DEFENCE DATA

**Manpower**
  Total Armed Forces. . . . . . . . . . . . . . . . . . . . . . . . . . . . . . . . . . .1,950
    (See Page 529)
  Population . . . . . . . . . . . . . . . . . . . . . . . . . . . . . . . . . . . . . . . . .1,203,000

**Spending**
  Military Expenditures . . . . . . . . . . . . . . . . . . . . . . . . . . . . . . . . . .$16 million
  Gross National Product . . . . . . . . . . . . . . . . . . . . . . . . . . . . . . . .$5.103 billion
  Military Expenditure as a Percentage of
    Gross National Product . . . . . . . . . . . . . . . . . . . . . . . . . . . . . . . .0.3%
  Military Expenditure as a Percentage of
    Central Government Expenditure . . . . . . . . . . . . . . . . . . . . . . . .0.9%

**Defence Treaties** *(See Part II for Additional Detail)*

  Bilateral:    United States

  Multilateral:   Inter-American Treaty for Reciprocal Assistance
          Treaty for the Prohibition of Nuclear Weapons in Latin
            America
          Treaty on the Non-Proliferation of Nuclear Weapons

# TUNISIA
## Republic of Tunisia
### al-Jumhuriyah al-Tunisiyah


## Defense Establishment Command Structure and Force Organization

The President is Commander-in-Chief of the armed forces of Tunisia. His authority is exercised through the Minister of Defense, who has responsibility for administrative, personnel and logistical affairs, and is in operational command of the armed forces. The Inspector-General is responsible for military discipline and efficiency. The Ministry of Interior controls internal security through the National Guard and National Police.

**Total armed forces:** 28,600 (Army: 24,000;   Navy: 2,600;   Air Force: 2,000). **Paramilitary forces:** 8,500 (Gendarmerie: 5,000;   National Guard: 3,500).


## HEAD OF STATE

H. E. The President-for-Life Habib Bourguiba


**OFFICE OF THE PRESIDENT FOR-LIFE**
*Palais Présidential*
*Tunis and Carthage*

Telephone: 260 348 (Tunis),
   275 911 (Carthage)

President-for-Life ..................................Habib Bourguiba
Special Counselor .............................Habib Bourguiba, Jr.
Special Secretary .......................................Allala Laouiti
Director, Protocol................................Abdul Majid Karoui


**OFFICE OF THE PRIME MINISTER**
*Place du Gouvernement*
*Tunis*

*Telephone: 260 322*
*Telex: 13566 otd*
      *12530 pmcab tn*
      *(Premier Ministère Cabinet)*

Prime Minister......................................Mohamed Mzali
Minister to the Prime Minister for the
   Destourian Socialist Party............................Mongi Kooli
Minister for Administrative Reform and
   Public Service .......................................Mezri Chekir


**MINISTRY OF NATIONAL DEFENSE**
*Boulevard Bab Menara*
*Tunis*

*Telephone: 260 244/5, 260 088, 262 088,*
   *262 011*
*Telex: 12580 defnat tn*
      *13570 defnat tn*

Minister .........................................Slaheddine Baly


**MINISTRY OF INTERIOR**
*Avenue Habib Bourguiba*
*Tunis*

*Telephone: 243 000*
*Telex: 13662 dsaf tn*

Minister .............................................Driss Guiga

# DEFENSE FORCES

**ARMED FORCES**
*c/o Ministry of National Defense*
*Boulevard Bab Menara*
*Tunis*

*Telephone: 260 244/5, 260 088, 262 088*
*Telex: 12580 defnat tn*

Chief of General Staff . . . . . . . . . . . . . . . Gen. de Div. Abdelhamid Escheikh
Inspector General, Armed Forces . . . . . . . . . Gen. de Div. Salah Makadden
Director, Military Security . . . . . . . . . . . . . Gen. de Div. Boubakar Balma
Director, Military Health . . . . . . . . . . . . . . . . . Gen.-Medecin Ben Moussas

**ARMY**
**Tunisian National Army**
*c/o Ministry of National Defense*
*Boulevard Bab Menara*
*Tunis*

*Telephone: 260 244/5, 260 088, 262 088*
*Telex: 12580 defnat tn*

Chief of Staff . . . . . . . . . . . . . . . . . . . . . . . . . . . . Gen. de Brig. Mohamed
Commander, Para Comando Brigade . . . . . . . . . . . Col. Hamid El Ferchichi

**NAVY**
*c/o Ministry of National Defense*
*Boulevard Bab Menara*
*Tunis*

*Telephone: 260 244/5, 260 088, 262 088*
*Telex: 12580 defnat tn*

Chief of Staff . . . . . . . . . . . . . . . . . . . . . . . . . . . . . . . . . Capt. Habib Fedhila

**AIR FORCE**
*c/o Ministry of National Defense*
*Boulevard Bab Menara*
*Tunis*

*Telephone: 260 244/5, 260 088, 262 088*
*Telex: 12580 defnat tn*

Chief of Staff . . . . . . . . . . . . . . . . . . . . . . . . . . . . . . Col. Touhami Machta
Chief, Training and Operations . . . . . . . . . . Lt. Col. Ridha Ben Sadok Attar

**NATIONAL GUARD**
*(Gendarmerie)*
*Tunis*

Director . . . . . . . . . . . . . . . . . . . . . . . . . . . . . . . . . . . . . . . Ameur Gheidra

\* \* \* \* \*

# GENERAL DEFENSE DATA

**Manpower**
 Total Armed Forces . . . . . . . . . . . . . . . . . . . . . . . . . . . . . . . . . . . . 28,600
  (See Page 531)
 Population . . . . . . . . . . . . . . . . . . . . . . . . . . . . . . . . . . . . . . . . . 6,842,000

**Spending**
 Military Expenditures . . . . . . . . . . . . . . . . . . . . . . . . . . . . . . . . $116 million
 Gross National Product . . . . . . . . . . . . . . . . . . . . . . . . . . . . . . . . $8.4 billion
 Military Expenditure as a Percentage of
  Gross National Product . . . . . . . . . . . . . . . . . . . . . . . . . . . . . . . . 1.4%
 Military Expenditure as a Percentage of
  Central Government Expenditure . . . . . . . . . . . . . . . . . . . . . . . . . 4.5%

**Defense Treaties** (*See Part II for Additional Detail*)

Bilateral:    France
United States

Multilateral:    Biological Weapons Convention
Environmental Weapons Convention
League of Arab States
Limited Test Ban Treaty
Organization of African Unity
Treaty on the Control of Arms on the Seabed
Treaty on the Non-Proliferation of Nuclear Weapons

**Military Rank Comparisons**
See Appendix A.

# TURKEY
## Republic of Turkey
### *Türkiye Cumhuriyeti*

## Defense Establishment Command Structure and Force Organization

The President exercises his authority as Commander-in-Chief of the armed forces through the House of Representatives and the Prime Minister. He is advised by the National Security Council. Administrative control of the military is exercised by the Minister of Defense. Operational control of the armed forces is the responsibility of the General Staff. There are no command links between the Ministry of Defense and the General Staff.

**Total armed forces:** 569,000 (Army: 470,000; Navy: 46,000; Air Force: 53,000). **Gendarmerie:** 120,000.

## HEAD OF STATE

H. E. Gen. Kenan Evren

**OFFICE OF THE PRESIDENT**
*Cumhurbaş Kanliği*
*Ankara*
Telephone: *(41) 27 13 38*
Telex: *42303 köşk tr*

President and Commander-in-Chief ............Gen. (Ret.) Kenan Evren

**National Security Council**
*(Millî Güvenlik Konseyi)*
*Türkiye Büyük Millet Meclisi*
*Ankara*
Telephone: *(41) 17 51 00*

Chairman .................................Gen. (Ret.) Kenan Evren
Member ...................................Gen. Nurettin Ersin
(Chief of the General Staff)
Member....................................Gen. Necdet Üruğ
(Chief of the Army)
Member ...................................Adm. Nejat Tümer
(Chief of the Navy)
Member ...................................Gen. Tahsin Şahinkaya
(Chief of the Air Force)
Member ...................................Gen. Sedat Celasun
(Chief of the Gendarmerie)
Secretary General .........................Gen. Necip Torumtay

**OFFICE OF THE PRIME MINISTER**
*Basbakanlik*
*Ankara*
Telephone: *(41) 18 57 76*

Prime Minister ...........................Adm. (Ret.) Büllend Ulusu
Deputy Prime Minister and State Minister ..............Zeyyat Baykara
State Minister.............................Mehmet Nimet Özdaş
State Minister ............................Mehmet Özgünes
State Minister ............................Ilhan Öztrak
State Minister ............................Sermet R. Pasin

**MINISTRY OF NATIONAL DEFENSE**
*(Milli Savunma Bakanliği)*
*Ankara*
Telephone: *(41) 18 64 19*

Minister .................................Ümit Halûk Bayülken
Undersecretary............................Gen. Ragip Uluğbay

# DEFENSE FORCES

**ARMED FORCES**
**Turkish General Staff**
*(Genelkurmay Başkanliği)*
*Ankara*

*Telephone:  (41) 18 21 00*
  *(General Staff Switchboard)*

| | |
|---|---|
| Chief of the General Staff | Gen. Nurettin Ersin |
| Deputy Chief | Gen. Necdet Öztorun |
| Deputy Chief | Brig. Gen. Erol Özalp |

**ARMY**
**Turkish Land Forces**
*(Kara Kuvvetleri Komutanliği)*
*Ankara*

*Telephone:  (41) 17 10 80, 17 53 20*

| | |
|---|---|
| Commander | Gen. Necdet Üruğ |
| Chief of Staff | Lt. Gen. Kemal Yamak |

    **First Army**
    *(European Turkey)*
    *Headquarters Istanbul*

| | |
|---|---|
| Commander | Gen. Haydar Saltik |
| Chief of Staff | Maj. Gen. Ekrem Dinc |

    **Second Army**
    *(Central and Southeastern Anatolia)*
    *Headquarters Malatya*

| | |
|---|---|
| Commander | Gen. Mehmet Buyruk |
| Chief of Staff | Maj. Gen. Dursun Pekel |

    **Third Army**
    *(Eastern Anatolia)*
    *Headquarters Erzincan*

| | |
|---|---|
| Commander | Gen. Celal Bulutlar |
| Chief of Staff | Maj. Gen. Kikmet Bayar |

    **Aegean Army**
    *Headquarters Izmir*

| | |
|---|---|
| Commander | Gen. M. Süreyya Yüksel |
| Chief of Staff | Maj. Gen. Arif Eryilmaz |

**NAVY**
**Turkish Naval Forces**
*(Türk Deniz Kuvvetleri Komutanliği)*
*Ankara*

*Telephone:  (41) 25 64 20*
*Telex:   0607 43492 Dz. Tk. Tr.*

| | |
|---|---|
| Commander | Adm. Nejat Tümer |
| Chief of Staff | Vice Adm. Irfan Tinaz |

    **Turkish Fleet**
    *Goluk Naval Base*

| | |
|---|---|
| Commander | Adm. Zahit Atakan |
| Chief of Staff | Rear Adm. Atilla Erkan |

    **Sea Area South**
    *Izmir*

| | |
|---|---|
| Commander | Vice Adm. Emin Göksan |

    **Sea Area North**
    *Istanbul*

| | |
|---|---|
| Commander | Vice Adm. Orhan Karabulut |

    **Naval Training Command**

| | |
|---|---|
| Commander | Rear Adm. Cahit Parpucu |

**AIR FORCE**
**Turkish Air Force**
*(Hava Kuvvetleri Komutanliği)*
*Ankara*

*Telephone:  (41) 19 90 90*

| | |
|---|---|
| Commander | Gen. Tahsin Şahinkaya |
| Deputy Commander | Gen. Halil Özer |
| Chief of Staff | Lt. Gen. Cemil Çuha |

    **First Tactical Air Force**
    *Eskeşehir*

| | |
|---|---|
| Commander | Lt. Gen. Yusuf Özer |

**Second Tactical Air Force**
*Diyarbekir*

Commander..................................Lt. Gen. Hikmet Kesim

**GENDARMERIE**
**Constabulary**
*(Jandarma Genel Komutangliği)*
*Ankara*

Commander....................................Gen. Sedat Celasun
Deputy Commander ..........................Lt. Gen. Mehmet Kiral

*Telephone: (41) 17 90 45, 17 29 70*
*Telex: 43235 jgnk, 42021 jgnk*

\* \* \* \* \*

# GENERAL DEFENSE DATA

**Manpower**
Total Armed Forces.............................................569,000
　　(See Page 535)
Population ..............................................48,105,000

**Spending**
Military Expenditures.........................................$3.5 billion
Gross National Product.......................................$78.4 billion
Military Expenditure as a Percentage of
　　Gross National Product ...........................................4.5%
Military Expenditure as a Percentage of
　　Central Government Expenditure ...............................19.1%

**Defense Treaties** *(See Part II for Additional Detail)*

Bilateral:　　Pakistan
　　　　　　United States

Multilateral:　Biological Weapons Convention
　　　　　　Limited Test Ban Treaty
　　　　　　North Atlantic Treaty Organization
　　　　　　Treaty of Establishment
　　　　　　Treaty on the Control of Arms on the Seabed
　　　　　　Treaty on the Non-Proliferation of Nuclear Weapons

# TUVALU

## Defence Establishment Command Structure and Force Organization

Tuvalu maintains no military forces and has no formal defence structure.

## HEAD OF STATE

H. M. Queen Elizabeth II

## GOVERNOR-GENERAL

H. E. Sir Fiatau Penitala Teo, G.C.M.G., I.S.O., M.B.E.

**OFFICE OF THE GOVERNOR-GENERAL**
*Funafuti Atoll*

Governor-General . . . . . . . . . . . . . . . . . . . . . . . . . . . . Sir Fiatau Penitala Teo, G.C.M.G., I.S.O., M.B.E.
Secretary Supernumerary . . . . . . . . . . . . . . . . . . . Angus McDonald, O.B.E.

**OFFICE OF THE PRIME MINISTER**
*Funafuti Atoll*

Prime Minister and Minister of Foreign Affairs . . . . . . . . Dr. Tomasi Puapua
Deputy Prime Minister and Minister of Finance . . . . . . . . . . . . Henry Naisali

**POLICE**
*Funafuti Atoll*

Chief . . . . . . . . . . . . . . . . . . . . . . . . . . . . . . . . . . . . . . . . . . . . . . . . . Saloa Tavia

\* \* \* \* \*

## GENERAL DEFENCE DATA

**Manpower**
Total Armed Forces . . . . . . . . . . . . . . . . . . . . . . . . . . . . . . . . . . . . . . . . . . .
Population . . . . . . . . . . . . . . . . . . . . . . . . . . . . . . . . . . . . . . . . . . . . . 9,000

**Spending**
Military Expenditures . . . . . . . . . . . . . . . . . . . . . . . . . . . . . . . . . . . . . . . . .
Gross National Product . . . . . . . . . . . . . . . . . . . . . . . . . . . . . . . . . . . . $4 million
Military Expenditure as a Percentage of
Gross National Product . . . . . . . . . . . . . . . . . . . . . . . . . . . . . . . . . . . . . . .
Military Expenditure as a Percentage of
Central Government Expenditure . . . . . . . . . . . . . . . . . . . . . . . . . . . . . . . . .

**Defence Treaties** *(See Part II for Additional Detail)*

Bilateral:     None

Multilateral:  Treaty on the Non-Proliferation of Nuclear Weapons

# UGANDA
## Republic of Uganda

### Defence Establishment Command Structure and Force Organization

The President is Commander-in-Chief of the armed forces. Administration is the responsibility of the Minister of Defence.

**Total armed forces:** 10,000 (Army: 9,000; Air Force: 1,000). **Para-military forces:** 10,500 (Police "Special Force": 500; People's Militia: 10,000).

### HEAD OF STATE

H. E. The Hon. Dr. Apollo Milton Obote

**OFFICE OF THE PRESIDENT**
*Parliamentary Buildings*
*Box 7168*
*Kampala*
*Telephone: 54881*

President of the Republic, Minister of Foreign Affairs, Minister of Finance, and Commander-in-Chief . . . . . . . . . . . . . . . . . . Dr. Apollo Milton Obote
Minister Without Portfolio . . . . . . . . . . . . . . . . . . . . . . . . . . . . Shafiq Arain
Minister of State . . . . . . . . . . . . . . . . . . . . . . . . . . . . . . . . . Chris Rwakasisi
Ambassador Extraordinary and Plenipotentiary . . . . . . . . . . . . . . . . . . . . . . . Sheikh Ali Senyonga

**OFFICE OF THE VICE PRESIDENT**
*Parliamentary Buildings*
*Box 3798*
*Kampala*
*Telephone: 58041*

Vice President and Minister of Defence . . . . . . . . . . . . . . . . Paulo Muwanga
Minister of State for Defence . . . . . . . . . . . . . . . . . . . . . . . . Peter A. I. Otai

**OFFICE OF THE PRIME MINISTER AND LEADER OF GOVERNMENT BUSINESS**
*Conference Centre*
*Box 3496*
*Kampala*
*Telephone: 59758*

Prime Minister and Leader of Government Business . . . . . . . . . . . . . . . . . . . . . . . . . . . . . Otema Allimade
Minister of State . . . . . . . . . . . . . . . . . . . . . . . . . . . . . Edward Rurangaranga

**MINISTRY OF DEFENCE**
*Republic House*
*Box 3798*
*Kampala*
*Telephone: 70331*
*Telex: 61221/01203 defence*

Minister of Defence and Vice President . . . . . . . . . . . . . . . . Paulo Muwanga
Minister of State . . . . . . . . . . . . . . . . . . . . . . . . . . . . . . . . . Peter A. I. Otai
Secretary of Defence . . . . . . . . . . . . . . . . . . . . . . . . . . . . . . . N. O. Obore
Under Secretary of Defence . . . . . . . . . . . . . . . . . . . . . . . S. Kyamuhangire
Principal Assistant Secretary . . . . . . . . . . . . . . . . . . . . . . . C. B. W. Wagooli
Senior Assistant Secretary . . . . . . . . . . . . . . . . . . . . Mwesigwa Jovie Basheija
Assistant Secretary . . . . . . . . . . . . . . . . . . . . . . . . . . . . . . . . S. Byakutaga
Assistant Secretary . . . . . . . . . . . . . . . . . . . . . . . . . . . . . . . . . . . . . Banya
Assistant Secretary . . . . . . . . . . . . . . . . . . . . . . . . . . . . . . . . . . . . Isabirye
Principal Accountant . . . . . . . . . . . . . . . . . . . . . . . . . . . . . . . J. S. Engoru
Chief Executive Officer (A) . . . . . . . . . . . . . . . . . . . . . . . . . . . . (Vacant)
Chief Executive Officer (E) . . . . . . . . . . . . . . . . . . . . . . . . . . M. E. Otwao
Chief Engineer . . . . . . . . . . . . . . . . . . . . . . . . . . . . . . . . . . . . (Vacant)
Chief Architect . . . . . . . . . . . . . . . . . . . . . . . . . . . . . . . . . . . . (Vacant)

# DEFENCE FORCES

**ARMED FORCES**
**Uganda Defence Forces**
*National Liberation Army*
*General Headquarters*
*Republic House—Mengo*
*Box 7069*
*Kampala*
*Telephone:   70331-9*

Chief of Defence Forces . . . . . . . . . . . . . . . . . . . . . . . . . . Lt. Gen. Tito Okello
Chief of Staff . . . . . . . . . . . . . . . . . . . . . . . . . . . . . . . . Maj. Gen. Oyite-Ojok

\* \* \* \* \*

# GENERAL DEFENCE DATA

**Manpower**
Total Armed Forces . . . . . . . . . . . . . . . . . . . . . . . . . . . . . . . . . . . . . . . . 10,000
  (See Page 541)
Population  . . . . . . . . . . . . . . . . . . . . . . . . . . . . . . . . . . . . . . . . 13,651,000

**Spending**
Military Expenditures . . . . . . . . . . . . . . . . . . . . . . . . . . . . . . . . . . $176 million
Gross National Product . . . . . . . . . . . . . . . . . . . . . . . . . . . . . . . $9.531 billion
Military Expenditure as a Percentage of
  Gross National Product  . . . . . . . . . . . . . . . . . . . . . . . . . . . . . . . 1.8%
Military Expenditure as a Percentage of
  Central Government Expenditure  . . . . . . . . . . . . . . . . . . . . . . . . . . . 20.6%

**Defence Treaties** *(See Part II for Additional Detail)*

Bilateral:      Soviet Union
                Sudan
                Tanzania

Multilateral:   Limited Test Ban Treaty
                Organization of African Unity
                Treaty on the Non-Proliferation of Nuclear Weapons

# UNION OF SOVIET SOCIALIST REPUBLICS
## (Soviet Union)
### *Soyuz Sovyetskikh Sotsialisticheskikh Respublic*

## Defense Establishment Command Structure and Force Organization

Under the terms of the 1977 Constitution, the Supreme Soviet is the highest body of state authority of the U.S.S.R. The Presidium has responsibility for appointing and dismissing the high command of the Armed Forces, ordering mobilization, and proclaiming a state of war, and it functions as a collective Head of State.

The Council of Defense, selected by the Presidium, formulates and directs military policies and plans. The Council is Chaired by the General Secretary of the Communist Party of the Soviet Union (CPSU), who may be considered de facto Commander-in-Chief. Other members include the Minister of Defense, the Minister of Internal Affairs (MVD), Chairman of the Committee for State Security (KGB), and others from the CPSU Central Committee.

The Council of Ministers, which is also selected by the Presidium, coordinates the activities of the executive branch. It is charged with implementing measures to defend the state, and with exercising "general direction of the development of the Armed Forces of the U.S.S.R."

Soviet military forces are administered by three executive departments. The main services and supporting branches are controlled by the Ministry of Defense; Border Troops are under the jurisdiction of the KGB; and Internal Troops are part of the MVD.

The Minister of Defense has operational control of the five major force components (Ground, Navy, Air, Air Defense, and Strategic Rocket Forces), which are deployed in military districts, air defense districts, naval fleets, and groups of forces. The Minister of Defense also chairs the Main Military Council, which carries out the directives of the Council of Defense. The General Staff acts as executive agent for the Main Military Council. The Chief of the General Staff implements all orders given by the Minister of Defense and coordinates the various directorates (i.e., intelligence, operations, communications, mobilization). The Main Political Directorate, a department of the Central Committee which is represented on the General Staff, is responsible for insuring the political reliability of the armed forces.

Ground Forces, divided into tank, motorized rifle, and rocket/artillery troops, are deployed in 16 military districts (within the USSR) and four group forces (headquartered in Poland, Czechoslovakia, Hungary, and East Germany). A commander of a military district or group of forces is responsible for the readiness of, and has operational control over, ground forces and Frontal Aviation aircraft within his area, and reports directly to the Chief of the General Staff.

The Commander-in-Chief of the Soviet Navy has administrative and operational control over the four naval fleets and Caspian Sea Flotilla. The forces under his authority include ballistic missile submarines, surface combatants, naval infantry, coastal defenses, bases, and naval aircraft within maritime regions.

Soviet Air Forces are organized into Long-Range Aviation, Military Transport Aviation, and Frontal Aviation components. Frontal Aviation tactical air armies are divided between military districts and groups of forces, and hence come under the direction of the local field commander, and through him, the Chief of the General Staff. Military Transport Aviation, as part of the strategic reserve, is directly subordinate to the Minister of Defense. Long-Range Aviation bombers, equipped for nuclear strike missions, along with tactical air armies participating in such strikes, are controlled by the Air Force Commander-in-Chief.

The Air Defense Forces (PVO) consist of antiballistic missiles, surface to air missiles, and interceptor aircraft. Forces are arrayed in two air defense districts and eight air defense regions. Air defense commanders report to the PVO Commander-in-Chief (who is under the Chief of the General Staff), and are not operationally subordinate to military district commanders. In the event of a national emergency, it is likely that PVO would command some fighters from Frontal Aviation.

The Strategic Rocket Forces (SRF) encompass all units possessing intercontinental, intermediate, and medium range ballistic missiles. The Commander-in-Chief of the SRF has seniority over other service commanders, although probably not operational authority over them (this being retained by the Minsiter of Defense through the Chief of the General Staff).

Interservice logistical functions are performed by the Rear Service (Troops of the Tyl), Construction and Billeting Troops, and Special Troops, all under the supervision of the General Staff.

**Total armed forces:** 3,705,000 (Army: 1,825,000; Navy: 450,000; Air Force: 475,000; Air Defense: 630,000; Strategic Rocket Forces: 325,000). **Para-military forces:** 560,000 (KGB border troops: 300,000; MVD Security Troops: 260,000).

## SUPREME SOVIET OF THE USSR

Presidium

**SUPREME SOVIET OF THE USSR**
*Kremlin, Moscow*
*Telephone:  295-90-51*

| | |
|---|---|
| Chairman | Yuri Andropov |
| First Deputy Chairman | Vasiliy Vasil'yevich |
| Deputy Chairman | Antanas Stasevich |
| Deputy Chairman | Pavel Georgiyevich Gilashvili |
| Deputy Chairman | Ivan Petrovich Kalin |
| Deputy Chairman | Kurban Ali ogly Khalilov |
| Deputy Chairman | Makhmadula Kholovich Kholov |
| Deputy Chairman | Bally Yazkuliyevich Yazkuliyev |
| Deputy Chairman | Temirbek Khudaybergenovich Koshoyev |
| Deputy Chairman | Inamdzhan Buzrukovich Usmankhodzhayev |
| Deputy Chairman | Sattar Nurmashevich Imashev |
| Deputy Chairman | Ivan Yevteyevich Polyakov |
| Deputy Chairman | Babken Yesayevich Sarkisov |
| Deputy Chairman | Petr Yakubovich Strautmanis |
| Deputy Chairman | Ivan Gustavovich Kebin |
| Deputy Chairman | Aleksey Fedoseyevich Vatchenko |
| Deputy Chairman | Mikhail Alekseyevich Yasnov |

**COUNCIL OF MINISTERS**
*Kremlin, Moscow*

| | |
|---|---|
| Chairman | Nikolay Aleksandrovich Tikhonov |
| First Deputy Chairman | Ivan Vasil'yevich Arkhipov |
| First Deputy Chairman | Geydar Ali ogly Aliyev |
| Deputy Chairman | Lenoid Arkad'yevich Kostandov |
| Deputy Chairman | Nikolay Konstantinovich Baybakov |
| Deputy Chairman | Veniamin Emmanuilovich Dymshits |
| Deputy Chairman | Nikolay Vladimorovich Talyzin |
| Deputy Chairman | Guriy Ivanovich Marchuk |
| Deputy Chairman | Nikolasy Vasil'yevich Martynov |
| Deputy Chairman | Ignatiy Trofimovich Novikov |
| Deputy Chairman | Alesey Konstantinovich Antonov |
| Deputy Chairman | Ziya Nuriyevich Nuriyev |
| Deputy Chairman | Leonid Vasil'yevich Smirnov |
| Deputy Chairman | Ivan Ivanovich Bodyul |

**COUNCIL OF DEFENSE**

| | |
|---|---|
| Chairman | Yuri Andropov (Chairman of the Presidium) |
| Member | MSU Dmitriy Fedorovich (Minister of Defense) |

Member . . . . . . . . . . . . . . . . . . . Army Gen. Vataliy Vasil'yevich Fedorchuk
(Minister of Internal Affairs—MVO)
Member . . . . . . . . . . . . . . . . . . . Col. Gen. Viktor Mikhaylovich Chebrikov
(Chairman, State Committee for State Security—KGB)

**MINISTRY OF INTERNAL AFFAIRS— MVO**
*Moscow*

Minister . . . . . . . . . . . . . . . . . . Army Gen. Vitaliy Vasil'yevich Fedorchuk

**COMMITTEE FOR STATE SECURITY— KGB**
*Moscow*

Chairman . . . . . . . . . . . . . . . . . . Col. Gen. Viktor Mikhaylovich Chebrikov

**MINISTRY OF DEFENSE**
*(Obshchesoyuznoye ministerstvo oborony SSSR)*
*Ulitsa Kirova 37*
*Moscow 103160*

**Main Military Council**

Minsiter . . . . . . . . . . . . . . . . . . . . . . . . . MSU Dmitriy Fedorovich Ustinov
First Deputy Minister . . . . . . . . . . . . . . . MSU Viktor Georgiyevich Kulikov
First Deputy Minister . . . . . . . . . . . . . . . MSU Nikolay Vasil'yevich Ogarkov
First Deputy Minister . . . . . . . . . . . . . . . MSU Sergey Leonidovich Sokolov
Deputy Minister . . . . . . . . . . . Army Gen. Aleksandr Terent'yevich Altunin
Deputy Minister . . . . . . . . . . . . . . Flt. Adm. Sergey Georgiyevich Gorshkov
Deputy Minister . . . . . . . . . . . Mar. Avn. Aleksandr Ivanovich Koldunov
Deputy Minister . . . . . . . . . Army Gen. Semen Konstantinovich Kurkotkin
Deputy Minister . . . . . . . . . . . . Ch. Mar. Avn. Pavel Stepanovich Kutakhov
Deputy Minister . . . . . . . . . . . . . . . . . . MSU Kirill Semenovich Moskalenko
Deputy Minister . . . . . . . . . . . . . . . . . . Army Gen. Vasiliy Ivanovich Petrov
Deputy Minister . . . . . . . . . . . . . . . . . . . . . . Army Gen. Vitaliy Shabanov
Deputy Minister . . . . . . . . . . . . Mar. Engr. Nikolay Fedorovich Shestopalov
Deputy Minister . . . . . . . . . . . . . Army Gen. Vladimir Fedorovich Tolubko

**Main Inspectorate**
*(Glavnaya inspektisya)*

Chief Inspector . . . . . . . . . . . . . . . . . . MSU Kirill Semenovich Moskalenko
First Deputy Inspector . . . . . . . . . . . . . . . . . . . . . . . . . . . . . . . . . . . . . . .
Deputy Inspector . . . . . . . . . . . . . Col. Gen. Sergey Ivanovich Molokoyedov
Inspector-General . . . . . . . . . . . . . . . MSU Ivan Khristoforovich Bagramyan
Inspector-General . . . . . . . . . . . . . . . . . . MSU Pavel Fedorovich Batitskiy

**Main Political Directorate of Soviet Army and Navy**
*(Glavonye politicheskoye upravleniye sovetskoy armii i voyenno-morskogo flota)*

Chief . . . . . . . . . . . . . . . . . . . . Army Gen. Aleksey Alekseyevich Yepishev
First Deputy Chief . . . . . . . . . . . . . . . . . . . Adm. Aleksey Ivanovich Sorokin
Deputy Chief . . . . . . . . . . . . . . . . . . . . . . . . Lt. Gen. Nikolay N. Gus'kov
Deputy Chief . . . . . . . . . . . . . Col. Gen. Aleksey Dmitriyevich Lizichev
Deputy Chief . . . . . . . . . . . . . . . . . Col. Gen. Mikhail Georgiyevich Sobolev
Deputy Chief . . . . . . . . . . . . . . . . . . . . . . Lt. Gen. Boris Pavlovich Utikin
Chief, External Relations
Directorate . . . . . . . . . . . . . . . . . . . . . . . . . . . . . . . . . . . . . . . . . . . . .
Chief, Military Press Directorate . . . . . . Lt. Gen. Vasiliy Sergeyevich Ryabov
Deputy Chief, Military Press
Directorate . . . . . . . . . . . . . . . . Maj. Gen. Pavel Vasil'yevich Kukushkin
Deputy Chief, Military Press Directorate . . . . . . . . . . . . . . . Col. A. Solov'yev
Chief, Organizational Party Work
Directorate . . . . . . . . . . . . . . . . . Lt. Gen. Vadim Dmitriyevich Lukinykh
Deputy Chief, Organizational Party Work
Directorate . . . . . . . . . . . . . . . . . . . . . . . . . . . . . . . . . . . . . . . . . . . . . . .
Chief, Organization Department . . . . . . . . . . . . . . . Maj. Gen. V. G. Soshnev
Chief, Personnel Directorate . . . . . . . . . . . . . . Lt. Gen. Aleksey N. Agafonov
Deputy Chief, Personnel
Directorate . . . . . . . . . . . . . Maj. Gen. Avn. Vasiliy Ivanovich Korolenko
Chief, Propaganda and
Agitation Directorate . . . . . . . . Lt. Gen. Dmitriy Antonovich Volkogonov
Deputy Chief, Propaganda and
Agitation Directorate . . . . . . . . . . . . . Lt. Gen. Nikolay Ivanovich Smorigo
Chief, Culture Department . . . . . . Maj. Gen. Vsevolod Ivanovich Anikovich
Deputy Chief, Culture
Department . . . . . . . . . . . . . . . . Col. Aleksey Yevgen'yevich Sabel'nikov

Chief, Komsomol Work Department . . . . . . . . . . . . . . . . . . . . . . . . . . . . . . . . .
Deputy Chief, Komsomol Work Department . . . . . . . .Lt. Col. O. Fedyunin
Deputy Chief, Komsomol Work Department . . . . . . .Maj. I. Nestrugin
Chief, Military-Sociological Research Department . . . . . . . . . . . . . . . . . . .
Deputy Chief, Military-Sociological Research
    Department . . . . . . . . . . . . . . . . . . . . . . . . . . . . . .Col. Yu. M. Biryukov
Chief, Social Sciences Teaching
    Department . . . . . . . . . . . . . . .Maj. Gen. Mikhail Ignat'yevich Yasyukov
Chief, Technical Means of Propaganda Department . . . .Col. V. Kondyurin

**Civil Defense**
*(Grazhdanskaya oborona)*

Chief . . . . . . . . . . . . . . . . . . . . .Army Gen. Aleksandr Terent'yevich Altunin
First Deputy Chief . . . . . . . . .Col. Gen. Tank Troops Boris Petrovich Ivanov
First Deputy Chief . . . . . . .Lt. Gen. Tank Troops Sergey Il'ich Kremenskiy
First Deputy Chief . . . . . . . . . . . . . . . . .Col. Gen. Ivan Dmitriyevich Yershov

**Construction and Troop Billeting**
*(Stroitel'stvo i raskvartirovaniye voysk)*

Chief . . . . . . . . . . . . . . . .Mar. Engr. Trps. Nikolay Fedorovich Shestopalov
First Deputy Chief . . . . .Col. Gen. Engr. Konstantin Mikhaylovich Vertelov
Deputy Chief . . . . . . . . . . . . . . . . . .Lt. Gen. Engr. Viktor Ivanovich Ivankov
Deputy Chief . . . . . . . . . . . . . . . . . . . . . . . . . . . . . .Lt. Gen. Engr. M. Klimov
Deputy Chief . . . . . . . . . . . . . . .Lt. Gen. Engr. Yevgeniy Ivanovich Maykov

**Rear Services**
*(Tyl vooruzhennykh sil)*

Chief . . . . . . . . . . . . . . . . . . .Army Gen. Semen Konstantinovich Kurkotkin
First Deputy Chief . . . . . . . . . . . . . . . .Col. Gen. Ivan Makarovich Golushko
First Deputy Chief . . . . . . . . . . . . . . . . . . . .Col. Gen. Petr Ivanovich Sysoyev
Deputy Chief . . . . . . . . . . . . . . . . . . . . . . . . . . . . .Col. Gen. N. Rozhkov
Deputy Chief . . . . . . . . . . . . . . . . . . . . . . . . . .Lt. Gen. G. T. Tarasov
Chief, Main Trade
    Directorate . . . . . . . . . . . . .Lt. Gen. Intend. Serv. Yefim Il'ich Gol'dberg
Chief, Administrative-Management
    Directorate . . . . . . . . . . . . . . . . . . . . . . . . . . . . . . . . . . . . . .Lt. Gen. Engr.
               Leonid Stepanovich Chuvakhin
Chief, Central Finance
    Directorate . . . . . . .Col. Gen. Intend. Serv. Vladimir Nikolayevich Dutov
Chief, Central Food
    Directorate . . . . . . . . . . . . . . . . .Lt. Gen. Intend. Serv. Ivan D. Isayenko
Chief, Central Military Medical
    Directorate . . . . . . . . . . . . . . . . . . . . . . . . . . . . . . . .Col. Gen. Med. Serv.
               Fedor Ivanovich Komarov
Chief, Central Military Transportation
    Directorate . . . . . . . . . . . . . . . . . . . . . . . . . . . . . . . .Lt. Gen. Tech. Trps.
               Anatoliy Stepanovich Klemin
Chief, Clothing Supply
    Directorate . . . . . . . . . . . . . .Lt. Gen. Intend. Serv. Fedor Pavlovich Petrov
Chief, Fuel Supply
    Directorate . . . . . . . . . . . . . . .Col. Gen. Engr. Vasiliy Vasil'yevich Nikitin
Chief, Highways Directorate . . . . . .Lt. Gen. Engr. Trps. M. G. Kokornikov
Chief, Personnel Directorate . . . . . . . . . . . . . . . . . . . .Lt. Gen. V. G. Zaytsev
Chief, Railroad
    Troops . . . . . . . . .Col. Gen. Tech. Trps. Aleksey Mikhaylovich Kruyukov

**Special Troops**

Chief, Chemical
    Troops . . . . . . . . . . . . .Col. Gen. Tech. Trps. Vladimir Karpovich Pikalov
Deputy Chief, Chemical Troops . . . . . . . . . .Lt. Gen. Tech. Trps. P. Krasota
Chief, Engineer Troops . . .Mar. Engr. Trps. Sergey Khristoforovich Aganov
Chief, Signal Troops . . . . . . . . . . . . .Mar. Sig. Trps. Andrey Ivanovich Belov
First Deputy Chief, Signal Troops . . . . . . . . . . .Lt. Gen. Trps. Yu A. Pavlov

**Administrative and Technical Agencies**

Chief, Main Armor Directorate . . . . .Col. Gen. Yuriy Mikhaylovich Potapov
Chief, Main Directorate for Military
    Educational Institutions . . . . . . . . . . . . . . . . . . . . . .Col. Gen. Tank Trps.
               Dmitriy Ivanovich Litoutsev
Chief, Main Directorate of Navigation
    and Oceanography . . . . . . . . . . . . . . .Adm. Anatoliy Ivanovich Rassokho

Chief, Main Personnel
    Directorate ..................Army Gen. Ivan Nikolayevich Shkadov
Chief, Main Rocket and Artillery
    Directorate ..................Mar. Arty. Pavel Nikolayevich Kuleshov
Chief, Affairs Directorate ....................Lt. Gen. Engr. V. Gorskiy
Chief, Central Archives Directorate ...Maj. Gen. Nikolay Ivanovich Lutsev
Chief, Central Motor Vechicle
    Directorate .....................Col. Gen. Tech. Trps. A. T. Smirnov
Chife, Civilian Military Training
    Directorate .................Col. Gen. Yuriy Andreyevich Naumenko
Chief, Construction Industry
    Directorate ......................................Maj. Gen. Engr.
        Leonid Veniaminovich Shumilov
Chief, Military Band Service
    Directorate ..............Maj. Gen. Nikolay Mikhaylovich Mikhyalov
Chief, Military Procuracy....Col. Gen. Justice Artem Grigor'yevich Gornyy
Chief, Military Tribunal Directorate ......Lt. Gen. Justice S. S. Maksimov

## DEFENSE FORCES

Chief ...........................MSU Nikolay Vasil'yevich Ogarkov
First Deputy Chief...........Army Gen. Sergey Fedorovich Akhromeyev
First Deputy Chief ..............Army Gen. Anatoliy Ivanovich Gribkov
First Deputy Chief ...........Army Gen. Valentin Ivanovich Varennikov
Deputy Chief ..................Col. Gen. Viktor Yakovlevich Abolins
Deputy Chief ....................Adm. Nikolay Nikolayevich Amel'ko
Deputy Chief .................Mar. Sig. Trps. Andrey Ivanovich Belov
Deputy Chief ....................Army Gen. Petr Ivanovich Ivashutin
Deputy Chief ..................Col. Gen. Anatoliy Vasil'yevich Volkov
Chief, Main Directorate of Foreign
    Military Assistance ...........................................
First Deputy Chief .......Lt. Gen. Vyacheslav Vyacheslavovich Postnikov
Chief, Main Intelligence
    Directorate (GRU) and Deputy
    Chief of the General Staff .........Army Gen. Petr Ivanovich Ivashutin
Chief, Main Operations Directorate (GOU) .........................
Chief, Main Organization and
    Mobilization Directorate ........Col. Gen. Anatoliy Vasil'yevich Volkov
Chief, Communications
    Directorate ..................Mar. Sig. Trps. Andrey Ivanovich Belov
Chief, External Relations
    Directorate (UVS) .........Lt. Gen. Gennadiy Aleksandrovich Borisov
Deputy Chief, External Relations
    Directorate (UVS) .......Rear Adm. Vladimir Zhankhovich Khuzhokov
Chief, Military Science Directorate .................................
Deputy Chief, Military Science
    Directorate ..................Maj. Gen. Stepan Konstantinovich Il'in
Chief, Military Topographic
    Directorate .....................Lt. Gen. Tech. Trps. B. Ye. Byzov
Deputy Chief, Political Affairs.....................Maj. Gen. V. Shilov
Cheif, Political Department ........Col. Gen. Aleksandr Ivanovich Bukov
Deputy Chief, Political Department ...............................

Commander-in-Chief...............Army Gen. Vasiliy Ivanovich Petrov
First Deputy Commander-
    in-Chief ...............Col. Gen. Dmitriy Aleksandrovich Grinkevich
First Deputy Commander-
    in-Chief ...............Army Gen. Aleksandr Mikhaylovich Mayorov
Deputy Commander-in-Chief
    for Combat Training ........Col. Gen. Mikhail Grigor'yevich Khomulo
Deputy Commander-in-Chief
    for Military Educational
    Institutions ..............Col. Gen. Khachik Minasovich Ambaryan
Deputy Commander-in-Chief ....Col. Gen. Yuriy Andreyevich Naumenko

**ARMED FORCES**
**General Staff of the Armed Forces**
*(General'nyy shtab vooruzhennykh sil)*
*Ulitsa Korova 37*
*Moscow 103160*

**ARMY**
**Ground Forces—VS**
*(Sukhoputnyye voyska)*
*Ulitsa Korova 37*
*Moscow 103160*

Chief, Political Department . . . . . . . . Lt. Gen. Nikolay Dmitriyevich Frolov
Secretary, Party Commission . . . . . . . . . . . . . . . . . . . . . . . . . . . Col. N. Bessonov

**Main Staff**
Chief . . . . . . . . . . . . . . . . . . . Col. Gen. Dmitriy Aleksandrovich Grinkevich
First Deputy Chief . . . . . . . . . . . . . . . . . . . . . . . . . Col. Gen. I. I. Beletskiy
Deputy Chief . . . . . . . . . . . . . . . . . . . . . . . . . . . . . Lt. Gen. I. F. Arkhipov
Deputy Chief . . . . . . . . . . . . . . . . . . . Lt. Gen. Tank Trps. A. A. Dunin
Deputy Chief . . . . . . . . . . . . Lt. Gen. Konstantin Konstantinovich Pashuk
Deputy Chief . . . . . . . . . . . . . . . . . . . . . . . . . . . . . . . Lt. Gen. V. D. Sergeyev

## MILITARY DISTRICTS

**Baltic Military District**

Commander . . . . . . . . . . . . . . . . . . . . Col. Gen. Stanislav Ivanovich Postnikov
First Deputy Commander . . . . . . . . Lt. Gen. Aleksandr Alekseyevich Ivanov
Deputy Commander, Civil Defense . . . . . . Lt. Gen. Ivan Andreyevich Kibal'
Deputy Commander, Civilian Military
 Training . . . . . . . . . . . . . . . . . . . . . Lt. Gen. Tank Trps. P. V. Butenko
Deputy Commander, Combat Training and
 Military Educational Insitutions . . . . . . . . . . . . . . Maj. Gen. I. Osadovskiy
Deputy Commander, Construction
 and Billeting . . . . . . . . . . . . . . . . . . . . . . . . . . . . . Col. Engr. O. Baykov
Deputy Commander, Rear Services . . . . . . . . . . . . . . . Lt. Gen. A. Tkachev
Chief, Political Directorate . . . . . . . . Col. Gen. Ivan Semenovich Mednikov

**Staff**
Chief . . . . . . . . . . . . . . . . . . . . . . . . . . . . Lt. Gen. Viktor M. Kozhbakhteyev
Deputy Chief . . . . . . . . . . . . . . . . . . . . Maj. Gen. Tank Trps. P. Ponomarev

**Belorussian Military Distrtict**

Commander . . . . . . . . . . . . . . . Army Gen. Yevgeniy Filippovich Ivanovskiy
First Deputy
 Commander . . . . . . . . . Lt. Gen. Tank Trps. Aleksey Ivanovich Semirenko
Deputy Commander,
 Combat Training . . . . Lt. Gen. Tank Trps. Pavel Stepanovich Pecherskiy
Deputy Commander, Construction and
 Billeting . . . . . . . . . . . . . . . . . . . . . . . . . . . . . . . . . . . . . . . . . . . . . . .
Deputy Commander, Rear Services . . . . . . . . . . . . . . . Lt. Gen. A. Voblikov
Chief, Political Department . . . . . . . . . . . . . . . . . . . . . . . . . . . . . . . . . . . .

**Staff**
Chief . . . . . . . . . . . . . . . . . . . . . . . . . . Lt. Gen. Ivan Andreyevich Gashkov
First Deputy Chief . . . . . . . . . . . . . . . . . . . . . . . . . . . . Maj. Gen. A. Ivanov
Deputy Chief . . . . . . . . . . . . . . . . . . . . . . . . . . . . . . . . . . Maj. Gen. Barudin
Deputy Chief . . . . . . . . . . . . . . . . . . . . . . . . . . . . Maj. Gen. V. M. Korolev

**Carpathian Military District**

Commander . . . . . . . . Col. Gen. Tank Trps. Valeriy Aleksandrovich Belikov
First Deputy Commander . . . . . . . . . Col. Gen. Nikolay Borisovich Abashin
Deputy Commander, Civilian Military
 Training . . . . . . . . . . . . . . . . . . . . . . . . . . Maj. Gen. Arty. N. V. Akimov
Deputy Commander, Combat Training and
 Military Educational Institutions . . . . . . . . . . . . . . . . . . . . . . . . . . . . . . .
Deputy Commander, Construction and
 Billeting . . . . . . . . . . . . . . . . . . . . . . . . Maj. Gen. Engr. N. Y. Gryaznov
Deputy Commander, Rear Services . . . . . . . . . . . . . . . . . . . . . . . . . . . . . . . .
Deputy Commander . . . . . . . . . Maj. Gen. Nikolay Alekseyevich Afanas'yev
Chief, Political Directorate . . . . . . . . . . Lt. Gen. Viktor Alekseyevich Silakov

**Staff**
Chief . . . . . . . . . . . . . . . . . . . . . . . . . . . . Lt. Gen. Tank Trps. N. Grachev
First Deputy Chief . . . . . . . . . . . . . . . . . . . . . . . . . . Maj. Gen. G. Grebenets

**Central Asian Military District**

Commander . . . . . . . . . . . . . . . . . . . . Col. Gen. Dmitriy Timofeyevich Yazov
First Deputy Commander . . . . . . . . . . . . . . . . . . . . . . . Lt. Gen. Tank Trps.
 Nail' Mirsaidovich Akhunov
First Deputy Commander . . . . . Col. Gen. Vladimir Mikhaylovich Arkhipov
First Deputy Commander . . . . . . . . . Lt. Gen. Vladimir Andreyevich Vostrov
Deputy Commander, Civil Defense . . . . . . . . . . . Maj. Gen. Kh. S. Depuyev

Deputy Commander, Combat Training and
    Military Educational Institutions...............Maj. Gen. B. Borodin
Deputy Commander, Construction and
    Billeting......................................Maj. Gen. Engr.
                Boris Vladimirovich Bel'skiy
Deputy Commander, Rear Services.............Maj. Gen. V. Ryabukhin
Deputy Commander...............Col. Gen. Aleksey Pavlovich Rudakov
Chief, Political Directorate...........Lt. Gen. Vitaliy Fedorovich Arapov

**Staff**
Chief..............Lt. Gen. Tank Trps. Vladimir Mikhaylovich Arkhipov

**Far East Military District**

Commander.....................Army Gen. Ivan Moiseyevich Tret'yak
First Deputy Commander.........................................
Deputy Commander, Civil Defense............Maj. Gen. I. P. Tarasenko
Deputy Commander, Civilian Military Training....Maj. Gen. V. Masenko
Deputy Commander, Combat Training and
    Military Educational Institutions.................................
Deputy Commander, Construction and
    Billeting.............................Maj. Gen. Engr. L. Kucherov
Deputy Commander, Rear Services..............Lt. Gen. R. G. Tavadze
Chief, Political Directorate...........Col. Gen. Vasiliy Petrovich Novikov

**Staff**
Chief..............................Col. Gen. Nikolay Ivanovich Popov
First Deputy Chief.............................................

**Kiev Military District**

Commander..............................Army Gen. Ivan Gerasimov
First Deputy Commander..........................Lt. Gen. A. Fomin
First Deputy Commander..Lt. Gen. Tank Trps. Yuriy Pavlovich Terent'yev
Deputy Commander, Civilian Military Training......Lt. Gen. V. I. Noskov
Deputy Commander, Combat Training and
    Military Educational Institutions.................Maj. Gen. A. Kozlov
Deputy Commander, Construction and Billeting......................
Deputy Commander, Rear Services............Maj. Gen. G. Kuropatkin

**Leningrad Military District**

Commander......................Col. Gen. Boris Vasil'yevich Snetkov
First Deputy Commander..........Lt. Gen. Vladimir Nikolayevich Lobov
Deputy Commander, Civilian
    Military Training.....................Maj. Gen. M. A. Baytuganov
Deputy Commander, Combat
    Training and Military
    Educational Institutions..........Maj. Gen. Vladimir Iosifovich Dolgiy
Deputy Commander, Construction and
    Billeting........................................Maj. Gen. Engr.
                Nikolay Andreyevich Vetelkin
Deputy Commander, Rear Services..............Lt. Gen. A. Lutoshkin
Deputy Commander.................Lt. Gen. Petr Semenovich Lazukin
Chief, Political Directorate........Lt. Gen. Viktor Stepanovich Nechayev

**Staff**
Chief...........................................................
Deputy Chief............................Lt. Gen. V. P. Cheremnykh

**Moscow Military District**

Commander......................Army Gen. Petr Georgiyevich Lushev
First Deputy Commander.............Lt. Gen. Aleksey Il'ich Bezotosov
First Deputy Commander.........Lt. Gen. Leonid Ivanovich Kuznetsov
Deputy Commander,
    Aviation.............Col. Gen. Avn. Vadim Konstantinovich Andreyev
Deputy Commander, Civilian
    Military Training..............Lt. Gen. Nikolay Alekseyevich Neyelov
Deputy Commander,
    Combat Training...Lt. Gen. Tank Trps. Nikolay Vasil'yevich Pronyayev
Deputy Commander, Construction and
    Billeting..............................Maj. Gen. Engr. Yu Yegorov

Deputy Commander,
   Rear Services ................. Lt. Gen. Mikhail Fedorovich Manakin
Chief, Political Directorate .............. Col. Gen. Ivan Petrovich Repin

**Staff**
Chief............................... Lt. Gen. Aleksey Il'ich Bezotosov
Deputy Chief ........................................ Col. V. Koval'
Secretary, Party Commission ...................... Lt. Col. A. Volkov

### North Caucasus Military District

Commander.................. Col. Gen. Vladimir Kirillovich Meretskov
First Deputy Commander ......................................
Deputy Commander, Civilian
   Military Training ................ Lt. Gen. Ivan Nikolayevich Indenko
Deputy Commander, Combat Training ............ Lt. Gen. Tank Trps.
                       Vladimir Aleksandrovich Bochkovskiy
Deputy Commander, Construction and
   Billeting ...................... Maj. Gen. Engr. V. F. Zakurdayev
Deputy Commander,
   Rear Services........................... Maj. Gen. M. F. Kruglov
Chief, Political Directorate ....... Lt. Gen. Fedor Kalistratovich Ishchenko

**Staff**
Chief....................................... Lt. Gen. Ye. Kondakov
Deputy Chief .................................. Maj. Gen. F. Vanin

### Odessa Military District

Commander.................... Col. Gen. Aleksandr Sidorovich Yelagin
First Deputy Commander ......................... Lt. Gen. A. Zaytsev
Deputy Commander ............................ Lt. Gen. L. Gorelov
Deputy Commander, Civil Defense .............. Maj. Gen. M. Subbotin
Deputy Commander, Combat Training ..............................
Deputy Commander, Construction and
   Billeting ............................. Maj. Gen. Engr. I. Ikayev
Deputy Commander,
   Rear Services ................... Lt. Gen. Intend. Serv. G. Belogrudov
Chief, Political Directorate ......... Lt. Gen. Pavel Vasil'yevich Fomichev

**Staff**
Chief ...................................... Lt. Gen. A. Betekhtin
First Deputy Chief ...................... Maj. Gen. G. K. Samoylenko

### Siberian Military District

Commander ........................ Col. Gen. Nikolay Ivanovich Popov
First Deputy Commander ........... Lt. Gen. Ivan Petrovich Volkhonskiy
Deputy Commander,
   Civil Defense ................................................
Deputy Commander, Combat Training ............... Lt. Gen. A. Kazak
Deputy Commander, Construction and
   Billeting.................................. Maj. Gen. V. Karpenko
Deputy Commander, Rear Services................. Maj. Gen. V. Litinov
Chief, Political Directorate ..... Lt. Gen. Viktor Grigor'yevion Samoylenko

**Staff**
Chief................................. Lt. Gen. Yu. A. Khvorost'yanov
Chief, Political Department ..................... Col. Ya. Murakhovskiy

### Transbaykal Military District

Commander ................... Army Gen. Grigoriy Ivanovich Salmanov
First Deputy Commander ......................................
Deputy Commander, Combat Training ........ Lt. Gen. A. M. Rubinchik
Deputy Commander, Construction and
   Billeting .................................................
Deputy Commander, Rear Services .............. Maj. Gen. V. Malyuga
Chief, Political Directorate .......... Lt. Gen. Viktor Matveyevich Lomov

**Staff**
Chief ............. Lt. Gen. Vladimir Nikolayevich Verevkin-Rakhal'skiy

**Transcaucasus Military District**

Commander ......................Col. Gen. Oleg Fedorovich Kulishev
First Deputy Commander ......Col. Gen. Vasiliy Konstantinovich Kirilyuk
First Deputy Commander ..........Lt. Gen. Vitaliy Vasil'yevich Saltykov
First Deputy Commander ........Lt. Gen. Mikhail Mikhaylovich Sotskov
Deputy Commander,
　Combat Training ...........Lt. Gen. Dmitriy Grigor'yevich Shkrudnev
Deputy Commander, Construction
　and Billeting ...................Maj. Gen. Engr. V. D. Zhivoglyadov
Deputy Commander, Rear Services ...............Lt. Gen. G. Dmitriyev
Deputy Commander .......Lt. Gen. Arty. Tofik Yakubovich Agaguseynov
Deputy Commander .......................Maj. Gen. K. Kazantsev
Deputy Commander................Maj. Gen. Tank Trps. P. Mamchur
Chief, Political Directorate .........Lt. Gen. Aleksey Ivanovich Shirinkin

**Staff**
Chief......................................Lt. Gen. V. K. Kirilyuk
First Deputy Chief ...............................................

**Turkestan Military District**

Commander .....................Col. Gen. Yuriy Pavlovich Maksimov
First Deputy Commander .......Lt. Gen. Grigoriy Fedorovich Krivosheyev
First Deputy Commander .......Lt. Gen. Yuriy Vladimirovich Tukharinov
Deputy Commander,
　Construction and
　Billeting .................Maj. Gen. Konstantin Fedorovich Pogorelov
Deputy Commander, Rear Services ..............Maj. Gen. A. I. Agudov
Deputy Commander .................Maj. Gen. Engr. A. Ya. Golovkin
Deputy Commander .............Lt. Gen. Il'ya Filippovich Ponomarenko
Deputy Commander ...............Lt. Gen. Grigoriy Pavlovich Strel'tsov
Chief, Political Directorate ............Lt. Gen. Viktor Semenovich Rodin

**Staff**
Chief ......................Lt. Gen. Grigoriy Fedorovich Krivosheyev
First Deputy Chief ...............................................
Deputy Chief .................................Maj. Gen. I. Tokarev

**Ural Military District**

Commander ..............Col. Gen. Mikhail Aleksandrovich Tyagunov
First Deputy Commander ..........................................
Deputy Commander, Civil Defense..................................
Deputy Commander, Combat Training and
　Military Educational Institutions ................Maj. Gen. V. Volkov
Deputy Commander, Construction and
　Billeting ...........................Mag. Gen. Engr. B. Naumenko
Deputy Commander, Rear Services ............Maj. Gen. V. A. Bulychev
Chief, Political Directorate ....................Lt. Gen. V. Serebryakov

**Staff**
Chief.......................................Lt. Gen. Ye. Kuznetsov
Deputy Chief .............................................Col. Susko

**Volga Military District**

Commander .................Col. Gen. Anatoliy Yakovlevich Ryakhov
First Deputy Commander .........................................
Deputy Commander, Civilian
　Military Training..............................Lt. Gen. Yu. Ivanov
Deputy Commander, Construction
　and Billeting.................Col. Engr. Yuriy Mikhaylovich Andreyev
Deputy Commander, Rear Services...............Maj. Gen. N. Neverov
Chief, Political Directorate ....Lt. Gen. Gennadiy Aleksandrovich Gromov

## GROUPS OF FORCES

**Central Group of Forces**
*Milovice*
*Czechoslovakia*

Commander ..................Lt. Gen. Grigoriy Grigor'yevich Borisov
First Deputy Commander .......................................S. Bokov
Deputy Commander, Combat Training ..............................
Deputy Commander, Rear Services................................
Chief, Political Directorate.......Lt. Gen. Nikolay Stepanovich Kovalenko

**Group of Soviet Forces in Germany—GSFG**
*Zossen—Wunsdorf*
*German Democratic Republic*

Commander-in-Chief . . . . . . . . . Army Gen. Mikhail Mitrofanovich Zaytsev
First Deputy Commander-
  in-Chief . . . . . . . . . . . . . . Lt. Gen. Vyacheslav Mitrofanovich Gordiyenko
Deputy Commander-in-Chief,
  Combat Training . . . . . . . . . . . . . . . . . . . . . . . . . . . . . . . . . . . . . . . . . . . .
Deputy Commander-in-Chief,
  Construction and Billeting . . . . . . . . . . . . . . . . . . . . . . . . . . . . . . . . . . . .
Deputy Commander-in-Chief,
  Rear Services . . . . . . . . . . . . . . . . . . . . . . . . . . Lt. Gen. Aleksey A. Nosov
Chief, Political Directorate . . . . . . . Col. Gen. Aleksey Dmitriyevich Lizichev

**Staff**
Chief . . . . . . . . . . . . . . . . . . . . . . . . Lt. Gen. Avn. Ivan Fedorovich Sviridov

**Northern Group of Forces**
*Legnica*
*Poland*

Commander . . . . . . . . . . . . . . . . . . . . . . Col. Gen. Yuriy Fedorovich Zarudin
First Deputy Commander . . . . . Lt. Gen. Vyacheslav Vladimirovich Dubinin
First Deputy Commander . . . . . . . . . . . . . . Maj. Gen. Aleksandr Kapochkin
First Deputy Commander . . . . . . . . . Lt. Gen. Tank Trps. Gennadiy Klusov
First Deputy Commander . . . . . . . . . Lt. Gen. Tank Trps. R. G. Rizatdinov
Deputy Commander, Combat Training . . . . . . . . . . . . . . . . . . . . . . . . . . . . .
Deputy Commander, Construction and
  Billeting . . . . . . . . . . . . . . . . . . . . Col. Engr. Ivan Donisovich Mit'Kovets
Deputy Commander, Rear Services . . . . . . . . . . . Maj. Gen. Ye. Shchepetov
Deputy Commander . . . . . . . . . . . . . . . . . . . Maj. Gen. Engr. A. I. Yatsenko
Chief, Political
  Directorate . . . . . . . . . . . . . Lt. Gen. Nikolay Andreyevich Lushnichenko

**Staff**
Chief . . . . . . . . . . . . . . . . . . . . . . . . . . . . . Maj. Gen. Aleksandr Kapochkin
First Deputy Chief . . . . . . . . . . . . . Maj. Gen. Mikhail Petrovich Shmelev

**Southern Group of Forces**
*Budapest*
*Hungary*

Commander . . . . . . . . . . . . . . . Col. Gen. Konstantin Alekseyevich Kochetov
First Deputy Commander . . . . . . . . . . . . . . . . . . . . . . . . . . . . . . . . . . Lt. Gen.
                       Sagadat Kozhakhmetovich Nurmagambetov
Deputy Commander, Combat Training . . . . . . . . . . . . . . . . . . . . . . . . . . . . .
Deputy Commander,
  Rear Services . . . . . . . . . . . . . . . . . . Lt. Gen. Mikhail Kirillovich Polyakov
Chief, Political Directorate . . . . . . . . Lt. Gen. Nikolay Dmitriyevich Shevkun

**Staff**
Chief . . . . . . . . . . . . . . . . . . . . . . . . . . . . . . . . . . . . . . . . . . . . . . . . . . . . . . .

**NAVY**
**Naval Forces—VMF**
*(Voyenno-morskoy flot)*
*Ulitsa Kirova 37*
*Moscow 103160*

Commander-in-Chief . . . . . . . . Flt. Adm. SU Sergey Georgiyevich Gorshkov
First Deputy Commander-
  in-Chief . . . . . . . . . . . . . . . . . . . . Adm. Vladimir Nikolayevich Chernavin
First Deputy Commander-
  in-Chief . . . . . . . . . . . . . . . . . . . . . . Flt. Adm. Nikolay Ivanovich Smirnov
Deputy Commander-in-Chief,
  Combat Training . . . . . . . . . . . . Adm. Grigoriy Alekseyevich Bondarenko
Deputy Commander-in-Chief,
  Naval Educational
  Institutions . . . . . . . . . . . . . . . . Vice Adm. Anatoliy Mikhavlovich Kosov
Deputy Commander-in-Chief,
  Rear Services . . . . . . . . . . . . . . . . . . . . . Adm. Leonid Vasil'yevich Mizin
Deputy Commander-in-Chief,
  Shipbuilding and Armaments . . . . Adm. Engr. Pavel Grigor'yevich Kotov
Deputy Commander-in-Chief . . . Adm. Engr. Vasiliy Grigor'yevich Novikov
Chief, Political Directorate . . . . . . . Vice Adm. Pavel Nikolayevich Medvedev

**Staff**
Chief . . . . . . . . . . . . . . . . . . . . . . . . Adm. Vladimir Nikolayevich Chernavin
First Deputy Chief . . . . . . . . . . . . . . . . Adm. Petr Nikolayevich Navoytsev
Deputy Chief . . . . . . . . . . . . . . . . . . . . . . . . . . . . Rear Adm. O. M. Kalinin
Deputy Chief . . . . . . . . . . . . . . . . . . . . . . Vice Adm. Yuriy Petrovich Kovel'
Chief, Observation and
  Communications Directorate . . . Rear Adm. Mikhail Mikhaylovich Krylov
Chief, Shipbuilding Directorate . . . . . . . . . . . . . . . . . . . . . . . . . . . . . . . . . .
Secretary, Party Commission . . . . . . . . . . . . . . . . . . . . . . Col. Ye. Vershinin

## FLEETS

**Baltic Fleet**

Commander . . . . . . . . . . . . . . . . . Vice Adm. Ivan Matveyevich Kapitanets
First Deputy Commander . . . . . . . Vice Adm. Aleksey Mikhaylovich Kalinin
Deputy Commander, Construction . . . . . . . . Maj. Gen. Engr. O. Anikanov
Deputy Commander, Rear Services . . . . . Rear Adm. Pavel Pavlovich Belous
Chief, Political Directorate . . . . . . . . . . . Vice Adm. Ivan Fedorovich Alikov

**Staff**
Chief . . . . . . . . . . . . . . . . . . . . . . . . . . . . . . . . Vice Adm. K. Makarov
Secretary, Party Commission . . . . . . . . . . . . . Capt. 1st Rank Ye. Gnitsevich

**Black Sea Fleet**

Commander . . . . . . . . . . . . . . . . . . . . . . . Adm. Nikolay Ivanovich Khovrin
Deputy Commander, Combat
  Training . . . . . . . . . . . . . . . . . . . . Rear Adm. Fedor Titovich Starozhilov
Deputy Commander, Construction . . . . . . . . . . . . . . . . . . . . . . . . . . . . . . .
Deputy Commander, Rear Services . . . . . . . . . . Rear Adm. N. A. Yermakov
Deputy Commander . . . . . . . . . . . . . . . . . . . . . Rear Adm. P. T. Zenchenko
Chief, Political
  Directorate . . . . . . . . . . . . . . . Rear Adm. Rudol'f Nikolayevich Likhvonin

**Staff**
Chief . . . . . . . . . . . . . . . . . . . . . . Rear Adm. Nikolay Gavrilovich Klitnyy

**Northern Fleet**

Commander . . . . . . . . . . . . . . . . . Adm. Arkadiy Petrovich Mikhaylovskiy
First Deputy Commander . . . . Vice Adm. Vladimir Sergeyevich Kruglyakov
Deputy Commander, Combat Training . . . . . . . . . . . Rear Adm. V. Ryabov
Deputy Commander, Rear Services . . . . . . . . . . . . . Vice Adm. V. M. Petrov
Deputy Commander . . . . . . . . . . . . . Rear Adm. Al'bert Vasil'yevich Akatov
Chief, Political Directorate . . . . . . . . Vice Adm. Nikolay Vital'yevich Usenko

**Staff**
Chief . . . . . . . . . . . . . . . . . . . . . . . . . . . . . . . . . Vice Adm. V. Korobov
First Deputy Chief . . . . . . . . . . . Rear Adm. Mars Dzhemalovich Iskanderov

**Pacific Fleet**

Commander . . . . . . . . . . . . . . . . . . . . . Adm. Vladimir Vasil'yevich Sidorov
First Deputy Commander . . . . . . . . Vice Adm. Nikolay Yakovlevich Yasakov
Deputy Commander, Combat Training . . . . . . . . . . . . . . . . . . . . . . . . . . . . . .
Deputy Commander, Construction . . . . . . . . . Maj. Gen. Engr. V. Skuratov
Deputy Commander,
  Rear Services . . . . . . . . . . . . Vice Adm. Mark Alekseyevich Kosyachenko
Deputy Commander . . . . . . . . Rear Adm. Aleksandr Nikolayevich Apollonov
Chief, Political
  Directorate . . . . . . . . . . . . . . . . Vice Adm. Nikolay Pavlovich D'yakonskiy

**Staff**
Chief . . . . . . . . . . . . . . . . . . . . . Vice Adm. Rudolf Aleksandrovich Golosov
Deputy Chief . . . . . . . . . . . . . . . . . . . . . . . . . . . Rear Adm. V. N. Perelygin
Chief, Observation and
  Communications Directorate . . . . . . . . . . . . . Rear Adm. Engr. A. Morev

**Caspian Flotilla**

Commander . . . . . . . . . . . . . . . Vice Adm. Gamid Gabibovich Kasumbekov
First Deputy Commander . . . . . . . . . . . . . . . . . . . . . . . . . . . . . . . . . . . . . .
Deputy Commander,
  Rear Services . . . . . . . . . Capt. 1st Rank Bagrat Rafaelovich Knyazchyan
Deputy Commander . . . . . . . . . . . . . . . . . . Capt. 1st Rank V. M. Zhuchkov
Chief, Political Directorate . . . . . . . . . . . . . . . . . Rear Adm. V. P. Nekrasov

**Staff**
Chief . . . . . . . . . . . . . . . . . . . . . . . . . . . . . . . . . . . . . . . . . . . . . . . . . . . . .
First Deputy Chief . . . . . . . . . . . . Capt. 1st Rank Aleksey S. Zakharchenko

## AIR FORCE
Air Forces—VVS
*(Voyenno-vozdushnyye sily)*
*Ulitsa Kirova 37*
*Moscow 103160*

Commander-in-Chief . . . . . . . . Ch. Mar. Avn. Pavel Stepanovich Kutakhov
First Deputy Commander-
in-Chief . . . . . . . . . . . . . . . . . . . . Mar. Avn. Grigoriy Petrovich Skorikov
First Deputy Commander-
in-Chief . . . . . . . . . . . . . . . . . Mar. Avn. Aleksandr Nikolayevich Yefimov
Deputy Commander-in-Chief,
Aviation Engineering
Service . . . . . . . . . . . . . . . . . Col. Gen. Engr. Viktor Zakharovich Skubilin
Deputy Commander-in-Chief,
Combat Training . . . . . . . . . Col. Gen. Avn. Sergey Vasil'yevich Golubev
Deputy Commander-in-Chief,
Military Educational
Institutions . . . . . . . . . . . . . . Col. Gen. Avn. Grigoriy Ustinovich Dol'nikov
Deputy Commander-in-Chief,
Military Transport
Aviation . . . . . . . . . . . . . . . . Col. Gen. Avn. Aleksandr Nikitovich Volkov
Deputy Commander-in-Chief,
Rear Services . . . . . . . . . . . . . Col. Gen. Avn. Vasily Samsonovich Loginov
Deputy Commander-in-Chief,
Space Navigation . . . . . . . Lt. Gen. Avn. Valimir Aleksandrovich Shatalov
Deputy Commander-
in-Chief . . . . . . . . . . . . . . . Col. Gen. Avn. Vasily Vasil'yevich Reshetnikov
Deputy Commander-
in-Chief . . . . . . . . . . . . . . . . . Mar. Avn. Aleksandr Petrovich Silant'yev
Chief, Political
Directorate . . . . . . . . . . . . . . . . Lt. Gen. Avn. Leonid Lukich Batekhin

**Staff**
Chief . . . . . . . . . . . . . . . . . . . . . . . . Mar. Avn. Grigoriy Petrovich Skorikov
First Deputy Chief . . . . . . Col. Gen. Avn. Aleksandr Nikolayevich Medvedev
Deputy Chief . . . . . . . . . . . . . Col. Gen. Avn. Ivan Dmitriyevich Gaydayenko
Deputy Chief . . . . . . . . . . . . . . . Lt. Gen. Avn. Boris Nikolayevich Khapayev
Deputy Chief . . . . . . . . . . . . . . . Col. Gen. Avn. Ivan Fedorovich Modyayev

## AIR DEFENSE FORCES—PVO
*(Voyska protivovozdushnoy oborony)*
*Ulitsa Kirova 37*
*Moscow 103160*

Commander-in-Chief . . . . . . . . . Mar. Avn. Aleksandr Ivanovich Koldunov
First Deputy Commander-
in-Chief . . . . . . . . . . . . . . . Col. Gen. Arty. Yuriy Timofeyevich Chesnokov
First Deputy Commander-
in-Chief . . . . . . . . . . . . . . . . Col. Gen. Avn. Ivan Dmitriyevich Podgornyy
First Deputy Commander-
in-Chief . . . . . . . . . . . . . . . . . . . . Col. Gen. Semen Fedorovich Romanov
First Deputy Commander-
in-Chief . . . . . . . . . . . . . . . . . . Col. Gen. Valentin Dmitriyevich Sozinov
First Deputy Commander-
in-Chief . . . . . . . . . . . . . . . Col. Gen. Arty. Yevgeniy Sergeyevich Yurasov
Deputy Commander-in-Chief,
Armaments . . . . . . . . . . . . . . . . . . . . . . . . . . . . . . . . . . . . . . . . . . . . .
Deputy Commander-in-Chief,
Aviation . . . . . . . . . . . . . . . Col. Gen. Avn. Nikolay Ivanovich Moskvitelev
Deputy Commander-in-Chief,
Combat Training . . . . . . . . Col. Gen. Arty. Aleksey Grigor'yevich Smirnov
Deputy Commander-in-Chief
for Maintenance (Ekspluatatsia) . . . . . . . . . Col. Gen. Engr. Tech. Trps.
Nikolay Danilovich Grebennikov
Deputy Commander-in-Chief,
Military Educational
Institutions . . . . . . . . . . . . . . Col. Gen. Avn. Vladimir Nikitovich Abramov
Deputy Commander-in-Chief,
Radio Technical Troops
(RTV) . . . . . . . . . . . . . . . . . . . . Lt. Gen. Mikhail Timofeyevich Bergovoy
Deputy Commander-in-Chief,
Rear Services . . . . . . . . . . . . . . . . . . . . . . . . . . . . . . . . . . Lt. Gen. M. Bobkov

Deputy Commander-in-Chief,
Surface to Air Missile
Troops (ZRV) ......................Lt. Gen. Arty. A. Khyupenen
Deputy Commander-
in-Chief ..................Col. Gen. Avn. Boris Viktorovich Bochkov
Deputy Commander-
in-Chief................Col. Gen. Engr. Leonid Mikhaylovich Leonov
Deputy Commander-
in-Chief................Lt. Gen. Arty. Yuriy Vsevolodovich Votintsev
Chief, Political Directorate.........Col. Gen. Sergey Andreyevich Bobylev

**Staff**
Chief ...................................Col. Gen. Semen Fedorovich
First Deputy Chief ...........Col. Gen. Valentin Vasil'yevich Druzhinin
First Deputy Chief......................Lt. Gen. Avn. I. Maltsev
Chief, Communications Directorate .................................
Deputy Chief, Communications
Directorate ...........Maj. Gen. Engr. Sergey Nikolayevich Skvortsov

**Moscow Air Defense District**

Commander ..........Col. Gen. Avn. Anatoliy Ustinovich Konstantinov
First Deputy Commander......................................
Deputy Commander, Combat Training.........Lt. Gen. Avn. P. Khatylev
Deputy Commander, Construction and
Billeting .............................Lt. Gen. Engr. V. Shekhovtsev
Deputy Commander, Rear Services ..............Maj. Gen. V. Bugorkov
Chief, Political
Directorate.............Lt. Gen. Avn. Vadim Alekseyevich Ponomarev

**Staff**
Chief .....................Lt. Gen. Arty. Nikolay Petrovich Mil'chenko

**Baku Air Defense District**

Commander .......................................................
First Deputy Commander...........................................
Deputy Commander, Combat Training ......Maj. Gen. Avn. M. D. Popov
Chief, Political Directorate............Lt. Gen. Ivan Fedorovich Sviridov

**Staff**
Chief................................Maj. Gen. Avn. V. Kraskovskiy
First Deputy Chief ........Maj. Gen. Avn. Arkadiy Mikhaylovich Selyutin
Deputy Chief ............................Lt. Gen. Avn. M. V. Vlasov

**STRATEGIC ROCKET FORCES—SRF**
*(Raketnyye voyska strategicheskogo*
*naznacheniya)*
*Ulitsa Kirova 37*
*Moscow 103160*

Commander-in-Chief .......Ch. Mar. Arty. Vladimir Fedorovich Tolubko
First Deputy
Commander-in-Chief ......Col. Gen. Vladimir Mikhaylovich Vishenkov
First Deputy
Commander-in-Chief ............Col. Gen. Yuriy Alekseyevich Yashin
Deputy Commander-in-Chief,
Combat Training ...........Col. Gen. Aleksey Dmitriyevich Melekhin
Deputy Commander-in-Chief,
Military Educational
Institutions ...................Col. Gen. Yuriy Petrovich Zabegaylov
Deputy Commander-in-Chief,
Rear Services .....................Lt. Gen. Demitriy Petrovich Petrov
Deputy Commander-in-Chief ....Lt. Gen. Nikolay Nikolyevich Smirnitskiy
Chief, Political Directorate ........Col. Gen. Petr Andreyevich Gorchakov

**Staff**
Chief ....................Col. Gen. Vladimir Mikhaylovich Vishenkov

* * * * *

## GENERAL DEFENSE DATA

**Manpower**

Total Armed Forces . . . . . . . . . . . . . . . . . . . . . . . . . . . . . . . . . . . . . . . . . . .3,705,000
    (See Page 543)
Population . . . . . . . . . . . . . . . . . . . . . . . . . . . . . . . . . . . . . . . . . . . . . . .269,876,000

**Spending**

Military Expenditures . . . . . . . . . . . . . . . . . . . . . . . . . . . . . . . . . . . . . .$207.4 billion
Gross National Product . . . . . . . . . . . . . . . . . . . . . . . . . . . . . . . . . . . . .$1,400 billion
Military Expenditure as a Percentage of
  Gross National Product . . . . . . . . . . . . . . . . . . . . . . . . . . . . . . . . . . . . . .14.6%
Military Expenditure as a Percentage of
  Central Government Expenditure . . . . . . . . . . . . . . . . . . . . . . . . . . . . . .48.3%

**Defense Treaties** *(See Part II for Additional Detail)*

Bilateral:

| | |
|---|---|
| Angola | Libya |
| Afghanistan | Mali |
| Bulgaria | Mongolia |
| Czechoslovakia | Poland |
| Ethiopia | Romania |
| Finland | Syria |
| German Demo- | Uganda |
|   cratic Republic | United States |
| Hungary | Vietnam |
| India | People's Democratic |
| Iraq |   Republic of Yemen |
| North Korea | Zambia |

Multilateral:

Biological Weapons Convention
Environmental Modification Convention
Limited Test Ban Treaty
Protocol II of Treaty of Tlateblco
Treaty on the Control of Arms on the Seabed
Treaty on the Non-Proliferation of Nuclear Weapons
Warsaw Treaty Organization

**Military Rank Comparisons**
See Appendix A.

# UNITED ARAB EMIRATES
## State of the United Arab Emirates
### *Dawlat al-Umarat al-Arabiya al-Mutaheeda*

## Defense Establishment Command Structure and Force Organization

The President is Supreme Commander of the Federal Armed Forces. His authority is exercised through the Deputy Supreme Commander and the Chief of Staff. The Minister of Defense is responsible for administrative, personnel and logistical matters. Theoretically, the armed forces of the member states are integrated under a single General Command. However, Dubai supports and runs its own force of about 6,000 men.

**Total armed forces:** 48,500 (Army: 46,000;    Navy: 1,000;    Air Force: 1,500).

## HEAD OF STATE

H. H. Sheikh Zayed bin Sultan Al-Nahayyan

**OFFICE OF THE PRESIDENT OF THE UNITED ARAB EMIRATES AND RULER OF ABU DHABI**
*Manhal Palace*
*P.O. Box 280*
*Abu Dhabi*

*Telephone:  (2) 341010*
*Telex:  22220 palace, 22878 dpahh em,*
*          22813 tahrir em (President Court)*

President of the United Arab Emirates, Ruler of Abu Dhabi, and Supreme Commander of the Federal Armed Forces............H. H. Sheikh Zayed Bin Sultan Al-Nahayyan

**OFFICE OF THE VICE PRESIDENT OF THE UNITED ARAB EMIRATES, RULER OF DUBAI AND PRIME MINISTER**
*Za'beel Palace*
*Dubai*

*Telephone:  (4) 431001/2, 431110*
*Telex:  45688 baldya db*

Vice President of the United Arab Emirates, Ruler of Dubai and Prime Minister...........H. H. Sheikh Rashid Bin Said Al-Maktoum

**SUPREME COUNCIL OF THE UNION**
*P.O. Box 545*
*Abu Dhabi*

*Telephone:  (2) 34392*

President of the United Arab Emirates and Ruler of Abu Dhabi.......H. H. Sheikh Zayed Bin Sultan Al-Nahayyan
Vice President of the United Arab Emirates, Ruler of Dubai, and Prime Minister............H. H. Sheikh Rashid Bin Said Al-Maktoum
Ruler of Sharjah.........H. H. Sheikh Sultan Bin Mohammed Al-Qasimi
Ruler of Ras Al-Khaiman............H. H. Sheikh Saqr Bin Mohammed Al-Qasimi
Ruler of Umm ...H. H. Sheikh Rashid Bin Ahmed Al-Moalla Al-Quawain
Ruler of Fujairah........H. H. Sheikh Hamad Bin Mohammed Al-Sharqi
Ruler of Ajman.............H. H. Sheikh Humaid Bin Rasaid Al-Nuaimi
Minister of State, Superior Council Affairs.................Abdul Al-Aziz Bin Hamid Al-Qasimi

**MINISTRY OF DEFENSE**
*P.O. Box 2838*
*Dubai*

*Telephone: (4) 432330, 62956*
*Telex: 45554 moduae em*
*and*
*P.O. Box 3755*
*Abu Dhabi*

Minister . . . . . . . . . . . . . . . .Sheikh Mohammed Bin Rashid Al-Maktoum
Under Secretary . . . . . . . . . . . . . . . .Col. Mohammed Obaid Al-Maktoum
Adjutant General . . . . . . . . . . . . . . . . . . . . . . . . . . . . . . . . . . .Awad Al Khalidi
Assistant Adjutant General, Operations . . . . . . . .Mohammad Said Al-Badi
Assistant Adjutant General,
    Administration . . . . . . . . . . . . . . . . . . . . . . . . .Col. Ahmed Bin Maktoum
Assistant Adjutant General, Rations
    and Provision Supplies . . . . . . . . . . . . .Col. Mohammad Salem Al-Qasmi

## DEFENSE FORCES

**ARMED FORCES**
**United Arab Emirates Federal Armed Forces**
*P.O. Box 309*
*Abu Dhabi*

*Telephone: (2) 343492*
*Telex: 22368 hqwmr em*

President of the United Arab
    Emirates, Ruler of Abu Dhabi,
    and Supreme Commander of the
    Federal Armed Forces . . . . .H. H. Sheikh Zayed Bin Sultan Al-Nahayyan
Crown Prince and Deputy Supreme
    Commander of the Federal
    Armed Forces . . . . . . . . . .H. H. Sheikh Khalifa Bin Zayed Al-Nahayyan
Chief of Staff . . . . . . . . . . . . . . . . . . . . . . . . .Brig. Mohammed Sa'id Al-Badi
Deputy Commander, Operations . . . . . . . . . . . . . . . . . . . .Col. Saif Mubarak
Deputy Commander, Administration
    and Requirements (Abu Dhabi) . . . . . . . . . . . . . . . . . . . . . .Hamed Hilal
Chief of Intelligence . . . . . . . . . . . . . . . . . . . . . . . . . . .Hammudah Ibn Ali
Air Defense Commander . . . . . . . . . . . . . . . . . . . . . . . . .Col. Khalifa Salim

**NAVY**
*P.O. Box 309*
*Abu Dhabi*

*Telephone: (2) 341980*

Commander . . . . . . . . . . . . . . . .Col. Mohammed Nabil Radha Mudawwar

**AIR FORCE**
*P.O. Box 906*
*Abu Dhabi*

*Telephone: 377300*

Commander . . . . . . . . . . . . . . . . . . . . . . . . . . . .Maj. Gen. Awad Al-Khalidi
Deputy Commander . . . . . . . . . . . . . . . . . . . . . . . . . . . .Brig. Gen. M. Rashid

**FRONTIER GUARDS**
*Abu Dhabi*

Director . . . . . . . . . . . . . . . . . . . . . . . . . . . . . . . . . . . . . .Hamed Al-Rawwas
Director-General . . . . . . . . . . . . . . . . . . . . . . . . . . . .Maj. Saif Al-Shaafar

* * * * *

## GENERAL DEFENSE DATA

**Manpower**
    Total Armed Forces . . . . . . . . . . . . . . . . . . . . . . . . . . . . . . . . . . . . . . . . . .48,500
        (See Page 557)
    Population . . . . . . . . . . . . . . . . . . . . . . . . . . . . . . . . . . . . . . . . . . . . .1,240,000

**Spending**
    Military Expenditures. . . . . . . . . . . . . . . . . . . . . . . . . . . . . . . . . .$1.658 billion
    Gross National Product . . . . . . . . . . . . . . . . . . . . . . . . . . . . . . .$26.035 billion
    Military Expenditure as a Percentage of
        Gross National Product . . . . . . . . . . . . . . . . . . . . . . . . . . . . . . . . . . . .6.4%
    Military Expenditure as a Percentage of
        Central Government Expenditure . . . . . . . . . . . . . . . . . . . . . . . . . . .41.4%

**Defense Treaties** *(See Part II for Additional Detail)*

    Bilateral:     United Kingdom
                   United States

    Multilateral:  Cooperation Council for the Arab States of the Gulf
                   League of Arab States

# UNITED KINGDOM
## United Kingdom of Great Britain and Northern Ireland

### Defence Establishment Command Structure and Force Organization

As Sovereign, the Queen is nominal Commander-in-Chief of the armed forces, but political control is exercised by the Prime Minister and Secretary of State for Defence.

Defence policy making is a collective governmental responsibility which may involve the full Cabinet. The highest policy body is the Defence and Overseas Policy Committee, which is chaired by the Prime Minister and includes the Secretary of State for Defence, the Chancellor and the Foreign and Home Secretaries.

The Ministry of Defence is a Department of State and the Secretary of State for Defence is responsible to Parliament for the administration of the armed forces. He is assisted by the Ministers of State and Parliamentary Under Secretaries for the Armed Forces and Defence Procurement. The senior official advising the Secretary of State is the Permanent Under Secretary.

The Defence Council is charged with administering control of the military and is chaired by the Secretary of State for Defence. Other members are the Ministers of State for the Armed Forces and Defence Procurement, the Under Secretaries of State, the Chief of the Defence Staff and Service Chiefs of Staff, the Vice Chief of the Defence Staff, and Chief Scientific Advisor, and the Permanent Under Secretary of State. Execution of Council directives is handled by three Service Boards, also chaired by the Secretary of State, which in addition, have their own staffs. A Chiefs of Staff Committee, consisting of the three Service Chiefs and headed by the Chief of the Defence Staff, is responsible for the preparation of military advice on operational matters and on the military implication of defence policy.

Research, development, production and purchase of weapons systems and equipment for the armed forces, along with export promotion of defense equipment, is the concern of the Procurement Executive of the Ministry of Defence.

There are two principal army commands: Headquarters United Kingdom Land Forces at Wilton, which commands all units stationed in the United Kingdom in peace (except those in Northern Ireland, which are controlled directly by the Ministry of Defence), and Headquarters British Army on the Rhine. In addition, there are garrisons in Gibraltar, Cyprus, Belize, Falkland Islands and Hong Kong, which are controlled directly by the Ministry of Defence. The Royal Air Force is organized into three commands: strike and support commands and RAF Germany.

The armed forces of Britain are highly centralized and integrated. Multi-service functions, such as logistics, are the responsibility of special agencies associated with the services.

**Total armed forces:** 321,300 (Army: 161,000;   Navy: 71,700;   Air Force: 88,700). **Paramilitary forces:** 6,950 (Royal Ulster Constabulary).

## HEAD OF STATE

H. M. Queen Elizabeth II

**HER MAJESTY'S HOUSEHOLD**
*The Private Secretary's Office*
*Buckingham Palace*

Queen of the United Kingdom of Great
   Britain and Northern Ireland . . . . . . . . . . . . . . . H. M. Queen Elizabeth II
Private Secretary  . . . . . . . . . Sir Philip Moore, K.C.V.O., K.C.B., C.M.G.

*London SW1A 1AA*
*Telephone: (1) 930 4832*

**PRIME MINISTER'S OFFICE**
*10 Downing Street*
*London SW1*
*Telephone: (1) 930 4433*

**Defence and Overseas Policy
Committee**

**MINISTRY OF DEFENCE**
*Main Building*
*Whitehall*
*London SW1A 2HB*
*Telephone: (1) 218 9000*
*Telex: 825911*

**Defence Council**

| | |
|---|---|
| Deputy Private Secretary | William Heseltine, C.B., C.V.O. |
| Assistant Private Secretary | Robert Fellowes |
| Press Secretary | Michael Shea |

| | |
|---|---|
| Prime Minister, First Lord of the Treasury and Minister of the Civil Service | (Mrs.) Margaret Thatcher, M.P. |
| Private Secretary, Overseas Affairs | A. J. Coles |
| Private Secretary, Home Affairs | M. C. Scholar |
| Private Secretary, Parliamentary Affairs | M. A. Pattison |

| | |
|---|---|
| Chairman | (Mrs.) Margaret Thatcher, M.P. (Prime Minister) |
| Member | Michael Heseltine, M.P. (Secretary of State for Defence) |
| Member | The Lord Hailsham of St. Marylebone, C.H. (Chancellor) |
| Member | Francis Pym, M.P. (Secretary of State for Foreign and Commonwealth Affairs) |
| Member | William Whitelaw, C.H., M.C., M.P. (Secretary of State for the Home Department) |

| | |
|---|---|
| Secretary of State for Defence | Michael Heseltine, M.P. |
| Private Secretary | D. B. Omand |
| Minister of State for the Armed Forces | John Stanley, M.P. |
| Minister of State for Defence Procurement | Geoffrey Pattie, M.P. |
| Parliamentary Under Secretary of State for the Armed Forces | The Lord Trefgarne |
| Parliamentary Under Secretary of State for Defence Procurement | Ian Stewart, R.D., M.P. |
| Deputy Under Secretary of State, Navy | D. C. Humphrey |
| Deputy Under Secretary of State, Army | B. Robson, B.A. |
| Deputy Under Secretary of State, Air | A.R.M. Jaffray, C.B. |
| Permanent Under Secretary of State | Cline A. Whitmore |
| Second Permanent Under Secretary of State | Sir Arthur Hockaday, K.C.B., C.M.G. |

| | |
|---|---|
| Chairman | Michael Heseltine, M.P. (Secretary of State for Defence) |

**Army Board**

| | |
|---|---|
| Chairman | Michael Heseltine, M.P. (Secretary of State for Defense) |
| Member | Peter Blaker, M.P. (Minister of State for the Armed Forces) |
| Member | The Lord Trefgarne (Parliamentary Under Secretary for the Armed Forces) |
| Member | Geoffrey Pattie, M.P. (Minister of State for Defence Procurement) |
| Member | Ian Stewart, M.P. (Parliamentary Under Secretary for Defence Procurement) |
| Member | Gen. Sir John Stanier, G.C.B., M.B.E., A.D.C. (Chief of the General Staff) |
| Member | Gen. Sir George Cooper, K.C.B. (Adjutant General) |
| Member | Lt. Gen. Sir Paul Travers, K.C.B. (Quartermaster General) |
| Member | Gen. Sir Peter Leng, K.C.B., M.B.E., M.C. (Master-General of the Ordnance) |

Member . . . . . . . . . . . . . . . . . . . . . . . . . . . E. Broadbent, M.B., C.M.B.
(Second Permanent
Under Secretary of State)
Member . . . . . . . . . . . . . . . . . . . . . . . . . . . . . . . C. C. Fielding, C.B.
(Controller, R & D Establishments
and Research and Nuclear Programmes)
Member . . . . . . . . . . . . . . . . . . . . . . . . . . . . . . . B. Robson, B.A.
(Deputy Under Secretary of State, Army)

**Admiralty Board**
Chairman . . . . . . . . . . . . . . . . . . . . . . . . . . . Michael Heseltine, M.P.
(Secretary of State for Defence)
Member . . . . . . . . . . . . . . . . . . . . . . . . . . . . . . Peter Blaker, M.P.
(Minister of State for the Armed Forces)
Member . . . . . . . . . . . . . . . . . . . . . . . . . . . . The Lord Trefgarne
(Parliamentary Under Secretary
for the Armed Forces)
Member . . . . . . . . . . . . . . . . . . . . . . . . . . . . Geoffrey Pattie, M.P.
(Minister of State
for Defence Procurement)
Member . . . . . . . . . . . . . . . . . . . . . . . . . . . . . . . Ian Stewart
(Parliamentary Under Secretary
for Defence Procurement)
Member . . . . . . . . . . . . . . . . . . . . . . . . . . . E. Broadbent, C.B., M.P.
(Second Permenent Under
Secretary of State)
Member . . . . . . . . . . . . . . . . . . . . . . . . . . . . . . . C. C. Fielding, C.B.
(Controller, R & D Establishments
and Research and Nuclear Progrmmes)
Member . . . . . . . . . . . Adm. Sir John Fieldhouse, G.C.B., G.B.E., A.D.C.
(Chief of the Naval Staff and First Sea Lord)
Member . . . . . . . . . . . . . . . . Vice Adm. Sir Simon Cassels, K.C.B., C.B.E.
(Chief of Naval Personnel
and Second Sea Lord)
Member . . . . . . . . . . . . . . . Vice Adm. Sir Lindsay Bryson, K.C.B., BS.c.,
F.I.E.E., F.R.A.E.S.
(Controller of the Navy)
Member . . . . . . . . . . . . . . . Vice Adm. Sir James Kennon, K.C.B., C.B.E.
(Chief of Fleet Support)
Member . . . . . . . . . . . . . . . . . . . . . . . . Vice Adm. P. M. Stanford, M.V.O.
(Vice Chief of the Naval Staff)
Member . . . . . . . . . . . . . . . . . . . . . . . . . . . . A.R.M. Jaffray, C.B.
(Deputy Under Secretary of State, Navy)

**Air Force Board**
Chairman . . . . . . . . . . . . . . . . . . . . . . . . . . . Michael Heseltine, M.P.
(Secretary of State for Defence)
Member . . . . . . . . . . . . . . . . . . . . . . . . . . . . . . . Peter Blaker, M.P.
(Minister of State for the Armed Forces)
Member . . . . . . . . . . . . . . . . . . . . . . . . . . . . The Lord Trefgarne
(Parliamentary Under Secretary
for the Armed Forces)
Member . . . . . . . . . . . . . . . . . . . . . . . . . . . . Geoffrey Pattie, M.P.
(Minister of State for Defence Procurement)
Member . . . . . . . . . . . . . . . . . . . . . . . . . . . . . . . Ian Stewart, M.P.
(Parliamentary Under Secretary
for Defence Procurement)
Member . . . . . . . . . . . . . . . . . . . . . . . . . . . E. Broadbent, M.B., C.M.B.
(Second Permanent Under Secretary of State)
Member . . . . . . . . . . . . . . . . . . . . . . . . . . . . . . . C. C. Fielding, C.B.
(Controller, R & D Establishments
and Research and Nuclear Programmes)
Member . . . . . . . . . . . . . . . . . . . . . . . . . . . . . . . D. C. Humphrey
(Deputy Under Secretary of State, Air)

Member . . . . . . . Air Chief Marshal Sir Keith Williamson, G.C.B., A.F.C., A.D.C., RAF
(Chief of the Air Staff)
Member . . . . . . . . Air Marshal Sir Thomas Kennedy, K.C.B., A.F.C., RAF
(Air Member for Personnel)
Member . . . . . . . . Air Marshal M. W. P. Knight, C.B., A.F.C., B.A., RAF
(Air Member for Supply and Organization)
Member . . . . . . . . . . . Air Marshal Sir John Rogers, K.C.B., C.B.E., RAF
(Controller Aircraft)
Member . . . . . . . . . . . Air Marshal Sir Peter Harding, K.C.B., FBIM, RAF
(Vice Chief of the Air Staff)

**Permanent Under Secretary of State's Organization**

Deputy Under Secretary of State
(Policy and Programmes) . . . . . . . . . . . . . . . . . . . . . . . R. M. Hastie-Smith
Deputy Under Secretary of State
(Finance and Budget) . . . . . . . . . . . . . . . . . . . . . . . . . . . . J. D. Bryars
Deputy Under Secretary of State
(Civilian Management) . . . . . . . . . . . . . . . . . . E. Broadbent, C.B., C.M.G.
Deputy Under Secretary of State
(Personnel and Logistics) . . . . . . . . . . . . . . . . . . . . . . . . . C. W. France
Deputy Under Secretary of State (Navy) . . . . . . . . . . A. R. M. Jaffray, C.B.
Deputy Under Secretary of State (Army) . . . . . . . . . . . . . . B. Robson, B.A.
Deputy Under Secretary of State (Air) . . . . . . . . . D. C. Humphrey, C.M.G.
Assistant Under Secretary of State
(Defence Staff) . . . . . . . . . . . . . . . . . . . . . . . . . . . . . . . . . . J. M. Stewart
Director-General of Defence Accounts . . . . . . . . . . . . . . . . . J. S. Goldsmith
Director-General of Management Audit . . . . . . . . . . . . . . . . . . . J. F. Mayne
Deputy Chief Scientific Officer,
Civilian Management (Specialists)
Division 1 . . . . . . . . . . . . . . . . . . . . . K. W. Jones, B. Sc., C Chem, F.R.I.C.
Executive Director, Civilian Management . . . . . . . . . . . . . . . . E. Pendlebury
Assistant Under Secretary of State
(Personnel and Logistics) . . . . . . . . . . . . . . . . . . . . . . . . . . . J. Dromgoole
Assistant Under Secretary of State
(Fleet Support) . . . . . . . . . . . . . . . . . . . . . . . . . . . . . . . . . . B. H. Cousins
Assistant Under Secretary of State
(Adjutant-General/Quarter-Master-
General) (Army Department) . . . . . . . . . . . . . . . . . . . . . . M. D. Hobkirk
Chief of Public Relations . . . . . . . . . . . . . . . . . . . . . . . . . . . L. E. E. Jeanes
Director, Public Relations, (Navy) . . . . . . . . . Captain I. B. Sutherland, R.N.
Director, Public Relations, (Army) . . . . . . . . . . Brigadier D. J. Ramsbotham
Director, Public Relations, (Royal
Air Force) . . . . . . . . . . . . . . . . . . . . . . . . . . . Air Commodore R. A. Miller
Chief Press Officer, Defence Press Office . . . . . . . . . . . . . . . . . . . . . J. Gee

**Meteorological Office**
*(Part of the Air Force Department)*
*Bracknell*
*Berkshire*
*RG12 2SZ*

*Telephone:    0344 20242*
*Telex:    848160, 847010*

Director-General . . . . . . . . . . . . . . . Sir John Mason, C.B., D. Sc., F.R.S.
Director of Research . . . . . . . . . . . . . . . . . . . . . . . . . . Dr. K. H. Stewart
Deputy Chief Scientific Officer,
Radar Research Laboratory . . . . . . . . . . . . . . Dr. K. A. Browning, F.R.S.

**Scientific Staff**
*Telephone:    (1) 218 3508*

Deputy Chief, Scientific Adviser (Projects) . . . . . . . . . . . . . . . . J. F. Barnes
Assistant Chief, Scientific Adviser (Research) . . . . . . . . . H. G. R. Robinson
Director, Defence Operational Analysis Establishment . . . . . . J. D. Culshaw

**Research and Development Establishments and Research**

Controller . . . . . . . . . . . . . . . . . . . . . . . . . . . . . . . . . . . . . . C. C. Fielding, C.B.
Deputy Controller, Research Programmes . . . . . . . . . . . . . . Dr. D. H. Davies
Director-General, Research (General) . . . . . . . . . . . . . . . . H. G. R. Robinson

|  | Director-General, Research A and |  |
|---|---|---|
|  | Chief Scientist (Royal Navy) | Dr. F. A. Johnson |
|  | Director, Admiralty Marine Technology Establishment | A. B. Mitchell |
|  | Director, Admiralty Surface Weapons Establishment | |
|  | Director, Admiralty Underwater Weapons Establishment | I. L. Davies |
|  | Director-General, Research B and Chief Scientist (Army) | L. R. Gray |
|  | Director, Atomic Weapons Research Establishment | C. C. Fielding, C.B. |
|  | Director, Propellants, Explosives and | |
|  | Rocket Motor Establishment | |
|  | Director, Royal Armament Research and | |
|  | Development Establishment | Dr. F. H. Panton, M.B.E. |
|  | Director-General, Research C and | |
|  | Chief Scientist (Royal Air Force) | D. J. Harper |
|  | Director, National Gas Turbine Establishment | |
|  | Director, Royal Aircraft Establishment | |
| **Navy Controllerate** | Controller | Vice-Admiral Sir Lindsay Bryson, K.C.B., B. Sc., F.I.E.E., F.R.Ae.S. |
|  | Principal Director of Navy Contracts | A. J. Figes |
|  | Director-General, Weapons (Naval) | Rear Admiral J. E. K. Croydon, M.A., F.I.E.E. |
|  | Director, Underwater Weapons | |
|  | Projects (Naval) | Commodore P. J. Oldridge, B. Sc. |
|  | Director, Surface Weapons | |
|  | Projects (Naval) | Dr. D. G. Kiely, B. Sc., M. Sc., D.S.C.I. F.I.E.E., F INST P |
|  | Director-General, Ships | Vice-Admiral Sir Ted Horlick, K.B.E., MI MECH E, M.I.M.A.R.E. |
|  | Director, Project Team | |
|  | Submarines/Polaris | S. A. T. Warren, B. Sc., F.R.I.N.A., FI MECH E, R.C.N.C. |
| **Master-General of the Ordnance Controllerate** | Master-General | General Sir Peter Leng, K.C.B., M.B.E., M.C. |
|  | Director-General, Guided Weapons | |
|  | and Electronics | I. B. Bott |
|  | Director-General, Fighting Vehicles | |
|  | and Engineer Equipment | Major General J. H. B. Dent, O.B.E. |
|  | Director-General, Weapons (Army) | Major General D. T. Crabtree |
| **Aircraft Controllerate** | Controller | Air Marshal Sir John Rogers, K.C.B., C.B.E., RAF |
|  | Principal Director, Contracts/Air | R. A. W. Baker |
|  | Director-General, Future Projects | D. E. Humphries |
|  | Deputy Controller | D. H. Perry |
|  | Director-General, Engines (Procurement Executive) | M. C. Neale |
|  | Director-General, Aircraft 1 | D. M. Spiers |
|  | Director-General, Aircraft 2 | Air Vice-Marshal R. K. Hooks, C.B.E. |
|  | Director-General, Aircraft 3 | C. Redmayne |
|  | Director-General, Air Weapons | |
|  | Electronics Systems | Dr. T. P. McLean, B. Sc., F INST P, F.R.S.E. |
|  | Director-General, Strategic Electronics Systems | Dr. J. W. Berry |
| **Strategic Systems Executive** | Chief | Rear Admiral J. S. Grove, O.B.E. |
|  | Director, Weapons | |
|  | (Strategic Systems) | Commodore J. S. Cooper, O.B.E. |
| **Royal Ordnance Factories Organisation** *Northumberland House* *Northumberland Avenue* *London WC2N 5BP* *Telephone: (1) 218 4177* | Managing Director | W. Meakin, C ENG, FI MECH E |
|  | Director-General, Ordnance Factories/ | |
|  | Finance and Procurement | J. E. Carruthers |
|  | Director-General, Ordnance | |
|  | Factories/Ammunition | H. Butterworth, C ENG, MI MECH E |
|  | Director-General, Ordnance Factories/ | |
|  | Weapons and Fighting Vehicles | H. Pointon, C. ENG, MI MECH E |

**Procurement Executive**

*Telephone: (1) 218 9000*

Chief of Defence Procurement . . . . . . . Air Chief Marshal Sir Douglas Lowe,
G.C.B., D.F.C., A.F.C.
Deputy Chief of Defence Procurement (Nuclear) . . . . . . . . . . C. C. Fielding
Director, Warhead Development (Nuclear) . . . . . . . . . . . . Dr. E. D. Dracott
Deputy Under Secretary of State (Policy) . . . . . . . . . . . . . . K. C. Macdonald
Assistant Secretary, International
and Industrial Policy Division 1 . . . . . . . . . . . . . . . . . . . . . . . . J. M. Gibbon
Assistant Secretary, International
and Industrial Policy Division 2 . . . . . . . . . . . . . . . . . . T. F. W. B. Knapp
Director-General,
Quality Assurance . . . . . . . . . . P. Corner, E ENG, MI MECH E, M.I.E.E.
Director-General, Defence Contracts . . . . . . . . . . . . . . . . . . . . . . B. R. Haigh
Assistant Secretary, Contracts Policy Division . . . . . . . . . . . . . . . . B. J. Slade
Principal Director of Patents . . . . . . . . . . . . . . . . . . . . . . . . . . A. N. Devereux

**Defence Sales Organisation**

Head . . . . . . . . . . . . . . . . . . . . . . . . . . . . . . . . . . . . . . . . . . . . . . . . R. M. Regan
Assistant Under Secretary of State/Sales . . . . . . . . . . . . . . . . . . . . K. P. Jeffs
Assistant Under Secretary of State
(Sales Administration) . . . . . . . . . . . . . . . . . . . . . . . . . . . . . . . . . . . P. Mehew
Director, Sales Finance and Support . . . . . . . . . . . . . . . . . . . . . . . J. W. Davey
Military Deputy to Head
of Defence Sales . . . . . Air Vice Marshal H. A. Merriman, O.B.E., A.F.C.
Director of Marketing . . . . . . . . . . . . . . . . . . . . . . . . . . . . . . . . . . . D. H. Hills

**Inter-Service and Ancillary
Organisations**

Commandant, Royal College of
Defense Studies . . . . . . . . . . . . . . . . . . . Admiral Sir William Pillar, K.C.B.
Commandant, National Defense College . . . . . . . Rear Admiral D. C. Jenkin
Secretary, Defence Press and
Broadcasting Committee . . . . . . . . . . . . . . . . . . Rear Admiral W. N. Ash,
C.B., M.V.O., (Ret.)
Director, British Forces, Broadcasting Service . . . . . . . . . . . . . . . . I. J. Woolf
Commandant, Royal Military
College of Science . . . . . . . . . . . . . . Major General R. F. Vincent, D.S.O.

# DEFENCE FORCES

**ARMED FORCES**
**Chiefs of Staff Committee**
*Main Building*
*Whitehall*
*London SW1A 2HB*
*Telephone: (1) 218 9000*
*Telex: 825911*

Chairman . . . . . . . Field Marshal Sir Edwin Bramall, G.C.B., O.B.E., M.C.
(Chief of the Defence Staff)
Member . . . . . . . . . . . . . . . Gen. Sir John Stanier, G.C.B., M.B.E., A.D.C.
(Chief of the General Staff)
Member . . . . . . . . . . . Adm. Sir John Fieldhouse, G.C.B., G.B.E., A.D.C.
(Chief of Naval Staff and First Sea Lord)
Member . . . . . . . . Air Chief Marshal Sir Keith Williamson, G.C.B., A.F.C.,
A.D.C., RAF
(Chief of Air Staff)

**Defence Staff**

Assistant Chief, Commitments . . . . . . . . . . Air Vice Marshal J. M. D. Sutton
Assistant Chief, Programmes . . . . . . . . . . . . . . . . . . . Rear Adm. J. J. Roswald
Assistant Chief, Command, Control and
Communications, and Information Systems . . . Rear Adm. D. M. E. Maslin
Director, Overseas Defence Relations . . . . . . . . . . Colonel A. C. Uloth (Ret.)
Director-General, Intelligence . . . . . Vice Admiral Sir Roy Halliday, K.B.E.
Deputy Director, Intelligence (Logistics) . . . . . . . . . . . . . D. E. Chamberlain
Deputy Director, Intelligence
(Administration and Security) . . . . . . . . . . . . . . . . . . . . Mrs. D. E. J. Brooke
Assistant Chief (Signals) . . . . . . . . . . . . . . Air Vice Marshal T. B. Stephenson
Controller, Defence
Communications Network . . . . . . . . . . . . . . . Group Captain T. P. Reagan
Deputy Chief of the
Defence Staff . . . . . . . . . . . Lt. General M. R. Johnston, K.C.B., O.B.E.

**ARMY**
**British Army**
*Main Building*
*Whitehall*
*London SW1A 2HB*
*Telephone:* *(1) 218 9000*

### General Staff

### Army Department

Chairman, Army Board of the
    Defence Council . . . . . . . . . . . . . . . . . . . . . . . . . .Michael Heseltine, M.P.
        (Secretary of State for Defence)

Chief of the
    General Staff . . . . . . . .General Sir John Stanier, G.C.B., M.B.E, A.D.C.
Vice-Chief . . . . . . . . . . . . . . . .Lt. Gen. Sir James Glover, M.B.E., K.C.B.
Director, Secretary (Army) . . . . . . . . . . . . . .Maj. Gen. H. E. M. L. Garrett,
        C.B.E. (Ret.)
Director, Military Operations . . . . . . . . . .Maj. Gen. J. L. Chapple, C.B.E.
Deputy Director, Military Operations . . . . . . . .Brig. C. A. Ramsay, O.B.E.
Director, Military Assistance Office . . . . .Maj. Gen. A. W. Dennis, O.B.E.
Director, Military Survey . . . . . . . . . . . . . .Maj. Gen. E. W. Barton, M.B.E.
Director, Army Staff Duties . . . . . .Maj. Gen. C. R. Huxtable, C.B.E., C.B.
Assistant Chief of the General
    Staff (Operational Requirements) . . . . .Maj. Gen. L. A. W. New, C.B.E.
Director, Operational
    Requirements 2 (Army). . . . . . . . . . . . . . . . . . . . . . . .Brig. J. E. Killick
Director, Operational
    Requirements 3 (Army) . . . . . . . . . . . . . . . . . . . . . . .Brig. C. W. Beckett
Director, Operational
    Requirements 4 (Army) . . . . . . . . . . . . . . . . . . . . . . .Brig. G. R. Oehlers
Director, Royal Armoured Corps . . . . . . . .Maj. Gen. R. M. Jerram, M.B.E.
Director, Royal Artillery . . . . . . . .Maj. Gen. M. J. Tomlinson, C.B., O.B.E.
Engineer-in-Chief, (Army). . . . . . . . . . . . . . . . . . . . .Maj. Gen. M. Mathews
Director of Infantry . . . . . . . . . . .Maj. Gen. P. F. A. Sibbald, C.B., O.B.E.
Headquarters Director, Army Air Corps . .Maj. Gen. W. N. J. Withall, C.B.
Director, Territorial Army
    and Cadets . . . . . . . . . . . . . .Maj. Gen. R. E. J. Gerrard-Wright, C.B.E.

Military Secretary . . . . . .Lt. Gen. Sir Roland Guy, K.C.B., C.B.E., D.S.O.
Deputy Military Secretary A . . . . . . . . . . . . .Brig. A. R. G. Mullens, O.B.E.
Deputy Military Secretary B . . . . . . . . . . . . .Brig. P. D. Alexander, M.B.E.
Adjutant-General . . . . . . . .Gen. Sir George Cooper, K.C.B., M.C., A.D.C.
Vice-Adjutant-General/Director
    of Manning . . . . . . . . . . . . . . . . . . . . . . . . . . .Maj. Gen. J. Boyne, M.B.E.
Director-General of Army Training . . . . . . . . .Lt. Gen. Sir Richard Vickers,
        K.C.B., O.B.E., M.V.O.
Assistant Chief of the General Staff
    (Training) . . . . . . . . . . . . . . . . . . . . . . . . . . . . . . . . .Maj. Gen. C. J. Rougier
Chief of Staff, The Arms Executive . . . . . . . . . . . . . . . . . . . . . .Brig. G. Read
Director-General, Army Medical Services . . . . . . . . .Lt. Gen. Sir Alen Reay,
        K.B.E., Q.H.P., M.B., F.R.C.P., F.R.C.P. (Edin)
Deputy Director-General, Army
    Medical Services . . . . . . . . . . . . . . . .Brig. D. S. Paton, M.B.E., Q.H.S.,
        M.F.C.M., M.B.
Director of Medical Supplies . . . . . . .Brig. A. J. Shaw, M.A., D.T.M., M.B.
Paymaster-in-Chief . . . . . . . . . . . . . . . . . . . . . . . . . .Maj. Gen. J. L. Bartlett
Director, Army Education . . . . . . . . . . . . . . .Maj. Gen. A. J. Trythall, M.A.
Provost Marshal . . . . . . . . . . . . . . . . . . . . . . . . . . . . .Brig. B. Thomas, O.B.E.
Chaplain-General . . . . .The Venerable Archdeacon W. F. Johnson, Q.H.C.
Quartermaster-General . . . . . . . . . . . . . .Lt. Gen. Sir Richard Trant, K.C.B.
Vice-Quartermaster-General . . . . . . . . . . . . .Maj. Gen. B. M. Lang, O.B.E.
Chief of Staff, Logistic Executive . . . . . . . . .Maj. Gen. B. W. Davis, C.B.E.
Director-General, Transport and
    Movements, Logistic Executive . . . . . . . . . .Maj. Gen. W. M. Allen, C.B.
Director-General, Ordnance
    Services, Logistic Executive . . . . . . . . . . . . . . . .Maj. Gen. W. L. Whalley
Director-General, Electrical and Mechanical
    Engineering, Logistic Executive . . . . . . . . . . . . . .Maj. Gen. T. B. Palmer,
        C ENG, FI MECH E, F.B.I.M.

**NAVY**
**Royal Navy**
*Main Building*
*Whitehall*
*London SW1A 2HB*
*Telephone:   (1) 218 9000*

Chairman, Admiralty Board
  of the Defence Council . . . . . . . . . . . . . . . . . . . . . Michael Heseltine, M.P.
                                                           (Secretary of State for Defence)

**Naval Staff**

Chief of the Naval Staff and
  First Sea Lord . . . . . . Adm. Sir John Fieldhouse, G.C.B., G.B.E., A.D.C.
Vice Chief . . . . . . . . . . . . . . . . . . . . . . Vice Adm. P. M. Stanford, M.V.O.
Director of Naval Security . . . . . . . . . . Rear Adm. W. D. Lang, C.B., (Ret.)
Assistant Chief (Policy) . . . . . . . . . . . . . . . . . . Rear Adm. G. T. J. O. Dalton
Director, Naval Plans . . . . . . . . . . . . . . . . . . . . . . . . Capt. B. N. Wilson
Director, Naval Assistance Overseas . . . . . . . . . . . . . . . . . . . . Cmdr. J. Parry
Assistant Chief (Operations) . . . . . . . . Rear Adm. L. E. Middleton, D.S.O.
Director, Naval Air Warfare . . . . . . . . . . . . . . . . . . . . . . . Capt. D. B. Bathurst
Director, Naval Warfare . . . . . . . . . . . . . . . . . . . . . . . . . Capt. M. H. Livesay
Hydrographer of the Navy . . . . . . . . . . . . . . . . . . Rear Adm. D. W. Haslam,
                                                           C.B., O.B.E., FRICS
Director, Hydrographic Administration and Supply . . . . . . . . . . R. H. Foote
Assistant Chief (Operational
  Requirements . . . . . . . . . . . . . . . . . . Rear Adm. C. G. W. Marsh, O.B.E.
Director, Naval Operational
  Requirements . . . . . . . . . . . . . . . . . . . . . . . . . . . Capt. R. I. T. Hogg, R.N.
Commandant-General,
  Royal Marines . . . . . . . . Lt. Gen. Sir Stewart R. Pringle, Bt, K.C.B., DSc.
Chief of Staff to Commandant-General,
  Royal Marines . . . . . . . . . . . . . . . . . . . . . Maj. Gen. J. C. Hardy, M.V.O.
Colonel (Operations and Plans) . . . . . . . . . . . . . . . . . . . . . Col. J. St. J. Grey
Military Secretary . . . . . . . . . . . . . . . . . . . . . . Col. H. J. Flamank, O.B.E.
Colonel (Personnel) . . . . . . . . . . . . . . . . . . . Col. H. Y. LaR. Beverley, O.B.E.
Colonel (SO1 Logistics) . . . . . . . . . . . . . . . . . . Lt. Col. R. C. Van Der Horst

**Navy Department**

Chief of Naval Personnel and
  Second Sea Lord . . . . . . . . Vice Adm. Sir Simon Cassels, K.C.B., O.B.E.
Naval Secretary . . . . . . . . . . . . . . . . . . . Rear Adm. W. R. S. Thomas, O.B.E.
Director-General of Naval
  Manpower and Training . . . . . . . . . . . . Rear Adm. N. J. S. Hunt, M.V.O.
Medical Director-
  General . . . . . . . . . . . . . . . . Surgeon Vice Adm. R. J. W. Lambert, Q.H.P.
Chief of Fleet Support . . . . . . Vice Adm. Sir James Kennon, K.C.B., C.B.E.
Director-General, Naval
  Personnel Services . . . . . . . . . . . . Rear Adm. K. D. E. Wilcockson, C.B.E.
Chaplain of the Fleet . . . . . . . . . . . . . . The Venerable Ritti Roberts, Q.H.C.
Chief Executive, Royal Dockyards . . . . K. H. W. Thomas, O.B.E., F ENG,
                                                           F.R.I.N.A., F.B.I.M., R.C.N.C.
Director-General, Supplies and Transport
  Head of the Royal Naval Supply
  and Transport Service . . . . . . . . . . . . . . . . . . . . . . . . . K. J. Pritchard
Director-General, Fleet Support
  Policy and Services . . . . . . . . . . . . . . . . Rear Adm. J. P. Edwards, M.V.O.
Director, Marine Services . . . . . . . . . . . . . . . . . . . . . M. D. Walker, Esq.
Director, Public Relations . . . . . . . . . . . . . . . . . Capt. I. B. Sutherland, R.N.
Deputy Director, Public Relations . . . . . . . . . . . . . . . . . R. A. A. Moore
Director, Naval Recruiting . . . . . . . . . . . . . . . . . . . . Capt. D. A. Wallis, R.N.

**Other Commands**

Commander-in-Chief
  Naval Home Command . . . . . . . Adm. Sir Desmond Cassidi, C.B., A.D.C.
Commander-in-Chief, Fleet . . . . . . . . . . Adm. Sir William Staveley, K.C.B.
Flag Officer, Naval Air Command . . . . . . . . Vice Adm. Sir John Cox, K.C.B.
Flag Officer, Scotland and
  Northern Ireland . . . . . . . . . . . . . . . . . . . . . . . . . Vice Adm. R. R. Squires

Flag Officer, Plymouth . . . . . . . . . . . . . . . . . . . . . . Vice Adm. D. W. Brown
Flag Officer, Medway . . . . . . . . . . . . . . . Rear Adm. W. A. Higgins, C.B.E.
Flag Officer, Portsmouth . . . . . . . . . . . . . . . . . . . . . Rear Adm. A. S. Tippet
Flag Officer, Submarines . . . . . . . . . . . . . . . . . Vice Adm. P. G. M. Herbert
Flag Officer, First Flotilla . . . . . . Rear Adm. J. J. BLack, D.S.O., M.B.E.
Flag Officer, Second Flotilla . . . . . . . . . Rear Adm. R. W. F. Gerken, C.B.E.
Flag Officer, Third Flotilla . . . . . . . . . . . . . . . . . . . . Rear Adm. R. G. A. Fitch

## AIR FORCE
**Royal Air Force—RAF**
*Main Building*
*Whitehall*
*London SW1A 2HB*
*Telephone: (1) 218 9000*

Chairman, Air Force Board of the
    Defence Council . . . . . . . . . . . . . . . . . . . . . . . . . Michael Heseltine, M.P.
                        (Secretary of State for Defence)

### Air Staff

Chief of the Air Staff . . . . . . . . . . . Air Chief Marshal Sir Keith Williamson,
                            G.C.B., A.F.C., A.D.C., RAF
Vice Chief . . . . . . . . Air Marshal Sir Peter Harding, K.C.B., F.B.I.M., RAF
Assistant Chief (Policy) . . . . . Air Vice Marshal F. D. G. Clark, C.B.E., RAF
Director of Air Staff Plans . . . . . . . . . . . . . . . . Air Cmdr. B. J. Jackson, B.A.
Assistant Chief (Operations) . . . . . . . . Air Vice Marshal J. W. Price, C.B.E.
                                MRAeS, F.B.I.M., RAF
Director of Operations (Air Support) . . . . . . . . . . . . Air Cmdr. J. F. H. Tetley
Director of Operations (Strike) . . . . . . . . . . . . . . Air Cmdr. M. G. Simmons
Director of Operations (Air Defence) . . . . . . . . Air Cmdr. R. I. Stewart-Paul
Assistant Chief (Operational
    Requirements . . . . . . Air Vice Marshal D. Harcourt-Smith, D.F.C., RAF
Commandant-General (RAF REGT) and
    Director-General of Security . . . . . . . . Air Vice Marshal H. Reed-Purvis,
                        O.B.E., BSc., C.B., MINucE, RAF
Controller, National Air
    Traffic Services . . . . . . . . . . . Air Marshal I. M. Pedder, O.B.E., D.F.C.,
                                  K.C.B., RAF

### Air Force Department

Air Member
    for Personnel . . . . . . . Air Marshal Sir Thomas Kennedy, A.F.C., K.C.B.
Director-General of
    Personnel Management . . . . . . . . Air Vice Marshal J. B. Duxbury, C.B.E.
Chaplain-in-Chief . . . . . . . . . Air Vice Marshal The Reverend G. Renawden
Director-General, Personal Services . . . . Air Vice Marshal L. W. F. Wheeler
Director-General, Training . . . . . . . . . . . . . . Air Vice Marshal B. Brownlow,
                              C.B., O.B.E., A.F.C.
Director-General, Medical
    Services . . . . . . . . . . . . . . . . . . . . . . Air Marshal D. W. Atkinson, M.B.,
                  Q.H.P., C.H.B., F.F.C.M., M.F.O.M.,
                              D.P.H., D.I.H.
Air Member for Supply and
    Organisation . . . . . . . . Air Marshal M. W. P. Knight, C.B., A.F.C., B.A.
Director-General,
    Organisation . . . . Air Vice Marshal P. S. Collins, A.F.C., B.A., F.B.I.M.
Chief Engineer . . . . . . . . . . . Air Vice Marshal E. C. Dunn, B.E.M., CEng,
                                MRAeS, F.B.I.M.
Director-General, Supply . . . . . . . . Air Vice Marshal A. R. Martindale, B.A.

### Commands

Air Officer Commanding in
    Chief, RAF Strike Command . . . . . . . . Air Chief Marshal Sir David Craig,
                            C.B., O.B.E., M.A.
Air Officer Commanding in
    Chief, RAF Support Command . . . . . . . . Air Marshal Sir Michael Beavies,
                          C.B.E., A.F.C., F.B.I.M.
Command-in-Chief, RAF Germany . . . Air Vice Marshal P. Hine, F.B.I.M.

\* \* \* \* \*

## GENERAL DEFENCE DATA

**Manpower**
Total Armed Forces...............................................327,600
   (See Page 559)
Population ...................................................56,095,000

**Spending**
Military Expenditures.......................................$22.8 billion
Gross National Product ......................................$445 billion
Military Expenditure as a Percentage of
   Gross National Product ...........................................5.1%
Military Expenditure as a Percentage of
   Central Government Expenditure ...............................12.5%

**Defence Treaties** *(See Part II for Additional Detail)*

| | | |
|---|---|---|
| Bilateral: | Bahrain | Singapore |
| | Kenya | Sri Lanka |
| | Malta | United Arab |
| | Mauritius | Emirates |
| | Qatar | United States |

Multilateral:   Biological Weapons Convention
Environmental Modification Convention
Five-Power Defence Arrangement
Limited Test Ban Treaty
Multinational Force and Observers in Sinai
North Atlantic Treaty Organization
Protocols I and II of Treaty for the Prohibition of Nuclear
   Weapons in Latin America
South-East Asia Collective Defence Treaty
Treaty of Establishment
Treaty on the Control of Arms on the Seabed
Treaty on the Non-Proliferation of Nuclear Weapons
*United Kingdom—Finland—France—Soviet Union*: Paris
   Peace Treaty restricting size and armament of Finnish
   armed forces (1947)

# UNITED STATES OF AMERICA

## Defense Establishment Command Structure
## and Force Organization

The President is the Commander-in-Chief of the armed forces. He is responsible for the formulation of defense policy and administration of the military. Under the Constitution, he has the power, with the consent of the Senate, to enter into treaties and appoint officers. Only Congress, however, can declare war and appropriate funds for defense.

The President exercises his authority through the Secretary of Defense, who is responsible for setting policy and directing defense programs and planning within the Department of Defense.

The President is advised by the National Security Council which is comprised of the Vice-President, Secretary of State, Secretary of Defense, Chairman of the Joint Chiefs of Staff, Director of the Central Intelligence Agency, and others within the Executive Office of the President.

The Joint Chiefs of Staff are the principal military advisors to the President, the National Security Council and the Secretary of Defense. The Joint Chiefs include the Army Chief of Staff, Chief of Naval Operations, Air Force Chief of Staff, the Commandant of the Marine Corps, and a Chairman, who is appointed by the President for a two-year term and may be appointed for one additional term.

Operational control of United States combat forces is assigned to the nine unified and specified commands, which are subordinate to the Joint Chiefs of Staff. A unified command is composed of forces from two or more services and is normally organized geographically. The Atlantic Command covers the North Atlantic up to European coastal waters, and the sea surrounding South and Central America. The European Command includes the U.S. contribution to the North Atlantic Treaty Organization, as well as North Africa and the Middle East as far as Iran. The Pacific Command covers the Pacific and Indian Oceans and most of Asia east of Iran's western border. The Southern Command includes all of Central and South America. The newest unified command, the Central Command (formerly the Rapid Deployment Joint Task Force) is responsible for protecting U.S. interests in South West Asia. The Readiness Command is a unified command not based on a geographic region. It controls Army and Air Force tactical units held as reserves.

The specified commands are organized functionally rather than geographically and are made up of forces from a single service. The Strategic Air Command controls all U.S. land-based ballistic missiles and long-range bombers. The Military Airlift Command is responsible for all air transport serving the United States Armed Forces. The Aero-space Defense Command is responsible for the air defense of the 48 contiguous states and Alaska. It has no assigned forces in peacetime.

The flow of command extends from the President to the Secretary of Defense to the Joint Chiefs of Staff, who maintain the World-Wide Military Command and Control System. Through this system, the orders of the President and Secretary of Defense are trasmitted to the unified and specified commanders.

Operating under the direction of the Secretary of Defense are the Secretaries of the Army, Navy and Air Force. The Marine Corps is a component of the Navy. The Secretaries are responsible to the Secretary of Defense for the administration and operation of their services. The services train, organize and equip forces for assignment to the unified and specified commands, and continue administrative and logistic support to assigned units. However, they exert no command authority once a unit is assigned to a specific or unified command. The services also are responsible for their own doctrine development and weapons research.

The Coast Guard is a branch of the armed forces and is a service within the Department of Transportation, except when operating as a part of the Navy in time of war or when the President directs. In peacetime, the Coast Guard is the primary maritime law enforcement agency for the federal government.

The National Guard is organized along state lines and serves essentially as a reserve of the regular army. The state governors are commanders of the National Guard units in their states. The National Guard comes under the control of the President, as Commander-in-Chief, only after Congress has declared the existence of a national emergency.

**Total armed forces:** 2,116,000 (Army: 790,000; Navy: 553,000; Marines: 192,000; Air Force: 581,000). **Para-military forces:** 45,000 (Coast Guard).

# HEAD OF STATE

President Ronald W. Reagan

**EXECUTIVE OFFICE OF THE PRESIDENT**
*The White House Office*
*1600 Pennsylvania Avenue, N.W.*
*Washington, D.C. 20500*

*Telephone: (202) 456-1414*
*Telex: ITT 440074 whitehouse*

**National Security Council**
*Old Executive Office*
*Washington, D.C. 20506*

*Telephone: (202) 395-3000*

President of the United States and
Commander-in-Chief of the Armed Forces . . . . . . . . . . Ronald W. Reagan
Counsellor to the President . . . . . . . . . . . . . . . . . . . . . . . . . . . Edwin Meese III
Chief of Staff and Assistant
to the President . . . . . . . . . . . . . . . . . . . . . . . . . . . . . . . . James A. Baker III
Deputy Chief of Staff and Assistant
to the President . . . . . . . . . . . . . . . . . . . . . . . . . . . . . . . Michael K. Deaver

Chairman *(ex officio)* . . . . . . . . . . . . . . . . . . . . . . . . . . . . . . Ronald Reagan
(President of the United States and Commander-in-Chief
of the Armed Forces)
Member *(ex officio)* . . . . . . . . . . . . . . . . . . . . . . . . . . . George H. W. Bush
(Vice President)
Member *(ex officio)* . . . . . . . . . . . . . . . . . . . . . . . . . . . . . . . George Shultz
(Secretary of State)
Member *(ex officio)* . . . . . . . . . . . . . . . . . . . . . . . . . . . Caspar Weinberger
(Secretary of Defense)
Member *(ex officio)* . . . . . . . . . . . . . . . . . . . . . . . . . . . . . . . William Casey
(Director, Central Intelligence Agency)
Member *(ex officio)* . . . . . . . . . . . . . . . . . . . . . . . . . . . . Gen. John Vessey
(Chairman, Joint Chiefs of Staff)
Member . . . . . . . . . . . . . . . . . . . . . . . . . . . . . . . . . . . . . . William P. Clark
(Assistant to the President, National Security Affairs)
Member . . . . . . . . . . . . . . . . . . . . . . . . . . . . . . . . . . Robert C. McFarlane
(Deputy Assistant to the President, National Security Affairs)
Member . . . . . . . . . . . . . . . . . . . . . . . . . . . . . . Rear Adm. John M. Poindexter
(Military Assistant to the Assistant to the President,
National Security Affairs)
Member . . . . . . . . . . . . . . . . . . . . . . . . . . . . . . . . . . . Richard C. Marris
(Special Assistant to the Assistant to the President,
National Security Affairs)
Member . . . . . . . . . . . . . . . . . . . . . . . . . . . . . . . . . . . Jacquelyn T. Hill
(Special Assistant to the Assistant to the President,
National Security Affairs)

**Staff**
Deputy Assistant to the President,
National Security Affairs (Coordination) . . . . . . . . . . . . . Charles P. Tyson
Special Assistant to the President,
Executive Secretary and General Counsel . . . . . . . . . Robert M. Kimmitt
Deputy Executive Secretary . . . . . . . . . . . . . . . . . . . . . . . Thomas C. Shull
Special Assistant to the President and
Senior Director, Public Affairs . . . . . . . . . . . . . . . . . . . . . Robert B. Sims
Deputy Director, Public Affairs . . . . . . . . . . . . . . . . . . . . . Marc S. Brazil
Special Assistant to the President and
Senior Director, Legislative Affairs . . . . . . . . . . . . Christopher M. Lehman

Staff Legal Counsel and Deputy
Director of Legislative Affairs ....................Paul B. Thompson
Director, Information Policy/Security Review ............Brenda S. Reger

**European and Soviet Affairs**
Special Assistant to the President
and Senior Director ..........................Jack F. Matlock, Jr.
Director ...........................................Peter R. Sommer
Director ............................................John Lenczowski
Deputy Director .............................Paula J. Dobrainsky

**Asian Affairs**
Special Assistant to the President
and Senior Director ..........................Gaston J. Sigur, Jr.
Director ............................................David N. Laux

**African Affairs**
Director.....................................Frederick L. Wettering

**Latin American Affairs**
Director ......................................Alfonso F. Sapia-Bosch
Director ..........................................Roger W. Fontaine

**Near East and South Asia Affairs**
Special Assistant to the President
and Senior Director ..........................Geoffrey T. H. Kemp
Director...........................................Howard J. Teicher

**Political-Military Affairs**
Special Assistant to the President
and Senior Director ..........................Donald R. Fortier
Director .............................................Robert H. Lilac
Deputy Director..............................Richard T. Childress
Deputy Director .......................................Philip A. Dur
Deputy Director....................................Oliver L. North

**Defense Programs and Arms Control**
Special Assistant to the President
and Senior Director ..........................Ronald F. Lehman, II
Director, Arms Control ............................Sven F. Kraemer
Director, Defense Programs .........................Robert S. Helm
Director, Defense Programs.......................Horace L. Russell
Director, Defense Programs.......................Robert E. Linhard
Director, Defense Programs............................Allan A. Myer
Director, Defense Programs........................Raymond Pollock
Deputy Director, Defense Programs .................Richard B. Levine

**Intelligence Programs**
Director, Intelligence Programs ...............Kenneth E. deGraffenreid
Director, Space Programs ..............................Gilbert D. Rye

**Crisis Management Support and Planning**
Special Assistant to the President
and Senior Director ..............................Richard S. Beal
Deputy Director ...........................................Lyle Cox

**International Economic Affairs**
Special Assistant to the President
and Senior Officer................................Norman A. Bailey
Director ......................................Roger W. Robinson, Jr.
Director ..........................................William F. Martin
Director .........................................Douglas W. McMinn

**International Communications and Information**
Special Assistant to the President
and Senior Director..........................Walter Raymond, Jr.
Director ..........................................Carnes R. Lord

**DEPARTMENT OF DEFENSE—DOD**
*Pentagon*
*Washington, D.C. 20301*
*Telephone:* *(703) 545-6700*

| | |
|---|---|
| **Office of the Secretary of Defense** *Pentagon* *Telephone:* *(703) 695-5261* | Secretary . . . . . . . . . . . . . . . . . . . . . . . . . . . . . . . . . . . . . . .Caspar W. Weinberger |
| | Military Assistant . . . . . . . . . . . . . . . . . . . . . . . . . . . . .Maj. Colin L. Powell |
| | Military Assistant . . . . . . . . . . . . . . . . . . . . . . . . . .Capt. James P. Cormack |
| | Assistant to the Secretary of Defense . . . . . . . . . . . . . . . . . . . .Kathleen Troia |
| | Deputy Secretary . . . . . . . . . . . . . . . . . . . . . . . . . . . . . . . . . . . .Paul Thayer |
| | Senior Military Assistant . . . . . . . . . . . . . . . . . . . . . . . . .Brig. Buford D. Lary |
| | Military Assistant . . . . . . . . . . . . . . . . . . . . . . . . . . . .Col. Nicholas Krawciw |
| | Executive Secretary . . . . . . . . . . . . . . . . . . . . . . . . . . .Col. John H. Stanford |

| | |
|---|---|
| **Assistant to the Secretary of Defense for Review and Oversight** *Telephone:* *(703) 695-4249* | Assistant to the Secretary . . . . . . . . . . . . . . . . . . . . . . . . . .Joseph H. Sherick |
| | Executive Assistant . . . . . . . . . . . . . . . . . . . . . . . . . . .Lt. Col. Stephen Luster |
| | Special Assistant . . . . . . . . . . . . . . . . . . . . . . . . . . . . .William T. Merriman |
| | Inspector-General . . . . . . . . . . . . . . . . . . . . . . . . . . . . . . . . . . .(Vacant) |

| | |
|---|---|
| **Inspector-General of the Department of Defense** *Telephone:* *(703) 695-4250* | Inspector-General . . . . . . . . . . . . . . . . . . . . . . . . . . . . . . . . . . .(Vacant) |
| | Deputy Inspector-General (Acting) . . . . . . . . . . . . . .Derek J. Vander Schaaf |

| | |
|---|---|
| **Director, Program Analysis and Evaluation** *Telephone:* *(703) 695-0971* | Director . . . . . . . . . . . . . . . . . . . . . . . . . . . . . . . . . . . . . .David S. C. Chu |
| | Deputy Director, General Purpose Programs . . . . . . . . . .Thomas P. Christie |
| | Deputy Director, Resource Analysis . . . . . . . . . . . . . . . .Milton A. Margolis |
| | Deputy Director, Strategic Programs . . . . . . . . . . . . . . . . . .Philip L. Major |
| | Deputy Director, Theater Assessments and Planning . . . . . . . . . . . . . . . . . . . . . . . . . . . . . . . . . .Michael Leonard |

| | |
|---|---|
| **General Counsel of the Department of Defense** *Telephone:* *(703) 695-3341* | General Counsel . . . . . . . . . . . . . . . . . . . . . . . . . . . . . .William H. Taft IV |
| | Deputy General Counsel . . . . . . . . . . . . . . . . . . . . . . .Leonard Niederlehner |

| | |
|---|---|
| **Defense Legal Services Agency** *Telephone:* *(703) 695-3341* | Director . . . . . . . . . . . . . . . . . . . . . . . . . . . . . . . . . . .William H. Taft IV |
| | Deputy Director . . . . . . . . . . . . . . . . . . . . . . . . . . . .Leonard Niederlehner |

| | |
|---|---|
| **Assistant Secretary of Defense for Legislative Affairs** *Telephone:* *(703) 697-6210* | Assistant Secretary . . . . . . . . . . . . . . . . . . . . . . . . . . . . .Russell A. Rourke |
| | Deputy Assistant Secretary, Plans and Operations . . . . . . . . . . . . . . . . . . . .Brig. Gen. Buford D. Lary |
| | Deputy Assistant Secretary, Senate Affairs . . . . . . . . . . . . . . . .Ernie Garcia |
| | Deputy Assistant Secretary, House Affairs . . . . . . . . . . . . . . . . . . .Al Barry |

| | |
|---|---|
| **Undersecretary of Defense for Policy** *Telephone:* *(703) 694-1363* | Undersecretary . . . . . . . . . . . . . . . . . . . . . . . . . . . . . . . . . . . .Fred C. Ikle |
| | Military Assistant . . . . . . . . . . . . . . . . . . . . . . . . . . .Col. Martin L. Brandtner |
| | Military Assistant . . . . . . . . . . . . . . . . . . . . . . . . . . .Lt. Col. Richard S. Siner |
| | Counselor. . . . . . . . . . . . . . . . . . . . . . . . . . . . . . . . . . . . . . .Philip Merrill |
| | Deputy Undersecretary, Policy . . . . . . . . . . . . . . . .Gen. Richard G. Stilwell |

| | |
|---|---|
| **Assistant Secretary for International Security Affairs** *Telephone:* *(703) 695-4351* | Assistant Secretary . . . . . . . . . . . . . . . . . . . . . . . . . . . . . . . . . . .(Vacant) |
| | Principal Deputy Assistant, DASD African Affairs . . . . . . . . . .Noel C. Koch |
| | Director, Africa Region . . . . . . . . . . . . . . . . . . . . . . . . . . . .James L. Woods |
| | Director, Special Planning . . . . . . . . . . . . . . . . . . . . . . . . .R. Lynn Rylander |
| | Director, Foreign Military Rights Affairs . . . . . . . . . . . . .Philip E. Barringer |
| | Department of Defense Representative for Law of the Sea Task Force . . . . . . . . . . . . . . .Rear Adm. Bruce A. Harlow |
| | Deputy Assistant Secretary, East Asia and Pacific Affairs . . . . . . . . . . . . . . . . . . . . . . . . . . . .Richard L. Armitage |
| | Director, East Asia and Pacific Region . . . . . . .Commodore Stewart A. Ring |

Principal Advisor, POW/MIA Affairs.........Lt. Col. Gerald S. Venanzi
Deputy Assistant Secretary,
    Inter-American Affairs...........................Nestor D. Sanchez
Director, Inter-American Region ..........Maj. Gen. William S. deCamp
Deputy Assistant Secretary, Near Eastern
    and South Asian Affairs ..................Maj. Gen. Edward L. Tixier
Director, Near East and South Asia Region ...........Phillip R. Mayhew
Deputy Assistant Secretary, Policy Analysis .............James R. Blaker
Director, International Economics
    and Energy Affairs .........................Col. Donald S. Kendall
Director, Plans and Requirements ....................Col. John L. Clark
Director, Force Planning Policy.......................David M. Shilling
Deputy Director, Defense Security
    Assistance Agency ...........................Lt. Gen. Philip C. Gast

**Assistant Secretary for International Security Policy**

*Telephone:    (703) 695-0942*

Assistant Secretary ....................................Richard N. Perle
Principal Deputy Assistant Secretary ..............William E. Hoehn, Jr.
Deputy Assistant Secretary, European
    and North Atlantic Treaty
    Organization (NATO) Policy ...................Brig. John R. Lasater
Principal Director, NATO Political-
    Military Policy and Advisor,
    NATO Affairs .........................Brig. Gen. Anotny A. Smith
Deputy Assistant Secretary, Strategic and
    Theater Nuclear Forces Policy .................Ronald F. Lehman, II
Director, Theater Nuclear Policy ...............Stephen R. Hanmer, Jr.
Director, Strategic Forces Policy.....................Franklin C. Miller
Director, Verification Policy ............................Sally K. Horn
Deputy Assistant Secretary, Negotiations Policy ................(Vacant)
Director, Multilateral Negotiations....................Sheila R. Buckley
Director, Intelligence and Space Policy ...........Maj. Gen. Earl G. Peck
Director, Strategic Arms Reduction Talks
    (START) Arms Control Policy ................Dr. Abram N. Shulsky
Secretary of Defense Representative, U.S.
    Delegation Intermediate Nuclear Forces (INF) ......John A. Woodworth
Secretary of Defense Representative,
    U.S. Delegation START .......................Michael H. Mobbs
Secretary of Defense Representative, U.S.
    Delegation Mutual and Balanced Forced
    Reduction (MBFR)/Committee on Security
    and Cooperation in Europe (CSLE) .................Raymond Tanter

**Deputy Assistant Secretary for International Security Policy**

*Telephone:    (703) 697-9347*

Deputy Assistant Secretary.......................Dr. Stephen D. Bryen
Director, International Policy ......................William M. George
Director, Strategic Trade Policy.......................John R. Konfala
Director, National Disc/Military
    Technology Cooperation .................Lt. Col. Gary T. Walters, Jr.

**Office of the Director of Net Assessment**

*Telephone:    (703) 695-1811*

Director .......................................Andrew W. Marshall

**Defense Investigative Service**
*1900 Half Street, S.W.*
*Buzzard Point*
*Washington, D.C. 20324*
*Telephone:    (202) 693-1427*

Director .........................................Thomas J. O'Brien
Inspector-General ................................James R. Connolly

**Defense Security Assistance Agency**
*Telephone:    (703) 695-3291*

Director......................................Lt. Gen. Philip C. Gast
Deputy Director ...................................Walter B. Ligon

**Defense Intelligence Agency—DIA**
*Office of the Director*
*Telephone: (703) 695-7353*

| | |
|---|---|
| Director | Lt. Gen. James A. Williams |
| Executive Director | Col. N. R. Temperley |
| Executive Assistant | Maj. David J. Piirto |
| Special Assistant | Lt. JG Betsy A. Fitzgerel |
| Chief of Staff | Brig. Gen. Donald W. Goodman |
| Vice Director, Foreign Intelligence | Maj. Gen. Edmund R. Thompson |
| Director, Office of Security | Charles J. Little |
| Director, General Defense Intelligence Program Staff (GDIP) | Martin Hurwitz |
| Deputy Director, GDIP | Harry C. Banford |
| General Counsel | John R. Brock |
| Inspector-General | Col. Gordon A. Noffsinger |
| Chairman, DIA Advisory Committee | Harold L. Brownman |
| Deputy Director, Intelligence and External Affairs | John T. Hughes |
| Vice Deputy Director | Col. H. F. Prewitt |
| Assistant Deputy Director, External Affairs | A. Denis Clift |
| Vice Director, Management and Operations | Maj. Gen. Schuyler Bissell |

**Assistant Secretary of Defense Comptroller**

| | |
|---|---|
| Assistant Secretary | Vincent Puritano |
| Principal Deputy Assistant Secretary | John R. Quetsch |

**Defense Contract Audit Agency**
*Cameron Station, Virginia*
*Telephone: (703) 274-7328*

| | |
|---|---|
| Director | Charles O. Starrett, Jr. |

**Assistant to the Secretary of Defense for Intelligence Oversight**
*Telephone: (703) 697-1346*

| | |
|---|---|
| Assistant to the Secretary | Werner E. Michel |

**Small and Disadvantaged Business Utilization Office**
*Telephone: (703) 694-1151*

| | |
|---|---|
| Director | Norma B. Leftwich |

**Assistant Secretary of Manpower Reserve Affairs and Logistics**
*Telephone: (703) 695-5254*

| | |
|---|---|
| Assistant Secretary | Lawrence J. Korb |
| Chairman, Reserve Forces Policy Board | Louis Conti |
| Deputy Assistant, Military Personnel and Force Management | Lt. Gen. R. Dean Tice |
| Deputy Assistant, Mobilization Planning and Requirements | Lt. Gen. Bennett L. Lewis |

**Defense Logistics Agency**
*Cameron Station, Virginia*
*Telephone: (703) 274-6000*

| | |
|---|---|
| Director | Vice Adm. Eugene A. Grinstead |
| Deputy Director | Maj. Gen. M. Roger Peterson |
| Deputy Director, Acquisition Management | Maj. Gen. Joseph H. Connolly |
| Staff Director, Office of Small and Disadvantaged Business Utilization | Ray W. Dellas |
| General Counsel | Karl Kabeiseman |
| Inspector-General | Col. J. F. Senna |
| Assistant Director, Plans, Policies and Programs | Brig. Gen. Charles H. Edmiston, Jr. |
| Assistant Director, Telecommunications and Information Systems | Rear Adm. Duncan P. McGillavary |
| Comptroller | William J. Cassell |
| Executive Director, Contracting | R. F. Chiesa |
| Executive Director, Supply Operations | Brig. Gen. James E. Cassity |
| Executive Director, Technology and Logistics Service | Richard G. Bruner |
| Executive Director, Contract Management | W. V. Gordon |
| Executive Director, Quality Assurance | Rear Adm. Frank C. Collins, Jr. |

**Assistant Secretary of Defense for**
**Public Affairs**

*Telephone:    (703) 697-9312*

Assistant Secretary ................................Henry E. Catto, Jr.
Deputy Assistant ............................Brig. Walter C. Cousland
Director, Directorate for Defense Information ......Col. Robert J. O'Brien
Director, News Division .........................Capt. Charles W. Klee
Director, Public Correspondence Division ................Philip A. Farris
Director, Directorate for Community Relations.......Col. Charles H. Senn
Director, Directorate for Freedom of
    Information and Security Review .................Charles W. Hinkle

**American Forces Information Service**

*Telephone:    (703) 696-5284*

Director (Acting) ..............................Col. Fredwin M. Odom
Director, American Forces Press and
    Publications Service .........................Capt. James S. Eaves
Director, Department of Defense
    Dependents Schools............................W. Beth Stephens
Director, Office of Economic Adjustment .............Robert M. Rauner
Director, Tri-Service Medical Information
    System Program Office SNBB ..................Col. John W. McGinnis

**Defense Audiovisual Agency**
*Office of the Director*
*Norton Air Force Base, Virginia*
*Telephone:    (703) 876-7047*

Director..............................................Robert Scott

**Assistant Secretary for Health Affairs**

*Telephone:    (703) 697-2113*

Assistant Secretary (Acting)..........................John F. Beary, III
Director, Medical Planning..................Lt. Col. Podge M. Reed, Jr.
Director, International Health Affairs ............Lt. Col. Jerry M. Brown
Director, Medical Logistics Readiness ..............Ronald G. Richards
Director, Health Programming and Budgeting...............John Dexter

**Undersecretary of Defense for**
**Research and Engineering**

*Telephone:    (703) 697-9111*

Undersecretary...................................Richard D. DeLauer
Principal Deputy Undersecretary ...................James P. Wade, Jr.
Deputy Undersecretary, Acquisition
    Management (Acting) ...........................Harvey J. Gordon
Director, International Acquisition ......................Col. Carlberg
Director, Contract Administration .....................Thomas J. Lelli
Director, Contract Policy ...........................Herbert L. Fisher
Director, Cost Pricing and Finance .......................John Kendig
Director, Contract Studies ..........................Benson D. Adams
Director, Defense Acquisition Regulatory Systems.........James Brannan
Director, Major Systems Acquisition .......................John Smith
Director, Federal Acquisition Group ...............Cdr. John Summers
Assistant Deputy Undersecretary,
    Production Support .............................John A. Mittino
Director, Industrial Productivity (Acting) ...........Richard A. Stimson
Director, Industrial Resources .....................Richard E. Donnelly
Director, Standardization and
    Acquisition Support ...........................Richard A. Stimson
Director, International Acquisition ..............Col. Ronald L. Carlberg
Director, Federal Acquisition Regulatory
    Project Office ................................................
Deputy Undersecretary, Command, Control,
    Communications, and Intelligence ................Donald C. Latham
Director, Command, Control, and
    Communications Resources...........................N. Cavallini
Director, Information Systems .....................Stephen T. Walker
Director, Electronic Warfare and Command,
    Control, and Communications Countermeasures ........John M. Porter
Director, Strategic and Theater Nuclear
    Forces Command, Control and Communications ...Arthur H. Bertapelle
Director, Theater and Tactical
    Command, Control and Communications ...........John C. Cittadino
Assistant Deputy Undersecretary, Intelligence ........Charles A. Hawkins

Director, Intelligence Resources .......................James I. Mayer
Director, National Intelligence Systems....................Mary J. Vajta
Director, Tactical Intelligence Systems .................Roger K. Engel
Assistant Deputy Undersecretary,
　Systems Integration ................................Robert D. Turner
Director, Systems Architecture and Analysis...........Dennis K. Leedom
Director, Long-Range Planning and System Evaluation ..........(Vacant)
Deputy Undersecretary, International
　Programs and Technology .......................Talbot S. Lindstrom
Assistant Deputy Undersecretary,
　International Programs...........................Gerald D. Sullivan
Director, NATO/European Affairs ..................Gerald D. Sullivan
Director, Far/Middle East and
　Southern Hemisphere Affairs......................Jeanne S. Mintz
Assistant Deputy Undersecretary,
　Technology Transfer (Acting) ....................Francis B. Kapper
Special Assistant/Special Coordinator,
　Technology Transfer...............................Les Lomacky
Director, Export Control (Acting).................Col. Roger L. Grossel
Director, Military Technology
　Sharing (Acting) .........................Lt. Col. Bruce R. Meiser
Deputy Undersecretary, Research and
　Advanced Technology ............................Edith W. Martin
Assistant Deputy Undersecretary, Research
　and Advanced Technology.........................H. Mark Grove
Director, Computer Software Systems ...........Lt. Col. Larry E. Druffel
Director, Electronics and Physical Sciences ...................(Vacant)
Director, Engineering Technology ..................Raymond F. Siewert
Director, Environmental and Life Sciences ..............Col. Paul D. Try
Director, Military Systems Technology ..............Raymond F. Siewert
Director, Research and Laboratory Management ..............Leo Young
Director, Very High Speed Integrated
　Circuits/Electronic Devices (Acting) ..........Egbert D. Maynard, Jr.
Deputy Undersecretary, Strategic and
　Theater Nuclear Forces ................................T. K. Jones
Military Assistant to Deputy Undersecretary,
　Strategic and Theater Nuclear Forces .......Brig. Gen. Elmer T. Brooks
Director, Cruise Missile Systems....................Stanley B. Alterman
Director, Defense Systems ...........................John L. Gardner
Director, Offensive and Space Systems ...............Cyrus P. Knowles
Director, START and Arms Control .................Lee P. Minichiello
Deputy Undersecretary, Tactical Warfare Programs .......Mac C. Adams
Assistant Deputy Undersecretary, Tactical
　Warfare Programs ...................Brig. Gen. Edwin M. Aguanno
Assistant Deputy Undersecretary, Mobility
　and Naval Warfare ..............................William D. O'Neil
Assistant Deputy Undersecretary, Land Warfare ......Charles W. Bernard
Assistant Deputy Undersecretary, Air Warfare .......Kenneth R. Hinman
Director, Defense Test and Evaluation ...................I. W. Linder
Deputy Undersecretary,
　Directed Energy Weapons ............Maj. Gen. Donald L. Lamberson

**Defense Science Board**
*1400 Wilson Boulevard*
*Arlington, Virginia*
*(Mailing Address: Washington, D.C.*
*　20305)*
*Telephone:　(703) 695-4157*

Chairman ....................................Norman R. Augustine
Vice Chairman ..................................Eugene G. Fubini

**Assistant to the Secretary of Defense**
**　for Atomic Energy**
*Telephone:　(703) 697-5161*

Assistant to the Secretary...........................Richard L. Wagner
Deputy Assistant, Military Applications .......Maj. Gen. David W. Einsel
Deputy Assistant, Chemical Matters ..............Dr. Theodore S. Gold

**Defense Advanced Research Projects Agency—DARPA**
*Telephone: (703) 694-3035*

Director ...........................................Robert S Cooper
Deputy Director, Research ...........................Carl F. Romney
Deputy Director, Technology .........................Verne L. Lynn

**Defense Communications Agency**
*Office of the Director*
*8th and South Courthouse Road*
*Arlington, Virginia*
*(Mailing Address: Washington, D.C. 20305)*
*Telephone: (703) 692-0018*

Director .................................Lt. Gen. Winston D. Powers
Vice Director ............................Rear Adm. P. Lautermilch
Director, Defense Communications
   System Organization ........................Brig. Gen. R. O. Petty
Deputy Director, Satellite
   Communications System....................Capt. P. E. Robinson, Jr.
Program Manager, Defense Data Network
   Program Management Office ......................Col. H. Heiden
Deputy Director, Joint Program Office ........Comdr. James F. Dorsy, Jr.

**Defense Communications Agency— Pacifica Area**
*Wheeler Air Force Base*
*Hawaii 96854*
*Telephone: (455) 655-1647*

Commander ......................................Col. T. D. Sargent

**Defense Commercial Communications Office**
*Scott Air Force Base*
*Illinois 62225*
*Telephone: (618) 256-4784*

Commander ...........................................D. L. Jones

**Defense Mapping Agency**
*Office of the Director*
*Building 56 NOBS*
*Washington, D.C. 20305*
*Telephone: (202) 653-1478*

Director.......................Rear Adm. Edward A. Wilkinson, Jr.
Deputy Director .........................Brig. Gen. William B. Webb
Deputy Director, Programs/Production Operation......Allen E. Anderson
Deputy Director, Plans
   and Requirements ..............Rear Adm. Laverne S. Severance, Jr.

**Defense Nuclear Agency**
*Office of the Director*
*Hybla Valley Federal Building*
*6801 Telegraph Road*
*Alexandria, Virginia*
*(Mailing Address: Washington, D.C. 20305)*
*Telephone: (703) 325-7595*

Director ..................................Lt. Gen. Richard U. Saxer
Deputy Director, Administration .........Maj. Gen. Grayson D. Tate, Jr.
Director, European Command
   Liaison Office ......................Lt. Col. Kenneth R. Lamison, Jr.
Director, Pacific Command Liaison Office...........Cdr. John B. Bartlett
Director, Joint Chiefs of Staff
   Communications Liaison Office.............Lt. Col. Frederick Tedesco
Director, Public Affairs Office ................Lt. Col. Dale F. Keller, Jr.
Inspector-General ...............................Capt. John W. Weed
General Counsel ...............................Robert L. Brittigan
Director, Biomedical Effects Directorate ..........Col. Bobby R. Adcock
Director, Arms Control and Policy Office.........Col. T. H. M. Crampton
Director, Operations Directorate .................Col. Charles R. Linton
Director, Acquisition Management Directorate .............John E. Reid
Director, Intelligence/Security Directorate .......Col. John L. Bohach, Jr.
Commander, Counterintelligence
   Detachment .......................Lt. Col. Lawrence N. Reiman
Director, Joint Atomic Information Exchange Group.....Cdr. Joh R. Lund
Director, Logistics and Engineering Directorate ........Thomas P. Jeffers
Director, Technical Information Directorate/
   Information Management Division ................Patricia H. Means
Deputy Director, Science and Technology ...................(Vacant)
Director, Nuclear Assessment Directorate.........Col. Donald D. Kunard
Director, Shock Physics Directorate ..................Col. M. I. Kovel
Director, Radiation Directorate .................Col. William E. Adams

**Armed Forces Radiobiology Research Institute**
*National Naval Medical Center*
*Bethesda, Maryland 20814*
*Telephone: (301) 295-0530*

Director ...........................................Capt. P. E. Tyler

**Military Liaison Committee to the Department of Energy**
*Telephone: (703) 697-5161*

Chairman ......................................Richard L. Wagner

**National Security Agency—NSA**
*Central Security Service*
*Headquarters Building*
*Ft. Meade, Maryland*
*Telephone: (301) 688-7111*

Director ..................................Lt. Gen. Lincoln D. Faurer
Deputy Director .................................Robert E. Rich
General Counsel ..............................Jon. T. Anderson
Inspector-General ..........................Albert D. Braeuninger
Defense Representative ...........................Robert K. Price
Assistant Deputy Director, Operations ........Maj. Gen. Thomas J. Flynn
Chief, Tactical Systems ...................Brig. Gen. David S. Watrous

## DEFENSE FORCES

**ARMED FORCES**
**United States Armed Forces**
*Pentagon*
*Washington, D.C. 20301*
*Telephone: (703) 697-9121*

**Joint Chiefs of Staff—JCS**
Chairman...................................Gen. John W. Vessey, Jr.
Member...................................Gen. John A. Wickham, Jr.
(Chief of Staff, Army)
Member ....................................Adm. J. D. Watkins
(Chief of Naval Operations)
Member....................................Gen. Charles A. Gabriel
(Chief of Staff, Air Force)
Member ....................................Gen. Paul X. Keiley
(Commandant of the Marine Corps)

Executive Assistant ....................Vice Adm. Arthur S. Moreau, Jr.
Member, Chairman's Staff Group ...............Col. Thomas Anderson
Member, Chairman's Staff Group .............Maj. Randolph M. Blanks
Member, Chairman's Staff Group................Capt. Alton Thompson
Member, Chairman's Staff Group ................Col. James D. Beans
Member, Chairman's Staff Group ...............Col. William M. Stokes

**Joint Staff**
*Telephone: (703) 694-5221*

Director...................................Lt. Gen. Jack N. Merritt
Vice Director ..............................Maj. Gen. George B. Crist
JCS Representative, Mutual and
    Balanced Force Reduction..............Maj. Gen. A. St. John II (Ret.)
DOD Representative, Mutual and
    Balanced Force Reduction .......................James R. Blaker
DOD Representative, Law of the Sea (Acting) ......Cdr. William Schachte
JCS Representative, Comprehensive
    Test Ban Negotiations ...................Maj. Gen. E. B. Giller (Ret.)
JCS Representative, Anti-
    Satellite Negotiations................Maj. Gen. D. D. Bradburn (Ret.)
DOD Representative, Panama Canal
    Treaty Affairs.........................Lt. Gen. W. G. Dolvin (Ret.)
JCS Representative, START
    Negotiations .........................Maj. Gen. Donald O. Aldridge
DOD Representative, START Negotiations ...........Michael H. Mobbs
Defense Adviser, U.S. Mission to NATO ..............Laurence J. Legere
U.S. Representative, NATO Military
    Committee Liaison Office .........................Col. R. H. Howe
Chairman, U.S. Section, Canada-U.S.
    Military Cooperation Committee ..........Maj. Gen. William E. Klein

Military Secretary, U.S. Delegation,
    Inter-American Defense Board and
    Military Secretary, U.S. Section,
    Joint Mexican U.S. Defense Commission . . . . . Lt. Col. Jose R. De Varona

**Studies Analysis and Gaming Agency**
*Telephone: (703) 695-9162*

Chief . . . . . . . . . . . . . . . . . . . . . . . . . . . . . . . . . . . . . . . Comdr. James M. Seely

**Marine Corps Liaison Office**
*Telephone: (703) 695-6952*

Cief . . . . . . . . . . . . . . . . . . . . . . . . . . . . . . . . . . . . . . Sgt. M. Janiszewzki

**J-3 Operations**
*Telephone: (703) 697-3702*

Director . . . . . . . . . . . . . . . . . . . . . . . . . . . . . . Lt. Gen. Richard L. Prillaman
Vice Director . . . . . . . . . . . . . . . . . . . . . . . . . Maj. Gen. Maurice C. Padden
Deputy Director, Current Operations . . . . . Brig. Gen. Larry D. Dillingham
Director, Environmental Services Division . . . . . . . . . . . Capt. J. R. Lincoln
Director, Joint Operations Division . . . . . . . . . . . . . . . . . . Col. P. R. Paxton
Director, Special Operations Division . . . . . . . . . . . . . . . . Col. R. W. Gingras
Deputy Director, Operational Plans
    and Capabilities . . . . . . . . . . . . . . . . . . . . . . . . Comdr. Edwin Anderson
Director, Joint Exercise Division . . . . . . . . . . . . . . . . . . . . Col. Donald R. Ley
Director, Readiness Programs Division . . . . . . . . . . . . . Capt. Robert C. Leslie
Division Chief, Operation Plans Division . . . . . . . . . . . . . . Col. H. M. Nelson
Deputy Director, Reconnaisance Space
    Electronic Warfare and Command,
    Control and Communications Division . . . . . . . Rear Adm. John R. Batzler
Deputy Director, National Military
    Command Center . . . . . . . . . . . . . . . . . . . . . . . . . . . . . . . . Gen. Goodrich
Director, Command Systems Operations Division . . . . . . Col. W. B. Preston
Director, Command and Control Division . . . . . . . . . . . . . . . . Col. P. E. Rice
Director, Strategic Operations Division . . . . . . . . . . . . . Col. R. B. Goetze, Jr.

**J-4 Logistics**
*Telephone: (703) 697-7000*

Director . . . . . . . . . . . . . . . . . . . . . . . . . . . . . . Vice Adm. William J. Cowhill
Deputy Director, Strategic Mobility . . . . . . . . . . . Maj. Gen. C. D. Smith, Jr.
Deputy Director, Planning and Resources . . . . . . . . . . . . . . . . . . . . . . . . . . . .
Director, Logistic Planning Division . . . . . . . . . . . . . . . . . . . Capt. Ted Ieber
Director, Plans, Programs and Mobilization Branch . . . . . . . . . Col. M. Cluff
Director, Logistics Resources Division . . . . . . . . . . . . . . . Col. L. F. Tigh, Jr.

**J-5 Plans and Policy**
*Pentagon*
*Telephone: (703) 695-5618*

Director . . . . . . . . . . . . . . . . . . . . . . . . . . . . . . Lt. Gen. Herman O. Thomson
Vice Director . . . . . . . . . . . . . . . . . . . . . . . . . . . Maj. Gen. William E. Klein
Deputy Director, Politico-Military Affairs . . . . . . . . . . Comdr. Jack N. Darby
Assistant Deputy Director, Politico-Military
    Affairs . . . . . . . . . . . . . . . . . . . . . . . . . . . . . . Brig. Gen. Andrew L. Cooley, Jr.
Director, European Division . . . . . . . . . . . . . . . . . . . . . . . Col. H. A. Shockley
Director, Far East/South Asia Division . . . . . . . . . . . . . . . . . . Col. R. Deitch
Director, Western Hemisphere Division . . . . . . . . . . . . . . Col. J. W. Connally
Director, Security Assistance/Arms Transfer Division . . . . . Col. J. P. Coyne
Director, Middle East/Africa Division . . . . . . . . . . . . . . . . Capt. J. D. Cossey
Deputy Director, International Negotiations . . . . . . . Brig. Gen. J. Nicholson
JCS Representative, START . . . . . . . . . . . . . . Rear Adm. W. A. Williams III
JCS Representative, INF . . . . . . . . . . . . . . . . . . . . . Brig. Gen. W. F. Burns
Deputy Director, Force Development
    and Strategic Plans . . . . . . . . . . . . . . . . . . . . . Brig. Gen. Randall D. Peat
Assistant Deputy Director, Force
    Development and Strategic Plans . . . . . . . . . . . . . . . . . . . . . . . . . . . . . . . .
Director, Nuclear/Chemical Division . . . . . . . . . . . . . . . . . . . Capt. H. Bauer
Director, Strategic Division . . . . . . . . . . . . . . . . . . . . . . . Col. M. E. Smith III
Director, General and Organizational Policy Division . . . . . . Col. G. A. Holt
Director, Program Budget Analysis Division . . . . . . . . . . . . . Col. J. J. Mastal
Director, Force Planning and
    Programming Divison . . . . . . . . . . . . . . . . . . . . . . Col. Steven Musselman

**Command Control and Communications Systems**
*Telephone: (703) 695-6478*

Director . . . . . . . . . . . . . . . . . . . . . . . . . . . . . . . . . . . Lt. Gen. Robert T. Herres
Executive Director . . . . . . . . . . . . . . . . . . . . . . . . . . . . . Col. John E. Counts
Deputy Director, Strategic Systems . . . . . . . . . . . . Rear Adm. Paul D. Tomb
Deputy Director, Tactical/Theater
    Systems . . . . . . . . . . . . . . . . . . . . . . . . . . . . . . . . Brig. Gen. Robert G. Lynn

## COMBINED COMMANDS AND AGENCIES

**North Atlantic Treaty Organization (NATO) Military Committee**
*Brussels, Belgium*

U.S. Representative . . . . . . . . . . . . . . . . . . . . . . . Gen. Roscoe Robinson, Jr.
Deputy U.S. Representative . . . . . . . . . . . . . . . . . Comdr. Richard F. Butts
Deputy Chairman . . . . . . . . . . . . . . . . . . . . . . . . Lt. Gen. Sinclair L. Melner
Commander, NATO Air
    Early Warning Force . . . . . . . . . . . . . . . . Maj. Gen. Leighton R. Palmerton

**Supreme Headquarters, Allied Powers, Europe—SHAPE**
*Stuttgart-Veihingen*
*West Germany*

Supreme Allied Commander . . . . . . . . . . . . . . . . . . Gen. Bernard W. Rogers
Chief of Staff . . . . . . . . . . . . . . . . . . . . . . . . . . . . . . . Gen. James E. Dalton
Executive to Commander . . . . . . . . . . . . . . . . . Brig. Gen. Charles P. Otstott

**Allied Forces Southern Europe**

Commander-in-Chief . . . . . . . . . . . . . . . . . . . . . . . . Adm. William N. Small
Chief of Staff . . . . . . . . . . . . . . . . . . . . . . . . . . . . . . Lt. Gen. John B. Blount
Assistant Chief of Staff, Logistics . . . . . . . . . . . . . Comdr. John J. Higginson
Assistant Chief of Staff, Plans
    and Policy . . . . . . . . . . . . . . . . . . . . . . . . . . . . Brig. Gen. Jack D. Woodall
Deputy Chief of Staff, Logistics and
    Administration, Land Forces . . . . . . . . . . . . . Brig. Gen. Lincoln Jones, III
Commander, Air Forces . . . . . . . . . . . . . . . . Lt. Gen. William E. Brown, Jr.
Chief of Staff, Air Forces . . . . . . . . . . . . . . . . . . Maj. Gen. Bill V. Brain
Deputy Commander, 5th Air Force . . . . . . . . . . Brig. Gen. Richard G. Head
Deputy Commander, 6th Air Force . . . . . . . Maj. Gen. Leon W. Babcock, Jr.
Commander, Striking and Support Services . . Vice Adm. Edward H. Martin
Deputy Commander, Land Forces
    Southeastern Europe . . . . . . . . . . . . . . . . . . Maj. Gen. Richard W. Anson

**Allied Forces Central Europe**

Deputy Commander-in-Chief, Operations
    and Intelligence . . . . . . . . . . . . . . . . . . . . . . . Maj. Gen. Edward A. Dinjes
Assistant Chief of Staff, Operations . . . . . . . . . . Brig. Gen. David W. Forjan
Assistant Chief of
    Staff, Logistics . . . . . . . . . . . . . . . Brig. Gen. Walter W. Kastenmeyer, Jr.
Commander, Air Forces . . . . . . . . . . . . . . . . . . . . . . Gen. Billy M. Minter
Deputy Chief of Staff, Operations,
    Air Forces . . . . . . . . . . . . . . . . . . . . . . . . . . Brig. Gen. Wilson C. Cooney
Commander, Central Army Group
    (CENTAG)—NATO . . . . . . . . . . . . . . . . . . . . . . . Gen. Glenn K. Otis
Deputy Commander-in-Chief
    (CENTAG), Support . . . . . . . . . . . . . . . . . Brig. Gen. Charles E. Honore
Air Deputy, Allied Forces
    Northern Europe . . . . . . . . . . . . . . . . . . . Maj. Gen. Lawrence D. Garrison

**Supreme Allied Command, Atlantic— SACLANT**
*Norfolk, Virginia 23511*
*Telephone: (804) 444-0000*

Commander . . . . . . . . . . . . . . . . . . . . . . . . . . . . Adm. Wesley L. McDonald
Chief of Staff . . . . . . . . . . . . . . . . . . . . . Rear Adm. Richard L. Thompson
Island Commander, Iceland . . . . . . . . . . . . . Rear Adm. Ronald E. Narmi
Deputy Commander-in-Chief, Iberian
    Atlantic Area . . . . . . . . . . . . . . . . . . . . . . Rear Adm. Louis A. Williams

**United Nations Command, US Forces Korea (Combined Forces Command, Korea)**

Commander-in-Chief . . . . . . . . . . . . . . . . . . . . . Gen. Robert W. Sennewald
Deputy Commander-in-Chief . . . . . . . . . . . . . . . . . Lt. Gen. John L. Pickitt
Chief of Staff . . . . . . . . . . . . . . . . . . . . . . . . . Maj. Gen. John W. Hudachek
Deputy Assistant Chief of Staff,
    Command and Control . . . . . . . . . . . . . . . . . Brig. Gen. Larry D. Church
Assistant Chief of Staff, J-3 . . . . . . . . . . . . . . Maj. Gen. Kenneth C. Lever

Assistant Chief of Staff, J-4 . . . . . . . . . . . . . . . . . Brig. Gen. James Piner, Jr.
Assistant Chief of Staff, J-5 . . . . . . . . . . . . . . . Brig. Gen. Charles H. Pitman
Commander, U.S. Naval Forces . . . . . . . . . . Rear Adm. Frederick W. Kelley
Commander, Combined Field Army . . . . . . . . . Lt. Gen. Louis C. Menetrey
Chief of Staff . . . . . . . . . . . . . . . . . . . . . . . . . . Brig. Gen. John C. Bahnsen, Jr.

## North American Aerospace Defense Command—NORAD (and Space Command—SPACECOM)
*Paterson Air Force Base*
*Colorado Springs, Colorado 80914*

*Telephone:   (303) 591-7321*

Commander-in-Chief . . . . . . . . . . . . . . . . . . . . . . . . Gen. James V. Hartinger
Vice Commander-in-Chief . . . . . . . . . . . . . . . . . Maj. Gen. Bruce K. Brown
Deputy Chief of Staff for
    Intelligence, J-2 . . . . . . . . . . . . . . . . . . . . . . Brig. Gen. Thomas C. Brandt
Vice Deputy Chief of Staff, Plans (NORAD), and
    Deputy Chief of Staff, Plans (SPACECOM) . . . . . Maj. Gen. Carl N. Beer
Assistant Deputy Chief of Staff,
    Combat Operations . . . . . . . . . . . . . . . . . . . . . Brig. Gen. Paul D. Wagoner
Deputy Chief of Staff, Communications . . . . . Maj. Gen. Winston D. Pauers
Assistant Deputy Chief of Staff, Communications . . . . . . . . . . . . . . . . . . . . .
Deputy Chief of Staff, J-3 . . . . . . . . . . . . . . . . Maj. Gen. Thomas W. Sawyer
Command Director . . . . . . . . . . . . . . . . Brig. Gen. J. Hollis V. McCrea, Jr.
Command Director . . . . . . . . . . . . . . . . . . . . . . . Brig. Gen. Billy J. Rhoten
Command Director . . . . . . . . . . . . . . . . . . . . . Brig. Gen. Melbourne Kimsey
Command Director . . . . . . . . . . . . . . . . . Brig. Gen. Christian F. Breyer, Jr.
Deputy Commander, Tactical Air Command,
    Air Defense (Langley Air Force Base, VA) . . . . Maj. Gen. Russel L. Violett
Commander, 21st NORAD Region
    (Hancock Field, NY) . . . . . . . . . . . . . . . . . . . Brig. Gen. Kenneth W. North
Deputy Commander, 22nd NORAD Region
    (North Bay Air Force Base, Ontario, Canada) . . . . . . . . . . . . . . . . . . . . . .
Commander, 25th NORAD Region
    (McChard Air Force Base, WA) . . . . . . . . . . Brig. Gen. Richard M. Pascoe
Commander, 26th NORAD Region
    (Luke Air Force Base, AZ) . . . . . . . . . . . . . Brig. Gen. Richard A. Pierson
Commander, NORAD/Air Defense Command
    Region (Elmendorf Air Force Base, AK) . . . . . Lt. Gen. Lynwood E. Clark

## UNIFIED COMMANDS

### United States European Command
*Stuttgart-Veihingen*
*West Germany*

Commander-in-Chief . . . . . . . . . . . . . . . . . . . . . . . Gen. Bernard W. Rogers
Deputy Commander-in-Chief . . . . . . . . . . . . . . . . Gen. Richard L. Lawson
Chief of Staff . . . . . . . . . . . . . . . . . . . . . . . . . . . . . Lt. Gen. Howard F. Stone
Director, J-1 . . . . . . . . . . . . . . . . . . . . . . . . Brig. Gen. Mildred E. P. Hedbers
Director, J-2 . . . . . . . . . . . . . . . . . . . . . . . . . . . . Brig. Gen. Edward J. Heinz
Director, J-3 . . . . . . . . . . . . . . . . . . . . . . . . . . . Rear Adm. James S. Elfelt
Deputy Director, J-3 . . . . . . . . . . . . . . . . . . . Brig. Gen. Ernest J. Cook, Jr.
Director, J-4/J-7 . . . . . . . . . . . . . . . . . . . . . . . Maj. Gen. Francis J. Toner
Deputy Director, J-4/J-7 . . . . . . . . . . . . . . . . Brig. Gen. Marion F. Tidwell
Director, J-5 . . . . . . . . . . . . . . . . . . . . . . . . . . . . . Maj. Gen. Davis C. Rohr
Director, J-6 . . . . . . . . . . . . . . . . . . . . . . . . . . . . Comdr. Robert K. Kihune
Chief, Office of Military
    Cooperation (Egypt) . . . . . . . . . . . . . . . . . . . Brig. Gen. Stanton R. Musser
U.S. Deputy Commander-in-Chief,
    Live Oak, SHAPE (Belgium) . . . . . . . . . . Brig. Gen. Jerome R. Barnes, Jr.

### United States Pacific Command
*Honolulu, Hawaii*

*Telephone:   (808) 471-7411*

Commander-in-Chief . . . . . . . . . . . . . . . . . . . . . . . . . Adm. William T. Crave
Deputy Commander-in-Chief and
    Chief of Staff . . . . . . . . . . . . . . . . . . . . . . . Lt. Gen. Joseph T. Palastra, Jr.
Director, Intelligence . . . . . . . . . . . . . . . . . . . Brig. Gen. Jimmy C. PettyJohn
Director, Operations . . . . . . . . . . . . . . . . . . . . . . . . Maj. Gen. John V. Cox
Deputy Director, Operations . . . . . . . . . . . . . . Brig. Gen. Thomas R. Olsen
Director, Logistics, Security Assistance . . . . . . . . . . Comdr. John R. Wilson
Director, Plans . . . . . . . . . . . . . . . . . . . . . . . . Rear Adm. Robert E. Kirksey
Director, Command, Control and
    Communications Systems . . . . . . . . . . . . . . . . Maj. Gen. Vaughn O. Lang
Deputy Chief of Staff . . . . . . . . . . . . . . . . . . . . Maj. Gen. Robert E. Messerli

**United States Forces, Japan**

Commander . . . . . . . . . . . . . . . . . . . . . . . . . . .Lt. Gen. Charles L. Donnelly, Jr.
Chief of Staff . . . . . . . . . . . . . . . . . . . . . . . . . . . .Maj. Gen. David B. Barker

**United States Atlantic Command**
*Norfolk, Virginia 23511*
*Telephone:  (804) 444-0000*

Commander-in-Chief . . . . . . . . . . . . . . . . . . . . . . .Adm. Wesley L. McDonald
Army Component Commander . . . . . . . . . . . . . . . .Gen. Richard E. Carazas
Air Force Component Commander . . . . . . . . . . . . . .Gen. Wilbur L. Creech
Deputy and Chief of Staff . . . . . . . . . . . . . . . .Vice Adm. Kenneth M. Carr
Deputy Chief of Staff . . . . . . . . . . . . . . . . . . . .Brig. Gen. Walter D. Fillmore
Commander, U.S. Forces Azores  . . . . . . . . . . . .Brig. Gen. Donald C. Smith

**United States Readiness Command**
*MacDill Air Force Base*
*Florida 33608*
*Telephone:  (813) 830-1110*

Commander-in-Chief . . . . . . . . . . . . . . . . . . . . . . .Gen. Wallace H. Nutting
Deputy Commander-in-Chief . . . . . . . . . . . . . . .Lt. Gen. James R. Brickel
Chief of Staff . . . . . . . . . . . . . . . . . . . . . . . . . . .Rear Adm. Charles B. Hunter
Army Component Commander  . . . . . . . . . . . . . . .Gen. Richard E. Cavazos
Air Force Component Commander . . . . . . . . . . . . . .Gen. Wilbur L. Creech
Director, Operations, J-3 . . . . . . . . . . . . . . . . . .Maj. Gen. John A. Hemphill
Deputy Director, Operations, J-3 . . . . . . . . . .Brig. Gen. John C. Scheidt, Jr.
Director, Logistics, J-4  . . . . . . . . . . . . . . . . . . . . . . . . . . . . . . . . . . . . . . . .
Director, Plans, Programs,
    and Policy, J-5 . . . . . . . . . . . . . . . . . . . .Maj. Gen. George A. Edwards, Jr.
Director, Command Control Communications
    and Computer Systems (CYS) . . . . . . . . . . . . .Brig. Gen. Donald L. Moore
Commander, U.S. Forces Caribbean . . . . . . . . .Rear Adm. Ralph R. Hedges

**Joint Deployment Agency**
Director . . . . . . . . . . . . . . . . . . . . . . . . . . . . . . . .Gen. Wallace H. Nutting
Vice Director . . . . . . . . . . . . . . . . . . . . . . . . . . . .Lt. Gen. James R. Brickel
Chief of Staff . . . . . . . . . . . . . . . . . . . . . . . . . . .Rear Adm. Charles B. Hunter
Director of Deployment . . . . . . . . . . . . . . . . . . .Maj. Gen. James I. Baginski
Deputy Director of Deployment . . . . . . . . . . . . . . . . . . . . . . . . . . . . . . . . . . .
Deputy Director of Command,
    Control, Communications and
    Computer Systems (CYS) . . . . . . . . . . . . . . . .Brig. Gen. Donald L. Moore

**United States Central Command**
*MacDill Air Force Base*
*Florida 33608*
*Telephone:  (813) 830-2667*

Commander . . . . . . . . . . . . . . . . . . . . . . . . . . . .Lt. Gen. Robert C. Kingston
Deputy Commander . . . . . . . . . . . . . . . . . . . . . .Maj. Gen. Robert C. Taylor
Chief of Staff . . . . . . . . . . . . . . . . . . . . . .Brig. Gen. James R. VanDen Elzen
Director, J-2 . . . . . . . . . . . . . . . . . . . . . . . . . . .Brig. Gen. Dedly J. Gordon
Director, J-3 . . . . . . . . . . . . . . . . . . . . . .Brig. Gen. Michael P. C. Carns
Director, J-4 . . . . . . . . . . . . . . . . . . . . . . . . . .Maj. Gen. David E. Watts
Director, J-5 . . . . . . . . . . . . . . . . . . . . . . . . . . .Comdr. James M. Glenn
Director, J-6 . . . . . . . . . . . . . . . . . . . . . . . . .Brig. Gen. Samuel J. Greene
Commander, Headquarters Forward  . . . . . . . . .Brig. Gen. Ray M. Franklin

**United States Southern Command**
*Quarry Heights*
*Panama*

Commander-in-Chief . . . . . . . . . . . . . . . . . . . . . . . .Gen. Paul E. Gorman
Deputy Commander-in-Chief . . . . . . . . . . .Maj. Gen. William E. Masterson

## SPECIFIED COMMANDS

**Strategic Air Command—SAC**
*Omaha, Nebraska 68113*
*Telephone:  (402) 294-5900*

Commander-in-Chief . . . . . . . . . . . . . . . . . . . . . . . .Gen. Bennie L. Davis

**Tactical Air Command—TAC**
*Langley Air Force Base*
*Virginia 23665*
*Telephone:  (804) 764-9990*

Commander-in-Chief . . . . . . . . . . . . . . . . . . . . . . . .Gen. Wilbur L. Creech

**Military Airlift Command—MAC**
*Scott Air Force Base*
*Illinois 62225*
*Telephone:   (618) 256-1110*

Commander-in-Chief . . . . . . . . . . . . . . . . . . . . . . . . . . . .Gen. Thomas Ryan

**Joint Service Schools**

Commandant, Industrial College of the
   Armed Forces (Washington, D.C.) . . . . . . . . . . . . . . . . . . . . . . . .(Vacant)
Commander, Armed Forces Staff
   College (Norfolk, VA) . . . . . . . . . .Maj. Gen. Thomas G. Darling (USAF)
Commander, Uniformed Services
   University of the Health Sciences
   (Bethesda, MD) . . . . . . . . . . . . . . . . . . . . . . . .Col. Craig Llewellyn (USA)
Director, Department of Defense
   Computer Institute (Washington, D.C.) . . . . . . .Capt. K. G. Clark (USN)
Director, Defense Institute of Security
   Assistance Management (Wright-Patterson
   Air Force Base, OH) . . . . . . . . . . . .Brig. Gen. James P. Callaghan (USAF)
Director, Defense Intelligence
   College (Washington, D.C.) . . . . . . . . . . . . . .Col. Lee D. Badgett (USAF)
Director, Defense Mapping School
   (Ft. Belvoir, VA) . . . . . . . . . . . . . . . .Col. William P. Stockhausen (USA)
Director, Defense Equal Opportunity
   Management Institute (Patrick Air
   Force Base, FL) . . . . . . . . . . . . . . . . . . . . . . . .Col. Shirley J. Bach (USAF)
Commander, Defense Systems
   Management College
   (Ft. Belvoir, VA) . . . . . . . . . . . . . . . . . .Brig. Gen. Ben J. Pelletrini (USA)
Commander, Defense Information School
   (Ft. Benjamin Harrison, IN) . . . . . . . . . . . . . .Col. Gary L. Werner (USA)
Commander, Defense Foreign Language
   Institute (Presido of Monterey, CA) . . . . .Col. David A. McNermey (USA)
Commandant, National War College,
   (Washington, D.C.) . . . . . . . . . . . . . .Maj. Gen. Perry M. Smith (USAF)
President, National Defense University
   (Washington, D.C.) . . . . . . . . . . . . . . . . .Lt. Gen. John S. Pustay (USAF)

**Service War Colleges and Intermediate**
   **Officers School**

Commandant, Army War College
   (Carlisle Barracks, PA) . . . . . . . . . . . . . .Maj. Gen. Richard D. Lawrence
President, Naval War College
   (Newport, RI) . . . . . . . . . . . . . . . . . . . . . . . . .Rear Adm. James E. Service
Commandant, Air War College
   (Maxwell Air Force Base, AL) . . . . . . . . . . . . . .Maj. Gen. Paul H. Hodges
Commandant, Army Command and General
   Staff College (Fort Leavenworth, KS) . . . . . . . . . . .Lt. Gen. Carl E. Vuono
Dean of Students, College of Naval
   Command and Staff (Newport, RI) . . . . . . . . . .Capt. William K. Sullivan
Commandant, Marine Corps Command
   and Staff College (Quantico, VA)
   and Deputy for Education and
   Director, Educational Center . . . . . . . . . . . . . .Maj. Gen. John I. Hudson
Commandant, Air Command and Staff
   College (Maxwell Air Force Base, AL) . . . . .Brig. Gen. Richard A. Ingram

**ARMY**
**United States Army**
*Office of the Secretary*
*Pentagon*
*Washington, D.C. 20310*

Secretary . . . . . . . . . . . . . . . . . . . . . . . . . . . . . . . . . . . . .John O. Marsh, Jr.
Undersecretary . . . . . . . . . . . . . . . . . . . . . . . . . . . . . . . .James R. Ambrose
Assistant Secretary, Civil Works . . . . . . . . . . . . . . . . . . .William R. Gianelli
Assistant Secretary, Installations
   Logistics and Financial Management . . . . . . . . . . . . . .Joel E. Bonner, Jr.

*Telephone:* *(703) 695-3211*

Assistant Secretary, Manpower and Reserve Affairs . . . . . . . . . . . . .(Vacant)
Assistant Secretary, Research Development and Acquisition . . Jay R. Sculley
Principal Deputy and Deputy Assistant
    Secretary, Research Development and Systems . . . .Amoretta M. Hoeber
Deputy Assistant Secretary, Acqusition (Acting) . . . . . .George E. Dausman
General Counsel . . . . . . . . . . . . . . . . . . . . . . . . . . . . . . .Delbert L. Spurlock
Chief, Public Affairs . . . . . . . . . . . . . . . . . . . . . . . . . .Maj. Gen. Llyle Barker
Chief, Legislative Liaison . . . . . . . . . . . . . . .Maj. Gen. Charles D. Franklin

**The Army General Staff**
*Telephone:* *(703) 695-2077*

Chief of Staff . . . . . . . . . . . . . . . . . . . . . . . . . . . . . .Gen. John A. Wickham, Jr.
Vice Chief of Staff . . . . . . . . . . . . . . . . . . . . . . . . . .Gen. Maxwell Thurman
Director, Army Staff . . . . . . . . . . . . . . . . . . . . . . . . . . .Lt. Gen. A. Brown, Jr.
Deputy to the Director of the
    Army Staff, Executive Services . . . . . . . . . . . . . . . .Lt. Col. F. H. Sawyer
Deputy to the Director of the
    Army Staff, Staff Action Control . . . . . . . . . . . . . . . . .Col. H. M. Wassom
Director, Program Analysis and
    Evaluation Directorate . . . . . . . . . . . . . . . . . . . . .Maj. Gen. Max W. Noah
Director, Management Directorate . . . . . . . . .Brig. Gen. Michael J. Conrad
Director, Eighth United States Army Korea . . . . . . . . . . . . . .Col. K. E. Cook
Program Manager, Ballistic Missile Defense . . .Maj. Gen. E. R. Heiberg III
Commander, Ballistic Missile Defense
    Systems Command . . . . . . . . . . . . . . . . . . . . . . . . .Brig. Gen. Eugene Fox

**Deputy Chief of Staff for Personnel**
*Telephone:* *(703)*

Deputy Chief of Staff . . . . . . . . . . . . . . . . . . . . . . .Lt. Gen. Robert M. Elton
Assistant Deputy Chief of Staff . . . . . . . . . . .Maj. Gen. Edward C. Peter, III
Director, Manpower, Programs and Budget . . . . .Maj. Gen. Walter J. Mehl
Director, Personnel Plans and Systems . . . . . . . .Brig. Gen. Johnie Forte, Jr.
Director, Military Personnel Management . . . . . .Maj. Gen. Bobby B. Porter
Director, Human Resources Development . . . . .Maj. Gen. John H. Mitchell

**Deputy Chief of Staff for Logistics**
*Telephone:* *(703) 695-4102*

Deputy Chief of Staff . . . . . . . . . . . . . . . . . .Lt. Gen. Richard H. Thompson
Assistant Deputy Chief of Staff . . . . . . . . . . . .Maj. Gen. Arthur Holmes, Jr.
Assistant Deputy Chief of Staff for
    Security Assistance . . . . . . . . . . . . . . . . . . . .Brig. Gen. Robert D. Weigand
Director, Supply and Maintenance . . . . . . .Maj. Gen. Kenneth A. Jolemore
Director, Transportation, Energy
    and Troop Support . . . . . . . . . . . . . . . . . . . . . .Brig. Gen. Jimmy D. Ross
Director, Plans and Operations . . . . . . . . . . . . . .Brig. Gen. James M. Hesson
Director, Resources and Management . . . . . . .Brig. Gen. James R. DeMoss

**Deputy Chief of Staff for**
**Operations and Plans**
*Telephone:* *(703) 695-2904*

Deputy Chief of Staff . . . . . . . . . . . . . . . . . . . . . .Lt. Gen. Fred K. Mahaffey
Assistant Deputy Chief of Staff . . . . . . . . . . . . . .Maj. Gen. James H. Johnson
Assistant Deputy Chief of Staff, Joint Affairs . . . . . . . . . . . . . . . . . . . . . . . . .
Assistant Deputy Chief of Staff, Command
    Control Communications and Computers . . . . .Maj. Gen. J. M. Rockwell
Deputy Director, Command, Control,
    Communications and Computers . . . . . . . . . . . . .Brig. Walter J. Bickston
Chief, Army Force Modernization
    Coordination Office
Deputy Director, Systems Development, Integration
    and Engineering . . . . . . . . . . . . . . . . . . . . . . . . . . . . . . . . . . . . . . . . . . . . . . .
Deputy Director, Strategy,
    Plans and Policy . . . . . . . . . . . . . . . . . . . .Brig. Gen. John M. Shalikashrili
Director of Operations, Readiness
    and Mobilization . . . . . . . . . . . . . . . . . . . . . .Maj. Gen. William C. Moore
Deputy Director, Operations and Readiness . . . . .Brig. Gen. Natnan C. Vail
Director, Nuclear and Chemical . . . . . . . . . . . .Brig. Gen. Gerald G. Watson
Director of Requirements . . . . . . . . . . . . . . .Maj. Gen. Louis C. Wagoner, Jr.

Deputy Director, Requirements, and
    Army Aviation Officer . . . . . . . . . . . . . . . . . Brig. Gen. Robert F. Molinelli
Director, Force Management . . . . . . . . . . . . . . . . Brig. Gen. Gary E. Luck
Director, Training . . . . . . . . . . . . . . . . . . . . . . . . . Brig. Gen. John M. Kirk
Director, Military Support . . . . . . . . . . . . . . . . . . . . . . . . . . . . . . . . . . . .
Deputy Director,
    Military Support . . . . . . . . . . Brig. Gen. Alexander K. Davidson (USAF)
Director, Special Task Force, All
    Source Analysis Systems . . . . . . . . . . . . . . . . Brig. Gen. Alan B. Salisbury

**Deputy Chief of Staff for Research,**
**Development and Acqusition**
*Telephone: (703) 697-8186*

Deputy Chief of Staff . . . . . . . . . . . . . . . . . . . . . Lt. Gen. James H. Merryman
Assistant Deputy Chief of Staff,
    International Programs . . . . . . . . . . . . . . . . . Maj. Gen. Stan R. Sheridan
Director, Combat Support Systems . . . . . . . . . . . . Brig. Gen. Donald S. Pihl
Deputy Director, Combat Support Systems . . . . . . . . . Brig. Gen. Ray H. Lee
Director, Weapons Systems . . . . . . . . . . . . . . Brig. Gen. Richard D. Kenyon
Deputy Director, Weapons Systems . . . . . . . . . . . Brig. Gen. James C. Cercy
Director, Materiel, Plans and Programs . . . . . . . . Brig. Gen. Joe J. Breedlove
Deputy Director, Materiel, Plans and Programs . . Col. Michael L. Ferguson

**Comptroller of the Army**
*Telephone: (703) 695-2510*

Comptroller . . . . . . . . . . . . . . . . . . . . . . . . . . . . . . Lt. Gen. Ernest D. Peixotto
Director, Army Budget . . . . . . . . . . . . . . . . . Maj. Gen. Harold M. Davis, Jr.
Director, Operations and Maintenance,
    Army Appropriations . . . . . . . . . . . . . . . . . . Brig. Gen. Gerald R. Jennings
Assistant Comptroller, Finance
    and Accounting . . . . . . . . . . . . . . . . . . . . . . . . . . Maj. Gen. Paul P. Burns

**Chief of Army Reserve Office**
*Telephone: (703) 697-1784*

Chief of Army Reserve . . . . . . . . . . . . . . . . . Maj. Gen. William R. Berkman
Deputy Chief . . . . . . . . . . . . . . . . . . . . . . . . . . . Brig. Gen. Harry J. Mott, III

**National Guard Bureau**
*Telephone: (703) 697-2430*

Chief . . . . . . . . . . . . . . . . . . . . . . . . . . . . . . . . Lt. Gen. Emmett H. Walker, Jr.
Director, Joint Staff . . . . . . . . . . . . . . . . . . . . . . . . Col. Gordon K. Pollard
Director, Policy Plans and Special
    Projects Group (Office of Public Affairs) . . . . . . . . . . . . . . . Dan Donohue
Director, Air National Guard . . . . . . . . . . . . . . . Maj. Gen. John B. Conaway
Deputy Director, Air National Guard . . . . . . . Brig. Gen. Wess P. Chambers
Director, Army National Guard . . . . . . . . Maj. Gen. Herbert R. Temple, Jr.
Deputy Director, Army National Guard . . . . . . Brig. Gen. Richard D. Dean

**Assistant Chief of Staff for Intelligence**
*Telephone: (703) 695-3033*

Assistant Chief of Staff . . . . . . . . . . . . . . . . . . . Maj. Gen. William E. Odom
Deputy Assistant Chief of Staff . . . . . . . . . . . . . Brig. Gen. James W. Shufelt
Deputy Assistant Chief of Staff,
    Intelligence Systems and Automation . . . . . . . Brig. Gen. Harry E. Soyster

**The Adjutant-General**
*Telephone: (703) 695-0163*

Adjutant-General . . . . . . . . . . . . . . . . . . . . . . . . . Maj. Gen. Robert M. Joyce
Deputy Adjutant-General,
    Administrative Systems . . . . . . . . . . . . . . . Brig. Gen. Donald J. Delandro

**Chief of Chaplains**
*Telephone: (703) 695-1133*

Chief of Chaplains . . . . . . . . . . . . . . . . . . . . . . . Maj. Gen. Patrick J. Hessian
Deputy Chief . . . . . . . . . . . . . . . . . . . . . . . . . . . . Brig. Gen. Paul O. Forsberg

**The Inspector-General**
*Telephone: (703) 695-1500*

Inspector-General . . . . . . . . . . . . . . . . . . . . . . . . . . . . . . . . . . . . . . . . . . . .
Deputy to the Inspector-General . . . . . . . . . . Maj. Gen. Robert B. Solomon

**The Judge Advocate-General**
*Telephone:   (703) 697-5151*

Judge Advocate-General . . . . . . . . . . . . . . . . . . . . . . .Maj. Gen. H. J. Clausen
Assistant Judge Advocate-General . . . . . . . . . .Maj. Gen. Hugh R. Overholt
Assistant for Military Law  . . . . . . . . . . . . . . . . . .Brig. Gen. Lloyd K. Rector
Assistant for Civil Law . . . . . . . . . . . . . . . . . . . .Brig. Gen. Richard J. Bednar

**The Surgeon-General**
*Telephone:   (703) 697-1295*

Surgeon-General  . . . . . . . . . . . . . . . . . . . . . . . . .Lt. Gen. B. T. Mittemeyer
Deputy Surgeon-General . . . . . . . . . . . . . . . . .Maj. Gen. Edward J. Huyche
Assistant Surgeon-General and Chief, Dental Corps . . . . . . . . . . . . . . . . . . . .

**Chief of Engineers**
*Telephone:   (703) 697-5474*

Chief . . . . . . . . . . . . . . . . . . . . . . . . . . . . . . . . . . . .Lt. Gen. Joseph K. Bratton
Deputy Chief . . . . . . . . . . . . . . . . . . . . . . . . . . . .Maj. Gen. Richard M. Wells
Assistant Chief  . . . . . . . . . . . . . . . . . . .Maj. Gen. Norman G. Delbridge, Jr.
Director of Civil Works . . . . . . . . . . . . . . . . . . . . . .Maj. Gen. John F. Wall
Deputy Director of Civil Works  . . . . . . . . . .Brig. Gen. Charles E. Edgar, III
Director of Engineering and
   Construction  . . . . . . . . . . . . . . . . . . . . . . . .Maj. Gen. Ames S. Albro, Jr.
Deputy Assistant Chief of Engineers . . . . . . . .Brig. Gen. George K. Witners

## ARMY FIELD STAFF
   ## OPERATING AGENCIES

**U.S. Army Operational Test and**
   **Evaluation Agency**
*Falls Church, Virginia 22041*
*Telephone:   (703) 756-2360*

Commander . . . . . . . . . . . . . . . . . . . . . . . . . . . .Maj. Gen. Benjamin E. Doty

**U.S. Army Concepts Analysis Agency**
*Bethesda, Maryland 20814*
*Telephone:   (202) 295-1605*

Director  . . . . . . . . . . . . . . . . . . . . . . . . . . . . . . . . . . . . . .David C. Hardison

**Military Personnel Center**
*Washington, D.C. 22332*
*Telephone:   (202) 325-8844*

Commander . . . . . . . . . . . . . . . . . . . . . . . . . . . . .Maj. Gen. Vincent E. Falter

**Recruiting Command**
*Ft. Sheridan, Illinois 60037*
*Telephone:   (312) 926-4111*

Commander . . . . . . . . . . . . . . . . . . . . . . . . . . . . .Maj. Gen. Jack O. Bradshaw
Deputy Commander, East . . . . . . . . . . . . . . . .Brig. Gen. Gerald E. Monteith
Deputy Commander, West  . . . . . . . . . . . . . . . . . .Brig. Gen. Allen K. Ono

**U.S. Army Military Enlistment**
   **Processing Command**
*Ft. Sheridan, Illinois 60037*
*Telephone:   (312) 926-4111*

Commander . . . . . . . . . . . . . . . . . . . .Brig. Gen. Wilma L. Vaught (USAF)

**United States Military Academy**
*West Point, New York 10996*
*Telephone:   (914) 938-4011*

Superintendent  . . . . . . . . . . . . . . . . . . . . . . . .Lt. Gen. Willard W. Scott, Jr.
Dean of the Academic Board . . . . . . . . . .Brig. Gen. Frederick A. Smith, Jr.
Commandant of Cadets  . . . . . . . . . . . . . . . . .Brig. Gen. John H. Moellering

**U.S. Army Security Assistance Agency**
*Panama*

Commander  . . . . . . . . . . . . . . . . . . . . . . .Brig. Gen. Frederick F. Woerner, Jr.

**U.S. Army Nuclear and Chemical Agency**
*Ft. Belvoir, Virginia 22060*
*Telephone: (703) 695-4912*

Commander .............................Brig. Gen. Gerald G. Watson

**Special Task Force, Corps Weapon Support System**
*Ft. Sill, Oklahoma 73503*
*Telephone: (405) 351-6000*

Director ........................................Col. Robert Lamons

**U.S. Army Troop Support Agency**
*Ft. Lee, Virginia 23801*
*Telephone: (804) 734-3600*

Commander .........................Brig. Gen. Eugene L. Stillions, Jr.

**U.S. Army Computer Systems Command**
*Ft. Belvoir, Virginia 22060*
*Telephone: (703) 664-2955*

Commander .............................Maj. Gen. Donald R. Lasher
Deputy Commander ..............................Col. J. R. Ralph, Jr.

**U.S. Army Finance and Accounting Center**
*Indianapolis, Indiana 46249*
*Telephone: (317) 546-9211*

Commander ...............................Maj. Gen. Paul P. Burns
Deputy Commander.......................Brig. Gen. Robert B. Adams

**U.S. Army Medical Research and Development Command**
*Ft. Detrick, Maryland 21701*
*Telephone: (301) 663-7377*

Commander ...........................Maj. Gen. Garrison Rapmund

## MAJOR CONUS COMMANDS

**U.S. Army Communications Command**
*Ft. Huachuca, Arizona 65613*
*Telephone: (602) 538-2151*

Commander .........................Maj. Gen. Clarence E. McKnight
Deputy Commander.......................Brig. Gen. Leonard J. Riley

**Military Traffic Management Command**
*Washington, D.C.*
*Telephone: (202) 289-1761*

Commander ..............................Maj. Gen. Harold I. Small
Vice Commander.................Brig. Gen. Archer L. Durham (USAF)

**U.S. Army Intelligence and Security Command**
*Falls Church, Virginia 22047*
*Telephone: (703) 222-6637*

Commander ......................Maj. Gen. Albert N. Stubblebine, III
Deputy Commander, Intelligence .............Brig. Gen. James W. Hunt
Deputy Commander, Support ........................................

**U.S. Army Military District of Washington**
*Washington, D.C.*
*Telephone: (202) 223-0135*

Commander...............................Maj. Gen. Jerry R. Curry

**U.S. Army Criminal Investigation Command**
*Falls Church, Virginia*
*Telephone:  (703) 289-2263*

Commander . . . . . . . . . . . . . . . . . . . . . . . . Maj. Gen. Paul M. Timmerberg

**U.S. Army Health Services Command**
*Ft. Sam, Houston, Texas 78234*
*Telephone:  (713) 471-6313*

Commander . . . . . . . . . . . . . . . . . . . . . . . . . . . Maj. Gen. Floyd W. Baker
Deputy Commander and Director,
    Dental Services . . . . . . . . . . . . . . . . . . . . . . Brig. Gen. Billie B. Lefler

**U.S. Army Corps of Engineers**
*Telephone:  (703) 697-5474*

Commander . . . . . . . . . . . . . . . . . . . . . . . . . . . Lt. Gen. Joseph K. Bratton
Deputy Commander . . . . . . . . . . . . . . . . . . . . . Maj. Gen. Richard M. Wells
Commander, Mississippi Valley Division
    (Vicksburg, MS) . . . . . . . . . . . . . . . . . . . . . . Maj. Gen. William E. Reed
Commander, Central Division
    (Chicago, IL) . . . . . . . . . . . . . . . . . . . . . . . Brig. Gen. Jerome B. Hilmes
Commander, Ohio River Division
    (Cincinnati, OH) . . . . . . . . . . . . . . . . . . . . Brig. Gen. Richard S. Kern
Commander, North Atlantic Division
    (New York, NY) . . . . . . . . . . . . . . . . . . . . . Brig. Gen. Thomas A. Sands
Commander, South Atlantic Division
    (Atlanta, GA) . . . . . . . . . . . . . . . . . . . . . . Brig. Gen. Forrest T. Gay, III
Commander, South Western Division
    (Dallas, TX) . . . . . . . . . . . . . . . . . . . . . . . Brig. Gen. Robert J. Dacey
Commander, South Pacific Division
    (San Francisco, CA) . . . . . . . . . . . . . . . . . . Brig. Gen. Donald J. Palladino
Commander, North Pacific Division
    (Portland, OR) . . . . . . . . . . . . . . . . . . Brig. Gen. James W. van Lobenseis
Commander, Missouri River Division
    (Omaha, NB) . . . . . . . . . . . . . . . . . . . . . . . Brig. Gen. Mark J. Sisinyak
Commander, MX Program Agency (Norton
    Air Force Base, CA) . . . . . . . . . . . . . . . . . . . . . . . . . . . . . . . . . . . . . . . . . . .
Engineers Missile Construction Agency
    (San Francisco, CA) . . . . . . . . . . . . . . . . . . Brig. Gen. Donald J. Palladino

**U.S. Army Training and Doctrine Command**
*Ft. Monore, Virginia 23651*
*Telephone:  (703) 680-3514*

Commander . . . . . . . . . . . . . . . . . . . . . . . . . Gen. William R. Richardson
Deputy Commander . . . . . . . . . . . . . . . . . . . . . . . . Lt. Gen. Carl E. Vuano
Deputy Commander, Training . . . . . . . . . . . . Maj. Gen. Charles W. Bagnal
Chief of Staff . . . . . . . . . . . . . . . . . . . . . . . . Maj. Gen. Robert H. Forman
Special Assistant to Commander . . . . . . . . . . . . . . Brig. Gen. Claude T. Ivey
Deputy Chief of Staff, Personnel,
    Administration and Logistics . . . . . . . . . . . . Maj. Gen. Archie S. Cannon
Deputy Chief of Staff, Combat
    Developments . . . . . . . . . . . . . . . . . . . . . . Maj. Gen. Carl H. McNair, Jr.
Deputy Chief of Staff, Training . . . . . . . . . Maj. Gen. Maurice O. Edmonds
Deputy Chief of Staff, Doctrine . . . . . . . . . . . Maj. Gen. Donald R. Morelli
Deputy Chief of Staff, ROTC . . . . . . . . . . . . . Maj. Gen. John P. Prillaman
Deputy Chief of Staff, Resource
    Management . . . . . . . . . . . . . . . . . . . . . . . Brig. Gen. Robert L. Gordon

Commander . . . . . . . . . . . . . . . . . . . . . . . . . . . . . . . Gen. Donald R. Keith

**U.S. Army Materiel Development and Readiness Command**
*Cameron Station*
*Alexandria, Virginia*

Deputy Commander, Research and
    Development and Acquisition . . . . . . . . . . . . . Lt. Gen. Robert L. Moore
Deputy Commander, Materiel Readiness . . . . . . Lt. Gen. Donald M. Babers
Deputy Commander, Resources
    and Management . . . . . . . . . . . . . . . . . . . . . . Maj. Gen. Jene W. Sharp
Chief of Staff . . . . . . . . . . . . . . . . . . . . . . . Maj. Gen. Claude M. Kicklghter
Deputy Executive Director,
    Conventional Ammunition . . . . . . . . . . . . . . Brig. Gen. Peter G. Burbules

Director, Development, Engineering
and Acquisition . . . . . . . . . . . . . . . . . . . . .Maj. Gen. John B. Oblinger, Jr.
Director, Procurement and Production . . . . . .Maj. Gen. David W. Stallings
Director, Personnel, Training and
Force Development . . . . . . . . . . . . . . . . . . . .Maj. Gen. Eugene S. Korpal
Director, Supply, Maintenance
and Transportation . . . . . . . . . . . . . . . . . . . .Maj. Gen. James S. Welch
Director, Readiness . . . . . . . . . . . . . . . . . . . . .Brig. Gen. William E. Potts
Director, Security Assistance . . . . . . . . . . . . . . . . . . . . . . . . . . . . . . . . . .
Comptroller. . . . . . . . . . . . . . . . . . . . . . . . . . . . .Brig. Gen. James F. McCall
Deputy Executive Director, Chemical
and Nuclear Matters . . . . . . . . . . . . . . . . . .Brig. Gen. Bobby C. Robinson

**U.S. Army Forces Command**
*Ft. McPherson, Georgia 30330*

*Telephone: (404) 752-3113*

Commander . . . . . . . . . . . . . . . . . . . . . . . . . . . .Gen. Richard E. Cavazos
Deputy Commander . . . . . . . . . . . . . . . . . . . . .Lt. Gen. William J. Livsey, Jr.
Deputy Commander, Mobilziation
Planning . . . . . . . . . . . . . . . . . . . . . . . . . . . . .Lt. Gen. LaVern E. Weber
Chief of Staff . . . . . . . . . . . . . . . . . . . . . . . . . . .Maj. Gen. David K. Doyle
Deputy Chief of Staff, Personnel . . . . . . . . .Maj. Gen. William G. O'Leksy
Deputy Chief of Staff, Intelligence . . . . . . . . . . . . .Brig. Gen. Roy M. Strom
Deputy Chief of Staff, Operations . . . . . . . . .Brig. Gen. Richard G. Graves
Assistant Deputy Chief of Staff,
Operations (Plans and Mobilization) . . . . . . . . . . . . . . . . . . . . . . . . . . .
Assistant Deputy Chief of Staff,
Operations (Training). . . . . . . . . . . . . . . . .Brig. Gen. Edwin S. Leland, Jr.
Deputy Chief of Staff, Logistics . . . . . . . . . . . .Maj. Gen. Vincent M. Russo
Deputy Chief of Staff, Comptroller . . . . . . . . . . .Brig. Gen. John M. Brown
Forces Command Engineer . . . . . . . . . . . . . . . . . . . . . . . . . . . . . . . . . . . . .

**First Army**
*Ft. George G. Meade*
*Maryland 20755*

*Telephone: (301) 677-6261*

Commander . . . . . . . . . . . . . . . . . . . . . . . . . . .Lt. Gen. Donald E. Rosenblum
Deputy Commander . . . . . . . . . . . . . . . . . . . . .Maj. Gen. Ronald L. Watts
Chief of Staff . . . . . . . . . . . . . . . . . . . . . . . . . . .Brig. Gen. Uri S. French, III

**Second Army**
*Ft. Gillem*
*Georgia 30050*

*Telephone: (404) 363-5000*

Commander. . . . . . . . . . . . . . . . . . . . . . . . . . . . .Lt. Gen. Charles P. Graham

**Third Army**
*Ft. McPherson*
*Georgia 30330*

*Telephone: (404) 752-3113*

Commander . . . . . . . . . . . . . . . . . . . . . . . . . . .Lt. Gen. William J. Livsey, Jr.
Chief of Staff . . . . . . . . . . . . . . . . . . . . . . . . .Brig. Gen. Houston P. Houser, III

**Fifth Army**
*Ft. Sam Houston*
*Texas 78234*

*Telephone: (512) 221-1211*

Commander . . . . . . . . . . . . . . . . . . . . . . . . . . . .Lt. Gen. Edward A. Partain
Deputy Commander. . . . . . . . . . . . . . . . . . . . . . .Maj. Gen. Joe S. Owens
Chief of Staff . . . . . . . . . . . . . . . . . . . . . . . . . . . .Brig. Gen. John E. Rogers

**Sixth Army**
*Presido of San Francisco*
*California 94129*

*Telephone: (415) 561-2211*

Commander . . . . . . . . . . . . . . . . . . . . . . . . . . .Lt. Gen. David E. Grange, Jr.
Deputy Commander . . . . . . . . . . . . . . . . . . .Maj. Gen. Kenneth E. Dohleman
Chief of Staff . . . . . . . . . . . . . . . . . . . . . . . . . . . . . .Brig. Jere L. Hickman

## MAJOR OVERSEAS COMMANDS

**U.S. Army, Europe and Seventh Army**
*Heidelberg*
*West Germany*

| | |
|---|---|
| Commander-in-Chief | Gen. Glenn K. Otis |
| Deputy Commander-in-Chief | Lt. Gen. Robert L. Wetzel |
| Chief of Staff | Maj. Gen. Thomas D. Ayers |
| Deputy Chief of Staff, Personnel | Maj. Gen. Charles C. Rogers |
| Deputy Chief of Staff, Intelligence | Brig. Gen. Julius Parker, Jr. |
| Deputy Chief of Staff, Operations | Maj. Gen. George R. Stotser |
| Deputy Chief of Staff, Logistics | Maj. Gen. William K. Hunzeker |
| Deputy Chief of Staff, Engineer | Maj. Gen. Henry J. Hatch |
| Surgeon | Maj. Gen. Floyd W. Baker |
| Deputy Chief of Staff, Resource Management | Brig. Gen. Stephen R. Woods, Jr. |
| Deputy Chief of Staff, Communications and Electronic | Brig. Gen. Norman E. Archibald |
| Provost Marshal | Brig. Gen. Eugene R. Cromartie |
| Adjutant-General | Brig. Gen. Charles F. Birggo |
| Judge Advocate | Brig. Gen. Ronald M. Holdaway |

**United States Army Japan**
*Camp Zama*
*Japan*

| | |
|---|---|
| Commander | Lt. Gen. Alexander M. Weyand |
| Deputy Commander and Chief of Staff | Brig. Gen. Joseph J. Skaff |

**Eighth U.S. Army**
*Seoul*
*South Korea*

| | |
|---|---|
| Commander | Gen. Robert W. Sennewald |
| Chief of Staff | Maj. Gen. John W. Hudachek |

**U.S. Army Western Command**
*Ft. Shafter*
*Hawaii 96858*
*Telephone: (808) 471-7411*

| | |
|---|---|
| Commander | Lt. Gen. James M. Lee |
| Deputy Commander and Chief of Staff | Brig. Gen. Todd P. Graham |

## NAVY

**United States Navy**
*Office of the Secretary*
*Pentagon*
*Washington, D.C. 20350*
*Telephone: (703) 695-3131*

| | |
|---|---|
| Secretary | John Lehman |
| Executive Assistant and Naval Aide | Capt. P. D. Miller |
| Administrative Aide | Cdr. D. J. Murphy, Jr. |
| Assistant, Public Affairs | Capt. John Dewey |
| Undersecretary | James F. Goodrich |
| Assistant, Administration | Oliver R. Ashe |
| Director, Fiscal Resources Management Division | John J. May |
| Assistant Secretary, Manpower and Reserve Affairs | John S. Herrington |
| Assistant Secretary, Shipbuilding and Logistics | George A. Sawyer |
| Director, Small and Disadvantaged Business Utilization | R. D. Ramirez |
| Deputy Undersecretary, Financial Management | Robert H. Conn |
| Assistant Secretary, Research, Engineering and Systems | Melvyn R. Paisley |
| General Counsel | Walter T. Skallerup |

**Office of the Auditor General**
*Telephone: (703) 756-2117*

| | |
|---|---|
| Auditor General | K. B. Hancock |

**Office of the Comptroller**
*Telephone: (703) 697-2325*

| | |
|---|---|
| Comptroller | R. H. Conn |
| Director, Office of Budget and Reports | Rear Adm. Daniel Cooper |
| Director, Budget Evaluation Group | Ronald L. Hass |
| Director, Investment and Development Division | R. G. Garant |

|  |  |
|---|---|
|  | Assistant Comptroller, Financial Management Systems . . . . . . . . . . . . . . . . . . . . . . . . . . . Capt. W. E. Kruse |
|  | Director, Resource Management Operations Division . . . . . . . . . . . . . . . . . . . . . . . . . Capt. A. K. Paszly, Jr. |
| **Office of Judge Advocate-General** *Telephone:  (703) 325-9820* | Judge Advocate-General . . . . . . . . . . . . . . . . . Rear Adm. James J. McHugh |
| **Office of Legislative Affairs** *Telephone:  (703) 697-7146* | Chief . . . . . . . . . . . . . . . . . . . . . . . . . . . . . . . . . . . . Rear Adm. Bruce Newell |
| **Office of Naval Research** *Telephone:  (703) 696-4258* | Chief . . . . . . . . . . . . . . . . . . . . . . . . . . . . . . . . Rear Adm. L. S. Kollmorgen<br>Director, Technology Programs . . . . . . . . . . . . . . . . . . . . Capt. F. H. Stodley<br>Director, Navy Patent Program . . . . . . . . . . . . . . . . . . . . . . . A. F. Kwitnieski<br>Director, Research Programs . . . . . . . . . . . . . . . . . . . . . . . Dr. F. E. Saalfield<br>Director, Financial Management, Comptroller . . . . . . . . . . . D. W. Rehorst<br>Director, Acquisition . . . . . . . . . . . . . . . . . . . . . . . . . . . . . . . . . . . J. T. Bolos |
| **Director of Navy Laboratories** *Telephone:  (703) 692-2766* | Director . . . . . . . . . . . . . . . . . . . . . . . . . . . . . . . . . . . . . . . . . . R. M. Hillyer |
| **Office of Program Appraisal** *Telephone:  (703) 697-9396* | Director . . . . . . . . . . . . . . . . . . . . . . . . . . . . . . . . . . Rear Adm. Frank Kelso |
| **Program Information Center** *Telephone:  (703) 697-0517* | Director . . . . . . . . . . . . . . . . . . . . . . . . . . . . . . . Rear Adm. Charles Prindle |
| **Office of Chief of Naval Operations— CNO** *Telephone:  (703) 695-6007* | Chief . . . . . . . . . . . . . . . . . . . . . . . . . . . . . . . . . . . . . . . Adm. J. D. Watkins<br>Vice Chief . . . . . . . . . . . . . . . . . . . . . . . . . . . . . . . . . . . Adm. Ronald J. Hays<br>Assistant Vice Chief and Director, Naval Administration . . . . . . . . . . . . . . . . . . . . . . . . . . Comdr. H. F. Boyle<br>Executive Assistant . . . . . . . . . . . . . . . . . . . . . . . . . . . . Comdr. D. E. Jeremiah<br>Administrative Assistant . . . . . . . . . . . . . . . . . . . . . . . . . . . Cdr. W. L. Putnam<br>Special Assistant, CNO/Public Affairs . . . . . . . . . . . . . . Capt. D. F. Dvornik<br>Director, Organization and OPNAV MNPR Budget and Security Division . . . . . . . . . . . Capt. George F. Lockeman, Jr.<br>Director, Support Services Division . . . . . . . . . . . . . . . . . . . . . . . . . . R. Ward<br>Director, Naval Reserve . . . . . . . . . . . . . . . . . . . . . . . . . Rear Adm. R. F. Dunn |
| **Program Planning Office** *Telephone:  (703) 695-2688* | Director and Scientific Officer, Center for Naval Analyses . . . . . . . . . . . . . . . . . . . . . . . . Vice Adm. C. A. H. Trost<br>Director, General Planning and Programming Division . . . . . . . . . . . . . . . . Rear Adm. George A. Aitcheson |
| **Office of Naval Medicine** *Telephone:  (703) 697-0587* | Director and Surgeon-General . . . . . . . . . . . . . . . Vice Adm. Lewis H. Seaton |
| **Command and Control** *Telephone:  (703) 695-3239* | Director . . . . . . . . . . . . . . . . . . . . . . . . . . . . . . . . . . . . Vice Adm. G. R. Nagler<br>Executive Assistant . . . . . . . . . . . . . . . . . . . . . . . . . . . . Capt. E. F. Bronson |

**Office of Naval Warfare**
*Telephone:   (703) 697-1098*

Director . . . . . . . . . . . . . . . . . . . . . . . . . . . . . . . . . . . Vice Adm. L. Baggett
Director, Anti-Submarine Warfare
  (ASW) Division . . . . . . . . . . . . . . . . . . . . . . . Rear Adm. R. A. Martini
Director, Surface ASW Systems Branch . . . . . . . . . . . Capt. J. D. Henderson
Director, Undersea Surveillance Branch . . . . . . . . . . Capt. M. J. Schneider
Director, Naval Oceanography Division . . . . . . Rear Adm. J. B. Mooney, Jr.
Director, Tactical Readiness Division . . . . . . . . Comdr. Clarence Armstrong
Director, Operations Evaluation Group . . . . . . . . . . . . . . . . Dr. Phill DePoy
Director, Strike and Amphibious Warfare Division . . . Rear Adm. J. J. Barth

**Office of Research, Development,
  Test and Evaluation**
*Telephone:   (703) 697-5533*

Director . . . . . . . . . . . . . . . . . . . . . . . . . . . . Rear Adm. Albert J. Baciocco
Assistant Director, Operational Test and Evaluation . . . . . . . . . . .(Vacant)
Special Assistant, Intelligence. . . . . . . . . . . . . . . . . . . . . . . . . . . . .P. Mantle
Assistant, Medical and Allied Sciences . . . . . . . . . . . . . . Capt. R. G. Ireland
Assistant, International Research and Development . . . . .Capt. J. A. Luper
Officer, International Research and
  Development Progarms. . . . . . . . . . . . . . . . . . . . . . Cdr. I. W. Frenzinger
Director, Undersea and Strategic Warfare and
  Nuclear Energy Development Division . . . . . . . . . Comdr. Norm Johnson
Director, Tactial Air Surface and Electronic Warfare Division . . . .(Vacant)
Director, Command and Control
  Development Division . . . . . . . . . . . . . . . . . . . . . . . Capt. J. R. Seesholtz
Director, Technology Assessment Division . . . . . . . . . . . . . . . .P. J. Mantle

**Naval Audiovisual Center**
*Washington, D.C. 20374*
*Telephone:   (202) 433-2102*

Commanding Officer and Assistant,
  Navy Audiovisual Management . . . . . . . . . . . . . . . . . . . .Capt. R. Kuhike

**Navy Broadcasting Service**
*1420 South Eads Street*
*Arlington, Virginia 22202*
*Telephone:   (703) 692-6558*

Director. . . . . . . . . . . . . . . . . . . . . . . . . . . . . . . . . . . . . . . . . . .J. E. Rizer

**Office of Naval Intelligence**
*Telephone:   (703) 695-3944*

Director . . . . . . . . . . . . . . . . . . . . . . . . . . . . . . . . Rear Adm. John L. Butts

**Deputy Chief of Naval Operations
  (Manpower, Personnel and Training)**
*Telephone:   (703) 694-1101*

Deputy Chief. . . . . . . . . . . . . . . . . . . . . . . . Vice Adm. William P. Lawrence
Deputy Chief . . . . . . . . . . . . . . . . . . . . . Rear Adm. Laurence Burkhardt III
Assistant, Joint Chief of Staff, Manpower Matters . . . . . . Capt. J. G. Stevens
Director, Total Force Planning, Training Division . . . . . Cdr. D. G. Primeau
Director, Total Force Programming,
  Manpower Division . . . . . . . . . . . . . . . . . . . . . . Rear Adm. Verle W. Klein
Director, Military Personnel
  Policy Division . . . . . . . . . . . . . . . . . . . . . Rear Adm. Albert J. Herberger

**Deputy Chief of Naval Operations
  (Submarine Warfare)**
*Telephone:   (703) 695-0058*

Deputy Chief. . . . . . . . . . . . . . . . . . . . . . . . . . . . . Vice Adm. N. R. Thunman
Director, Strategic Submarine Division
  and Trident Program Coordination . . . . . . . . . . . . . . . Comdr. Guy Curtis
Director, Attack Submarine Division . . . . . . . . . . . . . Cdr. R. M. Eytchinson
Director, Deep Submergence Systems Division . . . . . . . Capt. J. H. Howland
Director, Submarine Manpower and
  Training Requirements Division . . . . . . . . . . . . . . . . . . Capt. W. P. Chase

**Deputy Chief of Naval Operations
  (Surface Warfare)**

Deputy Chief . . . . . . . . . . . . . . . . . . . . . . . . . . . Vice Adm. Robert L. Walters
Director, Surface Warfare Division . . . . . . . . . . . Rear Adm. William Walsh

*Telephone:    (703) 697-7469*

Director, Surface Combat Systems Division ...Rear Adm. John W. Nyquist
Mobile Logistics Support Force,
   Amphibious Mine and Special
   Warfare Division ......................Comdr. B. C. McCaffree, Jr.
Director, Surface Warfare Manpower and
   Training Requirements Division .................Capt. John J. Gelke

**Deputy Chief of Naval Operations**
**(Logistics)**

*Telephone:    (703) 695-2154*

Deputy Chief ......................Rear Adm. Thomas J. Hughes, Jr.
Assistant Deputy Chief .................Rear Adm. Stanley J. Anderson
Executive Assistant ...............................Capt. E. J. Knapp
Director, Logistics Plans Division ...........Rear Adm. Richard C. Avrit
Director, Materiel Division ........................Comdr. Carl Webb
Director, Ships Maintenance and
   Modernization Division ...............Rear Adm. James K. Nunneley
Director, Shore Activities Planning
   and Program Division ...................Rear Adm. James T. Taylor
Director, Environmental Protection and
   Occupational Safety and Health Division .........Capt. S. A. Martinelli

**Deputy Chief of Naval Operations**
**(Air Warfare)**

*Telephone:    (703) 695-2374*

Deputy Chief ..........................Vice Adm. Robert F. Schoultz
Assistant Deputy Chief ......................Rear Adm. Cecil J. Kempf
Director, Aviation Plans and
   Requirements Division ...................Rear Adm. Paul T. Gillcrist
Director, Naval Aviation
   Maintenance Programs Division ..........Rear Adm. Allen D. Williams
Director, Aviation Department.............Lt. Gen. W. H. Fitch (USAF)
Director, Civil and Air Station Program
   Division and Aviation Manpower and
   Training Division ..................Rear Adm. Richard M. Dunleavy
Director, Air Anti Submarine
   Warfare Training Branch .....................Capt. R. W. Youmans

**Deputy Chief of Naval Operations**
**(Plans, Policy and Operations)**

*Telephone:    (703) 695-3707*

Deputy Chief ..........................Vice Adm. James A. Lyons, Jr.
Assistant Deputy Chief .................Rear Adm. Huntington Hardisty
Executive Assistant and Senior Aide .................Capt. J. B. Castano
Director, Strategy, Plans and Policy Division .....Rear Adm. Ron Marryott
Director, Strategy/Concepts Branch .................Capt. P. D. Smityh
Director, NATO Strategy Concepts
   and Force Planning ............................Cdr. R. P. Conrad
Director, Politico-Military Policy
   and Current Plans Division ...............Rear Adm. Ronald J. Kurth
Director, Technology Transfer Policy
   and Control Division ............................Capt. R. P. Coe
Director, Security Assistance
   Division ...................Rear Adm. Theodore A. Almstedt, Jr.
Director, Fleet Operations Readiness
   and Navy Command Center Division ............Capt. Jack W. Tomion
Director, Strategic and Theater
   Nuclear Warfare Division......................Comdr. Roger Bacon

**U.S. Marine Corps Headquarters**

*Telephone:    (703) 694-2500*

Commandant....................................Gen. Paul X. Kelley
Assistant Commandant...........................Gen. John K. Davis
Chief of Staff ..............................Lt. Gen. Gray Diwayne
Aide-de-Camp ...........................Lt. Col. W. R. McPherson
Director, Special Project Directorate ..................Col. F. L. Loving
Deputy Chief of Staff, Plans and Policy ...........Lt. Gen. B. E. Trainer
Director, Joint Strategy and Planning
   Branch (Plans Division) ..........................Col. T. J. Solak
Director, Joint Strategic Branch .....................Col. H. E. Pierpan

| | |
|---|---|
| | Director, Western Regional Branch .................Col. P. L. Harrington |
| | Director, Eastern Regional Branch ....................Col. F. E. Wirkus |
| | Director, Strategic Initiatives Branch ....................Col. E. P. Noll |
| | Director, Service Plans and Policies Division ...........Col. J. H. Redgate |
| | Director, Operations Division .................Maj. Gen. H. G. Glasgow |
| | Deputy Chief of Staff, Training ....................Maj. Gen. J. L. Day |
| | Deputy Chief of Staff, Manpower ..........Lt. Gen. William R. Maloney |
| | Director, Manpower, Plans and Policy Division ....Maj. Gen. A. Lukeman |
| | Director, Manpower, Policy, Planning, |
| |     Programs and Budgeting Branch ..............Lt. Col. R. B. Rothwell |
| | Director, Manpower Control Branch .....................Col. D. Festa |
| | Director, Manpower Management |
| |     Information Systems Branch ......................Col. D. L. Morris |
| | Deputy Chief of Staff, Aviation ...................Lt. Gen. W. H. Fitch |
| | Director, Aviation Plans, Policy and |
| |     Requirements Division ......................Brig. Gen. J. R. Dailey |
| | Director, Aviation Logistics Support |
| |     Branch (Aviation Supply and Support Division) ......Col. V. P. Hart, Jr. |
| | Director, Fiscal Division .........................E. T. Comstock |
| | Deputy Director, Fiscal Division ............Brig. Gen. Hollis E. Davison |
| | Director, Personnel Procurement Division ...Brig. Gen. Carl E. Mundy, Jr. |

**Marine Corps Reserve Division**

*Telephone:    (703) 694-1161*

Deputy Chief of Staff .......................Maj. Gen. S. G. Olmstead
Inspector-General ...........................Brig. Gen. C. D. Dean
Judge-Advocate ....................Brig. Gen. Walter J. Donovan, Jr.

**Marine Corps Division of Public Affairs**

*Telephone:    (703) 694-8010*

Director (Acting)...............................Col. J. L. McManaway

**Marine Corps Command, Control, Communications and Computer (C4) Systems Division**

*Telephone:    (703) 694-2604*

Director ........................................Brig. Gen. G. H. Leach
Director, Marine Corps Central Design
    and Programming Activity .........................Col. B. J. Cassidy

**Headquarters Naval Material Command**

*Telephone:    (703) 692-3002*

Chief of Naval Material ........................Adm. Steven A. White
Vice Chief ...............................Rear Adm. Richard A. Miller
Director, Information Systems and Administration .....Capt. R. A. Dropp
Deputy Chief, Resources Management .........Capt. W. J. M. O'Connor
Assistant Deputy Chief, Program Budget and Finance ........J. H. Brown
Director, Procurement Division ....................Capt. R. N. Nitschke
Assistant Deputy Chief, Manpower and Personnel ...........L. G. Ratto
Assistant Deputy Chief, Contracts
    and Business Management ..........................J. H. Flaherty
Deputy Chief, Logistics .....................Rear Adm. Ralph G. Bird

**Designated Project Managers**

*Telephone:    (703) 695-2064*

Director, Strategic Systems Projects .......Rear Adm. Glenwood Clark, Jr.
Director, Plans and Programs Division .................G. E. Keightley
Director, Technical Division .......................Capt. K. C. Malley
Director, Joint Cruise Missile
    Project Office .......................Rear Adm. Steven J. Hostettler
Program Manager, Anti-Submarine
    Warfare Systems Project ...................Rear Adm. R. A. Martini
Program Manager, Saudi Naval
    Expansion Program ........................Cdr. Richard Donnelly

**Naval Air Systems Command Headquarters**

Commander ............................Rear Adm. James E. Busey
Vice Commander ....................................................

*Telephone:    (703) 692-2260*

Secretary to the Vice Commander .................... Comdr. P. Cavada
Director, Small Business Office .......................... J. F. Lenahan
Management Consultant to the Commander .............. A. J. DiMascio
Inspector-General ..................................... E. M. Tupman
Patent Counsel ..................................... W. C. Townsend
Deputy Commander, Plans and Programs .... Rear Adm. Roger D. Johnson
Assistant Deputy Commander, Anti-Air Warfare .....................
Director, Reconnaisance and Electronic Warfare Projects .. H. E. Goldstein
Assistant Deputy Commander, Strike
    Warfare and Assault Projects ..................... C. M. Mitchell III
Assistant Deputy Commander, Anti-
    Sumbarine Warfare and Support Projects ................ W. R. Hunt
Program Manager, Support Aircraft
    and Submarine Warefare Project .............. Capt. J. W. Holtzclaw
Assistant Commander, Contracts .................... Capt. P. DeMayo
Assistant Commander, Research
    and Technology ......................... Capt. R. D. Friichtenicht
Assistant Commander, Systems and Engineering ...... Cdr. W. J. Finneran

## Naval Electronic Systems Command Headquarters

*2511 Jefferson Davis Highway*
*Arlington, Virginia*

*(Mailing Address: Washington, D.C.*
*20363)*

*Telephone:    (703) 692-3006*

Commander .......................... Rear Adm. George B. Shick, Jr.
Vice Commander ..................... Rear Adm. Albert A. Gallotta, Jr.
Project Manager, Navy Space Project ............. Cdr. Dennis M. Brooks
Project Manager, Rewson Systems Project ............. Capt. G. Flannery
Project Manager, Joint Tactical
    Information Distribution System ................... Capt. R. C. May
Project Manager, Communications Systems Project Office ..... D. C. Bailey
Project Manager, Command Systems Project .......... Capt. S. W. Adams
Project Manager, Undersea Surveillance Project ......... Capt. C. A. Rose
Project Manager, Marine Corps Systems Project ........ Col. J. A. Bracken
Deputy Commander, Contracts Directorate .......... Capt. D. E. Dedwig
Deputy Commander, Command, Control,
    Communications and Intelligence Systems
    and Technology Directorate ..................... Cdr. R. O. Simon
Deputy Commander, Management and
    Operations Directorate .......................... Capt. D. R. Bilicki
Deputy Commander, Life Cycle Engineering
    and Platform Integration Directorate ....... Rear Adm. Richard J. Grich

## Naval Sea Systems Command Headquarters

*National Building 3*
*Room 12E10*
*Arlington, Virginia*

*(Mailing Address: Washington, D.C.*
*20362)*

*Telephone:    (703) 692-3381*

Commander .......................... Vice Adm. Earl B. Fowler, Jr.
Vice Commander ...................... Rear Adm. James H. Webber
Deputy Commander, Contracts ................. Cdr. Stuart F. Platt
Deputy Commander, Ship Design
    and Engineering ...................... Cdr. Myron V. Ricketts
Director, Ship Hull Engineering Group ........ Capt. Millard S. Firebaugh
Director, Naval Architecture Sub-Group ............ Robert G. Keane, Jr.
Director, Survivability and Readiness Sub-Group ....... Capt. F. S. Hering
Director, Structural Integrity Sub-Group ............... John B. O'Brien
Director, Specifications and Standards Sub-Group ... Victor R. Burnett, Jr.
Director, Machinery Group ................. Capt. George M. Lachance
Director, Hull Systems Sub-Group ................... Vincent Liszcynski
Director, Auxiliary Systems Sub-Group ........ Capt. Frederick Richmond
Deputy Commander, Combat Systems
    Directorate ........................... Rear Adm. Wayne E. Meyer
Director, Combat Systems Engineering Group .... Capt. Lowell J. Holloway
Director, Combat Systems Architecture and
    Tactical Planning Sub-Group ..................... Capt. T. Fleming
Director, Class Combat Systems Engineering Sub-Group ... Capt. W. Long
Director, Combat Systems Design
    and Test Sub-Group ......................... Thomas R. Sarnecky
Director, Combat Direction Systems Sub-Group ....... Capt. Joel Crandall

Director, Combat Support Systems/
Equipment Sub-Group ............................ Capt. F. Jonasz
Director, Surface Warfare Systems Group .............. Capt. R. R. Hatch
Director, Surface Gun Weapon Systems Sub-Group ....... John P. Carroll
Director, Surface Missile Weapons
Systems Sub-Group ............................. Robert L. Mallonee
Director, Undersea Warfare Systems Group ...... Capt. James R. Williams
Director, Submarine Systems Sub-Group ....... Capt. Jermiah F. Sullivan
Director, Surface Systems Sub-Group .......... Capt. William C. Carlson
Director, Undersea Weapons/Test
Sub-Group ............................. Capt. Leland E. Wood, Jr.
Director, Ammunition Systems Group.......... Capt. Kenneth P. Hughes
Deputy Commander, Industrial and
Facility Management Directorate ........ Rear Adm. John C. McArthur
Deputy Commander, Nuclear Propulsion
Directorate ................................... Adm. K. R. McKee
Deputy Commander, Acqustion and
Logistics .............................. Rear Adm. James W. Lisanby
Deputy Commander, Surface
Ships Directorate ................... Rear Adm. George W. Davis, Jr.
Director, Electrical Systems Sub-Group .......... Capt. John H. McCorry
Deputy Commander, Submarine
Directorate ....................... Rear Adm. Edward M. Peebles
Deputy Commander, Management Support
Directorate (Acting)............................. Thomas E. Jackson
Project Manager, Light Airborne
Multi-Purpose Systems (Lamps) Project ........ Capt. Joseph M. Purtell
Project Manager, Combatant Craft/Service
Craft/Amphibious Acquisition Project....... Capt. Robert R. Gardenier
Project Manager, Steam Propulsion
Improvement Project............................ Capt. Ronald Owens
Project Manager, Patrol Hydrofoil Missile/
Mine Countermeasures Ship
Acquisition Project Office ..................... Capt. John R. Young
Project Manager, Ship Support
Improvement Project ..................... Cdr. George A. Mayfield
Project Manager, Saudi Naval Expansion Program ... Capt. S. P. Carpenter
Deputy Commander, New Combatants ...... Rear Adm. Donald R. Roane
Project Manager, Information Systems
Improvement Project ...................... Capt. John F. Leahy III
Project Manager, Spanish Ship Support Project ............ G. H. Lindsay
Project Manager, Amphibious Ship
Acquisition Project ....................... Capt. Charles H. Piersall
Project Manager, Battleship Acquisition/
Modernization Project .................... Capt. John B. Champlain
Project Manager, Auxiliary/Special
Mission Ship Acquisition Project........... Capt. Edmund C. Mortimer
Project Manager, Destroyer Ship Acquisition Project .... Joseph F. Grosson
Project Manager, Aircraft Carrier Ship
Acquisition Project........................ Capt. William A. Rehder
Project Manager, Attack Submarine
Acquisition Project ............................. Capt. Robert Fox
Project Manager, Deep Submergence Systems Project .... John J. O'Connor
Project Manager, Trident Submarine
Ship Acquisition Project .................... Capt. Walter H. Cantrell
Project Manager, Guided Missile Frigate
Ship Acquisition Project ................. Capt. David M. Stembel, Jr.
Project Manager, Aegis
Shipbuilding Project..................... Rear Adm. Wayne E. Meyer
Project Manager, Torpedo MK 48 Project ........ Capt. James G. Reynolds
Project Manager, Directed Energy
Weapons Project ........................... Capt. Alfred Skolnick

Project Manager, Advanced Light-
weight Torpedo Project . . . . . . . . . . . . . . . Capt. Richard M. Wellborn, Jr.
Project Manager, Mine Warfare
Systems Project . . . . . . . . . . . . . . . . . . . . . . Capt. Joseph M. P. Wright, Jr.
Project Manager, Navy Shipboard Tactical
Embedded Components Resources Project . . . . Capt. James P. Odonovan
Project Manager, Submarine Combat
Systems Project . . . . . . . . . . . . . . . . . . . . . . . Capt. James M. Vanmetre
Project Manager, Vertical Launch
Project Office . . . . . . . . . . . . . . . . . . . . . . . . . . Capt. James J. Kulesz
Project Manager, NATO Seasparrow
Project Office . . . . . . . . . . . . . . . . . . . . . . . . . Capt. Charles O. Johnson

**Naval Facilities Engineering Command**
*200 Stovall Street*
*Alexandria, Virginia 22332*
*Telephone: (703) 325-0589*

Commander . . . . . . . . . . . . . . . . . . . . . . . . . . Rear Adm. William M. Zobel

**Naval Supply Systems Command
Headquarters**
*Telephone: (703) 695-4009*

Commander . . . . . . . . . . . . . . . . . . . . . . . . Rear Adm. Andrew A. Giordano
Vice Commander . . . . . . . . . . . . . . . . . . . . . . Rear Adm. Bruno A. Pompanio
Assistant Commander, Inventory and
Systems Integrity . . . . . . . . . . . . . . . . . . . . . . . . . . . . . . . Cdr. C. R. Webb

**Oceanographer of the Navy**
*Washington, D.C. 20390*
*Telephone: (202) 653-1299*

Oceanographer . . . . . . . . . . . . . . . . . . . . . . . . Rear Adm. J. B. Mooney, Jr.

**Military Sealift Command
Headquarters**
*Washington, D.C. 20390*
*Telephone: (202) 282-2800*

Commander . . . . . . . . . . . . . . . . . . . . . . . . . . Vice Adm. William H. Rowden
Deputy Commander and Director
of Operations . . . . . . . . . . . . . . . . . . . . . . . . . Rear Adm. W. C. Hamm, Jr.
Director, Legislative and Public Affairs . . . . . . . . . . . . . . . . . . . . . Tacy Cook
Director, Staff Support/Maritime Affairs Office . . . . . . . . . . . W. T. Sansone
Administration and Manpower Officer . . . . . . . . . . . . . . . . . . . . . R. P. Lord
Civilian Personnel Officer . . . . . . . . . . . . . . . . . . . . . . . . . . . . . . . M. Lewis
Assistant Chief of Staff, Sealift Readiness . . . . . . . . . Capt. P. K. Fitzwilliam
Assistant Chief of Staff, Transportation . . . . . . . . . . . . . . Capt. B. W. Strong
Engineering Officer . . . . . . . . . . . . . . . . . . . . . . . . . . . . . . . . . . . I. W. Allen

**Naval Military Personnel Command**
*Telephone: (703) 694-2243*

Commander . . . . . . . . . . . . . . . . . . . . . . . . . . Rear Adm. David L. Harlow

**Naval Civilian Personnel Command**
*Telephone: (703) 696-4908*

Commander . . . . . . . . . . . . . . . . . . . . . . . . . . . . . . . . . . . . . . . J. K. Bohren

**Naval and Marine Reserve
Headquarters**
*Anacostia, Washington, D.C.*
*Telephone: (202) 433-4494*

Commander . . . . . . . . . . . . . . . . . . . . . . . . . . Rear Adm. Robert F. Dunn

**Naval Data Automation Command**
*Build 166*
*Washington Navy Yard*
*Washington, D.C. 20374*
*Telephone: (202) 433-4067*

Commander . . . . . . . . . . . . . . . . . . . . . . . . Rear Adm. Paul E. Sutherland

**Naval Telecommunications Command**
*4401 Massachusetts Avenue, N.W.*
*Washington, D.C. 20390*
*Telephone:   (202) 282-0550*

Commander . . . . . . . . . . . . . . . . . . . . . . . . . . . . Vice Adm. Ralph M. Ghormley
Deputy Commander . . . . . . . . . . . . . . . . . . . . . . . . . . . . Capt. R. O. Simon

**Naval Intelligence Command**
*4600 Silver Hill Road*
*Capitol Heights, Maryland*
*(Mailing Address: Washington, D.C.*
  *20389)*
*Telephone:   (301) 763-3552*

Commander . . . . . . . . . . . . . . . . . . . . . . . . . . . . . . . . . Capt. C. F. Hoffman
Deputy Chief of Staff . . . . . . . . . . . . . . . . . . . . . . . Capt. P. F. McKnight
Special Assistant, Long Range Planning . . . . . . . . . . . . . . . . . D. P. Harmon
Coordinator, Legal Affairs . . . . . . . . . . . . . . . . . . . . . . . H. W. Baumgardner
Special Assistant, Research and Development . . . . . . . . . . . Capt. R. G. Riley
Inspector-General, Naval Intelligence Command . . . . . . . . . . A. V. Krochalis

**Naval Intelligence Processing System**
  **Support Activity**
*4600 Silver Hill Road*
*Capitol Heights, Maryland*
*(Mailing Address: Washington, D.C.*
  *20389)*
*Telephone:   (301) 763-3506*

Commanding Officer . . . . . . . . . . . . . . . . . . . . . . . . . . . . Capt. E. D. Sheafer

**Naval Investigative Service**
  **Headquarters**
*Washington, D.C. 20388*
*Telephone:   (202) 763-3750*

Director . . . . . . . . . . . . . . . . . . . . . . . . . . . . . . . . . . . . Capt. P. D. Hoskins

**Naval Intelligence Support Center**
*4301 Suitland Road*
*Capitol Heights, Maryland*
*(Mailing Address: Washington, D.C.*
  *20390)*
*Telephone:   (301) 763-2120*

Commanding Officer . . . . . . . . . . . . . . . . . . . . . . . . . . . . Capt. D. S. Cooper

**Navy Field Operational Intelligence**
  **Office**
*4301 Suitland Road*
*Capitol Heights, Maryland*
*(Mailing Address: Washington, D.C.*
  *20390)*
*Telephone:   (301) 763-3694*

Commanding Officer . . . . . . . . . . . . . . . . . . . . . . . . . . . Capt. W. O. Studeman

**Naval Security Group Command**
  **Headquarters**
*3801 Nebraska Avenue, N.W.*
*Washington, D.C.*
*Telephone:   (202) 282-0444*

Commander . . . . . . . . . . . . . . . . . . . . . . . . . . . . Rear Adm. Don A. Mcdowell

**Navy Recruiting Command**
*Telephone:   (703) 696-4181*

Commander . . . . . . . . . . . . . . . . . . . . . . . . . . . . Rear Adm. James D. Williams

**Navy Accounting and Finance Center/**
  **Assistant Comptroller Financial**
  **Management Systems**
*Telephone:   (703) 697-3195*

Commander . . . . . . . . . . . . . . . . . . . . . . . . . . . . . . . . . . . Capt. W. E. Kruse
Deputy Commander, Financial Systems, Policy and
  Planning Operations Directorate . . . . . . . . . . . . . . . . . Capt. J. O. Carlson

**Other Major Naval Commands**

Commander-in-Chief, Pacific ...............Adm. William J. Crawe, Jr.
Commander-in-Chief, Allied Forces
  Southern Europe and Commander-in-
  Chief, U.S. Naval Forces, Europe..............Adm. William N. Small
Commander-in-Chief, U.S. Pacific Fleet .........Adm. Sylvester R. Foley
Commander-in-Chief, Atlantic and
  Atlantic Fleet and Supreme Allied
  Commander, Atlantic.....................Adm. Wesley L. Mcdonald
Commander, Naval Surface Force,
  U.S. Atlantic Fleet ......................Vice Adm. Edward S. Briggs
Commander, Naval Air Force,
  U.S. Atlantic Fleet ....................Vice Adm. Thomas J. Kilcline
Commander, Naval Air Force,
  U.S. Pacific Fleet .................Vice Adm. Crawford A. Easterling
Commander, Naval Surface Force,
  U.S. Pacific Fleet ..................Vice Adm. Harry C. Schrader, Jr.
Commander, Seventh Fleet ...................Vice Adm. James R. Hogg
Commander, Submarine Force,
  U.S. Atlantic Fleet .................Vice Adm. Bernard M. Kauderer
Commander, Sixth Fleet .................Vice Adm. Edward H. Martin
Commander, Second Fleet ...............Vice Adm. Joseph Metcalf, III
Commander, Third Fleet ...................Rear Adm. Donald S. Jones
Commander, Naval Air Force,
  U.S. Atlantic Fleet.....................Vice Adm. Carol C. Smith, Jr.
Commander, U.S. Naval Forces,
  Caribbean .............................Rear Adm. Ralph R. Hedges
Chief, Naval Education and Training
  (Pensacola, FL) ......................Vice Adm. James A. Sagerholm
Commander, Mine Warfare Command
  (Charleston, SC) ...................Rear Adm. Charles F. Horne, III
Superintendent, U.S. Naval Academy
  (Annapolis, MD).......................Rear Adm. Charles R. Larson

**Major Marine Corps Commands**

Commander, Fleet Marine Force, Atlantic
  (Norfolk, VA) and Commander, II Marine
  Amphibious Force (Camp Lejeune, NC)........Lt. Gen. John A. Miller
Commander, Fleet Marine Force,
  Pacific (Camp H. M. Smith, HI) ...........Lt. Gen. Charles G. Gopper
Commander, Marine Corps Development and
  Education Command (Quantico, VA) .....Maj. Gen. David M. Twomey
Commander, I Marine Amphibious
  Force (Camp Pendleton, CA)..........Maj. Gen. Earnest C. Cheatham
Commander, III Marine Amphibious
  Force (Camp Butler, Okinawa)...........Maj. Gen. Robert E. Haebel
Commander, Marine Corps Air Ground
  Combat Center (Twentynine Palms, CA)...Brig. Gen. William R. Etnyre

**AIR FORCE**
**United States Air Force**
*Office of the Secretary*
*Pentagon*
*Washington, D.C. 20330*
*Telephone: (703) 697-7376*

Secretary of the Air Force .................................Verne Orr
Military Assistant ...........................Brig. Gen. C. C. Rogers
Deputy Military Assistant ..................Col. Charles H. MacNevin
Under Secretary ...............................Edward C. Aldridge
Administrative Assistant .......................Robert J. McCormick

**Deputy Under Secretary of the Air**
**Force for Space Systems**
*Telephone: (703) 697-8531*

Deputy Under Secretary .............................Jimmie D. Hill
Director....................................Col. Donald L. Cromer
Assistant Secretary, Manpower Reserve
  Affairs and Installations...........................Tidal W. McCoy
Principal Deputy Assistant Secretary,
  Manpower Reserve Affairs and Installation ...........James W. Lucas

Deputy Assistant Secretary, Manpower
  Resources and Military Personnel ..................Karen R. Keesling
Deputy Assistant Secretary, Civilian Personnel
  Policy and Equal Employment Opportunity ..........J. Craig Cumbey
Deputy Assistant Secretary, Installations,
  Environment and Safety .........................James F. Boatright

**Assistant Secretary for Financial
Management**

*Telephone: (703) 697-2302*

Assistant Secretary ....................................Russell D. Hale
Principal Deputy Assistant .......................Willard H. Mitchell
Deputy Assistant Secretary,
  Information Systems .......................Dr. Thomas D. Conrad
Deputy, Management Systems ...................A. Ernest Fitzgerald

**Assistant Secretary for Research
Development and Logistics**

*Telephone: (703) 697-6361*

Assistant Secretary ...............................Thomas E. Cooper
Deputy Assistant Secretary, Systems .........................(Vacant)
Deputy Assistant Secretary,
  Acquisition/Management ....................James E. Williams, Jr.
Deputy Assistant Secretary, Logistics
  and Communications .......................Lloyd K. Mosemann II

**General Counsel**

*Telephone: (703) 697-0941*

General Counsel .....................................David E. Place

**Office of Public Affairs**

*Telephone: (703) 697-6061*

Director .......................................Brig. Gen. R. F. Abel
Chief, Media Relations Division .................Col. Marvin L. Braman

**Office of Legislative Liaison**

*Telephone: (703) 697-8153*

Director...............................Maj. Gen. James P. McCarthy

**Office of Small and Disadvantaged
Business Utilization**

*Telephone: (703) 697-4126*

Director .......................................Donald E. Rellins

**Air Force Audit Agency**

*Telephone: (703) 697-6281*

Assistant Auditor-General .........................Col. Robert D. Reid

**Office of the Chief of Staff**

*Telephone: (703) 697-9225*

Chief of Staff.................................Gen. Charles A. Gabriel
Vice Chief of Staff...........................Gen. Jerome F. O'Malley
Assistant Vice Chief of Staff ..................Lt. Gen. Howard W. Leaf
Director, Directorate of Air Force Board Structure .....Col. T. B. Schmidt

**Directorate of Administration**

*Telephone: (703) 697-0135*

Director .....................................Col. James L. Wyatt, Jr.
Deputy Director and Director, Plans Office .......Col. Robert N. Meredith

**Assistant Chief of Staff for Intelligence**

*Telephone: (703) 695-5613*

Assistant Chief of Staff ......................Maj. Gen. James C. Pfautz
Deputy Assistant Chief of Staff................Brig. Gen. Paul H. Martin
Director, Directorate of Estimates .................Col. Cortlandt Taylor
Assistant, Joint Matters ........................Lt. Col. James O'Brien
Chief, Electronic Combat Intelligence Group ........Col. Robert Dunham
Director, Intelligence Plans and Systems ..........Col. James Clapper, Jr.

**Office of Air Force Reserve**

*Telephone: (703) 695-9225*

Chief......................................Maj. Gen. Sloan R. Gill

**Assistant Chief of Staff for Studies
and Analyses**
*Telephone:    (703) 697-7546*

Assistant Chief of Staff . . . . . . . . . . . . . . . .Maj. Gen. Robert A. Rosenberg

**Office of the Inspector-General**
*Telephone:    (703) 697-6733*

Inspector-General . . . . . . . . . . . . . . . . . . . . . . .Lt. Gen. Robert W. Bazley

**Office of the Judge Advocate-General**
*Telephone:    (703) 694-5732*

Judge Advocate-General . . . . . . . . . . . . . . . . . . . . . .Maj. Gen. T. B. Bruton

**Scientific Advisory Board**
*Telephone:    (703) 697-4811*

Chairman  . . . . . . . . . . . . . . . . . . . . . . . . . . . . . . .Dr. Eugene E. Covert

**The Surgeon-General**
*Bolling Air Force Base*
*Washington, D.C. 20332*
*Telephone:    (202) 767-4343*

Surgeon-General . . . . . . . . . . . . . . . . . . . . . . . .Lt. Gen. Max B. Bralliar

**Comptroller of the Air Force**
*Telephone:    (703) 697-4774*

Comptroller . . . . . . . . . . . . . . . . . . . . . . . . . . .Lt. Gen. G. M. Browning, Jr.

**Deputy Chief of Staff for Manpower
and Personnel**
*Telephone:    (703) 697-6088*

Deputy Chief of Staff . . . . . . . . . . . . . . . . . . . .Lt. Gen. Kenneth L. Peek, Jr.

**Deputy Chief of Staff for Plans
and Operations**
*Telephone:    (703) 697-9991*

Deputy Chief of Staff . . . . . . . . . . . . . . . . . . . . . .Lt. Gen. John T. Chain, Jr.
Assistant Deputy Chief of Staff . . . . . . . . . . . . . .Maj. Gen. David L. Nichols
Director, Electronic Combat . . . . . . . . . . . . . . . . . .Brig. Gen. J. W. Tietge
Director, Command and Control
    Telecommunications . . . . . . . . . . . . . . . . . . .Maj. Gen. Gerald L. Prather
Director, Directorate of Space . . . . . . . . . . . . . . . . .Maj. Gen. J. H. Storrie
Chief, Space Operations Division . . . . . . . . . . . . . . . . . . .Col. R. Knecht
Chief, Space Plans Division . . . . . . . . . . . . . . . . . . . . .Lt. Col. S. C. Beamer
Chief, Space Joint Congressional Matters . . . . . . . . . .Lt. Col. D. E. Rossing
Director, Plans . . . . . . . . . . . . . . . . . . . . . . . . . . .Maj. Gen. John A. Shaud
Deputy Director, Plans . . . . . . . . . . . . . . . . . . .Brig. Gen. Charles R. Hamm
Assistant Director, Joint and
    National Security Matters . . . . . . . . . . . . . . . . . . . . . . .Col. C. G. Boyd
Assistant Director, Special Plans . . . . . . . . . . . . . . . . . . . .Col. R. C. Dutton
Assistant Director, Resources . . . . . . . . . . . . . . . . . . . . . .Col. Z. Zakrzeski
Deputy Director, Force Development . . . . . . . . . . . . . . . .Col. R. O. Bennett
Deputy Director, Regional Plans
    and Policy . . . . . . . . . . . . . . . . . . . . . . . .Brig. Gen. Robert B. Plowden, Jr.
Chief, Western Hemisphere Division . . . . . . . . . . . . . . .Col. A. Maldonado
Chief, Europe NATO Division . . . . . . . . . . . . . . . . . . . .Col. J. M. Johnston
Chief, Middle East/Africa Division . . . . . . . . . . . . . . . . .Col. R. S. Fisher
Chief, Pacific East Asia Division . . . . . . . . . . . . . . . . . . .Lt. Col. F. C. Boli
Chief, Arms Contingent
    Negotiations Division . . . . . . . . . . . . . . . . . . . . . . . . .Col. A. E. Johnson
Deputy Director, Doctrine Strategy
    and Plans Integration . . . . . . . . . . . . . . . . . . . . . . . .Col. H. S. Coyle, Jr.
Director, Directorate of Operations . . . . . . . . . . . . .Maj. Gen. R. D. Beckel
Deputy Director, Operational Support . . . . . . . . . . . . . . .Col. L. E. Bustle

**Deputy Chief of Staff for Programs
and Resources**
*Telephone:    (703) 694-8000*

Deputy Chief of Staff . . . . . . . . . . . . . . . . . . . . . . .Lt. Gen. Larry D. Welch
Director, Directorate of Programs
    and Evaluation . . . . . . . . . . . . . . . . . . . .Maj. Gen. C. J. Cunningham, Jr.
Director, Directorate of
    International Programs . . . . . . . . . . . . . . . .Brig. Gen. Thomas A. Baker

Chief, Americas/Anzus Division . . . . . . . . . . . . . . . . .Col. James G. Andrus
Chief, Middle East/Africa Division . . . . . . . . . . . . . .Col. Joseph J. Vecchio
Chief, Asia Division . . . . . . . . . . . . . . . . . . . . . . . . . . .Col. James L. Jamerson
Chief, Policy and Management Division . . . . . . . . . . . . . .Col. Roy T. Baker
Chief, Weapons Programs Division . . . . . . . . . . . . . . . .Col. Bruce N. Smith
Chief, Saudi Division . . . . . . . . . . . . . . . . . . . . . . . . . .Col. Charles D. Loney
Chief, Europe/NATO Division . . . . . . . . . . . . . . . . .Col. C. Thomas Keeney
Chief, Foreign Military
    Training Advisory Group . . . . . . . . . . . . . . . . . . . . .Lt. Col. David Hawley

## Deputy Chief of Staff for Research and Acquisition

*Telephone: (703) 697-7151*

Deputy Chief of Staff . . . . . . . . . . . . . . . . . . . .Lt. Gen. Lawrence A. Skantze
Management Secretariat . . . . . . . . . . . . . . . . . . . . . . . . .Maj. J. B. Gahagan
Special Assistant, MX Matters . . . . . . . . . . . . . . . . . .Brig. Gen. G. E. Fornell
Special Assistant, International Cooperative
    Research Development and Acquisition . . . . . . . . . . . . . .Col. K. S. Coryell
Director, Directorate of Contracting
    and Manufacturing Policy . . . . . . . . . . . . . . . . . . . .Brig. Gen. B. L. Weiss
Director, Directorate of
    Development and Production . . . . . . .Maj. Gen. George L. Monahan, Jr.
Director, Directorate of
    Operational Requirements . . . . . . . . . . . . . . . . .Maj. Gen. W. A. Gorton
Director, Directorate of Space
    Systems and Command Control
    Communications . . . . . . . . . . . . . . . . . .Brig. Gen. Robert R. Rankine, Jr.
Director, Directorate of
    Program Integration . . . . . . . . . . . . . . . . . . . .Brig. Gen. R. C. Preston, Jr.

## Deputy Chief of Staff for Logistics and Engineering

*Telephone: (703) 695-3153*

Deputy Chief of Staff . . . . . . . . . . . . . . . . . . . . . . . . .Lt. Gen. Leo Marquez
Director, Directorate of Logistics,
    Plans and Programs . . . . . . . . . . . . . . . . . . . . . . .Maj. Gen. A. G. Hansen
Chief, Logistics Budget Integration Office . . . . . . . . . . . . . .Col. R. F. Swarts
Director, Directorate of
    Engineering and Services . . . . . . . . . . . . . . . .Maj. Gen. Clifton D. Wright
Director, Directorate of
    Maintenance and Supply . . . . . . . . . . . .Brig. Gen. Gordon P. Masterson

## Air Force Academy
*Colorado Springs*
*Colorado 80840*
*Telephone: (303) 259-4140*

Superintendent . . . . . . . . . . . . . . . . . . . . . . .Lt. Gen. Winfield W. Scott, Jr.

## MAJOR AIR FORCE COMMANDS

### Air Force Communications Command—AFCC
*Scott Air Force Base*
*Belleville, Illinois 62225*
*Telephone: (309) 638-2571*

Commander . . . . . . . . . . . . . . . . . . . . . . . . . .Maj. Gen. Robert F. McCarthy
Vice Commander . . . . . . . . . . . . . . . . . . . . . . .Brig. Gen. Duncan W. Campbell

### Air Force Logistics Command—AFLC
*Wright-Patterson Air Force Base*
*Dayton, Ohio 45433*
*Telephone: (513) 787-6033*

Commander . . . . . . . . . . . . . . . . . . . . . . . . . . . . . . . .Gen. James P. Mullins
Vice Commander . . . . . . . . . . . . . . . . . . . . . . .Lt. Gen. Earl T. O'Laughlin
Chief of Staff . . . . . . . . . . . . . . . . . . . . . . . .Maj. Gen. Charles McCausland
Deputy Chief of Staff, Operations . . . . . . . . . .Maj. Gen. William P. Bauden
Commander, International Logistics Center . . . .Maj. Gen. Jack W. Waters
Deputy Chief of Staff, Manpower
    and Personnel . . . . . . . . . . . . . . . . . . . . . . . .Brig. Gen. Robert P. McCoy
Deputy Chief of Staff, Comptroller . . . . . . . . .Brig. Gen. Charles D. Metcalf
Deputy Chief of Staff, Contracting
    and Manufacturing . . . . . . . . . . . . . . . . . . . .Brig. Gen. Eugene M. Poe, Jr.
Deputy Chief of Staff, Engineering
    and Services . . . . . . . . . . . . . . . . . . . . . .Brig. Gen. William M. Shaw, Jr.
Deputy Chief of Staff, Plans
    and Programs . . . . . . . . . . . . . . . . . . . . . .Brig. Gen. Charles P. Skipton

**Air Force Systems Command—AFSC**
*Andrews Air Force Base*
*Camp Springs, Maryland 20334*
*Telephone: (301) 858-6200/6209*

Commander . . . . . . . . . . . . . . . . . . . . . . . . . . . . . . . . . . .Gen. Robert T. Marsh
Vice Commander . . . . . . . . . . . . . . . . . . . . . . . . . . .Lt. Gen. Robert M. Bond
Deputy Chief of Staff, Systems . . . . . . . . . . . . .Maj. Gen. Melvin F. Chubb
Deputy Chief of Staff, Acquisitions
and Logistics . . . . . . . . . . . . . . . . . . . . . . . .Maj. Gen. Graham W. Rider
Deputy Chief of Staff, Test
and Evaluation . . . . . . . . . . . . . . . . . . . . . .Maj. Gen. William T. Twinting
Director of Laboratories . . . . . . . . . . . . . . . . . . . .Maj. Gen. Brien D. Ward
Deputy Chief of Staff, Contracting
and Manufacturing . . . . . . . . . . . . . . . . . . . .Brig. Gen. James C. Dever, Jr.
Deputy Chief of Staff, Comptroller . . . . . . . . . .Brig. Gen. Daniel B. Geran

**Air Force Training Command—AFTC**
*Randolph Air Force Base*
*San Antonio, Texas 78150*
*Telephone: (512) 487-5512*

Commander . . . . . . . . . . . . . . . . . . . . . . . . . . . . . . . . . .Gen. Andrew P. Iosue
Vice Commander . . . . . . . . . . . . . . . . . . . .Maj. Gen. James P. Smothermon
Deputy Chief of Staff, Technical Training . . . .Maj. Gen. Thomas J. Hickey
Deputy Chief of Staff, Operations . . . . . . . . . . .Brig. Gen. Chris O. Divich
Deputy Chief of Staff, Logistics . . . . . . . . . . . . .Brig. Gen. Richard F. Gillis
Deputy Chief of Staff, Recruiting . . . . . . . . . . .Brig. Gen. Winfield S. Harpe
Deputy Chief of Staff, Personnel . . . . . . . . . . . .Brig. Gen. Donald C. Metz

**Alaskan Air Command—AAC**
*Elmendorf Air Force Base*
*Anchorage, Alaska 99506*
*Telephone: (907) 552-3100*

Commander . . . . . . . . . . . . . . . . . . . . . . . . . . . . .Lt. Gen. Lynwood W. Clark

**Electronic Security Command—ESC**
*San Antonio, Texas 78243*
*Telephone: (512) 945-2001*

Commander . . . . . . . . . . . . . . . . . . . . . . . . . . . .Maj. Gen. John B. Marks, Jr.
Vice Commander . . . . . . . . . . . . . . . . . . . . . . .Brig. Gen. Regis F. A. Urschler

**Military Airlift Command—MAC**
*Scott Air Force Base*
*Belleville, Illinois 62225*
*Telephone: (309) 638-3205*

Commander . . . . . . . . . . . . . . . . . . . . . . . . . . . . .Gen. Thomas M. Ryan, Jr.
Vice Commander . . . . . . . . . . . . . . . . . . . . . . .Lt. Gen. Robert E. Coverdale
Chief of Staff . . . . . . . . . . . . . . . . . . . . . . .Maj. Gen. James L. Gardner, Jr.
Deputy Chief of Staff, Plans . . . . . . . . . . . . . . .Maj. Gen. Donald D. Brown
Deputy Chief of Staff, Operations . . . . . . . . . . .Maj. Gen. Duane H. Cassidy
Commander, 23rd Air Force . . . . . . . . . . . . . .Maj. Gen. William J. Mall, Jr.
Deputy Chief of Staff, Personnel . . . . . . . . . . .Brig. Gen. Jack W. Sheppard
Deputy Chief of Staff, Logistics . . . . . . . . . . . . .Brig. Gen. Larry D. Wright
Assistant Deputy Chief of Staff, Plans . . . .Brig. Gen. Claudius E. Watts, III

**Pacific Air Forces—PAF**
*Hickam Air Force Base*
*Honolulu, Hawaii, 96853*
*Telephone: (808) 449-1711*

Commander . . . . . . . . . . . . . . . . . . . . . . . . . . . .Lt. Gen. Arnold W. Bragwell
Vice Commander . . . . . . . . . . . . . . . . . . . . . . . .Maj. Gen. Fred A. Haeffner
Deputy Chief of Staff,
Operations and Intelligence . . . . . . . . . .Maj. Gen. Thomas G. McInerney
Deputy Chief of Staff, Logistics . . . . . . . . . . .Maj. Gen. Russell W. Mohney
Deputy Chief of Staff, Plans . . . . . . . . . . . . . .Brig. Gen. Bradley C. Hosmer

**North American Air Defense Command—NORAD, (and Space Command—SPACECOM)**
*Peterson Air Force Base*
*Colorado Springs, Colorado 80914*
*Telephone: (303) 692-3001*

Commander . . . . . . . . . . . . . . . . . . . . . . . . . . . . .Gen. James V. Hartinger
Vice Commander . . . . . . . . . . . . . . . . . . . . . . . . .Maj. Gen. Bruce K. Brown
Deputy Chief of Staff, Plans . . . . . . . . . . . . . . . . .Maj. Gen. Carl N. Beer
Deputy Chief of Staff, Operations . . . . . . . . . .Maj. Gen. Thomas W. Sawyer
Deputy Chief of Staff, Intelligence . . . . . . . . . .Brig. Gen. Brandt C. Thomas
Commander, 1st Space Wing . . . . . . . . . . . . . . . . . . . . .Ralph E. Spraker

**Cheyene Mountain Complex**
Director, NORAD Combat
Operations . . . . . . . . . . . . . . . . . . . . . .Maj. Gen. Carles W. Bartholomew
Director, NORAD Combat Operations . . . . .Brig. Gen. Melbourne Kimsey
Director, NORAD Combat Operations . . . . . . . . .Brig. Gen. Billy J. Rhoten
Assistant Deputy Chief of Staff, Combat
Operations NORAD/SPACECOM . . . . . . . .Brig. Gen. Paul D. Wagoner

**Strategic Air Command—SAC**
*Offut Air Force Base*
*Omaha, Nebraska 68113*
*Telephone:   (402) 271-4111*

Commander . . . . . . . . . . . . . . . . . . . . . . . . . . . . . . . .Gen. Bernie L. Davis
Vice Commander . . . . . . . . . . . . . . . . . . . . . . . . .Lt. Gen. George D. Miller
Chief of Staff . . . . . . . . . . . . . . . . . . . . . . . .Maj. Gen. Monroe W. Hatch, Jr.
Deputy Chief of Staff, Operations . . . . . . . . . . . .Maj. Gen. John A. Brashear
Deputy Chief of Staff,
    Operations and Plans . . . . . . . . . . . . . . . . . . .Maj. Gen. Harley A. Hughes
Deputy Chief of Staff, Plans . . . . . . . . . . .Maj. Gen. Harold J. M. Williams
Deputy Chief of Staff, Data Systems . . . . . . . . .Brig. Gen. James L. Crouch
Deputy Chief of Staff, Logistics . . . . . . . . . . . . .Brig. Gen. John J. Poran, Jr.
Deputy Chief of Staff, Intelligence . . . . . . . .Brig. Gen. William L. Doyle, Jr.
Director, Command and Control . . . . . . . . . .Brig. Gen. Charles A. May, Jr.

**Tactical Air Command—TAC**
*Langley Air Force Base*
*Hampton, Virginia 23665*
*Telephone:   (703) 432-3205*

Commander . . . . . . . . . . . . . . . . . . . . . . . . . . . . .Gen. Wilbur L. Creech
Vice Commander . . . . . . . . . . . . . . . . . . . . . . . . .Lt. Gen. Robert E. Kelley
Chief of Staff . . . . . . . . . . . . . . . . . . . . . . . . . .Maj. Gen. James G. Jones
Deputy Chief of Staff, Plans . . . . . . . . . . . . . .Maj. Gen. Merrill A. McPeak
Deputy Commander for Air Defense . . . . . . . . .Maj. Gen. Russell L. Violett
Deputy Chief of Staff, Requirements . . . . . . . . .Maj. Gen. Thomas L. Craig
Deputy Chief of Staff,
    Engineering and Services . . . . . . . . . . . . . . . .Brig. Gen. George E. Ellis
Deputy Chief of Staff, Logistics . . . . . . . . . . . . . .Brig. Gen. Jerry D. Holmes

**U.S. Air Forces Europe**
*Ramstein Air Force Base*
*West Germany*

Commander . . . . . . . . . . . . . . . . . . . . . . . . . . . . .Gen. Billy M. Minter
Vice Commander . . . . . . . . . . . . . . . . . . . . . . . . .Lt. Gen. Carl H. Catney
Chief of Staff . . . . . . . . . . . . . . . . . . . . .Maj. Gen. William J. Breckner, Jr.
Deputy Commander, (Southern Area) . . . . .Lt. Gen. William E. Brown, Jr.
Commander, 3rd Air Force . . . . . . . . . . . . . . .Maj. Gen. William P. Acker
Commander, 16th Air Force . . . . . . . . . . . . .Maj. Gen. Robert W. Clement
Commander, 17th Air Force . . . . . . . . . . . . . .Maj. Gen. Harry A. Goodall
Deputy Chief of Staff, Operations . . . . . . . . . . . .Maj. Gen. William L. Kirk
Deputy Chief of Staff,
    Engineering and Services . . . . . . . . . . . . . .Brig. Gen. Joseph A. Ahearn
Deputy Chief of Staff, Logistics . . . . . . . . . . . . . .Brig. Gen. Lewis G. Curtis
Deputy Chief of Staff, Plans . . . . . . . . . . . . . .Brig. Gen. Wilfred L. Goodson
Deputy Chief of Staff, Intelligence . . . . . . . .Brig. Gen. Leonard H. Perroots

**COAST GUARD**
**Department of Transportation**
*Washington, D.C. 20593*
*Telephone:   (202) 426-2158*

Commandant, Coast Guard Headquarters . . . . . . . . .Adm. James S. Gracey
Chief of Staff . . . . . . . . . . . . . . . . . . . . . . . . . . . . . . . .Adm. Paul A. Yost
Commander, Atlantic Area (New York, NY) . . . . .Adm. Wayne E. Caldwell
Commander, Pacific Area (Long Beach, CA) . . . . . . . .Adm. A. P. Manning
Commander, Coast Guard Academy
    (New London, CT) . . . . . . . . . . . . . . . . . . . . . . . .Capt. Joseph E. Vorbach

\* \* \* \* \*

# GENERAL DEFENSE DATA

**Manpower**
    Total Armed Forces . . . . . . . . . . . . . . . . . . . . . . . . . . . . . . . . . . . . . . . . . . .2,116,000
        (See Page 569)
    Population . . . . . . . . . . . . . . . . . . . . . . . . . . . . . . . . . . . . . . . . . . . . . . .239,195,000

**Spending**
    Military Expenditures . . . . . . . . . . . . . . . . . . . . . . . . . . . . . . . . . . . . . .$182.8 billion
    Gross National Product . . . . . . . . . . . . . . . . . . . . . . . . . . . . . . . . . .$2,925.5 billion
    Military Expenditure as a Percentage of
        Gross National Product . . . . . . . . . . . . . . . . . . . . . . . . . . . . . . . . . . . . .6.2%
    Military Expenditure as a Percentage of
        Central Government Expenditure . . . . . . . . . . . . . . . . . . . . . . . . . . . . . .24.9%

**Defense Treaties** *(See Part II for Additional Detail)*

Bilateral:

| | | |
|---|---|---|
| Antigua | Guyana | Philippines |
| Argentina | Haiti | Portugal |
| Australia | Honduras | Rwanda |
| Austina | Iceland | St. Lucia |
| Bahamas | India | St. Vincent and |
| Belgium | Indonesia |    the Grenadines |
| Belize | Iran | Saudi Arabia |
| Benin | Israel | Senegal |
| Bermuda | Italy | Sierra Leone |
| Bolivia | Jamaica | Singapore |
| Botswana | Japan | Somalia |
| Brazil | Jordan | South Africa |
| Burma | Kenya | Spain |
| Cameroon | Republic of Korea | Sri Lanka |
| Canada | Kuwait | Sudan |
| Chile | Lebanon | Sweden |
| Columbia | Liberia | Suriname |
| Costa Rica | Luxembourg | Thailand |
| Cuba | Malawi | Togo |
| Denmark | Malaysia | Trinidad and |
| Dominican | Mali |    Tobago |
|    Republic | Morocco | Tunisia |
| Dominica | Netherlands | Turkey |
| Egypt | New Zealand | United Arab |
| El Salvador | Nicaragua |    Emirates |
| Ethiopia | Niger | Union of Soviet |
| France | Nigeria |    Socialist Republics |
| Federal Republic | Norway | United Kingdom |
|    of Germany | Oman | Uruguay |
| Ghana | Pakistan | Venezuela |
| Greece | Panama | Yugoslavia |
| Guatemala | Paraguay | Zaire |
| Guinea | Peru | |

Multilateral:
Act of Chapultepec
ANZUS
Biological Weapons Convention
Central American Democratic Community
Environmental Modification Convention
Inter-American Treaty of Reciprocal Assistance
Limited Test Ban Treaty
Multinational Force in Beirut
Multinational Force and Observers in Sinai
North Atlantic Treaty Organization
South-East Asia Collective Defense Treaty
Treaty for the Prohibition of Nuclear Weapons in
   Latin-America
Treaty on the Control of Arms on the Seabed
Treaty on the Non-Proliferation of Nuclear Weapons

# UPPER VOLTA

## Defense Establishment Command Structure and Force Organization

The President of the People's Salvation Council, is Minister of National Defense and Veterans Affairs. All services form part of the Army.

**Total armed forces:** 4,070 (Army: 4,000; Air Force: 70). **Para-military forces:** 1,850.

## HEAD OF STATE

Médecin-Cdt. Jean-Baptiste Ouedraogo

**OFFICE OF THE PRESIDENT**
*B.P. 7031*
*Ouagadougou*
*Telephone: 345 43*
*Telex: 221 pregouv*

President of the People's Salvation Council and
   Minister of National Defense and
   Veterans Affairs ...... Médecin-Commandant Jean-Baptiste Ouedraogo
Director of Cabinet ........................ Robert Badini Nabasnogho
Chief, Military Cabinet ................. Lt. Gaongo Guessirina Martin
Aide-de-Camp ..................................... Lt. Louliga Zongo

**MINISTRY OF INTERIOR AND SECURITY**
*B.P. 7034*
*Ouagadougou*
*Telephone: 324 01*

Minister .............................. Cdt. Harouna Noné Tarnagda
Director of Cabinet ....................... Tingnínian Bernard Nabure
Director-General, National Police ................... Emmanuel Kyelem
Deputy Director-General ................. Nongoma Ernest Ouedraogo
Director, State Security ................. Adama Jean-Marie Bakouan
Chief, Republican Security Corps .................. Barthélémy Ouaba
Commander, Ouagadougou Airport ............. Soulaymane Ouedrago

**MINISTRY OF NATIONAL DEFENSE AND VETERANS AFFAIRS**
*(Ministère de la Défense Nationale et des Anciens Combattants)*
*B.P. 496*
*Ouagadougou*
*Telephone: 346 77, 326 50*
*Telex: 5297 uv*
*Cable: MINIDEF*

Minister and
   President ........... Médecin-Commandant Jean-Baptiste Ouedraogo
Director of Cabinet .............................. Joachim Zabramba
Secretary-General ........................... Col. Mamadou Djerma
Director, Operations Division.............. Lt. Col. Ousmane Ouedraogo
Senior Commisariat Officer ............. Int. Mil. Soré Daniel Ouedraogo
Deputy Senior Commisariat
   Officer ......................... Int. Mil. Kountiahir Désiré Dabire

## DEFENSE FORCES

**ARMY**
*(Armée Nationale)*
*B.P. 509*
*Ouagadougou*
*Telephone: 345 43*
*Telex: 5298*

Chief of Staff............................ Col. Yoryan Gabriel Some
Deputy Chief of Staff ..................... Col. Yaoua Marcel Tamini

**Air Force**
*B.P. 96*
*Ouagadougou*
*Telephone: 321 61*

Commander .......................... Christophe Laurent Kielwasser
Adjunct Commander ................................ Maj. Dô Sanou

**NATIONAL CONSTABULARY**
*(Gendarmerie Nationale)*
*Ouagadougou*

Commander .................................... Lt. Col. Sié Ouattara
Adjunct Commander ........................... Maj. Abel Ouedraogo
Adjunct Commander ................ Lt. Kango Barthélémy Ouedraogo

\* \* \* \* \*

## GENERAL DEFENSE DATA

**Manpower**

Total Armed Forces ............................................... 4,070
    (See Page 607)
Population ............................................... 6,208,000

**Spending**

Military Expenditures ......................................... $35 million
Gross National Product ........................................ $1.1 billion
Military Expenditure as a Percentage of
    Gross National Product ........................................ 3.1%
Military Expenditure as a Percentage of
    Central Government Expenditure ................................ 18.2%

**Defense Treaties** (*See Part II for Additional Detail*)

Bilateral:    Mali

Multilateral:    Economic Community of West African States
                Organization of African Unity
                Treaty on the Non-Proliferation of Nuclear Weapons

# URUGUAY
## Oriental Republic of Uruguay
### *República Oriental del Uruguay*

### Defense Establishment Command Structure and Force Organization

The President is nominal Commander-in-Chief of the Armed Forces. He is advised by the National Security Council, which consists of cabinet members, the three service chiefs, and the Chief of the Joint Staff. The authority of the President is exercised through the Minister of National Defense, who is responsible for the administration of the military.

**Total armed forces:** 29,700 (Army: 22,000;   Navy: 4,700;   Air Force: 3,000). **Para-military forces:** 1,500 (Coastguard).

## HEAD OF STATE

Tte. Gral. Gregorio Álvarez

**OFFICE OF THE PRESIDENT**
*(Oficina de la Presidencia)*
*Casa de Gobierno*
*Plaza Independencia 776*
*Montevideo*
Telephone:   98 93 10 ext. 143

President of the Republic and Commander-in-Chief of the Armed Forces .............. Tte. Gral. Gregorio Álvarez

**National Security Council**

*(Consejo de Seguridad Nacional)*

Chairman .................................. Tte. Gral. Gregorio Álvarez
(President and Commander-in-Chief of the Armed Forces)
Member *(ex officio)* ............................... Dr. Carlos A. Maeso
(Minister of Foreign Affairs)
Member *(ex officio)* .......................... Gral. Yamandú Trinidad
(Minister of the Interior)
Member *(ex officio)* ........................ Walter Lusiardo Aznarez
(Minister of Economics and Finance)
Member *(ex officio)* ............................. Gral. Boscan Hontou
(Commander of Army)
Member *(ex officio)* ............................. Valm. Rodolfo Invídio
(Commander of Navy)
Member *(ex officio)* ......................... Tte. Gral Manuel Buadas
Permanent Secretary ............................. Cap. Jorge Laborde
(Chief of the Joint Staff)

**MINISTRY OF NATIONAL DEFENSE**
*(Ministério de Defensa Nacional)*
*25 de Mayo 279*
*Montevideo*

Telephone:   95 18 21, 95 28 16, 95 59 56
Telex:   721 urusid uy

Minister ....................................... Dr. Justo M. Alonso
Under Secretary ................................. Dr. Héctor Frugone
Director-General ................................ Cnel. Carlos Legnani
Army Assistant to Defense Minister ........... Cnel. Washington Bertran
Navy Assistant to Defense Minister ................. Cap. Alberto Sghirle
Air Force Assistant to Defense Minister ............. Cnel. Carlos Palermo
Chief, Central Division ..................................... (Vacant)
Chief, 2nd Division ........................................ (Vacant)
Chief, 3rd Division ........................................ (Vacant)
Chief, 4th Division ........................................ (Vacant)
Director-General, Materials and Armament Services ........................ Cnel. Alfredo Rúbio

# DEFENSE FORCES

## ARMED FORCES
*Avenida 8 de Octubre 2628*
*Montevideo*
*Telephone:    4 33 67, 98 93 10 ext. 354*

Chief of the Joint Staff . . . . . . . . . . . . . . . . . . . . . . . . . . . . .Capt. Jorge Laborde

## ARMY
*Commando General del Ejército*
*Avenida Garibaldi 2313*
*Montevideo*
*Telephone:    28 15 42/46*
*Telex:    931 ejuru uy*

Commander-in-Chief, Army . . . . . . . . . . . . . . . . .Tte. Gral. Boscan Hontou
Chief of Staff . . . . . . . . . . . . . . . . . . . . . . . . . . . . . .Gral. Héctor S. Álvarez
President, Secretariat for Planning
   Coordination and Information . . . . . . . . . . . . . . . . . .Gral. Pedro J. Aranco
Director, School of Arms . . . . . . . . . . . . . . . . . . . . . . . . . . .Gral. Alfonso Feola
Commander, Fourth Army Division . . . . . . . . . . . . .Gral. Abdon Raimúndez
First Deputy Chief of Staff . . . . . . . . . . . . . . . . . . . . . . .Cnel. Sergio Sosa
Chief, Department I—Personnel . . . . . . . . . . . . . . . . . .Cnel. Esteban Souto
Chief, Department II—Information . . . . . . . . . . . . . .Cnel. Alberto F. Mira
Chief, Department III—
   Operations and Instruction . . . . . . . . . . . . . . . . . . .Cnel. Daniel E. García
Chief, Department IV—Logistics
   (In charge of procurement) . . . . . . . . . . . . . . . . .Cnel. Alberto P. Loureiro
Chief, Department of Public Relations . . . . . . . . . .Cnel. Victor M. Escobal

## NAVY
*Commando General de la Armada*
*Edificio Aduana, 4 Piso*
*Montevideo*
*Telephone:    90 46 11 ext. 329, 95 29 53,*
*95 64 01*
*Telex:    746 armwda uy*

Commander-in-Chief, Navy . . . . . . . . . . . . . . . . .Vice Alm. Rodolf Invidio
Chief, Coast Guard . . . . . . . . . . . . . . . . . . . . .Contra Alm. Pedro José Imizcoz
Chief, Forces Afloat . . . . . . . . . . . . . . . . . . . . . . . . . . . . .Cap. Yamandú Ubal
Chief of Staff . . . . . . . . . . . . . . . . . . . . . . . . . . . . . . .Cap. Jorge Fernandez
Chief, Customs . . . . . . . . . . . . . . . . . . . . . . . . . . . . . . . .Cap. Jorge Laborde
Chief, Naval Education and Training . . . . . . . . . . . . . .Cap. Luis Chiaparro
Chief, Naval Aviation . . . . . . . . . . . . . . . . . . . . . . . . . .Cap. Reclus Cavalleri

## AIR FORCE
*Commando General de la Fuerza Aérea*
*Avenida Don Pedro de Mendoza 5553*
*Montevideo*
*Telephone:    22 34 21/09, 22 44 01*
*Telex:    906 fau uy*

Commander-in-Chief, Air Force . . . . . . . . . . . . . .Tte. Gral. Manuel Buadas
Chief, Materiel Command . . . . . . . . . . . . . . . . . . .Brig. Gral. Fernando Arbe
Chief of Staff . . . . . . . . . . . . . . . . . . . . . . . . . . .Brig. Gral. Walther Machado
Assistant Chief of Staff, Personnel . . . . . . . . . . . . . . . . . .Cnel. Adan Da Luz
Assistant Chief of Staff, Intelligence . . . . . . . . . . . . . . . . .Cnel. Edwin Noble
Assistant Chief of Staff, Operations . . . . . . . . . . . . . . .Cnel. Werner Malates
Assistant Chief of Staff, Materiel . . . . . . . . . . . . . . . .Cnel. Esperanza Pintos

\* \* \* \* \*

# GENERAL DEFENSE DATA

**Manpower**
   Total Armed Forces . . . . . . . . . . . . . . . . . . . . . . . . . . . . . . . . . . . . . . . . .29,700
      (See Page 609)
   Population . . . . . . . . . . . . . . . . . . . . . . . . . . . . . . . . . . . . . . . . . . . .2,961,000

**Spending**
   Military Expenditures . . . . . . . . . . . . . . . . . . . . . . . . . . . . . . . . . . . .$130 million
   Gross National Product . . . . . . . . . . . . . . . . . . . . . . . . . . . . . . . . . . .$7.9 billion
   Military Expenditure as a Percentage of
      Gross National Product . . . . . . . . . . . . . . . . . . . . . . . . . . . . . . . . . . .1.6%
   Military Expenditure as a Percentage of
      Central Government Expenditure . . . . . . . . . . . . . . . . . . . . . . . . . . . .9.9%

**Defense Treaties** *(See Part II for Additional Detail)*

    Bilateral:     United States

    Multilateral:    Act of Chapultepec
                      Biological Weapons Convention
                      Inter-American Defense Board
                      Inter-American Treaty of Reciprocal Assistance
                      Limited Test Ban Treaty
                      Multinational Force and Observers in the Sinai
                      Treaty for the Prohibition of Nuclear Weapons in
                         Latin America
                      Treaty on the Non-Proliferation of Nuclear Weapons

**Military Rank Comparisons**
  See Appendix A.

# VANUATU
## Republic of Vanuatu

### Defense Establishment Command Structure and Force Organization

Vanuatu does not maintain a defense force.

### HEAD OF STATE

H. E. Ati George Sokomanu, M.B.E.

**OFFICE OF THE PRESIDENT**
*Port Vila*

President . . . . . . . . . . . . . . . . . . . . . . . . . . . . . Ati George Sokomanu, M.B.E.

**OFFICE OF THE PRIME MINISTER**
*Port Vila*
*Telex: 1040 vangov nh*

Prime Minister . . . . . . . . . . . . . . . . . . . . Father Walter Hayde Lini, C.B.E.
Deputy Prime Minister
   and Minister of Home Affairs . . . . . . . . . . . . . . . . . . . . . . Sethy Regenvanu

\* \* \* \* \*

### GENERAL DEFENSE DATA

**Manpower**
   Total Armed Forces . . . . . . . . . . . . . . . . . . . . . . . . . . . . . . . . . . . . . . . . . . . . .
   Population . . . . . . . . . . . . . . . . . . . . . . . . . . . . . . . . . . . . . . . . . . . . . 123,000

**Spending**
   Military Expenditures . . . . . . . . . . . . . . . . . . . . . . . . . . . . . . . . . . . . . . . . . .
   Gross National Product . . . . . . . . . . . . . . . . . . . . . . . . . . . . . . . . . . . . . $60 million
   Military Expenditure as a Percentage of
      Gross National Product . . . . . . . . . . . . . . . . . . . . . . . . . . . . . . . . . . . . . . . .
   Military Expenditure as a Percentage of
      Central Government Expenditure . . . . . . . . . . . . . . . . . . . . . . . . . . . . . . . .

**Defense Treaties** *(See Part II for Additional Detail)*

   Bilateral:     Papua New Guinea

   Multilateral:  None

# THE VATICAN CITY STATE
## The Holy See

The Vatican City State is governed by a Pontifical Commission appointed by the Supreme Pontiff. The President of the Commission is also the Secretary of State.

Defense for the Vatican City is the responsibility of the government of Italy. However, the Vatican City has its own private security force, (the Swiss Guards) which also serves ceremonial functions.

**Swiss Guards:** 24.

## HEAD OF STATE
### (The Supreme Pontiff)

His Holiness Pope John Paul II (Karol Wojtyla)

**PONTIFICAL COMMISSION**
*(Pontificia Commissione)*
*00120 Citta del Vaticano*

*Telex:* *2019 pccs va*
*(Pontificia Commissione per le*
*Comunicazioni Sociali)*

President and Secretary of State . . . . . . . . . . . . . . . Cardinal Agostino Casaroli

**SWISS GUARDS**

Captain Commander . . . . . . . . . . . . . . . . . . . . . . . . . . . . . Col. Roland Buchs
Chaplain . . . . . . . . . . . . . . . . . . . . . . . . . . . . . . Monsignor Paul Grichting
Lieutenant . . . . . . . . . . . . . . . . . . . . . . . . . . . . . . . . . . . . . Gregor Volken
Sub-Lieutenant . . . . . . . . . . . . . . . . . . . . . . . . . . . . . . Alois. Esthermann

\* \* \* \* \*

## GENERAL DEFENSE DATA

**Manpower**
Total Armed Forces . . . . . . . . . . . . . . . . . . . . . . . . . . . . . . . . . . . . . . . .24
Population . . . . . . . . . . . . . . . . . . . . . . . . . . . . . . . . . . . . . . . . . . . . .1,000

**Spending**
Military Expenditures . . . . . . . . . . . . . . . . . . . . . . . . . . . . . . . . . . . . . .
Gross National Product . . . . . . . . . . . . . . . . . . . . . . . . . . . . . . . . . . . . .
Military Expenditure as a Percentage of
   Gross National Product . . . . . . . . . . . . . . . . . . . . . . . . . . . . . . . . . . .
Military Expenditure as a Percentage of
   Central Government Expenditure . . . . . . . . . . . . . . . . . . . . . . . . . . . .

**Defense Treaties** *(See Part II for Additional Detail)*

Bilateral:    None

Multilateral:   Treaty on the Non-Proliferation of Nuclear Weapons

# VENEZUELA
## Republic of Venezuela
*República de Venezuela*

The President is Commander-in-Chief of the armed forces of Venezuela. His authority is exercised through the Minister of Defense. A National Defense Council advises the President on security matters.

**Total armed forces:** 40,800 (Army: 27,000; Navy: 9,000; Air Force: 4,800). **Para-military forces:** 20,000 (Fuerzas Armadas de Cooperacion).

## HEAD OF STATE

H. E. Dr. Luis Herrera Campins

**OFFICE OF THE PRESIDENT**
*(Oficina del Presidente)*
*Palacio de Miraflores*
*Caracas 101*
*Telephone: (2) 810811*

President of the Republic and
   Commander-in-Chief . . . . . . . . . . . . . . . . . . . . . Dr. Luis Herrera Campins

**National Defense Council**

| | |
|---|---|
| Chairman . . . . . . . . . . . . . . . . . . . . . . | Gral. Div. Humberto Alcalde Álvarez (Minister of Defense) |
| Member . . . . . . . . . . . . . . . . . . . . . . . . . . . | Gral. Div. Felipe Arrieta Ávila (Commander, Armed Forces) |
| Member . . . . . . . . . . . . . . . . . . . . . . . . . . . | Gral. Div. Octavio Romero (Commander, Army) |
| Member . . . . . . . . . . . . . . . . . . . . . . . | Vice Alm. Aroldo Rodríquez Figueroa (Commander-General, Navy) |
| Member . . . . . . . . . . . . . . . . . . . . . . . . . . . | Gral. Div. Carlos Pinaud Areila (Commander, Air Force) |
| Member . . . . . . . . . . . . . . . . . . . . . . . . . . . | Vice Alm. Julio Fernando Fosse (Inspector-General, Armed Forces) |
| Member . . . . . . . . . . . . . . . . . . . . . . . . . | Gral. Div. Alfredo Quintana Romero (Chairman, Joint Chiefs of Staff) |

**MINISTRY OF DEFENSE**
*(Ministério de la Defensa)*
*Fuerte Tiana, El Valle*
*Caracas*
*Telephone:  (2) 622-2276, 662-1248,*
*662-1775*

| | |
|---|---|
| Minister . . . . . . . . . . . . . . . . . . . . . . . | Gral. Div. Humberto Alcalde Álvarez |
| Inspector-General . . . . . . . . . . . . . . . . . . . . . | Vice Alm. Julio Fernándo Fosse |
| Director, Intelligence . . . . . . . . . . . . . . . . . . . . | Contra Alm. Clemente Lange |
| Director, Operations . . . . . . . . . . . . . . . | Gral Brig. Ramón Benigno Aguilar |
| Director, Finances . . . . . . . . . . . . . | Gral Brig. Juan Arévalo Vásquez Cedeno |
| Director, Cabinet . . . . . . . . . . . . | Gral Brig. José António Rosseaun Vásquez |

## DEFENSE FORCES

**ARMED FORCES**
*(Fuerzas Armadas)*
*Fuerte Tiuna*
*Conejo Blanco, El Valle*
*Caracas*

| | |
|---|---|
| Commander-in-Chief and President . . . . . . . . . . . | Dr. Luis Herrera Campins |
| Commander . . . . . . . . . . . . . . . . . . . . . . . . | Gral. Div. Felipe Arrieta Ávila |

**Office of the Joint Chiefs of Staff**
*(Oficina del Estado Mayor Conjunto)*
*Telephone: (2) 662-3043*

Chairman, Joint Chiefs of Staff . . . . . . Gral. Div. Alfredo Quintana Romero

**ARMY**
*(Ejército Nacional)*
*Fuerte Tiuna*
*Conejo Blanco, El Valle*
*Caracas*
*Telephone: (2) 69 18 11*
*Telex: 21491, 21612*

Commander . . . . . . . . . . . . . . . . . . . . . . . . . . . . . . Gral. Div. Octavio Romero
Chief of Staff . . . . . . . . . . . . . . . . . . . . . . . . . . . . . . . . . . . . . . . . . . (Vacant)
Inspector-General . . . . . . . . . . . . . . . . . . . . . . . . Gral. Div. Ovaldo Plazola Gilly
Director, Personnel . . . . . . . . . . . . . . . . . Gral. Brig. Armando García Portillo
Director, Intelligence . . . . . . . . . . . . . . . Gral. Brig. Carlos Zamudio Ferretti
Director, Finance . . . . . . . . . . . . . . . . . . . . . Gral. Brig. Rafael Canache Mata

**NAVY**
*(La Marina Venezolana)*
*Avenida Vollmer*
*San Bernadino*
*Caracas 101*
*Telephone: (2) 52 33 33 (Commander-*
*General), 52 41 91 (Public*
*Relations)*

Commander-General . . . . . . . . . . . . . . Vice Alm. Aroldo Rodríquez Figueroa
Inspector-General . . . . . . . . . . . . . . . . . . . . . Vice Alm. Julio Lanz Castellanos
Chief, Operations . . . . . . . . . . . . . . . . . . . Vice Alm. José Rodríquez Mottola
Chief of Staff . . . . . . . . . . . . . . . . . . . . . Vice Alm. Justo Fernández Márquez
Commander, Naval Squadron . . . . Contra Alm. Alejandro Lander Landaeta
Commander, Marine Corps . . . . . . . . Contra Alm. Francisco Herrera Balduz
Chief, Personnel . . . . . . . . . . . . . . . . . Contra Alm. Cipriano Salazar Aquino
Director, Intelligence . . . . . . . . . . . . . Contra Alm. Ricardo de Lima Martínez
Chief, Education . . . . . . . . . . . . . . . . Contra Alm. Justo Fernández Márquez
Chief, Logistics . . . . . . . . . . . . . . . . . Contra Alm. Carlos Pulido Salvatierra
Director, Administration . . . . . . . . . . . Contra Alm. Tulio António Márquez

**AIR FORCE**
*(La Fuerza Aerea)*
*Vase Generalisimo*
*Francisco de Miranda*
*PB*
*La Carlota Air Base*
*Caracas*
*Telephone: (2) 239 2311, 239 0224, 239 2353*

Commander . . . . . . . . . . . . . . . . . . . . . . . . . . Gral. Div. Carlos Pinaud Areila
Chief of Staff . . . . . . . . . . . . . . . . . . . . . . . . . . Gral. Div. Pascual J. Azara
Inspector-General . . . . . . . . . . . . . . . . . . . . . Gral. Div. Calixtenes Fujuent
Director, Personnel . . . . . . . . . . . . . . . . . . . . . Gral. Div. Orlanda Coronel
Commander, Logistics . . . . . . . . . . . . . . . . . . . . Gral. Brig. Raymundo Aular
Commander, Operations . . . . . . . . . . . . . . . . . . . . . . . . Gral. Brig. Lionidas

**ARMED FORCES OF COOPERATION**
*(Fuerzas Armadas de Cooperacion–FAC)*
*Aven. Paez, Quinta*
*Las Acacia, El Paraiso*
*Caracas*
*Telephone: (2) 483-4533*

Commander . . . . . . . . . . . . . . . . . . . . Gral. Div. Felipe Mery Arrieta Ávila
Chief, Operations . . . . . . . . . . . . . . . . . . . . . . . Gral Div. José Enrique Berthe
Inspector-General . . . . . . . . . . . . . . . . Gral Div. Landys Ferreira Zambrano
Director, Personnel . . . . . . . . . . . . . . . . . . . Gral. Brig. Jesús Vargas Chirinos
Director, Intelligence . . . . . . . . . . . . . . . Gral. Brig. Miguel José Morales Paz
Director, Finance . . . . . . . . . . . . . . Gral. Brig. Alfredo Sandoval Hernández

\* \* \* \* \*

## GENERAL DEFENSE DATA

**Manpower**
    Total Armed Forces . . . . . . . . . . . . . . . . . . . . . . . . . . . . . . . . . . . . . . . . . . . 40,800
       (See Page 617)
    Population . . . . . . . . . . . . . . . . . . . . . . . . . . . . . . . . . . . . . . . . . . . . 18,427,000

**Spending**
    Military Expenditures . . . . . . . . . . . . . . . . . . . . . . . . . . . . . . . . . . . . . $671 million
    Gross National Product . . . . . . . . . . . . . . . . . . . . . . . . . . . . . . . . . . . . . $54 billion
    Military Expenditure as a Percentage of
       Gross National Product . . . . . . . . . . . . . . . . . . . . . . . . . . . . . . . . . . . . . 1.2%
    Military Expenditure as a Percentage of
       Central Government Expenditure . . . . . . . . . . . . . . . . . . . . . . . . . . . . . . 5%

**Defense Treaties** *(See Part II for Additional Detail)*

Bilateral:     United States

Multilateral:    Act of Chapultepec
Biological Weapons Convention
Inter-American Defense Board
Inter-American Treaty of Reciprocal Assistance
Limited Test Ban Treaty
Treaty for the Prohibition of Nuclear Weapons in Latin
   America
Treaty on the Non-Proliferation of Nuclear Weapons

**Military Rank Comparisons**
See Appendix A.

# VIETNAM
## Socialist Republic of Vietnam
### Cong-Hoa Xa-Hoi Chu-Nghia Viet-Nam

## Defense Establishment Command Structure and Force Organization

The Chairman of the Council of State has supreme command of the armed forces and is Chairman of the National Defense Council, an advisory group elected by the National Assembly. The Central Military Party Committee of the Vietnamese Communist Party provides the link between the party and the military.

The Air and Air-Defense Service forms an integral part of the Army. The Navy and Air Force operate as independent branches of the armed forces.

**Total armed forces:** 1,029,000 (Army: 1,000,000; Navy: 4,000; Air Force: 25,000). **Para-military forces:** 70,000 (Frontier, Coast Security, People's Armed Security Forces). **Militia:** 1,500,000.

## HEAD OF STATE

H. E. Chiang Ching-Kuo

| | | |
|---|---|---|
| **COUNCIL OF STATE** *Hanoi* | Chairman | Truong Cinh |
| | Vice Chairman | Chu Huy Man |
| | Vice Chairman | Le Thanh Nghi |
| | Vice Chairman | Huynh Tan Phat |
| | Vice Chairman | Nguyen Huu Tho |
| | Secretary General | Le Thanh Nghi |
| **National Defense Council** | Chairman | Truong Chinh |
| | Vice Chairman | Pham Van Dong |
| | Member | Pham Hung |
| | Member | Van Tein Dung |
| | Member | To Huu |
| **CENTRAL MILITARY PARTY COMMITTEE OF THE VIETNAMESE COMMUNIST PARTY—VCP** *Hanoi* | Secretary, VCP | Gen. Le Duan |
| | First Deputy Secretary | Senior Gen. Van Tien Dung |
| | Deputy Secretary | Senior Gen. Chu Huy Man |
| | Deputy Secretary | Le Duc Tho |
| | Member | Col. Gen. Le Duc Anh |
| | Member | Lt. Gen. Le Quang Dao |
| | Member | Lt. Gen. Bui Phung |
| | Member | Lt. Gen. Nguyen Quyet |
| | Member | Col. Gen. Le Trong Tan |
| | Member | Senior Gen. Hoang Van Thai |
| **MINISTRY OF NATIONAL DEFENSE** *Hanoi* | Minister of Defense | Senior Gen. Van Tien Dung |
| | Vice Minister | Lt. Gen. Bui Phung |
| | Vice Minister | Maj. Gen. Dang Vu Hiep |
| | Vice Minister | Senior Gen. Hoang Van Thai |
| | Vice Minister | Col. Gen. Le Duc Anh |

Vice Minister . . . . . . . . . . . . . . . . . . . . . . . . . . . . Lt. Gen. Le Quang Hoa
Vice Minister . . . . . . . . . . . . . . . . . . . . . . . . . . . . . Col. Gen. Le Trong Tan
Vice Minister . . . . . . . . . . . . . . . . . . . . . . . . . . . . .Lt. Gen. Tran Quy Hai
Vice Minister . . . . . . . . . . . . . . . . . . . . . . . . . . . .Lt. Gen. Tran Van Quang
Vice Minister . . . . . . . . . . . . . . . . . . . . . . . . . . . Maj. Gen. Vu Xuan Chiem

## DEFENSE FORCES

**ARMY**
**People's Army of Vietnam**
*(Quan Doi Nan Dan)*
*Hanoi*

Chief of Staff . . . . . . . . . . . . . . . . . . . . . . . . . . . . . Col. Gen. Le Trong Tan
Director, General Political Department . . . . . . .Senior Gen. Chu Huy Man
Commander, Military Region I . . . . . . . . . . . .Maj. Gen. Dam Quang Trung
Commander, Military Region III . . . . . . . . . . . . . .Maj. Gen. Nguyen Quyet
Commander, Military Region IV . . . . . . . . . . . . . . . . .Lt. Gen. Hoang Can
Commander, Military Region V . . . . . . . . . . . . . . . . . .Lt. Gen. Doan Khue
Commander, Military Region VII . . . . . . . . .Maj. Gen. Nguyen Minh Chau
Commander, Military Region IX . . . . . . . . . . . . . .Maj. Gen. Tran Nghiem

**Air and Air-Defense Service**

Commander . . . . . . . . . . . . . . . . . . . . . . . . . . .Maj. Gen. Hoang Van Khanh

**NAVY**
**People's Navy of Vietnam**
*Hanoi*

Commander . . . . . . . . . . . . . . . . . . . . . . . . . . . .Maj. Gen. Doan Ba Khanh

**AIR FORCE**
*Hanoi*

Commander . . . . . . . . . . . . . . . . . . . . . . . . . . . .Maj. Gen. Dao Dinh Luyer

\* \* \* \* \*

## GENERAL DEFENSE DATA

**Manpower**
Total Armed Forces . . . . . . . . . . . . . . . . . . . . . . . . . . . . . . . . . . . . . . . . .1,029,000
    (See Page 621)
Population . . . . . . . . . . . . . . . . . . . . . . . . . . . . . . . . . . . . . . . . . . .56,430,000

**Spending**
Military Expenditures . . . . . . . . . . . . . . . . . . . . . . . . . . . . . . . . . . . . . . . . .
Gross National Product . . . . . . . . . . . . . . . . . . . . . . . . . . . . . . . . . .$9.5 billion
Military Expenditure as a Percentage of
    Gross National Product . . . . . . . . . . . . . . . . . . . . . . . . . . . . . . . . . . . . . .
Military Expenditure as a Percentage of
    Central Government Expenditure . . . . . . . . . . . . . . . . . . . . . . . . . . . . . .

**Defense Treaties** *(See Part II for Additional Detail)*

| Bilateral: | Bulgaria | Kampuchea |
|---|---|---|
| | Czechoslovakia | Laos |
| | German Demo- | Mongolia |
| | cratic Republic | Soviet Union |

Multilateral:    Biological Weapons Convention
Environmental Modifications Convention
Limited Test Ban Treaty
Treaty on the Non-Proliferation of Nuclear Weapons

# WESTERN SAMOA
## Independent State of Western Samoa
### *Samoai Sisfo*

## Defense Establishment Command Structure
## and Force Organization

Western Samoa has no defense forces. The Prime Minister is head of the island's police force.

## HEAD OF STATE

H. H. Malietoa Tanumafili II, G.C.M.G., C.B.E.

**OFFICE OF THE HEAD OF STATE**
*Government House*
*Vailima, Apia*
*Telephone:   20840*
*Telex:   221 malo sx*

Head of State
   (O le o le Malo) . . . . . . . . . . . . . . . . . . . . . . . H. H. Malietoa Tanumafili II,
                                            B.C.M.G., C.B.E.

**OFFICE OF THE PRIME MINISTER**
*P.O. Box 193*
*Apia*
*Telephone:   21500*
*Telex:   221 malo sx*
*Cable:   MALO APIA*

Prime Minister, Attorney General and Minister in Charge of
   Finance, Customs, Legislative Affairs, Audit, Logistics,
   Police and Prisons, Internal Affairs, Immigration, Public
   Service Commission, Public Trust Development Bank,
   National Providence Fund, Somoan Forest Products,
   Monetary Board, Labor, and Fire Brigade . . . . . . . . . . . . . . . . . Tofilau Eti

\* \* \* \* \*

## GENERAL DEFENSE DATA

**Manpower**
   Total Armed Forces . . . . . . . . . . . . . . . . . . . . . . . . . . . . . . . . . . . . . . . . . . . . . . . . .
   Population . . . . . . . . . . . . . . . . . . . . . . . . . . . . . . . . . . . . . . . . . . . .158,000

**Spending**
   Military Expenditures . . . . . . . . . . . . . . . . . . . . . . . . . . . . . . . . . . . . . . . . . . . . . . .
   Gross National Product . . . . . . . . . . . . . . . . . . . . . . . . . . . . . . . . . . . . . .$50 million
   Military Expenditure as a Percentage of
      Gross National Product . . . . . . . . . . . . . . . . . . . . . . . . . . . . . . . . . . . . . . . . . . .
   Military Expenditure as a Percentage of
      Central Government Expenditure . . . . . . . . . . . . . . . . . . . . . . . . . . . . . . . . . . .

**Defense Treaties** *(See Part II for Additional Detail)*

   Bilateral:     New Zealand

   Multilateral:   Limited Test Ban Treaty
               Treaty on the Non-Proliferation of Nuclear Weapons

# YEMEN ARAB REPUBLIC

## (North Yemen)
### *al-Jumhuriya al-Arabiya al-Yamaniya*

## Defense Establishment Command Structure and Force Organization

The President is Commander-in-Chief of the armed forces. The Chief of Staff, also serving as Deputy Commander-in-Chief, exercises operational control over all three armed services and is directly responsible to the President.

**Total armed forces:** 32,050 (Army: 30,000;    Navy: 550;    Air Force: 1,500). **Para-military forces:** 20,000 (tribal levies).

## HEAD OF STATE

H. E. Col. Ali Abdullah Saleh

**OFFICE OF THE STATE PRESIDENCY**
*Zubairy Street*
*Sana'a*

*Telephone:  71392, 74191-5*
*Telex:   2422 riasah ye*

President of the Republic
and Commander-in-Chief . . . . . . . . . . . . . . . . . . . Col. Ali Abdullah Saleh
Personal Representative of the President . . . . . . . . . . . . . . Hussein al-Dafaa
Minister of State and Legal Advisor. . . . . . . . . . . . . . . . . Husayn al-Hubaishi
Minister of State for Cabinet Affairs . . . . . . . . . . . . . . Lt. Col. Lutif al-Kilabi
Minister for State and Chairman
of the Yemen Oil and
Mineral Resources Corporation . . . . . . . . . . . . Ali Abdul Rahman al-Bahr
Military Advisor . . . . . . . . . . . . . . . . . . . . . . . . . . . . . . . . . . . Ali al-Shaybah

**OFFICE OF THE VICE PRESIDENT**
*Street of 26th September*
*Sana'a*

*Telephone:  78673/4*

Vice President and Chairman of the
Constitutional People's Council . . . . . . . . . Qadhi Abdul-Karim al-Arashi
Vice President . . . . . . . . . . . . . . . . . . . . . . . . . . . Abdul Aziz Abdul Ghani

## DEFENSE FORCES

**ARMED FORCES**
**Armed Forces Headquarters**
*Airport Street*
*Sana'a*

*Telephone:  71392*

President of the Republic
and Commander-in-Chief . . . . . . . . . . . . . . . . . . . Col. Ali Abdullah Saleh
Chief of Staff and Deputy
Commander-in-Chief . . . . . . . . . . . Col. Abdullah Hussein al-Bashiry
Deputy Chief of Staff, Military Affairs . . . . . . . . . . . . . . . . . Lt. Col. Ali Salih
Director, Military Intelligence . . . . . . . . . . . . . . . . Lt. Col. Ghaled Gamash
Deputy Chief, Moral
Orientation Directorate . . . . . . . . . . . . . . . . . . . . . . . . Maj. Ali al-Shatar

**ARMY**
*Airport Street*
*Sana'a*

*Telephone:  75772-5*

Chief of Staff . . . . . . . . . . . . . . . . . . . Lt. Col. Abdullah Hussein al-Bashiry
Commander, Armored Corps . . . . . . . . . . . . . Maj. Mohammad al-Wasimi
Commander, 1st Armored
Brigade . . . . . . . . . . . . . . . . . . . . . . . . . . . Lt. Col. Ali Mohasan al-Ahmar
Commander, Infantry Division . . . . . . . . . . . . . . . . . . Lt. Col. Ahmed Farrag
Commander, 2nd Artillery
Brigade . . . . . . . . . . . . . . . . . . . . . . . . . . . . Lt. Col. Ali Saleh al-Ahmar

**NAVY**
*Hodiedah*

Commander . . . . . . . . . . . . . . . . . . . . . . . . . . Lt. Col. Abdul Karim Muharram
Chief of Staff . . . . . . . . . . . . . . . . . . . . . . . . . . . . . . Lt. Col. Yahya al-Ulufi

**AIR FORCE**
*International Airport*
*Sana'a*
*Telephone:    7411/2*

Commander . . . . . . . . . . . . . . . . . . . . . . . . . . . . . . Lt. Col. Faris al-Sharif
Chief of Staff . . . . . . . . . . . . . . . . . . . . . . . . . . . . . Maj. Mohammed Wahas

**✶ ✶ ✶ ✶ ✶**

## GENERAL DEFENSE DATA

**Manpower**
Total Armed Forces . . . . . . . . . . . . . . . . . . . . . . . . . . . . . . . . . . . . . . . . 32,050
  (See Page 625)
Population  . . . . . . . . . . . . . . . . . . . . . . . . . . . . . . . . . . . . . . . .5,490,000

**Spending**
Military Expenditures . . . . . . . . . . . . . . . . . . . . . . . . . . . . . . . . . . . .$325 million
Gross National Product . . . . . . . . . . . . . . . . . . . . . . . . . . . . . . . . . . . .$3.897 billion
Military Expenditure as a Percentage of
  Gross National Product  . . . . . . . . . . . . . . . . . . . . . . . . . . . . . . . . . . .8.3%
Military Expenditure as a Percentage of
  Central Government Expenditure  . . . . . . . . . . . . . . . . . . . . . . . . . . . .30.0%

**Defense Treaties** *(See Part II for Additional Detail)*

   Bilateral:    China
                 Czechoslovakia

   Multilateral:   Environmental Modification Convention
                   League of Arab States

# PEOPLE'S DEMOCRATIC REPUBLIC OF YEMEN
## (South Yemen)
### *Jumhuriyat al-Yaman al-Democratiya al-Sha'abiya*

## Defence Establishment Command Structure and Force Organization

The Chairman of the Presidium is the Supreme Commander of the armed forces and exercises control through the Ministry of Defence. Operational command of the military is the responsibility of the Chief of the General Staff. There are eight regional commands coinciding with the country's administrative districts.

The General Security Units are under the direction of the Minister of the Interior. The Popular Militia, which nominally includes every adult male, is directly controlled by the Secretary-General of the ruling party.

**Total armed forces:** 26,000 (Army: 22,000; Navy: 1,000; Air Force: 3,000). **Paramilitary forces:** 15,000 (Public Security Force). **Popular Militia:** (unspecified).

## HEAD OF STATE

Ali Nasser Mohammed Al-Hasani

**PRESIDIUM OF THE SUPREME PEOPLE'S COUNCIL**
*Aden*

Chairman of the Presidium, Prime Minister and Supreme Commander .......... Ali Nasser Mohammed Al-Hasani
Secretary General ........................ Abdullah Ahmed Ghanem

**OFFICE OF THE PRIME MINISTER**
*Aden*

Prime Minister, Chairman of the Presidium of the Supreme People's Council, Secretary General of the Central Committee for the Yemeni Socialist Party .............. Ali Nasser Mohammed Al-Hasani
First Deputy Prime Minister and Minister of Local Administration ........ Staff Brigadier Ali Ahmad Nasir Antar

**State Security Committee**
*Aden*

Chairman ............................... Salih Munassar al-Siyayli
Deputy Chairman ............................... Ali Mansur Rahim

**MINISTRY OF THE INTERIOR**
*Aden*

Minister ........................ Col. Mohammad Abdullah Al-Batani
Deputy Minister........................ Lt. Col. Abd Al-Wasi Sallam

**MINISTRY OF DEFENCE**
*Aden*
*Telex: 2294 ad defence*

Minister .............................. Brig. Gen. Salih Muslih Qasim
First Deputy Minister and Chief of General Staff ...................... Lt. Col. Abdullah Ali 'Ulaywah

## DEFENCE FORCES

**ARMY**
*Aden*

Chief, General Staff .................... Lt. Col. Abdullah Ali 'Ulaywah
Commander, Militia National Commands...... Mohamed Abdur-Rahman

**NAVY**
*Aden*

Commander ...................... Capt. Ahmad Abdullah Muhammed

**AIR FORCE**
*Aden*

Commander .......................... Lt. Col. Abdullah Ali 'Ulaywah

\* \* \* \* \*

## GENERAL DEFENCE DATA

**Manpower**
Total Armed Forces ............................................ 26,000
   (See Page 627)
Population ................................................. 2,022,000

**Spending**
Military Expenditures ......................................... $126 million
Gross National Product ........................................ $989 million
Military Expenditure as a Percentage of
   Gross National Product ..................................... 12.8%
Military Expenditure as a Percentage of
   Central Government Expenditure ............................. 45.7%

**Defence Treaties** (*See Part II for Additional Detail*)

    Bilateral:    Bulgaria
                   Ethiopia
                   Hungary
                   Soviet Union

    Multilateral:    Aden Treaty Tripartite Alliance
                   Biological Weapons Convention
                   Environmental Modification Convention
                   League of Arab States
                   Limited Test Ban Treaty
                   Treaty on the Control of Arms on the Seabed
                   Treaty on the Non-Proliferation of Nuclear Weapons

# YUGOSLAVIA
## Socialist Federal Republic of Yugoslavia
### Socijalisticka Federativna Republika Jugoslavia

## Defense Establishment Command Structure and Force Organization

The President of the Presidency is Commander-in-Chief of the Yugoslavian armed forces. Administration of the military is the responsibility of the Federal Secretariat for National Defense, which formulates policy and coordinates military affairs.

**Total armed forces:** 252,500 (Army: 190,000; Navy: 17,500; Air Force: 45,000). **Paramilitary forces:** 20,000 (Frontier Guards).

## HEAD OF STATE

Petar Stambolić

**PRESIDENCY OF THE SOCIALIST FEDERAL REPUBLIC OF YUGOSLAVIA**
*Bulevar Lenjïna 2*
*11000 Belgrade*
*Telephone: (11) 339-301, 636-466, 334-281, 635-822, 338-281, 673-033*
*Telex: 11448 yu siv*

| | |
|---|---|
| President of the Presidency | Petar Stambolić |
| Vice President | Mika Spiljak |
| Member | Fadilj Hodža |
| Member | Lazar Kološevski |
| Member | Sergej Kraigher |
| Member | Cvijetin Mijatović |
| Member | Radovan Vlajković |
| Member | Vidoje Žarković |
| Member *(ex officio)* | Mitja Ribicic |

**FEDERAL SECRETARIAT FOR NATIONAL DEFENSE**
*Kneza Milosa 35*
*11000 Belgrade*
*Telephone: (11) 454-061*

| | |
|---|---|
| Federal Secretary | Adm. Branko Mamula |
| Deputy Secretary | Col. Gen. Dane Petkovski |
| Federal Under Secretary | Col. Gen. Asim Hodžić |
| Assistant Secretary, Rear Services | Col. Gen. Ilija Radaković |
| Assistant Secretary, Civil Defense | Col. Gen. Bruno Vuletić |
| Assistant Secretary, Inter-Army Cooperation | Col. Gen. Radovan Vojvodić |
| Assistant Secretary, Military Economy | Col. Gen. Janko Susnjar |
| Assistant Secretary, Political and Legal Affairs | Col. Gen. Dane Petkovski |
| Assistant Secretary | Col. Gen. Milan Daljević |
| Assistant Secretary | Col. Gen. Veljko Kadijević |
| Assistant Secretary | Col. Gen. Spasoje Todorović |
| Chief Inspector for National Defense | Col. Gen. Rade Suša |
| Chief, Foreign Military Liaison Section | Col. Nebojša Govedarica |

## DEFENSE FORCES

**ARMY**
**Yugoslav People's Army**
*Federal Secretariat for National Defense*
*Kneza Milosa 35*
*11000 Belgrade*

| | |
|---|---|
| Chief, General Staff | Col. Gen. Petar Gračanin |
| Inspector-General | Col. Gen. Dusan Pekić |
| Deputy Chief of General Staff, Army | Lt. Gen. Spasoje Todorović |
| Chief, Ground Services | Lt. Gen. Veljko Kadijević |

**NAVY**
*Federal Secretariat for National Defense*
*Kneza Milosa 35*
*11000 Belgrade*

Commander, Navy .............................Adm. Tihomer Vilović
Deputy Chief of General Staff, Navy ..............Rear Adm. Drago Štok
Chief, Naval Directorate ...............Vice Adm. Miodrag Radosavljević

**AIR FORCE**
*Federal Secretariat for National Defense*
*Kneza Milosa 35*
*11000 Belgrade*

Commander, Aircraft Defense...............Maj. Gen. Slobodan Atlagić
Deputy Chief of General Staff,
    Air Force and Air Defense...................Lt. Gen. Ismet Kulenović

* * * * *

## GENERAL DEFENSE DATA

**Manpower**
    Total Armed Forces................................................252,500
        (Scc Page 629)
    Population ................................................22,689,000

**Spending**
    Military Expenditures.........................................$3.5 billion
    Gross National Product .........................................$73 billion
    Military Expenditure as a Percentage of
        Gross National Product .........................................4.8%
    Military Expenditure as a Percentage of
        Central Government Expenditure ................................20.8%

**Defense Treaties** *(See Part II for Additional Detail)*

    Bilateral:     United States

    Multilateral:  Biological Weapons Convention
                   Limited Test Ban Treaty
                   Treaty on the Control of Arms on the Seabed
                   Treaty on the Non-Proliferation of Nuclear Weapons
                   Warsaw Treaty Organization

# ZAIRE

## Defense Establishment Command Structure and Force Organization

The President is State Commissioner for National Defense and Commander-in-Chief of the armed forces.

**Total armed forces:** 26,000 (Army: 22,000;     Navy: 1,500;     Air Force: 2,500). **Paramilitary forces:** 22,000 (Gendarmerie).

## HEAD OF STATE

H. E. Marshal Mobutu Sese Seko Kuku Ngbendu Wa Za Banga

**OFFICE OF THE PRESIDENT AND STATE COMMISSIONER FOR NATIONAL DEFENSE AND VETERAN'S AFFAIRS**
*Mont Ngaliema*
*Kinshasa*

Telephone:  31312, 59903
Telex:  21368 presidence, 21200, 21250, 21371, 21405 (Chief of Staff)

President of the Republic State Commissioner for National Defense and Veteran's Affairs and Commander-in-Chief . . . . . . . . . . . . . . . . . . . Marshal Mobutu Sese Seko
Chief of Staff . . . . . . . . . . . . . . . . . . . . . . . . Niny Mayidiki Ngimbi
Assistant to the Chief of Staff . . . . . . . . . . . . . . . . . . . . . . . . Tshunza Mbiye
Commander, Military House . . . . . . . . . . . . . Col. Bosange Bompese Bakolo
Commander, Special Presidential Brigade . . . . . . . . . . . . . . . . . . . . . . . Lt. Col. Nzimbi Ngbale
Deputy Commander, Special Presidential Brigade . . . . . . . . . . . . . . . . . . . . . . . Cdt. Sumahili Busangu
Special Presidential Advisor on National Security . . . . . . . . . . . . . . . . . . . . . . . . . . . . . . . . . . . . . . . Yale Seti
Administrator General, National Intelligence Service . . . . . . . . . . . . . . . . . . . . . . . . . . . . . . . Liloo Nkema

**OFFICE OF THE FIRST STATE COMMISSIONER**
*Hotel du Conseil Executif*
*Kinshasa/Gombe Avenue 3 "Z"*
Telephone:  30892, 30979, 31372

First State Commissioner . . . . . . . . . . . . . N'singa Udjuu Ongwakebi Untube

**OFFICE OF THE DEPUTY FIRST STATE COMMISSIONER**
*Hotel du Conseil Executif*
*Kinshasa/Gombe Avenue 3 "Z"*

Deputy First State Commissioner . . . . . . . . . . . . . . . . Vunduawe Te Pemako

**DEPARTMENT OF NATIONAL AND VETERANS' AFFAIRS**
*B.P. 8635*
*Kinshasa 1*

Telephone:  30528, 59894 (Secretary of State)
Telex:  21363 ddn zr

President and State Commissioner for National Defense and Veterans' Affairs . . . . . . Marshal Mobutu Sese Seko
Secretary of State, National Defense . . . . . . . . . . . . . . . . . Vice Amr. Wa Botende Lomponda
Secretary of State, Veterans' Affairs . . . . . . . . . . . Gen. de Div. Kambing Dikuta Ebilansang

631

# DEFENSE FORCES

**ARMED FORCES**
*(Forces Armées Zairoises—FAZ)*
*c/o Department of National Defense*
*B.P. 8635*
*Kinshasa 1*

*Telephone: 59371*
*Telex: 21363 ddn zr*

President of the Republic and State
  Commissioner for National Defense . . . . . . . . Marshal Mobutu Sese Seko
Chief of Staff . . . . . . . . . . . . . . . . . Gén. d'Armée Boyenge Mosambay Nsinga
Deputy Chief . . . . . . . . . . . . Gén. de Corp d'Armée Boteti Nkok Ea Nkango

**ARMY**
*c/o Department of National Defense*
*B.P. 8635*
*Kinshasa 1*

*Telephone: 68503*
*Telex: 21363 ddn zr*

Chief of Staff . . . . . . . . . . . . . . . . . . . . . . Gén. de Div. Eluki Mongo Aundu
Commander, City of Kinshasa . . . . . . . . Col. Longelo Mbule Wa Mouzomba
Commander, Region 1 . . . . . . . . . . . . . . . . . . Gén. de Brig. Yoku Mamgbau
Commander,
  Region 2 . . . . . . . . . Gén. de Corps d'Armée Itambo Mukina Wa Kambula
Commander,
  Region 3 . . . . . . . . . . . . . . . . . . . Gén. de Corps d'Armée Danga Ngbokoli
1st Armored Brigade . . . . . . . . . . . . . . . . . . . . . . . . . . . . . . . . . . . . Gén. Somao
31st Parachutist Brigade, (N'Dijili) . . . . . . . . . . . . . . . . . . . . . . . Col. Mathiote
312th Battalion, (Kinshasa) . . . . . . . . . . . . . . . . . . . . . . . . . . . . Col. Bourdeau
Commander, Kintona
  Army Base . . . . . . . . . . . . . . . . . . . Gén. de Brig. Yeka Mangbou Lowanga
Commander, Kamanyola
  Division . . . . . . . . . . . . . . . . . . . . Gén. de Brig. Mukoba Mundend Popolo

**NAVY**
*c/o Department of National Defense*
*B.P. 8635*
*Kinshasa 1*

*Telephone: 23306*
*Telex: 21363 ddn zr, 21569 em/fr zr*

Chief of Staff . . . . . . . . . . . . . . . . . . . . . . . . . . . . . . . . Cdt. Mambu Nsenga
Deputy Chief . . . . . . . . . . . . . . . . . . . . . . . . . . . . . . Lt. Col. Mavua Mudima

**AIR FORCE**
*c/o Department of National Defense*
*B.P. 8635*
*Kinshasa 1*

*Telephone: 23560*
*Telex: 21363 ddn zr, 21560 em/faza zr*

Chief of Staff . . . . . . . . . . . . . . . . . . . . . . . . . . Gén. de Div. Kikunda Ombala
Deputy Chief . . . . . . . . . . . . . . . . . . . . . . . . . . . . . . . . . . . Gén. de Brig. Baruti

**GENDARMERIE NATIONALE**
  **(CONSTABULARY)**
*c/o Department of National Defense*
*B.P. 8635*
*Kinshasa 1*

*Telephone: 59371*
*Telex: 21363 ddn zr, 21523 em/gd nat zr*

Chief of Staff . . . . . . . . . . . . . . . . . . . . . . Gén. de Brig. Mulama Pene Lowe

\* \* \* \* \*

# GENERAL DEFENSE DATA

**Manpower**
  Total Armed Forces . . . . . . . . . . . . . . . . . . . . . . . . . . . . . . . . . . . . . . . . . . . . 26,000
    (See Page 631)
  Population . . . . . . . . . . . . . . . . . . . . . . . . . . . . . . . . . . . . . . . . . . . . . 30,289,000

**Spending**

Military Expenditures . . . . . . . . . . . . . . . . . . . . . . . . . . . . . . . . . . . . . . . .$199 million
Gross National Product . . . . . . . . . . . . . . . . . . . . . . . . . . . . . . . . . . . . . .$6.489 billion
Military Expenditure as a Percentage of
    Gross National Product . . . . . . . . . . . . . . . . . . . . . . . . . . . . . . . . . . . . . . . .3.1%
Military Expenditure as a Percentage of
    Central Government Expenditure . . . . . . . . . . . . . . . . . . . . . . . . . . . . . .12.4%

**Defense Treaties** *(See Part II for Additional Detail)*

| | |
|---|---|
| Bilateral: | Belgium |
| | Egypt |
| | France |
| | United States |
| | |
| Multilateral: | Biological Weapons Convention |
| | Limited Test Ban Treaty |
| | Organization of African Unity |
| | *Zaire—Burundi—Rwanda*: Mutual Security Pact (1966, 1974) |
| | *Zaire—Zambia—Angola*: Non-Aggression Pact (1979) |

**Military Rank Comparisons**

See Appendix A.

# ZAMBIA
## Republic of Zambia

### Defense Establishment Command Structure and Force Organization

The President is Commander-in-Chief and exercises command through the Minister of Defence.

**Total armed forces:** 15,800 (Army: 14,000; Air Force: 1,800). **Para-military forces:** 1,200; Police: 6,300.

## HEAD OF STATE

H. E. Dr. Kenneth David Kaunda

**OFFICE OF THE PRESIDENT**
**State House**
*P.O. Box 30208*
*Lusaka*

*Telephone: 221833*
*Telex: 41460*

President of the Republic, President of the
    United National Independence Party
    (UNIP), and Commander-in-Chief ........Dr. Kenneth David Kaunda
Special Assistant, Political ...........................Wilted J. Phiri
Special Assistant, Press .......................J. C. Mililo Punabantu
Special Assistant, Economics ...................Dominic C. Mulaisho
Special Assistant, Technical Cooperation
    and Administration...............................Dr. Siteke Mwale
Principal Private Secretary .........................Q. X. Shimabale
Commissioner, Police (State House) ...................Herbert Mapili

**OFFICE OF THE SECRETARY OF STATE FOR DEFENCE AND SECURITY**
*P.O. Box 30208*
*Lusaka*

*Telephone: 211411*
*Telex: 43640 unip za*

Secretary of State, Defence and Security, and
    Member, Central Committee ......Alexander Grey Zulu, M.C.C., M.P.
Principal Advisor and Head, Research Bureau........Festus P. Muyawala

**MINISTRY OF DEFENCE**
*Lusaka*

Minister ................................Wilson M. Chakulya, M. P.
Minister of State ..........................................(Vacant)
Permanent Secretary ...........................Phineas K. Musukwa

## DEFENCE FORCES

**ARMY**
**Zambia Army**
*Arakan Barracks*
*P.O. Box 31931*
*Lusaka*

*Telephone: 21667*
*Telex: 41620*

Commander, Zambia Army ................Gen. Malimba N. Masheke
Deputy Commander and Chief of Staff........Maj. Gen. Christon Tembo

**AIR FORCE**
*Lusaka*
*Telephone:  216677*
*Telex:  41620*

Commander, Zambian Air Force  . . . . . . Maj. Gen. Hananiah B. M. Lungu
Deputy Commander . . . . . . . . . . . . . . . . . . . . . Brig. Gen. H. R. C. Simutowe

\* \* \* \* \*

## GENERAL DEFENCE DATA

**Manpower**
Total Armed Forces  . . . . . . . . . . . . . . . . . . . . . . . . . . . . . . . . . . . . . . . . . . . .15,800
    (See Page 635)
Population  . . . . . . . . . . . . . . . . . . . . . . . . . . . . . . . . . . . . . . . . . . . . . .6,222,000

**Spending**
Military Expenditures . . . . . . . . . . . . . . . . . . . . . . . . . . . . . . . . . . . . . . .$130 million
Gross National Product  . . . . . . . . . . . . . . . . . . . . . . . . . . . . . . . . . . . . .$3.4 billion
Military Expenditure as a Percentage of
    Gross National Product . . . . . . . . . . . . . . . . . . . . . . . . . . . . . . . . . . . . . .3.8%
Military Expenditure as a Percentage of
    Central Government Expenditure . . . . . . . . . . . . . . . . . . . . . . . . . . . . . . .8.6%

**Defence Treaties** *(See Part II for Additional Detail)*

    Bilateral:      Angola
                    Soviet Union

    Multilateral:   Limited Test Ban Treaty
                    Organization of African Unity
                    Treaty on the Control of Arms on the Seabed
                    *Zambia—Angola—Mozambique—Tanzania*: Agreement con-
                        cerning joint defense strategy against external attack
                        (1976)

# ZIMBABWE
## Republic of Zimbabwe

## Defence Establishment Command Structure and Force Organization

The President is the nominal Commander-in-Chief. Actual control of the armed forces is exercised by the Prime Minister. The Minister of Defence has responsibility for the administration of the military.

**Total armed forces:** 63,000 (Army: 60,000; Air Force: 3,000). **Para-military forces:** 11,500 (Police).

## HEAD OF STATE

Hon. Canaan Sodindo Banana

**OFFICE OF THE PRESIDENT**
*P.O. Box 368*
*Harare*
*Telephone: 26666*
*Telex: 4478*

President .................................. Canaan Sodindo Banana

**OFFICE OF THE PRIME MINISTER**
*Milton Building*
*Private Bag 7700, Causeway*
*Samora Machel Avenue*
*Harare*
*Telephone: 707091*
*Telex: 4478*

Prime Minister and Minister
of Defence .......................... Robert Gabriel Mugabe, M.P.
Minister of State ..................... Emerson D. Munangagwa, M.P.
Minister of State with
Special Responsibility
for Defence .......................... Dr. Sydney Sekeramayi, M.P.

**OFFICE OF THE DEPUTY PRIME MINISTER**
*Milton Building*
*Private Bag 18511, Causeway*
*Samora Machel Avenue*
*Harare*
*Telephone: 707091*
*Telex: 4478*

Deputy Prime Minister in Charge
of Coordination .................... Simon Vengayi Muzenda, M.P.
Permanent Secretary ......................... Dr. Charles M. B. Utete

**MINISTRY OF DEFENCE**
*Milton Building*
*Private Bag 7713, Causeway*
*Samora Machel Avenue*
*Harare*
*Telephone: 700155*
*Telex: 2141*
*Cable: MINDEF*

Minister of Defence and
Prime Minister ...................... Robert Gabriel Mugabe, M.P.
Deputy Minister ..................... William Ndangana, M.P.
Permanent Secretary ..................................... (Vacant)
Under Secretary ....................................... R. W. H. Tait

**Ministry of Para-Military Training**
*Harare*

Deputy Minister ........................... William Ndangana, M.P.

# DEFENCE FORCES

**ARMY**
**Zimbabwe National Army—ZNA**
*Private Bag 7720, Causeway*
*Borrowdale Road*
*Harare*

*Telephone:   707451, 707461, 793861*
*Telex:   2323 armyhq zw*

Commander, Defence Forces ................... Gen. A. L. C. MacLean
Commander, Zimbabwe National
   Army ........................................ Lt. Gen. Rex Nhongo
Deputy Commander, Zimbabwe
   National Army............................ Lt. Gen. L. K. V. Masuku
Chief of Staff (G) ................................. Brig. S. Gava
Chief of Staff (A) ......................... Maj. Gen. J. L. Thompson
Chief of Staff (Q) .......................... Maj. Gen. J. B. Maseko
Chief of Staff (D) .................... Maj. Gen. M. D. Shute, O.L.M.

**Services Directorate**
*(in charge of procurement)*
*Army Headquarters*
*Private Bag 7720*
*Causeway*
*Harare*

Director, Army Service Corps ................. Col. C. N. Dhauramanzi

**G Branch**
*(military training institution)*
*Army Headquarters*
*Private Bag 7720*
*Causeway*
*Harare*

Brigadier "G" ............................... Brig. R. A. R. Maponga

## FORCE DIVISIONS

**First Brigade**
*P.O. Box 698*
*Bulawayo*

Commander ...................................... Brig. D. Chinenge

**Second Brigade**
*P.O. Box 6320*
*Cranborne*
*Harare*

Commander....................................... Brig. S. Ndlovu

**Third Brigade**
*P.O. Box 7068*
*Mutare*

Commander ...................................... Brig. A. Kembeu

**Fourth Brigade**
*P.O. Box 750*
*Nyanda*

Commander .......................................... Brig. C. Grey

**Fifth Brigade**
*P.O. Box 1249*
*Gweru*

Commander ...........................................

**Harare Districts**
*P.O. Box 8320*
*Causeway*
*Harare*

Commander .......................................... Col. T. Nyika

**Bulawayo Districts**
*Llewellin Barracks*
*Bulawayo*

Commander ................................... Col. B. Hurungudo

**Midlands Districts**
*P.O. Box 22*
*Gweru*

Commander . . . . . . . . . . . . . . . . . . . . . . . . . . . . . . . . . . . . . . . . Col. C. Munyoro

**AIR FORCE**
*Milton Building*
*Private Bag 7721*
*Causeway*
*Harare*

Commander . . . . . . . . . . . . . . . . . . . . . . . . Air Vice Marshall Azim Daudpota
Deputy . . . . . . . . . . . . . . . . . . . . . . . . . . . . . . . . . . . Gen. Josiah Tungamirai

*Telephone:  794661*
*Telex:   4318*
*Cable:   AIRHEAD*

**POLICE HEADQUARTERS**
*P.O. Box 8007, Causeway*
*7th Street, Montag Avenue*
*Harare*

Commissioner . . . . . . . . . . . . . . . . . . . . . . . . . . . . . . . . . . . . . . . . . J. Denley

*Telephone:   700171*
*Telex:   4328*

\* \* \* \* \*

## GENERAL DEFENCE DATA

**Manpower**
Total Armed Forces . . . . . . . . . . . . . . . . . . . . . . . . . . . . . . . . . . . . . . 63,000
    (See Page 637)
Population . . . . . . . . . . . . . . . . . . . . . . . . . . . . . . . . . . . . . . . . . 8,090,000

**Spending**
Military Expenditures . . . . . . . . . . . . . . . . . . . . . . . . . . . . . . . . . . . $380 million
Gross National Product . . . . . . . . . . . . . . . . . . . . . . . . . . . . . . . . . . $4.551 billion
Military Expenditure as a Percentage of
    Gross National Product . . . . . . . . . . . . . . . . . . . . . . . . . . . . . . . . . 8.4%
Military Expenditure as a Percentage of
    Central Government Expenditure . . . . . . . . . . . . . . . . . . . . . . . . . . . 25.9%

**Defence Treaties** *(See Part II for Additional Detail)*

Bilateral:      Mozambique

Multilateral:   Organization of African Unity

# PART II

# INTERNATIONAL DEFENSE ORGANIZATIONS, TREATIES AND AGREEMENTS

# A. MULTILATERAL DEFENSE ORGANIZATIONS, TREATIES AND AGREEMENTS

# ACT OF CHAPULTEPEC

## SIGNATORIES

| | | |
|---|---|---|
| Argentina | Dominican Republic | Panama |
| Bolivia | Ecuador | Paraguay |
| Brazil | Guatemala | Peru |
| Chile | Honduras | United States |
| Colombia | Haiti | Uruguay |
| Costa Rica | Mexico | Venezuela |
| Cuba | Nicaragua | |

Signed in March and April, 1945, this Act declared that, in response to any aggression, the members would consult and agree upon appropriate measures, including armed force. There is no institutional or administrative structure.

# ADEN TRIPARTITE ALLIANCE

## MEMBERS

Ethiopia, Libya, People's Democratic Republic of Yemen

Established in August, 1981, the Aden Tripartite Alliance was formed as a "joint defense commitment" and for defense cooperation. There is no institutional structure for the Alliance.

# ANZUS

## MEMBERS

Australia, New Zealand, United States

The ANZUS Security Treaty, signed in September, 1951, commits each party to "consult together whenever . . . the territorial integrity, political independence or security of any of the parties is threatened in the Pacific." This treaty, coordinating the defense of the region, was later supplemented by the South-East Asia Collective Defense Treaty (the Manila Pact) in 1954.

Military co-operation involves the free exchange of strategic intelligence and information, as well as military exercises, official visits and exchanges. The Treaty also provides to American naval vessels free access to the port facilities of the other partners.

The three parties are organized into the ANZUS Council, composed of the Foreign Ministers (or their deputies) and a military representative from each country. The Council meets annually, the location rotating among the three capitals. The military officers, who advise the Council on military co-operation, also meet separately.

The organization has no institutional life. There is no secretariat or permanent staff, and costs of the meetings are borne by the host-country.

**ANZUS COUNCIL**
*c/o Department of Foreign Affairs*
*Administration Building*
*Parkes, A.C.T. 2600*
*Australia*
*Telephone:* *(62) 619111*
          *(62) 613134 (After Hours)*
*Telex:* *62041*

Member .............................................. William Hayden
(Minister for Foreign Affairs, Australia)
Member .............................................. Warren E. Cooper
(Minister of Foreign Affairs, New Zealand)
Member .............................................. George P. Shultz
(Secretary of State, United States)

# BIOLOGICAL WEAPONS CONVENTION

*Convention on the Prohibition of the Development, Production and Stockpiling of Bacteriological (Biological) and Toxin Weapons and on Their Destruction*

## SIGNATORIES

| | | |
|---|---|---|
| Afghanistan | Hungary | Portugal |
| Argentina | Iceland | Qatar |
| Australia | India | Romania |
| Austria | Iran | Rwanda |
| Barbados | Ireland | San Marino |
| Belgium | Italy | São Tomé and Príncipe |
| Benin | Jamaica | Saudi Arabia |
| Bhutan | Japan | Senegal |
| Bolivia | Jordan | Seychelles |
| Brazil | Kenya | Sierra Leone |
| Bulgaria | Kuwait | Singapore |
| Canada | Laos | South Africa |
| Cape Verde | Lebanon | Spain |
| Congo | Libya | Sweden |
| Costa Rica | Luxembourg | Switzerland |
| Cuba | Malta | Taiwan |
| Cyprus | Mauritius | Thailand |
| Czechoslovakia | Mexico | Togo |
| Denmark | Mongolia | Tonga |
| Dominican Republic | Netherlands | Tunisia |
| Ecuador | New Zealand | Turkey |
| Ethiopia | Nicaragua | Union of Soviet Socialist |
| Fiji | Niger |    Republics |
| Finland | Nigeria | United Kingdom |
| German Democratic | Norway | United States |
|    Republic | Pakistan | Uruguay |
| Ghana | Panama | Venezuela |
| Greece | Papau New Guinea | Vietnam |
| Guatemala | Paraguay | People's Democratic |
| Guinea-Bissau | Philippines |    Republic of Yemen |
| Honduras | Poland | Zaire |

The Biological Weapons Convention was approved by the General Assembly of the United Nations in 1971, and took effect in 1975. The parties to the convention undertake not to develop, produce, stockpile, or acquire biological agents or toxins "of types and in quantities that have no justification for prophylactic, protective, and other peaceful purposes."

# CENTRAL-AMERICAN DEMOCRATIC COMMUNITY
*Communidad Democratica Centroamericana*

## MEMBERS

Costa Rica, El Salvador, Honduras

Observers: Colombia, United States, Venezuela

This regional grouping was formed in January 1982 to provide mutual aid in the event of armed aggression against any of the parties.

# COOPERATION COUNCIL FOR THE ARAB STATES OF THE GULF
## Gulf Cooperation Council (GCC)

## MEMBERS

| | |
|---|---|
| Bahrain | Qatar |
| Kuwait | Saudi Arabia |
| Oman | United Arab Emirates |

The Cooperation Council for the Arab States of the Gulf was founded in January 1981 to co-ordinate, economic, social, cultural, internal security and defense affairs among the six Gulf States.

The principle policy-making body of the GCC is the Supreme Council. It comprises the heads of state of the six countries, and its Presidency rotates annually. Attached to the Supreme Council is the Commission for Settlement of Disputes (or "Conciliation Commission"), which attempts to resolve disputes among the members peacefully. Reporting to the Supreme Council is a Ministerial Council, consisting of the Foreign Ministers. This body meets bi-monthly to draw up and recommend policies, studies and projects. The GCC's institutional headquarters, the Secretariat-General, is based in Riyadh. This office prepares reports and budgets, and is responsible for implementing the policies and recommendations of the Councils. The Secretary-General is appointed by the Supreme Council for a three-year term.

**SUPREME COUNCIL**

President . . . . . . . . . . . . . . . . . . . . . . . . . . . . . Zayid bin Sultan Al-Nuhayyan
(United Arab Emirates)
Member (*ex officio*) . . . . . . . . . . Amir 'Isa bin Salman Al-Khalifa (Bahrain)
Member (*ex officio*) . . . . . . Amir Jabir al-Ahmad al-Jabir Al-Sabah (Kuwait)
Member (*ex officio*) . . . . . . . . . . . . . . . . . . Sultan Qaboos bin Said (Oman)
Member (*ex officio*) . . . . . . . . . . . Amir Khalifa bin Hamid Al-Thani (Qatar)
Member (*ex officio*) . . . . . . . . . . . . . . . King Fahd bin 'Abd al-Aziz Al-Sa'ud
(Saudi Arabia)

**MINISTERIAL COUNCIL**

Chairman . . . . . . . . . . . . . . . . . . . . . . . . . . . . . . . . . . . . . . . . . . . . . (Rotates)
Member (*ex officio*) . . . . . . . . . . . . . . Muhammad bin Mubarak Al-Khalifa
(Minister of Foreign Affairs, Bahrain)
Member (*ex officio*) . . . . . . . . . . . . . . . . Sabah al-Ahmad al-Jabir Al-Sabah
(Minister of Foreign Affairs, Kuwait)

Member (*ex officio*) . . . . . . . . . . . . . . . . . . . . . . . . . . . . . . . Qaboos bin Said
(Minister of Foreign Affairs, Oman)
Member (*ex officio*) . . . . . . . . . . . . . . . . . . . . . . Suhaym bin Hamad al-Thani
(Minister of Foreign Affairs, Qatar)
Member (*ex officio*) . . . . . . . . . . . . . . . . . . . . . . . . . . Sa'ud Al-Faisal Al-Sa'ud
(Minister of Foreign Affairs, Saudi Arabia)
Member (*ex officio*) . . . . . . . . . . . . . . . . . . . . . . . . . . . . . Rashid Abdullah
(Minister of Foreign Affairs, United Arab Emirates)

**SECRETARIAT GENERAL**
*GCC Headquarters*
*P.O. Box 7153*
*Riyadh, Saudi Arabia*
*Telex:  203635 Riyadh*

Secretary-General . . . . . . . . . . . . . . . . . . Abdullah Yacoub Bishara (Kuwait)
Assistant Secretary-General,
Political Affairs . . . . . . . . . . . . . . . . Ibrahim Hamud al-Subhi (Oman)
Assistant Secretary-General
Economic Affairs . . . . . . . . . . . . . . . . . . Abdullah Quaysi (Saudi Arabia)

# COUNCIL FOR CENTRAL-AMERICAN DEFENSE
## (CONDECA)

### MEMBERS

El Salvador, Guatemala, Honduras, Nicaragua

Observers: Costa Rica, Panama

The Agreement on the establishment and operation of CONDECA was signed on December 14, 1963 and entered into force on May 18, 1964 for an indefinite duration. It is responsible for the collective security of the participating states and forms part of the Organization of Central-American States.

The Council is comprised of the Ministers of Defense, or other officials, from each country. There is a Permanent Commission consisting of military attaches from each country, acting as delegates. This commission acts as a General Staff, performs administrative duties, and appoints a General Secretary.

**CENTRAL AMERICAN DEFENSE**
**COUNCIL**
*(CONDECA)*

Member . . . . . . . . . . . . . . . . . . . . . . . . Gen. Carloz Eugenio Vides Casanova
(Minister of Defense and Public Security, El Salvador)
Member . . . . . . . . . . . . . . . . . . . . . . . . . . . . . . . . . . Gen. Oscar Ortega Rivas
(Minister of Defense, Guatemala)
Member . . . . . . . . . . . . . . . . . . . . . . . . Angel Edmundo Solano Calderon
(Minister of Public Security, Costa Rica)

**PERMANENT COMMISSION**
*(Cope Condeca)*
*6 Avenida 11-57*
*Zone 9*
*Guatemala City*
*Guatemala*

*Telephone:  (502) 2 66270*

President . . . . . . . . . . . . . . . Gen. Jose Pablo Coronado Robles (Costa Rica)
Secretary . . . . . . . . . . . . . . . . . . . . . . . . . . . . . . . . . . . . Leticia de Nichols
Delegate . . . . . . . . . . . . . . . Cap. de Navio Arturo Rubio Ruiz (Guatemala)
Delegate . . . . . . . . . . . Cnel. de Cab. Julio Ramiro Marroquin (Guatemala)
Delegate . . . . . . . . . . . Cnel. de Art. Marco Tulio Bucaro Ruiz (Guatemala)
Delegate . . . . . . . . . . . . . . . . . . . . Cnel. Julip Gonzalez Paloma (El Salvador)
Delegate . . . . . . . Tte. Cnel. de Inf. Jose Alfredo Rodriguez M. (El Salvador)
Delegate . . . . . . . . . . . . Tte. Cnel. de Inf. Isidor Tapia Martinez (Honduras)
Delegate . . . . . . . . . . . . . . . . May. Eric Ricardo Aquilera Prescott (Panama)

# ECONOMIC COMMUNITY OF WEST AFRICAN STATES (ECOWAS)

## MEMBERS

Benin
Cape Verde
Gambia
Ghana
Guinea
Guinea-Bissau

Ivory Coast
Liberia
Mali
Mauritania
Niger

Nigeria
Senegal
Sierra Leone
Togo
Upper Volta

The Economic Community of West African States was established in accordance with the Treaty of Lagos, signed in May, 1975. Its purpose is to promote trade, cooperation and self-reliance in West Africa, including such areas as regional industrial policy, agricultural development, customs unions, communications and energy.

The organization is comprised of an Authority of Heads of State and Government, a Council of Ministers, a Tribunal, an Executive Secretariat with a permanent staff, and four specialized commissions.

At the Third Conference of Heads of State and Government in May, 1981, 13 of the 16 members (excluding Cape Verde, Guinea-Bissau and Mali) signed a protocol of non-aggression, the "Protocol on Mutual Assistance on Defense Matters." This called for the establishment of a Defense Commission, composed of Defense Ministers and Chiefs of Staff, and a Defense Council of the Heads of State. The Protocol also called for the creation of a joint force, using assigned units from each national army, for intervention and peace-keeping duties.

**EXECUTIVE SECRETARIAT**
*6 King George V Rd.*
*Lagos, Nigeria*
*Telephone: 26001*
*Telex: 22633 ecowas ng*

Executive Secretary . . . . . . . . . . Dr. Abubakr Diaby-Ouattara (Ivory Coast)
Deputy Executive Secretary . . . . . . . . . . . . . . . . . . . Dr. James Nti (Ghana)
Deputy Executive Secretary . . . . . . Dr. Dakoum Toumany Sakho (Guinea)
Financial Controller . . . . . . . . . . . . . . . . Isaac Oladeinde Adeyale (Nigeria)

# ENVIRONMENTAL MODIFICATION CONVENTION

*Convention on the Prohibition of Military or any other Hostile use of Environmental Modification Techniques*

## SIGNATORIES

Bangladesh
Belgium
Bulgaria
Canada
Cape Verde
Cuba
Cyprus
Czechoslovakia
Denmark
Egypt
Finland
German Democratic
   Republic

Ghana
Hungary
India
Ireland
Italy
Japan
Kuwait
Laos
Malawi
Mongolia
Norway
Papua New Guinea
Poland

São Tomé and Príncipe
Solomon Islands
Spain
Sri Lanka
Tunisia
Union of Soviet Socialist
   Republics
United Kingdom
United States
Vietnam
Yemen Arab Republic
People's Democratic
   Republic of Yemen

The Environmental Modification Convention was approved by the General Assembly of the United Nations in 1976, and took effect in 1978. The parties undertake "not to engage in military or any other hostile use of environmental modification techniques having widespread, long-lasting or severe effects as the means of destruction, damage or injury..."

# FIVE-POWER DEFENSE ARRANGEMENTS (ANZUK)

## SIGNATORIES

Australia
Malaysia
New Zealand

Singapore
United Kingdom

This treaty, which went into effect on November 1, 1971, is related to the defense of Malaysia and Singapore. All parties are to consult for the purpose of deciding the appropriate actions to take in the event of an attack, or threat against Malaysia or Singapore. Although Britain withdrew its forces from the area in 1976, New Zealand still maintains troops in Singapore, and Australia continues to base part of its Air Force in Malaysia.

# INTER-AMERICAN DEFENSE BOARD (IADB)
*Junta Inter-Americano de Defensa*

## MEMBERS

| | | |
|---|---|---|
| Argentina | Ecuador | Panama |
| Bolivia | El Salvador | Paraguay |
| Brazil | Guatemala | Peru |
| Chile | Haiti | United States |
| Colombia | Honduras | Uruguay |
| Costa Rica | Mexico | Venezuela |
| Dominican Republic | Nicaragua | |

The Inter-American Defense Board was founded on March 30, 1942, to plan for the collective defense of the Western Hemisphere. It is essentially a military advisory group attached to the Organization of American States, although it operates independently. It maintains its own headquarters and staff but has no standing troops or authority to raise troops.

The IADB is composed of high-ranking military representatives from each member state. It is organized into (1) the Council of Delegates, which meets every two weeks and sets policy; (2) the International Staff, to develop plans, prepare studies, and generally implement the policies enacted by the Council; and (3) the Secretariat which is responsible for the budget and all support services for the IADB.

**COUNCIL OF DELEGATES**
*2600 16th St., N.W.*
*Washington, D.C. 20441*
*United States*
*Telephone: (202) 387-7860*

Chairman . . . . . . . . . . . . Lt. Gen. John W. McEnery (United States, Army)
Vice Chairman . . . . . . . . . Brig. Gen. Fernando Soto-Harrison (Costa Rica)
Chief, Argentine Delegation . . . . . . . Rear Adm. Enrique Pedro Montemayor (Navy)
Chief, Bolivian Delegation . . . . . . . . . . . Capt. Jorge Bustos Da Ponte (Navy)
Chief, Brazilian Delegation . . . . . . . . . Brig. Gen. Jose Pinto dos Reis (Army)
Chief, Chilean Delegation . . . . . . . . Rear Adm. Sergio Sanchez Luna (Navy)
Chief, Colombian Delegation . . . . Maj. Gen. Rafael Obdulio Forero (Army)
Chief, Costa Rican Delegation . . . . . . . . Brig. Gen. Fernanco Soto-Harrison (Civil Guard)
Chief, Dominican Republic
  Delegation . . . . . . . . . . . . . . . . Vice Adm. Olgo Santana Carrasco (Navy)
Chief, Ecuadoran Delegation . . . . . . . . Rear Adm. Guillermo Duenas (Navy)
Chief, El Salvadoran Delegation . . . . . . Col. Gustavo Martinez Isassi (Army)
Chief, Guatemalan Delegation . . . . . . . . . . . . . . . . . . . . . . . . . . . . . . . (Vacant)
Chief, Haitian Delegation . . . . . . . . . . . . . . . . . . Col. Cecilio Dorce (Army)
Chief, Honduran Delegation . . . . . . . . . . Col. Ramon Rayes Sanchez (Army)
Chief, Mexican Delegation . . . . . . Brig. Gen. Ernesto Perez Robledo (Army)
Chief, Nicaraguan Delegation . . . . . . . . . . . . . . Capt. Sergio Buitrago (Army)
Chief, Panamanian Delegation . . . . . . . . . . . . . . Lt. Col. Rogelio Alba Barnal (National Guard)
Chief, Paraguayan Delegation . . . . . . . Capt. Sergio Rolando Alcaraz (Navy)
Chief, Peruvian Delegation . . . . . . . . Lt. Col. Javier Elias Vargas (Air Force)
Chief, United States Delegation . . . . . . . . . . Maj. Gen. Bernard E. Trainor (Marines)
Chief, Uruguayan Delegation . . . . . . . Brig. Gen. Jorge A. Borad (Air Force)
Chief, Venezuelan Delegation . . . . Rear Adm. Alfredo Jose Vegas Torrealba (Navy)

**INTERNATIONAL STAFF**
*2600 16th St., N.W.*
*Washington, D.C. 20441*
*United States*
*Telephone: (202) 387-7860*

Director . . . . . . . . . . . . . . . . . Brig. Gen. Duane H. Erickson (United States)
Head, Plans Division . . . . . . . . . . . . . . . . . . Col. Thomas Vargas (Venezuela)
Head, Logistics Division . . . . . . . . . . . . . . . . . Col. Adolfo Carujo (Uruguay)
Head, Intelligence Division . . . . . . . . . . . . Col. Nedo Cardarrelli (Argentina)

**SECRETARIAT**
*2600 16th St., N.W.*
*Washington, D.C. 20441*
*United States*
*Telephone: (202) 387-7860*

Secretary . . . . . . . . . . . . . . . . . . . . . . . Capt. James B. Rodgers (United States)
Deputy Secretary, Administration . . . . Capt. William Leslie (United States)
Deputy Secretary, Conferences and Documents . . . . . . . . . . . . . . . . (Vacant)
Deputy Secretary, Protocol and Public Relations . . . . . Maj. Thomas A. Cseh (United States)
Deputy Secretary, Finance and Liaison . . . . . . . . Capt. Francisco Gonzalez (United States)

**INTER-AMERICAN DEFENSE COLLEGE**
*Fort Leslie J. McNair*
*Washington, D.C.*
*United States*
*Telephone: (202) 693-8218*

Director . . . . . . . . . . . . . . Rear Adm. Sayre A. Swarztrauber (United States)
Chief, Administration . . . . . . . . . . Col. Francis J. McCarthy (United States)

# INTER-AMERICAN TREATY OF RECIPROCAL ASSISTANCE
## (The Rio Treaty)

### SIGNATORIES

| | | |
|---|---|---|
| Argentina | Ecuador | Panama |
| Bolivia | El Salvador | Paraguay |
| Brazil | Guatemala | Peru |
| Chile | Haiti | Trinidad and Tobago |
| Colombia | Honduras | United States |
| Costa Rica | Mexico | Uruguay |
| Dominican Republic | Nicaragua | Venezuela |

This agreement was signed in September, 1947 and went into effect on December 3, 1948 for an indefinite period. The treaty commits the signatories to peaceful settlement of disputes among themselves, and provides for collective self-defense of the Americas.

# THE LEAGUE OF ARAB STATES
## (Arab League)

### MEMBERS

| | | |
|---|---|---|
| Algeria | Libya | Sudan |
| Bahrain | Mauritania | Syria |
| Djibouti | Morocco | Tunisia |
| Egypt (suspended) | Oman | United Arab Emirates |
| Iraq | Palestine | Yemen Arab Republic |
| Jordan | Qatar | People's Democratic |
| Kuwait | Saudi Arabia | Republic of Yemen |
| Lebanon | Somalia | |

The League of Arab States was established in March 1945. It is a voluntary association of sovereign states, with no real executive power.

Its aims are to strengthen relations among the member states and to coordinate their policies. Its principles and goals, outlined in Article II of the Charter, are as follows: the protection of the independence of member states; the protection of peace and security in the region; cooperation between the League and other international organizations; the accomplishment of Arab political cooperation; cooperation and coordination in social, cultural and economic affairs; and dedication to national independence movements and the removal of colonialism in the region.

It is comprised of the Council of the League of Arab States, Permanent Committees, the General Secretariat, and specialized councils or agencies.

The Council is responsible for general policy, and helps settle disputes among or involving member-states. Representatives of each member-state meet twice a year.

The Secretariat-General is the permanent administrative and financial headquarters of the League. It prepares the agendas and budgets. It is subdivided into several bureaus which implement the decisions of the Council and its committees. The Secretary-General is appointed by the Council for a five-year tenure, and holds the rank of Ambassador.

There are five specialized councils including the Joint Defence Council. Assisting the Joint Defense Council is a Permanent Military Commission. It is composed of representatives of the General Staffs of the armies of the member-states, and is charged with the formulation and implementation of plans for collective defense, including proposals for the organization of forces, and exchange of training missions, exercises and maneuvers.

There is also a Unified Arab Command, formed in 1964. This body is responsible for coordinating policies for the liberation of Palestine. The Council of the Arab League established an Arab Deterrent Force in 1976. This was designed to supervise successive attempts to cease hostilities and maintain peace in Lebanon.

**GENERAL SECRETARIAT**
*37 Khereddine Pasha St.*
*Tunis, Tunisia*

*Telephone:   890 100, 890 314*
*Telex:   (934) 13241, 13242*

Secretary-General . . . . . . . . . . . . . . . . . . . . H. E. Mr. Chedli Klibi (Tunisia)
Assistant Secretary-General
   Political Bureau . . . . . . . . . . . . . . . . . . . . . . . . . Adnan Omran (Syria)
Assistant Secretary-General
   Economic Affairs Bureau . . . . . . . . . . . . . . Abdul Hassan Zalzalah (Iraq)
Assistant Secretary-General
   Social and Labor Affairs Bureau . . . . . . . . . . . . Assad el-Assad (Lebanon)
Assistant Secretary-General
   Legal Affairs Bureau . . . . . . . . . . . . . . . . . Mohamed bin Slama (Tunisia)
Assistant Secretary-General
   Administrative and Financial Bureau . . . . . . . . . . . . . . . . . . . . . (Vacant)
Assistant Secretary-General
   Health Bureau . . . . . . . . . . . . . . . . . . . . . . . . . . . . . . . . . . . . (Vacant)
Assistant Secretary-General
   Media Bureau . . . . . . . . . . . . . . . . . . . . . . . . . . . . . . . . . . . . . . . . . .
Assistant Secretary-General
   Bureau of Council Affairs . . . . . . . . . . . . . . . . . . . . . . . . . . . . . . . . . . .
Adviser and Head of Bureau of
   Palestinian Affairs . . . . . . . . . . . . . . . . . . . . . . . . Mohamed el-Farrah
Adviser for African Affairs . . . . . . . . . . . . . . . . . . Abdullah Adam (Somalia)
Adviser and Head of Cabinet of
   Secretariat-General . . . . . . . . . . . . . . . . . . . . . Mongi el-Fakih (Tunisia)

**JOINT DEFENSE COUNCIL**

Member (*ex officio*) . . . . . . . . . . . . . . . . . . . . . . . . Dr. Ahmed Taleb Ibrahimi [f. 1]
   (Minister of Foreign Affairs, Algeria)
Member (*ex officio*) . . . . . . . . . . . . . . . . . . . . . . . . . . . . . Col. Chadli Benjedid
   (Minister of National Defense, Algeria)
Member (*ex officio*) . . . . . . . . . . . . . . . . . . . . . . . Hamad bin 'Isa Al-Khalifa
   (Minister of Defense, Bahrain)
Member (*ex officio*) . . . . . . . . . . . . . . . . Muhmed bin Mubarak Al-Khalifa
   (Minister of Foreign Affairs, Bahrain)
Member (*ex officio*) . . . . . . . . . . . . . . . . . . . . . . . . . Habib Mohamid Loita
   (Minister of National Defense, Djibouti)
Member (*ex officio*) . . . . . . . . . . . . . . . . . . . . . . . . Moumin Bahdon Farah
   (Minister of Foreign Affairs and Cooperation, Djibouti)

Member (*ex officio*) . . . . . . . . . . . . . . . . . . Staff General Adnan Khayrallah
(Minister of Defense, Iraq)

Member (*ex officio*) . . . . . . . . . . . . . . . . . . . . . . . Tarik Mikhayl Aziz
(Minister of Foreign Affairs, Iraq)

Member (*ex officio*) . . . . . . . . . . . . . . . . . . . . . . . . Mudar Badran
(Minister of Defense, Jordan)

Member (*ex officio*) . . . . . . . . . . . . . . . . . . . . . . . Maiwan al-Kasim
(Minister of Foreign Affairs, Jordan)

Member (*ex officio*) . . . . . . . . . . . . . . . . . . Salim al-Sabah al-Salim Al-Sabah
(Minister of Defense, Kuwait)

Member (*ex officio*) . . . . . . . . . . . . . . . . . Sabah al-Ahmed al-Jabir Al-Sabah
(Minister of Foreign Affairs, Kuwait)

Member (*ex officio*) . . . . . . . . . . . . . . . . . . . . . . . . . . . Elie Salem
(Minister of Foreign Affairs, Lebanon)

Member (*ex officio*) . . . . . . . . . . . . . . . . . . . . . . . . . . . Issam Khuri
(Minister of National Defense,
Education and Fine Arts, Lebanon)

Member (*ex officio*) . . . . . . . . . . . . . . . . . . . . . . . 'Abd al-'Ati al-'Ubaydi
(Minister of Foreign Liaison, Libya)

Member (*ex officio*) . . . . . . . . . . . . . . . Col. Maaouiya Ould Sid Ahmen Taya
(Minister of Defense, Mauritania)

Member (*ex officio*) . . . . . . . . . . . . . . . . . . . . . Maj. Ahmed Ould Minnih
(Minister of Foreign Affairs
and Cooperation, Mauritania)

Member (*ex officio*) . . . . . . . . . . . . . . . . . . . . . . . . M'Hamed Boucetta
(Minister of State in Charge
of Foreign Affairs, Morocco)

Member (*ex officio*) . . . . . . . . . . . . . . . . . . . . . . . . Qaboos bin Said
(Minister of Defense, Oman)

Member (*ex officio*) . . . . . . . . . . . . . . . . . . . . . . . . Qaboos bin Said
(Minister of Foreign Affairs, Oman)

Member (*ex officio*) . . . . . . . . . . . . . . . . . . . Hamad bin Khalifa Al-Thani
(Minister of Defense, Qatar)

Member (*ex officio*) . . . . . . . . . . . . . . . . . . . Suhaym bin Hamad Al-Thani
(Minister of Foreign Affairs, Qatar)

Member (*ex officio*) . . . . . . . . . . . . . . . . . . Sultan bin Abd-al-Aziz Al-Sa'ud
(Minister of Defense and Aviation, Saudi Arabia)

Member (*ex officio*) . . . . . . . . . . . . . . . . . . . . . . . Sa'ud al-Faysal Al-Sa'ud
(Minister of Foreign Affairs, Saudi Arabia)

Member (*ex officio*) . . . . . . . . . . . . . . . Lt. Gen. Mohamed Ali Samantar
(Minister of Defense, Somalia)

Member (*ex officio*) . . . . . . . . . . . . . . . . . . . . . Abdurahman Jama Barre
(Minister of Foreign Affairs, Somalia)

Member (*ex officio*) . . . . . . . . . . . . . . . . . Maj. Gaafer Mohamed Nimeiri
(Minister of Defense, Sudan)

Member (*ex officio*) . . . . . . . . . . . . . . . . . Muhamed Mirghani Mubarak
(Minister of Foreign Affairs, Sudan)

Member (*ex officio*) . . . . . . . . . . . . . . . . . . . . . . . . . Mustafa Talas
(Minister of Defense, Syria)

Member (*ex officio*) . . . . . . . . . . . . . . . . . . . . . Abd al-Halim Khaddam
(Minister of Foreign Affairs, Syria)

Member (*ex officio*) . . . . . . . . . . . . . . . . . . . . . . . Slaheddine Baly
(Minister of National Defense, Tunisia)

Member (*ex officio*) . . . . . . . . . . . . . . . . . . . . . . . Beji Caid es-Sebsi
(Minister of Foreign Affairs, Tunisia)

Member (*ex officio*) . . . . . . . . . Muhamed ibn Rashid ibn Sa'id Al-Maktum
(Minister of Defense, United Arab Emirates)

Member (*ex officio*) . . . . . . . . . . . . . . . . . . . . . . . Ali Lutfi al-Thawr
(Minister of Foreign Affairs, Yemen Arab Republic)

Member (*ex officio*) . . . . . . . . . . . . . . . . . Brig. Gen. Salih Muslih Qasim
(Minister of Defense,
People's Democratic Republic of Yemen)

Member (*ex officio*) . . . . . . . . . . . . . . . . . . . . . . Dr. Abd al-Aziz al-Dali
(Minister of Foreign Affairs,
People's Democratic Republic of Yemen)

# LIMITED TEST-BAN TREATY

*Treaty Banning Nuclear Weapons Tests in the Atmosphere, in Outer Space and Under Water*

## SIGNATORIES

Afghanistan
Australia
Austria
Bahamas
Belgium
Benin
Bhutan
Bolivia
Botswana
Brazil
Bulgaria
Burma
Canada
Cape Verde
Central African Republic
Chad
Chile
Costa Rica
Cyprus
Czechoslovakia
Denmark
Dominican Republic
Ecuador
Egypt
El Salvador
Fiji
Finland
Gabon
Gambia
German Democratic
    Republic
Federal Republic of Germany
Ghana
Greece
Guatemala
Honduras
Hungary
Iceland

India
Indonesia
Iran
Iraq
Ireland
Israel
Italy
Ivory Coast
Japan
Jordan
Kenya
Korea
Kuwait
Laos
Lebanon
Liberia
Libya
Luxembourg
Madagascar
Malawi
Malaysia
Malta
Mauritania
Mauritius
Mexico
Mongolia
Morocco
Nepal
Netherlands
New Zealand
Nicaragua
Niger
Nigeria
Norway
Panama
Papua New Guinea
Peru
Philippines

Poland
Romania
Rwanda
San Marino
Senegal
Sierra Leone
Singapore
South Africa
Spain
Sri Lanka
Sudan
Swaziland
Sweden
Switzerland
Syria
Taiwan
Tanzania
Thailand
Togo
Tonga
Trinidad and Tobago
Tunisia
Turkey
Uganda
Union of Soviet Socialist
    Republics
United Kingdom
United States
Uruguay
Venezuela
Western Samoa
Democratic People's
    Republic of Yemen
Yugoslavia
Zaire
Zambia

This treaty was signed in 1963. It prohibits nuclear weapon tests "or any other nuclear explosion" in the atmosphere, in outer space and under water. Moreover, it bans tests underground if they cause "radioactive debris" to be present outside that state's territorial limits.

# THE MULTINATIONAL FORCE AND OBSERVERS IN SINAI

## Troop Contributing Countries

| | | |
|---|---|---|
| Australia | Italy | United Kingdom |
| Colombia | Netherlands | United States |
| Fiji | New Zealand | Uruguay |
| France | Norway | |

**Troop Strength:** 2,600 armed troops, 50 Observers.

The Multinational Force and Observers in Sinai was established on April 25, 1982, in accordance with the Egyptian-Israeli Peace Treaty and Protocol to supervise the security arrangements upon the withdrawal of Israeli forces.

It has a North Base, in El Gorah, and a South Base, in Sharm esh-Sheikh.

**MULTINATIONAL FORCE
 AND OBSERVERS**
*CP 642
00187 Roma,
Italy*

Director-General . . . . . . . . . . . . . . . . . . . . . . Leamon R. Hunt (United States)
Force Commander, and Commander
 of the North Base . . . . . . . . . . . . Lt. Gen. Frederik Bull-Hansen (Norway)

# THE MULTINATIONAL FORCE IN BEIRUT

## Troop Contributing Countries

France, Italy, United Kingdom, United States

**Force Strength:** Approximately 4,200 (France: 1,500;    Italy: 1,400;    United Kingdom: 100;    United States: 1,200).

The Multinational Force is operating in Beirut at the invitation of the Lebanese government. Formally, each of the four contributing countries reached separate, bilateral agreements with the government of Lebanon in an exchange of notes.

The Multinational Force has no single force commander or headquarters. It is run by a Multinational Force Liaison and Coordinating Committee, which is chaired by the President of Lebanon and includes an ambassador from each contributing country. There is also a Military Committee, composed of the four individual commanders and chaired by the Commander-in-Chief of the Lebanese Armed Forces.

**MULTINATIONAL FORCE LIAISON
 AND COORDINATING COMMITTEE**
*c/o Office of the President
Ba'abda*

*Telephone: 220000
Telex: 21000*

Chairman . . . . . . . . . . . . . . . . . . . . . . . . . . . . . . . . . President Amin Gemayal
Member . . . . . . . . . . . . . . . . . . . . . Ambassador Paul-Marc Henry (France)
Member . . . . . . . . . . . . . . . . . . . . . Ambassador Franco Lucioli-Ottieri (Italy)
Member . . . . . . . . . . . . . . . . Ambassador D. A. Roberts, C.M.G., C.V.U.
 (United Kingdom)
Member . . . . . . . . . . . . . . . . . . . . Ambassador Robert Dillon (United States)

**MILITARY COMMITTEE**

Chairman . . . . . . . . . . . . . . . . . . . . . . . . . . . . . . . . Gen. Ibrahim Tannous
 (Commander-in-Chief of the Lebanese Armed Forces)
Commander, French Forces . . . . . . . . . . . . . Brig. Gen. Jean-Claude Coullon
 (French Foreign Legion, 31st Brigade)
Commander, Italian Forces . . . . . . . . . . . Brig. Gen. Franco Angioni (Army)
Commander, British Forces . . . . . . . . . . . . . . . . . . Lt. Col. John C. Cochrane
 (Royal Irish Rangers)
Commander, American Forces . . . . . . . . . . . . . . . . Col. Timothy J. Geraghty
 (24th Marine Amphibious Unit)

# NORTH ATLANTIC TREATY ORGANIZATION (NATO)

## MEMBERS

| | | |
|---|---|---|
| Belgium | Greece | Portugal |
| Canada | Iceland | Spain |
| Denmark | Italy | Turkey |
| France | Luxemburg | United Kingdom |
| Federal Republic of | Netherlands | United States |
| Germany | Norway | |

The North Atlantic Treaty Organization (NATO) was founded on April 4, 1949, as an international collective defense organization linking a group of European states with the United States of America and Canada. Article V of the Treaty stipulates that: "The Parties agree that an armed attack against one or more of them shall be considered an attack against them all," and pledges the members to take "such action as it deems necessary, including the use of armed force, to restore and maintain the security of the North Atlantic area."

The highest governing body is the North Atlantic Council (NAC) which consists of representatives from the 15 member countries and permanent ambassadors who represent each government. The Council has a President, appointed annually from each member nation in alphabetical order. The Secretary General is a permanent appointment; he is Chairman of the Council. With the International Staff, he advises the Council and its committees on political, military, financial and scientific aspects of defense planning.

At the Ministerial Meetings of the Council, member nations are represented by Ministers of Foreign Affairs. These meetings are held twice a year. The Council also meets on occasion at the level of Heads of State and government. In permanent session, at the level of ambassadors (Permanent Representatives), the Council meets at least once a week.

The Council controls a number of special committees. They include Committees of Political Affairs, Economics, Defense Review, Armaments, Civil Emergency Planning, Logistics, Air Defense and Nuclear Defense Affairs. Their recommendations or decisions represent the collective views of the member governments. Decisions by the Council are taken by common consent and not by majority vote.

The Committees established by the Council are supported by the International Staff, made up of personnel drawn from all member countries and responsible to the Secretary-General.

The highest military body in the NATO Alliance is the Military Committee. It is responsible for making recommendations to the Council and providing guidance on military questions to Allied Commanders and subordinate military authorities. It is composed of the Chiefs-of-Staff of all member countries, except France and Iceland.

The Defense Planning Committee (DPC) shares the same level of authority as the North Atlantic Council. The Secretary-General of NATO is the Chairman of both the NAC and DPC and heads the International Staff. The NAC and DPC have the authority to establish auxiliary committees as they see fit. The DPC is composed of representatives of the member countries participating in NATO's integrated military structure. France, Iceland and Spain, although members of the alliance, do not take part in the integrated military structure. The DPC deals with matters specifically related to defense. Like the council, it meets both in permanent session at the level of Ambassadors and twice a year at the Ministerial level. At Ministerial Meetings, member nations are represented by Defense Ministers.

The Chiefs-of-Staff meet three times a year and whenever else they deem necessary. To enable the Military Committee to function in permanent session with effective powers of decision, each Chief-of-Staff appoints a Permanent Military Representative. Liaison between the Military Committee and the French High Command is effected through the Chief of the French Military Mission to the Military Committee.

The Presidency of the Military Committee rotates annually by country in alphabetical order. The Chairman is elected by the Committee for a period of two to three years. There is a Deputy Chairman who is also responsible for the co-ordination of nuclear matters within the International Military Staff and for all questions pertaining to mutual and balanced force reductions. The Military Committee is assisted by an integrated International Military Staff (IMS) headed by a Director selected from one of the member nations. The Director is assisted by six Assistant Directors and the Secretary of the IMS who are of general officer rank. The Assistant Directors head six ancillary divisions.

The strategic area covered by the North Atlantic Treaty is divided among three commands: Allied Command Europe; Allied Command Atlantic; and Allied Command Channel. Plans for the defense of the North American area are developed by the Canada-United States Regional Planning Group, which makes recommendations to the Military Committee. It meets alternately in the United States and Canada.

The authority exercised by the commands varies in accordance with geographical and political factors and with peace and wartime exigencies. Generally, the forces of member countries are under national command in peacetime; some, however, are already assigned to NATO commands. Others remain under national control in all circumstances. The NATO commanders are responsible for the development of defense plans for their respective areas, for the determination of force requirements and for the deployment and exercise of the forces under their command.

f. 1-2

# CIVILIAN ORGANIZATION

**NORTH ATLANTIC COUNCIL**
*Brussels 1110*
*Belgium*
*Telephone:   241 00 40*
*            241 44 00*
*            241 44 90*
*Telex:   23 867*

President . . . . . . . . . . . . . . . . . . . . . . . Mr. Uffe Ellemann-Jensen (Denmark)
Chairman (Secretary-General) . . . . . . . . . . . . . . . . . . . Joseph M. A. H. Luns
Deputy Secretary-General . . . . . . . . . . . . . . . . . . . . . . . Eric Da Rin (Italy)
Permanent Representative . . . . . . . . . . . . . . . . . . . Juan Cassiers (Belgium)
Deputy . . . . . . . . . . . . . . . . . . . . . . . . . . . . . . . . . . Pierre Bassette
Permanent Representative . . . . . . . . . . . James Hutchings Taylor (Canada)
Permanent Representative . . . . . . . . . . . . . . . . . . . Anker Svart (Denmark)
Deputy . . . . . . . . . . . . . . . . . . . . . . . . . . . . . . . . Flemming Morch
Permanent Representative . . . . . . . . . . . . . . Jean-Marie Merillon (France)
Deputy . . . . . . . . . . . . . . . . . . . . . . . . . . . Francis Beauchataud
Permanent Representative . . . . . . . . . . . . . . . . . . . . . . Hans-Georg Wieck
(Federal Republic of Germany)
Deputy . . . . . . . . . . . . . . . . . . . . . . . . . . . . . . . Alfons Bocker
Permanent Representative . . . . . . . . . . . . . . . . . Stylianos Vassilicos (Greece)
Deputy . . . . . . . . . . . . . . . . . . . . . . . . . . . . . . Spiridon Dokianos
Permanent Representative . . . . . . . . . . . . . Henrik Sv. Bjornsson (Iceland)
Deputy . . . . . . . . . . . . . . . . . . . . . . . . . . . . . Thordur Einarsson
Permanent Representative . . . . . . . . . . . . . . . . . . . . Vinenzo Jornetta (Italy)
Deputy . . . . . . . . . . . . . . . . . . . . . . . . . . . . . Amadeo de Franchis
Permanent Representative . . . . . . . . . . . . . . . . . Pierre Wurth (Luxembourg)
Deputy . . . . . . . . . . . . . . . . . . . . . . . . . . . . . . Alphonse Berns
Permanent Representative . . . . . . . . J. G. N. de Hoop Scheffer (Netherlands)
Deputy . . . . . . . . . . . . . . . . . . . . . . . . . . . . . . Bernard R. Bot
Permanent Representative . . . . . . . . . . . . . . . . . . . . . Kjeld Vibe (Norway)
Deputy . . . . . . . . . . . . . . . . . . . . . . . . . . . . . . . Kjell Ostrem
Permanent Representative . . . . . . . Jose Manuel P. de Villas-Boas (Portugal)
Deputy . . . . . . . . . . . . . . . . . . . . . . . . . . . . Octavio N. Valerio
Permanent Representative . . . . . . . . . . . . . . . . . . Jaime de Ojeda (Spain)
Permanent Representative . . . . . . . . . . . . . . . . . Osman Olcay (Turkey)
Deputy . . . . . . . . . . . . . . . . . . . . . . . . . . . . . . Teoman Surenkok
Permanent Representative . . . . . . . . . . Sir John Graham (United Kingdom)
Deputy . . . . . . . . . . . . . . . . . . . . . . . . . . . . . . Timothy Daunt
Permanent Representative . . . . . . . . . . . W. Tapley Bennett (United States)
Deputy . . . . . . . . . . . . . . . . . . . . . . . . . . . . . Stephen J. Ledogar

**INTERNATIONAL SECRETARIAT**

Secretary General ...................Joseph M. A. H. Luns (Netherlands)
Deputy Secretary General..........................Eric Da Rin (Italy)
Assistant Secretary General for Political Affairs ....Dr. Fredo Dannenbring
(Federal Republic of Germany)
Assistant Secretary General for Defense Planning
and Policy ......................David A. Nicholls (United Kingdom)
Assistant Secretary General for Infrastructure,
Logistics, and Council Operations..............David Collins (Canada)
Assistant Secretary General for Scientific and
Environmental Affairs ......................Robert Chabbal (France)
Directeur du Cabinet, Office
of the Secretary General .........Dr. S. I. P. van Campen (Netherlands)

**Division of Defense Support**

Assistant Secretary General
for Defense Support ....................Vitalij Garber (United States)

**Directorate of Planning and Support**
Director ..........................................J. Stone (2431, 2254)
Chief, Intellectual Property, Administrative
Problems and Liaison .....................S. Tsambiras (2279, 2280)
Chief, Planning Section ...................................A. Leblanc
Chief, Materiel Management and Systems ................H. Schurkens

**Directorate of Armaments & Defense Research**
(Responsible for procurement and replacement plans)
Director..........................................M. Weiss (2303, 2304)
Chief, Air Armaments ........................Charles Epstein (2268)
Chief, Maritime Patrol Air Raft ......................(Vacant) (2260)
Chief, Land Armaments ..............................J. H. Hill (2273)
Chief, Naval Armaments...........Rear Adm. L. Piamonte (Ret.) (2270)
Chief, Defense Research ...................Ing. Gen. P. Naslin (2262)
Chief, Electronic Warfare .................Ing. Gen. F. Romano (2382)

## MILITARY ORGANIZATION

**DEFENSE PLANNING**
**COMMITTEE—DPC**

Chairman ........Joseph M. A. H. Luns (Secretary General, Netherlands)
Members ........................Same as the North Atlantic Council,
with the exception of France

**CHIEFS OF DEFENSE STAFF**

Belgium ..............................Lt. Gen. Maurice J. Gysemberg
Canada ........................................Gen. G. C. Theriault
Denmark........................................Gen. Knud Jorgensen
France ........................................Gen. Jeannou Lacaze
Germany ......................Herr Gen. Wolfgang Attenburg
Greece........................................Adm. Theodore Beyannis
Iceland ....................................(No Defense Forces)
Italy ....................................Gen. Victtorio Santini
Luxembourg ................................Col. Francis Welfring
The Netherlands ..............................Gen. Govert Huyser
Norway ....................................Gen. Svenaage Hauge
Portugal................................Gen. Nuno de Melo Egidio
Spain........................Lt. Gen. Alvaro de la Calle Leloup
Turkey ........................................Gen. Kenan Evren
United Kingdom ...............Field Marshal Sir Edwin Bramall
United States ............................Gen. John W. Vessey, Jr.

**NATO MILITARY COMMITTEE**

President ...............Gen. N. V. T. de Melo Egidio (Portugal)
Chairman ...............Gen. Cornelius de Jager (Netherlands)
Deputy Chairman ..........Lt. Gen. Sinclair L. Melner (United States)

**Permanent Representatives**
Military Representative ..............Amr. de Div. E. Poullet (Belgium)
Deputy .........................................Col. Fraz Leblanca

Military Representative ............... Lt. Gen. R. Gutknecht (Canada)
Deputy ..................................... Col. Andre Simon
Military Representative ......... Maj. Gen. N. Holst-Sorensen (Denmark)
Deputy ..................................... Col. Mannus Sund
Deputy ..................................... Lucien Klein (France)
Military Representative ...................... Lt. Gen. E. D. Bernhard
.................................................. (Federal Republic of Germany)
Deputy ........................... Brig. Gen. Klaus Goldschmidt
Military Representative ........... Lt. Gen. E. Papefstathiou (Greece)
Deputy ........................... Capt. John Theofilopolous
Military Representative ................ Lt. Gen. B. Cottone (Italy)
Deputy ........................... Brig. Gen. Ilio Innocenzi
Military Representative ................ Col. P. Bergem (Luxembourg)
Military Representative ............... Lt. Gen. B. Mus (Netherlands)
Deputy ..................................... Capt. Ono Denboeft
Military Representative ............ Maj. Gen. Ole Mioen (Norway)
Deputy ..................................... Lt. Col. Randolph Abby
Military Representative ............ Gen. P. A. G. Cardoso (Portugal)
Deputy ..................................... Col. Rui Pereira
Military Representative ............ Maj. Gen. Rodriguez (Spain)
Deputy ..................................... Capt. Florencio Careno
Military Representative ............... Lt. Gen. B. Tulunay (Turkey)
Deputy ..................................... Col. Berkan Gonenc
Military Representative ..... Adm. Sir Anthony Morton (United Kingdom)
Deputy ........................... Air Cdr. Vivian Warrington
Military Representative .............. Gen. R. Robinson (United States)
Deputy ..................................... Brig. Donald Aldridge

**INTERNATIONAL MILITARY STAFF—IMS**

Director, International Staff .............. Lt. Gen. T. Huifeldt (Norway)
Deputy Commander .......... Lt. Gen. Sinclair L. Melner (United States)
Assistant to Chairman, Military
    Committee ................. Brig. Gen. Maurice Archdeacon (Canada)
Secretary ........................... Brig. Gen. J. C. Hayter (Canada)
Assistant Director, Intelligence ........ Maj. Gen. Franciscus H. Alkemade
.................................................. (Netherlands)
Assistant Director, Plans and Policy ....... Maj. Gen. Michael F. Reynolds
.................................................. (United Kingdom)
Deputy Assistant, Plans and Policy ..... Brig. Gen. Heinz-Guunter Donner
.................................................. (Federal Republic of Germany)
Assistant Director, Operations .......... Brig. Gen. Giovanni Baldi (Italy)
Assistant Director, Management
    and Logistics ....... Maj. Gen. Jacques R. M. P. A. Matthhys (Belgium)
Assistant Director, Command, Control, and Communications ...........
Assistant Director, Armaments, Standarization and
    Interoperability .................. Maj. Gen. Pat J. Mitchel (Canada)
Deputy Assistant, Armaments, Standarization and
    Interoperability ........................... Maj. Gen. A. Barbanos
.................................................. (Federal Republic of Germany)

**NUCLEAR PLANNING GROUP—NPG**

Chairman ........ Joseph M. A. H. Luns (Secretary General, Netherlands)
Members ........ Same as the North Atlantic Council, with the exception of
.................................................. France and Iceland

# NATO ALLIED COMMANDS

**SUPREME HEADQUARTERS ALLIED POWERS EUROPE—SHAPE**
*Headquarters: SHAPE, B-7010 Belgium*
*Telephone:    (32) 065 44 5000*

Supreme Allied Commander Europe
    (SACEUR) .................. Gen. Bernard W. Rogers (United States)
Deputy Supreme Allied
    Commander ....... Air Chief Marshal Sir Peter Terry (United Kingdom)
Deputy Supreme Allied
    Commander .......................... Gen. Dr. Gunter Kiessling
.................................................. (Federal Republic of Germany)
Chief of Staff, SHAPE ............. Gen. James E. Dalton (United States)

**Commands Subordinate to Supreme Allied Command Europe—SACEUR**

Commander, Northern European,
(AFNORTH) . . . . . . . . . . . . . Gen. Sir Richard Lawson (United Kingdom)
Commander, Central European,
(AFCENT) . . . . . . . . . . . . . . . . . . . . . . . . . . . . . . Gen. Leopold Chalupa
(Federal Republic of Germany)
Commander, Southern European,
(AFSOUTH) . . . . . . . . . . . . . . . Adm. William N. Small (United States)
Commander, United Kingdom Air Forces
(UKAIR) . . . . . . . . . . . Air Chief Marshal David Craig (United Kingdom)
Commander, Allied Command Europe
Mobile Force (AMF) . . . . . . . . . . . . . . Maj. Gen. A. G. Christie (Canada),
Commander, NATO Early Warning
(NAEW) . . . . . . . . . . . Maj. Gen. Leighton R. Palmerton (United States)
SACEUR Official Representative to NATO
Headquarters . . . . . . . . . . . . . . . . . . . . Maj. Gen. Kramer (Netherlands)

**SUPREME ALLIED COMMAND ATLANTIC—SACLANT**
*Headquarters: Norfolk, Virginia*
*United States*

*Telephone:   (804) 444-4333*

Supreme Allied Commander Atlantic
(SACLANT) . . . . . . . . . . . . . . Adm. Wesley L. McDonald (United States)
Deputy Supreme Allied Commander Atlantic
(SACLANT) . . . . . . . . . . . Vice Adm. David J. Hallifax (United Kingdom)

**Commands Subordinate to SACLANT**

Commander, Western Atlantic
(WESTLANT) . . . . . . . . . . . . . Adm. Wesley L. McDonald (United States)
Commander, Eastern Atlantic
(EASTLANT) . . . . . . . . . . . Adm. Sir William Staveley (United Kingdom)
Commander, Standing Naval Force Atlantic
(STANAVFORLANT) . . . . . . . . . . . . . . . . . Capt. Streeter (United States)
Commander, Striking Fleet Atlantic
(COMSTRIKEFLTLANT) . . . . . . . . . . . . . . . . . . . . . . (United States)
Submarine Allied Commander Atlantic
(SUBACLANT) . . . . . . . Vice Adm. Bernard M. Kauderer (United States)
Commander, Iberian Atlantic . . . . . . . . . . . . . . . . . . . . . . . . . . . . . . . . . . . . . .
SACLANT Official Representative to NATO
Headquarters . . . . . . . . . . . . . . . . . . . . . . . . Vice Adm. Johann Scheuer

**ALLIED COMMAND CHANNEL— ACCHAN**
*Headquarters: Northwood, Middlesex*
*HA6 3HR*
*England*
*Telephone:   Northwood 26161*
*Telex:   23139*

Commander-in-Chief, Channel
(CINCHAN) . . . . . . . . . . . . . Adm. Sir William Staveley (United Kingdom)
Deputy Commander-in-Chief
(CINCHAN) . . . . . . Rear Adm. Huibert Pieter Propper (The Netherlands)

**Commands Subordinate to ACCHAN**

Commander, Maritime Air Force
Channel. . . . . . . . . . . . . . . . . . . . Air Marshall J. Fitzpatrick CB (RAF)
Commander, Benelux Sub-Area
Channel . . . . . . . . . . . . . . . . . . . . . . . . . . Rear Adm. R. Krijger (RNLN)
Commander, North Sub-Area
Channel . . . . . . . . . . . . . . . . . . . . . . . . . . . Vice Adm. R. R. Squires (RN)
Commander, Standing Naval Force
Channel . . . . . . . . . . . . . . . . . . . . . . . . . . Commander G. Busard (BNF)

**Canada—U.S. Regional Planning Group**

Chairman . . . . . . . . . . . . . . . . . . . . . . . . Col. G. E. C. McArthur (Canada)
Chairman . . . . . . . . . . . . . . . . . . . . Capt. Charles E. Ryan (United States)
Secretary . . . . . . . . . . . . . . . . . . . . . . . . . . . . . . . . . . . . J. C. Allard (Canada)
Secretary. . . . . . . . . . . . . . . . . . . . Lt. Col. Roy L. Linden, Jr. (United States)
Committee Member . . . . . . . . . . . . . . . . . . . . Capt. J. R. O'Reilly (Canada)
Committee Member . . . . . . . . . . . . . . . . . . . . . . . Col. E. C. Quinn (Canada)
Committee Member . . . . . . . . . . . . . . Commander R. J. Lancshire (Canada)
Committee Member . . . . . . . . . . . . . . . . . . . . Lt. Col. V. A. Coroy (Canada)
Committee Member . . . . . . . . . . . . . . . . . . . . . Lt. Col. T. O. Cue (Canada)
Committee Member . . . . . . . . . . . . . . . . . . . . . Maj. R. D. Neeve (Canada)
Committee Member . . . . . . . . . . . . . . . Col. Paul W. Grenier (United States)
Committee Member . . . . . Commander Gary W. Gottschalk (United States)
Committee Member. . . . . . . . Lt. Col. Merrill E. Eastcott, Jr. (United States)
Committee Member . . . . . . . . . Lt. Col. Bardon Blizzard, Jr. (United States)
Committee Member . . . . . . . . . . . . Maj. Francis J. NcHnoh (United States)

# ORGANIZATION OF AFRICAN UNITY (OAU)

## MEMBERS

| | | |
|---|---|---|
| Algeria | Ghana | Rwanda |
| Angola | Guinea | São Tomé and Príncipe |
| Benin | Guinea-Bissau | Senegal |
| Botswana | Ivory Coast | Seychelles |
| Burundi | Kenya | Sierra Leone |
| Cameroon | Lesotho | Somalia |
| Cape Verde | Liberia | Sudan |
| Central African Republic | Libya | Swaziland |
| Chad | Madagascar | Tanzania |
| Comoros | Malawi | Togo |
| Congo | Mali | Tunisia |
| Djibouti | Mauritania | Uganda |
| Egypt | Mauritius | Upper Volta |
| Equatorial Guinea | Morocco | Zaire |
| Ethiopia | Mozambique | Zambia |
| Gabon | Niger | Zimbabwe |
| Gambia | Nigeria | |

The Organization of African Unity was established on May 25, 1963 in Addis Ababa, Ethiopia. The stated purposes of the organization are to: (1) promote unity and solidarity among African states, (2) intensify and coordinate efforts to improve living standards, (3) defend the sovereignty, territorial integrity and independence of African states, (4) eradicate colonialism, and (5) promote international cooperation, in keeping with the United Nations Charter.

There are four main organs of the OAU. The Assembly of Heads of State and Government, which meets annually in rotating countries, is the highest authority. The Council of Ministers, comprised of the members' Foreign Ministers, meets twice per year, elects its own Chairman each session, and prepares for the Assembly meetings. The Secretariat-General is the permanent headquarters of the OAU. Its Secretary-General is elected to a four-year term by the Assembly. The fourth organ of the OAU is the Council of Mediation, Conciliation and Arbitration, which meets when necessary to hear and settle disputes between member-countries by peaceful means.

There are also several "specialized commissions" attached to the OAU, one of which is the Defense Commission. It was established by the Assembly of Heads of State and Government in 1963 under Article XX of the OAU Charter and consists of all African Defense Ministers (or other ministers and plenipotentiaries designated by the member countries). It has its own rules of procedure and is responsible for questions referred to it by the Assembly and Council of Ministers, and for promoting inter-African cooperation in defense matters. The Commission meets every two years, electing its bureau for each session.

The Commission has defined the guidelines for the establishment of an OAU defense force, and has studied the legal and financial implications of such a move. The Commission does not, however, have the authority to raise troops independently. There is no committee of military experts nor an office of the OAU military advisor within the OAU Secretariat. However, an office called the "Defense and Security Section" is charged with defense matters.

**ASSEMBLY OF HEADS OF STATE AND GOVERNMENT**     Chairman . . . . . . . . . . . . . . . . . . . . . . . . . . Pres. Daniel T. Arap Moi (Kenya)

**COUNCIL OF MINISTERS**     Chairman . . . . . . . . . . . . . . . . . . . . . . . . . . . . . . . . . . . . . . . . . . . . . . . . .

**GENERAL SECRETARIAT**
*P.O. Box 3242*
*Addis Ababa, Ethiopia*

*Telephone:   15 77 00*
*Telex:   21046*
*Cable:   OAU ADDIS ABABA*

Secretary-General . . . . . . . . . . . . . . . . . . . . . . . . . . . . . . Edem Kodjo (Togo)
Assistant Secretary—General, Political Department
 (Acting) . . . . . . . . . . . . . . . . . . . . . . . . . . . . . . . . . . . Dawit G. Egziabher
Assistant Secretary—General, Finance
 Department . . . . . . . . . . . . . . . . . . . . Dr. Sylvester Nsazimana (Rwanda)
Assistant Secretary—General, Economic Development
 and Cooperation Department . . . . . . . . . . . . . . . . . Paul Etiang (Uganda)
Assistant Secretary—General, Administration and
 Conferences Department . . . . . . . . . . . . Augustine N. Chimuka (Zambia)
Assistant Secretary—General, Cultural and
 Social Affairs . . . . . . . . . . . . . . . . . . . . . . . . . . . . . . . Noureddine Djoudi
Head, Defense and Security Section . . . . . . . . . . . . . . . . . . . . . Major Zoula

**COMMISSION OF MEDIATION,
 CONCILIATION AND ARBITRATION**

President . . . . . . . . . . . . . . . . . . . . . . . . . . . . . . . . . . . . . . . . . . . . . . . . . . . . .
First Vice-President . . . . . . . . . . . . . . . . . . . . . . . . . . . . . . . . . . . . . . . . . . . . . .
Second Vice-President . . . . . . . . . . . . . . . . . . . . . . . . . . . . . . . . . . . . . . . . . . . .
Members . . . . . . . . . . . . . . . . . . . . . . . . . . . . . . . . . . . . . . . . . . . . . . . . . . . . . .

**DEFENSE COMMISSION**
 **(7th Session)**

Chairman . . . . . . . . . . . . . . . . . . . . . . Na Polkuu Konkuu Chiiri (Ghana)
First Vice Chairman . . . . . . . . . . . . Maj. Gaafer Mohammed Nimeiri (Sudan)
Second Vice Chairman . . . . . . . . . . . . . . . . . . . . . . . . . . . . . . . . . . . . . (Kenya)
Rapporteur . . . . . . . . . . . . . . . . . . . . . . . . . . . . . . . . . . . . . . . . . . . . . (Morocco)

# SOUTH-EAST ASIA COLLECTIVE DEFENSE TREATY
## (The Manila Pact)

### SIGNATORIES

| | |
|---|---|
| Australia | Thailand |
| New Zealand | United Kingdom |
| Philippines | United States |

Signed on September 8, 1954, this treaty is still in force, though the organization established to implement it (SEATO) was dissolved in 1977. The pact calls for action to meet armed aggression, or consultation should the territory, sovereignty or political independence of any member be threatened.

# TREATY FOR THE PROHIBITION OF NUCLEAR WEAPONS IN LATIN AMERICA
## (Treaty of Tlatelolco)

## SIGNATORIES

| | | |
|---|---|---|
| Argentina (not ratified) | Ecuador | Nicaragua |
| Bahamas | El Salvador | Panama |
| Barbados | Grenada | Paraguay |
| Bolivia | Guatemala | Peru |
| Brazil (not in force) | Haiti | Suriname |
| Chile (not in force) | Honduras | Trinidad and Tobago |
| Colombia | Jamaica | Uruguay |
| Costa Rica | Mexico | Venezuela |
| Dominican Republic | | |

Protocol I:  France (not ratified)
Netherlands
United Kingdom
United States

Protocol II:  China
France
Union of Soviet Socialist
Republics
United Kingdom
United States

Signed in 1967, the Treaty of Tlatelolco prevents the introduction of nuclear weapons into an area hitherto free of them. The basic obligations of the treaty commit the parties to use the nuclear material and facilities in their jurisdiction exclusively for peaceful purposes.

In addition to the treaty itself, signed by the nations of Latin America and the Caribbean, there are also two "Protocols" signed by other nations. Protocol I calls for countries with possessions in the area to apply these provisions to their territories. In Protocol II, nuclear weapons states commit themselves to (1) respect the denuclearized states of the area, (2) not to use or threaten to use nuclear weapons against the contracting parties, and (3) not to contribute to acts violating the obligations of the parties to the treaty.

# TREATY OF ESTABLISHMENT

## SIGNATORIES

Cyprus, Greece, Turkey, United Kingdom

Signed in August, 1960, this agreement recognizes British sovereignty over two base areas in Cyprus, Akrotini and Dhekelia. The treaty also confers on the United Kingdom specific rights within Cyprus, such as rights of movement and the use of designated training areas.

**HEADQUARTERS**
*Episkopi*
*British Forces Post Office 53*
*Cyprus*

Administrator..........................Air Vice-Marshal R. L. Davis
Chief Officer of Administration ...........................M. D. Tidy
Senior Judge of Senior Judge's Court ..........W. A. Sime, M.B.C., Q.C.
Resident Judge of Judge's Court ...........................J. M. Long

# TREATY ON THE CONTROL OF ARMS ON THE SEABED

*Treaty on the Prohibition of the Emplacement of Nuclear Weapons and other weapons of Mass Destruction on the Seabed and the Ocean Floor and in the Subsoil Thereof*

## SIGNATORIES

Afghanistan
Antigua and Barbuda
Australia
Austria
Belgium
Botswana
Bulgaria
Canada
Cape Verde
Central African Rep.
Congo
Cyprus
Czechoslovakia
Denmark
Dominica
Dominican Rep.
Ethiopia
Finland
German Democratic
    Republic
Federal Republic
    of Germany
Ghana
Grenada
Guinea-Bissau
Hungary

Iceland
India
Iran
Iraq
Ireland
Italy
Ivory Coast
Japan
Jordan
Laos
Lesotho
Luxembourg
Malaysia
Malta
Mauritius
Mongolia
Morocco
Nepal
Netherlands
New Zealand
Nicaragua
Niger
Norway
Panama
Poland
Portugal

Qatar
Romania
Rwanda
St. Lucia
São Tomé and Princípe
Saudi Arabia
Seychelles
Singapore
Solomon Islands
South Africa
Swaziland
Sweden
Switzerland
Taiwan
Togo
Tunisia
Turkey
Union of Soviet Socialist
    Republics
United Kingdom
United States
Vietnam
People's Democratic
    Republic of Yemen
Yugoslavia
Zambia

The General Assembly of the United Nations approved the Treaty on the Control of Arms on the Seabed in 1971, and the Treaty went into effect in 1972. The principal obligation of the treaty is to prohibit the parties from emplacing nuclear weapons or weapons of mass destruction on the seabed and ocean floor beyond a 12-mile coastal zone.

# TREATY ON THE NON-PROLIFERATION OF NUCLEAR WEAPONS

## SIGNATORIES

Afghanistan
Australia
Austria
Bahamas
Bangladesh
Barbados
Belgium
Benin
Bolivia
Botswana
Bulgaria
Burundi
Cameroon
Canada
Cape Verde
Central African Republic
Chad
Congo
Costa Rica
Cyprus
Czechoslovakia
Denmark
Dominican Rep.
Ecuador
Egypt
El Salvador
Ethiopia
Fiji
Finland
Gabon
Gambia
German Democratic
  Republic
Federal Republic
  of Germany
Ghana
Greece
Grenada
Guatemala
Guinea-Bissau
Haiti

Honduras
Hungary
Iceland
Indonesia
Iran
Iraq
Ireland
Italy
Ivory Coast
Jamaica
Japan
Jordan
Kampuchea
Kenya
Republic of Korea
Laos
Lebanon
Lesotho
Liberia
Libya
Liechtenstein
Luxembourg
Madagascar
Malaysia
Maldives
Mali
Malta
Mauritius
Mexico
Mongolia
Morocco
Nauru
Nepal
Netherlands
New Zealand
Nicaragua
Nigeria
Norway
Panama
Papua New Guinea
Paraguay

Peru
Philippines
Poland
Portugal
Romania
Rwanda
St. Lucia
San Marino
Senegal
Sierra Leone
Singapore
Somalia
Sri Lanka
Sudan
Suriname
Swaziland
Sweden
Switzerland
Syria
Taiwan
Thailand
Togo
Tonga
Tunisia
Turkey
Tuvalu
Uganda
Union of Soviet Socialist
  Republics
United Kingdom
United States
Upper Volta
Uruguay
Venezuela
Vietnam, Socialist Rep.
Vatican City
Western Samoa
People's Democratic
  Republic of Yemen
Yugoslavia
Zaire

Approved by the United Nations General Assembly in 1968, the Treaty on the Non-Proliferation of Nuclear Weapons went into effect in 1970. The basic aim of the treaty is to prevent the spread of nuclear weapons (Articles I and II). The treaty provides for an international system of safeguards designed to detect and deter the diversion of nuclear materials from peaceful uses by those countries which have not yet developed nuclear weapons (Article III). Moreover, the treaty seeks to promote full cooperation in the peaceful uses of nuclear energy by providing for the sharing of nuclear technology with non-nuclear states (Articles IV and V). Finally, the treaty includes a commitment by the nuclear powers to negotiate comprehensive arms control and disarmament issues in good faith (Article VI).

# UNITED NATIONS PEACE-KEEPING FORCES

The United Nations was established on October 24, 1945 with its first purpose being the maintenance of international peace and security. The Security Council, now consisting of 15 Members, has primary responsibility for maintaining the peace, with specific powers granted for that purpose. All members undertake to make available "armed forces, assistance and facilities" when called upon to do so and in accordance with specific agreement, "in order to enable the U.N. to take urgent military measures."

Plans for the actual deployment of armed forces are made by the Security Council with the aid of the Military Staff Committee.

**MILITARY STAFF COMMITTEE**
*Room 3540-A*
*United Nations*
*New York, N.Y. 10017*
*Telephone: (212) 754-5278*

Chairman . . . . . . . . . . . . . . . . . . . . . . . . . . . . . . . . . . . . . . . . (rotates monthly)
Liaison Officer, Military Staff Committee Secretariat . . . . . . . Yongyi Huang

**China**
Head of Delegation . . . . . . . . . . . . . . . . . . . . . . . . . . . . . . . . . . . . Yixian Sun
Member . . . . . . . . . . . . . . . . . . . . . . . . . . . . . . . . . . . Jinkun Shi (Navy)
Member . . . . . . . . . . . . . . . . . . . . . . . . . . . . . . . . . . . Shiwen Li (Army)
Member . . . . . . . . . . . . . . . . . . . . . . . . . . . . . . . . . Zhenxi Jiang (Army)
Member . . . . . . . . . . . . . . . . . . . . . . . . . . . . . . . . . Desheng Bou (Army)
Member . . . . . . . . . . . . . . . . . . . . . . . . . . . . . . . . . . . . . . . (Air Force)
Secretariat . . . . . . . . . . . . . . . . . . . . . . . . . . . . . . . . . . . . . . . Shiwen Li

**France**
Member . . . . . Brig. Gen. Michel M. J. Jouslin de Pisseloup de Noray (Army)
Member . . . . . . . . . . . . . . . . . . . . . Col. Antoine G. L. M. de Virieu (Army)
Member . . . . . . . . . . . . . . . . . . . . . . . . . . . Col. Jacques L. Pons (Army)
Member . . . . . . . . . . . . . . Lt. Col. Alain Joseph M. E. Gantelmi D'ille (Army)
Member . . . . . . . . . . . . . . . . . . . . . . . . Lt. Col. Alain Marie Faupin (Army)
Member . . . . . . . . . . . . . . . . . . . . . . . . . Col. Guy J. Archer (Air Force)
Member . . . . . . . . . . . . . . . . . . . . . Commander Yves P. de Kersauson (Navy)
Secretariat . . . . . . . . . . . . . . . . . . . . . . Col. Antoine G. L. M. de Virieu

**Union of Soviet Socialist Republics**
Member . . . . . . . . . . . . Capt. First Class Evgeny A. Smirnov (Armed Forces)
Member . . . . . . . . . . . . Capt. First Class Nikolai I. Spassky (Armed Forces)
Member . . . . . . . . . . . . . . . . . . . Col. Anatoly V. Makhov (Armed Forces)
Member . . . . . . . . . . . . . . . . . . Lt. Col. Nikolai N. Zlenko (Armed Forces)
Secretariat . . . . . . . . . . . . . . . . . . . . . . . . . . . . Lt. Col. Nikolai N. Zlenko

**United Kingdom**
Chief Representative . . . . . . . . . . . . . . Maj. Gen. Thomas A. Boam, C.B.E.
Member . . . . . . . . . . . . . . . . . . . Rear Adm. Patrick J. Symons, R.N. (Navy)
Member . . . . . . . . . . . . . . . . . . . Capt. Jeremy B. D. Read, R.N. (Navy)
Member . . . . . . . . . . . . . . . . Col. Michael J. Reece, O.B.E., R.M. (Navy)
Member . . . . . . . . . . . . . . . . . . . . . . Col. Brian T. Pennicott (Army)
Member . . . . . . . . . . . . . . . . . . . . . . . . . . . Maj. Philip L. Pearce (Army)
Member . . . . . . . . . . . . . . . . Air Commodore L. Swart, R.A.F. (Air Force)
Member . . . . . . . . . . . . . . . . . Group Capt. Brian T. Sills, R.A.F. (Air Force)
Secretariat . . . . . . . . . . . . . . . . . . . Col. Michael J. Reece, O.B.E., R.M.

**United States**
Member . . . . . . . . . . . . . . . . . . . . . . . . . Vice Adm. A. S. Moreau (Navy)
Member . . . . . . . . . . . . . . . . . . . . . . . . . . Capt. W. R. Gentry (Navy)
Member . . . . . . . . . . . . . . . . . Lt. Gen. Hans H. Driessnack (Air Force)
Member . . . . . . . . . . . . . . . . . . . . . . . . Col. Dan C. Allen (Air Force)
Member . . . . . . . . . . . . . . . . . . . Lt. Gen. William R. Richardson (Army)
Member . . . . . . . . . . . . . . . . . . . . . Col. John M. Shalikashvili (Army)
Secretariat . . . . . . . . . . . . . . . . . . . . . . . Col. Dan C. Allen (Air Force)

The Military Staff Committee was established under the United Nations Charter, Article 47, "to advise and assist the Security Council on all questions relating to the Security Council's military requirements for the maintenance of international peace and security, the employment and command of forces placed at its disposal, the regulation of armaments, and possible disarmament."

The Committee is composed of the Chiefs of Staff of the five permanent members of the Security Council (China, France, the Union of Soviet Socialist Republics, the United Kingdom, the United States) or their representatives. Chairmanship rotates monthly among each of the five members.

**UNITED NATIONS INTERIM FORCE IN LEBANON—UNIFIL**
*P.O. Box 75*
*Main Post Office*
*Nahariya, Israel*
*22100*
*Telephone:   (4) 929341*

Force Commander . . . . . . . . . . . . . . . .Lt. Gen. William Callaghan (Ireland)
Force Strength . . . . . . . . . . . . . . . . . . . . . . . . . . . . . . . . . . . . . . . . .5,848
Troop Contributing Countries . . . . . .Fiji, Finland, France, Ghana, Ireland, Italy, Netherlands, Norway, Senegal, Sweden

The United Nations Interim Force in Lebanon was established in accordance with Security Council Resolution No. 425 of March 19, 1978, for the purpose of "confirming the withdrawal of Israeli forces, restoring international peace and security and assisting the government of Lebanon in ensuring the return of its effective control in the area." Its local base is in Naqoura, Lebanon. UNIFIL is assisted by a group of 74 observers from UNTSO, forming "Observer Group Lebanon."

**UNITED NATIONS FORCE IN CYPRUS—UNFICYP**
*P.O. Box 1642*
*Nicosia, Cyprus*
*Telephone:   64000*

Force Commander . . . . . . . . . . . . .Maj. Gen. Gunther G. Greindl (Austria)
Special Representative of the Secretary-General . . . . . . . . Hujo Juan Gobbi (Argentina)
Force Strength . . . . . . . . . . . . . . . . . . . . . . . . . . . . . . . . . . . . . . . . . .2,300
Troop Contributing Countries . . . . . . . . . . . . . .Australia, Austria, Canada, Denmark, Finland, Ireland, Sweden, United Kingdom

The United Nations Peace-Keeping Force in Cyprus was established in accordance with Security Council Resolution No. 186 of March 4, 1964, to keep the peace between the Greek and Turkish Cypriot communities. Its purpose was "to use its best efforts to prevent a recurrence of fighting and, as necessary, to contribute to the maintenance and restoration of law and order and a return to normal conditions."

The original three-month mandate has been extended in three or six-month intervals. UNFICYP now performs additional functions, supervising the cease-fire between the armed forces of Turkey and Cyprus and assisting the United Nations High Commissioner for Refugees in providing humanitarian aid across military lines.

**UNITED NATIONS DISENGAGEMENT OBSERVER FORCE—UNDOF**
*P.O. Box 5368*
*Damascus, Syrian Arab Republic*
*Telephone:   (11) 81 69 38*

Force Commander . . . . . . . . . . . . . . . . . . . .Maj. Gen. C. G. Stahl (Sweden)
Force Strength . . . . . . . . . . . . . . . . . . . . . . . . . . . . . . . . . . . . . . . . . .1,287
Troop Contributing Countries . . . . . . . . .Austria, Canada, Finland, Poland

The United Nations Disengagement Observer Force was established in accordance with Security Resolution No. 350 of May 31, 1974 for an initial period of six months, following the signing of a troop disengagement agreement between Syria and Israel. It has been extended by successive resolutions. The UNDOF mans the area of separation between Israeli and Syrian troops, inspects the areas of limited deployment and generally maintains the cease-fire.

**UNITED NATIONS TRUCE SUPERVISION ORGANIZATION— UNTSO**

*P.O. Box 490*
*Government House*
*Jerusalem 91004*
*Israel*

*Telephone:  (2) 716223*
*Telex:    25282*

Chief of Staff . . . . . . . . . . . . . . . . . . . . .Lt. Gen. Emmanuel Erskine (Ghana)
Deputy Chief of Staff . . . . . . . . . . . . . . . . . . . .Col. .R. Wrangdahl (Sweden)
Chief of Operations . . . . . . . . . . . . . . . . . . . . . . . . . . . .Col. R. Sholly (USA)
Chief, Military Personnel . . . . . . . . . . . . . . . .Lt. Col. B. Isaksen (Denmark)
Chief Observer, Group Golan . . . . . . . . . . . . . . . .Lt. Col. D. Swan (Ireland)
Chief Observer, Detachment Damascus . . . . .Lt. Col. V. Petrounev (USSR)
Chief Observer, Group Egypt . . . . . . . . . . . . . .Lt. Col. M. Verreschi (Italy)
Chief Observer, Group Beirut . . . . . . . . . . . .Lt. Col. P. Letourneur (France)
Chief Observer, Group Lebanon . . . . . . . . . . . . . . . .Lt. Col. P. Bond (USA)
Chief Liaison, Amman  . . . . . . . . . . . . . . . . . . .Lt. Col. K. Gnasser (Austria)
Officer-in-Charge, Observer Group
    Jerusalem . . . . . . . . . . . . . . . . . . . . . . . . . . . . . . .Maj. J. Olsen (Denmark)
Liaison Officer, Gaza . . . . . . . . . . . . . . . . . . . . . . . .Cpt. J. Fondain (France)
Countries Providing Military Observers  . . . . .Argentina, Australia, Austria,
            Belgium, Canada, Chile, Denmark, Finland,
    France, Ireland, Italy, Netherlands, New Zealand, Norway,
    Sweden, United States, Union of Soviet Socialist Republics

UNTSO was officially established as the "Truce Commission for Palestine" in accordance with Security Council Resolution No. 48 (April 23, 1948) and reiterated by Security Council Resolution No. 50 (May 29, 1948). Its original purpose was to assist the Security Council in supervising the implementation of Resolution No. 46 (April 17, 1948), calling on all parties to cease fire. It has assisted in the application of the 1949 Armistice Agreements.

UNTSO is now manned by 300 unarmed military observers from 17 countries. UNTSO also assists other United Nations peace-keeping forces in the Middle East (UNIFIL, UNDOF).

**UNITED NATIONS MILITARY OBSERVER GROUP IN INDIA AND PAKISTAN—UNMOGIP**

*P.O. Box 68*
*Rawalpindi, Pakistan*
*P.O. Box 58*
*Srinagar, Kashmir*
*India*

Chief Military Observer . . . . . . . . . . . .Brig. Gen. Thor A. Johnsen (Norway)
Force Strength . . . . . . . . . . . . . . . . . . . . . . . . . . . . . . . . . . . . . . . . . . . . . . . . .36
Countries Contributing Military Observers . . . . . . . . . . .Australia, Belgium,
            Chile, Denmark, Finland,
            Italy, New Zealand, Norway,
            Sweden, Uruguay, United States

The United Nations Military Observer Group in India and Pakistan was established by Security Council Resolution No. 39 of January 20, 1948. It consists of unarmed observers who help maintain the truce along the India-Pakistan border.

# THE WARSAW TREATY ORGANIZATION
*(Warsaw Pact)*

## MEMBERS

| | |
|---|---|
| Bulgaria | Hungary |
| Czechoslovakia | Poland |
| German Democratic | Romania |
| Republic | USSR |

The "Warsaw Treaty of Friendship, Cooperation and Mutual Assistance" was signed on May 14, 1955. It is a military and political alliance, supplementing bilateral agreements between the Soviet Union and the other member countries. All senior command posts are held by Soviet officers.

The principal political decision-making body in the organization is the Political Consultative Committee (PCC). It comprises the First Secretaries of the members' Communist Parties, the Heads of State or their representatives, the Foreign and (sometimes) Defense Ministers, and the Commander-in-Chief and Chief of Staff of the Pact's Joint Armed Forces Command.

There are two administrative organizations directly responsible to the PCC: a Joint Secretariat and a Permanent Commission. The committees of the Pact consist of the Committee of Foreign Ministers, the Committee of Defense Ministers, and the Military Council. The Defense Ministers' Committee is the senior military body and meets annually to review the reports and recommendations of the Commander-in-Chief of the Joint Armed Forces Command. The Military Council, an advisory body for both the Defense Ministers and the Joint Command, usually meets semi-annually.

On the operational level, military matters are the purview of the Joint Armed Forces Command. It formulates operational plans for maneuvers and exercises. It is always commanded by a General of the Soviet Union (who is also the first Deputy Minister of Defense).

The Military Council, which consists of Deputy Defense Ministers and/or Chiefs of Staff of member countries, is chaired by the Commander-in-Chief and is assisted by the Pact's Chief of Staff. It advises the Joint Armed Forces Command on non-operational matters and supervises the work of a Technical Committee. The Technical Committee is the principal body responsible for ensuring co-operation in the development and procurement of military equipment and the exchange of information on science and technology relating to weapons and equipment.

The Warsaw Pact has four groups of armed forces under its command. The Group of Soviet Forces Germany is headquartered in Zosser-Wundsdorf, near Berlin. The Soviet Northern Group of Forces is based in Legnica, Poland. The Soviet Central Group of Forces is located in Milovice, Czechoslovakia. The Soviet Southern Group of Forces is based in Budapest, Hungary. These four commands all have Soviet tactical air forces and air-defense systems attached to them, under the centralized command of the Commander-in-Chief of the Soviet Air Defense Forces in Moscow.

In addition, it is generally assumed that elements of the armed forces of non-Soviet Warsaw Pact members are assigned to the Joint Armed Forces Command. Moreover, the three Western Military Districts of the Soviet Union (Baltic, Belorussian and Carpathian) are also assumed to be oriented toward the Warsaw Pact Command structure.

**POLITICAL CONSULTATIVE COMMITTEE**
*Warsaw Pact Headquarters*
*Moscow*

Chairman . . . . . . . . . . . . . . . . . . . . . . . . . . . . . . . . . . . . . . . . . . (host country)
**Party Chiefs**
First Secretary, Bulgaria . . . . . . . . . . . . . . . . . . . . . . . . . . . . Todor Zhivkov
First Secretary, Czechoslovakia . . . . . . . . . . . . . . . . . . . . . . . Gustav Husak
First Secretary, German Democratic Republic . . . . . . . . . . . . Erick Honecker
First Secretary, Hungary . . . . . . . . . . . . . . . . . . . . . . . . . . . . . Janos Kadar
First Secretary, Poland . . . . . . . . . . . . . . . . . . . . . Gen. Woyciech Jaruzelski
First Secretary, Romania . . . . . . . . . . . . . . . . . . . . . . . . . Nicolae Ceausescu
First Secretary, Union of Soviet Socialist Republics . . . . . . . . Yuri Andropov

**Foreign Ministers**

Minister of Foreign Affairs, Bulgaria . . . . . . . . . . . . . . . . . . . .Petur Mladena
Minister of Foreign Affairs, Czechoslovakia . . . . . . . . . .Bohuslav Chňoupek
Minister of Foreign Affairs,
    German Democratic Republic . . . . . . . . . . . . . . . . . . . . . . . .Oskar Fischer
Minister of Foreign Affairs, Hungary . . . . . . . . . . . . . . . . . . . . .Frigyes Puja
Minister of Foreign Affairs, Poland . . . . . . . . . . . . . . . . . .Stefan Olszowski
Minister of Foreign Affairs, Romania . . . . . . . . . . . . . . . . . . .Stefan Andrei
Minister of Foreign Affairs,
    Union of Soviet Socialist Republics . . . . . . . . . . . . . . . . .Andrey Gromyko

Member . . . . . . . . . . . . . . . . . . . . . . .Marshal Viktor Georgiyevich Kulikov
    (Commander-in-Chief, Joint Armed Forces Command—
        Union of Soviet Socialist Republics)
Member . . . . . . . . . . . . . . . . . . . . . . . . . . .Gen. Anatoly Ivanovich Gribkov
    (Chief of Staff, Joint Armed Forces Command—
        Union of Soviet Socialist Republics)

**Joint Secretariat**

Secretary-General . . . . . . . . . . . . . . . . . . . . . . . . . . . . . . . . . . . . .(Vacant)

**Permanent Commission**

(Inactive)

**COMMITTEE OF FOREIGN MINISTERS**

Chairman . . . . . . . . . . . . . . . . . . . . . . . . . . . . . . . . . . . . . . .(host country)
Member . . . . . . . . . . . . . . . . . . . . . . . . .Petur Toshev Mladenov (Bulgaria)
Member . . . . . . . . . . . . . . . . . . . . . . .Bohuslav Chnoupek (Czechoslovakia)
Member . . . . . . . . . . . . . . . . .Oskar Fischer (German Democratic Republic)
Member . . . . . . . . . . . . . . . . . . . . . . . . . . . . . . . . . .Frigyes Puja (Hungary)
Member . . . . . . . . . . . . . . . . . . . . . . . . . . . . . .Stefan Olszowski (Poland)
Member . . . . . . . . . . . . . . . . . . . . . . . . . . . . . . . . .Stefan Andrei (Romania)
Member . . . . . . . . . . . . . . . . . . . . . . . . . . .Andrey Andreyevich Gromyko
    (Union of Soviet Socialist Republics)

**COMMITTEE OF DEFENSE MINISTERS**

Chairman . . . . . . . . . . . . . . . . . . . . . . . . . . . . . . . . . . . . . . .(host country)
Member . . . . . . . . . . . . . . . . . . . . . . . .Marshal Dmitri Fedorovich Ustinov
    (Union of Soviet Socialist Republics)
Member . . . . . . . . . . . . . . . . . .Maj. Gen. Constantin Olteanu (Romania)
Member . . . . . . . . . . . . . . . . . . . . . . . . .Gen. Dobri Dzhurov (Bulgaria)
Member . . . . . . . . . . . . . . . . . . . . . . . . . .Gen. Martin Dzur (Czechoslovakia)
Member . . . . . . . . . .Gen. Heinz Hoffmann (German Democratic Republic)
Member . . . . . . . . . . . . . . . . . . . . . . . . . . . .Gen. Lajos Czinege (Hungary)
Member . . . . . . . . . . . . . . . . . . . . . . . . . .Gen. Wojciech Jaruzelski (Poland)

**JOINT ARMED FORCES COMMAND**

Commander-in-Chief . . . . . . . . . . . . . .Marshal Viktor Georgiyevich Kulikov
First Deputy Commander-in-Chief . . . . . . .Gen. Anatoly Ivanovich Gribkov
Deputy Commander-in-Chief for Air
    Defense Forces . . . . . . . . . . . .Marshal of Aviation Aleksandr I. Koldunov
Deputy Commander-in-Chief for
    Air Forces . . . . . . . . . . . . . .Col. Gen. Avn. Aleksey Nikolayevich Katrich
Deputy Commander-in-Chief for
    Naval Forces . . . . . . . . . . . . . . . . .Adm. Vladimir Vasil'yevich Mikhaylin
Deputy Commander-in-Chief for Rear
    Services . . . . . . . . . . . . . . . . . . . . . . . . . . . . . . . .Lt. Gen. G. T. Khoreshko

**Joint Armed Forces Staff**

Chief of Staff . . . . . . . . . . . . . . . . . . . . . . . .Gen. Anatoly Ivanovich Gribkov
First Deputy Chief of Staff . . . .Col. Gen. Mikhail Nikitovich Tereshchenko
Deputy Chief . . . . . . . . . . . . . .Col. Gen. Aleksey Alekseyevich Dement'yev
Deputy Chief . . . . . . . . . . . . . . . .Col. Gen. Anatoly Grigoryevich Merezhko
Deputy Chief . . . . . . . . . . . . . . . . . . . .Vice Adm. Fedor Ivanovich Savel'yev
Inspector-General . . . . . . . . . . . . . . . . . . . . .Lt. Gen. Yefim Ye. Patushenko

**Non-Soviet Warsaw Pact Representatives**

Permanent Representative . . . . . . . . . Lt. Gen. Khristo Radonov (Bulgaria)
Permanent Representative . . . . . . . . . Maj. Gen. Laszlo Fazekas (Hungary)
Permanent Representative . . . . . . . . . . . . . . . . . . . Maj. Gen. Kurt Gottwald
(German Democratic Republic)
Permanent Representative . . . . . . . . . . . . . . . Gen. Stanislaw Antos (Poland)
Permanent Representative . . . . . . . Maj. Gen. Dumitru Panescu (Romania)
Permanent Representative . . . . . . . Maj. Gen. Jan Husak (Czechoslovakia)

**MILITARY COUNCIL**

Chairman . . . . . . . . . . . . . . . . . . . . . Marshal Viktor Georgiyevich Kulikov
Deputy Chairman . . . . . . . . . . . . . . . . . . . Gen. Anatoly Ivanovich Gribkov
(Chief of Staff, Joint Armed Forces Command—
Union of Soviet Socialist Republics)

**Technical Committee**

Chairman . . . . . . . . . . . . . . . . . . . . . . . . . . . . . . . . . . . . . . . . . . . . . . . . .

**REGIONAL COMMANDS**

**Central Group of Forces**
*Milovice*
*Czechoslovakia*

Commander . . . . . . . . . . . . . . . . . . . . Lt. Gen. Grigory Grigor'yevich Borisov
First Deputy Commander . . . . . . . . . . . . . . . . . . . . . . . . . Lt. Gen. S. Bokov
Chief, Political Directorate . . . . . . . . . . . Lt. Gen. Mikhail Ivanovich Goglev
Commander, Rocket and Artillery
Forces . . . . . . . . . . . . . . . . . . . . . . . . . . . . Maj. Gen. Arty. I. Makarenko
Chief of Staff . . . . . . . . . . . . . . . . . . . . . Lt. Gen. Viktar M. Kozhbakhteyev

**Group of Soviet Forces Germany**
*Zossen-Wunsdorf,*
*German Democratic Republic*

Commander-in-Chief . . . . . . . . . . . . . . . . . . . . . . . . Gen. Mikhail M. Zaytsev
First Deputy Commander-
in-Chief . . . . . . . . . . . . . . Lt. Gen. Vyacheslav Mitrofanovich Gordiyenko
Deputy Commander-in-Chief and Chief for
Rear Services . . . . . . . . . . . . . . . . . . . . . . . . . . . Lt. Gen. Aleksey A. Nosov
Chief of Staff . . . . . . . . . . . . . . . . . . . Lt. Gen. Avn. Ivan Fedorovich Sviridov
Chief, Political Directorate . . . . . . . . . . . . . . . . . . . Col. Gen. Alekei Lizichev
Commander, Aviation . . . . . Col. Gen. Avn. Vladimir Fedorovich Korochkin
Chief, Military Procuracy . . . . . . . . . . . . . . . . . . . . . . . . Maj. Gen. B. Popov
Chief, Personnel . . . . . . . . . . . . . . . . . Maj. Gen. Grigory Ivanovich Lozovoy
Commander, Rocket and
Artillery Troops . . . . . . . . . . . . . . . . . . . . . . Lt. Gen. Arty. Ye. Me Komarov

**Northern Group of Forces**
*Legnica, Poland*

Commander . . . . . . . . . . . . . . . . . . . . . . . . Col. Gen. Yuri Fedorovich Zarudin
First Deputy Commander and Chief
of Staff . . . . . . . . . . . . . . . . . . . . . . . . . . . Maj. Gen. Aleksandr Kapochkia
Chief, Political Directorate . . . Lt. Gen. Nikolay Andreyevich Lushnichenko
Chief, Military Procuracy . . . . . . . . . . . . . . . . . . . . . . Col. Justice A. Abdeyer
Chief of Staff . . . . . . . . . . . . . . . . . . Lt. Gen. Tank Troops R. G. Rizatdinov

**Southern Group of Forces**
*Budapest, Hungary*

Commander . . . . . . . . . . . . . . . . . . . . . . . . . . Col. Gen. Vladimir I. Sivenok
First Deputy Commander . . . . . . . . . . Lt. Gen. Sagadat K. Nurmagambetov
Deputy Commander and Chief,
Rear Services . . . . . . . . . . . . . . . . . . . . . . . . Lt. Gen. Mikhail K. Polyakov
Chief, Political Directorate . . . . . . . . . . . . . . . . Lt. Gen. Nikolay D. Shevkun

# WESTERN EUROPEAN UNION (WEU)

## MEMBERS

Belgium
France
Federal Republic
 of Germany

Italy
Luxembourg
Netherlands
United Kingdom

The Western European Union is based on the Brussels Treaty which was signed on March 17, 1948, for the purpose of "collaboration in economic, social and cultural matters, and for collective self-defense." On December 20, 1950, the functions of the Western Union defense organization were assumed by NATO. However, the reorganization did not end the meetings of Western European Union Defense Ministers and Chiefs of Staff.

The WEU is formally organized into a Council, Secretariat-General, Assembly (with several permanent committees), the Agency for the Control of Armaments, and the Standing Armaments Committee.

The Council of the WEU is the senior decision-making body. It is responsible for formulating policy, directing the work of the Secretariat and the agencies and committees, and cooperating with NATO authorities. It consists of the seven nations' Foreign Ministers or their permanent representatives, and usually meets twice per month. The permanent chairman is the Secretary-General. The chairman at the ministerial level rotates.

The Assembly, comprised of delegates to the Parliamentary Assembly of the Council of Europe, meets twice a year to consider defense policy and make further reports and recommendations.

**COUNCIL OF THE WESTERN EUROPEAN UNION**
*9 Grosvenor Place*
*London, 8W1X 7HL*
*United Kingdom*
*Telephone:   (1) 235-5351*

Chairman . . . . . . . . . . . . . . . . . . . . . . . . . . . . . . . . . . .Claude Cheysson
(Minister of External Relations, France)
Member . . . . . . . . . . . . . . . . . . . . . . . . . . . . . . . . . . .Leo Tindemans
(Minister of Foreign Relations, Belgium)
Member . . . . . . . . . . . . . . . . . . . . . . . . . . . . . .Hans-Dietrich Genscher
(Minister of Foreign Affairs
Federal Republic of Germany)
Member. . . . . . . . . . . . . . . . . . . . . . . . . . . . . . . . . . .Emilio Colombo
(Minister of Foreign Affairs, Italy)
Member . . . . . . . . . . . . . . . . . . . . . . . . . . . . . . . . . . .Colette Flesch
(Minister of Foreign Affairs, Foreign Commerce and
Foreign Assistance, Luxembourg)
Member . . . . . . . . . . . . . . . . . . . . . . . . . . . . . . . . . . .Hans van den Broek
(Minister of Foreign Affairs, Netherlands)
Member . . . . . . . . . . . . . . . . . . . . . . . . . . . . . . . . . . .Geoffrey Hawe
(Secretary of State for Foreign and
Commonwealth Affairs, United Kingdom)

**Permanent Representatives**

Belgium . . . . . . . . . . . . . . . . . . . . . . . . . . . . . . . . . . . . .Robert Vaes
France . . . . . . . . . . . . . . . . . . . . . . . .Emmanuel Jacquin de Margerie
Federal Republic of Germany . . . . . . . . . . . . . . . . . . . . .Dr. Jurgen Ruhfus
Italy . . . . . . . . . . . . . . . . . . . . . . . . . . . . . . . . . . . . . . . .Andrea Cagiati
Luxembourg . . . . . . . . . . . . . . . . . . . . . . . . . . . . . . . . . . .Roger Hastert
Netherlands . . . . . . . . . . . . . . . . . . . . . . . . . . . . . . .J. L. R. Huydecoper
United Kingdom . . . . . . . . . . . . . . . . . . . . . . . . . . . . . . .Kenneth James

**SECRETARIAT-GENERAL**

Secretary-General . . . . . . . . . . . . . . . . . . . . . .Edouard Longerstaey (Belgium)
Deputy Secretary-General . . . . . . . . . . . . . . . . . . . . . . . .Dr. Jürgen Diesel
(Federal Republic of Germany)
Assistant Secretary-General and Head of
 the International Secretariat . . . . . . . . . . . . . . . . . . . . . . .Eric Hinterman
Assistant Secretary-General (and Press Officer) . . . . . . . . . . . . . .Peter Fraser
(United Kingdom)
Legal Advisor . . . . . . . . . . . . . . . . . . . . . . . . . . . . . . . .J. Westhof (Belgium)

## THE AGENCY FOR THE CONTROL OF ARMAMENTS
*43 Ave. du President Wilson*
*75775 Paris Cedex 16*
*France*
*Telephone:    (1) 723-5432*

Director . . . . . . . . . . . . . . . . . . . . . . . . . . . . . . . . . Lt. Gen. E. Rambaldi (Italy)

## THE STANDING ARMAMENTS COMMITTEE
*43 Ave. du President Wilson*
*75775 Paris Cedex 16*
*France*
*Telephone:    (1) 723-5432*

Chairman . . . . . . . . . . . . . . . . . . . . . . . . . . . . . . . . Eric Hinterman (France)

## THE ASSEMBLY
*43 Ave. du President Wilson*
*75775 Paris Cedex 16*
*France*
*Telephone:    (1) 723-5432*

President . . . . . . . . . . . . . . . . . . . . . . . . . . . . . . . Mr. Alfredo De Poi (Italy) f. 1.
Vice-President . . . . . . . . . . . . . . . . . Sir Frederick Bennet (United Kingdom)
Vice-President . . . . . . . . . . . . . . . . . . . . . Mr. Albert Berchem (Luxembourg)
Vice-President . . . . . . . . . . . . . . . . . . . . . . . . . . Mr. Raoul Bunnel (Belgium)
Vice-President . . . . . . . . . . . . . . . . . . . . . . . . . . Mr. Lucien Pignion (France)
Vice-President . . . . . . Mr. Herman Unland (Federal Republic of Germany)
Vice-President . . . . . . . . . . . . . . . . . . . . . . Mr. J. N. Scholten (Netherlands)
Chairman of the Federated Group of Christian Democrats
    and European Democrats . . . . . . . . . . . . . . . . . . . . . . M. Valiante (Italy)
Chairman of the Liberal Group . . . . . . . . . . . . . . . . . . . A. Mayoud (France)
Chairman of the Socialist Group . . . . . . . . . . . . . P. Stoffelen (Netherlands)
Chairman of the Communist Group . . . . . . . . . . . . . . . Ugo Pecchioli (Italy)
Clerk . . . . . . . . . . . . . . . . . . . . . . . . . . . . . . . . . . . . . . . . Georges Moulias
Spokesman . . . . . . . . . . . . . . . . . . . . . . . . . . . . . . . Paul Borchier (France)

## PERMANENT COMMITTEES

Chairman, Defense Questions and Armaments . . . . . . . . Mr. Lucien Pignion
(France)

Chairman, General Affairs . . . . . . . . . . . . . . . . . . . . . . . . . . . . . . . . . . . . . .
Chairman, Scientific Affairs . . . . . . . . . . . . . . . . . . . . . . . . . . . . . . . . . . . . .
Chairman, Budgetary Affairs and Administration . . . . . . . . . . . . . . . . . . . .
Chairman, Rules of Procedure and Privileges . . . . . . . . . . . . . . . . . . . . . . .
Chairman, Relations with Parliaments . . . . . . . . . . . . . . . . . . . . . . . . . . . . .

# B. BILATERAL DEFENSE
# TREATIES AND AGREEMENTS

# AFGHANISTAN

**Afghanistan—Czechoslovakia**
Treaty of Friendship, Cooperation and Mutual Assistance (1981)

**Afghanistan—Union of Soviet Socialist Republics**
(1) Treaty of Friendship, Cooperation and Mutual Assistance (1978)
(2) Stationing of Forces Agreement (1980)

\* \* \* \* \*

# ALBANIA

None

\* \* \* \* \*

# ALGERIA

**Algeria—Libya**
Defense Agreement (1975)

\* \* \* \* \*

# ANGOLA

**Angola—Cuba**
Agreement concerning Cuban military training and assistance in internal security, and the stationing of Cuban personnel (1977)

**Angola—Union of Soviet Socialist Republics**
(1) Treaty of Friendship, Cooperation and Mutual Assistance (1976)
(2) Military Cooperation Agreement (for military aid)

**Angola—Zambia**
Mutual Defense Agreement (1979)

\* \* \* \* \*

677

# ANTIGUA AND BARBUDA

**Antigua—United States**
    (1)  Status of Forces Agreement (concerning U.S. bases) (1978)
    (2)  Agreement concerning the provision of military training (1981)

* * * * *

# ARGENTINA

**Argentina—United States**
    Military Assistance Agreement (1964)
    Agreement concerning armed forces cooperation projects (1970)

* * * * *

# AUSTRALIA

**Australia—India**
    Agreement on aid in defense of India (1963)

**Australia—New Zealand**
    (1)  ANZAC Agreement concerning joint policy on the Southwest Pacific (including defense) (1944, 1947)
    (2)  Agreement concerning integrated defense planning and equipment (1969)

**Australia—United States**
    (1)  Reciprocal Aid in War Agreement (1942)
    (2)  Military Defense Assistance Agreements (1951, 1963, 1974, 1980)
    (3)  Agreement concerning weapons development program (1960)
    (4)  Agreement concerning joint defense space research facility (1966, 1977)
    (5)  Agreement concerning training exchange program (1976)

* * * * *

# AUSTRIA

**Austria—United States**
    Exchanges of Notes concerning military sales (1957)

* * * * *

# BAHAMAS

**Bahamas—United States**
Exchanges of Notes concerning U.S. "military rights" and maritime practices (continuation of agreements between United Kingdom and United States) (1973)

\* \* \* \* \*

# BAHRAIN

**Bahrain—Saudi Arabia**
Security Cooperation Pact (1981)

**Bahrain—United Kingdom**
Treaty of Friendship (1971)

\* \* \* \* \*

# BANGLADESH

None

\* \* \* \* \*

# BARBADOS

None

\* \* \* \* \*

# BELGIUM

**Belgium—United Kingdom**
Mutual Aid Agreement (1944)

**Belgium—United States**
(1) Mutual Defense Assistance Agreement (1950, 1968, 1969)
(2) Exchanges of Notes concerning weapons production (1960)
(3) Memorandum of Understanding concerning mutual cooperation in research, development, production, procurement and logistic support of defense equipment (1979)

**Belgium—Zaire**
Military Aid Agreement (1977/78)

\* \* \* \* \*

# BELIZE

**Belize—United Kingdom**
Agreement for British troops to remain in Belize to train Belizean defense forces (1981)

**Belize—United States**
Agreement concerning the provision of military training (1982)

\* \* \* \* \*

# BENIN

**Benin—France**
Cooperation Agreement (1975)

**Benin—United States**
Military Assistance Agreement (1962)

\* \* \* \* \*

# BERMUDA

**Bermuda—United States**
Agreement to lease 2.3 square miles to the U.S. for naval and air bases.

\* \* \* \* \*

# BHUTAN

**Bhutan—India**
Treaty of Perpetual Peace and Friendship (1949)

\* \* \* \* \*

# BOLIVIA

**Bolivia—United States**
(1) Military Assistance Agreement (1958)
(2) Agreement concerning the furnishing of military supplies (1962)

\* \* \* \* \*

# BOTSWANA

**Botswana—United States**
Agreement concerning the provision of military training (1980)

\* \* \* \* \*

# BRAZIL

**Brazil—United States**
(1) Military Assistance Agreement (1952)
(2) Exchanges of Notes concerning military assistance (1964)
(3) Memorandum of Understanding concerning Brazilian acquisition of military aircraft (1973)

\* \* \* \* \*

# BRUNEI

None

\* \* \* \* \*

# BULGARIA

**Bulgaria—Angola**
Treaty of Friendship, Cooperation and Mutual Assistance (1978)

**Bulgaria—Cambodia**
Treaty of Friendship, Cooperation and Mutual Assistance (1960)

**Bulgaria—Czechoslovakia**
Treaty of Friendship, Cooperation and Mutual Assistance (1968)

**Bulgaria—German Democratic Republic**
Treaty of Friendship, Cooperation and Mutual Assistance (1967)

**Bulgaria—Hungary**
Treaty of Friendship, Cooperation and Mutual Assistance (1948)

**Bulgaria—Laos**
Treaty of Friendship, Cooperation and Mutual Assistance (1979)

**Bulgaria—Mongolia**
Treaty of Friendship, Cooperation and Mutual Assistance (1967, 1977)

**Bulgaria—Poland**
Treaty of Friendship, Cooperation and Mutual Assistance (1948, 1967)

**Bulgaria—Romania**
Treaty of Friendship, Cooperation and Mutual Assistance (1970)

**Bulgaria—Union of Soviet Socialist Republics**
Treaty of Friendship, Cooperation and Mutual Assistance (1948, 1967)

**Bulgaria—Vietnam**
Treaty of Friendship, Cooperation and Mutual Assistance (1979)

**Bulgaria—People's Democratic Republic of Yemen**
(1) Protocol for Cooperation (signed by Defense Ministers, 1980)
(2) Treaty of Friendship, Cooperation and Mutual Assistance (1981)

\* \* \* \* \*

# BURMA

**Burma—United States**
Agreement concerning the provision of military training (1980)

\* \* \* \* \*

# BURUNDI

None

\* \* \* \* \*

# CAMEROON

**Cameroon—France**
Defense Agreement (February 1974)

**Cameroon—Libya**
Treaty of Friendship and Cooperation (1975)

**Cameroon—United States**
Agreement concerning the provision of military training (1980)

\* \* \* \* \*

# CANADA

**Canada—France**
Exchanges of Notes concerning the exchange of defense scientific information (1962)

**Canada—Federal Republic of Germany**
(1) Agreement on cooperation in peaceful use of atomic energy (1957)
(2) Exchanges of Notes concerning defense scientific information (1964)

**Canada—Norway**
Exchanges of Notes concerning defense scientific information (1960)

**Canada—Sweden**
Agreement concerning defense research, development and production (1975)

**Canada—Switzerland**
Cooperation agreement concerning peaceful use of atomic energy (1958, 1971)

**Canada—United States**
    (1) Ogdensburg declaration concerning creation of a Permanent Joint Board on Defense (1940—continued 1947)
    (2) Protocol concerning defense of Newfoundland (1941)
    (3) Exchanges of Notes concerning economic cooperation for defense (1950)
    (4) Agreement concerning extension and coordination of continental radar defense system (1951)
    (5) Agreement concerning establishment of early-warning stations in Canada (1955)
    (6) Agreement for cooperation concerning atomic information for mutual defense (1955, 1959)
    (7) Agreement providing for the creation of United States—Canadian Committee on Joint Defense (1958)
    (8) Agreement concerning North American Air Defense Command (1958, 1968, 1973, 1975, 1981)
    (9) Exchanges of Notes concerning establishment of integrated communications system to support ballistic missile early-warning system (1959)
    (10) Agreement concerning placement in Canada of short-range tactical air navigation facilities (1959)
    (11) Agreement concerning establishment and operation of improved ground-to-air military communications facility in Canada (1965)
    (12) Memorandum of understanding concerning NAVSTAR global positioning system, with annex (1978)
    (13) Exchanges of Notes concerning the testing and evaluation of U.S. defense weapons systems in Canada (1983)

\* \* \* \* \*

# CAPE VERDE

None

\* \* \* \* \*

# CENTRAL AFRICAN REPUBLIC

**Central African Republic—France**
Cooperation Agreement (1960)

\* \* \* \* \*

# CHAD

**Chad—France**
Cooperation Agreement (1960, 1964, 1974)

**Chad—Nigeria**
Treaty of Friendship, Cooperation and Mutual Assistance (1972)

\* \* \* \* \*

# CHILE

**Chile—United States**
Military Assistance Agreement (1952)

\* \* \* \* \*

# CHINA

**China—Egypt**
Supply Agreement (1979)

**China—Equatorial Guinea**
Military Assistance Agreement

**China—Guinea**
Military Assistance Agreement

**China—Japan**
Treaty of Peace and Friendship (1978)

**China—North Korea**
Treaty of Friendship, Cooperation and Mutual Assistance (1961)

**China—Mali**
Military Assistance Agreement

**China—Sudan**
Treaty of Friendship, Cooperation and Mutual Assistance (1982)

**China—Tanzania**
Military Assistance Agreement

**China—Yemen Arab Republic**
Treaty of Friendship, Cooperation and Mutual Assistance (1964)

\* \* \* \* \*

# COLOMBIA

**Colombia—United States**
(1) Military Assistance Agreement (1952)
(2) Agreement on military advisors (1955)
(3) Military Supply Agreement (1961)
(4) Agreement concerning general security of military information (1981)

\* \* \* \* \*

# COMOROS

None

\* \* \* \* \*

# CONGO

**Congo—France**
  Cooperation Agreement (1960, 1974)

\* \* \* \* \*

# COSTA RICA

**Costa Rica—United States**
  Exchanges of Notes concerning military supplies and services (1962)

\* \* \* \* \*

# CUBA

**Cuba—Angola**
  Agreement concerning Cuban military training and assistance in internal security, and the stationing of Cuban personnel (1977)

**Cuba—United States**
  Agreement concerning jurisdiction and control over Guantanamo Bay military base (1903, 1934)

\* \* \* \* \*

# CYPRUS

None

\* \* \* \* \*

# CZECHOSLOVAKIA

**Czechoslovakia—Afghanistan**
  Treaty of Friendship, Cooperation and Mutual Assistance (1981)

**Czechoslovakia—Bulgaria**
Treaty of Friendship, Cooperation and Mutual Assistance (1968)

**Czechoslovakia—Ethiopia**
Treaty of Friendship, Cooperation and Mutual Assistance (1978)

**Czechoslovakia—German Democratic Republic**
Treaty of Friendship, Cooperation and Mutual Assistance (1967)

**Czechoslovakia—Hungary**
Treaty of Friendship, Cooperation and Mutual Assistance (1968)

**Czechoslovakia—Laos**
Treaty of Friendship, Cooperation and Mutual Assistance (1980)

**Czechoslovakia—Poland**
Treaty of Friendship, and Mutual Aid (1947, 1967)

**Czechoslovakia—Romania**
Treaty of Friendship, Cooperation and Mutual Assistance (1968)

**Czechoslovakia—Union of Soviet Socialist Republics**
(1) Treaty of Friendship, Cooperation and Mutual Assistance (1970)
(2) Stationing of Forces Agreement (1968)

**Czechoslovakia—Vietnam**
Treaty of Friendship, Cooperation and Mutual Assistance (1980)

**Czechoslovakia—People's Democratic Republic of Yemen**
Treaty of Friendship, Cooperation and Mutual Assistance (1964)


\* \* \* \* \*


# DENMARK


**Denmark—United Kingdom**
Mutual Aid Agreement (1945)

**Denmark—United States**
(1) Mutual Defense Assistance Agreement (under NATO) (1950)
(2) Agreement concerning the defense of Greenland (1951, 1960)
(3) Exchanges of Notes concerning weapons production program (1960)
(4) Memorandum of Understanding concerning mutual cooperation in research, development, production, procurement and logistic support of defense equipment (1980)
(5) Exchanges of Notes concerning general security of military information (1981)
(6) Mutual Logistical Support Agreement (1982)


\* \* \* \* \*


# DJIBOUTI


**Djibouti—France**
Agreement permitting stationing of French forces (1977)


\* \* \* \* \*

# DOMINICA

**Dominica—United States**
   Exchanges of Notes concerning the provision of military training (1981)

\* \* \* \* \*

# DOMINICAN REPUBLIC

**Dominican Republic—United States**
   Military Assistance Agreement (1962)

\* \* \* \* \*

# ECUADOR

**Ecuador—Italy**
   Declaration of Friendship and Collaboration (1949)

\* \* \* \* \*

# EGYPT

**Egypt—China**
   Arms Supply Agreement (1979)

**Egypt—France**
   Arms Supply Agreement

**Egypt—Israel**
   (1) Sinai Force Separation Agreement (1975)
   (2) Peace Treaty (1979)

**Egypt—Sudan**
   Joint Defense Agreement (providing the basis for a "Joint Defense Council" and joint military training) (1977)

**Egypt—Union of Soviet Socialist Republics**
   Treaty of Friendship, Cooperation and Mutual Assistance (1971)

**Egypt—United States**
   (1) Mutual Defense Agreement (1952)
   (2) Agreement on U.S. use of Egyptian bases and facilities (1979, 1981)
   (3) Military Assistance Agreement (1979, 1980)
   (4) Memorandum of Understanding concerning Egyptian production of U.S. defense equipment (1979)
   (5) General Security of Military Information Agreement (1982)

**Egypt—Zaire**
   Technical Military Cooperation Agreement (1980)

\* \* \* \* \*

# EL SALVADOR

**El Salvador—United States**
   (1) Agreement concerning the furnishing of defense articles and services contributing to El Salvador's internal security (1962)
   (2) Agreement concerning U.S. Army mission to El Salvador (1954, 1959, 1963)
   (3) Agreement concerning U.S. Air Force mission to El Salvador (1957, 1959, 1960)


\* \* \* \* \*


# EQUATORIAL GUINEA

**Equatorial Guinea—China**
   Military Assistance Agreement


\* \* \* \* \*


# ETHIOPIA

**Ethiopia—Kenya**
   (1) Treaty of Friendship, Cooperation and Mutual Agreement (1979)
   (2) Mutual Aid Defence Agreement (1963)

**Ethiopia—Union of Soviet Socialist Republics**
   Treaty of Friendship, Cooperation and Mutual Assistance (including agreement on the use of Dahlak Island base) (1978, ratified April 1979)

**Ethiopia—United States**
   Exchanges of Notes concerning mutual defense assistance (1952)

**Ethiopia—People's Democratic Republic of Yemen**
   (1) Treaty of Friendship, Cooperation and Mutual Assistance (1979)
   (2) Protocol continuing Military cooperation (1980)


\* \* \* \* \*


# FIJI

None


\* \* \* \* \*

# FINLAND

**Finland—Union of Soviet Socialist Republics**
Treaty of Friendship, Cooperation and Mutual Assistance (1948, 1970)

**Finland—France, Union of Soviet Socialist Republics, United Kingdom**
Paris Peace Treaty (restricting the size and armament of armed forces of Finland) (1947)

\* \* \* \* \*

# FRANCE

**France—Benin**
Agreement of Cooperation (1975)

**France—Canada**
Agreement on the exchange of defense science information (1962)

**France—Cameroon**
Defense Agreement (1974)

**France—Central African Republic**
Agreement of Cooperation (1960)

**France—Chad**
Agreement of Cooperation (1960, 1964, 1974)

**France—Congo**
Agreement of Cooperation (1960, 1974)

**France—Djibouti**
Agreement concerning stationing of French forces (1977)

**France—Egypt**
Arms Supply Agreement

**France—Federal Republic of Germany**
(1) Agreement concerning mutual secrecy of defense-related inventions and technical experience (1961)
(2) Treaty of Cooperation (1963)

**France—Finland**
Paris Peace Treaty (restricting the size and armament of the armed forces of Finland) (1947)

**France—Gabon**
Agreement of Cooperation (1960, 1974)

**France—Ivory Coast**
Defense Agreement

**France—Lebanon**
Arms Supply Agreement

**France—Libya**
Arms Supply Agreement

**France—Madagascar**
Defense and/or Military Cooperation Agreements (1960, 1973)

**France—Mauritania**
Defense Agreement

**France—Monoco**
Mutual assistance between relief and civil defense services (1970)

**France—Morocco**
Arms Supply Agreement

**France—Niger**
Defense Agreement

**France—Portugal**
Agreement concerning the establishment of a tracking station for ballistic missiles in the Azores (1964)

**France—Saudi Arabia**
Agreement concerning training for Saudi navy (1982)

**France—Senegal**
Defense and/or Military Cooperation Agreement

**France—Spain**
Military Cooperation Agreement (1970)

**France—Togo**
Defense Agreement (1963, 1975)

**France—Tunisia**
Arms Supply Agreement

**France—Union of Soviet Socialist Republics**
(1) Agreement on the Principles of Cooperation (1971)
(2) Joint Declaration concerning the non-proliferation of nuclear weapons technology (1975)
(3) Exchange of Notes concerning measures to prevent the accidental or unauthorized use of nuclear weapons (1976)

**France—United Kingdom**
Agreement in principle on exchange of information on the world naval situation (1976)

**France—United States**
(1) Mutual Defense and Assistance Agreements (1950)
(2) Mutual Security Agreements (under NATO) (1952)
(3) Agreement concerning cooperation in the field of atomic weapons for mutual defense purposes (1959, 1961)
(4) Memorandum of Understanding concerning military procurement (1961)
(5) General security of information agreement (1977)
(6) Exchanges of Notes concerning weapons production (1960)

**France—Zaire**
Military Cooperation Agreement (1978 ratified)

\* \* \* \* \*

# GABON

**Gabon—France**
Agreement of Cooperation (1960, 1974)

\* \* \* \* \*

# GAMBIA

**Gambia—Senegal**
Confederation of Senegambia (1982)

\* \* \* \* \*

# GERMAN DEMOCRATIC REPUBLIC (East Germany)

**German Democratic Republic—Angola**
Treaty of Friendship, Cooperation and Mutual Assistance (1979)

**German Democratic Republic—Bulgaria**
Treaty of Friendship, Cooperation and Mutual Assistance (1967)

**German Democratic Republic—Czechoslovakia**
Treaty of Friendship, Cooperation and Mutual Assistance (1967)

**German Democratic Republic—Ethiopia**
Treaty of Friendship, Cooperation and Mutual Assistance (1979)
Military Cooperation Protocol (1979)

**German Democratic Republic—Hungary**
Treaty of Friendship, Cooperation and Mutual Assistance (1967)

**German Democratic Republic—Kampuchea**
Treaty of Friendship, Cooperation and Mutual Assistance (1980)

**German Democratic Republic—Mozambique**
Treaty of Friendship, Cooperation and Mutual Assistance
Military Cooperation Protocol (1979)

**German Democratic Republic—People's Democratic Republic of Yemen**
Treaty of Friendship, Cooperation and Mutual Assistance (1979)

**German Democratic Republic—Poland**
Treaty of Friendship, Cooperation and Mutual Assistance (1967)

**German Democratic Republic—Romania**
Treaty of Friendship, Cooperation and Mutual Assistance (1972)

**German Democratic Republic—Tanzania**
Treaty of Friendship, Cooperation and Mutual Assistance (1964)

**German Democratic Republic—Union of Soviet Socialist Republics**
Status of Forces Agreement (1957)
Treaty of Friendship, Cooperation and Mutual Assistance (1964)

**German Democratic Republic—Vietnam**
Treaty of Friendship, Cooperation and Mutual Assistance (1977)

\* \* \* \* \*

# FEDERAL REPUBLIC OF GERMANY (West Germany)

**Federal Republic of Germany—Union of Soviet Socialist Republics**
  Treaty on the Renunciation of the Use of Force (1972)

**Federal Republic of Germany—United States**
  (1) Mutual Defense Assistance Agreement (1955)
  (2) Exchanges of Notes concerning weapons production (1960)
  (3) Memorandum of Understanding concerning cooperative development of an advanced surface-to-air missile (1976)
  (4) Agreement concerning the provision of military training (1977)
  (5) Memorandum of Understanding concerning co-production of the Sidewinder AIM-9L Missile (1977)
  (6) Memorandum of Understanding concerning cooperation in research, development, production, procurement, and logistic support of defense equipment (1978)
  (7) Memorandum of Understanding concerning standardization and inter-operability of army tactical data systems (1980)
  (8) Wartime Host Nation Support Agreement (1982)


\* \* \* \* \*


# GHANA


**Ghana—United States**
  Mutual Defense Assistance Agreement (1950)


\* \* \* \* \*


# GREECE


**Greece—United States**
  (1) Agreement concerning military bases (1953)
  (2) Agreement concerning status of U.S. forces in Greece (1956)
  (3) Exchanges of Notes concerning weapons production (1960)
  (4) Agreement concerning status of personnel and establishment of joint standing committee (1972)
  (5) Military Supplies Agreement (1979, 1982)
  (6) Agreement concerning U.S. military bases (1983)


\* \* \* \* \*


# GRENADA

None


\* \* \* \* \*

# GUATEMALA

**Guatemala—United States**
  (1) Exchanges of Notes concerning transfer of military equipment (1954, 1964)
  (2) Military Assistance Agreement (1955)

* * * * *

# GUINEA

**Guinea—China**
  Military Assistance Agreement

**Guinea—Liberia**
  Non-aggression and Mutual Defense Treaty (1979)

**Guinea—Sierra Leone**
  Defense Agreement (1971)
  Mutual Defense Pact (1981)

**Guinea—Union of Soviet Socialist Republics**
  Military Cooperation Agreement

**Guinea—United States**
  Exchanges of Notes concerning military assistance (1965)

* * * * *

# GUINEA-BISSAU

**Guinea-Bissau—Portugal**
  Military Assistance Agreement (1978)

**Guinea-Bissau—Union of Soviet Socialist Republics**
  Military Cooperation Agreement

* * * * *

# GUYANA

**Guyana—United States**
  Exchanges of Notes concerning provision of military training (1981)

* * * * *

# HAITI

**Haiti—United States**
(1) Exchanges of Notes concerning transfer of military equipment (1960)
(2) Military Assistance Agreement (1975)

\* \* \* \* \*

# HONDURAS

**Honduras—United States**
(1) Military Assistance Agreement (1954, 1982)
(2) Exchanges of Notes concerning U.S. military assistance advisory group (1956)
(3) Military Assistance Agreement (1962)

\* \* \* \* \*

# HONG KONG

None

\* \* \* \* \*

# HUNGARY

**Hungary—Bulgaria**
Treaty of Friendship, Cooperation and Mutual Assistance (1948, 1969)

**Hungary—Czechoslovakia**
Treaty of Friendship, Cooperation and Mutual Assistance (1968)

**Hungary—German Democratic Republic**
Treaty of Friendship, Cooperation and Mutual Assistance (1967)

**Hungary—Poland**
Treaty of Friendship, Cooperation and Mutual Assistance (1948, 1968)

**Hungary—Romania**
Treaty of Friendship, Cooperation and Mutual Assistance (1972)

**Hungary—Union of Soviet Socialist Republics**
Treaty of Friendship, Cooperation and Mutual Assistance (1967)

**Hungary—People's Democratic Republic of Yemen**
Treaty of Friendship, Cooperation and Mutual Assistance (1964)

\* \* \* \* \*

# ICELAND

**Iceland—United States**
    (1) Defense Agreement (pursuant to NATO) (1951, 1974)
    (2) Exchanges of Notes concerning stationing of troops, U.S. use of bases and facilities and setting up of Iceland Defense Standing Group (1956)

\* \* \* \* \*

# INDIA

**India—Union of Soviet Socialist Republics**
    Treaty of Friendship, Cooperation and Mutual Assistance (1971)

**India—United States**
    (1) Exchanges of Notes concerning transfer of Military supplies and equipment (1951, 1962)
    (2) Exchanges of Notes concerning military assistance (1965)

\* \* \* \* \*

# INDONESIA

**Indonesia—United States**
    (1) Exchanges of Notes concerning military assistance program (1950)
    (2) Exchanges of Notes concerning military sales (1958)
    (3) Exchanges of Notes concerning the furnishing of military equipment (1967, 1970)
    (4) Exchanges of Notes concerning U.S. provision of pilot training (1969)

\* \* \* \* \*

# IRAN

**Iran—United States**
    (1) Exchanges of Notes concerning mutual defense assistance agreement (1950, 1952)
    (2) Exchanges of Notes concerning safeguarding of classified information (1974)
    (3) Agreement concerning the furnishing of certain federal catalogue data and cataloging services to Iran (1975)

\* \* \* \* \*

# IRAQ

**Iraq—Jordan**
Defense Agreement (1981)

**Iraq—Union of Soviet Socialist Republics**
(1) Treaty of Friendship, Cooperation and Mutual Assistance (1972)
(2) Arms Supply Agreement (1978)

\* \* \* \* \*

# IRELAND

None

\* \* \* \* \*

# ISRAEL

**Israel—Egypt**
(1) Sinai Force Separation Agreement (1975)
(2) Peace Treaty (1979)

**Israel—Lebanon**
Security Agreement (1983, pending implementation)

**Israel—United States**
(1) Mutual Defense Assistance Agreement (1952)
(2) Exchanges of Notes concerning general procurement arrangements for goods and services (1965)
(3) Exchanges of Notes concerning purchase from Israel of goods for U.S. Navy ships' stores overseas (1965)
(4) Agreement concerning payment of tooling costs of accelerated production of M-60 A1 tanks (1975)
(5) Memorandum of Understanding concerning mutual cooperation in research, development, production, procurement and logistic support of selected defense equipment (1979)
(6) Agreement concerning construction of airbases (1979)
(7) Memorandum of Understanding concerning assurances, consultations and U.S. policy on matters relating to Middle East peace (1975)
(8) Memorandum of Understanding concerning U.S. role at any future Geneva peace conference (1975)
(9) Memorandum of Understanding concerning assurances concerning Middle East peace (1979)
(10) Letter concerning implementation of Egypt-Israel peace treaty (1979)
(11) Agreement concerning U.S. personnel of Multinational Force and Observers in Israel (1982)

\* \* \* \* \*

# ITALY

**Italy—Malta**
Agreement protecting the neutrality of Malta (1980)

**Italy—United States**
(1) Exchanges of Notes concerning mutual defense assistance (1950)
(2) Agreement concerning the use of facilities in Italy (1956)
(3) Exchanges of Notes concerning weapons production (1960)
(4) Exchanges of Notes concerning the safeguarding of classified information (1964)
(5) Memorandum of Understanding on mutual cooperation in the research, development, production and procurement of defense materials (1978)

\* \* \* \* \*

# IVORY COAST

**Ivory Coast—France**
Defense Agreement

\* \* \* \* \*

# JAMAICA

**Jamaica—United States**
Exchanges of Notes concerning the furnishing of defense articles and services (1963)

\* \* \* \* \*

# JAPAN

**Japan—United States**
(1) Mutual Defense Assistance Agreement (1954)
(2) Exchanges of Notes concerning revision of 1954 agreement (1960)
(3) Exchanges of Notes concerning transfer of military equipment (1954)
(4) Exchanges of Notes concerning the furnishing of military equipment (1955)
(5) Exchanges of Notes concerning aircraft production (1955, 1960, 1969, 1972, 1977, 1978)
(6) Exchanges of Notes concerning cost-sharing in weapons production (1958, 1963, 1964, 1965)
(7) Treaty of Mutual Cooperation and Security (1960, 1970)
(8) Agreement under 1960 Treaty concerning facilities and status of U.S. forces in Japan (1960)
(9) Exchanges of Notes concerning weapons production (1967, 1972, 1977)
(10) Exchanges of Notes concerning change in name of Military Assistance Advisory Group to Mutual Defense Assistance Office (1969)

\* \* \* \* \*

# JORDAN

**Jordan—Iraq**
Defense Agreement (1981)

**Jordan—Saudi Arabia**
Military Cooperation Agreement (1962)

**Jordan—United States**
Exchanges of Notes concerning the furnishing of defense articles and services (1976, 1979, 1980, 1982)

\* \* \* \* \*

# KAMPUCHEA

**Kampuchea—German Democratic Republic**
Treaty of Friendship, Cooperation and Mutual Assistance (1980)

**Kampuchea—Vietnam**
Series of agreements containing military provisions and border pact (1979)

\* \* \* \* \*

# KENYA

**Kenya—Ethiopia**
(1) Treaty of Friendship, Cooperation and Mutual Assistance (1979)
(2) Defense Agreement for mutual aid (1963)

**Kenya—United Kingdom**
Overflight, training and defense agreements

**Kenya—United States**
(1) Mutual Defense Assistance Agreement (1980)
(2) Agreement for consultation and expanded relations concerning security assistance (1980)

\* \* \* \* \*

# KIRIBATI

None

\* \* \* \* \*

# DEMOCRATIC PEOPLE'S REPUBLIC OF KOREA (North Korea)

**Democratic People's Republic of Korea—Togo**
Treaty of Friendship, Cooperation and Mutual Assistance (1981)

**Democratic People's Republic of Korea—Union of Soviet Socialist Republics**
Treaty of Friendship, Cooperation and Mutual Assistance (1961)

\* \* \* \* \*

# REPUBLIC OF KOREA (South Korea)

**Republic of Korea—United States**
  (1) Mutual Defense Assistance Agreement (1950)
  (2) Mutual Defense Treaty (1954)
  (3) Agreed minute concerning continued economic and military cooperation (1954, 1962)
  (4) Exchanges of Notes concerning establishment of facilities (1955)
  (5) Agreement under Mutual Defense Treaty of 1954 concerning facilities and status of United States forces in Korea
     (1966)
  (6) Memorandum of Agreement concerning conventional ammunitions logistics (1974)
  (7) Memorandum of Understanding concerning weapons production (1971, 1976, 1977)
  (8) Memorandum of Understanding concerning construction of Tactical Air Control Center (1981)
  (9) Memorandum of Understanding concerning pre-positioning of equipment (1981)
(10) Memorandum of Understanding concerning construction of facilities (1982)

\* \* \* \* \*

# KUWAIT

**Kuwait—United States**
  (1) Exchanges of Notes concerning procurement of defense articles and services and establishment of U.S. Liaison Officer in Kuwait (1975)
  (2) Technical security arrangement (1976, 1977)

\* \* \* \* \*

# LAOS

**Laos—Bulgaria**
Treaty of Friendship, Cooperation and Mutual Assistance (1979)

**Laos—Czechoslovakia**
Treaty of Friendship, Cooperation and Mutual Assistance (1980)

**Laos—Vietnam**
Series of agreements containing military provisions and border pact (1977)

\* \* \* \* \*

# LEBANON

**Lebanon—France**
Arms Supply Agreement

**Lebanon—Israel**
Security agreement (1983, pending implementation)

**Lebanon—United States**
(1) Exchanges of Notes concerning military assistance (1957, 1958)
(2) Exchanges of Notes concerning U.S. participation in Multinational Force in Beirut (1982, 1982)

\* \* \* \* \*

# LESOTHO

None

\* \* \* \* \*

# LIBERIA

**Liberia—Guinea**
Non-Aggression and Mutual Defense Treaty (1979)

**Liberia—United States**
(1) Exchanges of Notes concerning mutual defense assistance (1951, 1958)
(2) Agreement of Cooperation (1959)
(3) Exchanges of Notes concerning the furnishing of military equipment (1961, 1962)
(4) Exchanges of Notes concerning transfer of the port of Monrovia to Liberia (1964)
(5) Mutual Defense Assistance Agreement (1972)

\* \* \* \* \*

# LIBYA

**Libya—Algeria**
Defense Agreement (1975)

**Libya—France**
Arms Supply Agreement

**Libya—Niger**
Defense and Security Treaty (1974)

**Libya—Togo**
Mutual Defense and Assistance Treaty (1976)

\* \* \* \* \*

# LIECHTENSTEIN

None

\* \* \* \* \*

# LUXEMBOURG

**Luxembourg—United States**
    (1)  Mutual Defense Assistance Agreement (1950)
    (2)  Agreement concerning general security of military information (1981)
    (3)  Memorandum of Understanding concerning reciprocal defense procurement (1982)

\* \* \* \* \*

# MADAGASCAR

**Madagascar—France**
    Defense and/or military cooperation agreements (1960, 1973)

\* \* \* \* \*

# MALAWI

**Malawi—United States**
    Exchanges of Notes concerning the provision of military training (1980)

\* \* \* \* \*

# MALAYSIA

**Malaysia—United States**
    (1)  Exchanges of Notes concerning the purchase of military equipment and services (1958)
    (2)  Agreement relating to eligibility for U.S. military assistance and training (1977)

\* \* \* \* \*

# MALDIVES

None

* * * * *

# MALI

**Mali—People's Republic of China**
Military Assistance Agreement

**Mali—Nigeria**
Treaty of Friendship, Cooperation and Mutual Assistance (1973)

**Mali—Union of Soviet Socialist Republics**
Arms Supply Agreement, including Soviet advisors to modernize Mali's armed forces (1976)

**Mali—United States**
(1) Exchanges of Notes concerning military assistance agreement (1961)
(2) Exchanges of Notes concerning mutual defense and assistance (1972)

* * * * *

# MALTA

**Malta—Italy**
Agreement concerning protecting the neutrality of Malta (1980)

**Malta—United Kingdom**
Mutual Defense and Assistance Agreement (1964, 1966)

* * * * *

# MAURITIUS

**Mauritius—United Kingdom**
Mutual Defense and Assistance Agreement (1968)

* * * * *

# MAURITANIA

**Mauritania—France**
Defense Agreement

* * * * *

# MEXICO

**Mexico—United States**
Agreement relating to the deposit by Mexico of ten percent of the value of military training scholarships provided by the U.S. (1972)

\* \* \* \* \*

# MONACO

**Monaco—France**
Agreement between relief and civil defense services concerning mutual assistance (1970)

\* \* \* \* \*

# MONGOLIA

**Mongolia—Bulgaria**
Treaty of Friendship, Cooperation and Mutual Assistance (1967)

**Mongolia—Union of Soviet Socialist Republics**
Treaty of Friendship, Cooperation and Mutual Assistance (1966)

\* \* \* \* \*

# MOROCCO

**Morocco—France**
Arms Supply Agreement

**Morocco—United States**
Exchanges of Notes concerning use of bases (1982)

\* \* \* \* \*

# MOZAMBIQUE

**Mozambique—Tanzania**
Defense Agreement (1976)

**Mozambique—Union of Soviet Socialist Republics**
Treaty of Friendship, Cooperation and Mutual Assistance (1977)

**Mozambique—Zimbabwe**
Agreement on joint military action against Mozambique rebels (1980)

\* \* \* \* \*

# NAURU

None

* * * * *

# NEPAL

None

* * * * *

# NETHERLANDS

**Netherlands—United States**
   (1) Mutual Defense Assistance Agreement (1950)
   (2) Stationing of U.S. forces agreement (1954)
   (3) Exchanges of Notes concerning establishment of Air Defense Technical Center (1954)
   (4) Exchanges of Notes concerning weapons production (1960)
   (5) General arrangements concerning coproduction of M109 vehicle (1966, 1969, 1979)
   (6) Memorandum of Understanding concerning mutual cooperation in research, development, production and procurement of conventional defense equipment (1978)
   (7) Exchanges of Notes concerning pre-positioning of equipment (1981)
   (8) Exchanges of Notes concerning establishment of transmitter at Soesterberg Airfield (1982)

* * * * *

# NETHERLANDS ANTILLES

None

* * * * *

# NEW ZEALAND

**New Zealand—Australia**
(1) ANZAC Agreement concerning joint policy, including defense, in the South West Pacific
(2) Agreement concerning integration of defense planning and equipment (1969)

**New Zealand—United States**
(1) Exchanges of Notes concerning mutual defense assistance (1952, 1960)
(2) Exchanges of Notes concerning reciprocal support of armed forces in specific circumstances (1969)
(3) Memorandum of Understanding concerning Communications Center support for Royal New Zealand Air Force, Orion Modernization Unit (1981)
(4) Memorandum of Understanding concerning logistic support (1982)

\* \* \* \* \*

# NICARAGUA

**Nicaragua—France**
Arms supplies and sales agreement

**Nicaragua—United States**
(1) Military Assistance Agreement (1954)
(2) Exchanges of Notes concerning military advisory group mission (1957)
(3) Military Assistance Agreement (1972)

\* \* \* \* \*

# NIGER

**Niger—France**
Defense Agreement

**Niger—Libya**
Defense and Security Treaty (1974)

**Niger—United States**
(1) Exchanges of Notes concerning the furnishing of military equipment and services (1962)
(2) Exchanges of Notes concerning the provision of military training (1980)

\* \* \* \* \*

# NIGERIA

**Nigeria—Chad**
Treaty of Friendship, Cooperation and Mutual Assistance (1972)

**Nigeria—Mali**
Treaty of Friendship, Cooperation and Mutual Assistance (1973)

**Nigeria—United States**
Military Assistance Agreement (1972)

\* \* \* \* \*

# NORWAY

**Norway—United States**
  (1) Mutual Defense Assistance Agreement (1950, amended 1966, 1975)
  (2) Exchanges of Notes concerning status of military advisory group under Status of Forces Agreement (1954)
  (3) Exchanges of Notes concerning weapons production program (1960)
  (4) Agreement concerning coproduction of M109A vehicle (1966, 1976)
  (5) Exchanges of Notes concerning the safeguarding of classified information (1970)
  (6) Memorandum of Understanding concerning mutual cooperation in research, development, production and procurement of defense equipment (1978)
  (7) Memorandum of Understanding concerning pre-positioning of equipment and the reinforcement of Norway (1981)
  (8) Agreement concerning mutual logistic support (1982)

\* \* \* \* \*

# OMAN

**Oman—United States**
  Agreement concerning cooperation in economic development, trade and security—including use of Salalah and Masirah bases and joint training exercises (1981)

\* \* \* \* \*

# PAKISTAN

**Pakistan—China**
  Border Pact (1963, 1965)

**Pakistan—India**
  Simla Agreement concerning withdrawal of armed forces after Bangladesh war and respect of the line of control in Jammu and Kashmir (1972)

**Pakistan—Turkey**
  Arms manufacturing agreement (1981)

**Pakistan—United States**
  (1) Exchanges of Notes concerning the transfer of military supplies and equipment (1950)
  (2) Mutual Defense Assistance Agreement (1954)
  (3) Defense Support Assistance Agreement (1955, 1961)
  (4) Construction agreement (1956)
  (5) Agreement of Cooperation (1959)
  (6) Exchanges of Notes concerning general security of military information (1982)

\* \* \* \* \*

# PANAMA

**Panama—United States**
    (1) Canal Zone treaty (1903, renegotiated 1977, in force 1979)
    (2) Exchanges of Notes concerning the sale of military supplies and services (1959)
    (3) Exchanges of Notes concerning the furnishing of defense equipment to Panama for internal security (1962)
    (4) Military Assistance Agreement (1972)
    (5) Exchanges of Notes concerning economic and military cooperation (1978)

\* \* \* \* \*

# PAPUA NEW GUINEA

None

\* \* \* \* \*

# PARAGUAY

**Paraguay—United States**
    (1) Exchanges of Notes concerning the furnishing of assistance to the Paraguayan Air Force (1962)
    (2) Exchanges of Notes concerning assistance for road construction to the Paraguayan Army (1964)
    (3) Exchanges of Notes concerning military assistance (1966)

\* \* \* \* \*

# PERU

**Peru—United States**
    (1) Military Assistance Agreement (1952)
    (2) Exchanges of Notes concerning military mission of duties (1955)
    (3) Exchanges of Notes concerning the furnishing of defense equipment and services
    (4) Military Assistance Agreement (1972)

\* \* \* \* \*

# PHILIPPINES

**Philippines—United States**
- (1) Agreements concerning military bases (1947, amended 1947, 1948, 1953, 1965, 1966, 1971, 1979)
- (2) Mutual Defense Treaty (1951)
- (3) Exchanges of Notes concerning military assistance (1953, 1955, 1956, 1957, 1958)
- (4) Exchanges of Notes concerning joint use of Manilla Air Station (1959)
- (5) Exchanges of Notes concerning establishment of Mutual Defense Board and assignment of Philippine military liaison officers to U.S. bases in Philippines (1958)
- (6) Exchanges of Notes concerning transfer of entire Manila Air Station to Philippines (1958)
- (7) Exchanges of Notes concerning establishment of a communications facility at Mt. Cabyao (1965)
- (8) Exchanges of Notes concerning the grant of defense articles and services (1979, 1980, 1981, 1982)
- (9) Memorandum of Understanding concerning exchange of military personnel between U.S. Army Western Command and Armed Forces of the Philippines (1981)

* * * * *

# POLAND

**Poland—Bulgaria**
Treaty of Friendship, Cooperation and Mutual Assistance (1967)

**Poland—Czechoslovakia**
Treaty of Friendship, Cooperation and Mutual Assistance (1947, 1967)

**Poland—Ethiopia**
Treaty of Friendship, Cooperation and Mutual Assistance (1979)

**Poland—German Democratic Republic**
Treaty of Friendship, Cooperation and Mutual Assistance (1967)

**Poland—Hungary**
Treaty of Friendship, Cooperation and Mutual Assistance (1948, 1961)

**Poland—Romania**
Treaty of Friendship, Cooperation and Mutual Assistance (1970)

**Poland—Union of Soviet Socialist Republics**
Stationing of forces agreement (1956)
Treaty of Friendship, Cooperation and Mutual Assistance (1965)

* * * * *

# PORTUGAL

**Portugal—Guinea-Bissau**
Military Assistance Agreement (1978)

**Portugal—United States**
(1) Mutual Defense Assistance Agreement (1951)
(2) Defense Agreement concerning Azores air base (1951, 1957, 1971, 1979)
(3) Exchanges of Notes concerning weapons production program (1960)
(4) Memorandum of Understanding concerning mutual cooperation in research, development, production, procurement and logistic support of defense equipment (1979)
(5) Exchanges of Notes concerning the grant of defense articles and services (1979, 1980, 1981, 1982)
(6) Exchanges of Notes concerning general security of military information (1982)

\* \* \* \* \*

# QATAR

**Qatar—United Kingdom**
Treaty of Friendship (1971)

\* \* \* \* \*

# ROMANIA

**Romania—Angola**
Treaty of Friendship, Cooperation and Mutual Assistance (1978)

**Romania—Bulgaria**
Treaty of Friendship, Cooperation and Mutual Assistance (1970)

**Romania—Burundi**
Treaty of Friendship, Cooperation and Mutual Assistance (1970)

**Romania—Czechoslovakia**
Treaty of Friendship, Cooperation and Mutual Assistance (1968)

**Romania—Gabon**
Treaty of Friendship, Cooperation and Mutual Assistance (1979)

**Romania—German Democratic Republic**
Treaty of Friendship, Cooperation and Mutual Assistance (1972)

**Romania—Hungary**
Treaty of Friendship, Cooperation and Mutual Assistance (1972)

**Romania—Kampuchea**
Treaty of Friendship, Cooperation and Mutual Assistance (1978)

**Romania—Mozambique**
Treaty of Friendship, Cooperation and Mutual Assistance (1979)

**Romania—Poland**
Treaty of Friendship, Cooperation and Mutual Assistance (1970)

**Romania—Sudan**
Treaty of Friendship, Cooperation and Mutual Assistance (1979)

**Romania—Union of Soviet Socialist Republics**
Treaty of Friendship, Cooperation and Mutual Assistance (1970)

**Romania—Vietnam**
Treaty of Friendship, Cooperation and Mutual Assistance (1978)

**Romania—Zaire**
Treaty of Friendship, Cooperation and Mutual Assistance (1980)

**Romania—Zambia**
Treaty of Friendship, Cooperation and Mutual Assistance (1979)

\* \* \* \* \*

# RWANDA

**Rwanda—United States**
Exchanges of Notes concerning the provision of military training (1980)

\* \* \* \* \*

# ST. CHRISTOPHER-NEVIS (ST. KITTS)

None

\* \* \* \* \*

# ST. LUCIA

**St. Lucia—United States**
Exchanges of Notes concerning the provision of military training (1981)

\* \* \* \* \*

# ST. VINCENT AND THE GRENADINES

**St. Vincent—United States**
Exchanges of Notes concerning the provision of military training (1981)

\* \* \* \* \*

# SÃO TOMÉ AND PRINCIPE

None

* * * * *

# SAUDI ARABIA

**Saudi Arabia—United States**
(1) Exchanges of Notes concerning the transfer of military supplies (1951)
(2) Exchanges of Notes concerning military advisory group (1953)
(3) Exchanges of Notes concerning construction of military facilities (1965, 1978, 1981, 1982)
(4) Exchanges of Notes concerning transfer of military aircraft (1965)
(5) Memorandum of Understanding concerning Saudi National Guard  modernization (1973)
(6) Agreement of economic, technical, industrial and defense cooperation (1974)
(7) Exchanges of Notes concerning the provision of military training (1977)

* * * * *

# SENEGAL

**Senegal—France**
Treaty of Friendship and Cooperation, including a military agreement providing for the transfer to Senegal of the French base at Dakas, with France retaining certain facilities, and the phased reduction of French forces (1974)

**Senegal—Gambia**
Senegambia Confederation (1982)

**Senegal—United States**
Exchanges of Notes concerning the furnishing of military supplies and services (1962)

* * * * *

# SEYCHELLES

None

* * * * *

# SIERRA LEONE

**Sierra Leone—Guinea**
Defense Agreement (1971)
Mutual Defense Pact (1981)

**Sierra Leone—United States**
Exchanges of Notes concerning the provision of military training (1982)

\* \* \* \* \*

# SINGAPORE

**Singapore—United States**
(1) Exchanges of Notes concerning the establishment of U.S. Air Force management training assistance team (1977)
(2) Memorandum of Understanding for the exchange of military personnel (1981, 1982)
(3) Exchanges of Notes concerning the provision of military training (1981)

\* \* \* \* \*

# SOLOMAN ISLANDS

None

\* \* \* \* \*

# SOMALIA

**Somalia—Union of Soviet Socialist Republics**
Treaty of Friendship, Cooperation and Mutual Assistance (1974)

**Somalia—United States**
(1) Exchanges of Notes concerning the furnishing of defense articles and services (1978)
(2) Agreement concerning military sales and U.S. use of Berbera base, an airstrip in the north and port facilities in Mogadishu
(3) Exchanges of Notes concerning the provision of military training (1981)

\* \* \* \* \*

# SOUTH AFRICA

**South Africa—United States**
Exchanges of Notes concerning mutual defense assistance (1951)

\* \* \* \* \*

# SPAIN

**Spain—United States**
    (1) Mutual Defense Assistance Agreement (1953)
    (2) Exchanges of Notes concerning arrangements for facilities (1954, 1955, 1956)
    (3) Declaration of Principles concerning continued defense cooperation within NATO framework (1974)
    (4) Treaty of Friendship and Cooperation, including U.S. use of bases (1976)
    (5) Exchanges of Notes concerning the grant of defense articles and services (1979, 1981)
    (6) Agreement concerning master data exchange for mutual development of weapons (1980)
    (7) Memorandum of Understanding concerning installation of a satellite ground terminal in Spain (1982)

\* \* \* \* \*

# SRI LANKA

**Sri Lanka—United Kingdom**
    Defense Agreement (1947)

**Sri Lanka—United States**
    Exchanges of Notes concerning military sales (1956)

\* \* \* \* \*

# SUDAN

**Sudan—China**
    Treaty of Friendship, Cooperation and Mutual Assistance (1982)

**Sudan—Egypt**
    Agreement of mutual defense (the authority for a "Joint Defense Council" and joint exercises) (1977)

**Sudan—Uganda**
    Mutual Defense Assistance Agreement (1972)

**Sudan—United States**
    (1) Military Assistance Agreement (1973)
    (2) Exchanges of Notes concerning mutual defense assistance agreement (1981)
    (3) Exchanges of Notes concerning the status of U.S. personnel in Sudan (1981)
    (4) Exchanges in Notes concerning the grant of defense articles and services (1981, 1982)

\* \* \* \* \*

# SURINAME

**Suriname—United States**
    Exchanges of Notes concerning the provision of military training (1980)

\* \* \* \* \*

# SWAZILAND

None

\* \* \* \* \*

# SWEDEN

**Sweden—United States**
   (1) Exchanges of Notes concerning the procurement of military equipment (1952)
   (2) Exchanges of Notes concerning general security of military information (1981)

\* \* \* \* \*

# SWITZERLAND

None

\* \* \* \* \*

# SYRIA

**Syria—Union of Soviet Socialist Republics**
   Treaty of Friendship, Cooperation and Mutual Assistance (1980)

# TAIWAN

None

\* \* \* \* \*

# TANZANIA

**Tanzania—China**
Military Assistance Agreement

**Tanzania—Mozambique**
Defense Agreement (1976)

**Tanzania—Uganda**
Defense Pact (1981)

\* \* \* \* \*

# THAILAND

**Thailand—United States**
(1) Military Assistance Agreement (1950, 1975)
(2) Memorandum of Understanding concerning pre-positioning of military stocks (1977)
(3) Memorandum of Understanding concerning integrated communications system (1977)

\* \* \* \* \*

# TOGO

**Togo—France**
Defense Agreement (1963)

**Togo—Libya**
Treaty of Mutual Defense and Assistance (1976)

**Togo—North Korea**
Treaty of Friendship, Cooperation and Mutual Assistance (1981)

**Togo—United States**
Exchanges of Notes concerning the provision of military training (1980)

\* \* \* \* \*

# TONGA

None

\* \* \* \* \*

# TRINADAD AND TOBAGO

**Trinadad and Tobago—United States**
Exchanges of Notes concerning use of the Five Islands (1954)

\* \* \* \* \*

# TUNISIA

**Tunisia—France**
Arms Supply Agreement

**Tunisia—United States**
(1)  Exchanges of Notes concerning military assistance (1974)
(2)  Strategic cooperation agreement (1981)

\* \* \* \* \*

# TURKEY

**Turkey—Pakistan**
Agreement to cooperate in arms and equipment manufacturing (1981)

**Turkey—United States**
(1)  Stationing of Forces Agreement (1954)
(2)  Mutual Defense Assistance program (1955, 1962)
(3)  Agreement of Cooperation (1959)
(4)  Exchanges of Notes concerning introduction of modern weapons into NATO forces in Turkey (1959)
(5)  Exchanges of Notes concerning establishment of facilities (1959)
(6)  Exchanges of Notes concerning weapons production (1960)
(7)  Military Assistance Agreement (1974)
(8)  Exchanges of Notes concerning the grant of defense articles and services (1979, 1980)
(9)  Agreement concerning cooperation in defense and economy with supplementary agreements concerning defense support, industrial cooperation and installations (1980)
(10)  Agreement concerning U.S. use of Turkish airfields (1982)

\* \* \* \* \*

# TUVALU

None

\* \* \* \* \*

# UGANDA

**Uganda—Soviet Union**
Arms Supply Agreement (1976)

**Uganda—Sudan**
Mutual Defense Assistance Agreement (1972)

**Uganda—Tanzania**
Defense Pact (1981)

\* \* \* \* \*

# UNION OF SOVIET SOCIALIST REPUBLICS (Soviet Union)

**Union of Soviet Socialist Republics—Angola**
Treaty of Friendship, Cooperation and Mutual Assistance (1976)

**Union of Soviet Socialist Republics—Afghanistan**
Stationing of Forces Agreement (1980)

**Union of Soviet Socialist Republics—Bulgaria**
Treaty of Friendship, Cooperation and Mutual Assistance (1967)

**Union of Soviet Socialist Republics—Czechoslovakia**
(1) Agreement of the stationing of troops (1968)
(2) Treaty of Friendship, Cooperation and Mutual Assistance (1970)

**Union of Soviet Socialist Republics—Ethiopia**
(1) Arms Supply Agreement (1977)
(2) Treaty of Friendship, Cooperation and Mutual Assistance (1978)
(3) Agreement concerning base on Dahlok Island

**Union of Soviet Socialist Republics—Finland**
(1) Paris Peace Treaty (restricting the size and armament to armed forces of Finland) (1947)
(2) Treaty of Friendship, Cooperation and Mutual Assistance (1948, 1955, 1970)

**Union of Soviet Socialist Republics—German Democratic Republic**
(1) Stationing of Forces Agreement (1957)
(2) Agreement concerning the stationing of troops (1957)
(3) Treaty of Friendship, Cooperation and Mutual Assistance (1964, 1975)

**Union of Soviet Socialist Republics—Ghana**
Treaty of Friendship, Cooperation and Mutual Assistance (1965)

**Union of Soviet Socialist Republics—Guinea**
Treaty of Friendship, Cooperation and Mutual Assistance

**Union of Soviet Socialist Republics—Guinea-Bissau**
Treaty of Friendship, Cooperation and Mutual Assistance

**Union of Soviet Socialist Republics—Hungary**
(1) Agreement concerning the stationing of troops (1957)
(2) Treaty of Friendship, Cooperation and Mutual Assistance (1967)

**Union of Soviet Socialist Republics—India**
Treaty of Friendship, Cooperation and Mutual Assistance (1971)

**Union of Soviet Socialist Republics—Iraq**
(1) Treaty of Friendship, Cooperation and Mutual Assistance (1972)
(2) Arms Supply Agreement (1978)

**Union of Soviet Socialist Republics—Democratic People's Republic of Korea**
Treaty of Friendship, Cooperation and Mutual Assistance (1961)

**Union of Soviet Socialist Republics—Libya**
(1) Arms Supply Agreements (1975)
(2) Agreement of Cooperation on the peaceful use of atomic energy (1975)

**Union of Soviet Socialist Republics—Mali**
Arms Supply Agreement, including experts to modernize Mali's armed forces (1976)

**Union of Soviet Socialist Republics—Mongolia**
Treaty of Friendship, Cooperation and Mutual Assistance (1966)

**Union of Soviet Socialist Republics—Mozambique**
Treaty of Friendship, Cooperation and Mutual Assistance (1977)

**Union of Soviet Socialist Republics—Poland**
Stationing of Forces Agreement (1956)

**Union of Soviet Socialist Republics—Romania**
(1) Agreement concerning the stationing of troops (1957)
(2) Treaty of Friendship, Cooperation and Mutual Assistance (1970)

**Union of Soviet Socialist Republics—People's Democratic Republic of Yemen**
(1) Treaty of Friendship, Cooperation and Mutual Assistance (1979)
(2) Agreement concerning naval base at Aden

**Union of Soviet Socialist Republics—Syria**
(1) Arms Supply Agreements (1979)
(2) Treaty of Friendship, Cooperation and Mutual Assistance (1980)

**Union of Soviet Socialist Republics—Uganda**
Arms Supply Agreement (1975)

**Union of Soviet Socialist Republics—United States**
(1) Memorandum of Understanding concerning establishment of direct communications link, or "Hot Line", for use in emergency (1973)
(2) Agreement concerning measures to reduce the risk of outbreak of nuclear war by accidental or unauthorized use of nuclear weapons, provision for immediate notification should an accident occur, and advanced notification of any planned missile launches (1971)
(3) Agreement concerning "Hot Line" modernization and improvement (1971, 1975)
(4) Treaty on the Limitation of Anti-Ballistic Missile Systems, leaving unchallenged the penetration capability of retaliatory missile forces (1972)
(5) Interim Agreement concerning certain measures with respect to the limitations of strategic offensive arms, plus Protocol (1972)
(6) Agreement concerning the Prevention of Nuclear War (1973)
(7) Threshold Test Ban Treaty, concerning the limitation of underground nuclear weapons tests, plus Protocol (1974)*
(8) Protocol to the 1972 Treaty on the Limitations of ABM systems, permitting each side to only one ABM deployment site (1974)
(9) Peaceful Nuclear Treaty, concerning underground nuclear explosions for peaceful purposes, and Protocol (1976)*
(10) Agreement of Cooperation on the exploration and use of outer space for peaceful purposes (1977)
(11) Treaty on the Limitation of Strategic Offensive Arms, plus Protocol, a Joint Statement of Principles and a Memorandum of Understanding concerning the establishment of a data base (SALT II), signed 1979*
*NOTE: Although U.S. Senate consent has not been given, both sides have declared that they would not jeopardize these treaties as long as the other side continues to abide by them.

**Union of Soviet Socialist Republics—Vietnam**
Treaty of Friendship, Cooperation and Mutual Assistance (1978)

**Union of Soviet Socialist Republics—Zambia**
Treaty of Friendship, Cooperation and Mutual Assistance

* * * * *

# UNITED ARAB EMIRATES

**United Arab Emirates—United Kingdom**
Treaty of Friendship (1971)

**United Arab Emirates—United States**
Exchanges of Notes concerning the sale of defense articles and services (1975)

\* \* \* \* \*

# UNITED KINGDOM

**United Kingdom—Bahrain**
Treaty of Friendship (1971)

**United Kingdom—Finland**
Paris Peace Treaty (restricting the size and armament of the armed forces of Finland) (1947)

**United Kingdom—Kenya**
Overflight training and defense agreement (1964)

**United Kingdom—Mauritius**
Mutual Defense and Assistance Agreement (1968)

**United Kingdom—Qatar**
Treaty of Friendship (1971)

**United Kingdom—Singapore**
Assistance Agreement (1971, amended 1978)

**United Kingdom—Sri Lanka**
Defense Agreement (1947)

**United Kingdom—United Arab Emirates**
Treaty of Friendship (1971)

**United Kingdom—United States**
(1) Exchanges of Notes concerning naval and air bases (1940)
(2) Protocol concerning defense of Newfoundland (1941)
(3) Agreement concerning leased bases (1941, 1950, 1978)
(4) Mutual Defense Assistance Agreement (1950)
(5) Exchanges of Notes concerning U.S. supply of intermediate range ballistic missiles (1958)
(6) Agreement to cooperate in use of nuclear energy for mutual defense (1958, 1959, 1968, 1969, 1974)
(7) Exchanges of Notes concerning establishment of ballistic missile early warning station at Fylingdale's Moor (1960)
(8) Exchanges of Notes concerning establishment of defense alarm system in United Kingdom (1961)
(9) Exchanges of Notes concerning weapons production program (1962)
(10) Exchanges of Notes concerning use of Ascension Island airfield (1962, 1973)
(11) Sales agreement concerning Polaris (1963)
(12) Memorandum of Understanding concerning cooperation in research, development, production and procurement of defense equipment (1975)
(13) Exchanges of Notes concerning U.S. use and expansion of Diego Garcia in Indian Ocean (1976)
(14) Exchanges of Notes concerning U.S. Navy use of Anegada in British Virgin Islands
(15) Agreement concerning U.S. bases in Antigua (1977)
(16) Agreement concerning U.S. bases in Turks and Caicos Islands (1979)

\* \* \* \* \*

## UNITED STATES OF AMERICA

**United States—Antigua**
(1) "Status of Forces" Agreement concerning U.S. bases (1978)
(2) Agreement concerning provision of military training (1981)

**United States—Argentina**
(1) Military Assistance Agreement (1964)
(2) Agreement concerning armed forces cooperative projects (1970)

**United States—Australia**
(1) Mutual Defense Assistance Agreement (1951, 1963, 1974, 1980)
(2) Agreement concerning mutual weapons development program (1960)
(3) Agreement concerning U.S. naval stations (1963)
(4) Agreement concerning joint defense space research facility (1966, 1977)
(5) Agreement concerning establishment of joint defense space communication facility (1969)
(6) Agreement on joint operation of U.S. naval communications station (1974)
(7) Agreement concerning exchange training program (1976)

**United States—Austria**
Exchanges of Notes concerning military sales (1957)

**United States—Bahamas**
Exchange of Notes concerning U.S. military rights in the Bahamas (1973)

**United States—Belgium**
(1) Mutual Defense Agreement (under NATO) (1950, 1968, 1969)
(2) Exchange of Notes concerning weapons production program (1960)
(3) Memorandum of Understanding concerning mutual cooperation in research, development, production, procurement and logistic support of defense equipment (1979)

**United States—Belize**
Agreement concerning provision of military training (1982)

**United States—Benin**
Military Assistance Agreement (1962)

**United States—Bermuda**
Agreement concerning leasing of bases (1941)

**United States—Bolivia**
(1) Military Assistance Agreement (1958)
(2) Agreement concerning furnishing of military equipment (1962)

**United States—Botswana**
Agreement concerning provision of military training (1980)

**United States—Brazil**
(1) Military Assistance Agreement (1952)
(2) Exchanges of Notes concerning military assistance (1964)
(3) Memorandum of Understanding concerning Brazilian acquisition of military aircraft (1973)

**United States—Burma**
Agreement concerning provision of military training (1980)

**United States—Cameroon**
Agreement concerning provision of military training (1980)

**United States—Canada**
(1) Ogdensburg declaration concerning creation of a Permanent Joint Board on Defense (1940—continued 1947)
(2) Protocol concerning defense of Newfoundland (1941)
(3) Exchanges of Notes concerning economic cooperation for defense (1950)
(4) Agreement concerning extension and coordination of continental radar defense system (1951)

(5) Agreement concerning establishment of early-warning stations in Canada (1955)
(6) Agreement for cooperation concerning atomic information for mutual defense (1955, 1959)
(7) Agreement providing for the creation of United States—Canadian Committee on Joint Defense (1958)
(8) Agreement concerning North American Air Defense Command (1958, 1968, 1973, 1975, 1981)
(9) Exchanges of Notes concerning establishment of integrated communications system to support ballistic missile early-warning system (1959)
(10) Agreement concerning placement in Canada short-range tactical air navigation facilities (1959)
(11) Agreement concerning establishment and operation of improved ground-to-air military communications facility in Canada (1965)
(12) Memorandum of understanding concerning NAVSTAR global positioning system, with annex (1978)
(13) Exchanges of Notes concerning the testing and evaluation of U.S. defense weapons systems in Canada (1983)

**United States—Chile**
Military Assistance Agreement (1952)

**United States—Colombia**
(1) Military Assistance Agreement (1952)
(2) Agreement concerning military advisors group (1955)
(3) Agreement concerning the furnishing of military supplies (1961)
(4) Agreement concerning general security of military information (1981)

**United States—Costa Rica**
Exchanges of Notes concerning military supplies and services (1962)

**United States—Cuba**
Agreement for the lease of Guantanamo Bay (1903, 1934)

**United States—Denmark**
(1) Mutual Defense Assistance (under NATO) (1950)
(2) Agreement concerning defense of Greenland (1951, 1960)
(3) Exchanges of Notes concerning weapons production program (1960)
(4) Memorandum of Understanding concerning mutual cooperation in research, development, production, procurement and logistic support of defense equipment (1980)
(5) Exchanges of Notes concerning general security of military information (1981)
(6) Mutual Logistical Support Agreement (1982)

**United States—Dominican Republic**
Military Assistance Agreement (1962)

**United States—Dominica**
Exchanges of Notes concerning provision of military training (1981)

**United States—Egypt**
(1) Exchanges of Notes concerning mutual defense assistance (1952)
(2) Exchanges of Notes concerning early-warning system in the Sinai (1975)
(3) Exchanges of Notes concerning military aid (1979, 1980)
(4) Memorandum of Understanding concerning Egyptian production of U.S. defense equipment (1979)
(5) Agreement concerning general security of military information (1982)

**United States—El Salvador**
Military Supply Agreement (1962)

**United States—Ethiopia**
Exchanges of Notes concerning mutual defense assistance (1952)

**United States—France**
(1) Mutual Defense Assistance Agreement (under NATO) (1950, 1958)
(2) Mutual Security Agreement (1952)
(3) Agreement concerning the U.S. use of French bases (1952)
(4) Exchanges of Notes concerning weapons production (1960)
(5) Agreement concerning general secrecy of military information (1977)

**United States—Federal Republic of Germany**
 (1) Mutual Defense Assistance Agreement (1955)
 (2) Exchanges of Notes concerning weapons production program (1960)
 (3) Memorandum of Understanding concerning development of an advanced surface-to-air missile (1976)
 (4) Agreement concerning the provision of military training (1977)
 (5) Memorandum of Understanding concerning the co-production of the Sidewinder AIM-9L Missile (1977)
 (6) Memorandum of Understanding concerning standardization and inter-operability of Army tactical data systems (1980)
 (7) Wartime Host Nation Support Agreement (1982)

**United States—Ghana**
 Mutual Defense Assistance Agreement (1950)

**United States—Greece**
 (1) Agreement concerning the use of military facilities (1953)
 (2) Status of Forces Agreement (1956)
 (3) Military Supplies Agreement (1979, 1982)
 (4) Exchanges of Notes concerning weapons production (1960)
 (5) Agreement concerning the status of personnel and establishment of a Joint Standing Committee (1972)

**United States—Guatemala**
 (1) Military Assistance Agreement (1955)
 (2) Exchanges of Notes concerning the transfer of military equipment (1962)

**United States—Guinea**
 Exchanges of Notes concerning assistance (1965)

**United States—Guyana**
 Exchanges of Notes concerning the provision of military training (1981)

**United States—Haiti**
 (1) Military Assistance Agreement (1955)
 (2) Exchanges of Notes concerning transfer of military equipment (1960)

**United States—Honduras**
 (1) Military Assistance Agreement (1954)
 (2) Exchanges of Notes concerning U.S. military assistance advisory group (1956)
 (3) Military Assistance Agreement (1960)

**United States—Iceland**
 (1) Defense Agreement pursuant to NATO (1951, 1974)
 (2) Agreement concerning the presence of forces, use of bases and establishment of the Iceland Defense Standing Committee (1956)

**United States—India**
 (1) Exchanges of Notes concerning transfer of military supplies and equipment (1951, 1962)
 (2) Exchange of Notes concerning military assistance (1965)

**United States—Indonesia**
 (1) Exchanges of Notes concerning military assistance program (1950)
 (2) Exchanges of Notes concerning military sales (1958)
 (3) Exchanges of Notes concerning the furnishing of military equipment (1967, 1970)
 (4) Exchanges of Notes concerning provision of pilot training (1969)

**United States—Iran**
 (1) Exchanges of Notes concerning mutual defense assistance agreement (1950, 1952)
 (2) Exchanges of Notes concerning the safeguarding of classified information (1974)
 (3) Agreement concerning the furnishing of certain federal catalog data and cataloging services to Iran (1975)

**United States—Israel**
 (1) Mutual Defense Assistance Agreement (1952)
 (2) Exchanges of Notes concerning general procurement arrangements for goods and services (1965)
 (3) Exchanges of Notes concerning purchase from Israel of goods for U.S. Navy ships stores overseas (1965)
 (4) Agreement concerning payment of tooling cost of accelerated production of the M-60 A1 tank (1975)

(5) Agreement concerning early-warning system in the Sinai (1975)
(6) Memorandum of Understanding concerning mutual cooperation in research, development, production, procurement and logistic support of selected defense equipment (1979)
(7) Agreement concerning construction of airbases (1979)
(8) Agreement concerning financing of airbases (1979)
(9) Memorandum of Understanding concerning assurances, consultation and U.S. policy on matters relating to Middle East peace (1975)
(10) Memorandum of Understanding concerning U.S. role at any future Geneva peace conference (1975)
(11) Memorandum of Understanding concerning assurances concerning Middle East peace (1979)
(12) Letter concerning implementation of Egypt—Israel peace treaty (1979)
(13) Agreement concerning U.S. personnel of the Multinational Force and Observers in Israel (1982)

**United States—Italy**
(1) Exchanges of Notes concerning mutual defense assistance (1950)
(2) Agreement concerning use of facilities in Italy (1955)
(3) Exchanges of Notes concerning weapons production (1960)
(4) Exchanges of Notes concerning the safeguarding of classified information (1964)
(5) Memorandum of Understanding concerning mutual cooperation in research, development, and procurement of defense material (1978)

**United States—Jamaica**
Exchanges of Notes concerning the furnishing of defense articles and services (1963)

**United States—Japan**
(1) Mutual Defense Assistance Agreement (1954)
(2) Exchanges of Notes concerning revision of Mutual Defense Assistance Agreement (1960)
(3) Exchanges of Notes concerning transfer of military equipment (1954)
(4) Exchanges of Notes concerning the furnishing of military equipment (1955)
(5) Exchanges of Notes concerning aircraft production (1955, 1960, 1969, 1972, 1977, 1978)
(6) Treaty of Mutual Cooperation and Security (1960, 1970)
(7) Agreement under (1960) treaty concerning facilities and status of U.S. forces in Japan (1960)
(8) Exchanges of Notes concerning cost-sharing of weapons production (1958, 1963, 1964, 1965)
(9) Exchanges of Notes concerning weapons production (1967, 1972, 1977)
(10) Exchange of Notes concerning change in name of Mutual Assistance Advisory Group to Mutual Defense Assistance Office pursuant to 1954 Mutual Defense Assistance Agreement (1969)

**United States—Jordan**
Exchanges of Notes concerning arms supplies (1974, 1979, 1980, 1982)

**United States—Kenya**
(1) Agreement for consultation and expanded relations concerning security assistance (1980)
(2) Mutual Defense Assistance Agreement (1980)

**United States—Republic of Korea**
(1) Mutual Defense Assistance Agreement (1950)
(2) Mutual Defense Treaty (1953, 1954)
(3) Agreed minute concerning configuration of economic and military cooperation (1954, 1962)
(4) Exchanges of Notes regarding establishment of facilities (1955)
(5) Agreement under Mutual Defense Treaty (1953) regarding facilities and status of U.S. forces in Korea (1966)
(6) Memorandum of Agreement concerning ammunition logistics (1974)
(7) Memorandum of Understanding concerning weapons production (1971, 1976, 1977)
(8) Memorandum of Understanding concerning construction of Tactical Air Control Center (1981)
(9) Memorandum of Understanding concerning pre-positioning of equipment (1981)
(10) Memorandum of Understanding regarding construction of facilities (1982)

**United States—Kuwait**
(1) Exchanges of Notes concerning procurement of defense articles and services and establishment of a U.S. liaison office (1975)
(2) Technical Security Arrangement (1976, 1977)

**United States—Lebanon**
(1) Exchanges of Notes concerning military assistance (1957, 1958)
(2) Exchanges of Notes concerning U.S. participation in multinational force in Beirut (1982, 1982)

**United States—Liberia**
(1) Exchange of Notes concerning mutual defense assistance (1951, 1958)
(2) Agreement of Cooperation (1959)
(3) Exchanges of Notes concerning the furnishing of military equipment (1961, 1962)
(4) Exchanges of Notes concerning transfer of Monrovia to Liberian jurisdiction (1964)
(5) Mutual Defense Assistance Agreement (1972)

**United States—Luxembourg**
(1) Mutual Defense Assistance Agreement (1950)
(2) Agreement concerning general security of military information (1981)
(3) Memorandum of Understanding on reciprocal defense procuremen' (1982)

**United States—Malawi**
Exchanges of Notes concerning the provision of military training (1980)

**United States—Malaysia**
Exchanges of Notes concerning the purchase of military equipment and services (1958)

**United States—Mali**
Exchanges of Notes concerning military assistance agreement (1961, 1972)

**United States—Mexico**
Agreement relating to the deposit by Mexico of ten percent of the value of military training scholarships provided by the U.S. (1972)

**United States—Morocco**
Exchanges of Notes concerning the use of bases (1982)

**United States—Netherlands**
(1) Mutual Defense Assistance Agreement (1950)
(2) Agreement concerning the stationing of U.S. forces (1954)
(3) Exchanges of Notes concerning the establishment of an air defense technical center (1954)
(4) Exchanges of Notes concerning weapons production program (1960)
(5) General arrangement concerning co-production of M-109 vehicle (1966, 1969, 1979)
(6) Memorandum of Understanding concerning mutual cooperation in research, development, production, and the procurement of conventional defense equipment (1978)
(7) Exchanges of Notes concerning pre-positioning of equipment (1981)
(8) Exchanges of Notes concerning the establishment of a transmitter at Soesterberg airfield (1982)

**United States—New Zealand**
(1) Exchanges of Notes concerning mutual defense assistance (1952, 1960)
(2) Exchanges of Notes concerning reciprocal support of armed forces in specific circumstances (1969)
(3) Memorandum of Understanding concerning Communication Center support for RNZAF *Orion Mod* Unit (1981)
(4) Memorandum of Understanding concerning logistic support (1982)

**United States—Nicaragua**
(1) Military Assistance Agreement (1954)
(2) Exchanges of Notes concerning a military advisory group mission (1957)
(3) Military Assistance Agreement (1972)

**United States—Niger**
(1) Exchanges of Notes concerning the furnishing of military equipment and services (1962)
(2) Exchanges of Notes concerning the provision of military training (1980)

**United States—Nigeria**
Military Assistance Agreement (1972)

**United States—Norway**
(1) Mutual Defense Assistance Agreement (1950, 1966, 1975)
(2) Exchanges of Notes concerning military advisory group under status of forces agreement (1954)
(3) Exchanges of Notes concerning weapons production program (1960)
(4) Exchanges of Notes concerning the safeguarding of classified information (1970)
(5) Agreement concerning the co-production for the M109A vehicle (1966, 1976)

(6) Memorandum of Understanding concerning mutual cooperation in the research, development, production, and the procurement of defense equipment (1978)
(7) Memorandum of Understanding concerning the pre-positioning of supplies and re-inforcement of Norway (use of bases, status of troops) (1981)
(8) Agreement concerning mutual logistical support (1982)

**United States—Oman**
Agreement concerning cooperation in economic development, trade, and security (including the use of Salalah and Masirah bases and joint training exercises) (1981)

**United States—Pakistan**
(1) Exchanges of Notes concerning the transfer of military equipment (1950)
(2) Mutual Defense Assistance Agreement (1954)
(3) Defense Support Assistance Agreement (1955, 1961)
(4) Construction Agreement (1956)
(5) Agreement of Cooperation (1959)
(6) Exchanges of Notes concerning the general security of military information (1982)

**United States—Panama**
(1) Canal Zone Treaty (1903) (renegotiated 1977, ratified 1979)
(2) Exchanges of Notes concerning the sales of military supplies and services (1959, 1962)
(3) Exchanges of Notes concerning the furnishing of defense equipment for internal security (1962)
(4) Military Assistance Agreement (1972)
(5) Exchanges of Notes concerning economic and military cooperation (1978)

**United States—Paraguay**
(1) Exchanges of Notes concerning the furnishing of assistance to the Paraguayan Air Force (1966)
(2) Exchanges of Notes concerning assistance for road construction to Paraguayan Army (1964)
(3) Exchanges of Notes concerning military assistance (1966)

**United States—Peru**
(1) Military Assistance Agreement (1952)
(2) Exchanges of Notes concerning missions of duties (1955)
(3) Exchanges of Notes concerning furnishing of defense equipment and services (1962)
(4) Military Assistance Agreement (1972)

**United States—Philippines**
(1) Agreement concerning military bases (1947, amended 1947, 1948, 1953, 1965, 1966, 1971, 1979)
(2) Mutual Defense Treaty (1951)
(3) Exchanges of Notes concerning military assistance (1953, 1955, 1956, 1957, 1958)
(4) Exchanges of Notes concerning joint use of the Manilla Air Station (1957)
(5) Exchanges of Notes concerning establishment of Mutual Defense Board and assignment of Philippine military liaison officers to U.S. military bases in the Philippines (1958)
(6) Exchanges of Notes concerning the transfer of the entire Manilla Air Station to the Philippines (1958)
(7) Exchanges of Notes concerning the establishment of a communication facility at Mt. Cabuyao (1965)
(8) Exchanges of Notes concerning grant of defense aid and services (1979, 1980, 1981, 1982)
(9) Memorandum of Understanding concerning exchange of military personnel between U.S. Army Western Command and the Air Force of the Philippines (1981)

**United States—Portugal**
(1) Mutual Defense Assistance Agreement (1951)
(2) Defense Agreement concerning the Azores (1951, 1957, 1971, 1979)
(3) Exchanges of Notes concerning weapons production program (1960)
(4) Exchanges of Notes concerning grant of defense arms and services (1979, 1980, 1981, 1982)
(5) Memorandum of Understanding concerning mutual cooperation in the research, development, production, procurement, and logistic support of defense equipment (1979)
(6) Exchanges of Notes concerning general security of military information (1982)

**United States—Rowanda**
Exchanges of Notes concerning the provision of military training (1980)

**United States—St. Lucia**
Exchanges of Notes concerning the provision of military training (1981)

**United States—St. Vincent and the Grenadines**
Exchanges of Notes concerning the provision of military training (1981)

**United States—Saudi Arabia**
(1) Exchanges of Notes concerning the transfer of military supplies (1951)
(2) Exchanges of Notes concerning military advisory group (1953)
(3) Exchanges of Notes concerning construction of facilities (1965, 1978, 1981, 1982)
(4) Exchanges of Notes concerning transfer of military aircraft (1965)
(5) Memorandum of Understanding concerning Saudi National Guard modernization (1973)
(6) Agreement of Cooperation (economic, technical, industrial and defense) (1974)
(7) Exchanges of Notes concerning the provision of U.S. military training (1977)

**United States—Senegal**
Exchanges of Notes concerning the furnishing of military supplies and services (1962)

**United States—Sierra Leon**
Exchanges of Notes concerning the provision of military training (1982)

**United States—Singapore**
(1) Exchanges of Notes concerning establishment of USAF training assistance team (1977)
(2) Memorandum of Understanding concerning the exchange of military personnel (1981, 1982)
(3) Exchanges of Notes concerning the provision of military training (1981)

**United States—Somalia**
(1) Exchanges of Notes concerning the furnishing of defense articles and services (1978)
(2) Agreement concerning base at Berbera air strip in northern Somalia, and port facilities at Mogadishu (1981)
(3) Exchanges of Notes concerning the provision of military training (1981)

**United States—South Africa**
Exchanges of Notes concerning mutual defense assistance (1981)

**United States—Spain**
(1) Mutual Defense Assistance Agreement (1953)
(2) Exchanges of Notes concerning arrangements for facilities (1954)
(3) Treaty of Friendship and Cooperation (including U.S. use of three air bases, firing range, and one naval base) (1976)
(4) Declaration of Principles, continuing defense cooperation within NATO (1974)
(5) Exchanges of Notes concerning grant of defense articles and services (1979, 1981)
(6) Agreement concerning master data exchange for mutual development of weapons systems (1980)
(7) Memorandum of Understanding concerning of installation of a satellite ground terminal in Spain (1982)

**United States—Sri Lanka**
Exchanges of Notes concerning military sales (1956)

**United States—Sudan**
(1) Military Assistance Agreement (1973)
(2) Exchanges of Notes concerning mutual defense assistance agreement (1981)
(3) Exchanges of Notes concerning grant of defense articles and services (1981, 1982)
(4) Exchanges of Notes concerning the status of U.S. personnel in the Sudan (1981)

**United States—Sweden**
(1) Exchanges of Notes concerning the procurement of military equipment (1952)
(2) Exchanges concerning general security of military information (1981)

**United States—Suriname**
Exchanges of Notes concerning the provision of military training (1980)

**United States—Thailand**
(1) Agreement concerning military assistance (1950, 1975)
(2) Memorandum of Understanding concerning pre-positioning of military supplies (1977)
(3) Memorandum of Understanding concerning integrated communications systems (1977)

**United States—Togo**
Exchanges of Notes concerning the provision of military training (1980)

**United States—Trinidad and Tobago**
Exchanges of Notes concerning the use of the Five Islands (1954)

**United States—Tunisia**
(1) Exchanges of Notes concerning military assistance (1974)
(2) Exchanges of Notes concerning strategic cooperation (1981)

**United States—Turkey**
(1) Status of Forces Agreement (1954)
(2) Mutual Defense Assistance Program (1955, 1962)
(3) Agreement of Cooperation (1959)
(4) Exchanges of Notes concerning introduction of modern weapons into NATO forces in Turkey (1959)
(5) Exchanges of Notes concerning the establishment of facilities (1959)
(6) Exchanges of Notes concerning weapons production program (1960)
(7) Military Assistance Agreement (1974)
(8) Exchanges of Notes concerning grant of defense articles and services (1979, 1982)
(9) Agreement concerning cooperation in defense and economics with supplementing agreements on defense support, defense industrial cooperation and installations (1980)

**United States—United Arab Emirates**
Exchanges of Notes concerning the sale of defense articles and services (1975)

**United States—Union of Soviet Socialist Republics**
(1) Memorandum of Understanding concerning establishment of direct communications link, or "Hot Line", for use in emergency (1973)
(2) Agreement concerning measures to reduce the risk of outbreak of nuclear war by accidental or unauthorized use of nuclear weapons, provision for immediate notification should an accident occur, and advanced notification of any planned missile launches (1971)
(3) Agreement concerning "Hot Line" modernization and improvement (1971, 1975)
(4) Treaty on the Limitation of Anti-Ballistic Missile Systems, leaving unchallenged the penetration capability of retaliatory missile forces (1972)
(5) Interim Agreement concerning certain measures with respect to the limitations of strategic offensive arms, plus Protocol (1972)
(6) Agreement concerning the Prevention of Nuclear War (1973)
(7) Threshold Test Ban Treaty, concerning the limitation of underground nuclear weapons tests, plus Protocol (1974)*
(8) Protocol to the 1972 Treaty on the Limitations of ABM systems, permitting each side to only one ABM deployment site (1974)
(9) Peaceful Nuclear Treaty, concerning underground nuclear explosions for peaceful purposes, and Protocol (1976)*
(10) Agreement of Cooperation on the exploration and use of outer space for peaceful purposes (1977)
(11) Treaty on the Limitation of Strategic Offensive Arms, plus Protocol, a Joint Statement of Principles and a Memorandum of Understanding concerning the establishment of a data base (SALT II), signed 1979*
    *NOTE: Although U.S. Senate consent has not been given, both sides have declared that they would not jeopardize these treaties as long as the other side continues to abide by them.

**United States—United Kingdom**
(1) Exchanges of Notes concerning naval and air bases (1940)
(2) Protocol on the defense of Newfoundland (1941)
(3) Agreement on leased bases (1941, 1950, 1978)
(4) Mutual Defense Assistance Agreement (1950)
(5) Agreement to cooperate in the use of nuclear energy for mutual defense (1958)
(6) Exchanges of Notes concerning the establishment of a ballistic missile early-warning station at Fylingdales Moor (1960)
(7) Exchanges of Notes concerning the use of the air field on Ascension Island (1962, 1973)
(8) Exchanges of Notes concerning Anegada (British Virgin Islands) by the U.S. (1973)
(9) Exchanges of Notes concerning U.S. use of Diego Garcia (Indian Ocean) (1976)
(10) Exchanges of Notes concerning U.S. defense areas and base on Antigua (1977)
(11) Agreement concerning U.S. bases in Turks and Caicos Islands (1979)
(12) Exchanges of Notes concerning the establishment of a missile defense alarm system in the U.K. (1961)
(13) Exchanges of Notes concerning weapons production program (1960)
(14) Memorandum of Understanding concerning cooperation in research, development, production, and procurement of defense equipment (1975)

**United States—Uruguay**
Military Assistance Agreement (1952, 1972)

**United States—Venezuela**
Exchanges of Notes concerning military assistance (1972, 1977)

**United States—Yugoslavia**
(1) Exchanges of Notes concerning military sales (1959)
(2) Agreement concerning expanded bilateral military cooperation (1978)

**United States—Zaire**
(1) Arms Supply Agreement (1977, 1979)
(2) Mutual Defense Assistance Agreement (1962)

\* \* \* \* \*

# UPPER VOLTA

**Upper Volta—Mali**
Border Pact, including a renunciation of the use of force (1975)

\* \* \* \* \*

# URUGUAY

**Uruguay—United States**
Military Assistance Agreement (1952, 1972)

\* \* \* \* \*

# VANUATU

**Vanautu—Papua New Guinea**
Agreement regarding the stationing of troops in Port Vila

\* \* \* \* \*

# VATICAN CITY STATE

None

\* \* \* \* \*

# VENEZUELA

**Venezuela—United States**
  Exchanges of Notes concerning military assistance (1972, 1977)

\* \* \* \* \*

# VIETNAM

**Vietnam—Bulgaria**
  Treaty of Friendship, Cooperation and Mutual Assistance (1979)

**Vietnam—Czechoslovakia**
  Treaty of Friendship, Cooperation and Mutual Assistance (1980)

**Vietnam—German Democratic Republic**
  Treaty of Friendship, Cooperation and Mutual Assistance (1977)

**Vietnam—Kampuchea**
  Treaty of Friendship, Cooperation and Mutual Assistance—military provisions and border pact included in series of agreements (1977)

**Vietnam—Laos**
  Treaty of Friendship, Cooperation and Mutual Assistance—military provisions and border pact included in series of agreements (1977)

**Vietnam—Mongolia**
  Treaty of Friendship, Cooperation and Mutual Assistance (1979)

**Vietnam—Union of Soviet Socialist Republics**
  Treaty of Friendship, Cooperation and Mutual Assistance (1978)

\* \* \* \* \*

# WESTERN SAMOA

**Western Samoa—New Zealand**
  Agreement providing for New Zealand to represent Western Samoa in all dealings with other countries and international organizations (1962)

\* \* \* \* \*

# YEMEN ARAB REPUBLIC (North Yemen)

**Yemen Arab Republic—China**
  Treaty of Friendship, Cooperation and Mutual Assistance (1964)

\* \* \* \* \*

# PEOPLE'S DEMOCRATIC REPUBLIC OF YEMEN (South Yemen)

**People's Democratic Republic of Yemen—Bulgaria**
  Protocol for Cooperation (1980)
  Treaty of Friendship, Cooperation and Mutual Assistance (1981)

**People's Democratic Republic of Yemen—Ethiopia**
  Treaty of Friendship, Cooperation and Mutual Assistance (1979)
  Protocol continuing military cooperation (1980)

**People's Democratic Republic of Yemen—Hungary**
  Protocol for Cooperation (1981)
  Treaty of Friendship, Cooperation and Mutual Assistance (1981)

**People's Democratic Republic of Yemen—Soviet Union**
  Treaty of Friendship, Cooperation and Mutual Assistance, including the use of Aden Naval base (ratified 1980)

\* \* \* \* \*

# YUGOSLAVIA

**Yugoslavia—United States**
  (1) Exchanges of Notes concerning military sales (1959)
  (2) Expanded bilateral military cooperation agreement (1978)

\* \* \* \* \*

# ZAIRE

**Zaire—Belgium**
  Military Aid Agreement (1977/1978)

**Zaire—Egypt**
  Technical Military Cooperation Agreement (1980)

**Zaire—France**
  Military Cooperation Agreement (ratified 1978)

**Zaire—United States**
  (1) Mutual Defense Assistance Agreement (1972)
  (2) Arms Supply Agreements (1977, 1979)

\* \* \* \* \*

# ZAMBIA

**Zambia—Angola**
Mutual Defense Agreement (1979)

**Zambia—Union of Soviet Socialist Republics**
Treaty of Friendship, Cooperation and Mutual Assistance

* * * * *

# ZIMBABWE

**Zimbabwe—Mozambique**
Agreement concerning joint military action against Mozambique rebels (1980)

* * * * *

# PART III
# MAPS AND
# MAJOR MILITARY BASES

# AFGHANISTAN

| ARMY: | Baghlan (Soviet Union) | Herat (Soviet Union) | Kandahar (Soviet Union) |
|---|---|---|---|
| | Gardez (Soviet Union) | Kabul (Soviet Union) | |

| AIR FORCE: | Bagram | Kabul (Soviet Union) | Qandahar |
|---|---|---|---|
| | Farah | Kunduz | Sherpur |
| | Faizabad | Mazar-i-Sharif | Shindand |
| | Jurm | | |

# ALBANIA

**ARMY:**      Tirane

**NAVY:**      Durres            Sarande          Shinjin
               Pasha Liman       Sazan Island     Valona

**AIR FORCE:** Berat             Sazan Island     Tirane
               Durazzo           Shijak           Valona
               Kucove

# ALGERIA

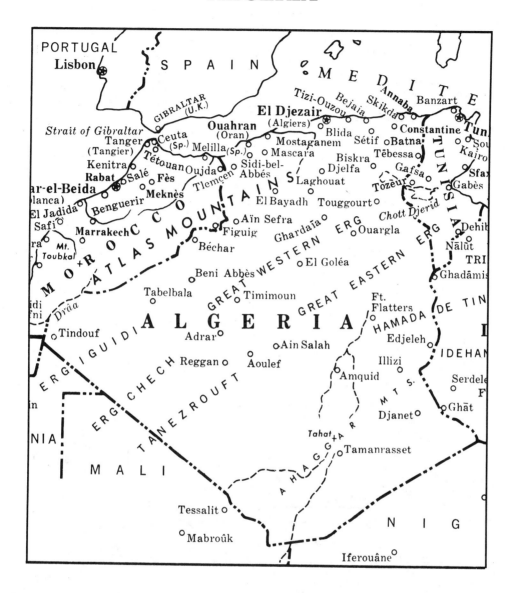

| ARMY: | Blida | Constantine | Ouargla |
| | Colomb-Bechar | Oran | Tamanrasset |
| | | | |
| NAVY: | Algiers | Mers-el-Kebir | |
| | Annaba | Oran | |
| | (Soviet Port Access) | Skikda | |
| | | | |
| AIR FORCE: | Algiers | La Calle | Ozukar |
| | Biskra | Maison Blanche | Paul-Cazelles |
| | Blida | Marine | Reggane |
| | Boufarak | Mers-el-Kebir | Sidi-bel-Abbes |
| | Bou-Sfer | Oran | Tafnaoui |
| | Colomb-Bechar | Ouargla | Zenate |
| | Dar-el-Beida | Oukda | |

# ANGOLA

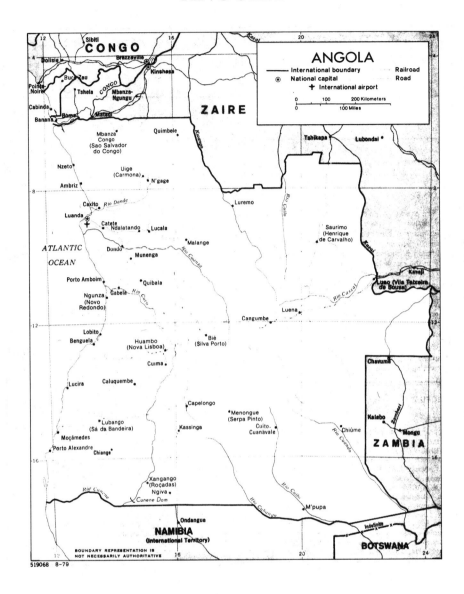

**ARMY:**

| | | |
|---|---|---|
| Cuando Cubango | Lula Sul | Mexico |
| Huambo | Melange | Mocamedes |
| Luanda | | |

**NAVY:**

| | | |
|---|---|---|
| Benguela | Luanda | Mocamedes |
| Lobito | (Soviet Port Access) | Porto Alexandre |

**AIR FORCE:**

| | | |
|---|---|---|
| Ambriz | Lubanga | Pereira de Eca |
| Benguela | Luso | Porto Amboin |
| Cabinda | Malanje | Portugalia |
| Camabatela | Menongue | Sa Da Bandera |
| Carmona | Mmbrizete | Santa Comba |
| Henrique de Carvalho | Mocamedes | Santo Antonio do Zaire |
| Lobito | Negage | Serpa Pinto |
| Luanda | Nova Lisboa | Silva Porto |
| (Soviet Air Access) | Novo Redondo | Texeira de Sousa |

# ANTIGUA & BARBUDA

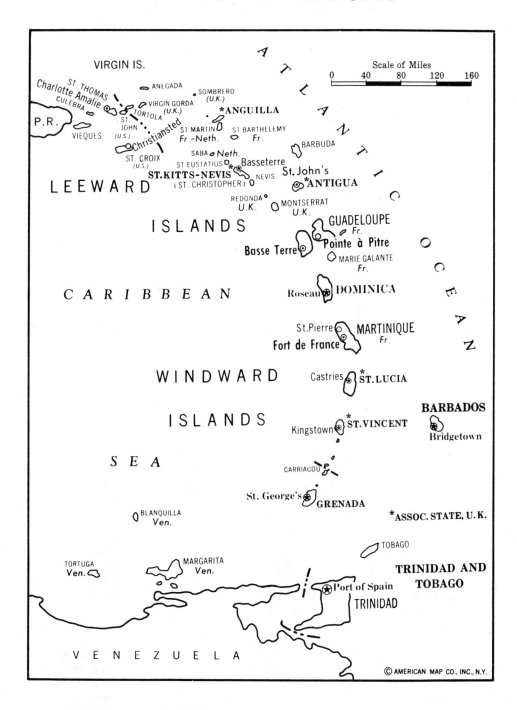

**ARMY:** St. John's

**NAVY:** St. John's (United States Oceanographic Research Facility)

# ARGENTINA

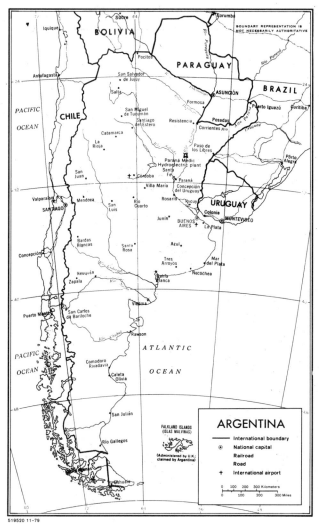

519520 11-79

**ARMY:**

Bahia Blanca
Campo de Mayo
  (near Buenos Aires)
Catamarca
Cordoba
Corrientes

Curuzu-Cuaha
Entre Rios
La Plata
Mendoza
Moron

Neuquen
Rosario
Salta
Tandil
Tucuman

**NAVY:**

Azul
Comandante
Darsena Norte
Espora
Ezeiza

Gallegos
Madryn
Mar de Plata
Petrel
Puerto Belgrano

Rio Grande
Rio Santiago
Trelew
Ushauaia
Zarate

**AIR FORCE:**

Aeroparque
Campo de Mayo
  (near Buenos Aires)
Chamical
Commodoro Rivadavia
Cordoba
El Palomar
El Plumerillo
General Pringles

General Urquiza
Mar de Plata
Mendoza
Moron
Parana
Posados
Puerto Deseado
Quilmes
Reconquista

Reynold
Rio Gallegos
Rivadavia
San Antonio Oeste
Tandil
Tenente Benjamin Matienzo
Tierra del Guego
Trelew

740

# AUSTRALIA

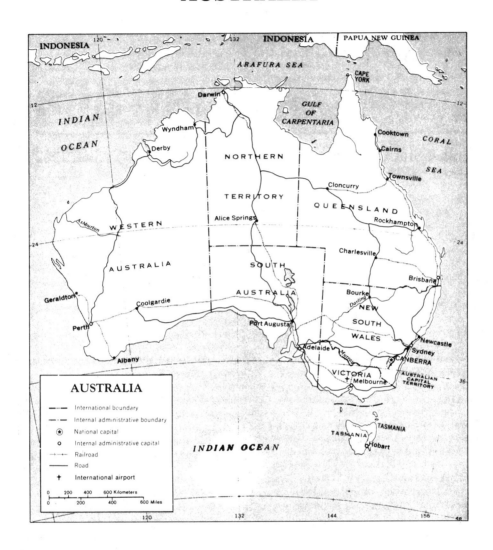

| ARMY: | Enoggera | Oakey | Sydney |
|---|---|---|---|
| | Holsworthy | Paddington | Townsville |

| NAVY: | Brisbane | Fremantle | Sterling |
|---|---|---|---|
| | Cairns | Jervis | (Cockburn Sound) |
| | Darwin | Nowra | Sydney |
| | Exmouth | | |
| | (United States Navy) | | |

| AIR FORCE: | Amberley | Learmont | Tullarmarine |
|---|---|---|---|
| | Canberra | Pearce | Wagga |
| | Darwin | Point Cook | Williamtown |
| | East Sale | Richmond | Woomera |
| | Ebinburg | Rindall | (United States Air |
| | Fairbain | Sydney | Force) |
| | Laverton | Townsville | |

# AUSTRIA

**ARMY:**    Burgenland       Graz       Tirol
             Carinthia       Salzburg     Vienna

**AIR FORCE:**   Aigen-Ennstal    Horsching
               Graz-Thalerhof   Zeltweg

# BAHAMAS

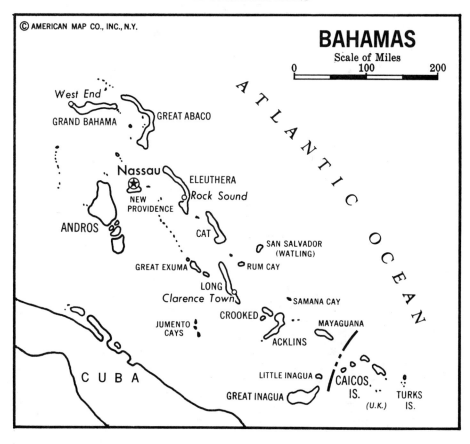

ARMY:      Nassau

NAVY:      Gleuthera (United States Oceanographic Research Facility)

# BAHRAIN

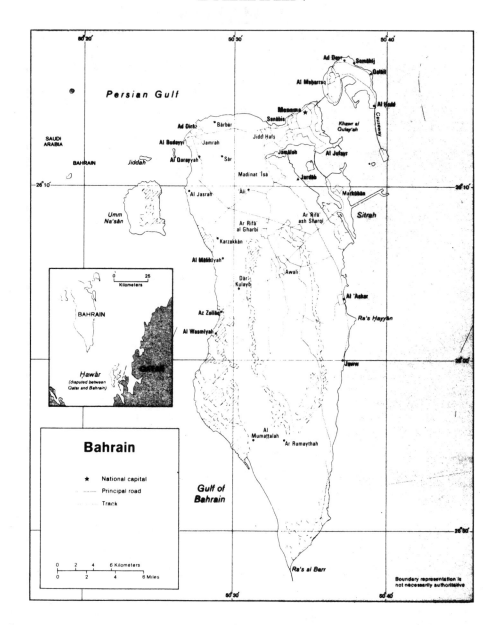

**ARMY:**       Manama

**NAVY:**       Manama

# BANGLADESH

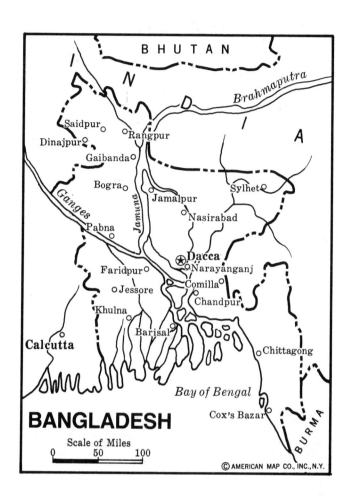

| ARMY: | Bogra | Dacca | Jessore |
|---|---|---|---|
| NAVY: | Chalna | Dacca | |
| | Chittagong | Khulna | |
| AIR FORCE: | Barisal | Hatnazari | Kurmitola |
| | Chiringa | Ishurdi | Lalmonirhat |
| | Chittagong | Jessore | Saldpur |
| | Cox's Bazar | Khulna | Tezagoon (Dacca) |
| | Dohazari | | |

# BARBADOS

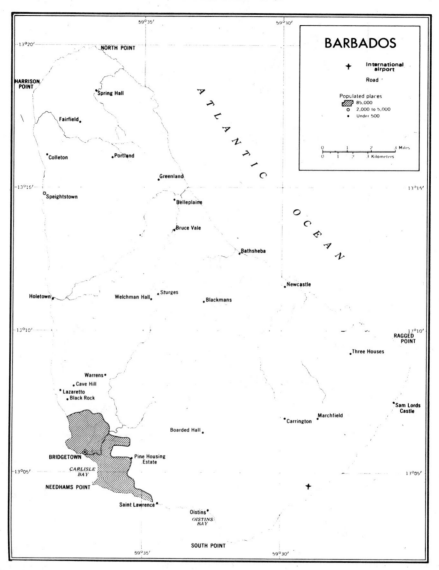

**ARMY:**      Bridgetown, St. Michael

# BELGIUM

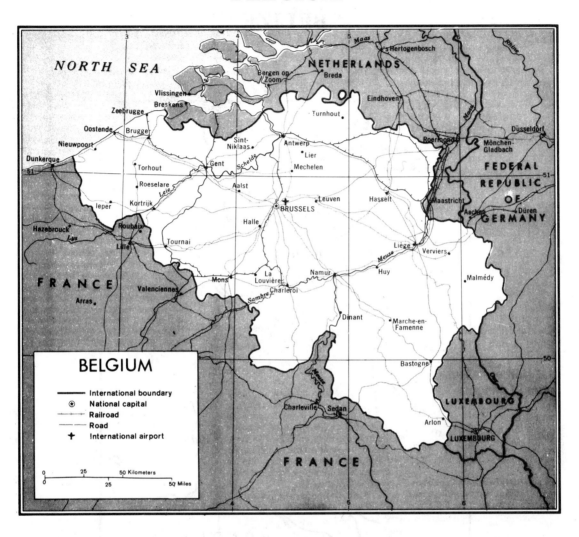

| | | |
|---|---|---|
| **ARMY:** | Mons | Tervuren |
| | (United States Army) | |
| | | |
| **NAVY:** | Brugge | Nieuport | Zeebrugge |
| | Kallo | Ostend | |
| | | | Koksyde |
| **AIR FORCE:** | Beauvechain | Florennes | Melsborek |
| | Bierset | Gosselies | Mons |
| | Brasschaat | Gossoncourt | Werl |
| | Brustem | Kleine Brohel | |
| | Butsweilerhof | | |

# BELIZE

**ARMY:**      Belize City            Belmopan

# BENIN

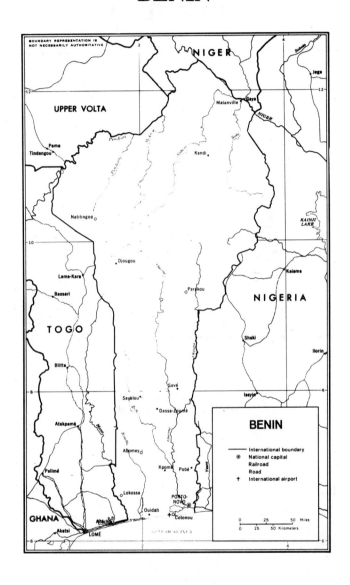

**ARMY:**    Cotonou        Parakou

**NAVY:**    Cotonou

**AIR FORCE:**    Aboumey        Kandi        Porto Nova
                Bemboreke      Natitingou   Save
                Cotonou

# BERMUDA

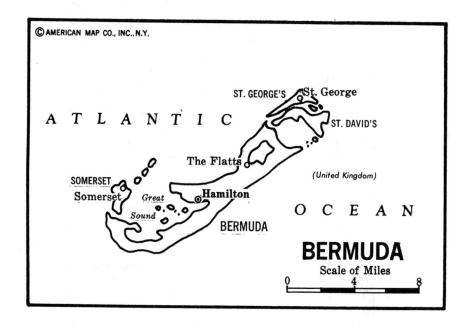

**ARMY:**        Hamilton

**NAVY:**        Hamilton

# BHUTAN

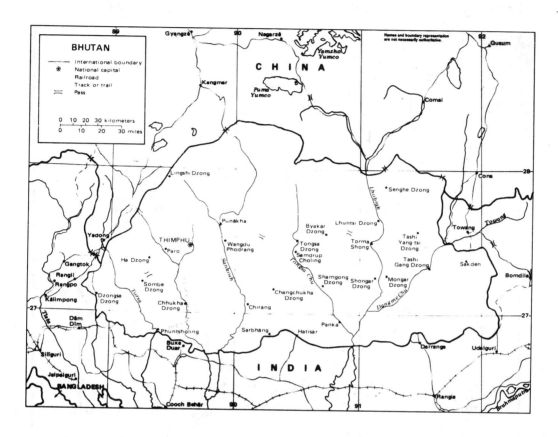

**ARMY:**       Thimphu

# BOLIVIA

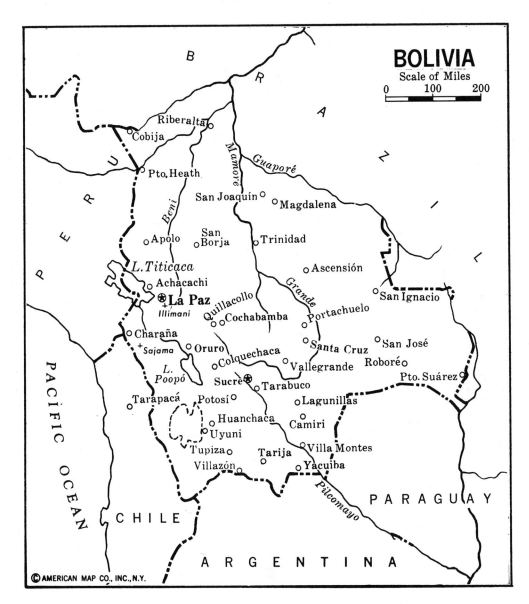

**ARMY:**

| | | |
|---|---|---|
| Camiri | Riberalta | Trinidad |
| Challapata | Robore | Tupiza |
| Cochabamba | Santa Cruz | Viacha |
| La Paz | Sucre | Villamontes |
| Ouru | Tarija | |

**NAVY:**

| | | |
|---|---|---|
| Guaramerin | Puerto Horquilla | San Juan de Tiquina |
| Lake Titicaca | Puerto Villarroel | Tiquina |
| La Paz | Riberalta | Trinidad |
| Loma Suarez | | |

**AIR FORCE:**

| | | |
|---|---|---|
| Charana | El Trompillo | Puerto Suarez |
| Colcapima | La Florida | Santa Cruz |
| El Tejar | La Paz | |

# BOTSWANA

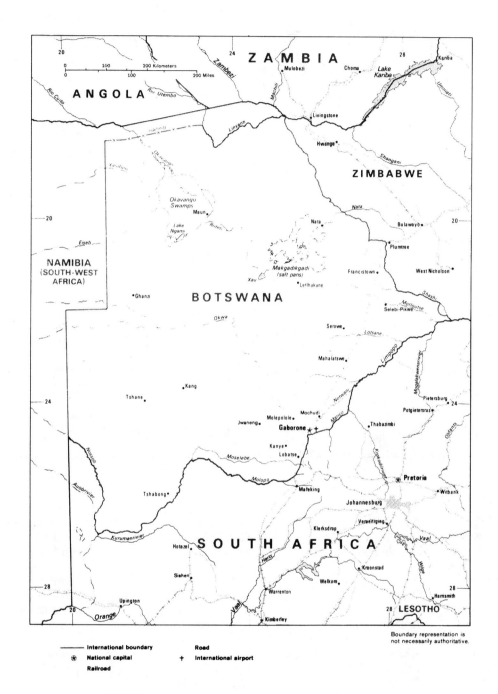

Boundary representation is
not necessarily authoritative.

—— International boundary    Road
⊛ National capital      + International airport
Railroad

**ARMY:**     Gabarone

**AIR FORCE:**   Francistown            Gabarone

# BRAZIL

| **ARMY:** | Belem | Manaus | Rio de Janeiro |
| | Curitiba | Porto Alegre | Sao Paulo |
| | Juiz de Fora | Recife | Sao Salvador |
| | | | |
| **NAVY:** | Aratu | Natal | Sao Paulo |
| | Belem | Niteroi | Sao Pedro de Aldeia |
| | Florianopols | Recife | Sao Salvador |
| | Ladario | Rio de Janeiro | |
| | | | |
| **AIR FORCE:** | Anapolis | Fortaleza | Rio de Janeiro |
| | Balterra | Galeao | Sao Salvador |
| | Belem | Gurantinqueta | Santa Cruz |
| | Brasilia | Jacareacanga | Santaren |
| | Cachijo | Manaus | Santos |
| | Campo Grande | Natal | Santos Dumont |
| | Campos dos Afonsos | Pirassununga | Sao Jose dos Campos |
| | Canoas | Porto Alegre | Sao Paulo |
| | Cumbica | Recife | Sao Pedro de Aldeia |
| | Florianopols | | |

# BRUNEI

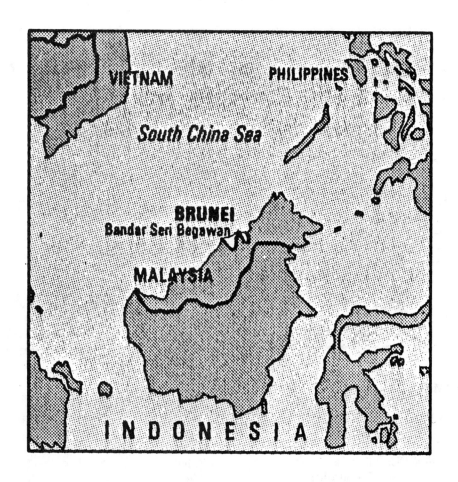

| | |
|---|---|
| **ARMY:** | Bandar Seri Begawan |
| **NAVY:** | Muara |
| **AIR FORCE:** | Bandar Seri Begawan |

# BULGARIA

**ARMY:**       Sofia

**NAVY:**       Atiya                Sozopol
               Burgas               Varna

**AIR FORCE:**  Balchik      Khin            Targoviste
               Bozhurishte  Pleven          Ternovo
               Burgas       Plovdiz         Tolbu
               Haskovo      Ruse            Varna
               Ignatiev     Silistra        Vrajdebna
               Kardzali     Sofia           Yambol
               Karlovo      Stara Zagora

# BURMA

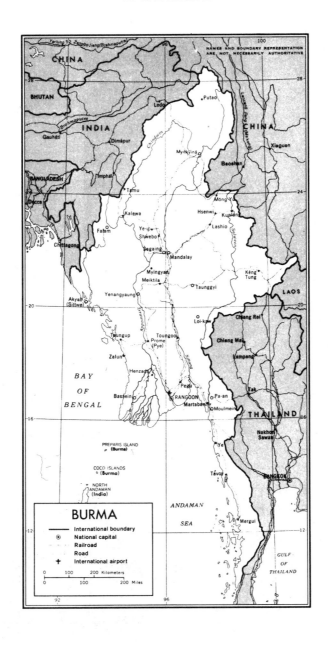

| **ARMY:** | Arakan | Kayah | Rangoon |
| | Irrawaddy | Magwe | Sagaing |
| | Kachin | Mandalay | Shan |
| | Karen | Pegu | Tenasserim |
| | | | |
| **NAVY:** | Bassein | Moulmeih | Sinmalaik |
| | Mergui | Seikyi | Sittwe (Akyab) |
| | Monkey Point | | |
| | | | |
| **AIR FORCE:** | Akyab | Mandalay | Mingaladon |
| | Hinawbi | Meiktila | Myitkyina |
| | Kengtung | Mergui | |

# BURUNDI

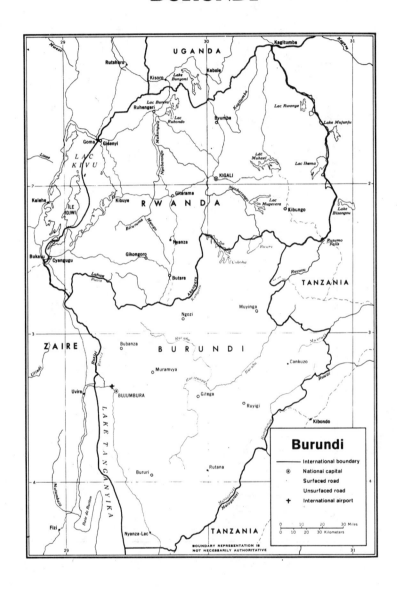

**ARMY:**      Bujumbura               Gitega

**AIR FORCE:**  Bujumbura

# CAMEROON

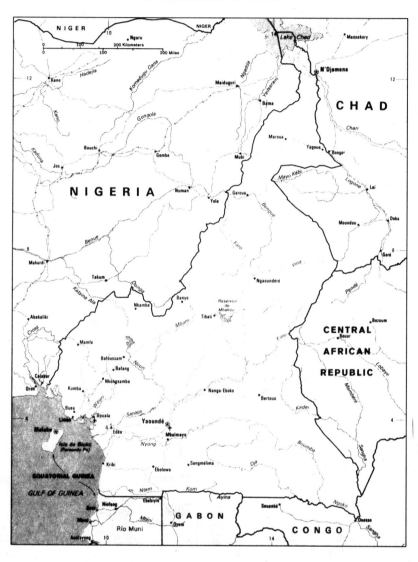

| **ARMY:** | Bafoussam | Ebolawa | Koutaba |
| | Douala | Garoua | Yaounde |
| **NAVY:** | Douala | | |
| **AIR FORCE:** | Batouri | Garoua | Salak |
| | Calabar | Kaele Maroua | Tiko |
| | Douala | N'Gaoundere | Yaounde |
| | Foumban | Port Pouet | |

# CANADA

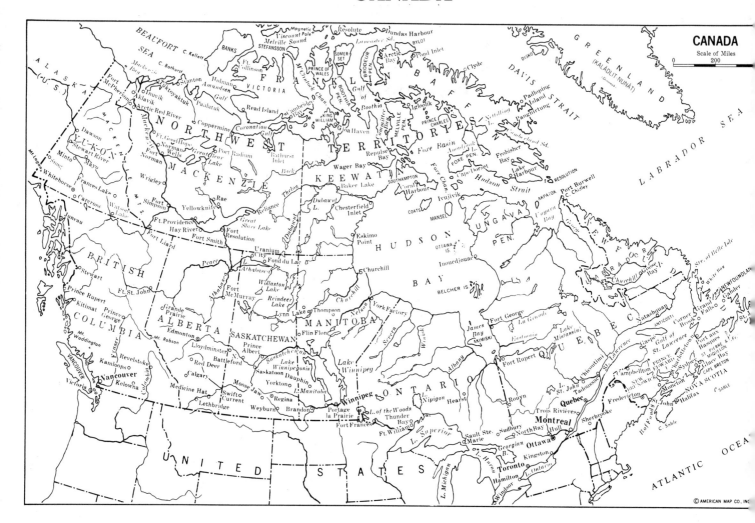

| | | | |
|---|---|---|---|
| **ARMY:** | Calgary | Kingston | Sukfield |
| | Edmonton | London | Toronto |
| | Esquimal | Montreal | Valcartier |
| | Gagetown | Petawaa | Winnipeg |
| | Halifax | Shila | |
| | | | |
| **NAVY:** | Argentia N'Land | Comox | Hamilton |
| | (United States Oceano- | Esquimalt | Patricia Bay |
| | graphic Research | Greenwood | Shearwater |
| | Facility) | Halifax | Summerside |
| | | | |
| **AIR FORCE:** | Bagotville | Knob Lake | Shilo |
| | Calgary | London | St. Hubert |
| | Chatham | Montreal | Summerside |
| | Cold Lake | Moose Jaw | Trenton |
| | Comox | Namao | Uplands |
| | Dartmouth | North Bay | Valcartier |
| | Downsville | Penhold | Val d'Or |
| | Gagetown | Portage | Whitehorse |
| | Goose Bay | Rockcliff | Winnipeg |
| | Greenwood | Shearwater | Yellowknife |

# CAPE VERDE

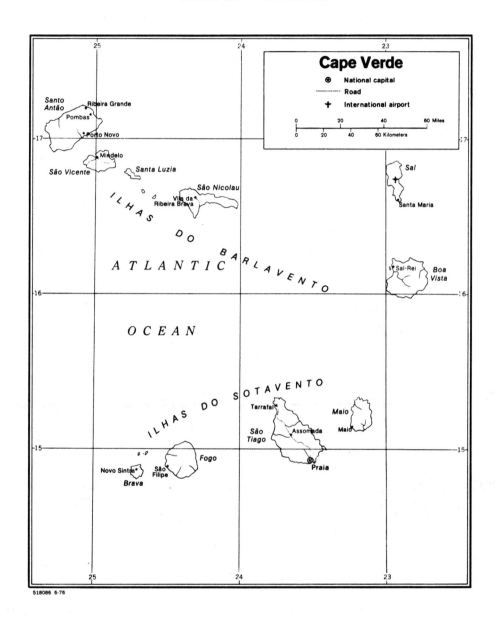

**ARMY:**        Praia                              Mindalo                          Sal Island

**AIR FORCE:**   Sal Island
                     (Amilcar Cabral)

# CENTRAL AFRICAN REPUBLIC

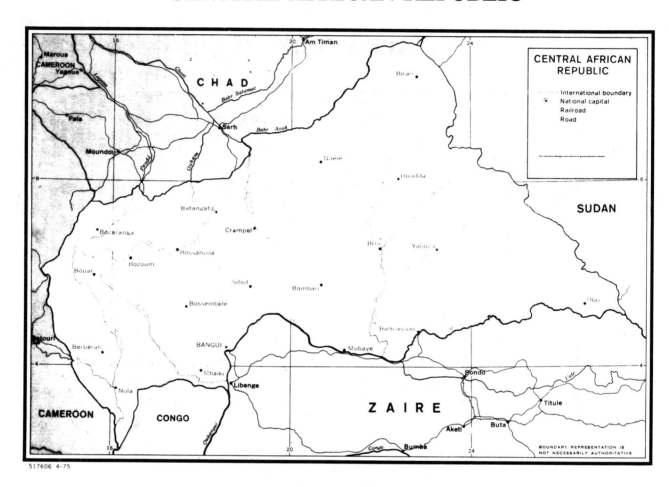

517606 4-75

| | | |
|---|---|---|
| **ARMY:** | Bangui | |
| **AIR FORCE:** | Bamburi | Berberati | Bouar |
| | Bangui | Birao | (French Air Access) |
| | (French Air Access) | | |

762

# CHAD

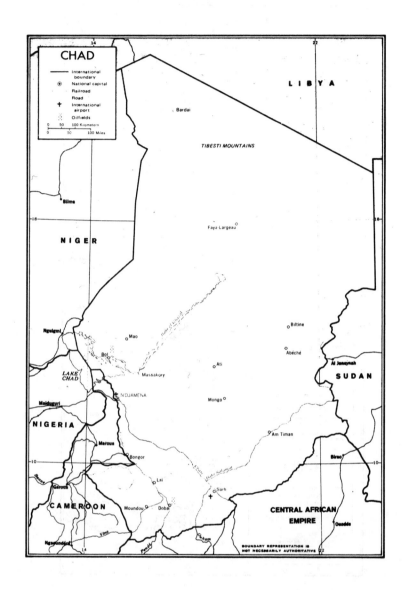

**ARMY:** N'Djamena

**NAVY:** Chari River      Lake Chad

**AIR FORCE:**

| | | |
|---|---|---|
| Abeche | Faya-Largeau | Ounianga |
| Ati | Fort Archambault | Pola |
| Bangor | Kebir | Sarn |
| Bardai | Mongo | Wour (Libya) |
| Douguia | Moundou | Zouar |
| Fada | N'Djamena | |

# CHILE

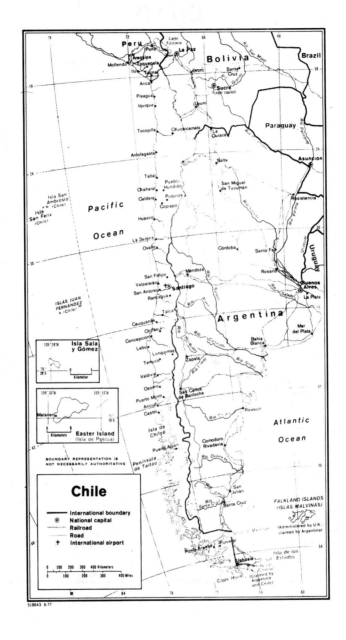

| ARMY: | Antofagasta | Iquique | Santiago |
| | Concepcion | Punta Arenas | Valdiva |
| | | | |
| NAVY: | Iquique | Puerto Williams | Talcahuano |
| | Puerto Montt | Punta Arenas | Valparaiso |
| | | | |
| AIR FORCE: | Antofagasta | Los Cerrillos | Quintero |
| | Cerro Moreno | Los Londores (Iniquique) | Tenuco |
| | El Bosque | Puerto Montt | Vallenar |
| | Iquique | Punta Arenas | |

# CHINA

**ARMY:**

| | | |
|---|---|---|
| Anhui | Henan | |
| Beijing | Hubei | Qinghai |
| Chengdu | Hunan | Shaanxi |
| East Xinjiang | Jiangsu | Shandong |
| Fujian | Jiangxi | Shanxi |
| Fuzhou | Jilin | Shenyand |
| Gansu | Jinan | Sichuan |
| Guangdong | Kunming | South Xinjiang |
| Guangzhou | Lanzhou | Urumqi |
| Guanxi | Liaoning | Wuhan |
| Guizhou | Nei Monggol | Xizang |
| Hainan | Ningxia | Yunnan |
| Hebei | North Xinjiang | Zhejiang |
| Heilongjiang | | |

**NAVY:**

| | | |
|---|---|---|
| Amoy | Huangpu | Tsamkong |
| Beihai | Huludao | Tsingtao |
| Changkiang | Luda | Weihai |
| Chengshan | Lushun | Wenzhou |
| Choushan | Ningbo | Whampoa |
| Fuzhou | Qingdao | Yulin |
| Guangzhou | Shantou | Zhanjiang |
| Haikou | Taku | Zhoushan |
| Haimen | Taohua Dao | |

**AIR FORCE:**

| | | |
|---|---|---|
| Beijing | Hungchiao | Nanking |
| Canton | Kwangchan | Pingtang |
| Changsha | Kunming | Shenyang |
| Chengchiao | Liencheng | Sian |
| Chienchiao | Lhassa | Tenghai |
| Fuzhou | Luchiao | Tsaochiao |
| Hsincheng | Nanhai | Wuhan |

# COLOMBIA

**ARMY:**

| | | |
|---|---|---|
| Armenia | Cali | Nevia |
| Baranquilla | Ibague | Tunja |
| Bogota | Medellin | Villavicencio |
| Bucaramanga | Melgar | |

**NAVY:**

| | |
|---|---|
| Baranquilla | Cartagena |
| Buenaventura | Santa Maria |

**AIR FORCE:**

| | | |
|---|---|---|
| Baranquilla | Eldorado | Palanquero |
| Berastegul | Leticia | Paranquero |
| Bogota | Medellin | Pasto |
| Cali | Melgar | Santa Marta |
| Cucata | Monteria | Tacho |

# COMOROS

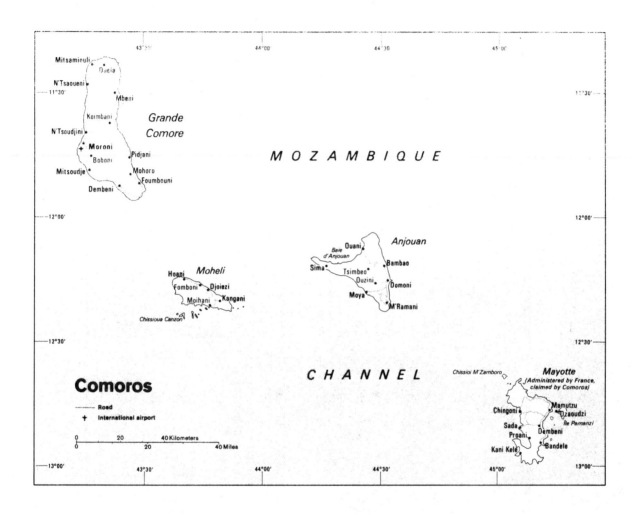

**ARMY:** Moroni

# CONGO

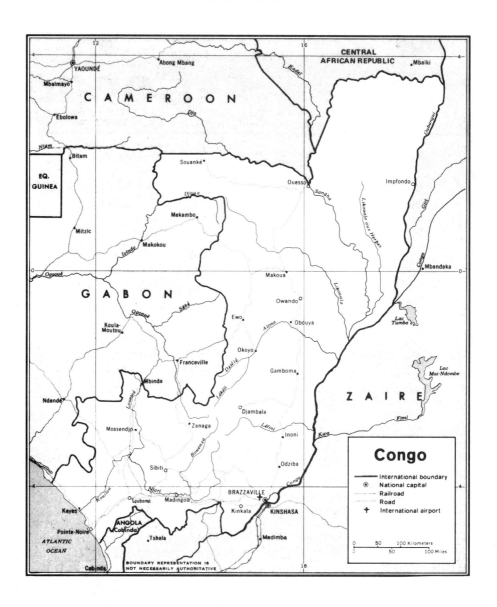

| ARMY: | Brazzaville | Loubomo | Onesso |
| --- | --- | --- | --- |
| | Djambalo | Onando | Pointe-Noire |
| | Impfondo | | |
| NAVY: | Etumbi | Pointe-Noire | |
| AIR FORCE: | Brazzaville | Dolisie | Pointe-Noire |

# COSTA RICA

**ARMY:**    San Jose

# CUBA

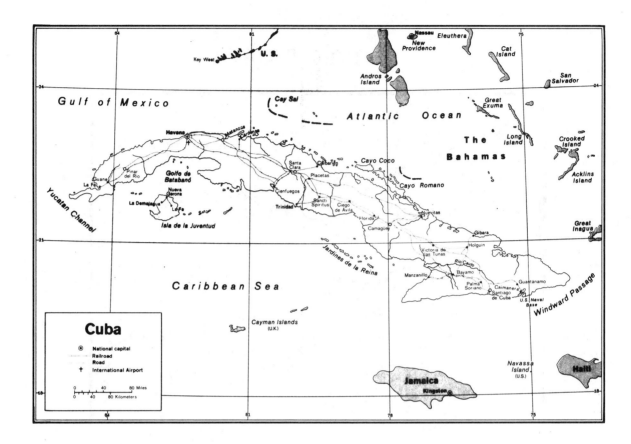

| **ARMY:** | Havana | Oriente provinces | |
| | Las Villas | Pinar del Rio | |

| **NAVY:** | Ballenatos | Cienfuegos (Soviet Union) | Havana |
| | Cabanas | Guantanamo Bay | Mariel |
| | Canasi | (United States) | Punta |

| **AIR FORCE:** | Camaguey | Holguin | Santa Clara |
| | Campo Libertad | San Antonio | Santiago |
| | Cienfuegos (Soviet Union) | San Julian | Veradero Habana |
| | Guines | | |

770

# CYPRUS

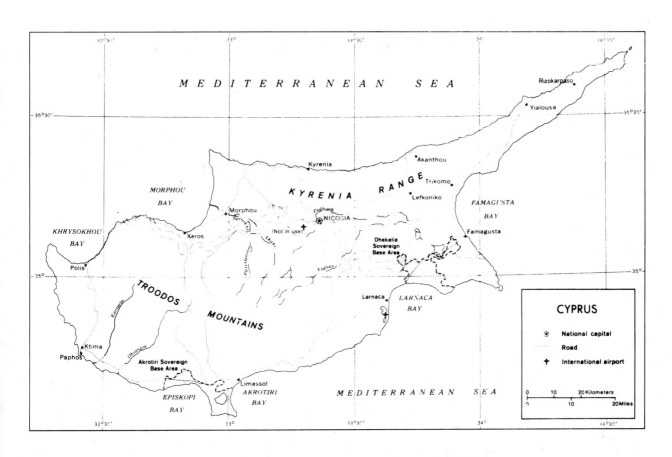

**ARMY:** Dhekelia          Nicosia

**AIR FORCE:** Akrotiri          Dhekelia          Troodos Mountains
(United Kingdom)

771

# CZECHOSLOVAKIA

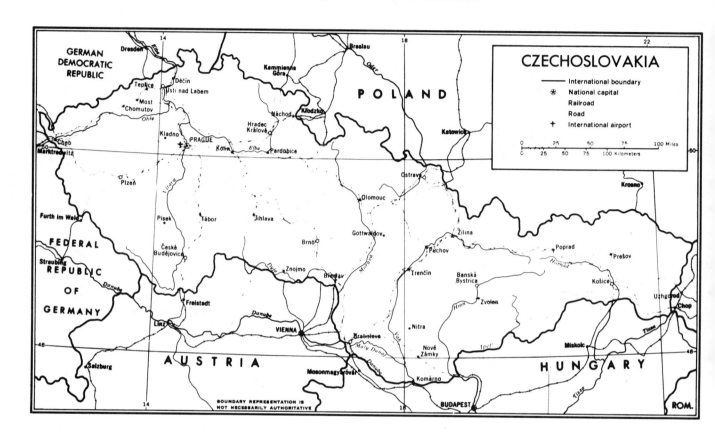

| ARMY: | Milovice | Prague (Soviet Union) | Trencin |
|---|---|---|---|
| **AIR FORCE:** | Brno | Ivanka | Minon |
| | Budejovice | Klecany | Pardubice |
| | Caslav | Kosice | Piestany |
| | Ceske | Kunovice | Plzen |
| | Cheh | Letnany | Prague |
| | Chocen | Machova | Prerov |
| | Debrany | Milovice | Spisska Nova Ves |
| | Gakovice | | |

# DENMARK

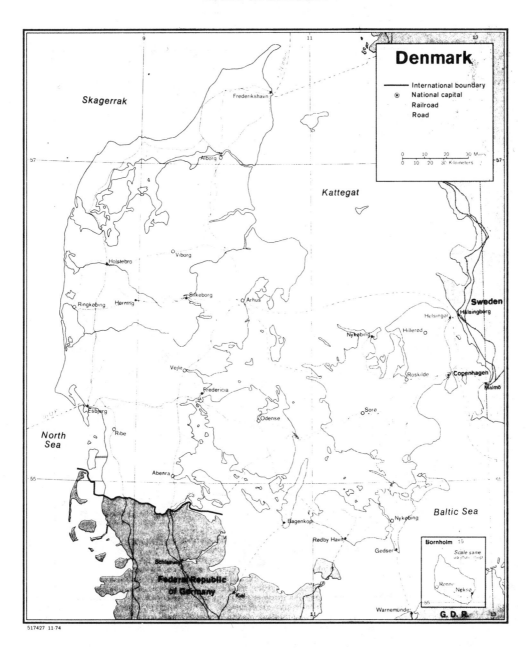

| ARMY: | Hjorring | Vandel | Vedbaek |
|---|---|---|---|
| **NAVY:** | Copenhagen<br>Frederikshaun | Korsor | |
| **AIR FORCE:** | Aalborg<br>Avno<br>Holdsteinborg<br>Karup<br>Narsarsuak (Greenland) | Skrydstrup<br>Sonderstrom-Stroemfjord<br>(Greenland—United States<br>Air Force) | Thule (Greenland—<br>United States Air Force)<br>Vaerlose |

# DJIBOUTI

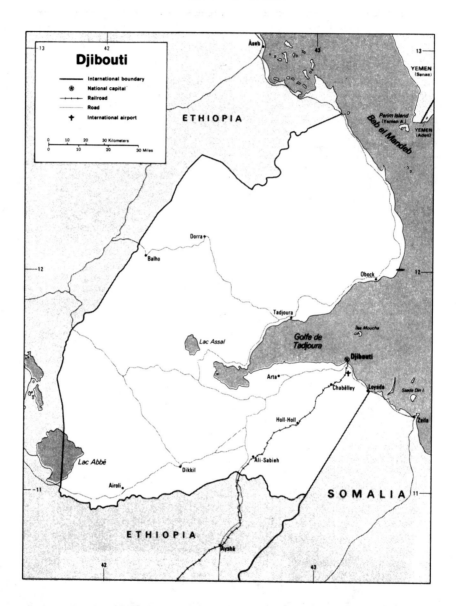

**ARMY:**     Djibouti

**NAVY:**     Djibouti (French Navy)

**AIR FORCE:**     Djibouti-Ambouli     Tadjourah Obock
                   (French Air Force)

# DOMINICA

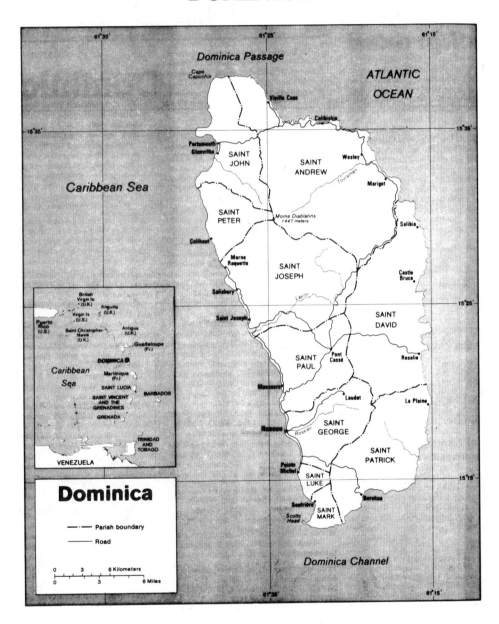

**ARMY:**     Roseau (Police)

# DOMINICAN REPUBLIC

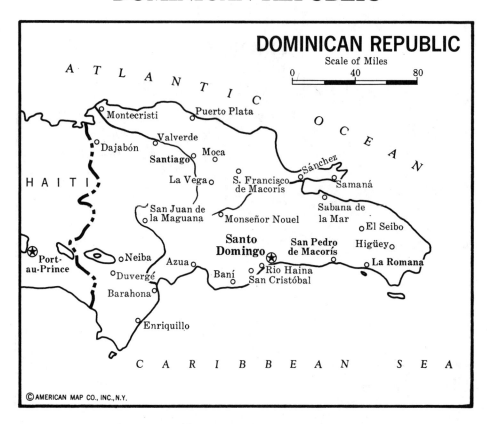

**ARMY:**      Santo Domingo

**NAVY:**
| Bani | Las Calderas | San Pedro de Macoris |
| Barahona | Monte Cristi | Santo Domingo |
| Haina | Puerto Plata | |

**AIR FORCE:**
| Azuza | La Vega | Saibo |
| Barahona | Monte Cristi | San Isidoro |
| La Romana | Puerto Plata | Santo Domingo |

# ECUADOR

| ARMY: | Cuenca | Loja | Pastaza |
|---|---|---|---|
| | Guayaquil | Machala | Quito |
| NAVY: | Galapagos Island | Guayaquil | San Lorenzo |
| AIR FORCE: | Guayaquil | Quito | Taura |
| | Manta | Salina | |

# EGYPT

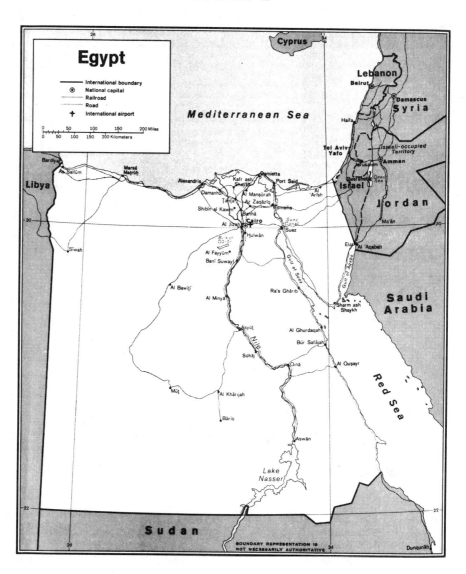

**ARMY:** Cairo

**NAVY:**

| | | |
|---|---|---|
| Alexandria | Port Said | Ras al Tin |
| Hurghada | Port Sagata | Ras Gharibi |
| Mersa Matruh | Port Twefiq | Safaga |

**AIR FORCE:**

| | | |
|---|---|---|
| Aboukir | Beni Sueif | Helwan |
| Abu Sueir | Bilbeis | Inchass |
| Alexandria | Bir Tamada | Ismailia |
| Almaza | Cairo West | Jiyanklis |
| Am Shas | Dekheila | Luxor |
| An Shas | El Mansura | Ras Banas (United States |
| Aswan | El Minya | Access) |
| Asyut | Fayid | |

# EL SALVADOR

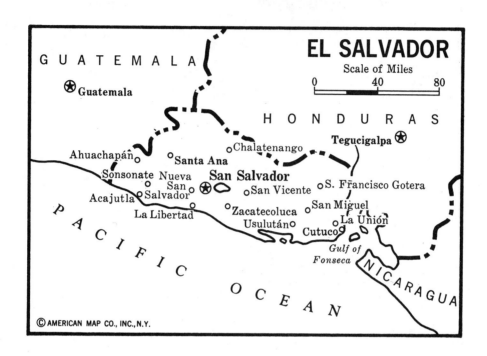

**ARMY:**     Atlacatl             San Salvador
                 San Miguel      Santa Ana

**NAVY:**     Acajutta          La Libertad        La Union

**AIR FORCE:**  Ilopango          San Salvador

# EQUITORIAL GUINEA

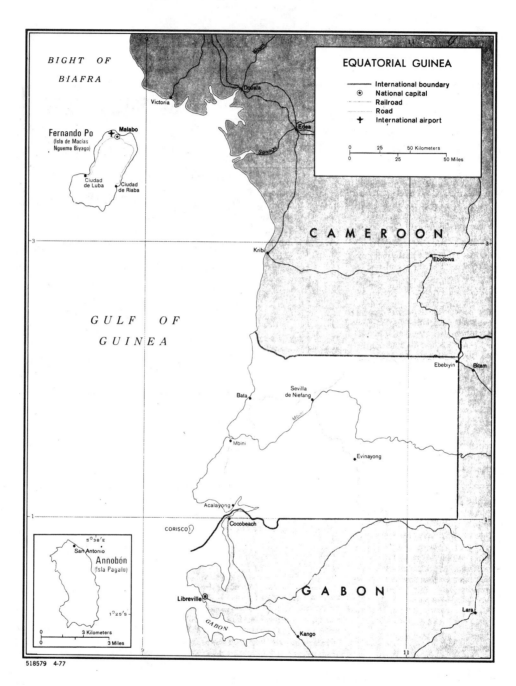

ARMY:      Bata                            Malabo
Coetiry                           Union Vale

| | | |
|---|---|---|
| **ARMY:** | Bata | Malabo |
| | Coetiry | Union Vale |
| **NAVY:** | Bata | Malabo |
| **AIR FORCE:** | Bata | Malabo |

# ETHIOPIA

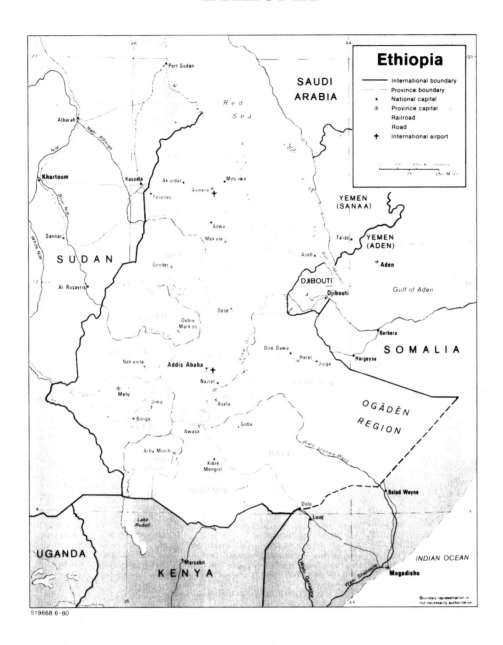

519668 6-80

**ARMY:**     Addis Ababa          Assab              Massawa
              Agordat              Barentu
              Asmara               Harar

**NAVY:**     Assab (Soviet Port Access)   Embaticalla        Massawa (Soviet Port
              Dahlak Islands (Soviet                          Access)
              Naval Facility)

**AIR FORCE:**  Addis Ababa         Desse              Gore
                Asmara (Soviet Air Access)   Dire-Dawa       Harar
                Bahar Dar           Djidjigga          Kabre Dehar
                Bishoftu            Goba               Negili
                Debre Zeit          Gondar

781

# FIJI

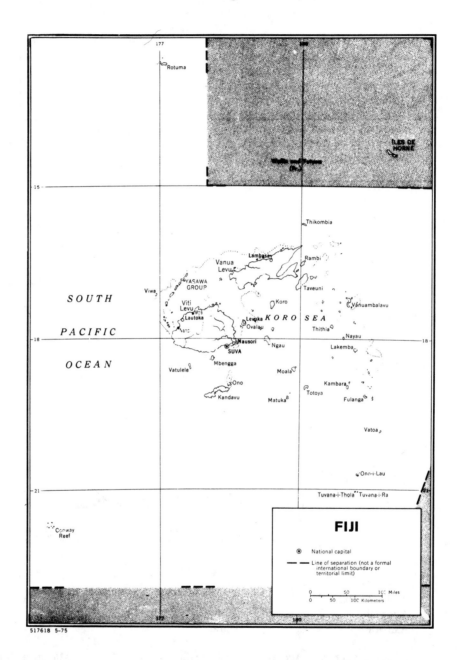

**ARMY:**    Nabua

**NAVY:**    Suva

# FINLAND

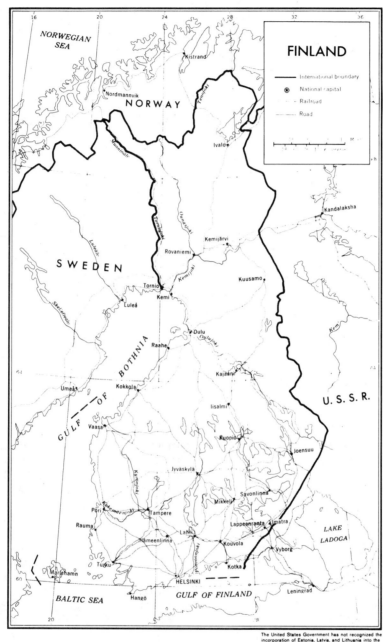

The United States Government has not recognized the
incorporation of Estonia, Latvia, and Lithuania into the
Soviet Union. Names and boundary representation
are not necessarily authoritative.

| ARMY: | Hameenlinna/Tarvastehus | Kuopio | Turku/Abo |
|---|---|---|---|
| | Luonetjarvi | Oulu/Uleaborg | Vassa/Vasa |
| | Kouvola | | |
| NAVY: | Hanko | Helsinki | Turku |
| AIR FORCE: | Jyvaskyla | Parote | Tampere |
| | Kauhava | Pori | Tikkakoski |
| | Kuopio-Rissala | Rissala | Utti |
| | Luonetjarvi | Rovaniemi | |

# FRANCE

**FRANCE**

Scale of Miles

0    100    200

© AMERICAN MAP CO., INC., N.Y.

**ARMY:**

| | | |
|---|---|---|
| Amicus | Lyon | Rennes |
| Beauvais | Marseilles | Rheims |
| Besancon | Metz | St. Germain |
| Bordeaux | Nancy | St. Malo |
| Constanz | Nantos | Strasbourg |
| Laon | Paris | Verdun |
| Lille | Pau | Versailles |
| Luneville | | |

**NAVY:**

| | | |
|---|---|---|
| Ajaccio | Corsica | Lorient |
| Aspretto | Hyeres | Nimes-Garons |
| Bordeaux | Landivisiau | Saint-Mandrier |
| Brest | Lann-Bihoue | St. Raphael |
| Cherbourg | Lanveoc-Poulmic | Toulon |

**AIR FORCE:**

| | | |
|---|---|---|
| Aix-les-Milles | Colmer | Orleans |
| Amberieu | Compiegne | Paris |
| Apt | Creil | Reims |
| Avord | Dijon | St. Didier |
| Bordeaux-Merignac | Evreaux | Salon-de-Provence |
| Bretigny | Istres | Solenzara |
| Cambrai | Le Bourget | Strasbourg |
| Cazaux | Luxeuil | Toul |
| Chambery | Metz | Toulouse-Francazal |
| Chateaudun | Mont-de-Marsan | Toul-Rosieres |
| Clermont-Ferrand | Nancy | Tours |
| Cognac | Orange | Villaboublay |

# GABON

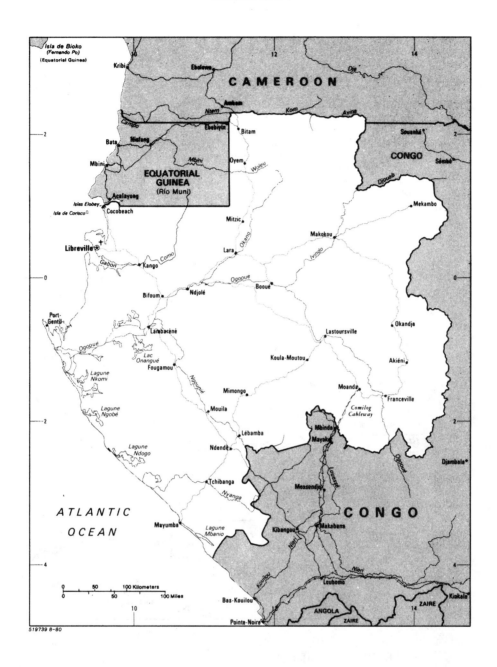

**ARMY:**        Libreville (French Army)

**NAVY:**        Libreville              Port Gentil

**AIR FORCE:**   Lambarene           Mvengue          Port Gentil
                Libreville           Oyem             Tchibanga

# GAMBIA

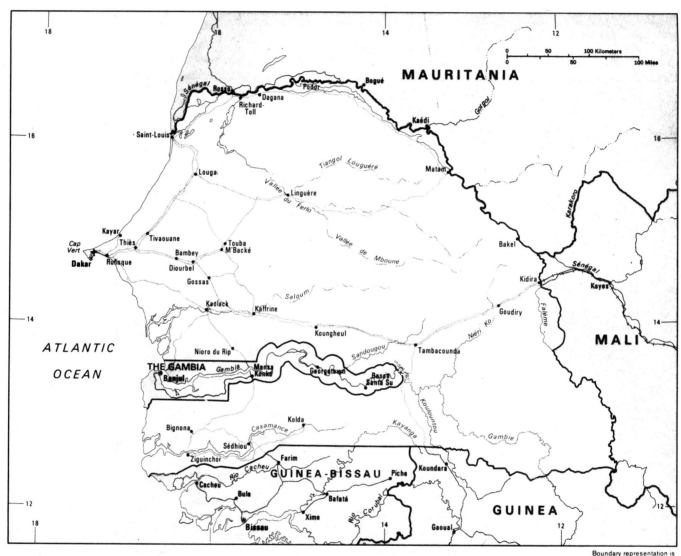

Boundary representation is
not necessarily authoritative

| | | |
|---|---|---|
| **ARMY:** | Banjul | Libreville |
| **NAVY:** | Banjul | |

# GERMAN DEMOCRATIC REPUBLIC

| **ARMY:** | Berlin (East) | Gera | Rostock |
|---|---|---|---|
| | Cottbus | Halle/Saale | Schwerin |
| | Dresden | Karl Marx Stadt | Suhl |
| | Eggesin | Leipzig | Zossen-Wunsdorf |
| | Erfurt | Magdenburg | (Soviet Union) |
| | Frankfurt An Der Oder | Potsdam | |

| **NAVY:** | Dranske-Bug | Sassnitz | Warnemunde |
|---|---|---|---|
| | Pennemunde | Stralsund | Wolgast |
| | Rostock | Tarnewitz | |

| **AIR FORCE:** | Bautzen | Janschwalde | Pennemunde |
|---|---|---|---|
| | Bergen | Jocksdorf | Prenzlau |
| | Brandenburg | Juterbog | Preschen |
| | Brusin | Kamenz | Puttnitz |
| | Cottbus | Kothen | Rothenburg |
| | Dessau | Marxwalde | Strausberg |
| | Dresden | Neubrandenburg | Tutow |
| | Drewitz | | |

# FEDERAL REPUBLIC OF GERMANY

**ARMY:**

Buckenburg
Celle
Dusseldorf
Frankfurt
   (United States Army)
Fritzlar
Hannover

Heidelberg (United States
   Army)
Itzehoe
Laupheim
Niedermendigl/Eifel
Niederstetten
Roth

Rothenburg/Hann
Rheine
Schleissheim
Seckenheim (NATO)
Stuttgart (United States
   Army)

**NAVY:**

Bremerhaven
Eggebeck
Hamburg

Kiel
Kiel-Holtenau
Nordholz

Olpenitz
Schleswig-Jagel
Wilhelshaven

**AIR FORCE:**

Ahlhorn/Oldenburg
Badlem Sollingem
   (Canadian Air Command)
Bitburg (United States
   Air Force)
Bremgarten/Baden
Buchel/Mosel
Diepholz
Erding
Fassburg/Celle
Frankfurt am Main
   (United States Air Force)
Furstenfeldbruck
Hohn
Husum
Ingolstadt

Jever
Kaufbeuren/Allgau
Koln/Nonn
Koln-Wahn
Lahr (Canadian Air
   Command)
Landsberg
Landstuhl
   (United States Air Force)
Lechfeld (Ausburg)
Leck/Schleswig
Leipheim
Memmingen/Allgau
Neuberg/Donau
Neubiberg

Norvenich bei Koln
Oldenburg
Pferdsfeld/Pfalz
Rheine-Hopsten
Sembach
   (United States Air Force)
Spangdahlem
   (United States Air Force)
Uetersen
Wahn
Wittmundhafen
Wunstorf/Hann
Zweibrucken
   (United States Air Force)

# GHANA

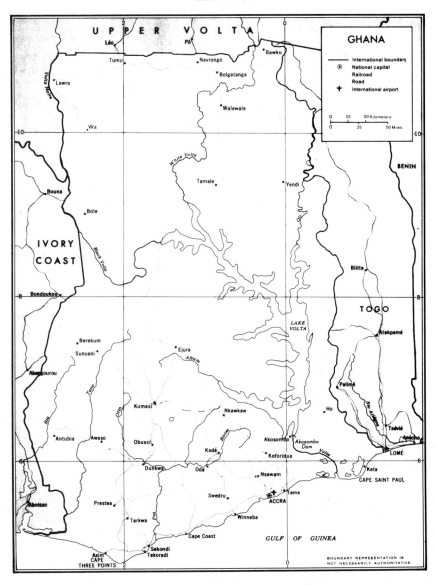

**ARMY:** Accra

**NAVY:** Sekondi    Tema

**AIR FORCE:** Accra    Takoradi
Kumasi    Tamali

# GREECE

| ARMY: | Athens | Megara | |
|---|---|---|---|
| NAVY: | Mitilini<br>Nea Makri (United States Navy)<br>Patrai<br>Piraeus | Salamis<br>Solonika<br>Souda Bay (United States Navy) | Thessaloniki<br>Valos |
| AIR FORCE: | Athens (United States Air Force)<br>Achialos<br>Andravidha<br>Araxos<br>Dhekelia | Eleusis<br>Iraklion (Crete— United States Air Force)<br>Kalamata<br>Larissa<br>Nea Ankhialos | Suda Bay<br>Tanagra<br>Tatoi<br>Thessaloniki-Mikra<br>Timbakion |

# GRENADA

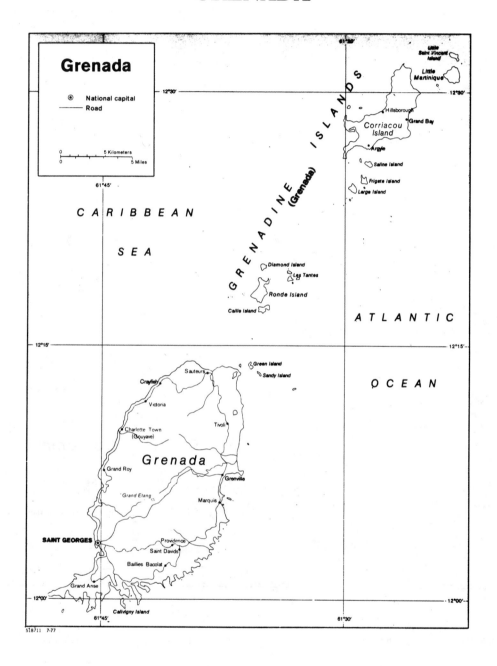

**ARMY:**     St. George's

# GUATEMALA

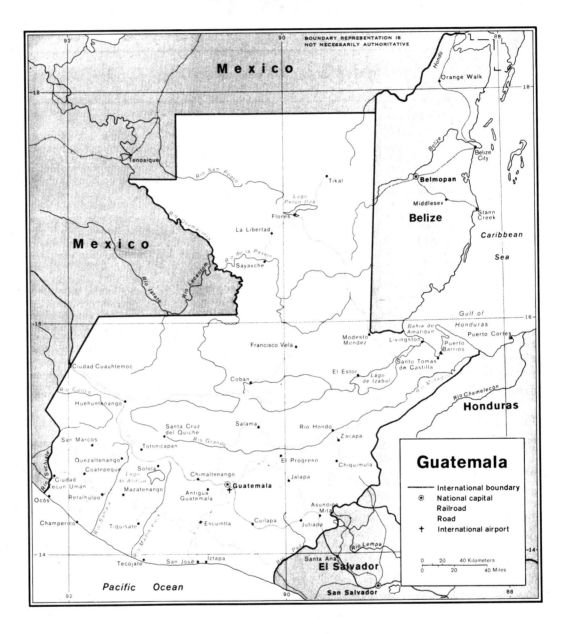

| ARMY: | Guatemala City | Puerto Barrios | San Jose |
|---|---|---|---|
| NAVY: | Santo Tomas de Castillos | Sipacate | |
| AIR FORCE: | Flores<br>Guatemala City | Los Cipresales<br>Puerto Barrios | Puerto San Jose<br>Retal Muleu |

# GUINEA

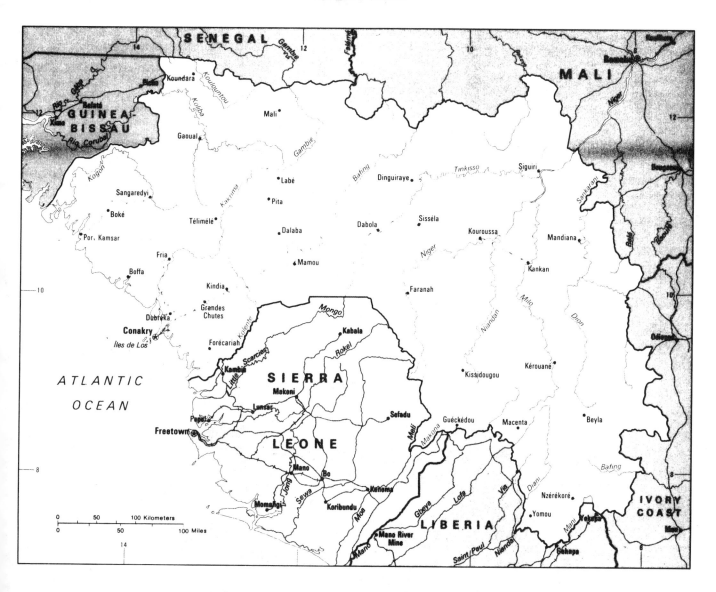

**ARMY:** Conakry

**NAVY:** Conakry
(Soviet Port Access)

**AIR FORCE:** 

| | | |
|---|---|---|
| Boke | Kakande | Labe |
| Conakry | Kankan | N'Zerekore |
| (Soviet Air Access) | Kissidougou | Siguiri |
| Gbessia | | |

# GUINEA-BISSAU

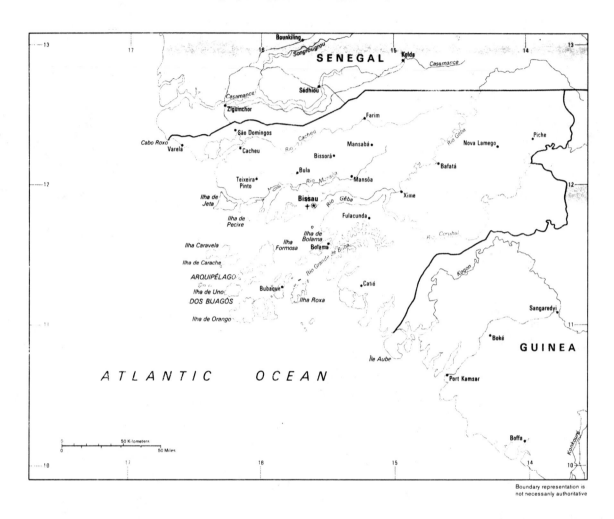

Boundary representation is
not necessarily authoritative

**ARMY:**        Bissau

**NAVY:**        Bissau (Soviet Port Access)

**AIR FORCE:**   Bissau          Nova Lamego
                 Bissora         Teixeira Pinto

# GUYANA

——— International boundary  Road
✳ National capital  ✚ International airport
Railroad

**ARMY:**   Camp Ayanganna (Thomas Lands, Georgetown)

# HAITI

**ARMY:**      Port-au-Prince

**NAVY:**      Bizoton

**AIR FORCE:**  Bowen Field          Duvalier Field          Les Cayes
          (Port-au-Prince)     Gonaives               Port-au-Paix
          Cap Haitien

# HONDURAS

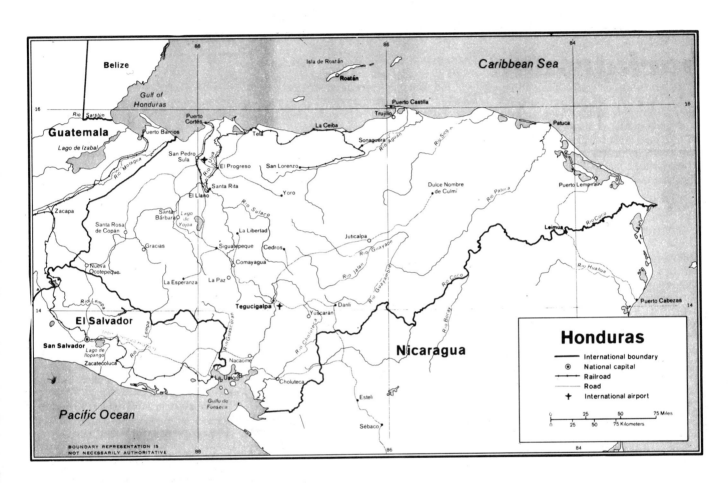

**ARMY:**        San Pedro Sula                Tegucigalpa

**NAVY:**        Ama Pala                      Puerto Cortes

**AIR FORCE:**  La Maesa                    Tegucigalpa
                 San Pedro Sula           Tocontin

# HONG KONG

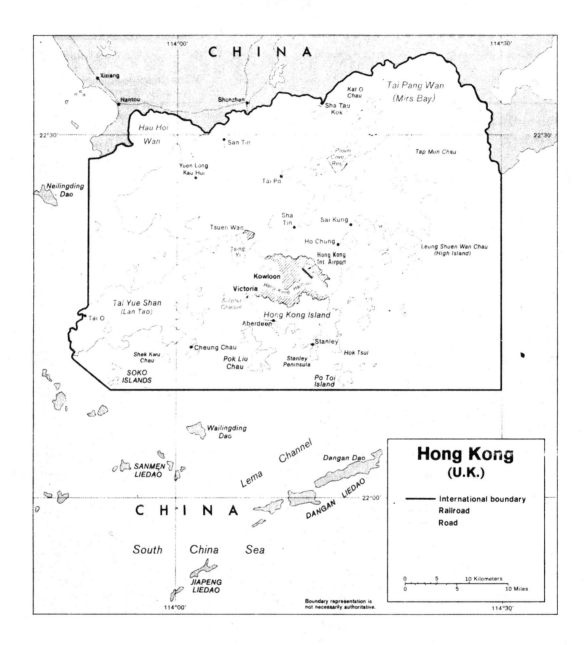

| | | | |
|---|---|---|---|
| **ARMY:** | Hong Kong | Kowloon | |
| **AIR FORCE:** | Kai Tak | Kowloon | Sek Kong |

# HUNGARY

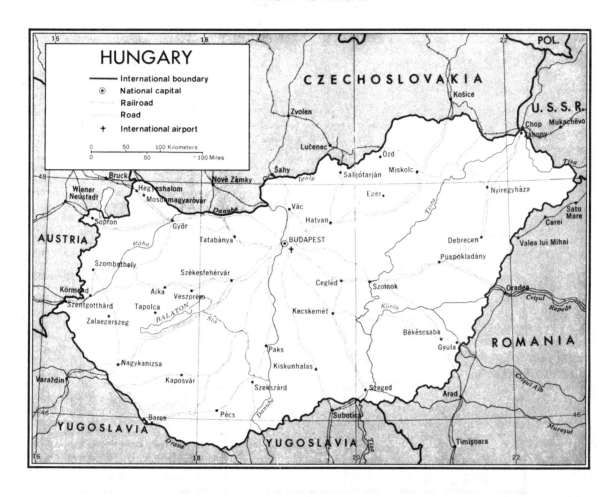

**ARMY:**    Budapest

**AIR FORCE:**

| | | |
|---|---|---|
| Budaors | Kecskemet | Pecs |
| Budapest | Kiskunfeleghaza | Szeged |
| Debrecen | Kiskunlachaza | Szekessehervar |
| Domboava Estergom | Kundmadaras | Szentkiralyaszabadja |
| Gyor | Matyasfold | Szolnok |
| Kalosca | Miskolc | Szombathely |
| Kaposvar | Papa | Tokol |

# ICELAND

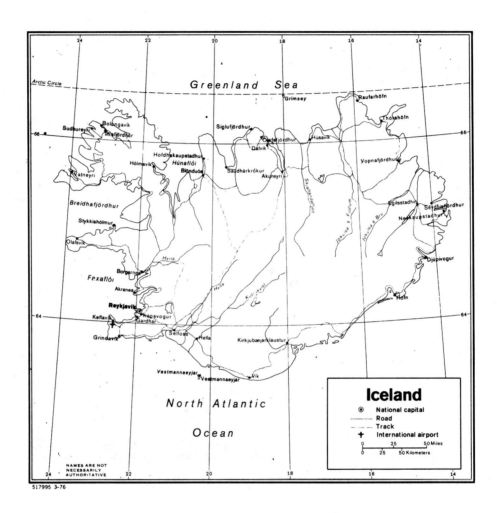

**ARMY:**    Reykjavik

**NAVY:**    Keflavik             Reykjavik
                (United States Navy)    (Coast Guard)

# INDIA

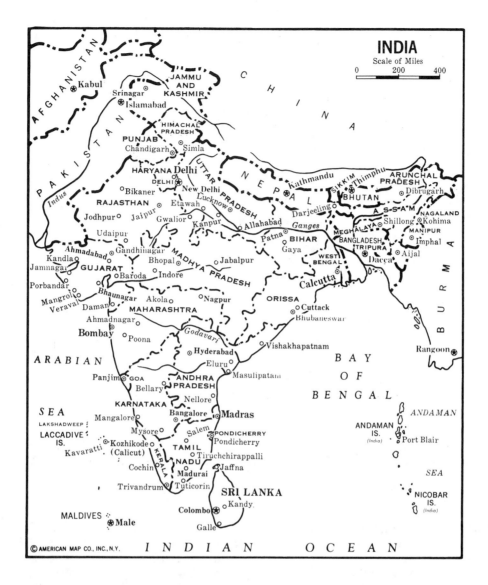

**ARMY:**

| | |
|---|---|
| Calcutta | Poona |
| Lucknow | Simla |

**NAVY:**

| | | |
|---|---|---|
| Bombay | Goa | Okha Jamgagar |
| Calcutta | Lonavala | Port Blair |
| Cochin | New Delhi | Vishakapatnam |

**AIR FORCE:**

| | | |
|---|---|---|
| Adampur | Chabua | Jorhat |
| Agartala | Chandigarh | Kalaikunda |
| Agra | Faridkot | Leh |
| Allahabad | Gauhati | Nagpur |
| Ambala | Gaya | New Delhi |
| Amritsar | Gorakhpur | Okha |
| Bagdogra | Gwalior | Palam |
| Bakshi-ka-Talab | Hakimpet | Panthankot |
| Bamrauli | Halwara | Pune Sulur |
| Bangalore | Hasimara | Shillong |
| Bareilly | Hindon | Srinagar |
| Barrackpore | Hyderabad | Tambaram |
| Begumpet | Jammu | Tezpur |
| Bhuj | Jamnagar | Uttarlai |
| Bikaner | Jodhpur | Yelahanka |
| Bombay | | |

# INDONESIA

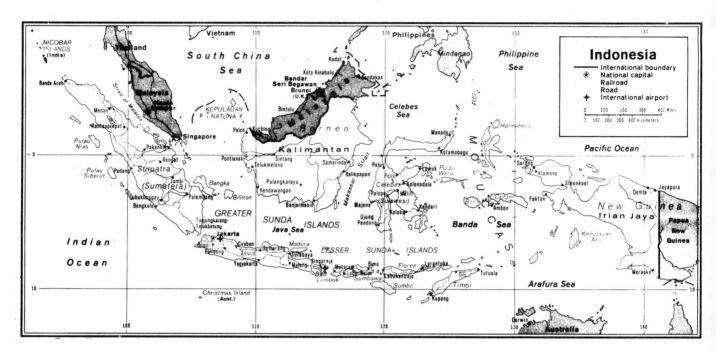

|  | | | |
|---|---|---|---|
| **ARMY:** | Central Java | Maluku | Sulawesi |
| | Central Kalimantan | North Sumatra | West Irian |
| | Djakarta | South Kalimantan | West Java |
| | East Kalimantan | South Sulawesi | West Kalimantan |
| | Lesser Sundas | South Sumatra | West Sumatra |
| **NAVY:** | Belawan | Kemajaran | Tanjungpinang |
| | Djakarta | Menado | Tanjung Uban |
| | Gorontolo | Surabaja | |
| **AIR FORCE:** | Abdul Rahmen Saleh | Halim | Menado |
| | Adisucipta | Husein | Morotai |
| | Amboina | Iswahjudi | Oeussi |
| | Ambon | Kalidjati | Padang |
| | Bacau | Kotaradji | Palembang |
| | Balikpapan | Kupang | Pangkalbinang |
| | Bandung | Lombok | Sabang |
| | Den Passar | Madium | Semarang |
| | Dili | Makassar | Surbaya |
| | Djakarta | Medan | Taraken |
| | Djambi | | |

# IRAN

| ARMY: | Chahbahar | Khouramshar | Tabriz |
|---|---|---|---|
| | Isfahan | Qous | Teheran |

| NAVY: | Bandar-e-Enzi | Chahbahar | Kharg Island |
|---|---|---|---|
| | Bandar Lengel (Abbas) | Hengham Island | Khorramshahr |
| | Busheyr | | |

| AIR FORCE: | Abadan | Hamadan | Nowshshr |
|---|---|---|---|
| | Ahwaz | Isfahan | Queys |
| | Bandar Abbas | Jask | Quchan |
| | Benshahr | Kapkan | Sarab |
| | Bisheh | Kazerun | Shahabad |
| | Boyuk Khnatu | Khaneh | Shahroki |
| | Busheyr | Khanian | Shiraz |
| | Chahbahar | Lali | Soga |
| | Dezful | Mahabad | Tabriz |
| | Doshan-Tappeh (Teheran) | Manzariyeh | Vandati |
| | Faharabad | Mashad | Zahidan |
| | Ghale-Marghi | Mehrabad | Zanjan |

**803**

# IRAQ

| ARMY: | Abadan<br>Baghdad | Kirkuk<br>Mosul | Tikrit |
|---|---|---|---|
| NAVY: | Basra<br>Umm Qasr<br>(Soviet Port Access) | | |
| AIR FORCE: | Baghdad<br>Basra<br>Habbaniyah | Kirkuk<br>Mosul<br>Rashid | Shaiba<br>Tikrit |

# IRELAND

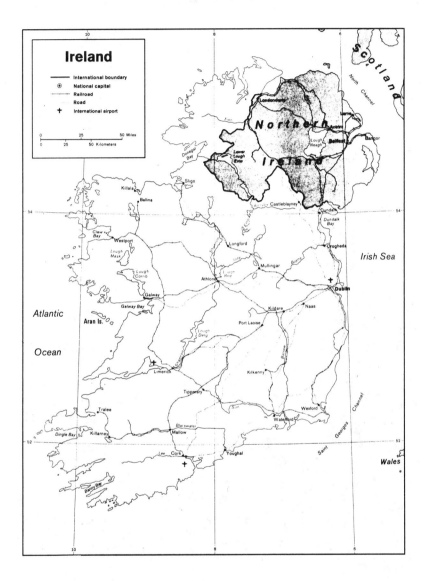

**ARMY:**      Dublin

**NAVY:**      Haulbowline
                (County Cork)

**AIR FORCE:**    Casement Airfield          Gormanston
                (Baldonnel)              (Meath)

# ISRAEL

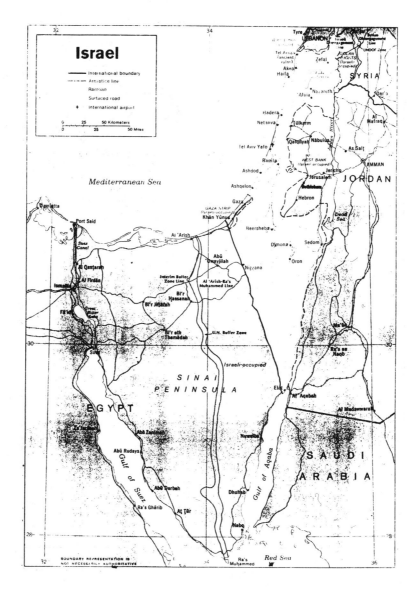

**ARMY:**    Beersheba        Jerusalem        Tel Aviv
Haifa        Negev

**NAVY:**    Ashdod        Eilat        Haifa

**AIR FORCE:**

| | | |
|---|---|---|
| Bir Hamma | El Bassa | Mahanayim |
| Bir Hasanah | Gebel Libni | Matred |
| Bir Jifjifah | Hatzerim | Ovda |
| Bir Thamada | Hatzor | Ramat David |
| Bir Yehouda | Herzliya | Sde Dov |
| Dov-Hoss | Isaab ben Yacov | Sedom |
| Ekron | Lod | Sharm el Sheikh |
| | | Yafo |

# ITALY

**ARMY:**

| | | |
|---|---|---|
| Bellino | Gorizia | Treviso |
| Bergamo | Naples | Trieste |
| Bologna | Novara | Udine |
| Bolzano | Padua | Veneto |
| Bressanone | Palermo | Venice |
| Bresso | Pisa (United States | Vercelli |
| Cagliari | Army Base) | Verona |
| Campoformido | Pordenon | Vicenza (United States |
| Casara | Portogruaro | Army Base) |
| Catania | Rome | Viterbo |
| Civitareehia | Salerno | Vittorio |
| Florence | Torino | |

**NAVY:**

| | | |
|---|---|---|
| Ancona | Cagliari | Leghorn |
| Arindisi (United States | Genoa | Messima |
| Navy Base) | La Maddalena | Naples |
| Augusta | (United States Navy Base) | Sigonella |
| Brindisi | La Spezia | Taranto |

**AIR FORCE:**

| | | |
|---|---|---|
| Amendola | Frosinone | Pisa |
| Bari | Ghedi | Pordenone |
| Brindisi | Gioia del Colle | (United States Air Force) |
| United States Air Force) | Grazzanise | Practicadi Mare (near Rome) |
| Cagliari-Elmos | Grosseto | Rimini |
| Cameri | Guidonia | Rivolto |
| Catawa | Istrana | Treviso |
| Cervia-San Giorgio | Latina | Treviso-San Angelo |
| Ciampino | Lecce | Verona |
| Decimomannu | Milan | Villafranca |

807

# IVORY COAST

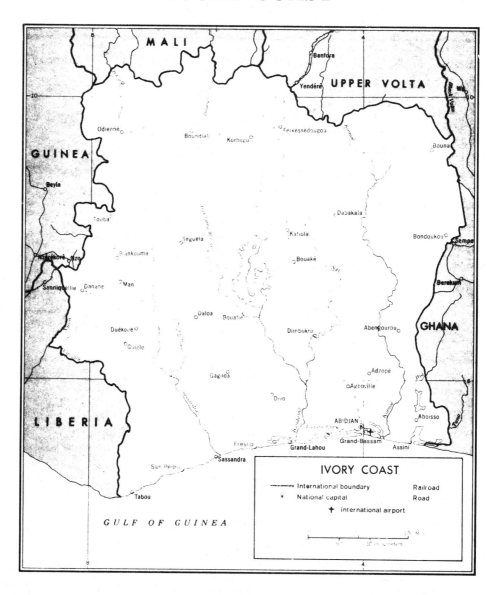

| | | |
|---|---|---|
| **ARMY:** | Akouedo | Daloa |
| | Bouake | Douala |
| **NAVY:** | Abidjan | Sassandra |
| | San Pedro | Tabou |
| **AIR FORCE:** | Abidjan-Porto Bouet | Bouake |
| | (French Air Force) | |

# JAMAICA

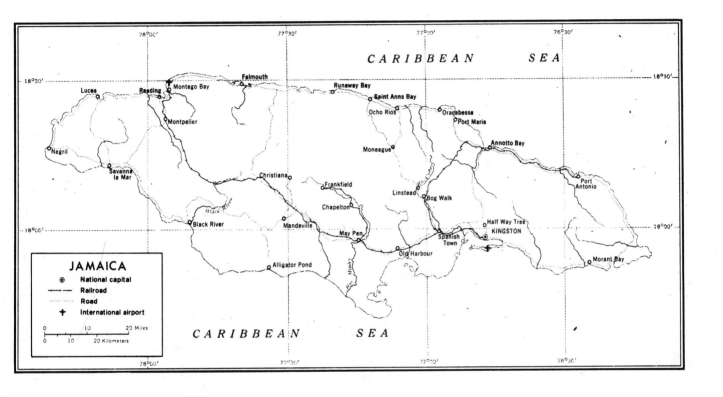

**ARMY:** Kingston

**NAVY:** Port Royal

**AIR FORCE:** Kingston      Palisades
               Montego Bay    Up Park Camp

# JAPAN

**ARMY:**

Akeno
Aomori
Asahigawa
Chitose
Fukuoka
Hachinoe
Hofu
Hokkaido (Island)
Ichigaya (near Tokyo)
Itami
Iwanuma

Jinmachi
Kaidichi
Kasumigaura
Kasuminone
Kisarazu
Kitakumamoto
Koza (Okinawa—
   United States Army)
Kumamoto
Makomanai
Moriyama

Nerima
Netabaru
Obihiro
Okadamy
Sapporo
Sendei
Sagamihara (United States
   Army)
Soomagahara
Tackikawa

**NAVY:**

Aburatsu
Atsugi
Hachinohe
Hakodate
Iwakuni
Kanoya
Kisarazu

Komatsujima
Kure
Maizuru
Ohminato
Ohmura
Okinawa
   (United States Navy)

Ozuki
Saiki
Sasebo (United States Navy)
Shimofusa
Shimonoseki
Tateyana
Yokosuka (United States Navy)

**AIR FORCE:**

Ashiya
Bofu-Kita
Chitose
Fuchu-shi
Gifu
Hamamatsu-Kita
Hamamatsu-Minani
Handa
Hofu
Huakuri
Iruma

Kasuga
Kamaki
Komatsu
Koza (Okinawa—
   United States Air Force)
Kumagaya
Kyakuri
Manda
Matsushima
Miho
Misawa

Miyazaki
Nana (Okinawa)
Niigata
Nyutabaru
Shizuhama
Tagchikawa
Tokyo (United States
   Air Force)
Tsuiki
Yokota

810

# JORDAN

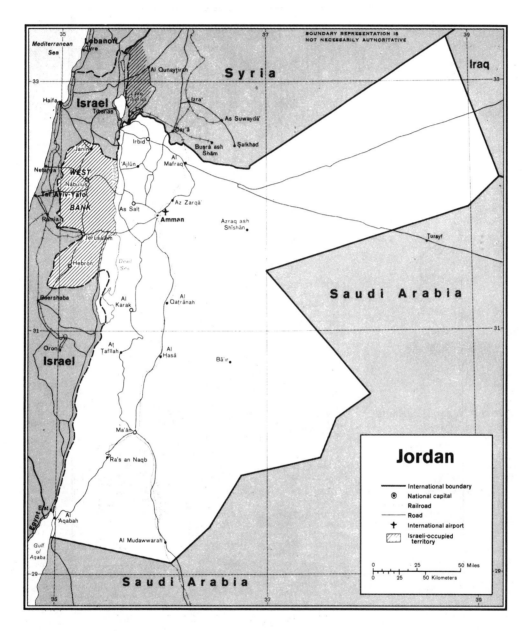

**ARMY:** Amman

**NAVY:** Aqaba

**AIR FORCE:** Al Mafraq (King Hussein)     El Azraq     Ma'an
Amman (King Abdullah)     Irbid     Prince Hassan
Aqaba     Koum

# KAMPUCHEA

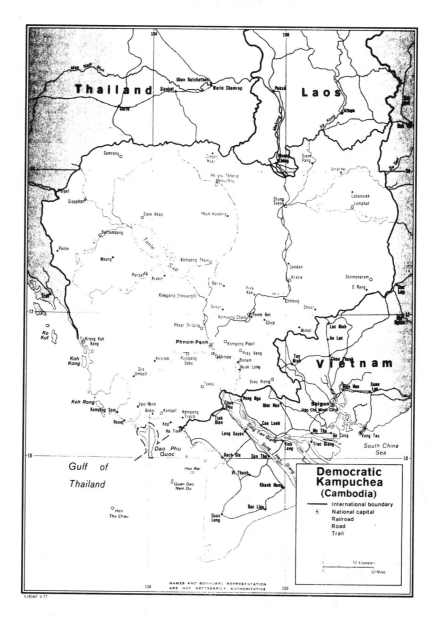

**ARMY:**      Phnom Penh

**NAVY:**      Kompong Som

**AIR FORCE:**    Angkor                 Kompong Chang
                      Battambang        Pochentong

# KENYA

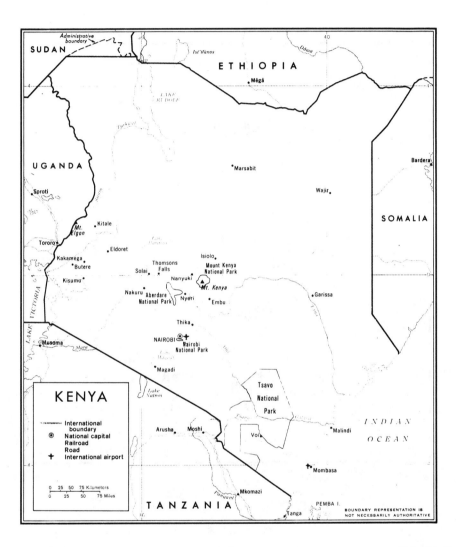

**ARMY:**
| | | |
|---|---|---|
| Kisumu | Lanet | Nairobi (Langata) |
| Kitale | Mombasa | Nakuru |

**NAVY:** Mombasa

**AIR FORCE:**
| | | |
|---|---|---|
| Eastleigh (Nairobi) | Kitale | Nakuri |
| Eldoret | Malindi | Nanyuki |
| Embakasi (Nairobi) | Mombasa | Nyeri |
| Kisumu | Moyale | Wilson (Nairobi) |

# KIRIBATI

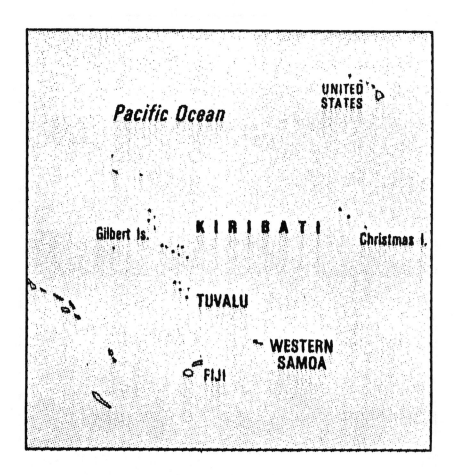

**ARMY:** Tarawa (Police)

# DEMOCRATIC PEOPLE'S REPUBLIC OF KOREA

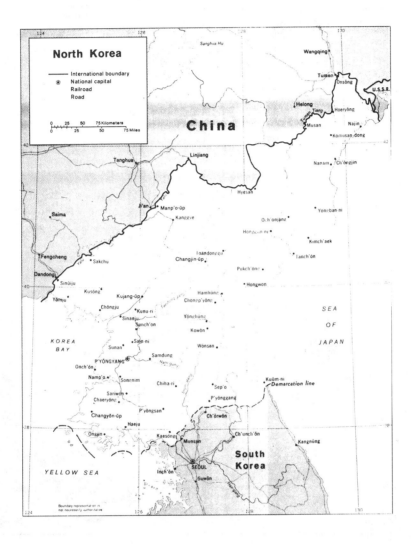

**ARMY:**      P'yongyang

**NAVY:**

| | | |
|---|---|---|
| Chaho | Kosong | Pipagot |
| Chinnamp'o | Mampo | Sagon Ni |
| Chongjin | Mayang Do | Taso Do |
| Haeju | Munchon | Wonsan |
| Kimch'aek | Nagin | |

**AIR FORCE:**

| | | |
|---|---|---|
| Namsi | Sinuiju | Uiju |
| Oksan-ni | Sunan | Wonsan |
| Pyong-ni | Taechon | Yenchi |
| P'yonyang | Ti Taung Kou | Yonpo |
| Saamchan | | |

# REPUBLIC OF KOREA

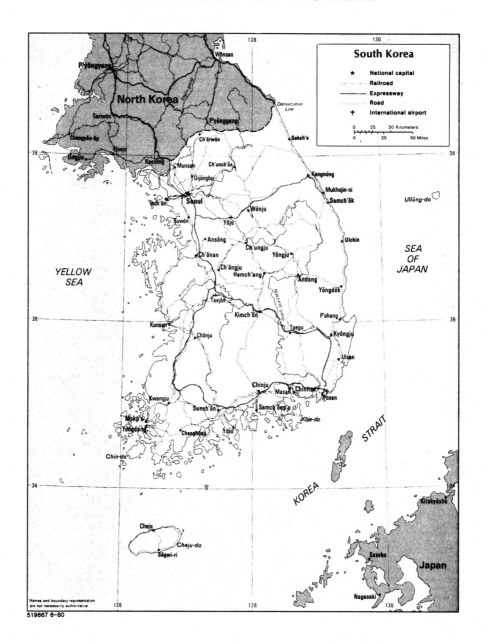

| ARMY: | Pyong Taek | Seoul | Tougduchon |
|---|---|---|---|
| | (United States Army) | (United States Army) | (United States Army) |
| | | | |
| NAVY: | Cheju | Mukho | Seoul |
| | Chinhae | Pohang | Tongyong |
| | Inchon (Chemulpo) | Pusan | Ulsan |
| | Mokpo | | |
| | | | |
| AIR FORCE: | Chinhae | Sachon | Taegu (United States |
| | Chungju | Seoul | Air Force) |
| | Osan | Suwon | Taejon |

# KUWAIT

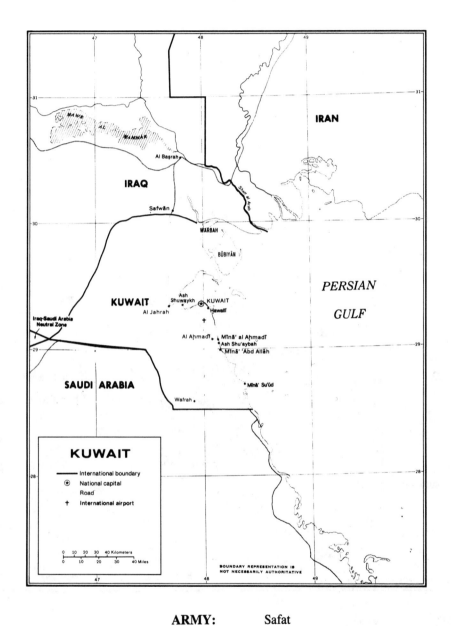

ARMY:        Safat

NAVY:        Safat

AIR FORCE:   Safat

# LAOS

**ARMY:**      Vientiane

**AIR FORCE:**    Luang-Prang            Phong Savan           Vientiane
                   Pakse                    Savannakhat

# LEBANON

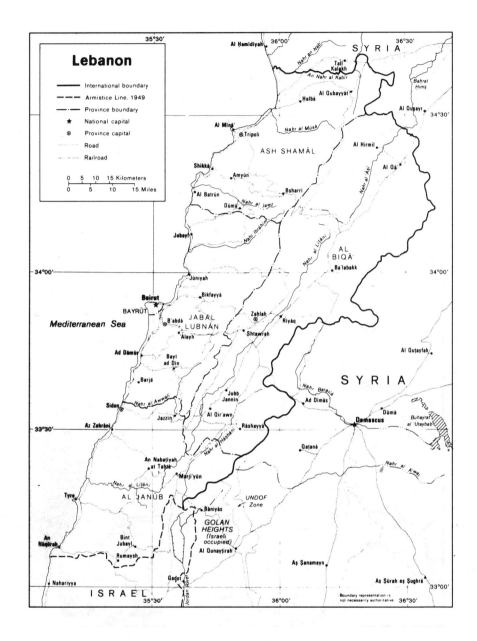

**ARMY:**

| | | |
|---|---|---|
| Armoun | Hamaana | Rayak |
| Baalbeck | Junich | Sidon |
| Batrun | Kfar Falouse | Tripoli |
| Beirut | Kleiat | Yazde |
| Byblos | | |

**AIR FORCE:** Beirut     Kleiat     Rayak

# LESOTHO

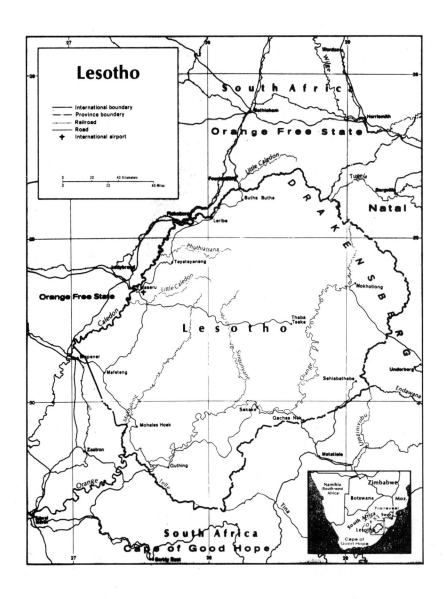

**ARMY:**      Maseru

# LIBERIA

**ARMY:** Egnis                    Monrovia                    Todec

**NAVY:** Monrovia

**AIR FORCE:** Roberts Field

# LIBYA

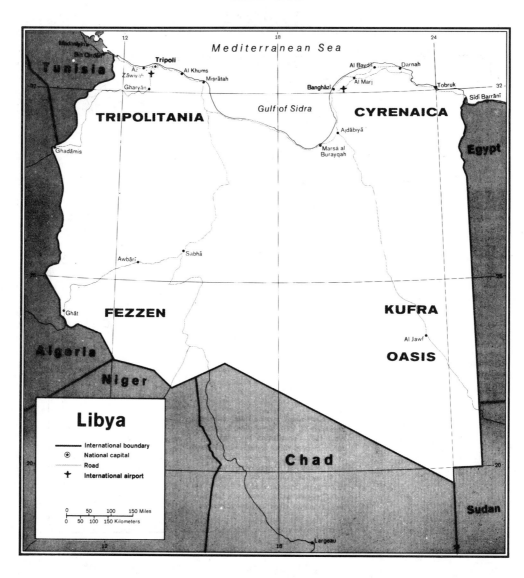

| ARMY: | Benghazi | Kufra | Tripoli |
|---|---|---|---|
| NAVY: | Benghazi | Tobruk | |
| | Darna | Tripoli | |
| AIR FORCE: | Banbah | El Awai | Okba ben Nafi |
| | Benghazi | Kufra | Tripoli |
| | Benina | Lutiyyah | Zawia |
| | El Adem | | |

# LIECHTENSTEIN

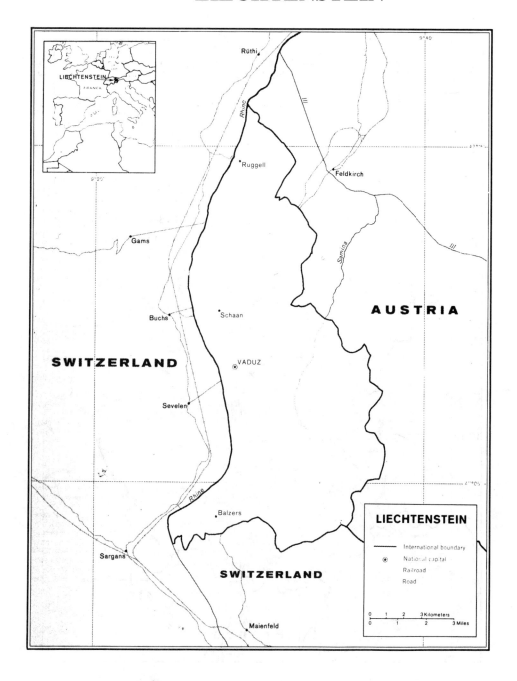

**ARMY:**    Vaduz (Police)

# LUXEMBORG

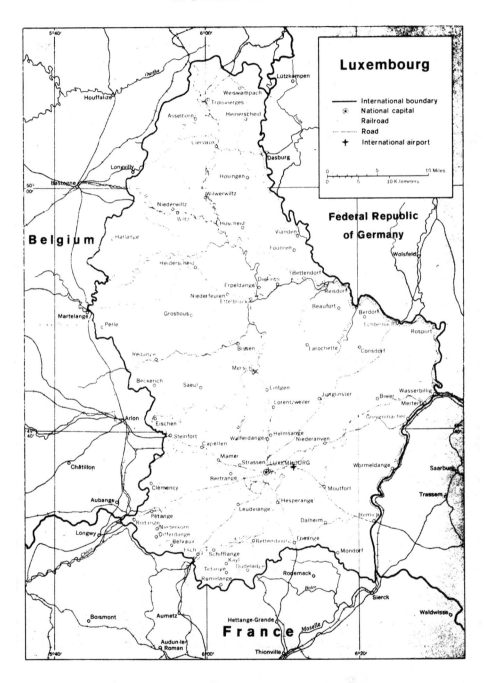

**ARMY:**      Luxembourg-Ville        Diekirch

# MADAGASCAR

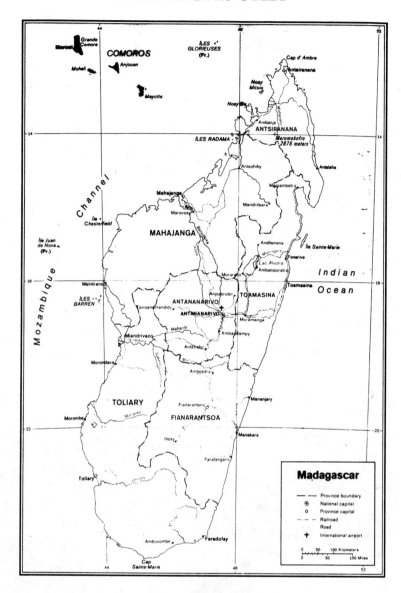

| ARMY: | Fianarantsoa | Majunga | Tamatave |
|---|---|---|---|
| | Fort Dauphin | Manakara | Tonanarive |
| | | | Tulear |
| NAVY: | Autisiranne | Fort Dauphin | Nossi-Be |
| | (Soviet Port Access) | Manakara | Tamatave |
| | Diego Suarez | Majunga | Tulear.20 |
| AIR FORCE: | Antalaha | Diego-Suarez | Majunga |
| | Antsohiky | Fianarantsoa | Nossi-Be |
| | Arivoniamamo | Fort Dauphin | Tamatave |
| | (Tananarive) | Ivato | Tulear |

# MALAWI

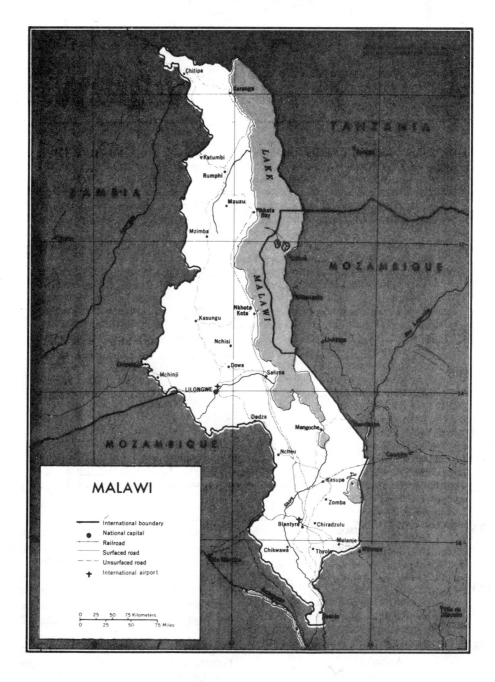

| | | |
|---|---|---|
| **ARMY:** | Blantyre | Lilongwe | Zomba |
| | Fort Johnston | Mzuzu | |
| **AIR FORCE:** | Blantyre | Mzuzu | Salima |

# MALAYSIA

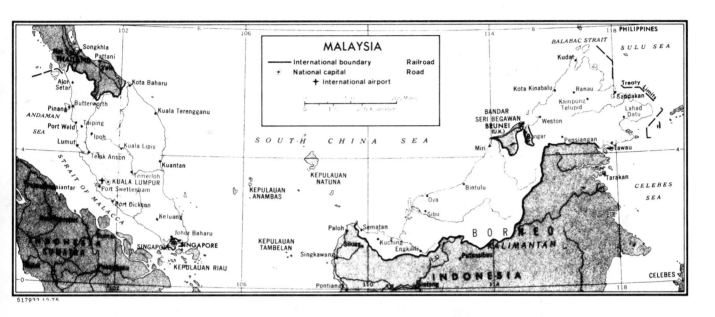

**ARMY:**
Ipoh
Jahore
Kota Belud
Kuala Lumpur
Port Dickson
Sungai Besi

**NAVY:**
Johore Straits
Kuantan
Labuan
Lumut Perak
Penang
Port Swethham
Sibu Rejang
Tanjong Gelang
Tawau
Tertendak
Woodlands

**AIR FORCE:**
Alor Star
Butterworth
Ipoh
Kedak
Kuala Lumpur
Kuantan
Kuching
Labuan
Paya Lebar

# MALDIVES

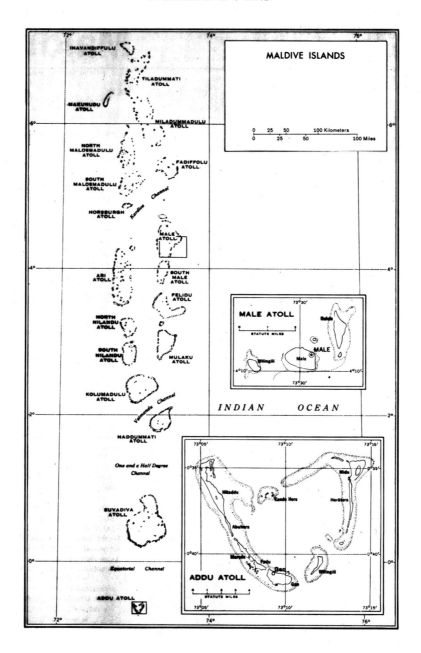

**ARMY:**        Male

# MALI

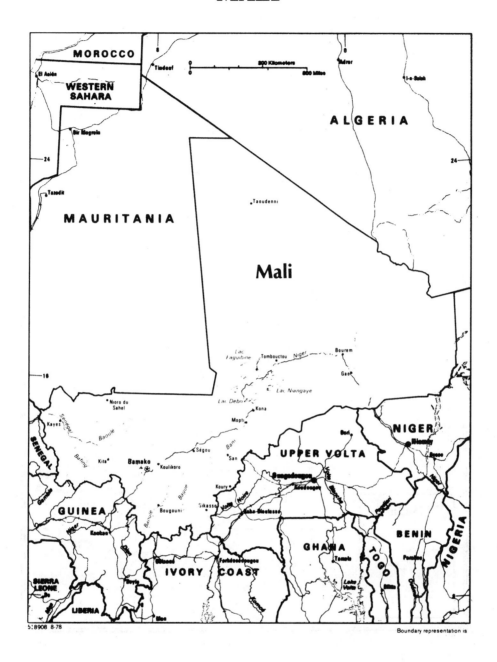

**ARMY:**      Bamako

**AIR FORCE:**   Bamako          Mopti          Tomboctou
               Gao            Nioro          Yelimane
               Kayes

# MALTA

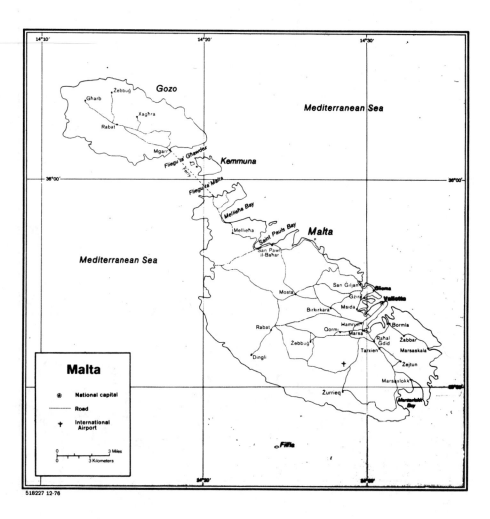

| | | | |
|---|---|---|---|
| **ARMY:** | Luqa Barracks | St. Andrew's Barracks | St. Patrick's Barracks (Sliema) |
| **NAVY:** | Hal Far | Valleta | |

# MAURITIUS

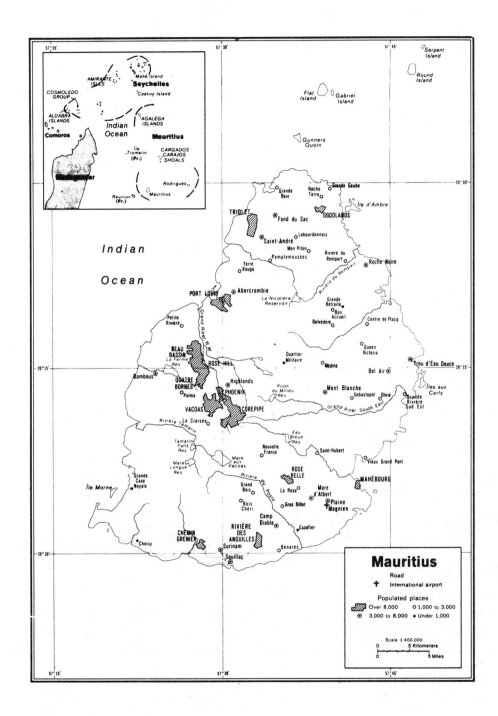

**ARMY:**      Port Luis

**NAVY:**      Port Luis (Soviet Port Access)

# MAURITANIA

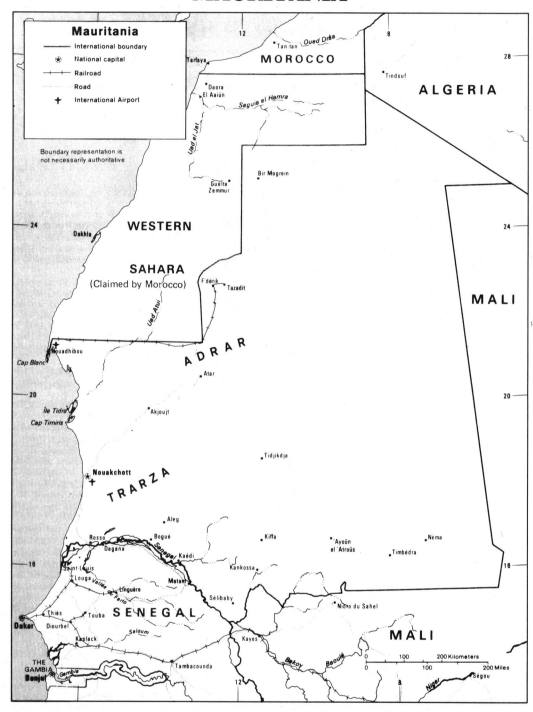

**ARMY:**

| | | |
|---|---|---|
| Ain ben Tili | Bir Moghrain | Oakhla |
| Akjouje | Nouadhibou | Tiris el-Gharbia |
| Atar | Nouakchott | Zouerake |

**NAVY:** Nouachchott     Nouadhibou

**AIR FORCE:**

| | | |
|---|---|---|
| Aion-el-Atrous | Fort Trinquet | Nouakchott |
| Akjoujt | Kaedi | Novadhibou |
| Atar | Kiffa | Rosso |
| Fort Gouraud | | |

# MEXICO

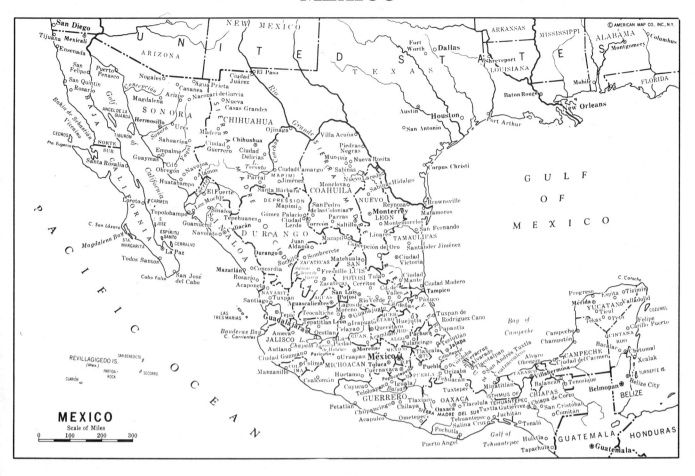

**ARMY:**
| | | |
|---|---|---|
| Aquacalientes | Hermosillo | Queretaro |
| Campeche | Heroica Puebla de Zaragoza | Saltillo |
| Chetumal | Jalapa Enriquez | San Luis Potosi |
| Chihuahua | La Paz | Tepic |
| Chilpancingo de los Bravos | Merida | Tlaxcala de Xicohtencatl |
| Ciudad Victoria | Mexicali | Toluca de Lerdo |
| Colima | Mexico City | Tuxtla Gutierrez |
| Cuernavaca | Monterrey | Victoria de Durango |
| Culiacan Rosales | Morelia | Villahermosa |
| Guadalajara | Oaxaca de Juarez | Zacatecas |
| Guanajuato | Pachuca de Soto | |

**NAVY:**
| | | |
|---|---|---|
| Acapulco | Jalisco | Salina Cruz |
| Bajo California Norte | La Paz | Sinaloa |
| Campeche | Lazaro Cardenas | Sonova |
| Chetumal | Mazatlan | Tabasco |
| Chiapas | Mexico City | Tamaulipas |
| Ciudad del Carmen | Oaxaca | Tampico |
| Ensenada | Puerto Cortes | Vera Cruz |
| Guayamas | Puerto Madero | Yikalpeten |
| Guerrero | Quintana Roo | Yucatan |

**AIR FORCE:**
| | | |
|---|---|---|
| Acapulco | Ensenada | Santa Luica |
| Cozumel | Ixtepec | Zapopan |
| Cuidad | Merida | |

# MONACO

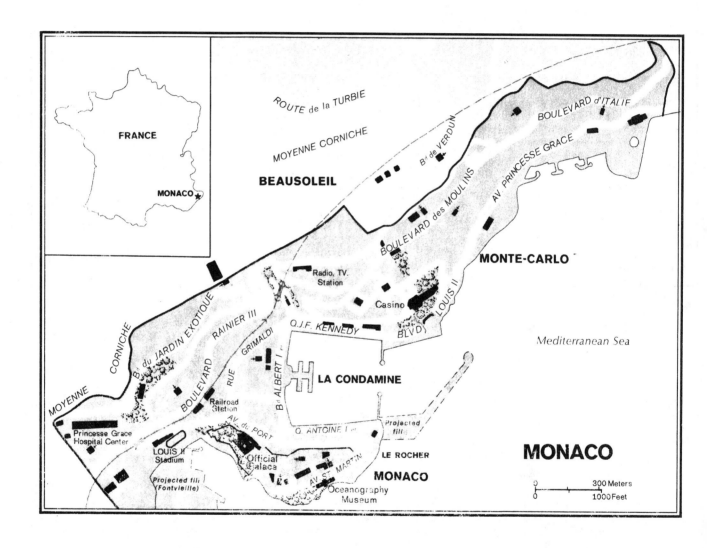

**ARMY:**        Monaco-ville (Police)

834

# MONGOLIA

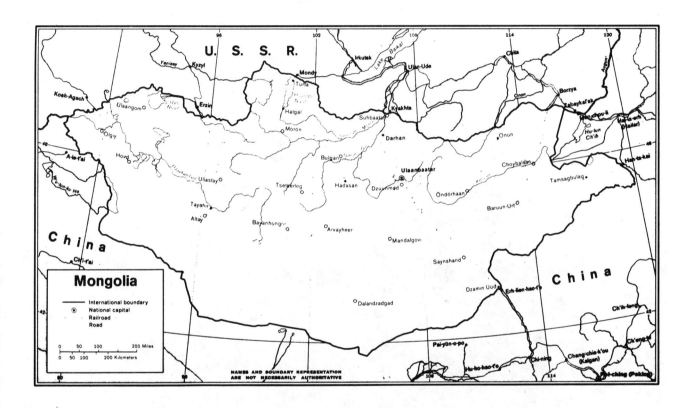

**ARMY:** Ulan Bator

**AIR FORCE:** Sayn Shanda          Ulan Bator

# MOROCCO

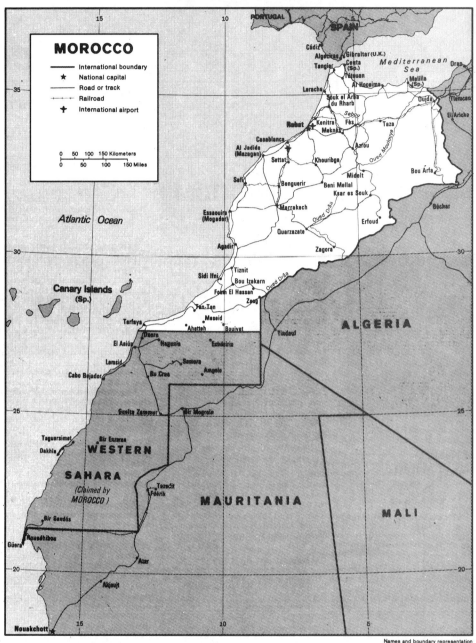

**ARMY:**

| | | |
|---|---|---|
| Bouizakara | Ohoud | Oujda |
| El Arak | Ouarzazate | Rabat |
| Errachidia | Oued ad Dakar | Saguiet El Hamra |
| Meknes | Oued Draa | Zellaka |

**NAVY:**

| | | |
|---|---|---|
| Agadir | Kenitra | Tangier |
| Casablance | Safi | |

**AIR FORCE:**

| | | |
|---|---|---|
| Agadir | Larache | Rabat |
| Ben Guerin | Marrakesh | Rabat Sale |
| Boulhat | Meknes | Safi |
| Casablanca | Melliila | Sidi Slimane |
| Fez | Mohammedia | Solon |
| Henitra | Nouasseur | Tanger |
| Khouribga | Port Lyautey | Tetuan |
| Laayoune | | |

# MOZAMBIQUE

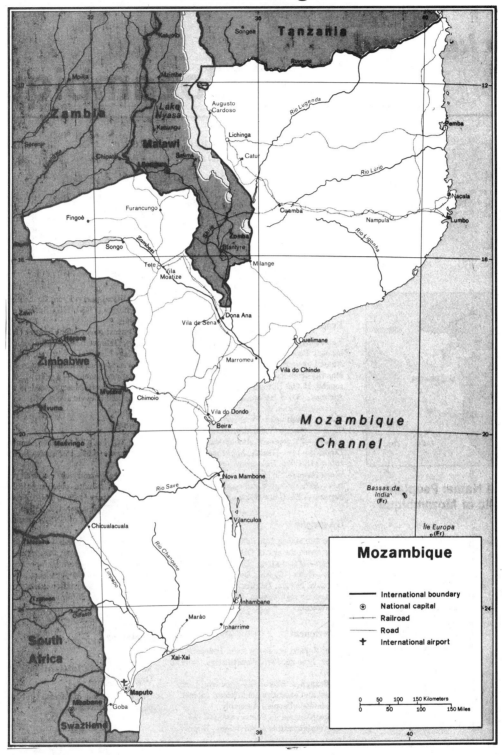

**ARMY:**      Maputo

**NAVY:**      Beira                    Metangula                Pemba
             Maputo                   Nacala

**AIR FORCE:** Beira                    Nacala
               (Soviet Port Access)       (Soviet Port Access)
             Chimoio                  Sofala
             Maputo                   Tete
               (Soviet Port Access)

# NAURU

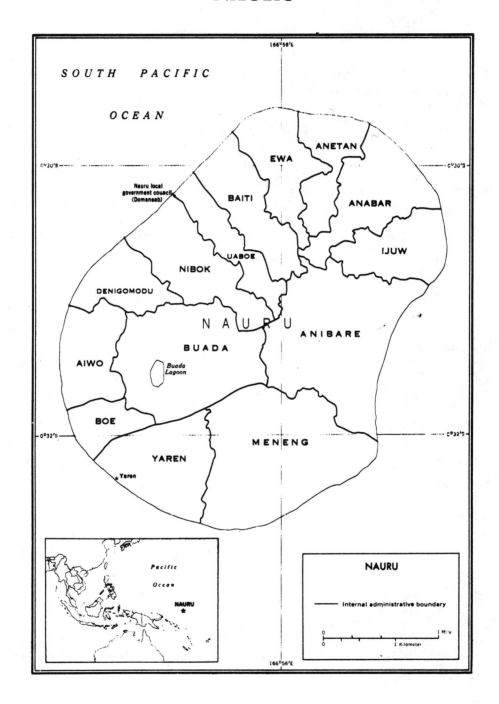

**ARMY:** Yaren (Police)

# NEPAL

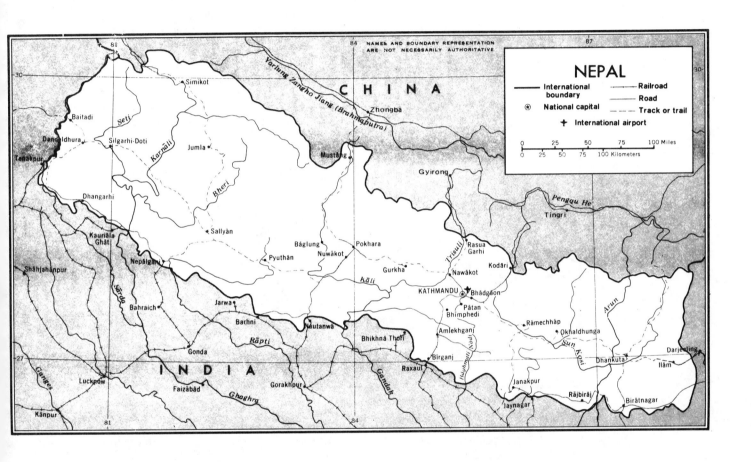

**ARMY:**     Biratnagur         Kathmandu
                 Dharan              Nepalgans

# NETHERLANDS

| ARMY: | Amersfoort | Breda | The Hague |
| --- | --- | --- | --- |
| | Apeldoorn | Deventer | Harderwijk |
| | Arnhem | Gouda | |
| NAVY: | Amsterdam | De Kooy | Rotterdam |
| | Curacao | Flushing | Valkenburg |
| | Den Helder | | |
| AIR FORCE: | Deelan | Rijswijk | Twente |
| | Eindhoven | Soesterberg | Volkel |
| | Gilze-Rijen | (United States Air Force) | Zelst |
| | Leeuwarden | | |

# NETHERLANDS ANTILLES

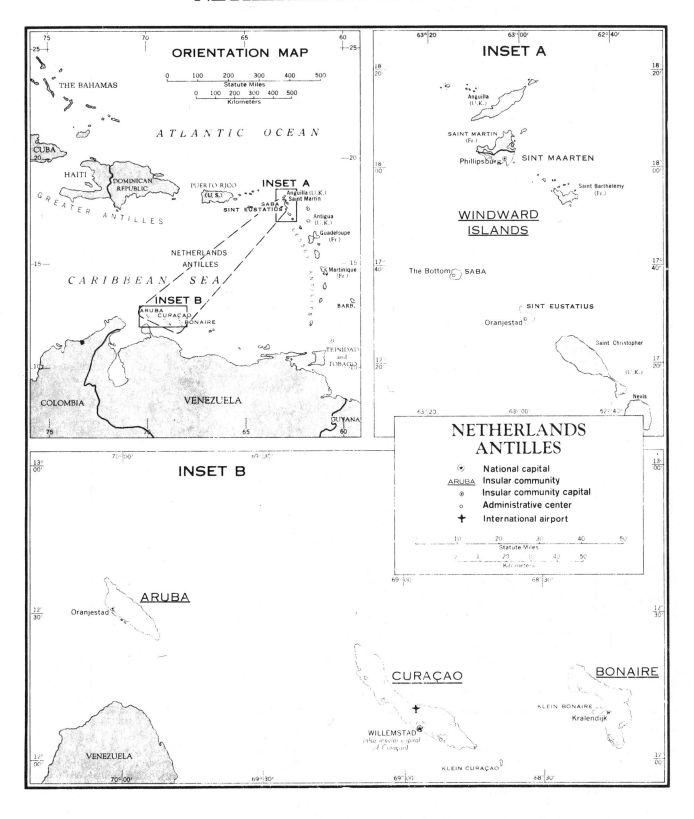

**ORIENTATION MAP**

Statute Miles
0   100   200   300   400   500

Kilometers
0   100   200   300   400   500

THE BAHAMAS

ATLANTIC OCEAN

CUBA

HAITI

DOMINICAN REPUBLIC

GREATER ANTILLES

PUERTO RICO (U.S.)

INSET A

Anguilla (U.K.)
Saint Martin

SABA
SINT EUSTATIUS

Antigua (U.K.)

Guadeloupe (Fr.)

NETHERLANDS ANTILLES

CARIBBEAN SEA

Martinique (Fr.)

LESSER ANTILLES

INSET B

ARUBA
CURAÇAO
BONAIRE

BARB.

COLOMBIA

VENEZUELA

TRINIDAD and TOBAGO

GUYANA

**INSET A**

Anguilla (U.K.)

SAINT MARTIN (Fr.)

Phillipsburg   SINT MAARTEN

Saint Barthélemy (Fr.)

WINDWARD ISLANDS

The Bottom   SABA

SINT EUSTATIUS
Oranjestad

Saint Christopher

(U.K.)

Nevis

## NETHERLANDS ANTILLES

⊛   National capital
ARUBA   Insular community
⊙   Insular community capital
o   Administrative center
✛   International airport

Statute Miles
10   20   30   40   50

Kilometers
1   20   30   40   50

**INSET B**

ARUBA
Oranjestad

CURAÇAO

WILLEMSTAD
(also insular capital of Curaçao)

BONAIRE

KLEIN BONAIRE
Kralendijk

VENEZUELA

KLEIN CURAÇAO

**NAVY:**   Marinebasis Parera (Willemstaf, Curacao)        Savaneta Camp

**AIR FORCE:**   Curacao

841

# NEW ZEALAND

**NEW ZEALAND**

⊛ National capital
Railroad
Road
✈ International airport

0   50   100   150 Kilometers
0   50      100    150 Miles

| ARMY: | Auckland | Palmerston North | Papakura Camp |
| | Christchurch | | (South Auckland) |
| NAVY: | Auckland | | |
| AIR FORCE: | Hobsonville (Auckland) | Te Rapa | Wigram |
| | Ohakea | Whenupai | Woodbourne |

# NICARAGUA

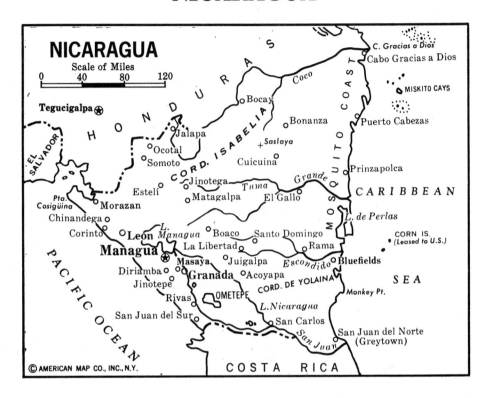

**ARMY:** Managua

**AIR FORCE:** Managua           Puerto Cabeza

# NIGER

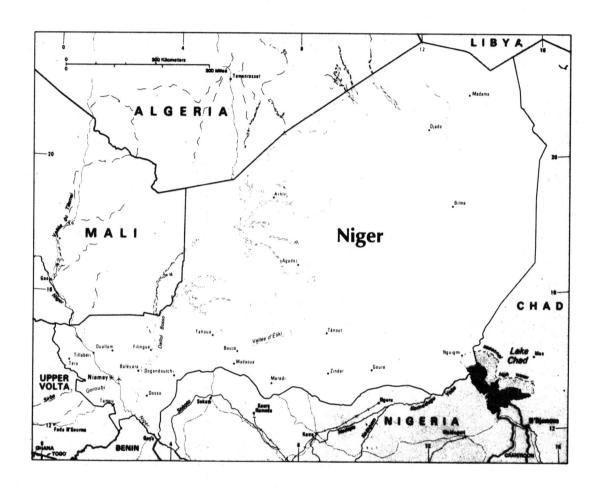

**ARMY:**    Niamey

**AIR FORCE:**    Agadez               Niamey                Zinder
                         Maradi               Tohoua

# NIGERIA

| ARMY: | Bauchi | Jali | Lagos |
| | Calabar | Jos | Minna |
| | Ibadan | Kaduna | Zaria |
| | Ikeja | Kano | |

| NAVY: | Abonema | Kaduna-Jayi | Onne Port |
| | Bonny | Koko | Port Harcourt |
| | Calabar | Lagos | Sapele |
| | Dagema Port | Lekki | Warri |
| | Escravos | | |

| AIR FORCE: | Abuja | Ilorin | Makurdi |
| | Benin City | Jos | Murtula Mohammed |
| | Calabar | Kaduna | Port Harcourt |
| | Ede | Kano | Sokolo |
| | Enugu | Lagos | Yola |
| | Ibadan | Maidurguri | Zaria |

# NORWAY

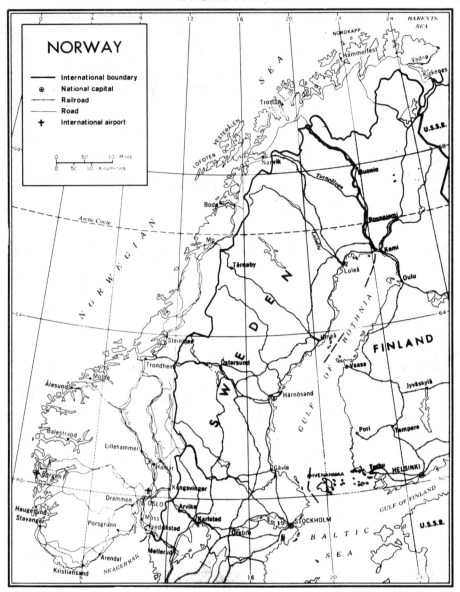

**ARMY:**

| | | |
|---|---|---|
| Bardutoss (Near Tromso) | Hamar | Oslo |
| Bergen | Harstad | Troncheim |
| Bodo | Kristiansand | |

**NAVY:**

| | | |
|---|---|---|
| Bergen | Hundrvaag | Tromsdalen |
| Haakonsvern | Kristiansand | Tromso |
| Harstad | Ramsund | Trondheim |
| Horten | | |

**AIR FORCE:**

| | | |
|---|---|---|
| Andenes | Gardemoen | Sola |
| Andoya | Kjeller | Stavanger |
| Banank | Laskelr | Stjordal |
| Bardufoss | Orland | Trondheim |
| Bergen | Oslo | Vaernes |
| Bodo | Rygge | Vanse |
| Brekstad | Sandefjord | |

# OMAN

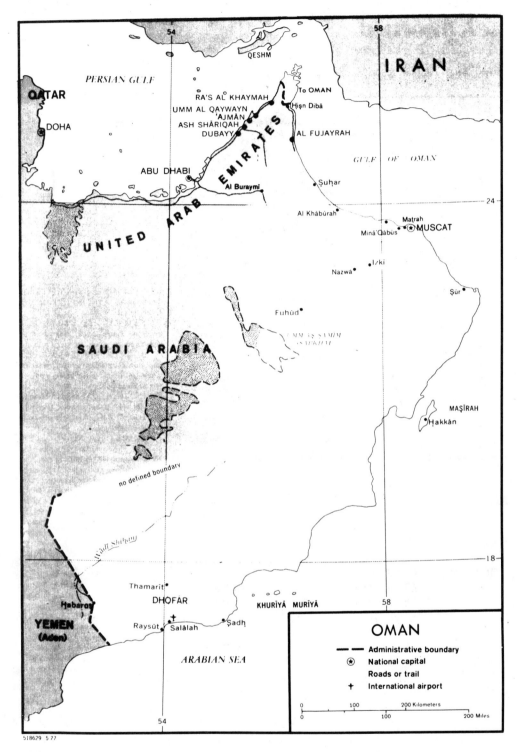

518629  5 77

| | | | |
|---|---|---|---|
| **ARMY:** | Muscat | | |
| **NAVY:** | Ghanam Island | Muscat | Raysut |
| **AIR FORCE:** | Khassab | Muscat | Seeb |
| | Masirah | Salalah | Thumrayt |

# PAKISTAN

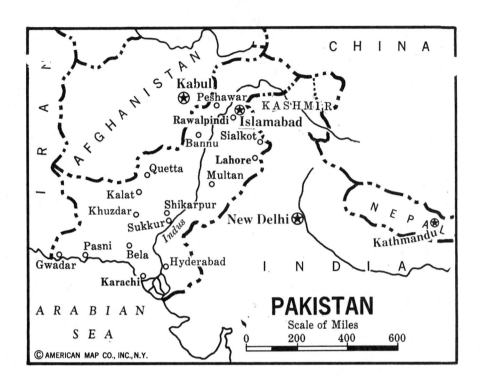

ARMY:      Islamabad      Lahore       Rawalpindi
           Karachi        Peshawar

NAVY:      Kaptai         Karachi

AIR FORCE: Chaklala       Mianwali     Risalawala
           Chanderi       Multan       Risalpur
           Drigh Road     Murid        Samungli
           Gilgit         Miramshar     Sargodha
           Kohat          Musroor      Shorkot
           Mauripur       Peshawar

# PANAMA

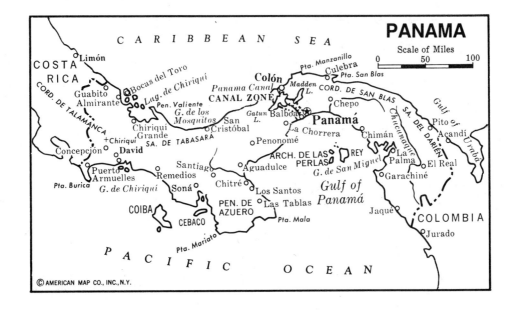

**ARMY:** Panama City
(United States Army)

**NAVY:** Balboa (United States Navy
Communications Facility)

**AIR FORCE:** Balboa (United States      France Field
Air Force)             Tocumen

# PAPUA NEW GUINEA

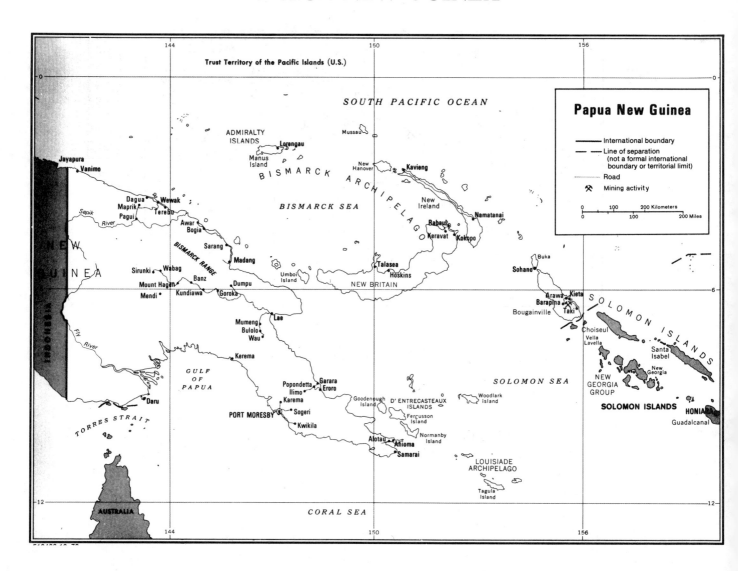

**ARMY:**      Port Moresby

**NAVY:**      Manus Island             Port Moresby

**AIR FORCE:**  Lae                Port Moresby      Wewak
                  Madang           Rabaul

# PARAGUAY

| ARMY: | Asuncion | Villarica | Mariscal Estigarribia |
|---|---|---|---|
| NAVY: | Asuncion | Puerto Sajonia | |
| AIR FORCE: | Asuncion | | |

# PERU

© AMERICAN MAP CO., INC., N.Y.

**PERU**

Scale of Miles

0    100    200

| | | | |
|---|---|---|---|
| **ARMY:** | Arequipa | Iquitos | Piura |
| | Callao | Lima | Tacna |
| | Cuzco | | |
| **NAVY:** | Callao | La Punta | San Lorenzo |
| | Iquitos (River) | Puno (Lake Titicaca) | Talara |
| **AIR FORCE:** | Ancon | La Joya | Piura |
| | Arequipa | Las Palmas | Pisco |
| | Callao | Lima | Talara |
| | Chiclayo | Limatambo | Trujillo |
| | Iquitos | Moquega | |
| | Jorge Chavez | | |

# PHILIPPINES

**PHILIPPINES**
Scale of Miles
0    100    200    300

**ARMY:**  Cobato Province        Lanao Province        Sulu Archipelago
           (Mindanoa)             (Mindanoa)            Zamboanga Province
                                                        (Mindanao)

**NAVY:**  Sangley Point          Subic Bay
                                  (United States Navy)

**AIR FORCE:**  Basa              Lipa City             San Fernando (United States
                (Florida Blanca)  Mactan                  Air Force Communica-
                Cebu              Nichols                 tions Facility)
                Clark (Angeles—   Paredes               Sangley Point
                United States Air Force)                Zamboanga City

853

# POLAND

| ARMY: | Legnica (Soviet Union) | Silesia | |
| | Pomerania | Warsaw | |

| NAVY: | Gdansk | Kohobrzeg | Szczecin |
| | Gdynia | Swinoujscie | Ustka |
| | Hel | | |

| AIR FORCE: | Bydgoszcz | Krosno | Siedlce |
| | Cracow | Kutno | Slupsk |
| | Deblin | Legnica | Sroda |
| | Elblag | Lublin | Swidnik |
| | Gdansk | Mielce | Szczecin |
| | Graudziadz | Olsztyn | Torun |
| | Inowroclaw | Poznan | Warsaw |
| | Jelenia Goria | Radom | Wroclaw |
| | Ketrzyn | Rzeszow | |

# PORTUGAL

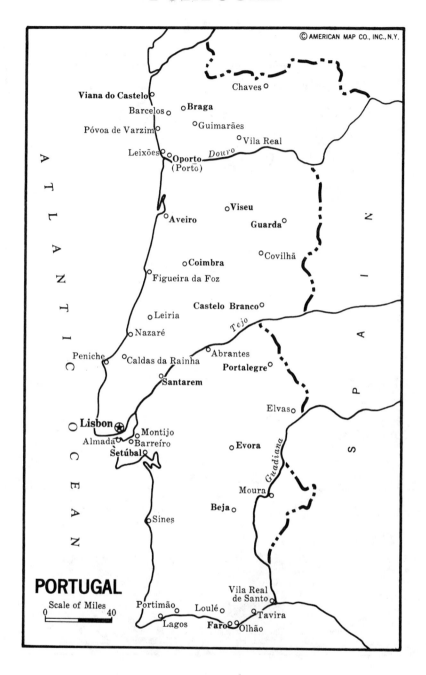

Viana do Castelo
Chaves
Barcelos
Braga
Guimarães
Póvoa de Varzim
Vila Real
Leixões
Oporto
(Porto)
Douro
Viseu
Aveiro
Guarda
Coimbra
Covilhã
Figueira da Foz
Castelo Branco
Leiria
Tejo
Nazaré
Abrantes
Peniche
Caldas da Rainha
Portalegre
Santarem
Elvas
Lisbon
Montijo
Almada
Barreíro
Evora
Setúbal
Guadiana
Moura
Beja
Sines
PORTUGAL
Scale of Miles
0        40
Vila Real
de Santo
Portimão
Loulé
Tavira
Lagos
Faro
Olhão

ATLANTIC OCEAN

SPAIN

© AMERICAN MAP CO., INC., N.Y.

| | | | |
|---|---|---|---|
| **ARMY:** | Azores | Evora | Medeira |
| | Coimbra | Lisbon | Porto |
| | | | |
| **NAVY:** | Alfeite | Lisbon | |
| | | | |
| **AIR FORCE:** | Beja | Monte Real | Sao Jacinto |
| | Lajes (United States Air Force) | Montijo | Sintra |
| | | Ota | Tancos |
| | Lisbon-Portela | Portela | |

855

# QATAR

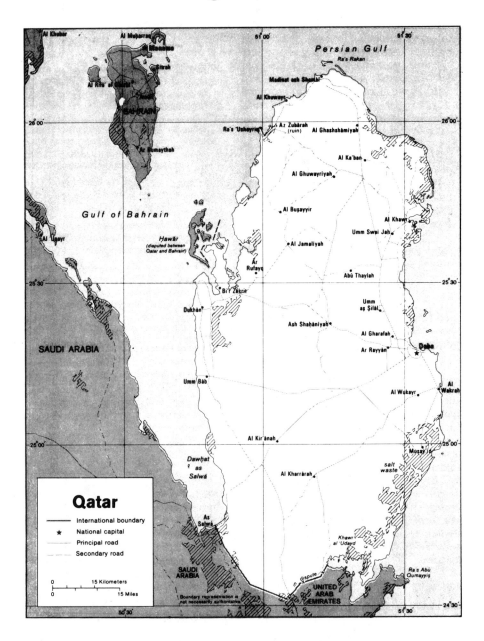

**ARMY:** Doha

**NAVY:** Doha

**AIR FORCE:** Doha

# ROMANIA

**ARMY:**    Bucharest

| **NAVY:** | Braila | Galati | Mongolia |
| --- | --- | --- | --- |
| | Constanta | Giurgiu | Sulina |
| | Danube | Mamaia | Tulcea |

| **AIR FORCE:** | Arad | Constanta | Otopeni |
| --- | --- | --- | --- |
| | Bacau | Craiova | Popesti-Leorden |
| | Baneasa | Galati | Satu Mare |
| | Brasov | Iasi | Tecuci |
| | Buzau | Mamaia | Timisoara |
| | Calarast | Medias | Tirqursor |
| | Cluji | Oradea | Zilistea |

# RWANDA

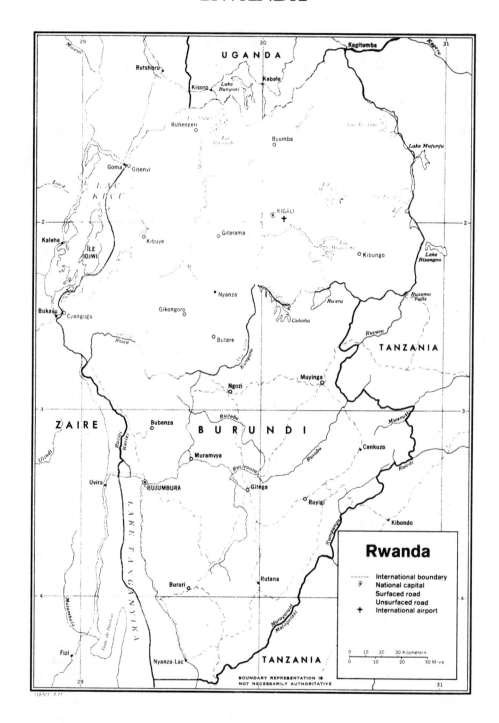

**ARMY:**    Butare               Kigale               Nyarugence
                  Kanobe            Muhima

**AIR FORCE:**   Kigali

# ST. CHRISTOPHER-NEVIS

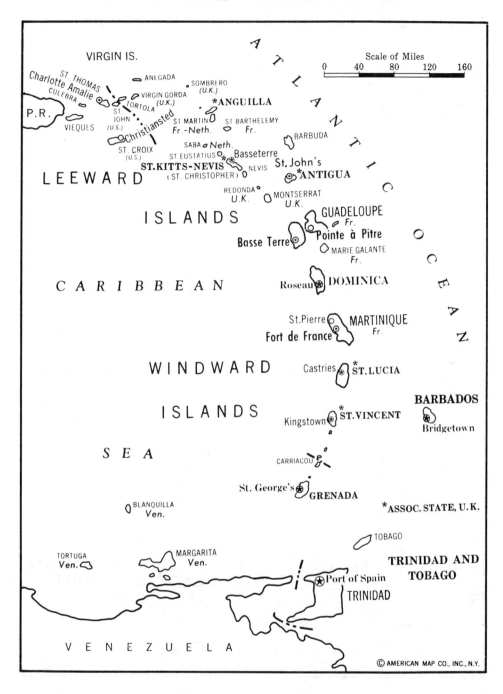

ARMY:        Springfield

NAVY:        Springfield

# ST. LUCIA

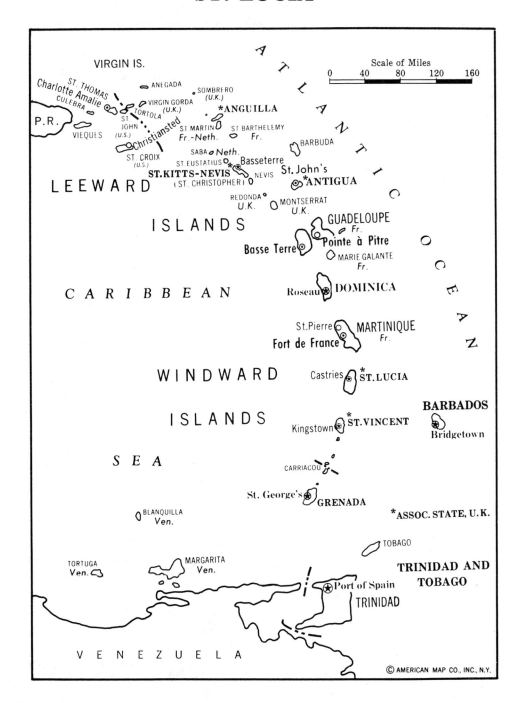

**ARMY:**     Castries (Police)

860

# ST. VINCENT AND THE GRENADINES

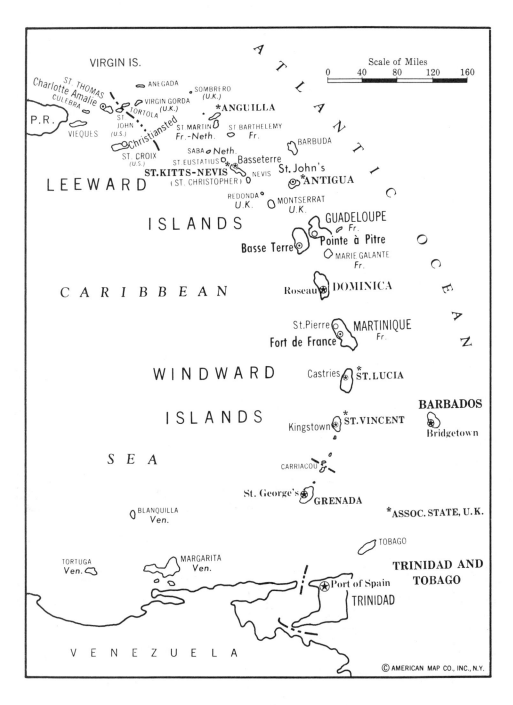

VIRGIN IS.

ATLANTIC

Scale of Miles
0   40   80   120   160

ST. THOMAS
Charlotte Amalie
CULEBRA
ANEGADA
SOMBRERO
(U.K.)
VIRGIN GORDA
(U.K.)
*ANGUILLA

P.R.
ST. JOHN
(U.S.)
TORTOLA
(U.K.)
Christiansted
ST MARTIN
Fr.-Neth.
ST BARTHELEMY
Fr.
VIEQUES
SABA o Neth.
BARBUDA

ST. CROIX
(U.S.)
ST. EUSTATIUS
Basseterre
St. John's

LEEWARD
ST.KITTS-NEVIS
(ST. CHRISTOPHER)
NEVIS
*ANTIGUA

REDONDA
U.K.
MONTSERRAT
U.K.

ISLANDS
GUADELOUPE
Fr.
Basse Terre
Pointe à Pitre
MARIE GALANTE
Fr.

CARIBBEAN
Roseau DOMINICA

St.Pierre MARTINIQUE
Fort de France      Fr.

WINDWARD
Castries *ST.LUCIA

ISLANDS
BARBADOS
Kingstown *ST.VINCENT
Bridgetown

SEA
CARRIACOU

St. George's GRENADA

*ASSOC. STATE, U.K.

BLANQUILLA
Ven.

TOBAGO

TORTUGA
Ven.
MARGARITA
Ven.

TRINIDAD AND
TOBAGO
Port of Spain
TRINIDAD

V E N E Z U E L A

© AMERICAN MAP CO., INC., N.Y.

**ARMY:**       Kingstown (Police)

# SAMOA

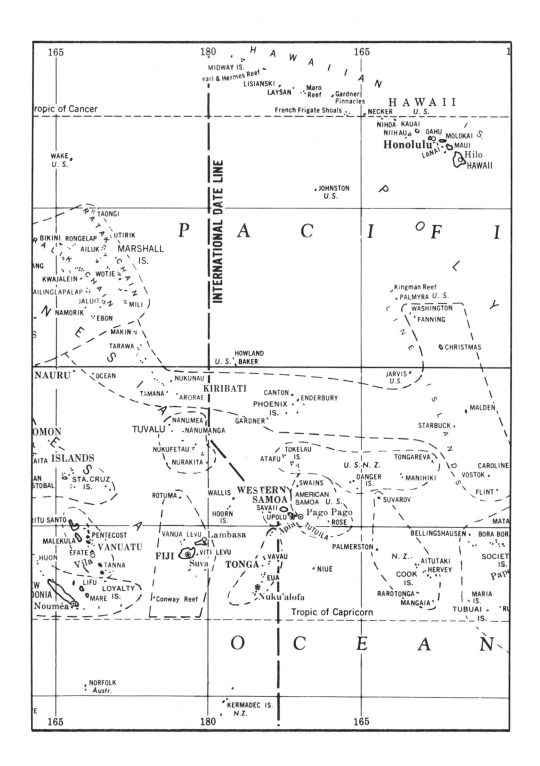

**ARMY:**        Apia (Police)

# SAO TOME & PRINCIPE

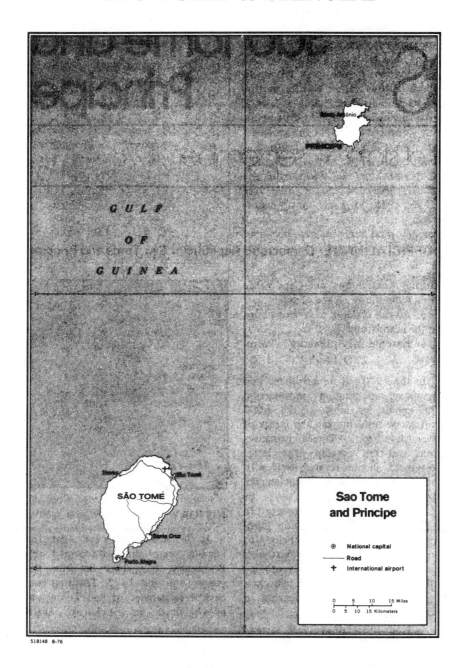

GULF

OF

GUINEA

Novas · ✠ São Tomé

**SÃO TOMÉ**

Santa Cruz

Porto Alegre

Santo António

Santo Cristo

**Sao Tome
and Principe**

⊕ National capital
— Road
✠ International airport

| 0 | 5 | 10 | 15 Miles |
| 0 | 5 | 10 | 15 Kilometers |

518148 8-76

**ARMY:**      Principe           Sao Tome

# SAUDI ARABIA

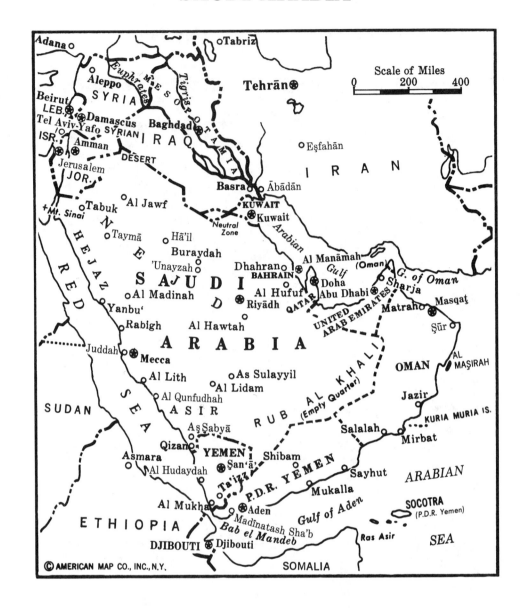

| ARMY: | Al-Hasa | Khamis Mushayt | Riyadh |
| | Al-Khuarj | Oyayna | Tabuk |
| | Hafar Al-Batin | Qassim | Taif |
| | Jeddah | | |

| NAVY: | Al Qatif/Jubail | Khasam Al-An | Ras Tanura |
| | Dammam | Ras al-Mishab | Yanbu |
| | Jeddah | | |

| AIR FORCE: | Abhar | Jizan | Tabuk |
| | Dhahran | Khamis Mushayt | Yaif |
| | Gurayat | Medina | Turayf |
| | Hofuf | Nejran | Yanbu |
| | Jeddah | Riyadh | |

# SENEGAL

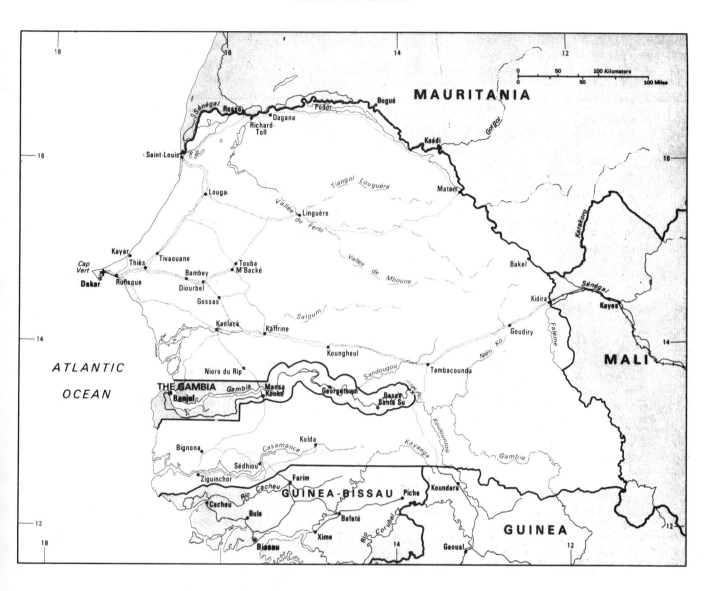

| ARMY: | Dakar | Sina Saloum | Wourossogui |
|---|---|---|---|
|  | Podor | Tambacounda | Zinguinchor |
|  | Saint Louis |  |  |
| NAVY: | Dakar | Kaolack | Saint Louis |
| AIR FORCE: | Cap Verte | Kedougou | Thies |
|  | (French Air Force) | Saint Louis | Yoff |
|  | Dakar-Yoff | Tambacounda | Zinguinchor |

865

# SEYCHELLES

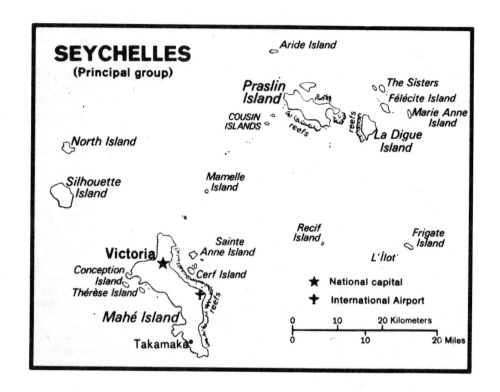

**ARMY:**       Pointe Larue

**NAVY:**       Victoria

**AIR FORCE:**  Victoria

# SIERRA LEONE

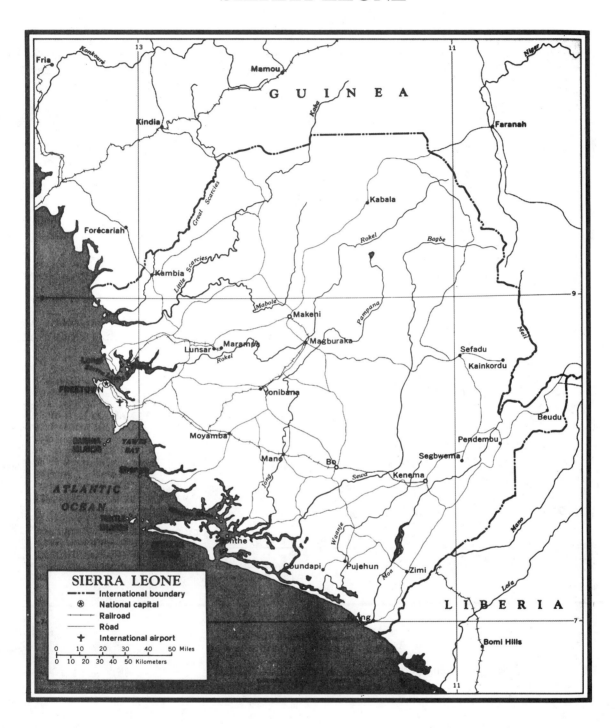

**ARMY:**     Murraytown Barracks (Freetown)

# SINGAPORE

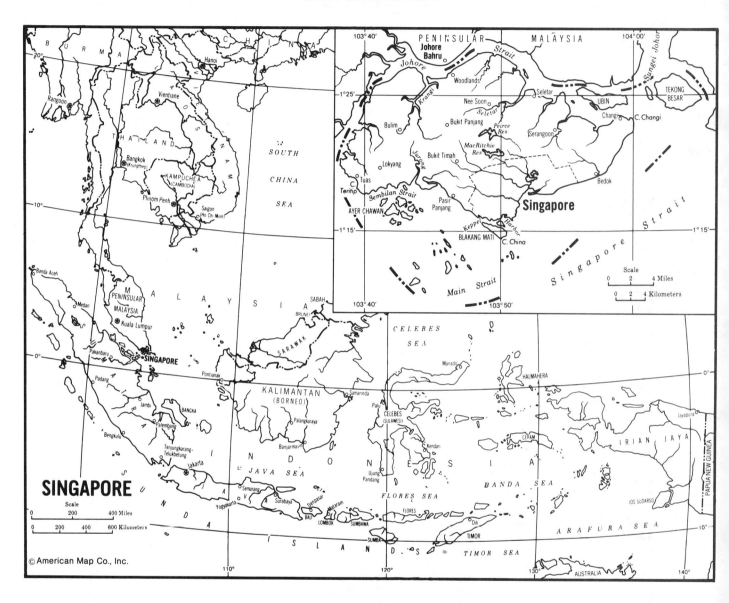

© American Map Co., Inc.

**ARMY:**       Singapore

**NAVY:**       Pulau Brani          Singapore

**AIR FORCE:**  Changi               Seletar              Tengah

868

# SOLOMON ISLANDS

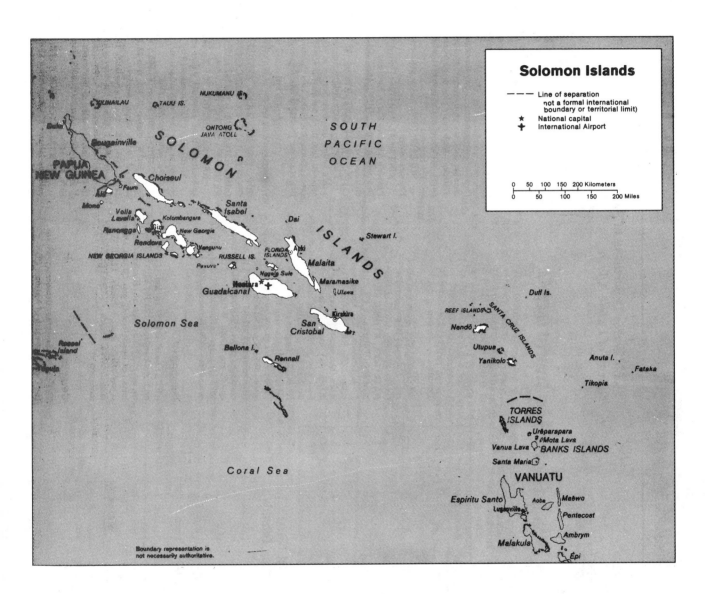

**ARMY:**     Avki (Police)          Honiara (Police)
              Gizo Island (Police)   Kirakira (Police)

# SOMALIA

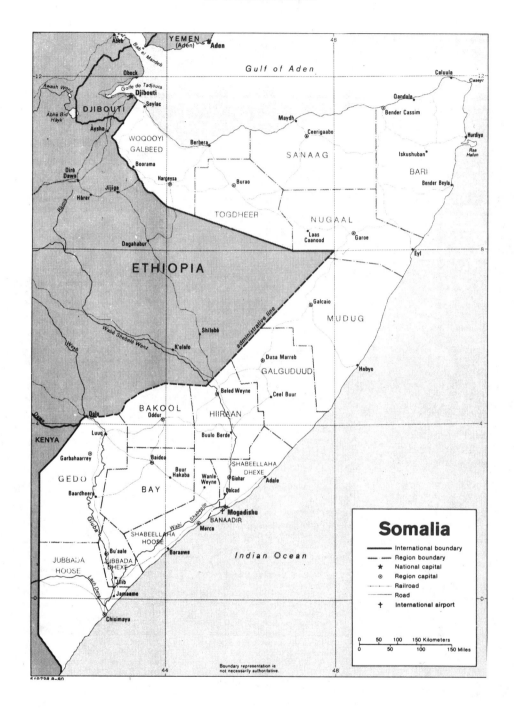

**ARMY:**    Mogadishu

**NAVY:**    Berbera (United States    Kismayu    Mogadishu
Navy Access)

**AIR FORCE:**    Berbera    Hargeisa    Mogadishu

# SOUTH AFRICA

| ARMY: | Bloemfontein | Johannesburg | Pretoria |
|---|---|---|---|
| | Cape Town | Kimberley | Stellenbosh |
| | Durban | Kroonstat | Vereening |
| | Eerste River | Ladybrand | Voortrekkehoogte |
| | Germiston | Lyttleton | Windhoek |
| | Grahamstown | Port Elizabeth | Wynberg |
| | Greytown | Potchefstroom | Youngsfield |

| NAVY: | Cape Town | Port Elizabeth | Simonstown |
|---|---|---|---|
| | Durban | Saldanha Bay | Walvis Bay |
| | East London | Silvermine | |

| AIR FORCE: | Alexander Bay | Grand Central | Rooikop |
|---|---|---|---|
| | Beaufort West | Hoedspruit | Springbok |
| | Bloemfontein | Langebaanweg | Swartkrops |
| | Bloemspruit | Lyttleton | Waterkloof |
| | Cape Town | Outshoorn | Windhoek |
| | Dunottar | Pietersburg | Youngsfield |
| | Durban | Port Elizabeth | Ysterplaat |
| | Germiston | Potchefstroom | Zwartkop |
| | George | Pretoria | |

# SPAIN

**SPAIN**

Scale of Miles

0    80    160

**ARMY:**

| | | |
|---|---|---|
| Agoncillo | El Copero | Minorca |
| Barcelona | Granada | Pamplona |
| Betera | Ibiza | Saragossa |
| Burgos | Levida | Seville |
| Ciudad Real | Los Remedios | Valencia |
| Colmenar Viejo | Madrid | Valladolid |
| Corunna | Mallorca | Virgen del Camino |

**NAVY:**

| | | |
|---|---|---|
| Cadiz | Gibraltar (United Kingdom) | Rota (United States Navy) |
| Cartagena | Las Palmas | |
| Ferrol | Mallocra | San Fernando (Cadiz) |

**AIR FORCE:**

| | | |
|---|---|---|
| Albacete | Los Llanos | Tablada |
| Alcantarilla | Malaga | Talavera |
| Armilla | Manises | Torrejan |
| Cuatro Vientos | Matacan | (United States Air Force) |
| Gando (Canary Islands) | Moron | Valenzuela |
| Getafe | Pollensa | Valladolid |
| Jerez | Rota | Villanubla |
| Las Palmas | San Javier | Zaragoza |
| La Parra | San Juan (Majorca) | (United States Air Force) |
| Los Alcazares | | |

# SRI LANKA

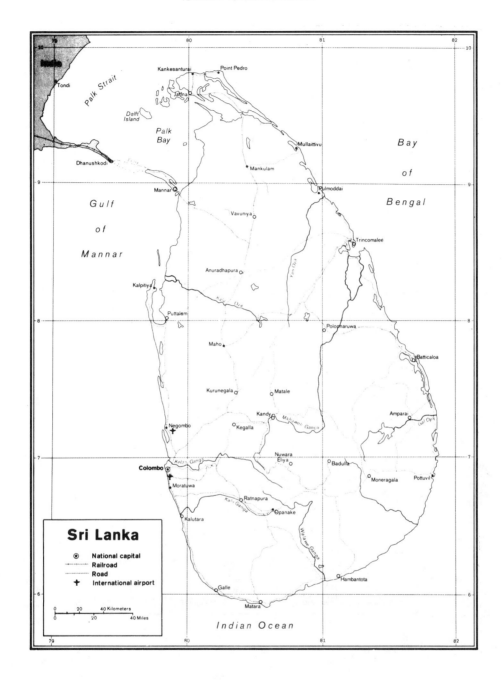

**ARMY:**      Colombo            Diyatalawa

**NAVY:**      Colombo            Tangala            Welisara
                   Karainager           Trincomalee

**AIR FORCE:**    China Bay         Katunayake       Trincomalee
                   Kalpitiya           Ratmalana

# SUDAN

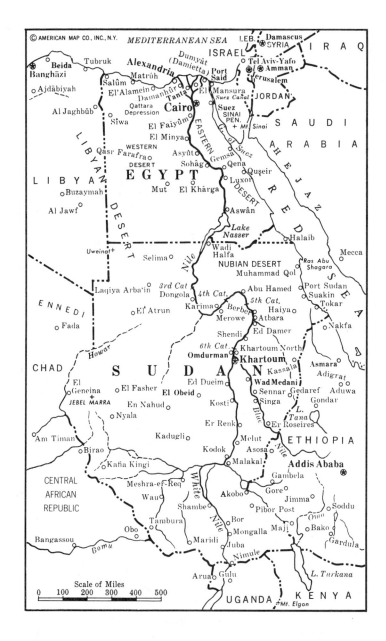

| ARMY: | Atbara | Khartoum | Omdurman |
|---|---|---|---|
| | Jubayt | North Khartoum | |
| **NAVY:** | Juba | Khartoum | Port Sudan |
| **AIR FORCE:** | Atbara | Geneina | Merowe |
| | Dongola | Juba | Port Sudan |
| | El Fashir | Khartoum | Wad Medani |
| | El Obeid | Malakal | Waw |

# SURINAME

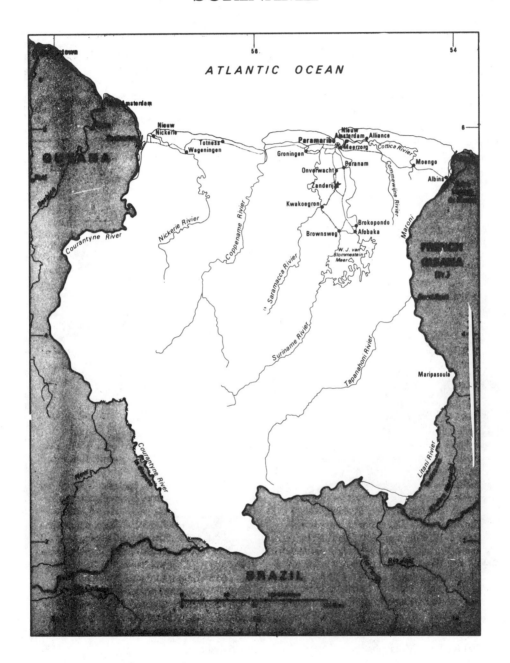

**ARMY:** Paramaribo

# SWAZILAND

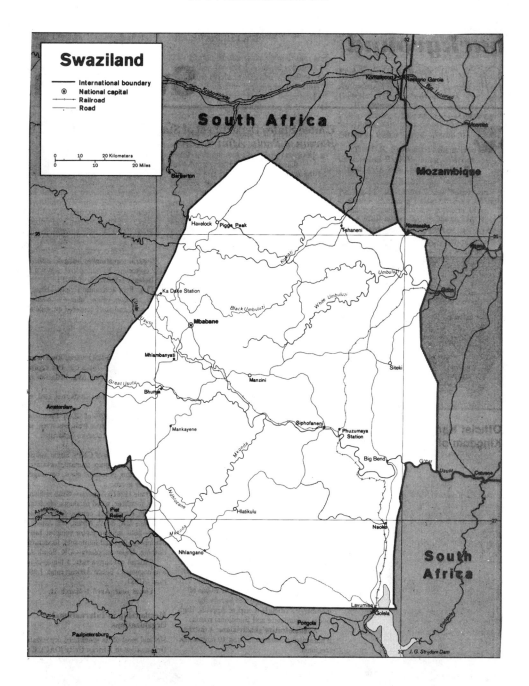

**ARMY:**      Kwaluseni          Lobamba          Mbabane

**AIR FORCE:**    Matsapha          Mbabane

# SWEDEN

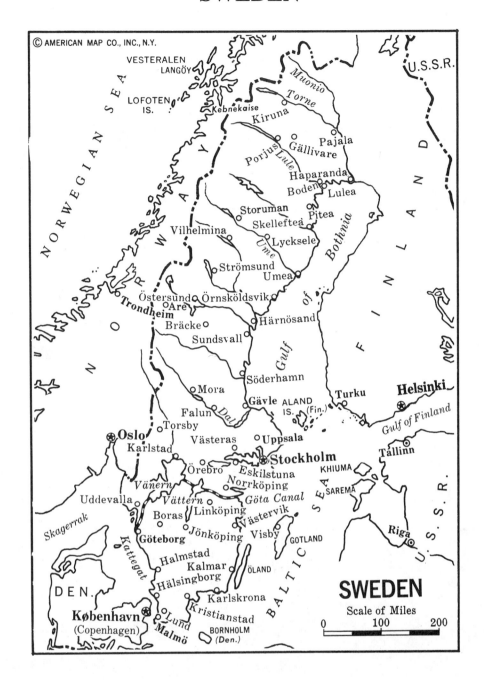

| **ARMY:** | Boden | Ostersund | Stranguas |
| | Karlstad | Skorde | Visby |
| | Krisnanstad | Stockholm | |
| | | | |
| **NAVY:** | Goteborg | Luleu | Stockholm |
| | Harnosand | Malmo | Vastra Frolunder |
| | Karlskrona | | |
| | | | |
| **AIR FORCE:** | Aengelholm | Karlsborg | Ostersund |
| | Froson | Linkoping | Ronneby |
| | Halmstad | Ljungbyhed | Satenas |
| | Halsholm | Lulea | Soderhamm |
| | Haslo | Malmslatt | Tullinge |
| | Kallinge | Norrkoping | Uppsola |
| | Kalmar | Nykoping | Vasteras |

# SWITZERLAND

| ARMY: | Aarau | Emmen | Sion |
|---|---|---|---|
| | Bellinzona | Kriens | Solothurn |
| | Bern | Lausanne | St. Maurice |
| | Chur | Magadino | Winterthur |
| | Colombier | Payerne | Zurich |
| | Dubendorf | | |
| AIR FORCE: | Bern | Emmen | Payerne |
| | Buochs | Magadino | Sion |
| | Dubendorf | Meiringen | |

# SYRIA

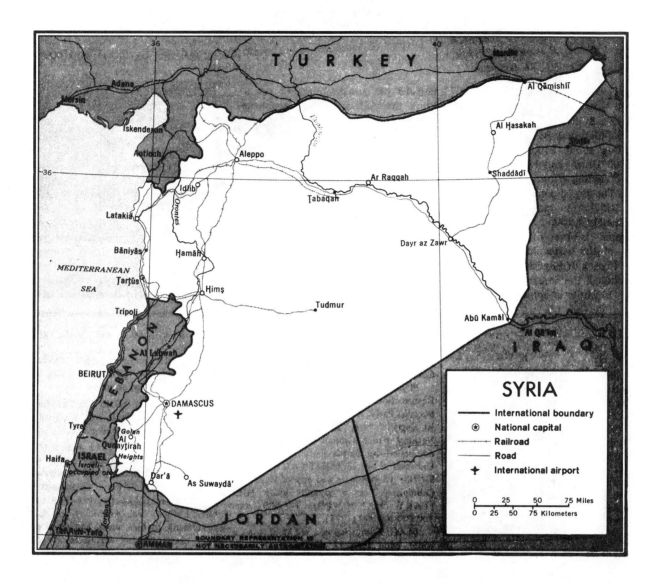

**ARMY:**    Aleppo        Damascus

**NAVY:**    Baniyas        Latakia        Tartus
                                 (Soviet Naval Facility)    (Soviet Port Access)

**AIR FORCE:**

| | | |
|---|---|---|
| Abu Dubor | Khalkhalah | Neirals |
| Aleppo | Marj Rhiyal | Palmyra |
| Blay | Masiriyah | Qatanah |
| Chliye | Mezze | Rasafa |
| Damascus | Midzh | Saigat |
| Djirah | Minak | Saikal |
| Dumayr | Minet el-Baida | Sueda |
| El Rasafa | (Soviet Air Access) | Tiyas |
| Hamah | Natzria | |

879

# TANZANIA

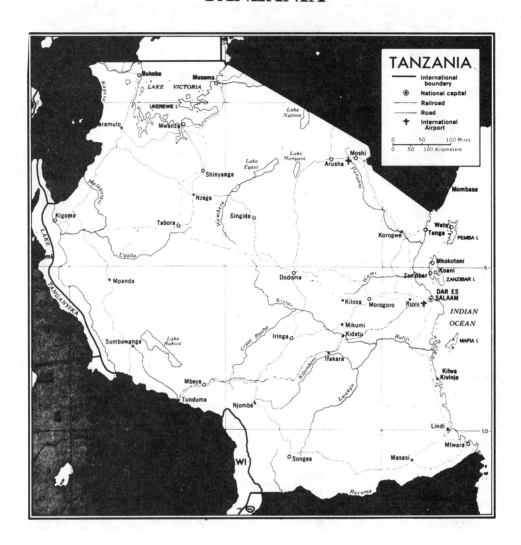

**ARMY:**

| | | |
|---|---|---|
| Arusha | Moaduli | Nachingwea |
| Dar es Salaam | Morogoro | Tabora |
| Mbeya | Moshi | Zanzibar |
| Mikumi | | |

**NAVY:**

| | |
|---|---|
| Dar es Salaam | Zanzibar |

**AIR FORCE:**

| | | |
|---|---|---|
| Arusha | Mbeya | Njombe |
| Dar es Salaam | Mikumi | Songea |
| Dodoma | Morogoro | Tabora |
| Iringa | Moshi | Tanga |
| Kilndoni | Mtwara | Zanzibar |
| Kilwa Kivinge | Mwanga | |

# THAILAND

| | | | |
|---|---|---|---|
| **ARMY:** | Bangkok | Nakhon Phanom | Saraburi |
| | Korat | Nakhon si Thammarat | U Tapao |
| | Lopburi | Phitsanuluk | |
| | | | |
| **NAVY:** | Bangkok | Phangnga | Songkla |
| | Paknam | Sattahip | |
| | | | |
| **AIR FORCE:** | Chieng Mai | Nakhon Ratchasima | Takli |
| | Don Muang (Bangkok) | Prachaub | Ubon |
| | Khon Kaen | Saraburi | Udorn |
| | Lop Buri | Sattahip | |

# TOGO

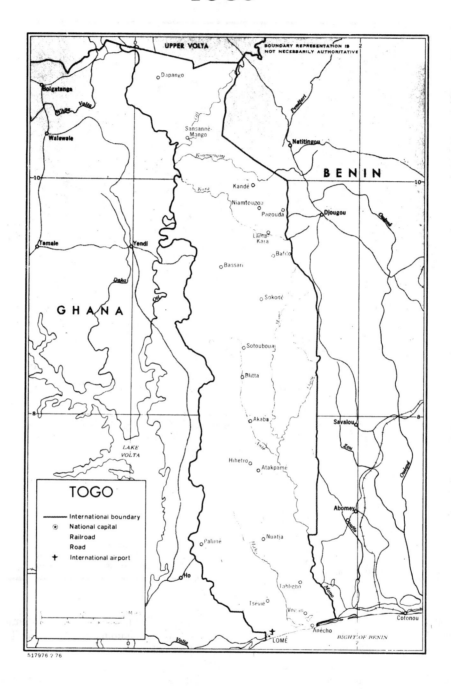

| | | | |
|---|---|---|---|
| **ARMY:** | Agoenyive | | Lome |
| | Lama Kara | | Temedja |
| **NAVY:** | Kpeme | | Lome |
| **AIR FORCE:** | Lome | | Sokode |
| | Niamtougou | | Tokoin |

# TAIWAN

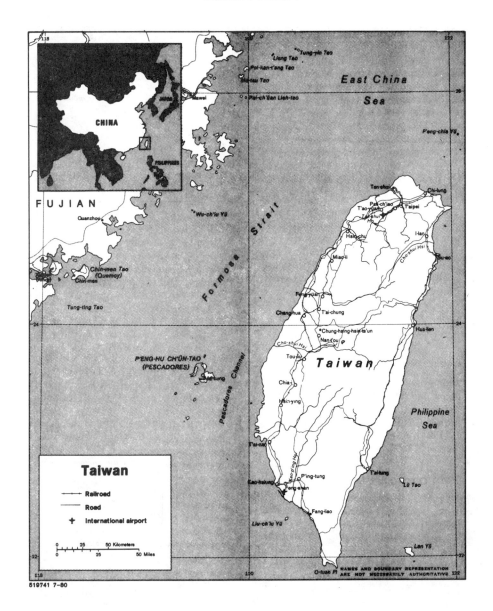

| ARMY: | Fenshan | Taipei | |
|---|---|---|---|
| NAVY: | Keelung | Makung (Pescadores) | Tsoying |
| AIR FORCE: | Chia-I | Kangshan | Shatou |
| | Chinchuankang | Kaohslung | Sungshan (Taipei) |
| | Hengchun | Kung-k'uang | Taichung |
| | Hsinchu | Makung | Tainan |
| | Hualien | Pingtung North | Taitung |
| | Ian Chinmen | Pingtung South | Taoydan |

# TRINIDAD & TOBAGO

**ARMY:**      Port-of-Spain

**NAVY:**      Chaguaramas                 Port-of-Spain                 Staubles Bay

# TUNISIA

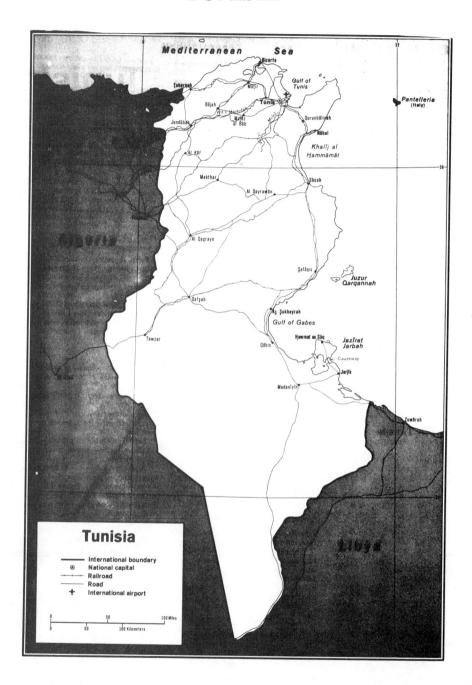

**ARMY:**      Tunis

**NAVY:**      Bizerte                    Susa                   Tunis

**AIR FORCE:**  Bizerte               El Aouina (Tunis)     Mouastir
               (Soviet Port Access)   Gabes               Sfax-el-Maou
               Djerba-Melita       Gafsa

# TURKEY

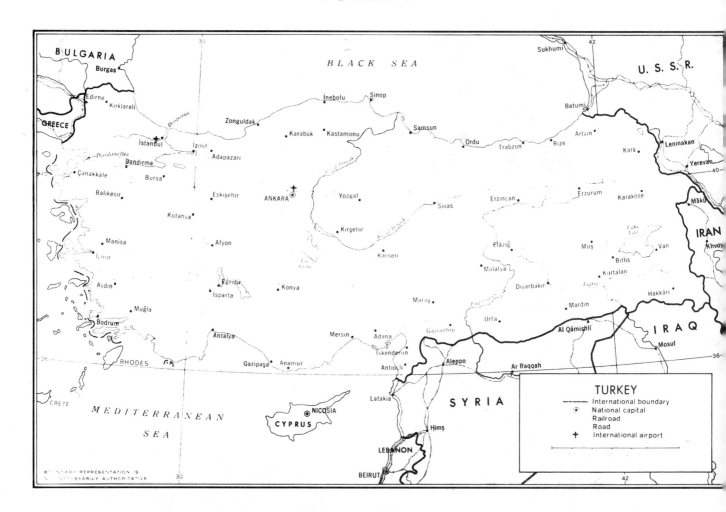

| ARMY: | Ankara | Izmir | Sinop (United States Army |
| | Erzincan | Malatya | Communications Facility) |
| | Istanbul | | |

| NAVY: | Ankara | Eregli | Iskenderun |
| | Bosphorus | Golcuk | Istanbul |
| | Dardanelles | Heybeli | Izmir |

| AIR FORCE: | Ankara | Erhac | Izmir |
| | (United States Air Force) | Eskisehir | (United States Air Force) |
| | Adana | Esluboga | Merzifon |
| | Balikersir | Etimesgut | Sivas |
| | Diyarbakir | Incirlik | Yesilkoy |
| | (United States Air Force) | (United States Air Force) | |

# TUVALU

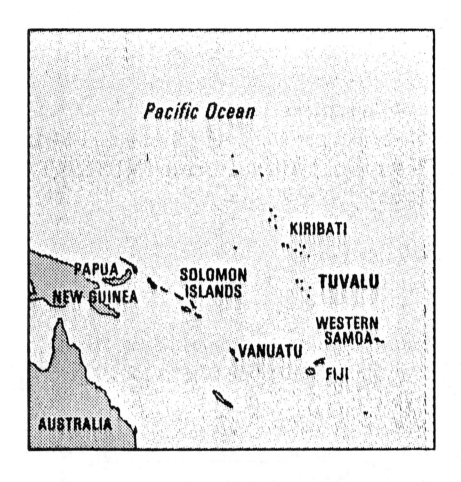

**ARMY:**     Funafuti Atoll (Police)

# UGANDA

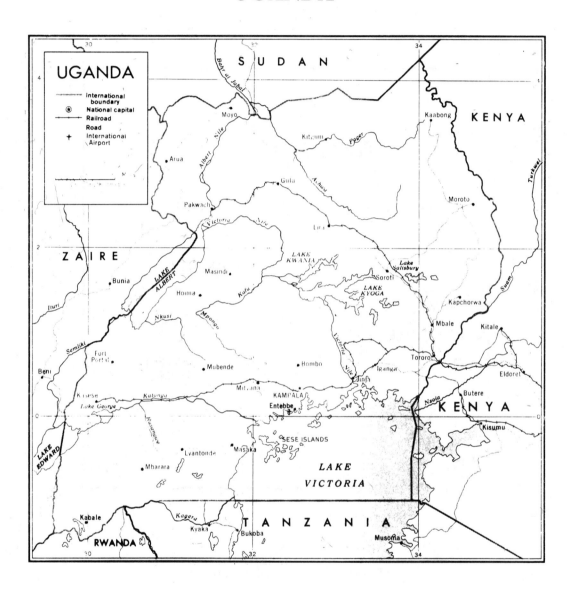

| **ARMY:** | Arua | Jinja | Nakasongola |
| | Entebbe | Kampala | Soroti |
| | Gulu | | |
| **AIR FORCE:** | Arua | Jinja | Nakasongola |
| | Entebbe | Kampala | Soroti |
| | Gulu | | |

# UNION OF SOVIET SOCIALIST REPUBLICS

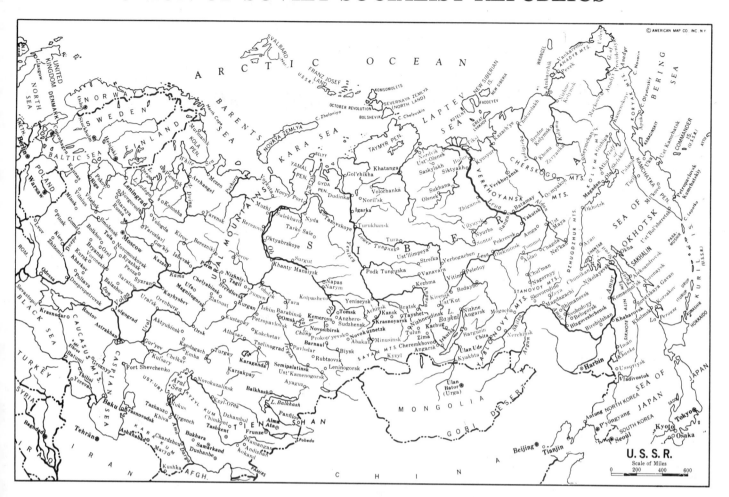

| ARMY: | Alma Ata | L'vov | Riga |
|---|---|---|---|
| | Chita | Minsk | Rostov-na-Donv |
| | Khabarousk | Moscow | Sverdlousk |
| | Kiev | Murmansk-Severomorsk | Tashkent |
| | Kuybyshev | Novosibirsk | Tbilisi |
| | Leningrad | Odessa | |

| NAVY: | Archangelsk | Odessa | Severodvinsk |
|---|---|---|---|
| | Baltiysk | Petropavlovsk | Sovetskaya Gavin |
| | Korsakov | Polyarny | Veveromorsk |
| | Kronstadt | Poti | Sovyetskaya |
| | Leipaja | Providenie | Tallin |
| | Magadan | Riga | Vladivostok |
| | Motovskij Gulf | Sevastopol | |

| AIR FORCE: | Aktyubinsk | Khabarousk | Okhotsk |
|---|---|---|---|
| | Arkhangel'sk | Kyzyl | Penza |
| | Baku | Laryak | Riga |
| | Chelyabinsk | Leningrad | Rostov-na-Donv |
| | Dushabe | Moscow | Simferopol |
| | Inarigda | Odessa | Svetly |

# UNITED ARAB EMIRATES

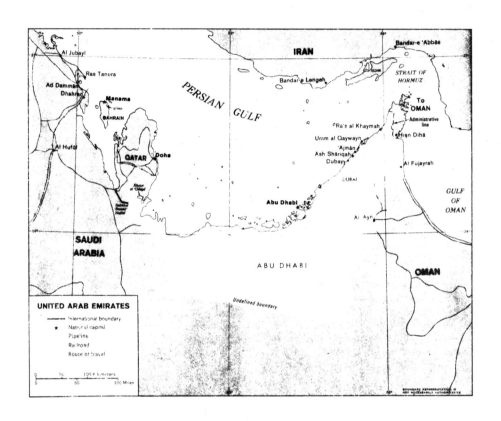

| | | | |
|---|---|---|---|
| **ARMY:** | Abu Dhabi | Dubai | |
| **NAVY:** | Abu Dhabi | | |
| **AIR FORCE:** | Abu Dhabi | Dubai | Sharjah |

# UNITED KINGDOM

UNITED KINGDOM

**ARMY:**

| | | |
|---|---|---|
| Aldershot | Edinburgh (Scotland) | Shrewsbury |
| Brecon | Lisbon (N. Ireland) | Warrington (United States |
| Bulford | London | Army Depot) |
| Colchester | Preston | York |

**NAVY:**

| | | |
|---|---|---|
| Chatham | Edzell (Scotland— | Portland |
| Culdrose | United States Navy) | Portsmouth |
| Devonport | Faslane | Roborough |
| Dunoon (United States | Honington | Rosyth |
| Navy) | Lee-on-Solent | Yeovilton |

**AIR FORCE:**

| | | |
|---|---|---|
| Abingdon | Greenham Common | Mildenhall |
| Alconbury | (Newbury—United States | (United States Air Force) |
| (United States Air Force) | Air Force) | Odiham |
| Benson | Honington | Saint Mawgan |
| Binbrook | Kinloss | Scampton |
| Bogotville | Lakenheath (United States | Sculthorpe |
| Brize Norton | Air Force) | (United States Air Force) |
| Casement | Leeming | Topcliffe |
| Church Fenton | Leuchars | Upper Heyford |
| Coltishall | Linton-on-Ouse | (United States Air Force) |
| Conningsby | Lossiemouty | Valley |
| Cottesmore | Lyneham | Waddington |
| Eyke (United States | Machrinhanish | Wittering |
| Air Force) | Manston | Woodbridge |
| Finningly | Marham | (United States Air Force) |
| | | Wyton |

# UNITED STATES OF AMERICA

# UNITED STATES

**ARMY:**

Fort Bragg (Fayetteville, North Carolina)
Fort Carson (Colorado Springs, Colorado)
Fort Devens (Ayer, Massachusetts)
Fort Dix (Wrightstown, New Jersey)
Fort Gillem (Atlanta, Georgia)
Fort Hood (Killeen, Texas)
Fort Knox (Louisville, Kentucky)

Fort Lewis (Tacoma, Washington)
Fort McClellan (Anniston, Alabama)
Fort McPherson (Atlanta, Georgia)
Fort Meade (Laurel, Maryland)
Fort Monroe (Hampton, Virginia)
Fort Ord (Monterey, California)
Fort Polk (Leesville, Louisiana)

Fort Riley (Junction City, Kansas)
Fort Sam Houston (San Antonio, Texas)
Fort Sheridan (Highland Park, Illinois)
Fort Stewart (Hinesville, Georgia)
Presidio of San Francisco (San Francisco, California)
Schofield Barracks (Honolulu, Hawaii)

**NAVY:**

Adak (Adak Island, Alaska)
Bangor (Bremerton, Washington)
Boston, Massachusetts
Brunswick, Maine
Camp Lejeune (Jacksonville, North Carolina)
Camp Pendleton (Oceanside, California)

Camp Smith (Honolulu, Hawaii)
Charleston, North Carolina
Jacksonville, Florida
Kings Bay (Kingsland, Georgia)
Long Beach, California
Mayport (Jacksonville Beach, Florida)

New London, Connecticut
New Orleans, Louisiana
Norfolk, Virginia
Pearl Harbor (Honolulu, Hawaii)
Quantico, Virginia
San Diego, California
Whidbey Island (Oak Harbor, Washington)

**AIR FORCE:**

Andrews (Camp Springs, Maryland)
Bolling (Washington, D.C.)
Edwards (Lancaster, California)
Eglin (Fort Walton Beach, Florida)
Elmendorf (Anchorage, Alaska)
Grand Forks, North Dakota
Griffis (Rome, New York)

Hanscom (Beford, Massachusetts)
Hickham (Honolulu, Hawaii)
Kelley (San Antonio, Texas)
Langley (Hampton, Virginia)
MacDill (Tampa, Florida)
Malmstrom (Great Falls, Montana)
Nellis, Las Vegas

Offut (Omaha, Nebraska)
Peterson (Colorado Springs, Colorado)
Randolf (San Antonio, Texas)
Scott (Belleville, Illinois)
Vandenberg (Lompoc, California)
Wright-Patterson (Dayton, Ohio)

# UPPER VOLTA

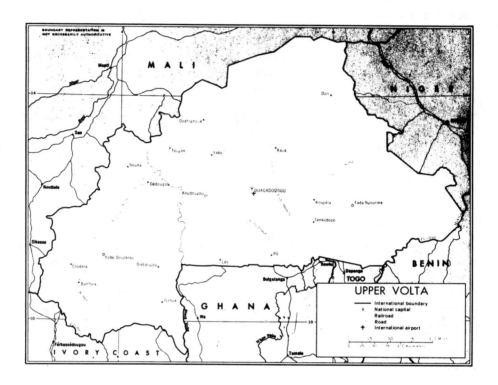

**ARMY:**       Ougadougou

**AIR FORCE:**  Bobo-Dioulasso                Ougadougou

# URUGUAY

URUGUAY
Scale of Miles
0   40   80   120

Artigas
Belén
Salto
Tacuarembó
Paysandú
Rivera
Melo
Mirim Lagoon
Negro
Mercedes
Treinta y Tres
Durazno
Colonia
Minas
Rocha
San José de Mayo
La Paloma
Buenos Aires
Montevideo
Maldonado
Río de la Plata
BRAZIL
ARGENTINA
ATLANTIC OCEAN
© AMERICAN MAP CO., INC., N.Y.

**ARMY:**      Montevideo

**NAVY:**      Laguna del Sauce          Montevideo          Punta del Este

**AIR FORCE:** Buranzo                   Montevideo
               Carrasco                  Pando

# VANUATU

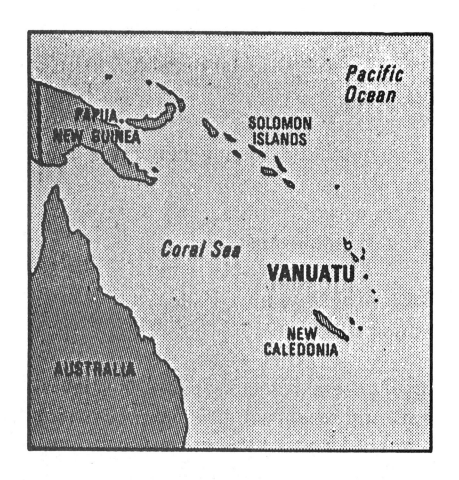

**ARMY:**     Port Vila (Police)

**NAVY:**     Port Vila

# VATICAN CITY STATE

**VATICAN CITY**

ITALY

VATICAN CITY

1000 Feet
300 Meters

41°54'30"

VIA LEONE IV

VIALE VATICANO

Wall

ITALY
(Rome)

Papal Gardens

Vatican Museums

VIA DI PORTA ANGELICA

VATICANO

Wall

Helicopter
Landing Pad

VIALE

Civil
Administration
Building

Sistine
Chapel

ST. PETER'S
SQUARE

Obelisk

St. Peter's Basilica

Radio Station

Wall

Wall

Railroad Station

VIALE VATICANO

Audience
Hall

LARGO DI PORTA
CAVALLEGGERI

ITALY
(Rome)

41°54'00"

Railroad

12°27'30"

12°28'30"

517538  3-75

# VENEZUELA

| | | | |
|---|---|---|---|
| **ARMY:** | Caracas | Maracay | San Cristobal |
| **NAVY:** | Caracas | La Guaira | Puerto de Hierro |
| | Falcon | Puerto Cabello | |
| **AIR FORCE:** | Barcelona | La Carlota | Maracay |
| | Barquisimento | Maiquetia | Maturin |
| | Caracas | Maracaibo | Palo Negro |

# VIETNAM

ARMY:

| | | |
|---|---|---|
| Dien Bien Phu | Ho Chi Minh City | Son La |
| Hanoi | Khesan | Vinh |

NAVY:

| | | |
|---|---|---|
| Cam Ranh Bay | Haiphong | Qui Nhon |
| Can Tho | Hue | Vinh |
| Chu Lai | Quang Khe | |
| Danang | | |
| (Soviet Navy Access) | | |

AIR FORCE:

| | | |
|---|---|---|
| Bien | Dalat | Hanoi |
| Bienhoa | Danang | Ho Chi Minh City |
| Binh Thuy | Dien Bien Phu | Phang Rang |
| Cam Ranh Bay | Dong Hoi | Pleiku |
| (Soviet Air Access) | Gia Lam Hoa Lae | Vinh |
| Cana | | |

# WESTERN SAMOA

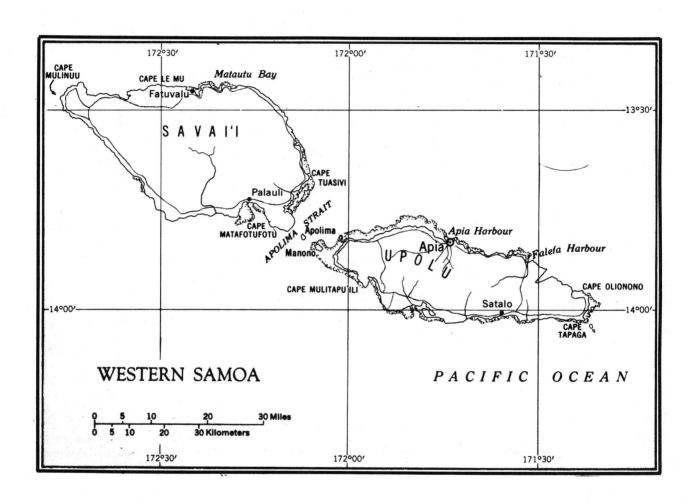

**ARMY:**      Apia (Police)

# YEMEN ARAB REPUBLIC

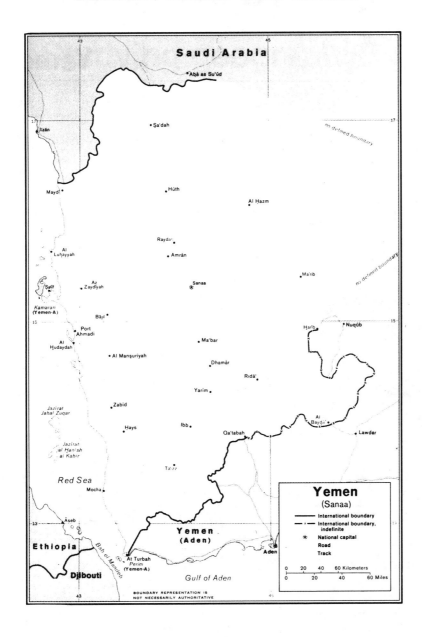

**ARMY:**      Hodeida

**NAVY:**      Hodeida

**AIR FORCE:**    Hodeida            Sana'a
                 Janad             Taiz

# PEOPLE'S DEMOCRATIC REPUBLIC OF YEMEN

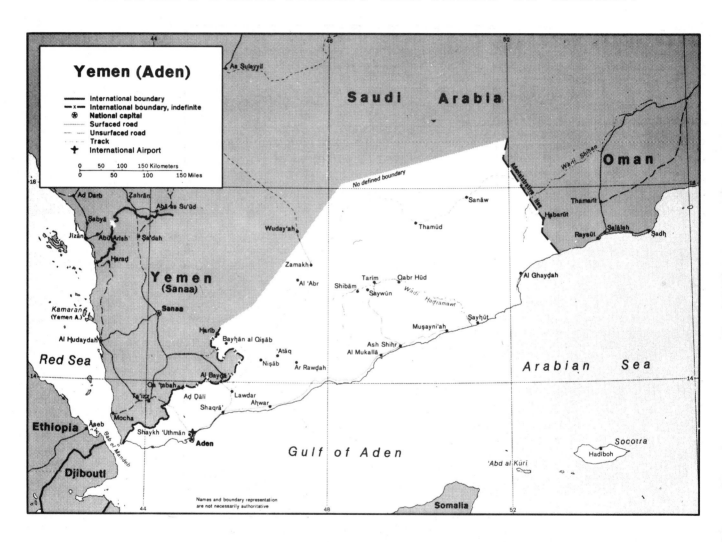

**ARMY:** Aden

**NAVY:**
Aden
(Soviet Navy)
Al Aned

Al-Mukalla
(Soviet Port Access)
Perim (Soviet Navy)

Riyan
Sacotra
(Soviet Navy)

**AIR FORCE:**
Adèn (Khormaksar
Soviet Air Access)
Al Dali
Al Mukalla
(Soviet Air Access)

Ansab
Ataq
Beihan
Beishan el-Qisab

Ir Fadhl Field
Lawdar
Mukayris
Zamakah

# YUGOSLAVIA

Map legend:

**YUGOSLAVIA**
- ——— International boundary
- ⊛ National capital
- ┼┼┼ Railroad
- ——— Road
- ✈ International airport

0   25   50   75   100 Miles
0  25  50  75  100 Kilometers

| ARMY: | Belgrade | Sisak | |
| | Kragujevac | Skopje | |

| NAVY: | Bay of Cattaro | Kotor | Pola |
| | Dubrovnik | Lora/Split | Sibenik |
| | Kardeljevo | Ploce | |

| AIR FORCE: | Banja Luka | Novi Sad | Sombor |
| | Batajnica | Petrovac | Titograd |
| | Ljubljana | Pleso/Zagreb | Vrsac |
| | Lucko/Zagreb | Pola | Zalusani |
| | Mostar | Sarajevo | Zemun |
| | Niksic | Skoplje | |

903

# ZAIRE

| **ARMY:** | Baki | Kinshasa | Mbanza |
| | Kamanyola | Kitona | Ndjili |
| | Kamina | Kota Kali | Ngunga |
| **NAVY:** | Kalemie | Kinshasa | Matadi |
| **AIR FORCE:** | Kamina | Libenge | Matadi |
| | Kinshasa | Likasi | Mbandaka |
| | Kisangani | Luluabourg | Ndjili |
| | Kolwesi | Lumumbashi | Ndolo |

# ZAMBIA

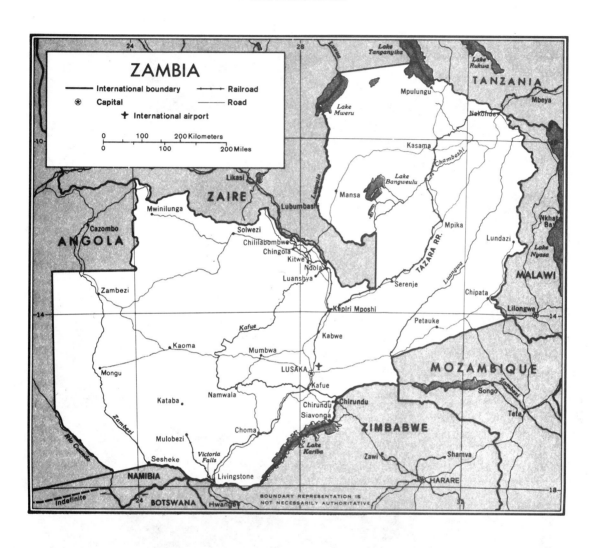

**ARMY:** Lusaka

**AIR FORCE:**

| | | |
|---|---|---|
| Abercorn | Livingstone | Mpika |
| Broken Hill | Lusaka | Mumbwa |
| Chingola | Luwingo | N'changa |
| Chipata | Mbala | Ndola |
| Kalabo | Mongu | Siluwe |
| Kasama | | |

# ZIMBABWE

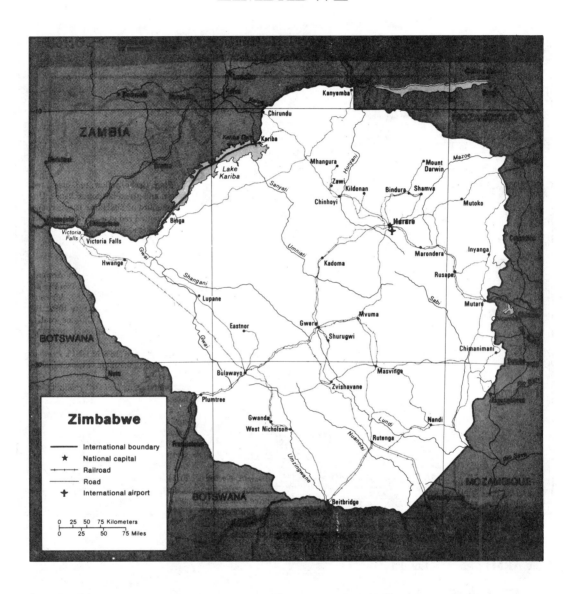

**ARMY:**  Bulawayo  Harare  Nyanda
 Gweru  Mutare

**AIR FORCE:**  Bulawayo  Kariba  Thornhill
 Cranbourne  Mutari  Victoria Falls
 Fort Victoria  New Sarum  Wankie
 Harare

906

# APPENDICES

## A. MILITARY RANK COMPARISONS

## B. INTERNATIONAL TELEPHONE DIALING CODES

# A. MILITARY RANK COMPARISONS

# Military Rank Comparisons

| ENGLISH<br>United States/United Kingdom | FRENCH | GERMAN |
|---|---|---|
| **Army** | **Army** | **Army** |
| General of the Army/Field Marshal† | Maréchal | Feldmarschall |
| General (Gen.) | Géneral d'Armée (Gén. d'Armée) | General (Gen.) |
| Lieutenant General (Lt. Gen.) | Géneral de Corps d'Armée (Gén. de Corps d'Armée) | Generalleutnant (GenLt) |
| Major General (Maj. Gen.) | Géneral de Division (Gén. de Div.) | Generalmajor (GenMaj) |
| | | |
| Brigadier General (Brig. Gen.)/Brigadier (Brig.) | Géneral de Brigade (Gén. de Brig.) | Brigadegeneral (BrigGen) |
| Colonel (Col.) | Colonel (Col.) | Oberst (Obst) |
| Lieutenant Colonel (Lt. Col.) | Lieutenant-Colonel (Lt.-Col.) | Oberstleutnant (ObstLt) |
| Major (Maj.) | Commandant (Cdt.) | Major (Maj) |
| Captain (Capt.) | Capitaine (Capt.) | Hauptmann (Hptm) |
| First Lieutenant (1st Lt.) | Lieutenant (Lt.) | Oberleutnant (Oblt) |
| Second Lieutenant (2nd Lt.) | Sous-Lieutenant (Sous Lt.) | Leutnant (Lt) |
| (No Corresponding Rank) | Aspirant | Fähnrich |
| | | |
| **Air Force** | **Air Force** | **Air Force** |
| General of the Air Force/Marshal of the Air Force | Maréchal | Luftmarschall |
| General (Gen.)/Air Chief Marshal | Géneral d'Armée Aérienne (Gén. d'Armée Aérienne) | General (Gen) |
| Lieutenant General (Lt. Gen.)/Air Marshal | Géneral de Corps d'Aerien (Gén. de Corps d'Aerien) | Generalleutnant (GenLt) |
| Major General (Maj. Gen.)/Air Vice Marshal | Géneral de Division Aérienne (Gén. de Div. Aérienne) | Generalmajor (GenMaj) |
| | | |
| Brigadier General (Brig. Gen.)/Air Commodore (Air Comdr.) | Géneral de Brigade Aérienne (Gén. de Brig. Aérienne) | Brigadegeneral (BrigGen) |
| Colonel (Col.)/Group Captain (Group Capt.) | Colonel (Col.) | Oberst (Obst) |
| Lieutenant Colonel (Lt. Col.)/Wing Commander (Wing Cdr.) | Lieutenant-Colonel (Lt.-Col.) | Oberstleutnant (Obstlt) |
| Major (Maj.)/Squadron Leader (Sqr. Ldr.) | Commandant (Cdt.) | Major (Maj) |
| Captain (Capt.)/Flight Lieutenant (Flt. Lt.) | Capitaine (Capt.) | Hauptmann (Hptm) |
| First Lieutenant (1st Lt.)/Flying Officer (Fg. Off.) | Lieutenant (Lt.) | Oberleutnant (Oblt) |
| Second Lieutenant (2nd Lt.)/Pilot Officer (Plt. Off.) | Sous Lieutenant (Sous Lt.) | Leutnant (Lt) |
| (No Corresponding Rank) | Aspirant | Fähnrich |
| | | |
| **Navy** | **Navy** | **Navy** |
| Admiral of the Fleet/Fleet Admiral | Amiral de la Flotte | Grossadmiral |
| Admiral (Adm.) | Amiral (Amr.) | Admiral (Adm) |
| Vice Admiral (Vice Adm.) | Vice Amiral (Vice Amr.) | Vizeadmiral (VAdm) |
| Rear Admiral (Rear Adm.) | Contre-Amiral (Contre-Amr.) | Konteradmiral (KAdm) |
| Commodore (Comdr.) | (No Corresponding Rank) | Flottillenadmiral (FltlAdm) |
| Captain (Capt.) | Capitaine de Vaisseau (Capt. de Vaisseau) | Kapitän zur See (KptzS) |
| Commander (Cdr.) | Capitaine de Frégate (Capt. de Frégate) | Fregattenkapitän |
| Lieutenant Commander (Lt. Cdr.) | Capitaine de Corvette (Capt. de Corvette) | Korvettenkapitän |
| Lieutenant (Lt.) | Lieutenant de Vaisseau (Lt. de Vaisseau) | Kapitänleutnant |
| Lieutenant Junior Grade (Lt. J.G.) | Enseigne de Vaisseau 1ére Classe | Oberleutnant (Oblt) |
| Ensign | Enseigne de Vaisseau 2éme Classe | Leutnant (Lt) |
| (No Corresponding Rank) | Aspirant | Fähnrich |

---

†With the exceptions of Marshal of the Air Force, Marshal (MSU/Mar.—Soviet Union), and Admiral of the Fleet (Fl. Adm. SU—Soviet Union), five star ranks are generally assigned only in wartime. For the purposes of comparison, five star ranks have been presented for all languages even though they are not used in every country.

---

Majors are called Chef de Bataillon in the infantry, Chief d'Escadrons in the cavalry, and Chef d'Escadron in the artillery.

Seargeants are known as Maréchal des Logis in the artillery, cavalry and constabulary.

Corporals are known as Brigadier in the cavalry, artillery and constabulary.

The rank of Adjutant is equivalent to that of a Warrant officer.

The rank of Colonel-Major is used by come countries to indicate the equivalent of a Brigadier-General.

---

Austria and Switzerland; The rank of Koprskommandant (Korpskdt.) is equivalent to that of Lt. Gen., the rank of Divisionär (Divr.) is equivalent to that of Major General, and the rank of Brigadier is equivalent to that of Brigadier General.

German Democratic Republic; The Highest rank in the *Volksarmee* is that of Armeegeneral (ArmeeGen) or Army General. The second-highest rank is Generaloberst (GenObst) or Colonel General. From the Lieutenant General rank down, the East German ranking system follows that of the Federal Republic of Germany.

# SCANDINAVIAN
## Norwegian/Swedish

## Army

Fält Marskall
General (Gen.)
Generalløytnant(Genlt.)/Generallöjtnanat (Glt.)
Generalmajor (Genmaj./Gmj)

Oberst I (Obl)/Överste av 1 graden (Övl)
Oberst II (Ob)/Överste (Öv)
Oberstloytnant (Oblt.)/Överstelitnant (Övlt.)
Major (Maj./Mj.)
Kaptein/Kapten (Kapt./Kn.)
Loytnant/Löjtnant (Lt.)
(No Corresponding Rank)
Fenrick (Fenr,)/Fänrick (Fänr)

## Air Force

Marskall
General (Gen.)
Generalløytnant (Genlt.)/Generallöjtnant (Glt.)
Generalmajor (Genmaj./Gmj)

Oberst I (Ob.I)/Överste av 1 graden (Öl)

Oberst II (Ob)/Överste (Öv)
Oberstloytnant (Oblt.)/Överstelöjtnant (Övlt.)
Major (Maj./Mj.)
Kaptein (Kapt.)/Kapten (Kn.)
Loytnant/Löjtnant (Lt.)
(No Corresponding Rank)
Fenrick (Fenr.)/Fänrick (Fänr.)

## Navy

Generaladmiral/Generalmiral
Admiral (Adm.)/Amiral (Am.)
Viseadmiral (Vadm.)/Viceadmiral (Vam.)
Kontreadmiral (Kadm.)/Koneramiral (Kam.)
Kommandør I (Kom.1)/Kommendör av 1 graden (Kmd. 1)
Kommandør II (Kom. II)/Kommenör (Kmd.)
Kommandørkaptein (K)/Kommedoŕrkaptan (Kk.)
Orlogskaptein (OK.)/Örlogskapten (Örkn.)
Kapteinløytnant (Kaptlt.)/Kaptenlöjtnant (Knlt.)
Løytnant/Löjtnant (Lt.)
Ferik (Fenr.)/Fänrick (Fär.)
Kadettferik

---

Denmark: The rank of Brigade General is equivalent to a Brigadier General, the rank of Premier Løjtnant is equivalent to a First Lieutenant, the rank of Løjtnant is equivalent to that of a Second Lieutenant, and the rank of Sekand Løjtnant is equivalent to that of an Ensign.

The rank of Flottiladmiral is equivalent to a Commodore, the rank of Premier Løjtnant is equivalent to a Lieutenant, and the rank of Sekandløjtnant is equivalent to Lieutenant Junior Grade.

# SPANISH

## Army

Mariscal
General de Ejercito (Gral.)/Capitan General (Cap. Gral.)
Tentiente General (Tte. Gral.)
Mayor General (May. Gen.)/General de Division (Gral. Div.)
General de Brigada/Brigadier General (Gral. Brig.)
Coronel (Cnel.)
Tentiente Coronel (Tte. Cnel.)
Mayor (May.)/Comandante (Cdte.)
Capitan (Cap.)
Primer Tentiente (1$^{er}$ Tte.)
Tentiente (Tte.)
Alferez

## Air Force

Mariscal de l'Aerea
General de Aviacion [Aerea] (Gral. de Av.)
Tentiente General (Tte. Gral.)
Mayor General (May. Gral.)/General de Division (Gral. Div.)
Brigadier General (Brig. Gral.)

Coronel (Cnel.)/Coronel de Aviacion (Cnel. de Av.)
Comandante de Gruppe (Cdte. de Gruppo)
Capitan de Escuadrilla (Cap. de Escuadrilla)
Tentiente Primero (Tte. 1$^{ero}$)
Tentiente Segundo (Tte. 2)
Sub Tentiente (Sub-Tte.)
Alferez

## Navy

Almirante de la Flota
Almirante (Alm.)
Vicealmirante (Vice Alm.)
Contraalmirante (Contra Alm.)
(No Corresponding Rank)
Capitan de Navio (Cap. Nav.)
Capitan de Fregata (Cap. Fregata)
Capitan de Corbeta (Cap. Corbeta)
Tentiente/de Navio (Tte. Nav.)
Tentiente Primero/de Fregata (Tte. Fregata)
Tentiente Segundo/de Corbeta (Tte. Corbeta)
Guardia Marina

---

The rank of General Brigada/Brigadier sometimes constitutes an intermediate rank between Coronel and General de Brigada/Brigadier General.

Some countries use Sub Tentiente as an intermediate rank between Guardia Marina and Tentiente Segundo de Corbeta.

# PORTUGUESE

## Army

Marechal (Mal.)
(No Corresponding Rank)
General-de-Exercito (Gen. Ex.)
General-de-Divisao (Gen. Div.)

General-de-Brigade (Gen.-de-Bda.)
Coronel (Cel.)
Tenente-Coronel (Ten. Cel.)
Major (Maj.)
Capitão (Cap.)
Primeiro-Tenente (1° Ten.)
Segundo-Tenente (2° Ten.)
Aspirante-a-Oficial

## Air Force

Marechal-do-Ar (Mal. Ar.)
(No Corresponding Rank)
Tenente-Brigadeiro (Ten. Brig.)
Major-Brigadeiro (Maj. Brig.)

Brigadeiro do Ar. (Brig.-do-Ar.)

Coronel (Cel.)
Tenente-Coronel (Ten. Cel.)
Major (Maj)
Capitão (Cap.)
Primeiro-Tenente (1° Ten.)
Segundo-Tenente (2° Ten.)
Aspirante-a-Official

## Navy

Almirante (Alte.)
Almirante-de-Esquadra (Alte.-de-Esq.)
Vice-Almirante (V. Alte.)
Contr-Almirante (C. Alte.)
(No Corresponding Rank)
Capitão-de-Mar-e-Guerra (CMG)
Capitão-de-Fragata (CF)
Capitão-de-Corveta (CC)
Capitão-Tenente (CT)
Primeiro-Tenente (1° Ten.)
Segundo-Tenente (2° Ten.)
Guarda-Marinha (GM)

---

Portugal; Generals are not noted by corps sizes but by a star ranking system in which a four star General is equivalent to a General de Exercito, a three star General is equivalent to a General de Division, and a Brigadier has two stars and is equivalent to a General de Brigada. The rank of Alferez is equivalent to that of an Aspirante.

# B. INTERNATIONAL TELEPHONE DIALING CODES

# International Telephone Dialing Codes

| Country | Country Code | City | City Code |
|---|---|---|---|
| Afghanistan | None | | |
| Albania | None | | |
| Algeria | None | | |
| Andorra | 33 | (all points) | 078 |
| Antigua & Barbuda[1] | 1 + 809 | St. Johns | NR |
| Argentina | 54 | Buenos Aires | 1 |
| | | Cordoba | 51 |
| | | Rosario | 41 |
| Australia | 61 | Canberra | 62 |
| | | Melbourne | 3 |
| | | Perth | 2 |
| | | Sydney | 9 |
| Austria | 43 | Graz | 316 |
| | | Innsbruck | 5222 |
| | | Linz | 732 |
| | | Vienna | 222 |
| Bahamas[1] | 1 + 809 | Nassau | NR |
| Bahrain | 973 | Manama | NR |
| Bangladesh | None | Dacca | * |
| Barbados[1] | 1 + 809 | Bridgetown | 42 |
| Belgium | 32 | Antwerp | 31 |
| | | Brussels | 2 |
| | | Ghent | 91 |
| | | Liege | 41 |
| Belize | 501 | Belize City | NR |
| Bermuda[1] | 1 + 809 | Hamilton | NR |
| Benin | * | Cotonou | * |
| Bhutan | * | Thimphu | * |
| Bolivia | 591 | La Paz | 2 |
| | | Santa Cruz | 33 |
| Botswana | * | Gaborone | * |
| Brazil | 55 | Brasilia | 61 |
| | | Porto Alegre | 51 |
| | | Recife | 81 |
| | | Rio de Janeiro | 21 |
| | | Sao Paulo | 11 |

| Country | Country Code | City | City Code |
|---------|-------------|------|-----------|
| Brunei | * | Bandar Seri Begawan | * |
| Bulgaria | * | Sofia | * |
| Burma | * | Rangoon | * |
| Burundi | * | Bujumbura | * |
| Cameroon | * | Yaounde | * |
| Canada | 1 | Calgary | 403 |
| | | Halifax | 902 |
| | | Montreal | 514 |
| | | Ottawa | 613 |
| | | Quebec | 418 |
| | | Toronto | 416 |
| | | Vancouver | 604 |
| | | Winnipeg | 204 |
| Cape Verde | * | Praia | * |
| Central African Republic | * | Bangui | * |
| Chad | * | N'Djamena | * |
| Chile | 56 | Penco | 42 |
| | | Santiago | 2 |
| | | Valparaiso | 31 |
| China | * | Beijing | * |
| Colombia | 57 | Barranquilla | 5 |
| | | Bogota | NR |
| | | Cali | 3 |
| | | Medellin | 4 |
| Comoros | * | Moroni | * |
| Congo | * | Brazzaville | * |
| Costa Rica | 506 | NR | NR |
| Cuba | * | Havana | * |
| Cyprus | 357 | Limassol | 51 |
| | | Nicosia | 21 |
| | | Paphos | 61 |
| Czechoslovakia | * | Prague | * |
| Denmark | 45 | Aarhus | 6 |
| | | Copenhagan | 1 or 2 |
| | | Odense | 9 |
| Djibouti | * | Djibouti | * |
| Dominica | | | |
| Dominican Republic[1] | 1 + 809 | Santo Domingo | NR |
| Ecuador | 593 | Cuenca | 4 |
| | | Guayaquil | 4 |
| | | Quito | 2 |

| Country | Country Code | City | City Code |
|---|---|---|---|
| Egypt | * | Cairo | * |
| El Salvador | 503 | San Salvador | NR |
| Equatorial Guinea | * | Malabo | * |
| Ethiopia | * | Addis Ababa | * |
| Fiji | 679 | Sura | NR |
| Finland | 358 | Helsinki | 0 |
| | | Tempere | 31 |
| France | 33 | Bordeaux | 56 |
| | | Lyon | 7 |
| | | Marseille | 91 |
| | | Nice | 93 |
| | | Paris | 1 |
| | | Strasbourg | 88 |
| | | Toulouse | 61 |
| Gabon | * | Libreville | * |
| Gambia | * | Banjul | * |
| German Democratic Republic | 37 | Berlin | 2 |
| | | Dresden | 51 |
| | | Leipzig | 41 |
| Federal Republic of Germany | 49 | Berlin | 30 |
| | | Bonn | 228 |
| | | Essen | 201 |
| | | Frankfurt | 611 |
| | | Hamburg | 40 |
| | | Munich | 89 |
| | | Stuttgart | 711 |
| | | Dusseldorf | 211 |
| Ghana | * | Accra | * |
| Greece | 30 | Athens | 1 |
| | | Rhodes | 241 |
| | | Thessaloniki | 31 |
| Grenada | * | St. George's | * |
| Guatemala | 502 | Guatemala City | 2 |
| Guinea | * | Conakry | * |
| Guinea-Bissau | * | Bissau | * |
| Guyana | 592 | Georgetown | 02 |
| | | Bartica | 05 |
| Haiti | 509 | Gonaive | 2 |
| | | Port-au-Prince | 1 |
| Honduras | 504 | Tegucigalpa | NR |
| Hong Kong | 852 | Hong Kong | 5 |
| | | Kowloon | 3 |

| Country | Country Code | City | City Code |
|---------|--------------|------|-----------|
| Hungary | * | Budapest | * |
| Iceland | 354 | Akureyi | 6 |
|  |  | Reykjavik | 1 |
| India | * | New Delhi | * |
| Indonesia | 62 | Jakarta | 21 |
|  |  | Medan | 61 |
|  |  | Surabaya | 31 |
| Iran | 98 | Esfahan | 31 |
|  |  | Tabriz | 41 |
|  |  | Teheran | 21 |
| Iraq | 964 | Baghdad | 1 |
|  |  | Mosul | 60 |
| Ireland | 353 | Cork | 21 |
|  |  | Dublin | 1 |
|  |  | Galway | 91 |
|  |  | Limerick | 61 |
| Israel | 972 | Haifa | 4 |
|  |  | Jerusalem | 2 |
|  |  | Tel Aviv | 3 |
| Italy | 39 | Bologna | 51 |
|  |  | Florence | 55 |
|  |  | Genoa | 10 |
|  |  | Milan | 2 |
|  |  | Naples | 81 |
|  |  | Palermo | 91 |
|  |  | Rome | 6 |
|  |  | Trieste | 40 |
|  |  | Turin | 11 |
|  |  | Venice | 41 |
| Ivory Coast | 225 | Abidjan | NR |
| Jamaica[1] | 1 + 809 | Kingston | NR |
| Japan | 81 | Hiroshima | 822 |
|  |  | Kitakyushu | 93 |
|  |  | Kobe | 78 |
|  |  | Kyoto | 75 |
|  |  | Nagoya | 52 |
|  |  | Osaka | 6 |
|  |  | Sapporo | 11 |
|  |  | Tokyo | 3 |
|  |  | Yokohama | 45 |
| Jordan | * | Amman | * |
| Kampuchea | * | Phnom Penh | * |
| Kenya | 254 | Mombasa | 11 |
|  |  | Nairobi | 2 |
|  |  | Nakuru | 37 |

| Country | Country Code | City | City Code |
|---|---|---|---|
| Kiribati | * | Tarawa Atoll | * |
| Korea, DPR | * | Pyongyang | * |
| Republic of Korea | 82 | Pusan | 51 |
| | | Seoul | 2 |
| | | Taegu | 53 |
| Kuwait | 965 | Kuwait | NR |
| Laos | * | Vientiane | * |
| Lebanon | * | Beirut | * |
| Lesotho | * | Maseru | * |
| Liberia | 231 | Monrovia | NR |
| Libya | 218 | Tripoli | 21 |
| Liechtenstein | 41 | (all points) | 75 |
| Luxembourg | 352 | Luxembourg | NR |
| Madagascar | * | Antananarivo | * |
| Malawi | * | Lilongwe | * |
| Malaysia | 60 | Ipoh | 5 |
| | | Kelang | 3 |
| | | Kuala Lumpur | 3 |
| Maldives | * | Malé | * |
| Mali | * | Bamako | * |
| Malta | * | Valletta | * |
| Mauritania | * | Nouakchott | * |
| Mauritius | * | Port Louis | * |
| Mexico | 52 | La Paz | 682 |
| | | Mexico City | 5 |
| | | Nogales | 631 |
| | | Tijuana | 688 |
| Monaco | 33 | (all points) | 93 |
| Mongolia | * | Ulan Bator | * |
| Morocco | * | Rabat | * |
| Mozambique | * | Maputo | * |
| Namibia | * | Windhoek | * |
| Nauru | * | Nauru | * |
| Nepal | * | Kathmandu | * |
| Netherlands | 31 | Amsterdam | 20 |
| | | The Hague | 70 |
| | | Rotterdam | 10 |

| Country | Country Code | City | City Code |
|---------|--------------|------|-----------|
| Netherlands Antilles | 599 | Aruba | 8 |
| | | Curacao | 9 |
| New Zealand | 64 | Auckland | 9 |
| | | Wellington | 4 |
| Nicaragua | 505 | Chinandega | 341 |
| | | Leon | 31 |
| | | Managua | 2 |
| Niger | * | Niamey | * |
| Nigeria | 234 | Lagos | 1 |
| Norway | 47 | Bergen | 5 |
| | | Oslo | 2 |
| Oman | * | Muscat | * |
| Pakistan | * | Islamabad | * |
| Panama | 507 | Panama | NR |
| Papua New Guinea | 675 | Port Moresby | NR |
| Paraguay | 595 | Asuncion | 21 |
| Peru | 51 | Arequipa | 54 |
| | | Lima | 14 |
| Philippines | 63 | Cebu | 32 |
| | | Manilla | 2 |
| Poland | * | Warsaw | * |
| Portugal | 351 | Lisbon | 1 |
| | | Ponta Delgada | 16 |
| | | Porto | 29 |
| Qatar | 974 | Doha | * |
| Romania | 40 | Bucharest | 0 |
| Rwanda | * | Kigali | * |
| St. Christopher-Nevis | * | Bassaterre | * |
| St. Lucia | * | Castries | * |
| St. Vincent & the Grenadines | * | Kingstown | * |
| San Marino | 39 | (all points) | 541 |
| São Tome & Principe | * | São Tomé | * |
| Saudi Arabia | 966 | Dahran | 3 |
| | | Jeddah | 2 |
| | | Mecca | 2 |
| | | Riyadh | 1 |
| Senegal | 221 | Dakar | NR |
| Seychelles | * | Victoria | * |

| Country | Country Code | City | City Code |
|---|---|---|---|
| Sierra Leone | * | Freetown | * |
| Singapore | 65 | Singapore | NR |
| Soloman Islands | * | Honiara | * |
| South Africa | 27 | Cape Town | 21 |
| | | Durban | 31 |
| | | Johannesburg | 11 |
| | | Pretoria | 12 |
| Spain | 34 | Barcelona | 3 |
| | | Bilbao | 4 |
| | | Las Palmas (Canary Is.) | 28 |
| | | Madrid | 1 |
| | | Seville | 54 |
| | | Valencia | 6 |
| Sri Lanka | 94 | Colombo | 1 |
| | | Kandy | 8 |
| | | Moratuwa | 72 |
| Sudan | * | Khartoum | * |
| Suriname | 597 | Paramaribo | NR |
| Swaziland | * | Mbabane | * |
| Sweden | 46 | Goteborg | 31 |
| | | Maimo | 40 |
| | | Stockholm | 8 |
| Switzerland | 41 | Basel | 61 |
| | | Berne | 31 |
| | | Geneva | 22 |
| | | Lucerne | 41 |
| | | Zurich | 1 |
| Syria | * | Damascus | * |
| Taiwan | 886 | Taipei | 2 |
| | | Kaohsiung | 7 |
| Tanzania | * | Dar-es-Salaam | * |
| Thailand | 66 | Bangkok | 2 |
| Togo | * | Lome | * |
| Tonga | * | Nuku'alofa | * |
| Trinidad & Tobago | * | Port-of-Spain | * |
| Tunisia | 216 | Tunis | 1 |
| Turkey | 90 | Adana | 711 |
| | | Ankara | 41 |
| | | Istanbul | 11 |
| | | Izmir | 51 |

| *Country* | *Country Code* | *City* | *City Code* |
|---|---|---|---|
| Tuvalu | * | Funafuti Atoll | * |
| Uganda | * | Kampala | * |
| Union of Soviet Socialist Republics | 7 | Kiev | 044 |
| | | Leningrad | 812 |
| | | Minsk | 017 |
| | | Moscow | 095 |
| | | Tallinn | 0142 |
| United Arab Emirates | 971 | Abu Dhabi | 2 |
| | | Ajman | 6 |
| | | Al Ain | 3 |
| | | Aweir | 49 |
| | | Dubai | 4 |
| | | Fujairah | 91 |
| | | Ras Al-Khaimah | 7 |
| | | Sharjah | 6 |
| | | Umm Al-Quwain | 6 |
| United Kingdom | 44 | Belfast | 232 |
| | | Birmingham | 21 |
| | | Cardiff | 222 |
| | | Edinburgh | 31 |
| | | Glasgow | 41 |
| | | Leeds | 532 |
| | | Liverpool | 51 |
| | | London | 1 |
| United States | 1 | Washington, DC | 202 |
| | | New York | 212 |
| Upper Volta | * | Ouagadougou | * |
| Uruguay | 598 | Canelones | 332 |
| | | Mercedes | 532 |
| | | Montevideo | 2 |
| Vanuatu | * | * | * |
| Vatican City | 39 | (all points) | 6 |
| Venezuela | 58 | Caracas | 2 |
| | | Maracaibo | 61 |
| | | Valencia | 41 |
| Vietnam | * | Hanoi | * |
| Western Sahara | * | * | * |
| Western Samoa | * | Apia | * |
| Yemen (PDRY) | * | Aden | * |
| Yemen (YAR) | * | Sanaa | * |
| Yugoslavia | 38 | Belgrade | 11 |
| | | Sarajevo | 71 |
| | | Skoplje | 91 |
| | | Zagreb | 41 |

| Country | Country Code | City | City Code |
|---------|-------------|------|-----------|
| Zaire | * | Kinshasa | * |
| Zambia | * | Lusaka | * |
| Zimbabwe | * | Harare | * |

---

*Not an international dial country. Operator assistance required.

NR—not required.

[1]To call most points in the Caribbean/Atlantic region from the United States, only the 809 area code is necessary, followed by the individual seven-digit number.